STUDENT'S SOLUTIONS MANUAL

HEIDI A. HOWARD
Florida Community College at Jacksonville

to accompany

COLLEGE ALGEBRA AND TRIGONOMETRY

THIRD EDITION

AND

PRECALCULUS

THIRD EDITION

Margaret L. Lial
American River College

John Hornsby
University of New Orleans

David I. Schneider
University of Maryland

PEARSON
Addison Wesley

Boston San Francisco New York
London Toronto Sydney Tokyo Singapore Madrid
Mexico City Munich Paris Cape Town Hong Kong Montreal

Reproduced by Pearson Addison-Wesley from electronic files supplied by the author.

Publishing as Pearson Addison-Wesley, 75 Arlington Street, Boston, MA 02116

ISBN 0-321-22770-0

5 6 BB 08 07 06

PEARSON
Addison
Wesley

CONTENTS

I wish to thank Faiz Al-Rubaee (a never-ending resource),
John Samons (a consummate professional), and Amanda Nunley
(a budding mathematician) for all their contributions to this supplement.
I also want to acknowledge the endless efforts of Joanne Ha,
Sandra Scholten, Sheila Spinney, and
Joe Vetere (aka Mr. Bender).
Thanks to you all.

Chapter R
REVIEW OF BASIC CONCEPTS

Section R.1: Real Numbers and Their Properties

1. 0 is a whole number. Therefore, it is also an integer, a rational number, and a real number. 0 belongs to B, C, D, F.

3. $-\frac{9}{4}$ is a rational number and a real number. $-\frac{9}{4}$ belongs to D, F.

5. $\sqrt{13}$ is an irrational number and a real number. $\sqrt{13}$ belongs to E, F.

7. Answers will vary. Possible answers include that *D. Rational Numbers and E. Irrational numbers* are two sets that have no common elements. Hence, a number could not belong to both sets.

9. Answers will vary.
Three examples are $\frac{2}{3}$, $-\frac{4}{9}$, and $\frac{21}{2}$.

11. 1 and 3 are natural numbers.

13. –6, $-\frac{12}{4}$ (or –3), 0, 1, and 3 are integers.

15. $-3^4 = -(3\cdot3\cdot3\cdot3) = -81$

17. $(-3)^4 = (-3)\cdot(-3)\cdot(-3)\cdot(-3) = 81$

19. $(-3)^5 = (-3)\cdot(-3)\cdot(-3)\cdot(-3)\cdot(-3) = -243$

21. $-2\cdot3^4 = -2\cdot(3\cdot3\cdot3\cdot3) = -2\cdot81 = -162$

23. Answers will vary.

i) $-5^2 = -(5\cdot5) = -(25) = -25$ is negative.
In this case, you are squaring a positive number, which yields a positive number. When you then find the opposite of this positive number, a negative number will be the outcome.

ii) $(-5)^2 = (-5)\cdot(-5) = 25$ is positive.
In this case, you are squaring a negative number, which yields a positive number.

iii) $-(-5)^2 = -[(-5)\cdot(-5)] = -(25) = -25$ is negative.
In this case, you are squaring a negative number, which yields a positive number. When you then find the opposite of this positive number, a negative number will be the outcome.

25. $16(-9)-4 = -144-4 = -148$

27. $9\cdot3-16\div4 = 27-16\div4 = 27-4 = 23$

29. $6(-5)-(-3)(2)^4 = 6(-5)-(-3)\cdot16 = -30-(-3)\cdot16 = -30-(-48) = -30+48 = 18$

31. $\left(4-2^3\right)\left(-2+\sqrt{25}\right) = (4-8)(-2+5) = (-4)(3) = -12$

33. $\left(-\frac{2}{9}-\frac{1}{4}\right)-\left[-\frac{5}{18}-\left(-\frac{1}{2}\right)\right] = \left(-\frac{8}{36}-\frac{9}{36}\right)-\left(-\frac{5}{18}+\frac{9}{18}\right) = \left(-\frac{17}{36}\right)-\left(\frac{4}{18}\right) = -\frac{17}{36}-\frac{8}{36} = -\frac{25}{36}$

35. $\dfrac{-8+(-4)(-6)\div 12}{4-(-3)}=\dfrac{-8+24\div 12}{4+3}=\dfrac{-8+2}{7}=\dfrac{-6}{7}=-\dfrac{6}{7}$

37. Let $q = 8$ and $r = -10$.
$2(q-r)=2\left[8-(-10)\right]=2(8+10)=2(18)=36$

39. Let $p = -4$, $q = 8$, and $r = -10$.
$2p-7q+r^2=2(-4)-7\cdot 8+(-10)^2=2(-4)-7\cdot 8+100=-8-7\cdot 8+100=-8-56+100=-64+100=36$

41. Let $p = -4$, $q = 8$, and $r = -10$.
$\dfrac{q+r}{q+p}=\dfrac{8+(-10)}{8+(-4)}=\dfrac{-2}{4}=-\dfrac{1}{2}$

43. Let $p = -4$, $q = 8$, and $r = -10$.
$\dfrac{3q}{r}-\dfrac{5}{p}=\dfrac{3\cdot 8}{-10}-\dfrac{5}{-4}=\dfrac{24}{-10}-\dfrac{5}{-4}=-\dfrac{12}{5}-\dfrac{5}{-4}=-\dfrac{12}{5}+\dfrac{5}{4}=-\dfrac{48}{20}+\dfrac{25}{20}=-\dfrac{23}{20}$

45. Let $p = -4$, $q = 8$, and $r = -10$.
$$\dfrac{-(p+2)^2-3r}{2-q}=\dfrac{-(-4+2)^2-3(-10)}{2-8}$$
$$=\dfrac{-(-2)^2-3(-10)}{-6}=\dfrac{-4-3(-10)}{-6}=\dfrac{-4-(-30)}{-6}=\dfrac{-4+30}{-6}=\dfrac{26}{-6}=-\dfrac{13}{3}$$

47. $A = 451$, $C = 281$, $Y = 3049$, $T = 22$, $I = 6$

$$\text{Passing Rating} = 85.68\left(\dfrac{C}{A}\right)+4.31\left(\dfrac{Y}{A}\right)+326.42\left(\dfrac{T}{A}\right)-419.07\left(\dfrac{I}{A}\right)$$
$$\approx 85.68\left(\dfrac{281}{451}\right)+4.31\left(\dfrac{3049}{451}\right)+326.42\left(\dfrac{22}{451}\right)-419.07\left(\dfrac{6}{451}\right)$$
$$\approx 53.38+29.14+15.92-5.58\approx 92.9$$

49. $A = 610$, $C = 375$, $Y = 4359$, $T = 24$, $I = 15$

$$\text{Passing Rating} = 85.68\left(\dfrac{C}{A}\right)+4.31\left(\dfrac{Y}{A}\right)+326.42\left(\dfrac{T}{A}\right)-419.07\left(\dfrac{I}{A}\right)$$
$$\approx 85.68\left(\dfrac{375}{610}\right)+4.31\left(\dfrac{4359}{610}\right)+326.42\left(\dfrac{24}{610}\right)-419.07\left(\dfrac{15}{610}\right)$$
$$\approx 52.67+30.80+12.84-10.31=86.0$$

51. $\text{BAC}=48\times 3.2\times 0.075\div 190-2\times 0.015\approx 0.031$

53. Ex 51: $\text{BAC}=48\times 3.2\times 0.075\div 215-2\times 0.015\approx 0.024$;
Ex 52: $\text{BAC}=36\times 4.0\times 0.075\div 160-3\times 0.015=0.023$
Increased weight results in lower BACs.

55. distributive

57. inverse

59. identity

61. No; in general $a-b\neq b-a$. Examples will vary.

63. $8p-14p=(8-14)p=-6p$

65. $-3(z-y)=-3z-(-3y)=-3z+3y$

67. $\frac{10}{11}(22z)=\left(\frac{10}{11}\cdot 22\right)z=20z$

69. $(m+5)+3=m+(5+3)=m+8$

71. $\frac{3}{8}\left(\frac{16}{9}y+\frac{32}{27}z-\frac{40}{9}\right)=\frac{3}{8}\left(\frac{16}{9}y\right)+\frac{3}{8}\left(\frac{32}{27}z\right)-\frac{3}{8}\left(\frac{40}{9}\right)=\left(\frac{3}{8}\cdot\frac{16}{9}\right)y+\left(\frac{3}{8}\cdot\frac{32}{27}\right)z-\frac{5}{3}=\frac{2}{3}y+\frac{4}{9}z-\frac{5}{3}$

73. Average $=\frac{64+65+65+67}{4}=\frac{261}{4}=65.25$

His average score was 65.25.

75. The distance around the Sun is equal to the circumference or $2\pi r$.

$2\pi r\approx 2(3.14)(92{,}960{,}000)=583{,}788{,}800$ miles

The average speed would be $\frac{583{,}788{,}800}{365.26}\approx 1{,}598{,}282.867\frac{\text{miles}}{\text{day}}\cdot\frac{1\text{ day}}{24\text{ hours}}\approx 66{,}595$ mph

Rounded to the nearest thousands the speed would be 67,000 mph.

77. In a sample of 3000 people, 31% of them, or 0.31(3000) = 930, are people in the United States who curse the ATM.

79. In a sample of 3000 people, 33% of them, or 0.33(3000) = 990, are people in Germany who tell the ATM to hurry up.

81. Finding a wind speed of 46.0 mph and then moving across to a 30-hour wind duration yields a wave height of 31 feet.

83. Answers will vary.

(a) $\frac{a^2}{b^2}=2\Rightarrow b^2\cdot\frac{a^2}{b^2}=b^2\cdot 2\Rightarrow a^2=2b^2$

(b) Since b is an integer (because $\frac{a}{b}$ is a rational number), b^2 will be a natural number. Since b^2 is multiplied by 2, $2b^2$ must be an even number.

(c) Each natural number has a unique prime factorization, so if one side has a factor of 2 then so does the other, namely a^2. Since a^2 is even, a must also be even because $a^2=a\cdot a$ has both factors a either even or odd. If they were both odd, then the square would also be odd so a must therefore be even.

(d) Substitute $2c$ for a.

(e) Divide both sides of $4c^2=2b^2$ by 2.

(f) Same reasoning as part b.

(g) $\frac{a}{b}$ is written in lowest terms thus a and b must have a greatest common factor of 1. Since both a and b are shown to be even, they have a common factor of 2.

85. The process in your head should be like the following:

$72\cdot 17+28\cdot 17=(72+28)(17)=(100)(17)=1700$

87. The process in your head should be like the following:

$123\frac{5}{8}\cdot 1\frac{1}{2}-23\frac{5}{8}\cdot 1\frac{1}{2}=\left(123\frac{5}{8}-23\frac{5}{8}\right)\left(1\frac{1}{2}\right)=(100)\left(1\frac{1}{2}\right)=(100)(1.5)=150$

Section R.2: Order and Absolute Value

1. Since $\sqrt{8} \approx 2.83$, $-\sqrt{3} \approx -1.73$ and $\sqrt{6} \approx 2.45$, the order is $-5, -4, -2, -\sqrt{3}, \sqrt{6}, \sqrt{8}, 3$.

3. Since $\frac{3}{4} = 0.75$, $\sqrt{2} \approx 1.414$, $\frac{7}{5} = 1.4$, $\frac{8}{5} = 1.6$, and $\frac{22}{15} \approx 1.47$, the order is $\frac{3}{4}, \frac{7}{5}, \sqrt{2}, \frac{22}{15}, \frac{8}{5}$.

5. Since $|-8| = 8$, $-|9| = -9$, and $-|-6| = -6$, the order is $-|9|, -|-6|, |-8|$.

7. Answers will vary.
In the second statement, $5 < x < 2$, there are no values that will satisfy this relation. There are no real numbers that are simultaneously greater than 5 and less than 2.

9. This statement is false since $|5-7| = |-2| = 2$ and $|5| - |7| = 5 - 7 = -2$. A corrected statement would be $|5-7| \neq |5| - |7|$ or $|5-7| \neq |7| - |5|$.

11. This statement is true since $|-5| \cdot |4| = 5 \cdot 4 = 20$ and $|-5 \cdot 4| = |-20| = 20$.

13. This statement is false. For example if you let $a = -2$ and $b = 3$ then $|-2-3| = |-5| = 5$ and $|a| - |b| = |-2| - |3| = 2 - 3 = -1$. A corrected statement is $|a-b| > |a| - |b|$, if $b > a$.

15. $|-9| = 9$

17. $-\left|\frac{4}{5}\right| = -\frac{4}{5}$

19. Let $x = -4$.
$|2x| = |2(-4)| = |-8| = 8$

21. Let $x = -4$ and $y = 2$.
$|x - y| = |-4 - 2| = |-6| = 6$

23. Let $x = -4$ and $y = 2$.
$$|3x + 4y| = |3(-4) + 4(2)| = |-12 + 8| = |-4| = 4$$

25. Let $x = -4$ and $y = 2$.
$$\frac{2|y| - 3|x|}{|xy|} = \frac{2|2| - 3|-4|}{|-4(2)|} = \frac{2(2) - 3(4)}{|-8|} = \frac{4-12}{8} = \frac{-8}{8} = -1$$

27. Let $x = -4$ and $y = 2$.
$$\frac{|-8y + x|}{-|x|} = \frac{|-8(2) + (-4)|}{-|4|} = \frac{|-16 + (-4)|}{-|-4|} = \frac{|-20|}{-(4)} = \frac{20}{-4} = -5$$

29. Since $\pi > 3$, $\pi - 3 > 0$, so $|\pi - 3| = \pi - 3$.

31. Since $y < 3$, $y - 3 < 0$, so $|y - 3| = -(y-3) = -y + 3 = 3 - y$.

33. If $k < 4$, $2k < 8$, and $2k - 8 < 0$, so $|2k - 8| = -(2k - 8) = -2k + 8 = 8 - 2k$.

35. If $x < y$, $x - y < 0$, so $|x - y| = -(x - y) = -x + y = y - x$.

37. Since $(3 + x^2) > 0$, so $|3 + x^2| = 3 + x^2$.

39. Property 2

41. Property 3

43. Since $|k-m|=|k+(-m)|$, $|k-m|\le|k|+|-m|$ by property 5, the triangle inequality.

45. Property 1

47. $12,243+5411+(-6)=17,648$ yards; No, it is not the same, because the sum of the absolute values is $|12,243|+|5411|+|-6|=12,243+5411+6=17,660$. The fact that $|-6|=6$ changes the two answers.

49. $P_d=|P-125|=|116-125|=|-9|=9$

The P_d value for a woman whose actual systolic pressure is 116 and whose normal value should be 125 is 9.

51. The absolute value of the difference in wind-chill factors for wind at 15 mph with a 30°F temperature and wind at 10 mph with a –10°F temperature is $|19°-(-28°)|=|47°|=47°$ F.

53. The absolute value of the difference in wind-chill factors for wind at 30 mph with a –30°F temperature and wind at 15 mph with a –20°F temperature is $|-67°-(-45°)|=|-22°|=22°$ F.

55. $d(P,Q)=|-1-(-4)|=|-1+4|=|3|=3$ or $d(P,Q)=|-4-(-1)|=|-4+1|=|-3|=3$

57. $d(Q,R)=|8-(-1)|=|8+1|=|9|=9$ or $d(Q,R)=|-1-8|=|-9|=9$

59. $d(Q,S)=|12-(-1)|=|13|=13$ or $d(Q,S)=|-1-12|=|-13|=13$

61. $xy>0$ if x and y have the same sign.

63. $\frac{x}{y}<0$ if x and y have different signs.

65. Since x^3 has the same sign as x, $\frac{x^3}{y}>0$ if x and y have the same sign.

Section R.3: Polynomials

1. Incorrect; $(mn)^2=m^2n^2$

3. Incorrect; $\left(\frac{k}{5}\right)^3=\frac{k^3}{5^3}=\frac{k^3}{125}$

5. $9^3\cdot 9^5=9^{3+5}=9^8$

7.
$$\begin{aligned}(-4x^5)(4x^2)&=(-4\cdot 4)(x^5x^2)\\&=-16x^{5+2}\\&=-16x^7\end{aligned}$$

9. $(2^2)^5=2^{2\cdot 5}=2^{10}$

11.
$$\begin{aligned}-(4m^3n^0)^2&=-\left[4^2(m^3)^2(n^0)^2\right]\\&=-4^2m^{3\cdot 2}n^{0\cdot 2}\\&=-4^2m^6n^0\\&=-(4^2)m^6\cdot 1\\&=-4^2m^6 \text{ or } -16m^6\end{aligned}$$

13. $\left(\frac{r^8}{s^2}\right)^3=\frac{(r^8)^3}{(s^2)^3}=\frac{r^{8\cdot 3}}{s^{2\cdot 3}}=\frac{r^{24}}{s^6}$

15. (a) $6^0 = 1$; B

(b) $-6^0 = -1$; C

(c) $(-6)^0 = 1$; B

(d) $-(-6)^0 = -1$; C

17. Answers will vary.
$x^2 + x^2 = 2x^2$

19. $-5x^{11}$ is a polynomial. It is a monomial since it has one term. It has degree 11 since 11 is the highest exponent.

21. $18p^5q + 6pq$ is a polynomial. It is a binomial since it has two terms. It has degree 6 because 6 is the sum of the exponents in the term $18p^5q$, and this term has a higher degree than the term $6pq$.

23. $\sqrt{2}x^2 + \sqrt{3}x^6$ is a polynomial. It is a binomial since it has two terms. It has degree 6 since 6 is the highest exponent.

25. $\frac{1}{3}r^2s^2 - \frac{3}{5}r^4s^2 + rs^3$ is a polynomial. It is a trinomial since it has three terms. It has degree 6 because the sum of the exponents in the term $-\frac{3}{5}r^4s^2$ is 6, and this term has the highest degree.

27. $\frac{5}{p} + \frac{2}{p^2} + \frac{5}{p^3}$ is not a polynomial since positive exponents in the denominator are equivalent to negative exponents in the numerator.

29. $\left(3x^2 - 4x + 5\right) + \left(-2x^2 + 3x - 2\right) = (3-2)x^2 + (-4+3)x + \left[5 + (-2)\right] = 1 \cdot x^2 + (-1)x + 3 = x^2 - x + 3$

31.
$$\begin{aligned}2\left(12y^2 - 8y + 6\right) - 4\left(3y^2 - 4y + 2\right) &= 2\left(12y^2\right) - 2(8y) + 2(6) - 4\left(3y^2\right) - 4(-4y) - 4 \cdot 2\\ &= 24y^2 - 16y + 12 - 12y^2 + 16y - 8 = 12y^2 + 4\end{aligned}$$

33.
$$\begin{aligned}\left(6m^4 - 3m^2 + m\right) - \left(2m^3 + 5m^2 + 4m\right) + \left(m^2 - m\right) &= 6m^4 - 3m^2 + m - 2m^3 - 5m^2 - 4m + m^2 - m\\ &= 6m^4 - 2m^3 + (-3-5+1)m^2 + (1-4-1)m\\ &= 6m^4 - 2m^3 + (-7)m^2 + (-4)m\\ &= 6m^4 - 2m^3 - 7m^2 - 4m\end{aligned}$$

35. $(4r-1)(7r+2) = 4r(7r) + 4r(2) - 1(7r) - 1(2) = 28r^2 + 8r - 7r - 2 = 28r^2 + r - 2$

37.
$$\begin{aligned}x^2\left(3x - \frac{2}{3}\right)\left(5x + \frac{1}{3}\right) &= x^2\left[\left(3x - \frac{2}{3}\right)\left(5x + \frac{1}{3}\right)\right] = x^2\left[(3x)(5x) + (3x)\left(\frac{1}{3}\right) - \frac{2}{3}(5x) - \frac{2}{3}\left(\frac{1}{3}\right)\right]\\ &= x^2\left(15x^2 + x - \frac{10}{3}x - \frac{2}{9}\right) = x^2\left(15x^2 + \frac{3}{3}x - \frac{10}{3}x - \frac{2}{9}\right)\\ &= x^2\left(15x^2 - \frac{7}{3}x - \frac{2}{9}\right) = 15x^4 - \frac{7}{3}x^3 - \frac{2}{9}x^2\end{aligned}$$

39. $4x^2\left(3x^3 + 2x^2 - 5x + 1\right) = 4x^2\left(3x^3\right) + 4x^2\left(2x^2\right) - 4x^2(5x) + 4x^2 \cdot 1 = 12x^5 + 8x^4 - 20x^3 + 4x^2$

41. $(2z-1)(-z^2+3z-4)=(2z-1)(-z^2)+(2z-1)(3z)-(2z-1)(4)$
$=2z(-z^2)-1(-z^2)+2z(3z)-1(3z)-(2z)(4)-(-1)(4)$
$=-2z^3+z^2+6z^2-3z-8z-(-4)=-2z^3+7z^2-11z+4$

We may also multiply vertically.

$$\begin{array}{rl} -z^2+3z-4 & \\ \underline{2z-1} & \\ z^2-3z+4 & \leftarrow -1(-z^2+3z-4) \\ \underline{-2z^3+6z^2-8z\quad} & \leftarrow 2z(-z^2+3z-4) \\ -2z^3+7z^2-11z+4 & \end{array}$$

43. $(m-n+k)(m+2n-3k)=(m-n+k)(m)+(m-n+k)(2n)-(m-n+k)(3k)$
$=m^2-mn+km+2mn-2n^2+2kn-3km+3kn-3k^2$
$=m^2+mn-2n^2-2km+5kn-3k^2$

We may also multiply vertically.

$$\begin{array}{rl} m-n+k & \\ \underline{m+2n-3k} & \\ -3km+3kn-3k^2 & \leftarrow -3k(m-n+k) \\ 2mn-2n^2\quad +2kn\quad & \leftarrow 2n(m-n+k) \\ \underline{m^2-mn\quad +km\qquad\qquad} & \leftarrow m(m-n+k) \\ m^2+mn-2n^2-2km+5kn-3k^2 & \end{array}$$

45. $(2m+3)(2m-3)=(2m)^2-3^2$
$=4m^2-9$

47. $(4x^2-5y)(4x^2+5y)=(4x^2)^2-(5y)^2$
$=16x^4-25y^2$

49. $(4m+2n)^2=(4m)^2+2(4m)(2n)+(2n)^2$
$=16m^2+16mn+4n^2$

51. $(5r-3t^2)^2=(5r)^2-2(5r)(3t^2)+(3t^2)^2$
$=25r^2-30rt^2+9t^4$

53. $\left[(2p-3)+q\right]^2=(2p-3)^2+2(2p-3)(q)+q^2=(2p)^2-2(2p)(3)+(3)^2+4pq-6q+q^2$
$=4p^2-12p+9+4pq-6q+q^2$

55. $[(3q+5)-p][(3q+5)+p]=(3q+5)^2-p^2=[(3q)^2+2(3q)(5)+5^2]-p^2=9q^2+30q+25-p^2$

57. $[(3a+b)-1]^2=(3a+b)^2-2(3a+b)(1)+1^2$
$=(9a^2+6ab+b^2)-2(3a+b)+1=9a^2+6ab+b^2-6a-2b+1$

59. $(y+2)^3=(y+2)^2(y+2)=(y^2+4y+4)(y+2)=y^3+4y^2+4y+2y^2+8y+8=y^3+6y^2+12y+8$

61. $(q-2)^4=(q-2)^2(q-2)^2=\left(q^2-4q+4\right)\left(q^2-4q+4\right)$

$=q^4-4q^3+4q^2-4q^3+16q^2-16q+4q^2-16q+16=q^4-8q^3+24q^2-32q+16$

63. $\left(p^3-4p^2+p\right)-\left(3p^2+2p+7\right)=p^3-4p^2+p-3p^2-2p-7=p^3-7p^2-p-7$

65. $(7m+2n)(7m-2n)=(7m)^2-(2n)^2=49m^2-4n^2$

67. $-3(4q^2-3q+2)+2(-q^2+q-4)=-12q^2+9q-6-2q^2+2q-8=-14q^2+11q-14$

69. $p(4p-6)+2(3p-8)=4p^2-6p+6p-16\ =4p^2-16$

71. $-y(y^2-4)+6y^2(2y-3)=-y^3+4y+12y^3-18y^2=11y^3-18y^2+4y$

73.
$$\begin{array}{r|l}
 & 2x^5+7x^4-5x^2+7 \\
\hline
-2x^2 & -4x^7-14x^6+10x^4-14x^2 \\
 & \underline{-4x^7} \\
 & \quad -14x^6 \\
 & \quad \underline{-14x^6} \\
 & \qquad 10x^4 \\
 & \qquad \underline{10x^4} \\
 & \qquad\quad -14x^2 \\
 & \qquad\quad \underline{-14x^2} \\
 & \qquad\qquad 0
\end{array}$$

$$\frac{-4x^7-14x^6+10x^4-14x^2}{-2x^2}=2x^5+7x^4-5x^2+7$$

75.
$$\begin{array}{r|l}
 & -5x^2+8 \\
\hline
-2x^6 & 10x^8-16x^6-4x^4 \\
 & \underline{10x^8} \\
 & \quad -16x^6 \\
 & \quad \underline{-16x^6} \\
 & \qquad -4x^4
\end{array}$$

$$\frac{10x^8-16x^6-4x^4}{-2x^6}=-5x^2+8-\frac{4x^4}{-2x^6}$$

$$=-5x^2+8+\frac{2}{x^2}$$

77.
$$\begin{array}{r|l}
 & 2m^2+m-2 \\
\hline
3m+2 & 6m^3+7m^2-4m+2 \\
 & \underline{6m^3+4m^2} \\
 & \quad 3m^2-4m \\
 & \quad \underline{3m^2+2m} \\
 & \qquad -6m+2 \\
 & \qquad \underline{-6m-4} \\
 & \qquad\qquad 6
\end{array}$$

$$\frac{6m^3+7m^2-4m+2}{3m+2}=2m^2+m-2+\frac{6}{3m+2}$$

79.
$$\begin{array}{r|l} & x^3 - x^2 - x + 4 \\ 3x+3 & 3x^4 - 0x^3 - 6x^2 + 9x - 5 \\ & \underline{3x^4 + 3x^3} \\ & -3x^3 - 6x^2 \\ & \underline{-3x^3 - 3x^2} \\ & -3x^2 + 9x \\ & \underline{-3x^2 - 3x} \\ & 12x - 5 \\ & \underline{12x + 12} \\ & -17 \end{array}$$

Thus, $\dfrac{3x^4 - 6x^2 + 9x - 5}{3x+3} = x^3 - x^2 - x + 4 + \dfrac{-17}{3x+3}$ or $x^3 - x^2 - x + 4 - \dfrac{17}{3x+3}$.

81. $99 \times 101 = (100-1)(100+1) = 100^2 - 1^2$
$= 10{,}000 - 1 = 9999$

83. $102^2 = (100+2)^2 = 100^2 + 2(100)(2) + 2^2$
$= 10{,}000 + 400 + 4 = 10{,}404$

82. $63 \times 57 = (60+3)(60-3) = 60^2 - 3^2$
$= 3600 - 9 = 3591$

84. $71^2 = (70+1)^2 = 70^2 + 2(70)(1) + 1^2$
$= 4900 + 140 + 1 = 5041$

85. **(a)** The area of the largest square is $s^2 = (x+y)^2$.

(b) The areas of the two squares are x^2 and y^2. The area of each rectangle is xy. Therefore, the area of the largest square can be written as $x^2 + 2xy + y^2$.

(c) Answers will vary. The total area must equal the sum of the four parts.

(d) It reinforces the special product for squaring a binomial: $(x+y)^2 = x^2 + 2xy + y^2$.

87. **(a)** The volume is
$V = \frac{1}{3}h(a^2 + ab + b^2) = \frac{1}{3}(200)(314^2 + 314 \times 756 + 756^2) \approx 60{,}501{,}000\,\text{ft}^3$.

(b) The shape becomes a rectangular box with a square base. Its volume is given by length × width × height or b^2h.

(c) If we let $a = b$, then $\frac{1}{3}h(a^2 + ab + b^2)$ becomes $\frac{1}{3}h(b^2 + bb + b^2)$, which simplifies to hb^2. Yes, the Egyptian formula gives the same result.

89. $x = 1940$
$0.000020591075(1940)^3 - 0.1201456829(1940)^2 + 233.5530856(1940) - 151{,}249.8184 \approx 6.2$
The formula is 0.1 high.

91. $x = 1978$
$0.000020591075(1978)^3 - 0.1201456829(1978)^2 + 233.5530856(1978) - 151{,}249.8184 \approx 2.3$
The formula is exact.

93. $\left(0.25^3\right)\left(400^3\right)=\left[(0.25)(400)\right]^3$
$=100^3=1{,}000{,}000$

95. $\dfrac{4.2^5}{2.1^5}=\left(\dfrac{4.2}{2.1}\right)^5=2^5=32$

97. $(y-x)^3=(y-x)^2(y-x)=\left(y^2-2yx+x^2\right)(y-x)=y^3-2y^2x+x^2y-y^2x+2yx^2-x^3$
$=y^3-3y^2x+3x^2y-x^3$

$-(x-y)^3=-(x-y)^2(x-y)=-\left(x^2-2xy+y^2\right)(x-y)=-\left(x^3-2x^2y+y^2x-x^2y+2xy^2-y^3\right)$
$=-\left(x^3-3x^2y+3xy^2-y^3\right)=-x^3+3x^2y-3xy^2+y^3$

Both expressions are equal to $-x^3+3x^2y-3xy^2+y^3$.

Section R.4: Factoring Polynomials

1. The greatest common factor is 12.
$12m+60=12(m)+12(5)=12(m+5)$

3. The greatest common factor is $8k$.
$8k^3+24k=8k\left(k^2\right)+8k(3)=8k\left(k^2+3\right)$

5. The greatest common factor is xy.
$xy-5xy^2=xy\cdot 1-xy(5y)=xy(1-5y)$

7. The greatest common factor is $-2p^2q^4$.
$-4p^3q^4-2p^2q^5=\left(-2p^2q^4\right)(2p)+\left(-2p^2q^4\right)(q)=-2p^2q^4(2p+q)$

9. The greatest common factor is $4k^2m^3$.
$4k^2m^3+8k^4m^3-12k^2m^4=\left(4k^2m^3\right)(1)+\left(4k^2m^3\right)\left(2k^2\right)-\left(4k^2m^3\right)(3m)=4k^2m^3\left(1+2z^2-3m\right)$

11. The greatest common factor is $2(a+b)$.
$2(a+b)+4m(a+b)=\left[2(a+b)\right](1)+\left[2(a+b)\right](2m)=2(a+b)(1+2m)$

13. $(5r-6)(r+3)-(2r-1)(r+3)=(r+3)[(5r-6)-(2r-1)]=(r+3)[5r-6-2r+1]=(r+3)(3r-5)$

15. $2(m-1)-3(m-1)^2+2(m-1)^3=(m-1)\left[2-3(m-1)+2(m-1)^2\right]=(m-1)\left[2-3m+3+2(m^2-2m+1)\right]$
$=(m-1)(2-3m+3+2m^2-4m+2)=(m-1)(2m^2-7m+7)$

17. $6st+9t-10s-15=(6st+9t)-(10s+15)=3t(2s+3)-5(2s+3)=(2s+3)(3t-5)$

19. $2m^4+6-am^4-3a=(2m^4+6)-(am^4+3a)=2(m^4+3)-a(m^4+3)=(m^4+3)(2-a)$

21. $20z^2-8x+5pz^2-2px=\left(20z^2-8x\right)+\left(5pz^2-2px\right)=4\left(5z^2-2x\right)+p\left(5z^2-2x\right)=\left(5z^2-2x\right)(4+p)$

23. The positive factors of 6 could be 2 and 3, or 1 and 6. Since the middle term is negative, we know the factors of 4 must both be negative. As factors of 4, we could have -1 and -4, or -2 and -2. Try different combinations of these factors until the correct one is found.
$6a^2-11a+4=(2a-1)(3a-4)$

25. The positive factors of 3 are 1 and 3. Since the middle term is positive, we know the factors of 8 must both be positive. As factors of 8, we could have 1 and 8, or 2 and 4. Try different combinations of these factors until the correct one is found.
$3m^2+14m+8=(3m+2)(m+4)$

27. The positive factors of 6 could be 2 and 3, or 1 and 6. As factors of –6, we could have –1 and 6, –6 and 1, –2 and 3, or –3 and 2. Try different combinations of these factors until the correct one is found.
$6k^2+5kp-6p^2=(2k+3p)(3k-2p)$

29. The positive factors of 5 can only be 1 and 5. As factors of –6, we could have –1 and 6, –6 and 1, –2 and 3, or –3 and 2. Try different combinations of these factors until the correct one is found.
$5a^2-7ab-6b^2=(5a+3b)(a-2b)$

31. $9x^2-6x^3+x^4=x^2(9-6x+x^2)=x^2(3-x)^2$

33. Factor out the greatest common factor, $2a^2$: $24a^4+10a^3b-4a^2b^2=2a^2\left(12a^2+5ab-2b^2\right)$

Now factor the trinomial by trial and error: $12a^2+5ab-2b^2=(4a-b)(3a+2b)$

Thus, $24a^4+10a^3b-4a^2b^2=2a^2\left(12a^2+5ab-2b^2\right)=2a^2(4a-b)(3a+2b)$.

35. $9m^2-12m+4=(3m)^2-12m+2^2=(3m)^2-2(3m)(2)+2^2=(3m-2)^2$

37. $32a^2+48ab+18b^2=2(16a^2+24ab+9b^2)=2[(4a)^2+24ab+(3b)^2]$
$=2[(4a)^2+2(4a)(3b)+(3b)^2]=2(4a+3b)^2$

39. $4x^2y^2+28xy+49=(2xy)^2+28xy+7^2=(2xy)^2+2(2xy)(7)+7^2=(2xy+7)^2$

41. $(a-3b)^2-6(a-3b)+9=(a-3b)^2-6(a-3b)+3^2$
$=(a-3b)^2-2(a-3b)(3)+3^2=[(a-3b)-3]^2=(a-3b-3)^2$

43. **(a)** Since $(x+5y)^2=x^2+10xy+25y^2$, a matches B.
(b) Since $(x-5y)^2=x^2-10xy+25y^2$, b matches C.
(c) Since $(x+5y)(x-5y)=x^2-25y^2$, c matches A.
(d) Since $(5y+x)(5y-x)=25y^2-x^2$, d matches D.

45. $9a^2-16=(3a)^2-4^2$
$=(3a+4)(3a-4)$

47. $25s^4-9t^2=(5s^2)^2-(3t)^2$
$=(5s^2+3t)(5s^2-3t)$

49. $(a+b)^2-16=(a+b)^2-4^2=[(a+b)+4][(a+b)-4]=(a+b+4)(a+b-4)$

51. $p^4-625=(p^2)^2-25^2=(p^2+25)(p^2-25)=(p^2+25)(p^2-5^2)$
$=(p^2+25)(p+5)(p-5)$ Note that p^2+25 is a prime factor.

53. $8-a^3=2^3-a^3=(2-a)(2^2+2\cdot a+a^2)=(2-a)(4+2a+a^2)$

55. $125x^3 - 27 = (5x)^3 - 3^3 = (5x-3)\left[(5x)^2 + 5x \cdot 3 + 3^2\right] = (5x-3)(25x^2 + 15x + 9)$

57. $27y^9 + 125z^6 = (3y^3)^3 + (5z^2)^3$

$$= (3y^3 + 5z^2)\left[(3y^3)^2 - (3y^3)(5z^2) + (5z^2)^2\right] = (3y^3 + 5z^2)(9y^6 - 15y^3z^2 + 25z^4)$$

59. $(r+6)^3 - 216 = (r+6)^3 - 6^3 = \left[(r+6) - 6\right]\left[(r+6)^2 + (r+6)(6) + 6^2\right]$

$$= \left[(r+6) - 6\right]\left[r^2 + 12r + 36 + (r+6)(6) + 6^2\right]$$

$$= \left[r + 6 - 6\right]\left[r^2 + 12r + 36 + 6r + 36 + 36\right] = r(r^2 + 18r + 108)$$

61. $27 - (m+2n)^3 = 3^3 - (m+2n)^3 = \left[3 - (m+2n)\right]\left[3^2 + (3)(m+2n) + (m+2n)^2\right]$

$$= \left[3 - (m+2n)\right]\left[3^2 + (3)(m+2n) + m^2 + 4mn + 4n^2\right]$$

$$= (3 - m - 2n)(9 + 3m + 6n + m^2 + 4mn + 4n^2)$$

63. The correct complete factorization of $x^4 - 1$ is B: $(x^2+1)(x+1)(x-1)$. Choice A is not a complete factorization, since $x^2 - 1$ can be factored as $(x+1)(x-1)$. The other choices are not correct factorizations of $x^4 - 1$.

65. $x^6 - 1 = (x^3)^2 - 1^2 = (x^3+1)(x^3-1)$ or $(x^3-1)(x^3+1)$

Use the patterns for the difference of cubes and sum of cubes to factor further. Since $x^3 - 1 = (x-1)(x^2+x+1)$ and $x^3 + 1 = (x+1)(x^2-x+1)$, we obtain the factorization $x^6 - 1 = (x^3-1)(x^3+1) = (x-1)(x^2+x+1)(x+1)(x^2-x+1)$.

66. $x^6 - 1 = (x^2)^3 - 1^3 = (x^2-1)\left[(x^2)^2 + x^2 \cdot 1 + 1^2\right] = (x^2-1)(x^4+x^2+1) = (x-1)(x+1)(x^4+x^2+1)$

67. From Exercise 65, we have $x^6 - 1 = (x-1)(x^2+x+1)(x+1)(x^2-x+1)$.

From Exercise 66, we have $x^6 - 1 = (x-1)(x+1)(x^4+x^2+1)$.

Comparing these answers, we see that $x^4 + x^2 + 1 = (x^2-x+1)(x^2+x+1)$.

68. Note: The reason for each step is given following that step.

$x^4 + x^2 + 1 = x^4 + 2x^2 + 1 - x^2$

Additive inverse property

(0 in the form $x^2 - x^2$)

$= (x^4 + 2x^2 + 1) - x^2$

Associative property of addition

$= (x^2+1)^2 - x^2$

Factoring a perfect square trinomial

$= (x^2 + 1 - x)(x^2 + 1 + x)$

Factoring the difference of squares

$= (x^2 - x + 1)(x^2 + x + 1)$

Commutative property of addition

69. The answer in Exercise 67 and the final line in Exercise 68 are the same.

70. $x^8 + x^4 + 1 = x^8 + 2x^4 + 1 - x^4 = (x^8 + 2x^4 + 1) - x^4 = (x^4 + 1)^2 - (x^2)^2$

$= (x^4 + 1 - x^2)(x^4 + 1 + x^2) = (x^4 - x^2 + 1)(x^4 + x^2 + 1) = (x^4 - x^2 + 1)(x^2 + x + 1)(x^2 - x + 1)$

Use result from Exercise 68.

71. $m^4 - 3m^2 - 10$

Let $x = m^2$, so that $x^2 = (m^2)^2 = m^4$. We have $x^2 - 3x - 10 = (x-5)(x+2)$. Replacing x with m^2 gives $m^4 - 3m^2 - 10 = (m^2 - 5)(m^2 + 2)$.

73. Let $x = 3k - 1$. This substitution gives $7(3k-1)^2 + 26(3k-1) - 8 = 7x^2 + 26x - 8 = (7x-2)(x+4)$. Replacing x with $3k - 1$ gives the following.

$$7(3k-1)^2 + 26(3k-1) - 8 = [7(3k-1) - 2][(3k-1) + 4] = (21k - 7 - 2)(3k - 1 + 4)$$
$$= (21k - 9)(3k + 3) = 3(7k - 3)(3)(k + 1) = 9(7k - 3)(k + 1)$$

75. Let $x = a - 4$. This substitution gives the following.

$$9(a-4)^2 + 30(a-4) + 25 = 9x^2 + 30x + 25 = (3x)^2 + 2(3x)(5) + 5^2 = (3x+5)^2$$

Replacing x by $a - 4$ gives $9(a-4)^2 + 30(a-4) + 25 = [3(a-4)+5]^2 = (3a - 12 + 5)^2 = (3a-7)^2$.

77. $4b^2 + 4bc + c^2 - 16 = (4b^2 + 4bc + c^2) - 16 = \left[(2b)^2 + 2(2b)(c) + c^2\right] - 16$

$= (2b+c)^2 - 4^2 = [(2b+c)+4][(2b+c)-4] = (2b+c+4)(2b+c-4)$

79. $x^2 + xy - 5x - 5y = (x^2 + xy) - (5x + 5y) = x(x+y) - 5(x+y) = (x+y)(x-5)$

81. $p^4(m-2n) + q(m-2n) = (m-2n)(p^4 + q)$

83. $4z^2 + 28z + 49 = (2z)^2 + 2(2z)(7) + 7^2$

$= (2z+7)^2$

85. $1000x^3 + 343y^3 = (10x)^3 + (7y)^3$

$= (10x + 7y)\left[(10x)^2 - (10x)(7y) + (7y)^2\right] = (10x + 7y)(100x^2 - 70xy + 49y^2)$

87. $125m^6 - 216 = (5m^2)^3 - 6^3 = (5m^2 - 6)\left[(5m^2)^2 + 5m^2(6) + 6^2\right] = (5m^2 - 6)(25m^4 + 30m^2 + 36)$

89. $64 + (3x+2)^3 = 4^3 + (3x+2)^3 = \left[4 + (3x+2)\right]\left[4^2 - (4)(3x+2) + (3x+2)^2\right]$

$= \left[4 + (3x+2)\right]\left[4^2 - (4)(3x+2) + 9x^2 + 12x + 4\right]$

$= (4 + 3x + 2)(16 - 12x - 8 + 9x^2 + 12x + 4) = (3x+6)(9x^2 + 12)$

$= 3(x+2)(3)(3x^2 + 4) = 9(x+2)(3x^2 + 4)$

91. $4p^2+3p-1$

The positive factors of 4 could be 2 and 2 or 1 and 4. The factors of –1 can only be 1 and –1. Try different combinations of these factors until the correct one is found.

$4p^2+3p-1=(4p-1)(p+1)$

93. $144z^2+121$

The sum of squares cannot be factored. $144z^2+121$ is prime.

95. $(x+y)^2-(x-y)^2=[(x+y)+(x-y)][(x+y)-(x-y)]$

$=(x+y+x-y)(x+y-x+y)=(2x)(2y)=4xy$

97. Answers will vary.

99. $4z^2+bz+81=(2z)^2+bz+9^2$ will be a perfect trinomial if $bz=\pm 2(2z)(9)$

$bz=\pm 36z$

$b=\pm 36.$

If $b=36$, $4z^2+36z+81=(2z+9)^2$.

If $b=-36$, $4z^2-36z+81=(2z-9)^2$.

101. $100r^2-60r+c=(10r)^2-\underbrace{2(10r)(3)}_{60r}+c$

will be a perfect trinomial if $c=3^2=9$.

If $c=9$, $100r^2-60r+9=(10r-3)^2$.

Section R.5: Rational Expressions

1. In the rational expression $\frac{x+3}{x-6}$, the solution to the equation $x-6=0$ is excluded from the domain.

$x-6=0 \Rightarrow x=6$

The domain is $\{x \mid x \neq 6\}$.

3. In the rational expression $\frac{3x+7}{(4x+2)(x-1)}$, the solution to the equation $(4x+2)(x-1)=0$ is excluded from the domain.

$$(4x+2)(x-1)=0$$

$$4x+2=0 \quad \text{or} \quad x-1=0$$

$$4x=-2 \qquad x=1$$

$$x=-\tfrac{1}{2}$$

The domain is $\left\{x \mid x \neq -\frac{1}{2}, 1\right\}$.

5. In the rational expression $\frac{12}{x^2+5x+6}$, the solution to the equation $x^2+5x+6=0$ is excluded from the domain.

$$x^2+5x+6=0$$

$$(x+3)(x+2)=0$$

$$x+3=0 \quad \text{or} \quad x+2=0$$

$$x=-3 \qquad x=-2$$

The domain is $\{x \mid x \neq -3, -2\}$.

7. If $x=4$ and $y=2$, then

(a) $\frac{1}{x}+\frac{1}{y}=\frac{1}{4}+\frac{1}{2}=\frac{1}{4}+\frac{2}{4}=\frac{3}{4}$ and

(b) $\frac{1}{x+y}=\frac{1}{4+2}=\frac{1}{6}$.

8. No; $\frac{1}{x}+\frac{1}{y}\neq\frac{1}{x+y}$.

9. If $x=3$ and $y=5$, then

(a) $\frac{1}{x}-\frac{1}{y}=\frac{1}{3}-\frac{1}{5}=\frac{5}{15}-\frac{3}{15}=\frac{2}{15}$ and

(b) $\frac{1}{x-y}=\frac{1}{3-5}=\frac{1}{-2}=-\frac{1}{2}$.

10. No; $\frac{1}{x}-\frac{1}{y}\neq\frac{1}{x-y}$.

11. $\frac{8k+16}{9k+18}=\frac{8(k+2)}{9(k+2)}=\frac{8}{9}$

13. $\frac{3(3-t)}{(t+5)(t-3)}=\frac{3(3-t)(-1)}{(t+5)(t-3)(-1)}=\frac{-3}{t+5}$

15. $\frac{8x^2+16x}{4x^2}=\frac{8x(x+2)}{4x^2}=\frac{2\cdot 4x(x+2)}{x\cdot 4x}$
$=\frac{2(x+2)}{x}$ or $\frac{2x+4}{x}$

17. $\frac{m^2-4m+4}{m^2+m-6}=\frac{(m-2)(m-2)}{(m-2)(m+3)}=\frac{m-2}{m+3}$

19. $\frac{8m^2+6m-9}{16m^2-9}=\frac{(2m+3)(4m-3)}{(4m+3)(4m-3)}=\frac{2m+3}{4m+3}$

21. $\frac{15p^3}{9p^2}\div\frac{6p}{10p^2}=\frac{15p^3}{9p^2}\cdot\frac{10p^2}{6p}=\frac{150p^5}{54p^3}$
$=\frac{25\cdot 6p^5}{9\cdot 6p^3}=\frac{25p^2}{9}$

23. $\frac{2k+8}{6}\div\frac{3k+12}{2}=\frac{2k+8}{6}\cdot\frac{2}{3k+12}$
$=\frac{2(k+4)(2)}{6(3)(k+4)}=\frac{2}{9}$

25. $\frac{x^2+x}{5}\cdot\frac{25}{xy+y}=\frac{x(x+1)}{5}\cdot\frac{25}{y(x+1)}=\frac{25x(x+1)}{5y(x+1)}=\frac{5x}{y}$

27. $\frac{4a+12}{2a-10}\div\frac{a^2-9}{a^2-a-20}=\frac{4a+12}{2a-10}\cdot\frac{a^2-a-20}{a^2-9}=\frac{4(a+3)}{2(a-5)}\cdot\frac{(a-5)(a+4)}{(a+3)(a-3)}=\frac{2(a+4)}{a-3}$ or $\frac{2a+8}{a-3}$

29. $\frac{p^2-p-12}{p^2-2p-15}\cdot\frac{p^2-9p+20}{p^2-8p+16}=\frac{(p-4)(p+3)}{(p-5)(p+3)}\cdot\frac{(p-5)(p-4)}{(p-4)(p-4)}=1$

31. $\frac{m^2+3m+2}{m^2+5m+4}\div\frac{m^2+5m+6}{m^2+10m+24}=\frac{m^2+3m+2}{m^2+5m+4}\cdot\frac{m^2+10m+24}{m^2+5m+6}$
$=\frac{(m+2)(m+1)}{(m+4)(m+1)}\cdot\frac{(m+6)(m+4)}{(m+3)(m+2)}=\frac{m+6}{m+3}$

33. $\frac{xz-xw+2yz-2yw}{z^2-w^2}\cdot\frac{4z+4w+xz+wx}{16-x^2}=\frac{x(z-w)+2y(z-w)}{(z+w)(z-w)}\cdot\frac{4(z+w)+x(z+w)}{(4+x)(4-x)}$
$=\frac{(z-w)(x+2y)}{(z+w)(z-w)}\cdot\frac{(z+w)(4+x)}{(4+x)(4-x)}=\frac{x+2y}{4-x}$

35. $\frac{x^3+y^3}{x^3-y^3}\cdot\frac{x^2-y^2}{x^2+2xy+y^2}=\frac{(x+y)(x^2-xy+y^2)}{(x-y)(x^2+xy+y^2)}\cdot\frac{(x+y)(x-y)}{(x+y)(x+y)}=\frac{x^2-xy+y^2}{x^2+xy+y^2}$

37. Expressions (B) and (C) are both equal to −1, since the numerator and denominator are additive inverses.

B. $\frac{-x-4}{x+4}=\frac{-1(x+4)}{x+4}=-1$

C. $\frac{x-4}{4-x}=\frac{-1(4-x)}{4-x}=-1$

39. $\frac{3}{2k}+\frac{5}{3k}=\frac{3\cdot 3}{2k\cdot 3}+\frac{5\cdot 2}{3k\cdot 2}=\frac{9}{6k}+\frac{10}{6k}=\frac{19}{6k}$

41. $\frac{1}{6m}+\frac{2}{5m}+\frac{4}{m}=\frac{1\cdot 5}{6m\cdot 5}+\frac{2\cdot 6}{5m\cdot 6}+\frac{4\cdot 30}{m\cdot 30}$
$=\frac{5}{30m}+\frac{12}{30m}+\frac{120}{30m}=\frac{137}{30m}$

43. $\frac{1}{a}-\frac{b}{a^2}=\frac{1\cdot a}{a\cdot a}-\frac{b}{a^2}=\frac{a}{a^2}-\frac{b}{a^2}=\frac{a-b}{a^2}$

45. $\frac{5}{12x^2y}-\frac{11}{6xy}=\frac{5}{12x^2y}-\frac{11\cdot 2x}{6xy\cdot 2x}$
$=\frac{5}{12x^2y}-\frac{22x}{12x^2y}=\frac{5-22x}{12x^2y}$

47. $\frac{17y+3}{9y+7}-\frac{-10y-18}{9y+7}=\frac{(17y+3)-(-10y-18)}{9y+7}=\frac{17y+3+10y+18}{9y+7}=\frac{27y+21}{9y+7}=\frac{3(9y+7)}{9y+7}=3$

49. $\frac{1}{x+z}+\frac{1}{x-z}=\frac{1\cdot(x-z)}{(x+z)(x-z)}+\frac{1\cdot(x+z)}{(x-z)(x+z)}=\frac{(x-z)+(x+z)}{(x-z)(x+z)}=\frac{x-z+x+z}{(x+z)(x-z)}=\frac{2x}{(x+z)(x-z)}$

51. Since $a-2=(-1)(2-a)$ we have

$\frac{3}{a-2}-\frac{1}{2-a}=\frac{3}{a-2}-\frac{1(-1)}{(2-a)(-1)}=\frac{3}{a-2}-\frac{-1}{a-2}=\frac{3-(-1)}{a-2}=\frac{4}{a-2}.$

We may also use 2 – a as the common denominator.

$\frac{3}{a-2}-\frac{1}{2-a}=\frac{3(-1)}{(a-2)(-1)}-\frac{1}{2-a}=\frac{-3}{2-a}-\frac{1}{2-a}=\frac{-4}{2-a}$

The two results, $\frac{4}{a-2}$ and $\frac{-4}{2-a}$, are equivalent rational expressions.

53. Since $2x-y=(-1)(y-2x)$

$\frac{x+y}{2x-y}-\frac{2x}{y-2x}=\frac{x+y}{2x-y}-\frac{2x(-1)}{(y-2x)(-1)}=\frac{x+y}{2x-y}-\frac{-2x}{2x-y}=\frac{x+y-(-2x)}{2x-y}=\frac{x+y+2x}{2x-y}=\frac{3x+y}{2x-y}.$

We may also use $y-2x$ as the common denominator. In this case, our result will be $\frac{-3x-y}{y-2x}$. The two results are equivalent rational expressions.

55. $\frac{4}{x+1}+\frac{1}{x^2-x+1}-\frac{12}{x^3+1}=\frac{4}{x+1}+\frac{1}{x^2-x+1}-\frac{12}{(x+1)(x^2-x+1)}$

$=\frac{4(x^2-x+1)}{(x+1)(x^2-x+1)}+\frac{1(x+1)}{(x+1)(x^2-x+1)}-\frac{12}{(x+1)(x^2-x+1)}=\frac{4(x^2-x+1)+(x+1)-12}{(x+1)(x^2-x+1)}$

$=\frac{4x^2-4x+4+x+1-12}{(x+1)(x^2-x+1)}=\frac{4x^2-3x-7}{(x+1)(x^2-x+1)}=\frac{(4x-7)(x+1)}{(x+1)(x^2-x+1)}=\frac{4x-7}{x^2-x+1}$

57. $$\frac{3x}{x^2+x-12}-\frac{x}{x^2-16}=\frac{3x}{(x-3)(x+4)}-\frac{x}{(x-4)(x+4)}=\frac{3x(x-4)}{(x-3)(x+4)(x-4)}-\frac{x(x-3)}{(x-4)(x+4)(x-3)}$$
$$=\frac{3x(x-4)-x(x-3)}{(x-3)(x+4)(x-4)}=\frac{3x^2-12x-x^2+3x}{(x-3)(x+4)(x-4)}=\frac{2x^2-9x}{(x-3)(x+4)(x-4)}$$

59. $$\frac{1+\frac{1}{x}}{1-\frac{1}{x}}=\frac{x\left(1+\frac{1}{x}\right)}{x\left(1-\frac{1}{x}\right)}=\frac{x\cdot 1+x\left(\frac{1}{x}\right)}{x\cdot 1-x\left(\frac{1}{x}\right)}=\frac{x+1}{x-1}$$

61. $$\frac{\frac{1}{x+1}-\frac{1}{x}}{\frac{1}{x}}=\frac{x(x+1)\left(\frac{1}{x+1}-\frac{1}{x}\right)}{x(x+1)\left(\frac{1}{x}\right)}=\frac{x(x+1)\left(\frac{1}{x+1}\right)-x(x+1)\left(\frac{1}{x}\right)}{x(x+1)\left(\frac{1}{x}\right)}=\frac{x-(x+1)}{x+1}=\frac{x-x-1}{x+1}=\frac{-1}{x+1}$$

63. $$\frac{1+\frac{1}{1-b}}{1-\frac{1}{1+b}}=\frac{(1-b)(1+b)\left(1+\frac{1}{1-b}\right)}{(1-b)(1+b)\left(1-\frac{1}{1+b}\right)}=\frac{(1-b)(1+b)(1)+(1-b)(1+b)\left(\frac{1}{1-b}\right)}{(1-b)(1+b)(1)-(1-b)(1+b)\left(\frac{1}{1+b}\right)}=\frac{(1-b)(1+b)+(1+b)}{(1-b)(1+b)-(1-b)}$$
$$=\frac{(1+b)[(1-b)+1]}{(1-b)[(1+b)-1]}=\frac{(1+b)(2-b)}{(1-b)b}\text{ or }\frac{(2-b)(1+b)}{b(1-b)}$$

65. $$\frac{m-\frac{1}{m^2-4}}{\frac{1}{m+2}}=\frac{m-\frac{1}{(m+2)(m-2)}}{\frac{1}{m+2}}$$

Multiply both numerator and denominator by the LCD of all the fractions, $(m+2)(m-2)$.

$$\frac{m-\frac{1}{m^2-4}}{\frac{1}{m+2}}=\frac{(m+2)(m-2)\left(m-\frac{1}{(m+2)(m-2)}\right)}{(m+2)(m-2)\left(\frac{1}{m+2}\right)}=\frac{(m+2)(m-2)(m)-(m+2)(m-2)\left(\frac{1}{(m+2)(m-2)}\right)}{(m+2)(m-2)\left(\frac{1}{m+2}\right)}$$
$$=\frac{m\left[(m+2)(m-2)\right]-1}{m-2}=\frac{m(m^2-4)-1}{m-2}=\frac{m^3-4m-1}{m-2}$$

67. $$\frac{\frac{1}{x+h}-\frac{1}{x}}{h}=\frac{x(x+h)\left(\frac{1}{x+h}-\frac{1}{x}\right)}{x(x+h)(h)}$$
$$=\frac{x(x+h)\left(\frac{1}{x+h}\right)-x(x+h)\left(\frac{1}{x}\right)}{x(x+h)(h)}=\frac{x-(x+h)}{x(x+h)(h)}=\frac{x-x-h}{x(x+h)(h)}=\frac{-h}{x(x+h)(h)}=\frac{-1}{x(x+h)}$$

69. Altitude of 7000 feet, $x = 7$ (thousand)

The distance from the origin is $\frac{7-7}{0.639(7)+1.75}=0$, which represents 0 miles.

71. $y=\frac{6.7x}{100-x}$; Let $x = 75$ (75%)

$$y=\frac{6.7(75)}{100-75}=\frac{502.5}{25}=20.1$$

The cost of removing 75% of the pollutant is 20.1 thousand dollars.

Section R.6: Rational Exponents

1. **(a)** $4^{-2} = \frac{1}{4^2} = \frac{1}{16}$; B

(b) $-4^{-2} = -\left(4^{-2}\right) = -\frac{1}{4^2} = -\frac{1}{16}$; D

(c) $(-4)^{-2} = \frac{1}{(-4)^2} = \frac{1}{16}$; B

(d) $-(-4)^{-2} = -\frac{1}{(-4)^2} = -\frac{1}{16}$; D

3. $(-4)^{-3} = \frac{1}{(-4)^3} = \frac{1}{-64} = -\frac{1}{64}$

5. $-(-5)^{-4} = -\frac{1}{(-5)^4} = -\frac{1}{625}$

7. $\left(\frac{1}{3}\right)^{-2} = \frac{1}{\left(\frac{1}{3}\right)^2} = \frac{1}{\frac{1}{9}} = 9$, also

$\left(\frac{1}{3}\right)^{-2} = \frac{1}{\left(\frac{1}{3}\right)^2} = \left(\frac{3}{1}\right)^2 = 3^2 = 9$

9. $(4x)^{-2} = \frac{1}{(4x)^2} = \frac{1}{16x^2}$

11. $4x^{-2} = 4 \cdot x^{-2} = 4 \cdot \frac{1}{x^2} = \frac{4}{x^2}$

13. $-a^{-3} = -\frac{1}{a^3}$

15. $\frac{4^8}{4^6} = 4^{8-6} = 4^2 = 16$

17. $\frac{x^{12}}{x^8} = x^{12-8} = x^4$

19. $\frac{r^7}{r^{10}} = r^{7-10} = r^{-3} = \frac{1}{r^3}$

21. $\frac{6^4}{6^{-2}} = 6^{4-(-2)} = 6^6$

Because 6^6 is a relatively large number, it is generally acceptable not to simplify it to be 46,656.

23. $\frac{4r^{-3}}{6r^{-6}} = \frac{4}{6} \cdot \frac{r^{-3}}{r^{-6}} = \frac{2}{3} r^{-3-(-6)} = \frac{2}{3} r^3 = \frac{2r^3}{3}$

25. $\frac{16m^{-5}n^4}{12m^2n^{-3}} = \frac{16}{12} \cdot \frac{m^{-5}}{m^2} \cdot \frac{n^4}{n^{-3}} = \frac{4}{3} m^{-5-2} n^{4-(-3)}$

$= \frac{4}{3} m^{-7} n^7 = \frac{4n^7}{3m^7}$

27. $-4r^{-2}\left(r^4\right)^2 = -4r^{-2}r^8 = -4r^{-2+8} = -4r^6$

29. $\left(5a^{-1}\right)^4\left(a^2\right)^{-3} = 5^4 a^{-4} a^{-6} = 5^4 a^{-4+(-6)}$

$= 5^4 a^{-10} = \frac{5^4}{a^{10}}$

Because 5^4 is a relatively large number, it is generally acceptable not to simplify to be $\frac{625}{a^{10}}$.

31. $\frac{\left(p^{-2}\right)^0}{5p^{-4}} = \frac{p^0}{5p^{-4}} = \frac{1}{5} \cdot \frac{p^0}{p^{-4}}$

$= \frac{1}{5} p^{0-(-4)} = \frac{1}{5} p^4 = \frac{p^4}{5}$

33. $\frac{(3pq)q^2}{6p^2q^4} = \frac{3pq^{1+2}}{6p^2q^4} = \frac{3pq^3}{6p^2q^4}$

$= \frac{3}{6} \cdot \frac{p}{p^2} \cdot \frac{q^3}{q^4} = \frac{1}{2} p^{1-2} q^{3-4}$

$= \frac{1}{2} p^{-1} q^{-1} = \frac{1}{2pq}$

35. $\frac{4a^5\left(a^{-1}\right)^3}{\left(a^{-2}\right)^{-2}} = \frac{4a^5a^{-3}}{a^4} = \frac{4a^{5+(-3)}}{a^4}$

$= \frac{4a^2}{a^4} = 4a^{2-4} = 4a^{-2} = \frac{4}{a^2}$

37. $169^{1/2} = 13$, because $13^2 = 169$.

39. $16^{1/4} = 2$, because $2^4 = 16$.

41. $\left(-\frac{64}{27}\right)^{1/3}=-\frac{4}{3}$, because $\left(-\frac{4}{3}\right)^{3}=-\frac{64}{27}$.

43. $(-4)^{1/2}$ is not a real number, because no real number, when squared, will yield a negative quantity.

45. (a) $\left(\frac{4}{9}\right)^{3/2}=\left[\left(\frac{4}{9}\right)^{1/2}\right]^3=\left(\frac{2}{3}\right)^3=\frac{8}{27}$; E

(b) $\left(\frac{4}{9}\right)^{-3/2}=\left(\frac{9}{4}\right)^{3/2}=\left[\left(\frac{9}{4}\right)^{1/2}\right]^3$

$=\left(\frac{3}{2}\right)^3=\frac{27}{8}$; G

(c) $-\left(\frac{9}{4}\right)^{3/2}=-\left[\left(\frac{9}{4}\right)^{1/2}\right]^3$

$=-\left(\frac{3}{2}\right)^3=-\frac{27}{8}$; F

(d) $-\left(\frac{4}{9}\right)^{-3/2}=-\left(\frac{9}{4}\right)^{3/2}=-\left[\left(\frac{9}{4}\right)^{1/2}\right]^3$

$=-\left(\frac{3}{2}\right)^3=-\frac{27}{8}$; F

47. $8^{2/3}=\left(8^{1/3}\right)^2=2^2=4$

49. $100^{3/2}=\left(100^{1/2}\right)^3=10^3=1000$

51. $-81^{3/4}=-\left(81^{1/4}\right)^3=-3^3=-27$

53. $\left(\frac{27}{64}\right)^{-4/3}=\left(\frac{64}{27}\right)^{4/3}$

$=\left[\left(\frac{64}{27}\right)^{1/3}\right]^4=\left(\frac{4}{3}\right)^4=\frac{256}{81}$

55. $3^{1/2}\cdot 3^{3/2}=3^{1/2+3/2}=3^{4/2}=3^2=9$

57. $\frac{64^{5/3}}{64^{4/3}}=64^{5/3-4/3}=64^{1/3}=4$

59. $y^{7/3}\cdot y^{-4/3}=y^{7/3+(-4/3)}=y^{3/3}=y^1=y$

61. $\frac{k^{1/3}}{k^{2/3}\cdot k^{-1}}=\frac{k^{1/3}}{k^{2/3+(-1)}}=\frac{k^{1/3}}{k^{2/3+(-3/3)}}$

$=\frac{k^{1/3}}{k^{-1/3}}=k^{1/3-(-1/3)}=k^{2/3}$

63. $\frac{\left(x^{1/4}y^{2/5}\right)^{20}}{x^2}=\frac{x^5y^8}{x^2}=x^{5-2}y^8=x^3y^8$

65. $\frac{\left(x^{2/3}\right)^2}{\left(x^2\right)^{7/3}}=\frac{x^{4/3}}{x^{14/3}}=x^{4/3-14/3}=x^{-10/3}=\frac{1}{x^{10/3}}$

67. $\left(\frac{16m^3}{n}\right)^{1/4}\left(\frac{9n^{-1}}{m^2}\right)^{1/2}=\frac{16^{1/4}m^{3/4}}{n^{1/4}}\cdot\frac{9^{1/2}n^{-1/2}}{m}=\frac{2m^{3/4}}{n^{1/4}}\cdot\frac{3n^{-1/2}}{m}=(2\cdot 3)\frac{m^{3/4}}{m}\cdot\frac{n^{-1/2}}{n^{1/4}}$

$=6m^{(3/4)-1}n^{(-1/2)-(1/4)}=6m^{(3/4)-(4/4)}n^{(-2/4)-(1/4)}=6m^{-1/4}n^{-3/4}=\frac{6}{m^{1/4}n^{3/4}}$

69. $\frac{p^{1/5}p^{7/10}p^{1/2}}{\left(p^3\right)^{-1/5}}=\frac{p^{1/5+7/10+1/2}}{p^{-3/5}}=\frac{p^{2/10+7/10+5/10}}{p^{-6/10}}=\frac{p^{14/10}}{p^{-6/10}}=p^{(14/10)-(-6/10)}=p^{20/10}=p^2$

71. (a) Let $w=25$

$t=\frac{31,293}{w^{1.5}}=\frac{31,293}{(25)^{3/2}}=\frac{31,293}{(25^{1/2})^3}=\frac{31,293}{(5)^3}=\frac{31,293}{125}\approx 250$ sec

(b) To double the weight, replace w with $2w$ to get $\frac{31,293}{(2w)^{1.5}}=\frac{31,293}{2^{3/2}w^{1.5}}=\frac{1}{2^{3/2}}(t)$; so the holding time changes by a factor of $\frac{1}{2^{3/2}}\approx .3536$.

73. $y^{5/8}(y^{3/8}-10y^{11/8}) = y^{5/8}y^{3/8} - 10y^{5/8}y^{11/8}$
$= y^{5/8+3/8} - 10y^{5/8+11/8}$
$= y - 10y^2$

75. $-4k(k^{7/3} - 6k^{1/3}) = -4k^1k^{7/3} + 24k^1k^{1/3}$
$= -4k^{10/3} + 24k^{4/3}$

77. $(x+x^{1/2})(x-x^{1/2})$ has the form $(a-b)(a+b) = a^2 - b^2$.
$(x+x^{1/2})(x-x^{1/2}) = x^2 - (x^{1/2})^2 = x^2 - x$

79. $\left(r^{1/2}-r^{-1/2}\right)^2 = \left(r^{1/2}\right)^2 - 2\left(r^{1/2}\right)\left(r^{-1/2}\right) + \left(r^{-1/2}\right)^2$
$= r - 2r^{(1/2)+(-1/2)} + r^{-1} = r - 2r^0 + r^{-1} = r - 2\cdot 1 + r^{-1} = r - 2 + r^{-1} = r - 2 + \frac{1}{r}$

81. Factor $4k^{-1} + k^{-2}$, using the common factor k^{-2}.
$4k^{-1} + k^{-2} = k^{-2}(4k+1)$

83. Factor $9z^{-1/2} + 2z^{1/2}$, using the common factor $z^{-1/2}$.
$9z^{-1/2} + 2z^{1/2} = z^{-1/2}(9+2z)$

85. Factor $p^{-3/4} - 2p^{-7/4}$, using the common factor $p^{-7/4}$.
$p^{-3/4} - 2p^{-7/4} = p^{-7/4}(p^{4/4} - 2) = p^{-7/4}(p-2)$

87. Factor $(p+4)^{-3/2} + (p+4)^{-1/2} + (p+4)^{1/2}$, using the common factor $(p+4)^{-3/2}$.
$(p+4)^{-3/2} + (p+4)^{-1/2} + (p+4)^{1/2} = (p+4)^{-3/2} \cdot [1 + (p+4) + (p+4)^2]$
$= (p+4)^{-3/2} \cdot (1 + p + 4 + p^2 + 8p + 16) = (p+4)^{-3/2}(p^2 + 9p + 21)$

89. $\dfrac{a^{-1}+b^{-1}}{(ab)^{-1}} = \dfrac{\frac{1}{a}+\frac{1}{b}}{\frac{1}{ab}} = \dfrac{\frac{1\cdot b}{a\cdot b}+\frac{1\cdot a}{b\cdot a}}{\frac{1}{ab}} = \dfrac{\frac{b+a}{ab}}{\frac{1}{ab}} = \dfrac{b+a}{ab}\cdot\dfrac{ab}{1} = b+a$

91. $\dfrac{r^{-1}+q^{-1}}{r^{-1}-q^{-1}}\cdot\dfrac{r-q}{r+q} = \dfrac{\frac{1}{r}+\frac{1}{q}}{\frac{1}{r}-\frac{1}{q}}\cdot\dfrac{r-q}{r+q} = \dfrac{rq\left(\frac{1}{r}+\frac{1}{q}\right)}{rq\left(\frac{1}{r}-\frac{1}{q}\right)}\cdot\dfrac{r-q}{r+q} = \dfrac{q+r}{q-r}\cdot\dfrac{r-q}{r+q} = \dfrac{r-q}{q-r} = \dfrac{r-q}{-1(r-q)} = -1$

93. $\dfrac{x-9y^{-1}}{\left(x-3y^{-1}\right)\left(x+3y^{-1}\right)} = \dfrac{x-\frac{9}{y}}{\left(x-\frac{3}{y}\right)\left(x+\frac{3}{y}\right)} = \dfrac{x-\frac{9}{y}}{x^2-\frac{9}{y^2}} = \dfrac{y^2\left(x-\frac{9}{y}\right)}{y^2\left(x^2-\frac{9}{y^2}\right)} = \dfrac{y^2x-9y}{y^2x^2-9}$ or $\dfrac{y(xy-9)}{x^2y^2-9}$

95. $a^7 = 30 \Rightarrow (a^7)^3 = 30^3 \Rightarrow a^{21} = 27{,}000$

97. Let x = length of side of cube. Then $3x$ = length of side of bigger cube (side tripled). x^3 is the volume of the cube, and $(3x)^3 = 3^3x^3 = 27x^3$ is the volume of the bigger cube.
The volume will change by a factor of 27.

99. $.2^{2/3}\cdot 40^{2/3} = (.2\cdot 40)^{2/3} = (8^{1/3})^2 = 2^2 = 4$

101. $\dfrac{2^{2/3}}{2000^{2/3}} = \left(\dfrac{2}{2000}\right)^{2/3} = \left(\dfrac{1}{1000}\right)^{2/3} = \left[\left(\dfrac{1}{1000}\right)^{1/3}\right]^2 = \left(\dfrac{1}{10}\right)^2 = \dfrac{1}{100}$

Section R.7: Radical Expressions

1. **(a)** $(-3x)^{1/3} = \sqrt[3]{-3x}$; F

(b) $(-3x)^{-1/3} = \dfrac{1}{(-3x)^{1/3}} = \dfrac{1}{\sqrt[3]{-3x}}$; H

(c) $(3x)^{1/3} = \sqrt[3]{3x}$; G

(d) $(3x)^{-1/3} = \dfrac{1}{\sqrt[3]{3x}}$; C

3. $m^{2/3} = \sqrt[3]{m^2}$ or $\left(\sqrt[3]{m}\right)^2$

5. $(2m+p)^{2/3} = \sqrt[3]{(2m+p)^2}$ or $\left(\sqrt[3]{2m+p}\right)^2$

7. $\sqrt[5]{k^2} = k^{2/5}$

9. $-3\sqrt{5p^3} = -3(5p^3)^{1/2} = -3 \cdot 5^{1/2} p^{3/2}$

11. A

13. It is true for all $x \geq 0$.

15. $\sqrt{(-5)^2} = |-5| = 5$

17. $\sqrt{25k^4m^2} = \sqrt{\left(5k^2m\right)^2} = \left|5k^2m\right| = 5k^2\,|m|$

19. $\sqrt{(4x-y)^2} = |4x-y|$

21. $\sqrt[3]{125} = 5$

23. This is not a real number since no real number raised to the fourth power will yield a negative quantity.

25. $\sqrt[3]{81} = \sqrt[3]{27 \cdot 3} = \sqrt[3]{27} \cdot \sqrt[3]{3} = 3\sqrt[3]{3}$

27. $-\sqrt[4]{32} = -\sqrt[4]{16 \cdot 2} = -\sqrt[4]{16} \cdot \sqrt[4]{2} = -2\sqrt[4]{2}$

29. $\sqrt{14} \cdot \sqrt{3pqr} = \sqrt{14 \cdot 3pqr} = \sqrt{42pqr}$

31. $\sqrt[3]{7x} \cdot \sqrt[3]{2y} = \sqrt[3]{7x \cdot 2y} = \sqrt[3]{14xy}$

33. $-\sqrt{\dfrac{9}{25}} = -\dfrac{\sqrt{9}}{\sqrt{25}} = -\dfrac{3}{5}$

35. $-\sqrt[3]{\dfrac{5}{8}} = -\dfrac{\sqrt[3]{5}}{\sqrt[3]{8}} = -\dfrac{\sqrt[3]{5}}{2}$

37. $\sqrt[4]{\dfrac{m}{n^4}} = \dfrac{\sqrt[4]{m}}{\sqrt[4]{n^4}} = \dfrac{\sqrt[4]{m}}{n}$

39. $3\sqrt[5]{-3125} = 3\sqrt[5]{(-5)^5} = 3(-5) = -15$

41. $\sqrt[3]{16(-2)^4(2)^8} = \sqrt[3]{2^4 \cdot (-2)^4 2^8} = \sqrt[3]{2^4 \cdot 2^4 \cdot 2^8} = \sqrt[3]{2^{15} \cdot 2} = \sqrt[3]{2^{15}} \cdot \sqrt[3]{2} = 2^5 \cdot \sqrt[3]{2} = 32\sqrt[3]{2}$

43. $\sqrt{8x^5z^8} = \sqrt{2 \cdot 4 \cdot x^4 \cdot x \cdot z^8} = \sqrt{4x^4z^8} \cdot \sqrt{2x} = 2x^2z^4\sqrt{2x}$

45. $\sqrt[4]{x^4 + y^4}$ cannot be simplified further.

47. $\sqrt{\dfrac{2}{3x}} = \dfrac{\sqrt{2}}{\sqrt{3x}} = \dfrac{\sqrt{2}}{\sqrt{3x}} \cdot \dfrac{\sqrt{3x}}{\sqrt{3x}} = \dfrac{\sqrt{2 \cdot 3x}}{\sqrt{9x^2}} = \dfrac{\sqrt{6x}}{3x}$

49. $\sqrt{\dfrac{x^5y^3}{z^2}} = \dfrac{\sqrt{x^5y^3}}{\sqrt{z^2}} = \dfrac{\sqrt{x^4xy^2y}}{z} = \dfrac{\sqrt{x^4y^2} \cdot \sqrt{xy}}{z} = \dfrac{x^2y\sqrt{xy}}{z}$

51. $\sqrt[3]{\frac{8}{x^2}} = \frac{\sqrt[3]{8}}{\sqrt[3]{x^2}} = \frac{2}{\sqrt[3]{x^2}} \cdot \frac{\sqrt[3]{x}}{\sqrt[3]{x}} = \frac{2\sqrt[3]{x}}{\sqrt[3]{x^3}} = \frac{2\sqrt[3]{x}}{x}$

53. $\sqrt[4]{\frac{g^3h^5}{9r^6}} = \frac{\sqrt[4]{g^3h^5}}{\sqrt[4]{9r^6}} = \frac{\sqrt[4]{h^4\left(g^3h\right)}}{\sqrt[4]{r^4\left(9r^2\right)}} = \frac{h\sqrt[4]{g^3h}}{r\sqrt[4]{9r^2}} = \frac{h\sqrt[4]{g^3h}}{r\sqrt[4]{3^2r^2}} \cdot \frac{\sqrt[4]{3^2r^2}}{\sqrt[4]{3^2r^2}} = \frac{h\sqrt[4]{3^2g^3hr^2}}{r\sqrt[4]{3^4r^4}} = \frac{h\sqrt[4]{9g^3hr^2}}{3r^2}$

55. $\sqrt[8]{3^4} = 3^{4/8} = 3^{1/2} = \sqrt{3}$

57. $\sqrt[3]{\sqrt{4}} = \sqrt[3]{4^{1/2}} = \left(4^{1/2}\right)^{1/3} = 4^{1/6} = \left(2^2\right)^{1/6} = 2^{2/6} = 2^{1/3} = \sqrt[3]{2}$

59. Cannot be simplified further

61. $8\sqrt{2x} - \sqrt{8x} + \sqrt{72x} = 8\sqrt{2x} - \sqrt{4 \cdot 2x} + \sqrt{36 \cdot 2x} = 8\sqrt{2x} - 2\sqrt{2x} + 6\sqrt{2x} = 12\sqrt{2x}$

63. $2\sqrt[3]{3} + 4\sqrt[3]{24} - \sqrt[3]{81} = 2\sqrt[3]{3} + 4\sqrt[3]{8 \cdot 3} - \sqrt[3]{27 \cdot 3} = 2\sqrt[3]{3} + 4(2)\sqrt[3]{3} - 3\sqrt[3]{3} = 2\sqrt[3]{3} + 8\sqrt[3]{3} - 3\sqrt[3]{3} = 7\sqrt[3]{3}$

65. $\sqrt[4]{81x^6y^3} - \sqrt[4]{16x^{10}y^3} = \sqrt[4]{\left(81x^4\right)x^2y^3} - \sqrt[4]{\left(16x^8\right)x^2y^3} = 3x\sqrt[4]{x^2y^3} - 2x^2\sqrt[4]{x^2y^3}$

67. This product has the pattern $(a+b)(a-b) = a^2 - b^2$, the difference of squares.

$\left(\sqrt{2}+3\right)\left(\sqrt{2}-3\right) = \left(\sqrt{2}\right)^2 - 3^2 = 2 - 9 = -7$

69. This product has the pattern $(a-b)(a^2+ab+b^2) = a^3 - b^3$, the difference of cubes.

Thus, $\left(\sqrt[3]{11}-1\right)\left(\sqrt[3]{11^2}+\sqrt[3]{11}+1\right) = \left(\sqrt[3]{11}\right)^3 - 1^3 = 11 - 1 = 10.$

71. This product has the pattern $(a+b)^2 = a^2 + 2ab + b^2$, the square of a binomial.

$\left(\sqrt{3}+\sqrt{8}\right)^2 = \left(\sqrt{3}\right)^2 + 2\left(\sqrt{3}\right)\left(\sqrt{8}\right) + \left(\sqrt{8}\right)^2 = 3 + 2\sqrt{24} + 8 = 11 + 2\sqrt{4 \cdot 6} = 11 + 2(2)\sqrt{6} = 11 + 4\sqrt{6}$

73. This product can be found by using the FOIL method.

$\left(3\sqrt{2}+\sqrt{3}\right)\left(2\sqrt{3}-\sqrt{2}\right) = 3\sqrt{2}\left(2\sqrt{3}\right) - 3\sqrt{2}\left(\sqrt{2}\right) + \sqrt{3}\left(2\sqrt{3}\right) - \sqrt{3}\sqrt{2}$

$= 6\sqrt{6} - 3 \cdot 2 + 2 \cdot 3 - \sqrt{6} = 6\sqrt{6} - 6 + 6 - \sqrt{6} = 5\sqrt{6}$

75. $\frac{\sqrt[3]{mn} \cdot \sqrt[3]{m^2}}{\sqrt[3]{n^2}} = \sqrt[3]{\frac{mnm^2}{n^2}} = \sqrt[3]{\frac{m^3}{n}} = \frac{\sqrt[3]{m^3}}{\sqrt[3]{n}} \cdot \frac{\sqrt[3]{n^2}}{\sqrt[3]{n^2}} = \frac{m\sqrt[3]{n^2}}{n}$

77. $\sqrt[3]{\frac{2}{x^6}} - \sqrt[3]{\frac{5}{x^9}} = \frac{\sqrt[3]{2}}{\sqrt[3]{x^6}} - \frac{\sqrt[3]{5}}{\sqrt[3]{x^9}} = \frac{\sqrt[3]{2}}{x^2} - \frac{\sqrt[3]{5}}{x^3} = \frac{\sqrt[3]{2} \cdot x}{x^2 \cdot x} - \frac{\sqrt[3]{5}}{x^3} = \frac{x\sqrt[3]{2}}{x^3} - \frac{\sqrt[3]{5}}{x^3} = \frac{x\sqrt[3]{2} - \sqrt[3]{5}}{x^3}$

79. $\frac{1}{\sqrt{2}}+\frac{3}{\sqrt{8}}+\frac{1}{\sqrt{32}}=\frac{1}{\sqrt{2}}+\frac{3}{\sqrt{4\cdot 2}}+\frac{1}{\sqrt{16\cdot 2}}=\frac{1}{\sqrt{2}}+\frac{3}{2\sqrt{2}}+\frac{1}{4\sqrt{2}}=\frac{4\cdot 1}{4\sqrt{2}}+\frac{3\cdot 2}{2\cdot 2\sqrt{2}}+\frac{1}{4\sqrt{2}}$

$=\frac{4}{4\sqrt{2}}+\frac{6}{4\sqrt{2}}+\frac{1}{4\sqrt{2}}=\frac{4+6+1}{4\sqrt{2}}=\frac{11}{4\sqrt{2}}=\frac{11\sqrt{2}}{4\sqrt{2}\cdot\sqrt{2}}=\frac{11\sqrt{2}}{4\cdot 2}=\frac{11\sqrt{2}}{8}$

81. $\frac{-4}{\sqrt[3]{3}}+\frac{1}{\sqrt[3]{24}}-\frac{2}{\sqrt[3]{81}}=\frac{-4}{\sqrt[3]{3}}+\frac{1}{\sqrt[3]{8\cdot 3}}-\frac{2}{\sqrt[3]{27\cdot 3}}=\frac{-4}{\sqrt[3]{3}}+\frac{1}{2\sqrt[3]{3}}-\frac{2}{3\sqrt[3]{3}}=\frac{-4\cdot 6}{\sqrt[3]{3}\cdot 6}+\frac{1\cdot 3}{2\sqrt[3]{3}\cdot 3}-\frac{2\cdot 2}{3\sqrt[3]{3}\cdot 2}$

$=\frac{-24}{6\sqrt[3]{3}}+\frac{3}{6\sqrt[3]{3}}-\frac{4}{6\sqrt[3]{3}}=\frac{-24+3-4}{6\sqrt[3]{3}}=\frac{-25}{6\sqrt[3]{3}}=\frac{-25}{6\sqrt[3]{3}}\cdot\frac{\sqrt[3]{3^2}}{\sqrt[3]{3^2}}=\frac{-25\sqrt[3]{9}}{6\cdot 3}=\frac{-25\sqrt[3]{9}}{18}$

83. $\frac{\sqrt{7}}{\sqrt{3}-\sqrt{7}}=\frac{\sqrt{7}}{\sqrt{3}-\sqrt{7}}\cdot\frac{\sqrt{3}+\sqrt{7}}{\sqrt{3}+\sqrt{7}}=\frac{\sqrt{7}\left(\sqrt{3}+\sqrt{7}\right)}{3-7}=\frac{\sqrt{21}+7}{-4}=\frac{-\left(\sqrt{21}+7\right)}{4}=\frac{-\sqrt{21}-7}{4}$

85. $\frac{\sqrt{7}-1}{2\sqrt{7}+4\sqrt{2}}=\frac{\sqrt{7}-1}{2\sqrt{7}+4\sqrt{2}}\cdot\frac{2\sqrt{7}-4\sqrt{2}}{2\sqrt{7}-4\sqrt{2}}=\frac{\left(\sqrt{7}-1\right)\left(2\sqrt{7}-4\sqrt{2}\right)}{\left(2\sqrt{7}+4\sqrt{2}\right)\left(2\sqrt{7}-4\sqrt{2}\right)}$

$=\frac{\sqrt{7}\cdot 2\sqrt{7}-\sqrt{7}\cdot 4\sqrt{2}-1\cdot 2\sqrt{7}+1\cdot 4\sqrt{2}}{\left(2\sqrt{7}\right)^2-\left(4\sqrt{2}\right)^2}=\frac{2\cdot 7-4\sqrt{14}-2\sqrt{7}+4\sqrt{2}}{4\cdot 7-16\cdot 2}$

$=\frac{14-4\sqrt{14}-2\sqrt{7}+4\sqrt{2}}{28-32}=\frac{14-4\sqrt{14}-2\sqrt{7}+4\sqrt{2}}{-4}$

$=\frac{-2\left(-7+2\sqrt{14}+\sqrt{7}-2\sqrt{2}\right)}{-4}=\frac{-7+2\sqrt{14}+\sqrt{7}-2\sqrt{2}}{2}$

87. $\frac{\sqrt{r}}{3-\sqrt{r}}=\frac{\sqrt{r}}{3-\sqrt{r}}\cdot\frac{3+\sqrt{r}}{3+\sqrt{r}}$

$=\frac{\sqrt{r}\left(3+\sqrt{r}\right)}{3^2-\left(\sqrt{r}\right)^2}=\frac{\sqrt{r}\left(3+\sqrt{r}\right)}{9-r}$

89. $\frac{3m}{2+\sqrt{m+n}}=\frac{3m}{2+\sqrt{m+n}}\cdot\frac{2-\sqrt{m+n}}{2-\sqrt{m+n}}=\frac{3m\left(2-\sqrt{m+n}\right)}{2^2-\left(\sqrt{m+n}\right)^2}=\frac{3m\left(2-\sqrt{m+n}\right)}{4-(m+n)}=\frac{3m\left(2-\sqrt{m+n}\right)}{4-m-n}$

91. Windchill temperature $=35.74+.6215T-35.75V^{.16}+.4275TV^{.16}$

Windchill temperature $=35.74+.6215(30)-35.75\left(15^{.16}\right)+.4275(30)\left(15^{.16}\right)\approx 19.0°$

The table gives 19°.

93. $\frac{\sqrt[3]{54}}{\sqrt[3]{2}}=\sqrt[3]{\frac{54}{2}}=\sqrt[3]{27}=3$

95. $\sqrt{.1}\cdot\sqrt{40}=\sqrt{.1\cdot 40}=\sqrt{4}=2$

97. $\sqrt[6]{2}\cdot\sqrt[6]{4}\cdot\sqrt[6]{8}=\sqrt[6]{2\cdot 4\cdot 8}=\sqrt[6]{64}=2$

99. $\frac{355}{113}=3.1415929\ldots$ and $\pi\approx 3.1415926\ldots$, so it gives six decimal places of accuracy.

Chapter R: Review Exercises

1. $-12, -6, -\sqrt{4}$ (or -2), 0, and 6 are integers.

3. 0 is a whole number, an integer, a rational number, and a real number.

5. $\frac{4\pi}{5}$ is an irrational number and a real number.

7. – 9. Answers will vary.

11. commutative

13. associative

15. identity

17. (a) 74°F
(b) 84°F

19. $(-4-1)(-3-5)-2^3=(-5)(-8)-8=40-8=32$

21. $\left(-\frac{5}{9}-\frac{2}{3}\right)-\frac{5}{6}=\left(-\frac{5}{9}-\frac{6}{9}\right)-\frac{5}{6}=\frac{-11}{9}-\frac{5}{6}=-\frac{22}{18}-\frac{15}{18}=-\frac{37}{18}$

23. $\frac{6(-4)-3^2(-2)^3}{-5[-2-(-6)]}=\frac{6(-4)-9(-8)}{-5[-2+6]}=\frac{6(-4)-9(-8)}{-5(4)}=\frac{-24-(-72)}{-20}=\frac{-24+72}{-20}=\frac{48}{-20}=-\frac{12}{5}$

25. Let $a=-1$, $b=-2$, $c=4$.
$-c(2a-5b)=-4[2(-1)-5(-2)]=-4[-2-(-10)]=-4(-2+10)=-4(8)=-32$

27. Let $a=-1$, $b=-2$, $c=4$.

$$\frac{9a+2b}{a+b+c}=\frac{9(-1)+2(-2)}{-1+(-2)+4}=\frac{-9+(-4)}{-3+4}=\frac{-13}{1}=-13$$

29. Simplify each number.
$|6-4|=|2|=2,\ -|-2|=-(2)=-2,\ |8+1|=|9|=9,\ -|3-(-2)|=-|3+2|=-|5|=-(5)=-5$
The correct order is $-|3-(-2)|, -|-2|, |6-4|, |8+1|$.

31. $-|-6|+|3|=-6+3=-3$

33. Since $\sqrt{8}<8$, $\sqrt{8}-8<0$, so
$\left|\sqrt{8}-8\right|=-\left(\sqrt{8}-8\right)=-\sqrt{8}+8=8-\sqrt{8}$.

35. $(3q^3-9q^2+6)+(4q^3-8q+3)=3q^3-9q^2+6+4q^3-8q+3=7q^3-9q^2-8q+9$

37. $(8y-7)(2y+7)=16y^2+56y-14y-49=16y^2+42y-49$

39. $(3k-5m)^2=(3k)^2-2(3k)(5m)+(5m)^2=9k^2-30km+25m^2$

41. **(a)** 51 million

(b) Evaluate $.146x^4 - 2.54x^3 + 11.0x^2 + 16.6x + 51.5$ when $x = 0$.

$$\begin{aligned}.146\cdot 0^4 - 2.54\cdot 0^3 + 11.0\cdot 0^2 + 16.6\cdot 0 + 51.5 &= .146\cdot 0 - 2.54\cdot 0 + 11.0\cdot 0 + 16.6\cdot 0 + 51.5\\ &= 0 - 0 + 0 + 0 + 51.5\\ &= 51.5 \text{ or approximately 52 million}\end{aligned}$$

(c) The approximation is 1 million high.

43. **(a)** 183 million

(b) Evaluate $.146x^4 - 2.54x^3 + 11.0x^2 + 16.6x + 51.5$ when $x = 5$.

$$\begin{aligned}.146\cdot 5^4 - 2.54\cdot 5^3 + 11.0\cdot 5^2 + 16.6\cdot 5 + 51.5 &= .146\cdot 625 - 2.54\cdot 125 + 11.0\cdot 25 + 16.6\cdot 5 + 51.5\\ &= 91.25 - 317.5 + 275 + 83 + 51.5\\ &= 183.25 \text{ or approximately 183 million}\end{aligned}$$

(c) They are the same.

45. $\dfrac{30m^3 - 9m^2 + 22m + 5}{5m+1}$

$$\begin{array}{r} 6m^2 - 3m + 5 \\ 5m+1\,\big)\overline{30m^3 - 9m^2 + 22m + 5} \\ \underline{30m^3 + 6m^2} \\ -15m^2 + 22m \\ \underline{-15m^2 - 3m} \\ 25m + 5 \\ \underline{25m + 5} \\ 0 \end{array}$$

$$\frac{30m^3 - 9m^2 + 22m + 5}{5m+1} = 6m^2 - 3m + 5$$

47. $\dfrac{3b^3 - 8b^2 + 12b - 30}{b^2 + 4}$

Insert the missing term in the divisor with a 0 coefficient.

$$\begin{array}{r} 3b - 8 \\ b^2 + 0b + 4\,\big)\overline{3b^3 - 8b^2 + 12b - 30} \\ \underline{3b^3 + 0b^2 + 12b} \\ -8b^2 + 0b - 30 \\ \underline{-8b^2 + 0b - 32} \\ 2 \end{array}$$

$$\frac{3b^3 - 8b^2 + 12b - 30}{b^2 + 4} = 3b - 8 + \frac{2}{b^2 + 4}$$

49. $3(z-4)^2 + 9(z-4)^3 = 3(z-4)^2[1 + 3(z-4)] = 3(z-4)^2(1 + 3z - 12) = 3(z-4)^2(3z-11)$

51. $z^2 - 6zk - 16k^2 = (z-8k)(z+2k)$

53. $48a^8 - 12a^7b - 90a^6b^2 = 6a^6(8a^2 - 2ab - 15b^2) = 6a^6(4a+5b)(2a-3b)$

55. $49m^8 - 9n^2 = (7m^4)^2 - (3n)^2 = (7m^4 + 3n)(7m^4 - 3n)$

57. $6(3r-1)^2 + (3r-1) - 35$

Let $x = 3r - 1$. With this substitution, $6(3r-1)^2 + (3r-1) - 35$ becomes $6x^2 + x - 35$.

Factor the trinomial by trial and error.

$6x^2 + x - 35 = (3x-7)(2x+5)$

Replacing x with $3r - 1$ gives

$[3(3r-1) - 7][2(3r-1) + 5] = (9r - 3 - 7)(6r - 2 + 5) = (9r-10)(6r+3) = 3(9r-10)(2r+1).$

59. $(3x-4)^2+(x-5)(2)(3x-4)(3)=(3x-4)[(3x-4)+(x-5)(2)(3)]$
$=(3x-4)[3x-4+6x-30]=(3x-4)(9x-34)$

61. $\dfrac{k^2+k}{8k^3}\cdot\dfrac{4}{k^2-1}=\dfrac{k(k+1)(4)}{8k^3(k+1)(k-1)}=\dfrac{4k}{8k^3(k-1)}=\dfrac{1}{2k^2(k-1)}$

63. $\dfrac{x^2+x-2}{x^2+5x+6}\div\dfrac{x^2+3x-4}{x^2+4x+3}=\dfrac{x^2+x-2}{x^2+5x+6}\cdot\dfrac{x^2+4x+3}{x^2+3x-4}=\dfrac{(x+2)(x-1)}{(x+3)(x+2)}\cdot\dfrac{(x+3)(x+1)}{(x+4)(x-1)}=\dfrac{x+1}{x+4}$

65. $\dfrac{p^2-36q^2}{(p-6q)^2}\cdot\dfrac{p^2-5pq-6q^2}{p^2-6pq+36q^2}\div\dfrac{5p}{p^3+216q^3}=\dfrac{p^2-36q^2}{(p-6q)^2}\cdot\dfrac{p^2-5pq-6q^2}{p^2-6pq+36q^2}\cdot\dfrac{p^3+216q^3}{5p}$
$=\dfrac{(p+6q)(p-6q)}{(p-6q)^2}\cdot\dfrac{(p-6q)(p+q)}{p^2-6pq+36q^2}\cdot\dfrac{(p+6q)(p^2-6pq+36q^2)}{5p}$
$=\dfrac{(p+q)(p+6q)^2}{5p}$

67. $\dfrac{m}{4-m}+\dfrac{3m}{m-4}=\dfrac{m(-1)}{(4-m)(-1)}+\dfrac{3m}{m-4}=\dfrac{-m}{m-4}+\dfrac{3m}{m-4}=\dfrac{2m}{m-4}$; We may also use 4 – *m* as the common denominator. In this case, the result will be $\dfrac{-2m}{4-m}$. The two results are equivalent rational expressions.

69. $\dfrac{\frac{1}{p}+\frac{1}{q}}{1-\frac{1}{pq}}=\dfrac{pq\left(\frac{1}{p}+\frac{1}{q}\right)}{pq\left(1-\frac{1}{pq}\right)}=\dfrac{pq\left(\frac{1}{p}\right)+pq\left(\frac{1}{q}\right)}{pq(1)-pq\left(\frac{1}{pq}\right)}=\dfrac{q+p}{pq-1}$

71. $2^{-6}=\dfrac{1}{2^6}=\dfrac{1}{64}$

73. $\left(-\dfrac{5}{4}\right)^{-2}=\left(-\dfrac{4}{5}\right)^2=\dfrac{16}{25}$

75. $(5z^3)(-2z^5)=-10z^{3+5}=-10z^8$

77. $(-6p^5w^4m^{12})^0=1$ Definition of a^0

79. $\dfrac{-8y^7p^{-2}}{y^{-4}p^{-3}}=-8y^{7-(-4)}p^{(-2)-(-3)}=-8y^{11}p$

81. $\dfrac{(p+q)^4(p+q)^{-3}}{(p+q)^6}=(p+q)^{4+(-3)-6}$
$=(p+q)^{-5}=\dfrac{1}{(p+q)^5}$

83. $(7r^{1/2})(2r^{3/4})(-r^{1/6})=-14r^{1/2+3/4+1/6}=-14r^{17/12}$

85. $\dfrac{y^{5/3}\cdot y^{-2}}{y^{-5/6}}=\dfrac{y^{5/3+(-2)}}{y^{-5/6}}=\dfrac{y^{5/3+(-6/3)}}{y^{-5/6}}=\dfrac{y^{-1/3}}{y^{-5/6}}=y^{-1/3-(-5/6)}=y^{-2/6+5/6}=y^{3/6}=y^{1/2}$

87. $2z^{1/3}(5z^2-2)=2z^{1/3}(5z^2)-2z^{1/3}(2)=10z^{1/3+2}-4z^{1/3}=10z^{1/3+6/3}-4z^{1/3}=10z^{7/3}-4z^{1/3}$

89. $\sqrt{200}=\sqrt{100\cdot 2}=\sqrt{100}\cdot\sqrt{2}=10\sqrt{2}$

91. $\sqrt[4]{1250}=\sqrt[4]{625\cdot 2}=\sqrt[4]{625}\cdot\sqrt[4]{2}=5\sqrt[4]{2}$

93. $-\sqrt[3]{\frac{2}{5p^2}}=-\frac{\sqrt[3]{2}}{\sqrt[3]{5p^2}}=-\frac{\sqrt[3]{2}}{\sqrt[3]{5p^2}}\cdot\frac{\sqrt[3]{25p}}{\sqrt[3]{25p}}=-\frac{\sqrt[3]{2\cdot 25p}}{\sqrt[3]{125p^3}}=-\frac{\sqrt[3]{50p}}{5p}$

95. $\sqrt[4]{\sqrt[3]{m}}=\left(\sqrt[3]{m}\right)^{1/4}=(m^{1/3})^{1/4}=m^{1/3\cdot 1/4}=m^{1/12}=\sqrt[12]{m}$

97. This product has the pattern $(a+b)(a^2-ab+b^2)=a^3+b^3$, the sum of two cubes.

$$\left(\sqrt[3]{2}+4\right)\left(\sqrt[3]{2^2}-4\sqrt[3]{2}+16\right)=\left(\sqrt[3]{2}+4\right)\left[\left(\sqrt[3]{2}\right)^2-\sqrt[3]{2}\cdot 4+4^2\right]=\left(\sqrt[3]{2}\right)^3+4^3=2+64=66$$

99.
$$\begin{aligned}\sqrt{18m^3}-3m\sqrt{32m}+5\sqrt{m^3}&=\sqrt{9m^2\cdot 2m}-3m\sqrt{16\cdot 2m}+5\sqrt{m^2m}\\&=3m\sqrt{2m}-4\cdot 3m\sqrt{2m}+5m\sqrt{m}=3m\sqrt{2m}-12m\sqrt{2m}+5m\sqrt{m}\\&=-9m\sqrt{2m}+5m\sqrt{m}\ \text{ or }\ m\left(-9\sqrt{2m}+5\sqrt{m}\right)\end{aligned}$$

101. $\frac{6}{3-\sqrt{2}}=\frac{6}{3-\sqrt{2}}\cdot\frac{3+\sqrt{2}}{3+\sqrt{2}}=\frac{6\left(3+\sqrt{2}\right)}{9-2}=\frac{6\left(3+\sqrt{2}\right)}{7}$

103. $x(x^2+5)=x\cdot x^2+x\cdot 5=x^3+5x$

105. $(m^2)^3=m^{2\cdot 3}=m^6$

107. $\frac{\left(\frac{a}{b}\right)}{2}=\left(\frac{a}{b}\right)\cdot\left(\frac{1}{2}\right)=\frac{a}{2b}$

109. One possible answer is $\frac{1}{\sqrt{a}+\sqrt{b}}=\frac{1}{\sqrt{a}+\sqrt{b}}\cdot\frac{\sqrt{a}-\sqrt{b}}{\sqrt{a}-\sqrt{b}}=\frac{\sqrt{a}-\sqrt{b}}{a-b}$.

111. $4-(t+1)=4-t-1$ or $3-t$

113. $(-5)^2=(-5)(-5)=25$ or 5^2

Chapter R: Test

1. **(a)** -13, $-\frac{12}{4}$ (or -3), 0, and $\sqrt{49}$ (or 7) are integers.

(b) -13, $-\frac{12}{4}$, 0, $\frac{3}{5}$, 5.9 (or $\frac{59}{10}$), and $\sqrt{49}$ (or 7) are rational numbers.

(c) All numbers in the set are real numbers.

2. Let $x=-2$, $y=-4$, $z=5$.

$$\left|\frac{x^2+2yz}{3(x+z)}\right|=\left|\frac{(-2)^2+2(-4)(5)}{3(-2+5)}\right|=\left|\frac{4+(-40)}{3(3)}\right|=\left|\frac{-36}{9}\right|=|-4|=4$$

3. **(a)** associative property
(b) commutative
(c) distributive
(d) inverse

4. $A = 419, C = 267, Y = 3075, T = 15, I = 10$

$$\text{Rating} \approx 85.68\left(\frac{C}{A}\right)+4.31\left(\frac{Y}{A}\right)+326.42\left(\frac{T}{A}\right)-419.07\left(\frac{I}{A}\right)$$

$$= 85.68\left(\frac{267}{419}\right)+4.31\left(\frac{3075}{419}\right)+326.42\left(\frac{15}{419}\right)-419.07\left(\frac{10}{419}\right) \approx 87.9$$

Matt Hasselbeck's rating is 87.9.

5. $(x^2-3x+2)-(x-4x^2)+3x(2x+1) = x^2-3x+2-x+4x^2+6x^2+3x = 11x^2-x+2$

6. $(6r-5)^2 = (6r)^2 - 2(6r)(5)+5^2 = 36r^2-60r+25$

7. $(t+2)(3t^2-t+4)$

$$\begin{array}{r} 3t^2 - t + 4 \\ t + 2 \\ \hline 6t^2 - 2t + 8 \\ 3t^3 - t^2 + 4t \quad\quad \\ \hline 3t^3 + 5t^2 + 2t + 8 \end{array}$$

8. $\dfrac{2x^3-11x^2+28}{x-5}$

$$\begin{array}{r} 2x^2 - x - 5 \\ x-5\overline{)2x^3 - 11x^2 + 0x + 28} \\ \underline{2x^3 - 10x^2 \quad\quad\quad\quad} \\ -x^2 + 0x \quad\quad \\ \underline{-x^2 + 5x \quad\quad} \\ -5x + 28 \\ \underline{-5x + 25} \\ 3 \end{array}$$

$$\frac{2x^3-11x^2+28}{x-5} = 2x^2 - x - 5 + \frac{3}{x-5}$$

9. $x = 3$

Adjusted poverty threshold

$\approx 5.476x^2 + 154.3x + 7889$

$= 5.476 \cdot 3^2 + 154.3 \cdot 3 + 7889$

$= 49.284 + 462.9 + 7889 = 8401.184$

approximately \$8401

10. $x = 5$

Adjusted poverty threshold

$\approx 5.476x^2 + 154.3x + 7889$

$= 5.476 \cdot 5^2 + 154.3 \cdot 5 + 7889$

$= 136.9 + 771.5 + 7889 = 8797.4$

approximately \$8797

11. $6x^2 - 17x + 7 = (3x-7)(2x-1)$

12. $x^4 - 16 = (x^2)^2 - 4^2 = (x^2+4)(x^2-4) = (x^2+4)(x^2-2^2) = (x^2+4)(x+2)(x-2)$

13. $24m^3 - 14m^2 - 24m = 2m(12m^2 - 7m - 12) = 2m(4m+3)(3m-4)$

14. $x^3y^2 - 9x^3 - 8y^2 + 72 = (x^3y^2 - 9x^3) - (8y^2 - 72) = x^3(y^2-9) - 8(y^2-9)$

$= (x^3-8)(y^2-9) = (x^3-2^3)(y^2-3^2) = (x-2)(x^2+2x+4)(y+3)(y-3)$

15. $$\frac{5x^2-9x-2}{30x^3+6x^2}\cdot\frac{2x^8+6x^7+4x^6}{x^4-3x^2-4}=\frac{(5x+1)(x-2)}{6x^2(5x+1)}\cdot\frac{2x^6(x^2+3x+2)}{(x^2-4)(x^2+1)}$$
$$=\frac{(5x+1)(x-2)}{6x^2(5x+1)}\cdot\frac{2x^6(x+2)(x+1)}{(x+2)(x-2)(x^2+1)}=\frac{2x^6(x+1)}{6x^2(x^2+1)}=\frac{x^4(x+1)}{3(x^2+1)}$$

16. $$\frac{x}{x^2+3x+2}+\frac{2x}{2x^2-x-3}=\frac{x}{(x+2)(x+1)}+\frac{2x}{(2x-3)(x+1)}$$

The least common denominator is $(x + 2)(x + 1)(2x - 3)$.

$$=\frac{x(2x-3)}{(x+2)(x+1)(2x-3)}+\frac{2x(x+2)}{(2x-3)(x+1)(x+2)}=\frac{2x^2-3x}{(x+2)(x+1)(2x-3)}+\frac{2x^2+4x}{(x+2)(x+1)(2x-3)}$$
$$=\frac{2x^2-3x+2x^2+4x}{(x+2)(x+1)(2x-3)}=\frac{4x^2+x}{(x+2)(x+1)(2x-3)}=\frac{x(4x+1)}{(x+2)(x+1)(2x-3)}$$

17. $\frac{a+b}{2a-3}-\frac{a-b}{3-2a}=\frac{a+b}{2a-3}-\frac{(a-b)(-1)}{(3-2a)(-1)}=\frac{a+b}{2a-3}+\frac{a-b}{2a-3}=\frac{2a}{2a-3}$; If $3 - 2a$ is used as the common denominator, the result will be $\frac{-2a}{3-2a}$. The rational expressions $\frac{2a}{2a-3}$ and $\frac{-2a}{3-2a}$ are equivalent.

18. $$\frac{y-2}{y-\frac{4}{y}}=\frac{y(y-2)}{y\left(y-\frac{4}{y}\right)}=\frac{y^2-2y}{y^2-4}=\frac{y(y-2)}{(y+2)(y-2)}=\frac{y}{y+2}$$

19. $$\left(\frac{x^{-2}y^{-1/3}}{x^{-5/3}y^{-2/3}}\right)^3=\frac{x^{-6}y^{-1}}{x^{-5}y^{-2}}=x^{-6-(-5)}y^{-1-(-2)}=x^{-1}y=\frac{y}{x}$$

20. $$\left(-\frac{64}{27}\right)^{-2/3}=\left(-\frac{27}{64}\right)^{2/3}=\left[\left(-\frac{27}{64}\right)^{1/3}\right]^2=\left(-\frac{3}{4}\right)^2=\frac{9}{16}$$

21. $$\sqrt{18x^5y^8}=\sqrt{(9x^4y^8)(2x)}=\sqrt{9x^4y^8}\cdot\sqrt{2x}=3x^2y^4\sqrt{2x}$$

22. $$\sqrt{32x}+\sqrt{2x}-\sqrt{18x}=\sqrt{16\cdot 2x}+\sqrt{2x}-\sqrt{9\cdot 2x}=4\sqrt{2x}+\sqrt{2x}-3\sqrt{2x}=2\sqrt{2x}$$

23. $$\left(\sqrt{x}-\sqrt{y}\right)\left(\sqrt{x}+\sqrt{y}\right)=\left(\sqrt{x}\right)^2-\left(\sqrt{y}\right)^2=x-y$$

24. $$\frac{14}{\sqrt{11}-\sqrt{7}}=\frac{14}{\sqrt{11}-\sqrt{7}}\cdot\frac{\sqrt{11}+\sqrt{7}}{\sqrt{11}+\sqrt{7}}=\frac{14\left(\sqrt{11}+\sqrt{7}\right)}{11-7}=\frac{14\left(\sqrt{11}+\sqrt{7}\right)}{4}=\frac{7\left(\sqrt{11}+\sqrt{7}\right)}{2}$$

25. Let $L = 3.5$.

$$t=2\pi\sqrt{\frac{L}{32}}=2\pi\sqrt{\frac{3.5}{32}}\approx 2.1$$

The period of a pendulum 3.5 ft long is approximately 2.1 seconds.

Chapter 1

EQUATIONS AND INEQUALITIES

Section 1.1: Linear Equations

1. Solve the equation $2x+3=x-5$.

$$2x+3=x-5$$
$$2x+3-x=x-5-x$$
$$x+3=-5$$
$$x+3-3=-5-3$$
$$x=-8$$

Moreover, replacing x with -8 in $2x+3=x-5$ yields a true statement. Therefore, the given statement is true.

3. The equations $x^2=4$ and $x+1=3$ are not equivalent. The first has a solution set $\{-2,2\}$ while the solution set of the second is $\{2\}$. Since the equations do not have the same solution set, they are not equivalent. The given statement is false.

5. Answers will vary.

7. B cannot be written in the form $ax+b=0$.
A can be written as $15x-7=0$ or $15x+(-7)=0$, C can be written as $2x=0$ or $2x+0=0$, and D can be written as $-.04x-.4=0$ or $-.04x+(-.4)=0$.

9.
$$5x+2=3x-6$$
$$2x+2=-6$$
$$2x=-8$$
$$x=-4$$

Solution set: $\{-4\}$

11.
$$6(3x-1)=8-(10x-14)$$
$$18x-6=8-10x+14$$
$$18x-6=22-10x$$
$$28x-6=22$$
$$28x=28$$
$$x=1$$

Solution set: $\{1\}$

13.
$$\frac{5}{6}x-2x+\frac{1}{3}=\frac{2}{3}$$
$$6\cdot\left[\frac{5}{6}x-2x+\frac{1}{3}\right]=6\cdot\frac{2}{3}$$
$$5x-12x+2=4$$
$$-7x+2=4$$
$$-7x=2$$
$$x=-\frac{2}{7}$$

Solution set: $\left\{-\frac{2}{7}\right\}$

15. $3x+2-5(x+1)=6x+4$
$$3x+2-5x-5=6x+4$$
$$-2x-3=6x+4$$
$$-3=8x+4$$
$$-7=8x$$
$$\frac{-7}{8}=x$$
$$-\frac{7}{8}=x$$
Solution set: $\left\{-\frac{7}{8}\right\}$

17. $2[x-(4+2x)+3]=2x+2$
$$2(x-4-2x+3)=2x+2$$
$$2(-x-1)=2x+2$$
$$-2x-2=2x+2$$
$$-2=4x+2$$
$$-4=4x$$
$$-1=x$$
Solution set: $\{-1\}$

19. $\frac{1}{7}(3x-2)=\frac{x+10}{5}$
$$35\cdot\left[\frac{1}{7}(3x-2)\right]=35\cdot\left[\frac{x+10}{5}\right]$$
$$5(3x-2)=7(x+10)$$
$$15x-10=7x+70$$
$$8x-10=70$$
$$8x=80$$
$$x=10$$
Solution set: $\{10\}$

21. $.2x-.5=.1x+7$
$$10(.2x-.5)=10(.1x+7)$$
$$2x-5=x+70$$
$$x-5=70$$
$$x=75$$
Solution set: $\{75\}$

23. $-4(2x-6)+7x=5x+24$
$$-8x+24+7x=5x+24$$
$$-x+24=5x+24$$
$$24=6x+24$$
$$0=6x$$
$$0=x$$
Solution set: $\{0\}$

25. $.5x+\frac{4}{3}x=x+10$
$$\frac{1}{2}x+\frac{4}{3}x=x+10$$
$$6\left(\frac{1}{2}x+\frac{4}{3}x\right)=6(x+10)$$
$$3x+8x=6x+60$$
$$11x=6x+60$$
$$5x=60$$
$$x=12$$
Solution set: $\{12\}$

27. $.08x+.06(x+12)=7.72$
$$100[.08x+.06(x+12)]=100\cdot 7.72$$
$$8x+6(x+12)=772$$
$$8x+6x+72=772$$
$$14x+72=772$$
$$14x=700$$
$$x=50$$
Solution set: $\{50\}$

29. $4(2x+7)=2x+25+3(2x+1)$
$$8x+28=2x+25+6x+3$$
$$8x+28=8x+28$$
$$28=28$$
$$0=0$$
identity; {all real numbers}

31. $2(x-7)=3x-14$
$$2x-14=3x-14$$
$$-14=x-14$$
$$0=x$$
conditional equation; $\{0\}$

33.
$$\begin{aligned}.3(x+2)-.5(x+2)&=-.2x-.4\\10[.3(x+2)-.5(x+2)]&=10[-.2x-.4]\\3(x+2)-5(x+2)&=-2x-4\\3x+6-5x-10&=-2x-4\\-2x-4&=-2x-4\\-4&=-4\\0&=0\end{aligned}$$
identity; $\{\text{all real numbers}\}$

35.
$$\begin{aligned}8(x+7)&=4(x+12)+4(x+1)\\8x+56&=4x+48+4x+4\\8x+56&=8x+52\\56&=52\end{aligned}$$
contradiction; $\varnothing$

37. Answers will vary.
In solving an equation, you cannot multiply (or divide) both sides of an equation by zero. This is essentially what happened when the student divided both sides of the equation by x. To solve the equation, the student should isolate the variable term, which leads to the solution set $\{0\}$.
$$\begin{aligned}5x&=4x\\5x-4x&=4x-4x\\x&=0\end{aligned}$$

39.
$$\begin{aligned}V&=lwh\\\frac{V}{wh}&=\frac{lwh}{wh}\\l&=\frac{V}{wh}\end{aligned}$$

41.
$$\begin{aligned}P&=a+b+c\\P-a-b&=c\\c&=P-a-b\end{aligned}$$

43.
$$\begin{aligned}A&=\frac{1}{2}(B+b)h\\2A&=2\left[\frac{1}{2}(B+b)h\right]\\2A&=(B+b)h\\2A&=Bh+bh\\2A-bh&=Bh\\\frac{2A-bh}{h}&=\frac{Bh}{h}\\B&=\frac{2A-bh}{h}=\frac{2A}{h}-b\end{aligned}$$

45.
$$\begin{aligned}S&=2\pi rh+2\pi r^2\\S-2\pi r^2&=2\pi rh\\\frac{S-2\pi r^2}{2\pi r}&=\frac{2\pi rh}{2\pi r}\\h&=\frac{S-2\pi r^2}{2\pi r}=\frac{S}{2\pi r}-r\end{aligned}$$

47.
$$\begin{aligned}S&=2lw+2wh+2hl\\S-2lw&=2wh+2hl\\S-2lw&=(2w+2l)h\\\frac{S-2lw}{2w+2l}&=\frac{(2w+2l)h}{2w+2l}\\h&=\frac{S-2lw}{2w+2l}\end{aligned}$$

49.
$$\begin{aligned}2(x-a)+b&=3x+a\\2x-2a+b&=3x+a\\-3a+b&=x\\x&=-3a+b\end{aligned}$$

51. $ax+b=3(x-a)\Rightarrow ax+b=3x-3a\Rightarrow 3a+b=3x-ax\Rightarrow 3a+b=(3-a)x\Rightarrow x=\dfrac{3a+b}{3-a}$

53.
$$\frac{x}{a-1} = ax+3$$
$$(a-1)\left[\frac{x}{a-1}\right] = (a-1)(ax+3)$$
$$x = a^2x + 3a - ax - 3$$
$$3 - 3a = a^2x - ax - x$$
$$3 - 3a = \left(a^2 - a - 1\right)x$$
$$\frac{3-3a}{a^2-a-1} = x$$
$$x = \frac{3-3a}{a^2-a-1}$$

55.
$$a^2x + 3x = 2a^2$$
$$\left(a^2+3\right)x = 2a^2$$
$$x = \frac{2a^2}{a^2+3}$$

57.
$$3x = (2x-1)(m+4)$$
$$3x = 2xm + 8x - m - 4$$
$$m + 4 = 2xm + 5x$$
$$m + 4 = (2m+5)x$$
$$\frac{m+4}{2m+5} = x$$
$$x = \frac{m+4}{2m+5}$$

59. (a) Here, $r = .08$, $P = 1575$, and $t = \frac{6}{12} = \frac{1}{2}$ (year).

$$I = Prt = 1575(.08)\left(\frac{1}{2}\right) = \$63$$

The interest is \$63.

(b) The amount Miguel must pay Julio at the end of the six months is \$1575 + \$63 = \$1638.

61.
$$F = \frac{9}{5}C + 32$$
$$F = \frac{9}{5}\cdot 20 + 32$$
$$F = 36 + 32$$
$$F = 68$$
Therefore, 20°C = 68°F.

63.
$$C = \frac{5}{9}(F-32)$$
$$C = \frac{5}{9}(59-32)$$
$$C = \frac{5}{9}\cdot 27$$
$$C = 15$$
Therefore, 59°F = 15°C.

65.
$$C = \frac{5}{9}(F-32)$$
$$C = \frac{5}{9}(100-32)$$
$$C = \frac{5}{9}\cdot 68$$
$$C \approx 37.8$$
Therefore, 100°F ≈ 37.8°C.

67.
$$C = \frac{5}{9}(F-32)$$
$$C = \frac{5}{9}(867-32)$$
$$C = \frac{5}{9}\cdot 835$$
$$C \approx 463.9$$
Therefore, 865°F ≈ 463.9°C.

69.
$$C = \frac{5}{9}(F-32)$$
$$C = \frac{5}{9}(5.2-32)$$
$$C = \frac{5}{9}\cdot(-28.8)$$
$$C \approx -14.9$$
Therefore, 5.2°F ≈ −14.9°C.

Section 1.2: Applications and Modeling with Linear Equations

Connections (page 100)
Step 1 compares to Polya's first step, Steps 2 and 3 compare to his second step, Step 4 compares to his third step, and Step 6 compares to his fourth step.

Exercises

1. 15 minutes is $\frac{1}{4}$ of an hour, so multiply 80 mph by $\frac{1}{4}$ to get a distance of 20 mi.

3. 4% is .04, so multiply $100 by .04 and by 2 yrs to get interest of $8

5. Concentration A, 36%, cannot possibly be the concentration of the mixture because it exceeds both the concentrations.

7. D

9. In the formula $P = 2l + 2w$, let $P = 98$ and $w = 19$.

$$98 = 2l + 2\cdot 19 \Rightarrow 98 = 2l + 38 \Rightarrow 60 = 2l \Rightarrow 30 = l$$

The length is 30 cm.

11. Let $w =$ width of rectangle.
Then $2w - 2.5 =$ length of rectangle.
Use the formula for the perimeter of a rectangle.

$$P = 2l + 2w \Rightarrow 40.6 = 2(2w - 2.5) + 2w \Rightarrow 40.6 = 4w - 5 + 2w$$
$$40.6 = 6w - 5 \Rightarrow 45.6 = 6w \Rightarrow 7.6 = w$$

The width is 7.6 cm.

13. Let $x =$ length of shortest side.
Then $2x - 200 =$ length of longest side.
Also, the length of the middle side will be $(2x - 200) - 200 = 2x - 400$.
The perimeter of a triangle is the sum of the measures of the three sides.

$$x + (2x - 200) + (2x - 400) = 2400 \Rightarrow x + 2x - 200 + 2x - 400 = 2400$$
$$5x - 600 = 2400 \Rightarrow 5x = 3000 \Rightarrow x = 600$$

The length of the shortest side is 600 ft. The middle side is $2\cdot 600 - 400 = 1200 - 400 = 800$ ft. The longest side is $2\cdot 600 - 200 = 1200 - 200 = 1000$ ft.

15. Let $w =$ width of the ticket.
Then $w + 4 =$ length of the ticket.
Use the formula for the perimeter of a rectangle.

$$P = 2l + 2w \Rightarrow 30 = 2\left[(w+4)+4\right] + 2(w+1)$$
$$30 = 2(w+8) + 2(w+1) \Rightarrow 30 = 2w + 16 + 2w + 2$$
$$30 = 4w + 18 \Rightarrow 12 = 4w \Rightarrow 3 = w$$

The width of the ticket is 3 mm and the length is $3 + 4 = 7$ mm.

17. Let h = the height of box.
Use the formula for the surface area of a rectangular box.

$$S = 2lw + 2wh + 2hl \Rightarrow 496 = 2 \cdot 18 \cdot 8 + 2 \cdot 8h + 2h \cdot 18$$
$$496 = 288 + 16h + 36h \Rightarrow 496 = 288 + 52h \Rightarrow 208 = 52h \Rightarrow 4 = h$$

The height of the box is 4 ft.

19. Let x = the time (in hours) spent on the way to the business appointment.

	r	t	d
Morning	50	x	$50x$
Afternoon	40	$x+\frac{1}{4}$	$40\left(x+\frac{1}{4}\right)$

Since the distance on the way to the business appointment is the same as the return trip, we have

$$50x = 40\left(x+\tfrac{1}{4}\right) \Rightarrow 50x = 40x + 10 \Rightarrow 10x = 10 \Rightarrow x = 1.$$

Since she drove 1 hr, her distance traveled would be $50 \cdot 1 = 50$ mi.

21. Let x = speed (in mph) of David on bike.
Then $x + 4.5$ = speed (in mph) of David driving.

	r	t	d
Car	$x+4.5$	20 min $= \frac{1}{3}$ hr	$\frac{1}{3}(x+4.5)$
Bike	x	45 min $= \frac{3}{4}$ hr	$\frac{3}{4}x$

Since the distance by bike and car are the same, we solve the following.

$$\tfrac{1}{3}(x+4.5) = \tfrac{3}{4}x \Rightarrow 12\left[\tfrac{1}{3}(x+4.5)\right] = 12\left[\tfrac{3}{4}x\right]$$
$$4(x+4.5) = 9x \Rightarrow 4x + 18 = 9x \Rightarrow 18 = 5x \Rightarrow \tfrac{18}{5} = x$$

Since his rate is $\frac{18}{5}$ (or 3.6) mph, David travels $\frac{3}{4}\left(\frac{18}{5}\right) = \frac{27}{10} = 2.7$ mi to work.

23. Let x = time (in hours) it takes for Russ and Janet to be $\frac{1}{2}$ mi apart.

	r	t	d
Russ	7	x	$7x$
Janet	5	x	$5x$

Since Russ's rate is faster than Janet's, he travels farther than Janet in the same amount of time. To have the difference between Russ and Janet to be $\frac{1}{2}$ mi, we must solve the following equation.

$$7x - 5x = \tfrac{1}{2} \Rightarrow 2x = \tfrac{1}{2} \Rightarrow x = \tfrac{1}{4}$$

It will take $\frac{1}{4}$ hr = 15 min for Russ and Janet to be $\frac{1}{2}$ mi apart.

25. We need to determine how many meters are in 26 miles.

$$26 \text{ mi} \cdot \frac{5,280 \text{ ft}}{1 \text{ mi}} \cdot \frac{1 \text{ m}}{3.281 \text{ ft}} \approx 41,840.9 \text{ m}$$

Tim Montgomery's rate in the 100-m dash would be $r = \frac{d}{t} = \frac{100}{9.78}$ meters per second.

Thus, the time it would take for Tim to run the 26-mi marathon would be $t = \frac{d}{r} = \frac{41,840.9}{\frac{100}{9.78}} = 41,840.9 \cdot \frac{9.78}{100} \approx 4,092$ sec. Since there is 60 seconds in one minute and $60 \cdot 60 = 3,600$ seconds in one hour, $4,092 \text{ sec} = 1 \cdot 3600 + 8 \cdot 60 + 12$ sec or 1 hr, 8 min, 12 sec. This is about $\frac{1}{2}$ the world record time.

27. Let x = speed (in km/hr) of Joanne's boat.
When Joann is traveling upstream, the current slows her down, so we subtract the speed of the current from the speed of the boat. When she is traveling downstream, the current speeds her up, so we add the speed of the current to the speed of the boat.

	r	t	d
Upstream	$x-5$	20 min $= \frac{1}{3}$ hr	$\frac{1}{3}(x-5)$
Downstream	$x+5$	15 min $= \frac{1}{4}$ hr	$\frac{1}{4}(x+5)$

Since the distance upstream and downstream are the same, we must solve the following equation.

$$\tfrac{1}{3}(x-5) = \tfrac{1}{4}(x+5) \Rightarrow 12\left[\tfrac{1}{3}(x-5)\right] = 12\left[\tfrac{1}{4}(x+5)\right]$$

$$4(x-5) = 3(x+5) \Rightarrow 4x - 20 = 3x + 15 \Rightarrow x - 20 = 15 \Rightarrow x = 35$$

The speed of Joann's boat is 35 km per hour.

29. Let x = the amount of time (in hours) it takes Joe and Sam to paint the house.

	r	t	Part of the Job Accomplished
Joe	$\frac{1}{3}$	x	$\frac{1}{3}x$
Sam	$\frac{1}{5}$	x	$\frac{1}{5}x$

Since Joe and Sam must accomplish 1 job (painting a house), we must solve the following equation.

$$\tfrac{1}{3}x + \tfrac{1}{5}x = 1 \Rightarrow 15\left[\tfrac{1}{3}x + \tfrac{1}{5}x\right] = 15 \cdot 1$$

$$5x + 3x = 15 \Rightarrow 8x = 15 \Rightarrow x = \tfrac{15}{8} = 1\tfrac{7}{8}$$

It takes Joe and Sam $1\frac{7}{8}$ hr working together to paint the house.

31. Let x = the amount of time (in hours) it takes plant A to produce the pollutant.
Then $2x$ = the amount of time (in hours) it takes plant B to produce the pollutant.

	Rate	Time	Part of the Job Accomplished
Pollution from A	$\frac{1}{x}$	26	$\frac{1}{x}(26)$
Pollution from B	$\frac{1}{2x}$	26	$\frac{1}{2x}(26)$

Since plant A and B accomplish 1 job (producing the pollutant), we must solve the following equation.

$$\frac{1}{x}(26)+\frac{1}{2x}(26)=1 \Rightarrow \frac{26}{x}+\frac{13}{x}=1 \Rightarrow x\left[\frac{39}{x}\right]=x\cdot 1 \Rightarrow 39=x$$

Plant B will take $2\cdot 39=78$ hr to produce the pollutant.

33. Let x = the amount of time (in hours) to fill the pool with both pipes open.

	Rate	Time	Part of the Job Accomplished
Inlet pipe	$\frac{1}{5}$	x	$\frac{1}{5}x$
Outlet pipe	$\frac{1}{8}$	x	$\frac{1}{8}x$

Filling the pool is 1 whole job, but because the outlet pipe empties the pool, its contribution should be subtracted from the contribution of the inlet pipe.

$$\frac{1}{5}x-\frac{1}{8}x=1 \Rightarrow 40\left[\frac{1}{5}x-\frac{1}{8}x\right]=40\cdot 1$$

$$8x-5x=40 \Rightarrow 3x=40 \Rightarrow x=\frac{40}{3}=13\tfrac{1}{3}\text{ hr}$$

It took $13\frac{1}{3}$ hr to fill the pool.

35. Let x = the amount of 5% acid solution (in gallons).

Strength	Gallons of Solution	Gallons of Pure Acid
5%	x	$.05x$
10%	5	$.10\cdot 5=.5$
7%	$x+5$	$.07(x+5)$

The number of gallons of pure acid in the 5% solution plus the number of gallons of pure acid in the 10% solution must equal the number of gallons of pure acid in the 7% solution.

$$.05x+.5=.07(x+5) \Rightarrow .05x+.5=.07x+.35$$

$$.5=.02x+.35 \Rightarrow .15=.02x \Rightarrow \frac{.15}{.02}=x$$

$$x=7.5=7\tfrac{1}{2}\text{gal}$$

$7\frac{1}{2}$ gallons of the 5% solution should be added.

37. Let x = the amount of 100% alcohol solution (in liters).

Strength	Liters of Solution	Liters of Pure Alcohol
100%	x	$1x = x$
10%	7	$.10 \cdot 7 = .7$
30%	$x+7$	$.30(x+7)$

The number of liters of pure alcohol in the 100% solution plus the number of liters of pure alcohol in the 10% solution must equal the number of liters of pure alcohol in the 30% solution.

$$x + .7 = .30(x+7) \Rightarrow x + .7 = .30x + 2.1$$

$$.7x + .7 = 2.1 \Rightarrow .7x = 1.4 \Rightarrow x = \frac{1.4}{.7} = \frac{14}{7} = 2 \text{ L}$$

2 L of the 100% solution should be added.

39. Let x = the amount of water (in mL).

Strength	Milliliters of Solution	Milliliters of Salt
6%	8	$.06(8) = .48$
0%	x	$0(x) = 0$
4%	$8+x$	$.04(8+x)$

The number of milliliters of salt in the 6% solution plus the number of milliliters of salt in the water (0% solution) must equal the number of milliliters in the 4% solution.

$$.48 + 0 = .04(8+x) \Rightarrow .48 = .32 + .04x$$

$$.16 = .04x \Rightarrow \frac{.16}{.04} = x \Rightarrow x = \frac{16}{4} = 4 \text{ mL}$$

To reduce the saline concentration to 4%, 4 mL of water should be added.

41. Let x = amount of short-term note.
Then 240,000 – x = amount of long-term note.

Amount of Note	Interest Rate	Interest
x	6%	$.06x$
$240{,}000 - x$	5%	$.05(240{,}000 - x)$
$240{,}000$		$13{,}000$

The amount of interest from the 6% note plus the amount of interest from the 5% note must equal the total amount of interest.

$$.06x + .05(240{,}000 - x) = 13{,}000 \Rightarrow .06x + 12{,}000 - .05x = 13{,}000$$

$$.01x + 12{,}000 = 13{,}000 \Rightarrow .01x = 1{,}000$$

$$x = 100{,}000$$

The amount of the short-term note is \$100,000 and the amount of the long-term note is \$240,000 – \$100,000 = \$140,000.

43. Let x = amount invested at 2.5%.
Then $2x$ = amount invested at 3%.

Amount in Account	Interest Rate	Interest
x	2.5%	$.025x$
$2x$	3%	$.03(2x)=.06x$
		850

The amount of interest from the 2.5% account plus the amount of interest from the 3% account must equal the total amount of interest.

$$.025x+.06x=850 \Rightarrow .085x=850 \Rightarrow x=\$10,000$$

Karen deposited \$10,000 at 2.5% and 2(\$10,000) = \$20,000 at 3%.

45. 30% of \$200,000 is \$60,000, so after paying her income tax, Marietta had \$140,000 left to invest.
Let x = amount invested at 1.5%.
Then $140,000 - x$ = amount invested at 4%.

Amount Invested	Interest Rate	Interest
x	1.5%	$.015x$
$140,000-x$	4%	$.04(140,000-x)$
140,000		4350

$$.015x+.04(140,000-x)=4350$$
$$.015x+5600-.04x=4350$$
$$-.025x+5600=4350$$
$$-.025x=-1250 \Rightarrow x=\$50,000$$

Marietta invested \$50,000 at 1.5% and \$140,000 – \$50,000 = \$90,000 at 4%.

47. **(a)** $k=\dfrac{.132B}{W}=\dfrac{.132\cdot 20}{75}=.0352$

(b) $R=(.0352)(.42)\approx .015$
An individual's increased lifetime cancer risk would be 1.5%.

(c) Using an average life expectancy of
72 yr, $\dfrac{.015}{72}\cdot 5000\approx 1$ case of cancer each year.

49. **(a)** The volume would be $10\times 10\times 8=800\text{ ft}^3$.

(b) Since the paneling has an area of $4\times 8=32$ sq ft, it emits $32\cdot 3365=107,680\ \mu g$ of formaldehyde.

(c) $F=107,680x$

(d) Since $33\ \mu g/ft^3$ causes irritation, the room would need $33\cdot 800=26,400\ \mu g$ to cause irritation.

$$F=107,680x$$
$$26,400=107,680x \Rightarrow \frac{26,400}{107,680}=x$$
$$x\approx .25 \text{ day or approximately 6 hours}$$

51. (a) In 2008, $x = 5$.

$$y = .2145x + 15.69$$
$$y = .2145 \cdot 5 + 15.69$$
$$y = 1.0725 + 15.69$$
$$y = 16.7625$$

Approximately 16.8 million

(b)

$$y = .2145x + 15.69$$
$$17 = .2145x + 15.69$$
$$1.31 = .2145x$$
$$\frac{1.31}{.2145} = x$$
$$x \approx 6.1$$

In the year 2009

(c) They are quite close.

(d) $y = .2145(-10) + 15.69$

$$y = -2.145 + 15.69$$
$$y \approx 13.5$$

Approximately 13.5 million

(e) Answers will vary.

Section 1.3: Complex Numbers

1. true

3. true

5. false (Every real number is a complex number.)

7. -6 is real and complex.

9. $10i$ is pure imaginary and complex.

11. $2 + i$ is complex.

13. π is real and complex.

15. $\sqrt{-9} = 3i$ is pure imaginary and complex.

17. $\sqrt{-25} = i\sqrt{25} = 5i$

19. $\sqrt{-10} = i\sqrt{10}$

21. $\sqrt{-288} = i\sqrt{288} = i\sqrt{144 \cdot 2} = 12i\sqrt{2}$

23. $-\sqrt{-18} = -i\sqrt{18} = -i\sqrt{9 \cdot 2} = -3i\sqrt{2}$

25. $\sqrt{-13} \cdot \sqrt{-13} = i\sqrt{13} \cdot i\sqrt{13}$
$$= i^2\left(\sqrt{13}\right)^2 = -1 \cdot 13 = -13$$

27. $\sqrt{-3} \cdot \sqrt{-8} = i\sqrt{3} \cdot i\sqrt{8} = i^2\sqrt{3 \cdot 8}$
$$= -1 \cdot \sqrt{24} = -\sqrt{4 \cdot 6} = -2\sqrt{6}$$

29. $\dfrac{\sqrt{-30}}{\sqrt{-10}} = \dfrac{i\sqrt{30}}{i\sqrt{10}} = \sqrt{\dfrac{30}{10}} = \sqrt{3}$

31. $\dfrac{\sqrt{-24}}{\sqrt{8}} = \dfrac{i\sqrt{24}}{\sqrt{8}} = i\sqrt{\dfrac{24}{8}} = i\sqrt{3}$

33. $\dfrac{\sqrt{-10}}{\sqrt{-40}} = \dfrac{i\sqrt{10}}{i\sqrt{40}} = \sqrt{\dfrac{10}{40}} = \sqrt{\dfrac{1}{4}} = \dfrac{1}{2}$

35. $\dfrac{\sqrt{-6} \cdot \sqrt{-2}}{\sqrt{3}} = \dfrac{i\sqrt{6} \cdot i\sqrt{2}}{\sqrt{3}} = i^2\sqrt{\dfrac{6 \cdot 2}{3}} = -1 \cdot \sqrt{\dfrac{12}{3}} = -\sqrt{4} = -2$

37. $\dfrac{-6 + \sqrt{-24}}{2} = \dfrac{-6 + \sqrt{-4 \cdot 6}}{2} = \dfrac{-6 + 2i\sqrt{6}}{2} = \dfrac{2\left(-3 + i\sqrt{6}\right)}{2} = -3 + i\sqrt{6}$

39. $\dfrac{10 - \sqrt{-200}}{5} = \dfrac{10 - \sqrt{-100 \cdot 2}}{5} = \dfrac{10 - 10i\sqrt{2}}{5} = \dfrac{5\left(2 - 2i\sqrt{2}\right)}{5} = 2 - 2i\sqrt{2}$

41. $\dfrac{3+\sqrt{-18}}{24}=\dfrac{3+\sqrt{-9\cdot 2}}{24}=\dfrac{3+3i\sqrt{2}}{24}=\dfrac{3\left(1+i\sqrt{2}\right)}{24}=\dfrac{1+i\sqrt{2}}{8}=\frac{1}{8}+\frac{\sqrt{2}}{8}i$

43. $(3+2i)+(4-3i)=(3+4)+\left[2+(-3)\right]i=7+(-1)i=7-i$

45. $(-2+3i)-(-4+3i)=\left[-2-(-4)\right]+(3-3)i=2+0i=2$

47. $(2-5i)-(3+4i)-(-2+i)=\left[2-3-(-2)\right]+(-5-4-1)i=1+(-10)i=1-10i$

49. $-i-2-(6-4i)-(5-2i)=(-2-6-5)+\left[-1-(-4)-(-2)\right]i=-13+5i$

51. $(2+i)(3-2i)=2(3)+2(-2i)+i(3)+i(-2i)=6-4i+3i-2i^2=6-i-2(-1)=6-i+2=8-i$

53. $(2+4i)(-1+3i)=2(-1)+2(3i)+4i(-1)+4i(3i)$
$=-2+6i-4i+12i^2=-2+2i+12(-1)=-2+2i-12=-14+2i$

55. $(-3+2i)^2=(-3)^2+2(-3)(2i)+(2i)^2$ Square of a binomial
$=9-12i+4i^2=9-12i+4(-1)=9-12i-4=5-12i$

57. $(3+i)(-3-i)=3(-3)+3(-i)+i(-3)+i(-i)=-9-3i-3i-i^2=-9-6i-(-1)=-9-6i+1=-8-6i$

59. $(2+3i)(2-3i)=2^2-(3i)^2$ Product of the sum and difference of two terms
$=4-9i^2=4-9(-1)=4+9=13$

61. $\left(\sqrt{6}+i\right)\left(\sqrt{6}-i\right)=\left(\sqrt{6}\right)^2-i^2=6-(-1)=6+1=7$

63. $i(3-4i)(3+4i)=i\left[(3-4i)(3+4i)\right]=i\left[3^2-(4i)^2\right]=i\left[9-16i^2\right]=i\left[9-16(-1)\right]=i(9+16)=25i$

65. $3i(2-i)^2=3i\left[2^2-2(2)(i)+i^2\right]$
$=3i\left[4-4i+(-1)\right]=3i(3-4i)=9i-12i^2=9i-12(-1)=9i+12=12+9i$

67. $(2+i)(2-i)(4+3i)=\left[(2+i)(2-i)\right](4+3i)$
$=\left[2^2-i^2\right](4+3i)=\left[4-(-1)\right](4+3i)=5(4+3i)=20+15i$

69. $i^{21}=i^{20}\cdot i=\left(i^4\right)^5\cdot i=1^5\cdot i=i$

71. $i^{22}=i^{20}\cdot i^2=\left(i^4\right)^5\cdot(-1)=1^5\cdot(-1)=-1$

73. $i^{23}=i^{20}\cdot i^3=\left(i^4\right)^5\cdot i^3=1^5\cdot(-i)=-i$

75. $i^{24}=\left(i^4\right)^6=1^6=1$

77. $i^{-9}=i^{-12}\cdot i^3=\left(i^4\right)^{-3}\cdot i^3=1^{-3}\cdot(-i)=-i$

79. $\dfrac{1}{i^{-11}}=i^{11}=i^8\cdot i^3=\left(i^4\right)^2\cdot i^3=1^2\cdot(-i)=-i$

81. Answers will vary.

83. $\dfrac{6+2i}{1+2i}=\dfrac{(6+2i)(1-2i)}{(1+2i)(1-2i)}$

$$=\frac{6-12i+2i-4i^2}{1^2-(2i)^2}=\frac{6-10i-4(-1)}{1-4i^2}=\frac{6-10i+4}{1-4(-1)}=\frac{10-10i}{1+4}=\frac{10-10i}{5}=\frac{10}{5}-\frac{10}{5}i=2-2i$$

85. $\dfrac{2-i}{2+i}=\dfrac{(2-i)(2-i)}{(2+i)(2-i)}=\dfrac{2^2-2(2i)+i^2}{2^2-i^2}=\dfrac{4-4i+(-1)}{4-(-1)}=\dfrac{3-4i}{5}=\dfrac{3}{5}-\dfrac{4}{5}i$

87. $\dfrac{1-3i}{1+i}=\dfrac{(1-3i)(1-i)}{(1+i)(1-i)}=\dfrac{1-i-3i+3i^2}{1^2-i^2}=\dfrac{1-4i+3(-1)}{1-(-1)}=\dfrac{1-4i-3}{2}=\dfrac{-2-4i}{2}=\dfrac{-2}{2}-\dfrac{4}{2}i=-1-2i$

89. $\dfrac{5}{i}=\dfrac{5(-i)}{i(-i)}=\dfrac{-5i}{-i^2}$

$$=\frac{-5i}{-(-1)}=\frac{-5i}{1}=-5i \text{ or } 0-5i$$

91. $\dfrac{-8}{-i}=\dfrac{-8\cdot i}{-i\cdot i}=\dfrac{-8i}{-i^2}$

$$=\frac{-8i}{-(-1)}=\frac{-8i}{1}=-8i \text{ or } 0-8i$$

93. $\dfrac{2}{3i}=\dfrac{2(-3i)}{3i\cdot(-3i)}=\dfrac{-6i}{-9i^2}=\dfrac{-6i}{-9(-1)}=\dfrac{-6i}{9}=-\dfrac{2}{3}i$ or $0-\dfrac{2}{3}i$

Note: In the above solution, we multiplied the numerator and denominator bye the complex conjugate of $3i$, namely $-3i$. Since there is a reduction in the end, the same results can be achieved by multiplying the numerator and denominator by $-i$.

95. We need to show that $\left(\dfrac{\sqrt{2}}{2}+\dfrac{\sqrt{2}}{2}i\right)^2=i.$

$$\left(\frac{\sqrt{2}}{2}+\frac{\sqrt{2}}{2}i\right)^2=\left(\frac{\sqrt{2}}{2}\right)^2+2\cdot\frac{\sqrt{2}}{2}\cdot\frac{\sqrt{2}}{2}i+\left(\frac{\sqrt{2}}{2}i\right)^2$$

$$=\frac{2}{4}+2\cdot\frac{2}{4}i+\frac{2}{4}i^2=\frac{1}{2}+i+\frac{1}{2}i^2=\frac{1}{2}+i+\frac{1}{2}(-1)=\frac{1}{2}+i-\frac{1}{2}=i$$

97. Let $z=3-2i$.

$$3z-z^2=3(3-2i)-(3-2i)^2=9-6i-\left[3^2-2(6i)+(2i)^2\right]=9-6i-\left(9-12i+4i^2\right)$$

$$=9-6i-\left[9-12i+4(-1)\right]=9-6i-\left[9-12i+(-4)\right]=9-6i-(5-12i)=9-6i-5+12i=4+6i$$

Section 1.4: Quadratic Equations

1. $x^2 = 4$

$x = \pm\sqrt{4} = \pm 2$; G

3. $x^2 + 2 = 0$

$x^2 = -2$

$x = \pm\sqrt{-2} = \pm i\sqrt{2}$; C

5. $x^2 = -8$

$x = \pm\sqrt{-8} = \pm 2i\sqrt{2}$; H

7. $x - 2 = 0$

$x = 2$; D

9. D is the only one set up for direct use of the zero-factor property.

$$(3x+1)(x-7)=0$$

$$3x+1=0 \quad \text{or} \quad x-7=0$$

$$x=-\tfrac{1}{3} \quad \text{or} \quad x=7$$

Solution set: $\left\{-\frac{1}{3}, 7\right\}$

11. C is the only one that does not require Step 1 of the method of completing the square.

$$x^2 + x = 12$$

$$x^2 + x + \tfrac{1}{4} = 12 + \tfrac{1}{4} \qquad \left[\tfrac{1}{2}\cdot 1\right]^2 = \left(\tfrac{1}{2}\right)^2 = \tfrac{1}{4}$$

$$\left(x+\tfrac{1}{2}\right)^2 = \tfrac{49}{4}$$

$$x + \tfrac{1}{2} = \pm\sqrt{\tfrac{49}{4}} = \pm\tfrac{7}{2}$$

$$x = -\tfrac{1}{2} \pm \tfrac{7}{2}$$

$$-\tfrac{1}{2} - \tfrac{7}{2} = \tfrac{-8}{2} = -4 \text{ and } -\tfrac{1}{2} + \tfrac{7}{2} = \tfrac{6}{2} = 3$$

Solution set: $\{-4, 3\}$

13. $x^2 - 5x + 6 = 0$

$(x-2)(x-3)=0$

$x-2=0$ or $x-3=0$

$x=2$ or $x=3$

Solution set: $\{2, 3\}$

15. $5x^2 - 3x - 2 = 0$

$(5x+2)(x-1)=0$

$5x+2=0$ or $x-1=0$

$x=-\frac{2}{5}$ or $x=1$

Solution set: $\left\{-\frac{2}{5}, 1\right\}$

17. $-4x^2 + x = -3$

$0 = 4x^2 - x - 3$

$0 = (4x+3)(x-1)$

$4x+3=0$ or $x-1=0$

$x=-\frac{3}{4}$ or $x=1$

Solution set: $\left\{-\frac{3}{4}, 1\right\}$

19. $x^2 = 16$

$x = \pm\sqrt{16} = \pm 4$

Solution set: $\{\pm 4\}$

21. $x^2 = 27$

$x = \pm\sqrt{27} = \pm 3\sqrt{3}$

Solution set: $\{\pm 3\sqrt{3}\}$

23. $x^2 = -16$

$x = \pm\sqrt{-16} = \pm 4i$

Solution set: $\{\pm 4i\}$

25. $(3x-1)^2 = 12$

$3x - 1 = \pm\sqrt{12}$

$3x = 1 \pm 2\sqrt{3}$

$x = \dfrac{1 \pm 2\sqrt{3}}{3}$

Solution set: $\left\{\frac{1\pm 2\sqrt{3}}{3}\right\}$

27. $(x+5)^2 = -3$

$x + 5 = \pm\sqrt{-3}$

$x + 5 = \pm i\sqrt{3}$

$x = -5 \pm i\sqrt{3}$

Solution set: $\left\{-5 \pm i\sqrt{3}\right\}$

29. $(5x-3)^2 = -3$

$5x - 3 = \pm\sqrt{-3}$

$5x - 3 = \pm i\sqrt{3}$

$5x = 3 \pm i\sqrt{3}$

$x = \dfrac{3 \pm i\sqrt{3}}{5} = \dfrac{3}{5} \pm \dfrac{\sqrt{3}}{5}i$

Solution set: $\left\{\frac{3}{5} \pm \frac{\sqrt{3}}{5}i\right\}$

31. $x^2 + 4x + 3 = 0$

$x^2 + 4x + 4 = -3 + 4 \qquad \left[\frac{1}{2}\cdot 4\right]^2 = 2^2 = 4$

$(x+2)^2 = 1$

$x + 2 = \pm\sqrt{1}$

$x + 2 = \pm 1$

$x = -2 \pm 1$

$-2 - 1 = -3$ and $-2 + 1 = -1$

Solution set: $\{-3, -1\}$

33. $2x^2 - x - 28 = 0$

$x^2 - \frac{1}{2}x - 14 = 0 \qquad$ Multiply by $\frac{1}{2}$.

$x^2 - \frac{1}{2}x + \frac{1}{16} = 14 + \frac{1}{16}$

Note: $\left[\frac{1}{2}\cdot\left(-\frac{1}{2}\right)\right]^2 = \left(-\frac{1}{4}\right)^2 = \frac{1}{16}$

$\left(x - \frac{1}{4}\right)^2 = \frac{225}{16}$

$x - \frac{1}{4} = \pm\sqrt{\frac{225}{16}}$

$x - \frac{1}{4} = \pm\frac{15}{4}$

$x = \frac{1}{4} \pm \frac{15}{4}$

$\frac{1}{4} - \frac{15}{4} = \frac{-14}{4} = -\frac{7}{2}$ and $\frac{1}{4} + \frac{15}{4} = \frac{16}{4} = 4$

Solution set: $\left\{-\frac{7}{2}, 4\right\}$

35. $x^2 - 2x - 2 = 0$

$x^2 - 2x + 1 = 2 + 1$

Note: $\left[\frac{1}{2}\cdot(-2)\right]^2 = (-1)^2 = 1$

$(x-1)^2 = 3$

$x - 1 = \pm\sqrt{3}$

$x - 1 = \pm\sqrt{3}$

$x = 1 \pm \sqrt{3}$

Solution set: $\left\{1 \pm \sqrt{3}\right\}$

37. $2x^2 + x - 10 = 0$

$x^2 + \frac{1}{2}x - 5 = 0$

$x^2 + \frac{1}{2}x + \frac{1}{16} = 5 + \frac{1}{16}$

Note: $\left[\frac{1}{2}\cdot\frac{1}{2}\right]^2 = \left(\frac{1}{4}\right)^2 = \frac{1}{16}$

$\left(x + \frac{1}{4}\right)^2 = \frac{81}{16}$

$x + \frac{1}{4} = \pm\sqrt{\frac{81}{16}}$

$x + \frac{1}{4} = \pm\frac{9}{4}$

$x = -\frac{1}{4} \pm \frac{9}{4}$

$-\frac{1}{4} - \frac{9}{4} = \frac{-10}{4} = -\frac{5}{2}$ and $-\frac{1}{4} + \frac{9}{4} = \frac{8}{4} = 2$

Solution set: $\left\{-\frac{5}{2}, 2\right\}$

39. $2x^2-4x-3=0$

$x^2-2x-\frac{3}{2}=0$

$x^2-2x+1=\frac{3}{2}+1$

Note: $\left[\frac{1}{2}\cdot(-2)\right]^2=(-1)^2=1$

$(x-1)^2=\frac{5}{2}$

$x-1=\pm\sqrt{\frac{5}{2}}$

$x-1=\pm\frac{\sqrt{10}}{2}$

$x=1\pm\frac{\sqrt{10}}{2}=\frac{2\pm\sqrt{10}}{2}$

Solution set: $\left\{\frac{2\pm\sqrt{10}}{2}\right\}$

41. $-4x^2+8x=7$

$x^2-2x=-\frac{7}{4}$

$x^2-2x+1=-\frac{7}{4}+1$

Note: $\left[\frac{1}{2}\cdot(-2)\right]^2=(-1)^2=1$

$(x-1)^2=\frac{-3}{4}$

$x-1=\pm\sqrt{\frac{-3}{4}}$

$x-1=\pm\frac{i\sqrt{3}}{2}$

$x=1\pm\frac{\sqrt{3}}{2}i$

Solution set: $\left\{1\pm\frac{\sqrt{3}}{2}i\right\}$

43. Answers will vary.

The quadratic formula, $x=\frac{-b\pm\sqrt{b^2-4ac}}{2a}$, can be evaluated with $a=1, b=-4,$ and $c=0$.

$$x=\frac{-(-4)\pm\sqrt{(-4)^2-4\cdot1\cdot0}}{2(1)}$$

$$=\frac{4\pm\sqrt{16-0}}{2}=\frac{4\pm\sqrt{16}}{2}=\frac{4\pm4}{2}$$

$$x=\frac{4+4}{2}=\frac{8}{2}=4 \text{ or } \frac{4-4}{2}=\frac{0}{2}=0$$

This agrees with the factoring approach.

$$x^2-4x=0\Rightarrow x(x-4)=0$$

$$x=0 \text{ or } x-4=0\Rightarrow x=0 \text{ or } x=4$$

45. $x^2-x-1=0$

Let $a=1, b=-1,$ and $c=-1$.

$$x=\frac{-b\pm\sqrt{b^2-4ac}}{2a}$$

$$=\frac{-(-1)\pm\sqrt{(-1)^2-4(1)(-1)}}{2(1)}$$

$$=\frac{1\pm\sqrt{1+4}}{2}=\frac{1\pm\sqrt{5}}{2}$$

Solution set: $\left\{\frac{1\pm\sqrt{5}}{2}\right\}$

47. $x^2-6x=-7$

$x^2-6x+7=0$

Let $a=1, b=-6,$ and $c=7$.

$$x=\frac{-b\pm\sqrt{b^2-4ac}}{2a}$$

$$=\frac{-(-6)\pm\sqrt{(-6)^2-4(1)(7)}}{2(1)}$$

$$=\frac{6\pm\sqrt{36-28}}{2}=\frac{6\pm\sqrt{8}}{2}$$

$$=\frac{6\pm2\sqrt{2}}{2}=3\pm\sqrt{2}$$

Solution set: $\left\{3\pm\sqrt{2}\right\}$

49. $x^2 = 2x - 5$

$x^2 - 2x + 5 = 0$

Let $a = 1, b = -2,$ and $c = 5.$

$$x = \frac{-b \pm \sqrt{b^2 - 4ac}}{2a} = \frac{-(-2) \pm \sqrt{(-2)^2 - 4(1)(5)}}{2(1)} = \frac{2 \pm \sqrt{4-20}}{2} = \frac{2 \pm \sqrt{-16}}{2} = \frac{2 \pm 4i}{2} = 1 \pm 2i$$

Solution set: $\{1 \pm 2i\}$

51. $4x^2 = 12x - 11 \Rightarrow 4x^2 - 12x + 11 = 0$

Let $a = 4, b = -12,$ and $c = 11.$

$$x = \frac{-b \pm \sqrt{b^2 - 4ac}}{2a} = \frac{-(-12) \pm \sqrt{(-12)^2 - 4(4)(11)}}{2(4)} = \frac{12 \pm \sqrt{144-176}}{8} = \frac{12 \pm \sqrt{-32}}{8} = \frac{12 \pm 4i\sqrt{2}}{8} = \frac{12}{8} \pm \frac{4\sqrt{2}}{8} i = \frac{3}{2} \pm \frac{\sqrt{2}}{2} i$$

Solution set: $\left\{\frac{3}{2} \pm \frac{\sqrt{2}}{2} i\right\}$

53. $\frac{1}{2}x^2 + \frac{1}{4}x - 3 = 0$

$4\left(\frac{1}{2}x^2 + \frac{1}{4}x - 3\right) = 4 \cdot 0$

$2x^2 + x - 12 = 0$

Let $a = 2, b = 1,$ and $c = -12.$

$$x = \frac{-b \pm \sqrt{b^2 - 4ac}}{2a} = \frac{-1 \pm \sqrt{1^2 - 4(2)(-12)}}{2(2)} = \frac{-1 \pm \sqrt{1+96}}{4} = \frac{-1 \pm \sqrt{97}}{4}$$

Solution set: $\left\{\frac{-1 \pm \sqrt{97}}{4}\right\}$

55. $.2x^2 + .4x - .3 = 0$

$10\left(.2x^2 + .4x - .3\right) = 10 \cdot 0$

$2x^2 + 4x - 3 = 0$

Let $a = 2, b = 4,$ and $c = -3.$

$$x = \frac{-b \pm \sqrt{b^2 - 4ac}}{2a} = \frac{-4 \pm \sqrt{4^2 - 4(2)(-3)}}{2(2)} = \frac{-4 \pm \sqrt{16+24}}{4} = \frac{-4 \pm \sqrt{40}}{4} = \frac{-4 \pm 2\sqrt{10}}{4} = \frac{-2 \pm \sqrt{10}}{2}$$

Solution set: $\left\{\frac{-2 \pm \sqrt{10}}{2}\right\}$

57. $4 + \frac{3}{x} - \frac{2}{x^2} = 0$

$x^2\left(4 + \frac{3}{x} - \frac{2}{x^2}\right) = x^2 \cdot 0, \; x \neq 0$

$4x^2 + 3x - 2 = 0$

Let $a = 4, b = 3,$ and $c = -2.$

$$x = \frac{-b \pm \sqrt{b^2 - 4ac}}{2a} = \frac{-3 \pm \sqrt{3^2 - 4(4)(-2)}}{2(4)} = \frac{-3 \pm \sqrt{9+32}}{8} = \frac{-3 \pm \sqrt{41}}{8}$$

Solution set: $\left\{\frac{-3 \pm \sqrt{41}}{8}\right\}$

59. $x^3-8=0 \Rightarrow x^3-2^3=0 \Rightarrow (x-2)(x^2+2x+4)=0$

$x-2=0$ or $x^2+2x+4=0$

$x=2$ $\quad a=1, b=2, \text{ and } c=4$

$$x=\frac{-b\pm\sqrt{b^2-4ac}}{2a}$$

$$=\frac{-2\pm\sqrt{2^2-4(1)(4)}}{2(1)}=\frac{-2\pm\sqrt{4-16}}{2}=\frac{-2\pm\sqrt{-12}}{2}=\frac{-2\pm 2i\sqrt{3}}{2}=-1\pm\sqrt{3}i$$

Solution set: $\{2,-1\pm\sqrt{3}i\}$

61. $x^3+27=0 \Rightarrow x^3+3^3=0 \Rightarrow (x+3)(x^2-3x+9)=0$

$x+3=0$ or $x^2-3x+9=0$

$x=-3$ $\quad a=1, b=-3, \text{ and } c=9$

$$x=\frac{-b\pm\sqrt{b^2-4ac}}{2a}$$

$$=\frac{-(-3)\pm\sqrt{(-3)^2-4(1)(9)}}{2(1)}=\frac{3\pm\sqrt{9-36}}{2}=\frac{3\pm\sqrt{-27}}{2}=\frac{3\pm 3i\sqrt{3}}{2}=\frac{3}{2}\pm\frac{3\sqrt{3}}{2}i$$

Solution set: $\left\{-3,\frac{3}{2}\pm\frac{3\sqrt{3}}{2}i\right\}$

63. $s=\frac{1}{2}gt^2$

$2s=2\left[\frac{1}{2}gt^2\right]$

$2s=gt^2$

$\frac{2s}{g}=\frac{gt^2}{g}$

$t^2=\frac{2s}{g}$

$t=\pm\sqrt{\frac{2s}{g}}=\frac{\pm\sqrt{2s}}{\sqrt{g}}\cdot\frac{\sqrt{g}}{\sqrt{g}}=\frac{\pm\sqrt{2sg}}{g}$

65. $F=\frac{kMv^2}{r} \Rightarrow rF=r\left[\frac{kMv^2}{r}\right]$

$Fr=kMv^2 \Rightarrow \frac{Fr}{kM}=\frac{kMv^2}{kM}$

$v^2=\frac{Fr}{kM}$

$v=\pm\sqrt{\frac{Fr}{kM}}$

$v=\frac{\pm\sqrt{Fr}}{\sqrt{kM}}\cdot\frac{\sqrt{kM}}{\sqrt{kM}}=\frac{\pm\sqrt{FrkM}}{kM}$

67. $h=-16t^2+v_0t+s_0$

$16t^2-v_0t+h-s_0=0 \Rightarrow \quad 16t^2-v_0t+(h-s_0)=0 \qquad a=16, b=-v_0, \text{ and } c=h-s_0$

$$x=\frac{-b\pm\sqrt{b^2-4ac}}{2a}$$

$$=\frac{-(-v_0)\pm\sqrt{(-v_0)^2-4(16)(h-s_0)}}{2(16)}=\frac{v_0\pm\sqrt{{v_0}^2-64(h-s_0)}}{32}=\frac{v_0\pm\sqrt{{v_0}^2-64h+64s_0}}{32}$$

69. $4x^2 - 2xy + 3y^2 = 2$

$4x^2 - 2xy + 3y^2 - 2 = 0$

(a) Solve for x in terms of y.

$4x^2 - (2y)x + (3y^2 - 2) = 0$

$a = 4$, $b = -2y$, and $c = 3y^2 - 2$

$$x = \frac{-b \pm \sqrt{b^2 - 4ac}}{2a} = \frac{-(-2y) \pm \sqrt{(-2y)^2 - 4(4)(3y^2 - 2)}}{2(4)}$$

$$= \frac{2y \pm \sqrt{4y^2 - 16(3y^2 - 2)}}{8} = \frac{2y \pm \sqrt{4y^2 - 48y^2 + 32}}{8} = \frac{2y \pm \sqrt{32 - 44y^2}}{8}$$

$$= \frac{2y \pm \sqrt{4(8 - 11y^2)}}{8} = \frac{2y \pm 2\sqrt{8 - 11y^2}}{8} = \frac{y \pm \sqrt{8 - 11y^2}}{4}$$

(b) Solve for y in terms of x.

$3y^2 - (2x)y + (4x^2 - 2) = 0$

$a = 3$, $b = -2x$, and $c = 4x^2 - 2$

$$y = \frac{-b \pm \sqrt{b^2 - 4ac}}{2a} = \frac{-(-2x) \pm \sqrt{(-2x)^2 - 4(3)(4x^2 - 2)}}{2(3)}$$

$$= \frac{2x \pm \sqrt{4x^2 - 12(4x^2 - 2)}}{6} = \frac{2x \pm \sqrt{4x^2 - 48x^2 + 24}}{6} = \frac{2x \pm \sqrt{24 - 44x^2}}{6}$$

$$= \frac{2x \pm \sqrt{4(6 - 11y^2)}}{6} = \frac{2x \pm 2\sqrt{6 - 11y^2}}{6} = \frac{x \pm \sqrt{6 - 11y^2}}{3}$$

71. $x^2 + 8x + 16 = 0$

$a = 1$, $b = 8$, and $c = 16$

$b^2 - 4ac = 8^2 - 4(1)(16) = 64 - 64 = 0$

one rational solution (a double solution)

73. $3x^2 - 5x + 2 = 0$

$a = 3$, $b = -5$, and $c = 2$

$b^2 - 4ac = (-5)^2 - 4(3)(2) = 25 - 24 = 1 = 1^2$

two distinct rational solutions

75. $4x^2 = 6x + 3$

$4x^2 - 6x - 3 = 0$

$a = 4$, $b = -6$, and $c = -3$

$b^2 - 4ac = (-6)^2 - 4(4)(-3) = 36 + 48 = 84$

two distinct irrational solutions

77. $9x^2 + 11x + 4 = 0$

$a = 9$, $b = 11$, and $c = 4$

$b^2 - 4ac = 11^2 - 4(9)(4) = 121 - 144 = -23$

two distinct nonreal complex solutions

79. $8x^2 - 72 = 0$

$a = 8$, $b = 0$, and $c = -72$

$b^2 - 4ac = 0^2 - 4(8)(-72) = 2304 = 48^2$

two distinct rational solutions

81. It is not possible for the solution set of a quadratic equation with integer coefficients to consist of a single irrational number. Additional responses will vary.

83.
$$x = 4 \quad \text{or} \quad x = 5$$
$$x - 4 = 0 \quad \text{or} \quad x - 5 = 0$$
$$(x-4)(x-5) = 0$$
$$x^2 - 5x - 4x + 20 = 0$$
$$x^2 - 9x + 20 = 0$$
$a = 1, b = -9,$ and $c = 20$

85.
$$x = 1 + \sqrt{2} \quad \text{or} \quad x = 1 - \sqrt{2}$$
$$x - \left(1 + \sqrt{2}\right) = 0 \quad \text{or} \quad x - \left(1 - \sqrt{2}\right) = 0$$
$$\left[x - \left(1 + \sqrt{2}\right)\right]\left[x - \left(1 - \sqrt{2}\right)\right] = 0$$
$$x^2 - x\left(1 - \sqrt{2}\right) - x\left(1 + \sqrt{2}\right) + \left(1 + \sqrt{2}\right)\left(1 - \sqrt{2}\right) = 0$$
$$x^2 - x + x\sqrt{2} - x - x\sqrt{2} + \left[1^2 - \left(\sqrt{2}\right)^2\right] = 0$$
$$x^2 - 2x + (1 - 2) = 0$$
$$x^2 - 2x - 1 = 0$$
$a = 1, b = -2,$ and $c = -1$

Section 1.5: Applications and Modeling with Quadratic Equations

Connections (page 129)

1. **(a)** $d = 16t^2$
$$= 16(5)^2$$
$$= 400$$
It will fall 400 feet in 5 seconds.

(b) $d = 16t^2$
$$= 16(10)^2$$
$$= 1600$$
It will fall 1600 feet in 10 seconds.

No, the second answer is $2^2 = 4$ times the first because the number of seconds is squared in the formula.

2. Both formulas involve the number 16 times the square of time. However, in the formula for the distance an object falls, 16 is positive, while in the formula for a propelled object, it is preceded by a negative sign. Also in the formula for a propelled object, the initial velocity and height affect the distance.

Exercises

1. The length of the parking area is $2x + 200$, while the width is x, so the area is $(2x + 200)x$. Set the area equal to 40,000.
$(2x + 200)x = 40{,}000$, so choice A is the correct choice.

3. Use the Pythagorean theorem with $a = x$, $b = 2x - 2$, and $c = x + 4$.
$x^2 + (2x-2)^2 = (x+4)^2$, so the correct choice is D.

5. Use the figure and equation A from Exercise 1.
$$x(2x + 200) = 40{,}000 \Rightarrow 2x^2 + 200x = 40{,}000$$
$$2x^2 + 200x - 40{,}000 = 0 \Rightarrow x^2 + 100x - 20{,}000 = 0 \Rightarrow (x - 100)(x + 200) = 0$$
$$x = 100 \text{ or } x = -200$$
The negative solution is not meaningful. If $x = 100$, then $2x + 200 = 400$. The dimensions of the lot are 100 yd by 400 yd.

7. Let x = the width of the strip of floor around the rug.

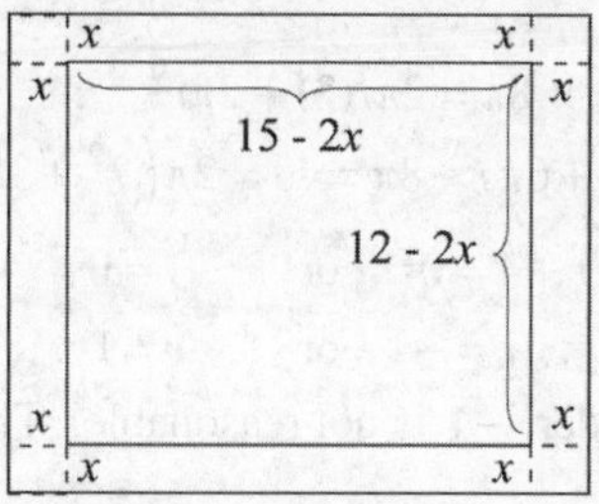

The dimensions of the carpet are $15 - 2x$ by $12 - 2x$. Since $A = lw$, the equation for the carpet area is $(15 - 2x)(12 - 2x) = 108$. Put this equation in standard form and solve by factoring.

$$(15-2x)(12-2x)=108 \Rightarrow 180-30x-24x+4x^2=108 \Rightarrow 180-54x+4x^2=108$$

$$4x^2-54x+72=0 \Rightarrow 2x^2-27x+36=0 \Rightarrow (2x-3)(x-12)=0$$

$$2x-3=0 \quad \text{or} \quad x-12=0$$

$$x=\tfrac{3}{2} \qquad\qquad x=12$$

The solutions of the quadratic equation are $\frac{3}{2}$ and 12. We eliminate 12 as meaningless in this problem. If $x = \frac{3}{2}$, then $15 - 2x = 12$ and $12 - 2x = 9$. The dimensions of the carpet are 9 ft by 12 ft.

9. Let x = the width of the metal. The dimensions of the base of the box are $x-4$ by $x+6$.

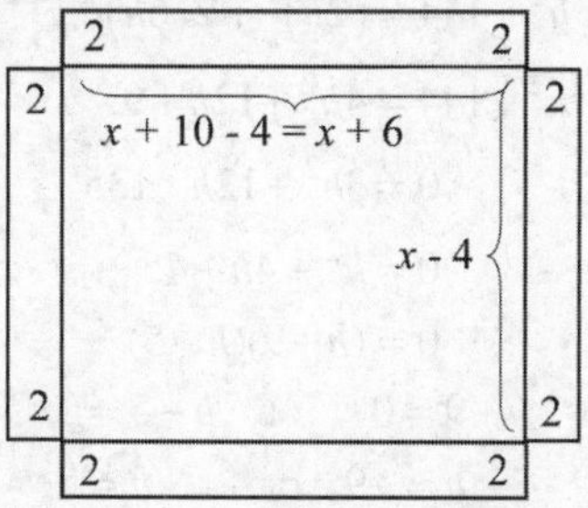

Since the formula for the volume of a box is $V = lwh$, we have

$$(x+6)(x-4)(2)=832 \Rightarrow (x+6)(x-4)=416 \Rightarrow x^2-4x+6x-24=416$$

$$x^2+2x-24=416 \Rightarrow x^2+2x-440=0 \Rightarrow (x+22)(x-20)=0$$

$$x+22=0 \quad \text{or} \quad x-20=0$$

$$x=-22 \quad \text{or} \quad x=20$$

The negative solution is not meaningful. If $x = 20$, then $x + 10 = 30$. The dimensions of the sheet of metal are 20 in by 30 in.

11. Let h = height and r = radius.
Area of side = $2\pi rh$ and Area of circle = πr^2
Surface area = area of side + area of top + area of bottom
Surface area = $2\pi rh + \pi r^2 + \pi r^2 = 2\pi rh + 2\pi r^2$
$371 = 2\pi r(12) + 2\pi r^2 \Rightarrow 371 = 24\pi r + 2\pi r^2 \Rightarrow 0 = 2\pi r^2 + 24\pi r - 371$
$a = 2\pi$, $b = 24\pi$, and $c = -371$

$$r=\frac{-b\pm\sqrt{b^2-4ac}}{2a}\quad r=\frac{-24\pi\pm\sqrt{(24\pi)^2-4(2\pi)(-371)}}{2(2\pi)}=\frac{-24\pi\pm\sqrt{576\pi^2+2968\pi}}{4\pi}$$

$r \approx -15.75$ or $r \approx 3.75$
The negative solution is not meaningful. The radius of the circular top is approximately 3.75 cm.

13. Let h = height and r = radius.
Surface area = $2\pi rh + 2\pi r^2$

$$8\pi = 2\pi r(3) + 2\pi r^2$$

$$8\pi = 6\pi r + 2\pi r^2 \Rightarrow 0 = 2\pi r^2 + 6\pi r - 8\pi \Rightarrow 0 = 2\pi\left(r^2 + 3r - 4\right) \Rightarrow 0 = (r+4)(r-1)$$

$$r + 4 = 0 \quad \text{or} \quad r - 1 = 0$$

$$r = -4 \quad \text{or} \quad r = 1$$

The r represents the radius of a cylinder, -4 is not reasonable. The radius of the circular top is approximately 1 ft.

15. Let x = length of side of square.
Area = x^2 and Perimeter = $4x$

$$x^2 = 4x \Rightarrow x^2 - 4x = 0 \Rightarrow x(x-4) = 0$$

$$x = 0 \text{ or } x = 4$$

We reject 0 since x must be greater than 0. The side of the square measures 4 units.

17. Let h = the height of the dock.
Then $2h + 3$ = the length of the rope from the boat to the top of the dock.
Apply the Pythagorean theorem to the triangle shown in the text.

$$h^2 + 12^2 = (2h+3)^2$$

$$h^2 + 144 = (2h)^2 + 2(6h) + 3^2$$

$$h^2 + 144 = 4h^2 + 12h + 9$$

$$0 = 3h^2 + 12h - 135$$

$$0 = h^2 + 4h - 45$$

$$0 = (h+9)(h-5)$$

$$h + 9 = 0 \quad \text{or} \quad h - 5 = 0$$

$$h = -9 \quad \text{or} \quad h = 5$$

The negative solution is not meaningful. The height of the dock is 5 ft.

19. Let r = radius of circle and x = length of side of square.
The radius is $\frac{1}{2}$ the length of the diagonal of the square.

Area = x^2

$800 = x^2$

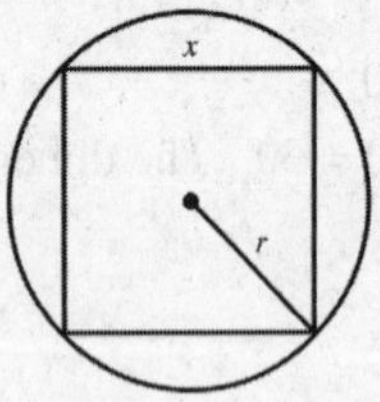

Apply the Pythagorean theorem.

$$a^2 + b^2 = c^2$$

$$x^2 + x^2 = (2r)^2 \Rightarrow 2x^2 = 4r^2$$

$$x^2 = 2r^2 \Rightarrow 800 = 2r^2$$

$$400 = r^2 \Rightarrow r = \pm\sqrt{400} = \pm 20$$

The radius is 20 feet. Disregard a negative radius.

21. Let x = length of ladder
Distance from building to ladder = 8 + 2 = 10.
Distance from ground to window = 13
Apply the Pythagorean theorem.

$$a^2 + b^2 = c^2 \Rightarrow 10^2 + 13^2 = x^2 \Rightarrow 100 + 169 = x^2 \Rightarrow 269 = x^2 \Rightarrow \pm\sqrt{269} = x$$

$$x \approx -16.4 \text{ or } x \approx 16.4$$

The negative solution is not meaningful. The worker will need a 16.4-ft ladder.

23. Let x = length of short leg, $x + 700$ = length of long leg, and $x + 700 + 100$ or $x + 800$ = length of hypotenuse.

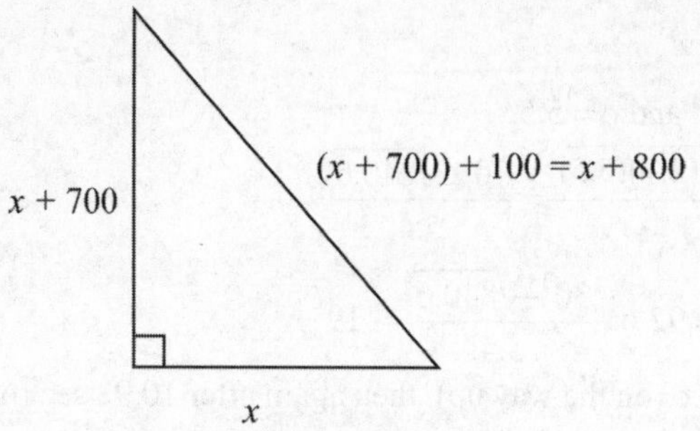

Apply the Pythagorean theorem.

$$c^2 = a^2 + b^2$$
$$(x+800)^2 = x^2 + (x+700)^2$$
$$x^2 + 1600x + 640{,}000 = x^2 + x^2 + 1400x + 490{,}000$$
$$0 = x^2 - 200x - 150{,}000$$
$$0 = (x+300)(x-500)$$

$x + 300 = 0$ or $x - 500 = 0$

$x = -300$ or $x = 500$

The negative solution is not meaningful.
500 = length of short leg
500 + 700 = 1200 = length of long leg
1200 + 100 = 1300 = length of hypotenuse
500 + 1200 + 1300 = 3000 = length of walkway.
The total length is 3000 yd.

25. (a) $s = -16t^2 + v_0 t$

$s = -16t^2 + 96t$

$80 = -16t^2 + 96t$

$16t^2 - 96t + 80 = 0$

$a = 16$, $b = -96$ and $c = 80$

$$t = \frac{-b \pm \sqrt{b^2 - 4ac}}{2a} = \frac{-(-96) \pm \sqrt{(-96)^2 - 4(16)(80)}}{2(16)} = \frac{96 \pm \sqrt{9216 - 5120}}{32} = \frac{96 \pm \sqrt{4096}}{32} = \frac{96 \pm 64}{32}$$

$$t = \frac{96-64}{32} = 1 \text{ or } t = \frac{96+64}{32} = 5$$

The projectile will reach 80ft at 1 sec and 5 sec.

(b) $s = -16t^2 + 96t$

$0 = -16t^2 + 96t$

$0 = -16t(t-6)$

$-16t = 0$ or $t - 6 = 0$

$t = 0$ or $t = 6$

The projectile will return to the ground after 6 sec.

27. (a) $s = -16t^2 + v_0 t$

$s = -16t^2 + 32t$

$80 = -16t^2 + 32t$

$16t^2 - 32t + 80 = 0$

$a = 16$, $b = -32$ and $c = 80$

$$t = \frac{-b \pm \sqrt{b^2 - 4ac}}{2a} = \frac{-(-32) \pm \sqrt{(-32)^2 - 4(16)(80)}}{2(16)} = \frac{32 \pm \sqrt{1024 - 5120}}{32} = \frac{32 \pm \sqrt{-4096}}{32} = \frac{32 \pm 64i}{32}$$

The projectile will not reach 80ft.

(b) $s = -16t^2 + 32t$

$0 = -16t^2 + 32t$

$0 = -16t(t-2)$

$-16t = 0$ or $t - 2 = 0$

$t = 0$ or $t = 2$

The projectile will return to the ground after 2 sec.

29. The height of the ball is given by $h = -2.7t^2 + 30t + 6.5$.

(a) When the ball is 12 ft above the moon's surface, $h = 12$.
Set $h = 12$ and solve for t.

$12 = -2.7t^2 + 30t + 6.5$

$2.7t^2 - 30t + 5.5 = 0$

Use the quadratic formula with $a = 2.7$, $b = -30$, and $c = 5.5$.

$$t = \frac{30 \pm \sqrt{900 - 4(2.7)(5.5)}}{2(2.7)} = \frac{30 \pm \sqrt{840.6}}{5.4}$$

$$\frac{30 + \sqrt{840.6}}{5.4} \approx 10.92 \text{ or } \frac{30 - \sqrt{840.6}}{5.4} \approx .19$$

Therefore, the ball reaches 12 ft first after .19 sec (on the way up), then again after 10.92 sec (on the way down).

(b) When the ball returns to the surface, $h = 0$.

$0 = -2.7t^2 + 30t + 6.5$

Use the quadratic formula with $a = -2.7$, $b = 30$, and $c = 6.5$.

$$t = \frac{-30 \pm \sqrt{900 - 4(-2.7)(6.5)}}{2(-2.7)} = \frac{-30 \pm \sqrt{970.2}}{-5.4}$$

$$\frac{-30 + \sqrt{970.2}}{-5.4} \approx -.21 \text{ or } \frac{-30 - \sqrt{970.2}}{-5.4} \approx 11.32$$

The negative solution is not meaningful. Therefore, the ball returns to the surface after 11.32 sec.

31. (a) Let $x = 50$.

$T = .00787(50)^2 - 1.528(50) + 75.89 \approx 19.2$

The exposure time when $x = 50$ ppm is approximately 19.2 hr.

(b) Let $T = 3$ and solve for x.

$3 = .00787x^2 - 1.528x + 75.89$

$.00787x^2 - 1.528x + 72.89 = 0$

Use the quadratic formula with $a = .00787$, $b = -1.528$, and $c = 72.89$.

$$x = \frac{-(-1.528) \pm \sqrt{(-1.528)^2 - 4(.00787)(72.89)}}{2(.00787)}$$

$$= \frac{1.528 \pm \sqrt{2.334784 - 2.2945772}}{.01574} = \frac{1.528 \pm \sqrt{.0402068}}{.01574}$$

$$\frac{1.528 + \sqrt{.0402068}}{.01574} \approx 109.8 \text{ or } \frac{1.528 - \sqrt{.0402068}}{.01574} \approx 84.3$$

We reject the potential solution 109.8 because it is not in the interval [50, 100]. So, 84.3 ppm carbon monoxide concentration is necessary for a person to reach the 4% to 6% CoHb level in 3 hr.

33. **(a)** Let $x = 600$ and solve for T.

$$T = .0002x^2 - .316x + 127.9 = .0002(600)^2 - .316(600) + 127.9 = 10.3$$

The exposure time when $x = 600$ ppm is 10.3 hr.

(b) Let $T = 4$ and solve for x.

$$4 = .0002x^2 - .316x + 127.9$$

$$.0002x^2 - .316x + 123.9 = 0$$

Use the quadratic formula with $a = .0002$, $b = -.316$, and $c = 123.9$.

$$x = \frac{-(-.316) \pm \sqrt{(-.316)^2 - 4(.0002)(123.9)}}{2(.0002)}$$

$$= \frac{.316 \pm \sqrt{.099856 - .09912}}{.0004} = \frac{.316 \pm \sqrt{.000736}}{.0004}$$

$$\frac{.316 + \sqrt{.000736}}{.0004} \approx 857.8 \text{ or } \frac{.316 - \sqrt{.000736}}{.0004} \approx 722.2$$

857.8 is not in the interval [500, 800]. A concentration of 722.2 ppm is required.

35. Let $x = 4$ and solve for y.

$$y = .808x^2 + 2.625x + .502$$

$$= .808(4)^2 + 2.625(4) + .502 = .808(16) + 10.5 + .502 = 12.928 + 11.002 = 23.93$$

Approximately 23.93 million households are expected to pay at least one bill online each month in 2004.

37. For each \$20 increase in rent over \$300, one unit will remain vacant. Therefore, for x \$20 increases, x units will remain vacant. Therefore, the number of rented units will be $80 - x$.

38. x is the number of \$20 increases in rent. Therefore, the rent will be $300 + 20x$ dollars.

39. $300 + 20x$ is the rent for each apartment, and $80 - x$ is the number of apartments that will be rented at that cost. The revenue generated will then be the product of $80 - x$ and $300 + 20x$, so the correct expression is $(80 - x)(300 + 20x) = 24{,}000 + 1600x - 300x - 20x^2 = 24{,}000 + 1300x - 20x^2$.

40. Set the revenue equal to \$35,000. This gives the equation $35{,}000 = 24{,}000 + 1300x - 20x^2$. Rewrite this equation in standard form: $20x^2 - 1300x + 11{,}000 = 0$.

41. $20x^2 - 1300x + 11{,}000 = 0 \Rightarrow x^2 - 65x + 550 = 0 \Rightarrow (x - 10)(x - 55) = 0$

$$x - 10 = 0 \quad \text{or} \quad x - 55 = 0$$

$$x = 10 \quad \text{or} \quad x = 55$$

Solution set: $\{10, 55\}$
If $x = 10$, $80 - x = 70$.
If $x = 55$, $80 - x = 25$.

Because of the restriction that at least 30 units must be rented, only $x = 10$ is valid here, and the number of units rented is 70.

43. Let x = number of passengers in excess of 75.
Then $225 - 5x$ = the cost per passenger (in dollars);
$75 + x$ = the number of passengers.
(Cost per passenger)(Number of passengers) = Revenue

$$(225-5x)(75+x)=16,000 \Rightarrow 16,875+225x-375x-5x^2=16,000 \Rightarrow 16,875-150x-5x^2=16,000$$
$$0=5x^2+150x-875 \Rightarrow 0=x^2+30x-175 \Rightarrow 0=(x+35)(x-5)$$
$$x+35=0 \quad \text{or} \quad x-5=0$$
$$x=-35 \quad \text{or} \quad x=5$$

The negative solution is not meaningful. Since there are 5 passengers in excess of 75, the total number of passengers is 80.

Section 1.6: Other Types of Equations

1. $\frac{5}{2x+3}+\frac{1}{x-6}=0$
$2x+3\neq 0$ or $x\neq -\frac{3}{2}$ and $x-6\neq 0$ or $x\neq 6$.

3. $\frac{3}{x-2}+\frac{1}{x+1}=\frac{1}{x^2-x-2}$ or $\frac{3}{x-2}+\frac{1}{x+1}=\frac{1}{(x-2)(x+1)}$
$x-2\neq 0$ or $x\neq 2$ and $x+1\neq 0$ or $x\neq -1$

5. $\frac{1}{4x}+\frac{2}{x}=3$
$4x\neq 0$ or $x\neq 0$

7. $\frac{2x+5}{2}-\frac{3x}{x-2}=x$
The least common denominator is $2(x-2)$, which is equal to 0 if $x=2$. Therefore, 2 cannot possibly be a solution of this equation.

$$2(x-2)\left[\frac{2x+5}{2}-\frac{3x}{x-2}\right]=2(x-2)(x)$$
$$(x-2)(2x+5)-2(3x)=2x(x-2)$$
$$2x^2+5x-4x-10-6x=2x^2-4x$$
$$-5x-10=-4x$$
$$-10=x$$

The restriction $x\neq 2$ does not affect the result. Therefore, the solution set is $\{-10\}$.

9. $\frac{x}{x-3}=\frac{3}{x-3}+3$
The least common denominator is $x-3$, which is equal to 0 if $x=3$. Therefore, 3 cannot possibly be a solution of this equation.

$$(x-3)\left(\frac{x}{x-3}\right)=(x-3)\left[\frac{3}{x-3}+3\right]\Rightarrow x=3+3(x-3)$$
$$x=3+3x-9\Rightarrow x=3x-6\Rightarrow -2x=-6\Rightarrow x=3$$

The only possible solution is 3. However, the variable is restricted to real numbers except 3. Therefore, the solution set is $\varnothing$.

11. $\frac{2}{x-3}-\frac{3}{x+3}=\frac{12}{x^2-9}$ or $\frac{2}{x-3}-\frac{3}{x+3}=\frac{12}{(x+3)(x-3)}$

The least common denominator is $(x+3)(x-3)$, which is equal to 0 if $x=-3$ or $x=3$. Therefore, -3 and 3 cannot possibly be solutions of this equation.

$$(x+3)(x-3)\left[\frac{2}{x-3}-\frac{3}{x+3}\right]=(x+3)(x-3)\left(\frac{12}{(x+3)(x-3)}\right)$$

$$2(x+3)-3(x-3)=12\Rightarrow 2x+6-3x+9=12\Rightarrow 15-x=12\Rightarrow -x=-3\Rightarrow x=3$$

The only possible solution is 3. However, the variable is restricted to real numbers except -3 and 3. Therefore, the solution set is $\varnothing$.

13. $\frac{4}{x^2+x-6}-\frac{1}{x^2-4}=\frac{2}{x^2+5x+6}$ or $\frac{4}{(x+3)(x-2)}-\frac{1}{(x+2)(x-2)}=\frac{2}{(x+2)(x+3)}$

The least common denominator is $(x+3)(x-2)(x+2)$, which is equal to 0 if $x=-3$ or $x=2$ or $x=-2$. Therefore, -3 and 2 and -2 cannot possibly be solutions of this equation.

$$(x+3)(x-2)(x+2)\left[\frac{4}{(x+3)(x-2)}-\frac{1}{(x+2)(x-2)}\right]=(x+3)(x-2)(x+2)\left(\frac{2}{(x+2)(x+3)}\right)$$

$$4(x+2)-1(x+3)=2(x-2)\Rightarrow 4x+8-x-3=2x-4$$

$$3x+5=2x-4\Rightarrow x+5=-4\Rightarrow x=-9$$

The restrictions $x\neq-3$, $x\neq 2$, and $x\neq-2$ do not affect the result. Therefore, the solution set is $\{-9\}$.

15. $\frac{2x+1}{x-2}+\frac{3}{x}=\frac{-6}{x^2-2x}$ or $\frac{2x+1}{x-2}+\frac{3}{x}=\frac{-6}{x(x-2)}$

Multiply each term in the equation by the least common denominator, $x(x-2)$, assuming $x\neq 0,2$.

$$x(x-2)\left[\frac{2x+1}{x-2}+\frac{3}{x}\right]=x(x-2)\left(\frac{-6}{x(x-2)}\right)\Rightarrow x(2x+1)+3(x-2)=-6$$

$$2x^2+x+3x-6=-6\Rightarrow 2x^2+4x-6=-6\Rightarrow 2x^2+4x=0\Rightarrow 2x(x+2)=0$$

$$2x=0 \quad\text{or}\quad x+2=0$$

$$x=0 \quad\text{or}\quad x=-2$$

Because of the restriction $x\neq 0$, the only valid solution is -2. The solution set is $\{-2\}$.

17. $\frac{-x}{x-1}+\frac{1}{x+1}=\frac{-2}{x^2-1}$ or $\frac{-x}{x-1}+\frac{1}{x+1}=\frac{-2}{(x+1)(x-1)}$

Multiply each term in the equation by the least common denominator, $(x+1)(x-1)$, assuming $x\neq\pm1$.

$$(x+1)(x-1)\left[\frac{-x}{x-1}+\frac{1}{x+1}\right]=(x+1)(x-1)\left(\frac{-2}{(x+1)(x-1)}\right)$$

$$-x(x+1)+(x-1)=-2\Rightarrow -x^2-x+x-1=-2\Rightarrow -x^2-1=-2\Rightarrow 0=x^2-1\Rightarrow 0=(x+1)(x-1)$$

$$x+1=0 \quad\text{or}\quad x-1=0$$

$$x=-1 \quad\text{or}\quad x=1$$

Because of the restriction $x\neq\pm1$, the solution set is $\varnothing$.

19. $\frac{5}{x^2}-\frac{43}{x}=18$

Multiply each term in the equation by the least common denominator, x^2, assuming $x \neq 0$.

$$x^2\left[\frac{5}{x^2}-\frac{43}{x}\right]=x^2(18) \Rightarrow 5-43x=18x^2 \Rightarrow 0=18x^2+43x-5 \Rightarrow 0=(2x+5)(9x-1)$$

$$2x+5=0 \quad \text{or} \quad 9x-1=0$$

$$x=-\tfrac{5}{2} \quad \text{or} \quad x=\tfrac{1}{9}$$

The restriction $x \neq 0$ does not affect the result. Therefore, the solution set is $\left\{-\frac{5}{2},\frac{1}{9}\right\}$.

21. $2=\frac{3}{2x-1}+\frac{-1}{(2x-1)^2}$

Multiply each term in the equation by the least common denominator, $(2x-1)^2$, assuming $x \neq \frac{1}{2}$.

$$(2x-1)^2(2)=(2x-1)^2\left[\frac{3}{2x-1}+\frac{-1}{(2x-1)^2}\right]$$

$$2(4x^2-4x+1)=3(2x-1)-1 \Rightarrow 8x^2-8x+2=6x-3-1$$

$$8x^2-8x+2=6x-4 \Rightarrow 8x^2-14x+6=0 \Rightarrow 2(4x^2-7x+3)=0 \Rightarrow 2(4x-3)(x-1)=0$$

$$4x-3=0 \quad \text{or} \quad x-1=0$$

$$x=\tfrac{3}{4} \quad \text{or} \quad x=1$$

The restriction $x \neq \frac{1}{2}$ does not affect the result. Therefore the solution set is $\left\{\frac{3}{4},1\right\}$.

23. $\frac{2x-5}{x}=\frac{x-2}{3}$

Multiply each term in the equation by the least common denominator, $3x$, assuming $x \neq 0$.

$$3x\left(\frac{2x-5}{x}\right)=3x\left(\frac{x-2}{3}\right) \Rightarrow 3(2x-5)=x(x-2)$$

$$6x-15=x^2-2x \Rightarrow 0=x^2-8x+15 \Rightarrow 0=(x-3)(x-5)$$

$$x-3=0 \quad \text{or} \quad x-5=0$$

$$x=3 \quad \text{or} \quad x=5$$

The restriction $x \neq 0$ does not affect the result. Therefore, the solution set is $\{3, 5\}$.

25. $\frac{2x}{x-2}=5+\frac{4x^2}{x-2}$

Multiply each term in the equation by the least common denominator, $x - 2$, assuming $x \neq 2$.

$$(x-2)\left(\frac{2x}{x-2}\right)=(x-2)\left[5+\frac{4x^2}{x-2}\right] \Rightarrow 2x=5(x-2)+4x^2$$

$$2x=5x-10+4x^2 \Rightarrow 0=4x^2+3x-10 \Rightarrow 0=(x+2)(4x-5)$$

$$x+2=0 \quad \text{or} \quad 4x-5=0$$

$$x=-2 \quad \text{or} \quad x=\tfrac{5}{4}$$

The restriction $x \neq 2$ does not affect the result. Therefore the solution set is $\left\{-2, \frac{5}{4}\right\}$.

27. $x-\sqrt{2x+3}=0 \Rightarrow x=\sqrt{2x+3} \Rightarrow x^2=\left(\sqrt{2x+3}\right)^2 \Rightarrow x^2=2x+3 \Rightarrow x^2-2x-3=0 \Rightarrow (x+1)(x-3)=0$

$x=-1$ or $x=3$

Check $x=-1$.

$$\begin{aligned} x-\sqrt{2x+3}&=0\\ -1-\sqrt{2(-1)+3}&=0 \ ?\\ -1-\sqrt{-2+3}&=0\\ -1-\sqrt{1}&=0\\ -1-1&=0\\ -2&=0 \end{aligned}$$

This is a false statement.
-1 is not a solution.

Check $x=3$.

$$\begin{aligned} x-\sqrt{2x+3}&=0\\ 3-\sqrt{2(3)+3}&=0 \ ?\\ 3-\sqrt{6+3}&=0\\ 3-\sqrt{9}&=0\\ 3-3&=0\\ 0&=0 \end{aligned}$$

This is a true statement.
3 is a solution.

Solution set: $\{3\}$

29. $\sqrt{3x+7}=3x+5 \Rightarrow \left(\sqrt{3x+7}\right)^2=(3x+5)^2$

$3x+7=9x^2+30x+25 \Rightarrow 0=9x^2+27x+18 \Rightarrow 0=9\left(x^2+3x+2\right) \Rightarrow 0=9(x+2)(x+1)$

$x=-2$ or $x=-1$

Check $x=-2$.

$$\begin{aligned} \sqrt{3x+7}&=3x+5\\ \sqrt{3(-2)+7}&=3(-2)+5 \ ?\\ \sqrt{-6+7}&=-6+5\\ \sqrt{1}&=-1\\ 1&=-1 \end{aligned}$$

This is a false statement.
-2 is not a solution.

Check $x=-1$.

$$\begin{aligned} \sqrt{3x+7}&=3x+5\\ \sqrt{3(-1)+7}&=3(-1)+5 \ ?\\ \sqrt{-3+7}&=-3+5\\ \sqrt{4}&=2\\ 2&=2 \end{aligned}$$

This is a true statement.
-1 is a solution.

Solution set: $\{-1\}$

31. $\sqrt{4x+5}-2=2x-7 \Rightarrow \sqrt{4x+5}=2x-5 \Rightarrow \left(\sqrt{4x+5}\right)^2=(2x-5)^2$

$4x+5=4x^2-20x+25 \Rightarrow 0=4x^2-24x+20$

$0=4\left(x^2-6x+5\right) \Rightarrow 0=4(x-1)(x-5)$

$x=1$ or $x=5$

Check $x=1$.

$$\begin{aligned} \sqrt{4x+5}-2&=2x-7\\ \sqrt{4(1)+5}-2&=2(1)-7 \ ?\\ \sqrt{4+5}-2&=2-7\\ \sqrt{9}-2&=-5\\ 3-2&=-5\\ 1&=-5 \end{aligned}$$

This is a false statement.
1 is not a solution.

Check $x=5$.

$$\begin{aligned} \sqrt{4x+5}-2&=2x-7\\ \sqrt{4(5)+5}-2&=2(5)-7 \ ?\\ \sqrt{20+5}-2&=10-7\\ \sqrt{25}-2&=3\\ 5-2&=3\\ 3&=3 \end{aligned}$$

This is a true statement.
5 is a solution.

Solution set: $\{5\}$

33. $\sqrt{4x}-x+3=0$

$$\sqrt{4x}=x-3$$
$$\left(\sqrt{4x}\right)^2=(x-3)^2$$
$$4x=x^2-6x+9$$
$$0=x^2-10x+9$$
$$0=(x-1)(x-9)$$

$x=1$ or $x=9$

Check $x=1$.

$$\sqrt{4x}-x+3=0$$
$$\sqrt{4(1)}-1+3=0 \ ?$$
$$\sqrt{4}-1+3=0$$
$$2-1+3=0$$
$$4=0$$

This is a false statement.
1 is not a solution.

Check $x=9$.

$$\sqrt{4x}-x+3=0$$
$$\sqrt{4(9)}-9+3=0 \ ?$$
$$\sqrt{36}-9+3=0$$
$$6-9+3=0$$
$$0=0$$

This is a true statement.
9 is a solution.

Solution set: $\{9\}$

35. $\sqrt{x}-\sqrt{x-5}=1$

$$\sqrt{x}=1+\sqrt{x-5}\Rightarrow\left(\sqrt{x}\right)^2=\left(1+\sqrt{x-5}\right)^2$$
$$x=1+2\sqrt{x-5}+(x-5)$$
$$x=x+2\sqrt{x-5}-4\Rightarrow 4=2\sqrt{x-5}$$
$$2=\sqrt{x-5}\Rightarrow 2^2=\left(\sqrt{x-5}\right)^2$$
$$4=x-5\Rightarrow 9=x$$

Check $x=9$.

$$\sqrt{x}-\sqrt{x-5}=1$$
$$\sqrt{9}-\sqrt{9-5}=1\ ?$$
$$3-\sqrt{4}=1$$
$$3-2=1$$
$$1=1$$

This is a true statement.
Solution set is: $\{9\}$

37. $\sqrt{x+7}+3=\sqrt{x-4}$

$$\left(\sqrt{x+7}+3\right)^2=\left(\sqrt{x-4}\right)^2$$
$$(x+7)+6\sqrt{x+7}+9=x-4$$
$$x+6\sqrt{x+7}+16=x-4\Rightarrow 6\sqrt{x+7}=-20$$
$$3\sqrt{x+7}=-10\Rightarrow\left(3\sqrt{x+7}\right)^2=(-10)^2$$
$$9(x+7)=100\Rightarrow 9x+63=100$$
$$9x=37\Rightarrow x=\frac{37}{9}$$

Check $x=\frac{37}{9}$.

$$\sqrt{x+7}+3=\sqrt{x-4}$$
$$\sqrt{\tfrac{37}{9}+7}+3=\sqrt{\tfrac{37}{9}-4}\ ?$$
$$\sqrt{\tfrac{37}{9}+\tfrac{63}{9}}+3=\sqrt{\tfrac{37}{9}-\tfrac{36}{9}}$$
$$\sqrt{\tfrac{100}{9}}+3=\sqrt{\tfrac{1}{9}}$$
$$\tfrac{10}{3}+3=\tfrac{1}{3}$$
$$\tfrac{10}{3}+\tfrac{9}{3}=\tfrac{1}{3}$$
$$\tfrac{19}{3}=\tfrac{1}{3}$$

This is a false statement.

Solution set: $\varnothing$

39. $\sqrt{x+2}=\sqrt{2x+5}-1 \Rightarrow \left(\sqrt{x+2}\right)^2=\left(\sqrt{2x+5}-1\right)^2 \Rightarrow x+2=(2x+5)-2\sqrt{2x+5}+1$

$x+2=2x+6-2\sqrt{2x+5} \Rightarrow 2\sqrt{2x+5}=x+4 \Rightarrow \left(2\sqrt{2x+5}\right)^2=(x+4)^2 \Rightarrow 4(2x+5)=x^2+8x+16$

$8x+20=x^2+8x+16 \Rightarrow 0=x^2-4 \Rightarrow 0=(x+2)(x-2)$

$x=\pm 2$

Check $x=2$.

$\sqrt{x+2}=\sqrt{2x+5}-1$

$\sqrt{2+2}=\sqrt{2(2)+5}-1\,?$

$\sqrt{4}=\sqrt{4+5}-1 \Rightarrow 2=\sqrt{9}-1$

$2=3-1 \Rightarrow 2=2$

This is a true statement.
2 is a solution.

Check $x=-2$.

$\sqrt{x+2}=\sqrt{2x+5}-1$

$\sqrt{-2+2}=\sqrt{2(-2)+5}-1\,?$

$\sqrt{0}=\sqrt{-4+5}-1 \Rightarrow 0=\sqrt{1}-1$

$0=1-1 \Rightarrow 0=0$

This is a true statement.
-2 is a solution.

Solution set: $\{\pm 2\}$

41. $\sqrt{3x}=\sqrt{5x+1}-1 \Rightarrow \left(\sqrt{3x}\right)^2=\left(\sqrt{5x+1}-1\right)^2 \Rightarrow 3x=(5x+1)-2\sqrt{5x+1}+1 \Rightarrow 3x=5x+2-2\sqrt{5x+1}$

$2\sqrt{5x+1}=2+2x \Rightarrow \sqrt{5x+1}=1+x \Rightarrow \left(\sqrt{5x+1}\right)^2=(1+x)^2 \Rightarrow 5x+1=1+2x+x^2$

$0=x^2-3x \Rightarrow 0=x(x-3)$

$x=0$ or $x=3$

Check $x=0$.

$\sqrt{3x}=\sqrt{5x+1}-1$

$\sqrt{3(0)}=\sqrt{5(0)+1}-1\,?$

$\sqrt{0}=\sqrt{0+1}-1 \Rightarrow 0=\sqrt{1}-1$

$0=1-1 \Rightarrow 0=0$

This is a true statement.
0 is a solution.

Check $x=3$.

$\sqrt{3x}=\sqrt{5x+1}-1$

$\sqrt{3(3)}=\sqrt{5(3)+1}-1\,?$

$\sqrt{9}=\sqrt{15+1}-1 \Rightarrow 3=\sqrt{16}-1$

$3=4-1 \Rightarrow 3=3$

This is a true statement.
3 is a solution.

Solution set: $\{0, 3\}$

43. $\sqrt{x+2}=1-\sqrt{3x+7} \Rightarrow \left(\sqrt{x+2}\right)^2=(1-\sqrt{3x+7})^2 \Rightarrow x+2=1-2\sqrt{3x+7}+(3x+7)$

$x+2=3x+8-2\sqrt{3x+7} \Rightarrow 2\sqrt{3x+7}=2x+6 \Rightarrow 2\sqrt{3x+7}=2(x+3)$

$\sqrt{3x+7}=x+3 \Rightarrow \left(\sqrt{3x+7}\right)^2=(x+3)^2 \Rightarrow 3x+7=x^2+6x+9 \Rightarrow 0=x^2+3x+2 \Rightarrow 0=(x+2)(x+1)$

$x=-2$ or $x=-1$

Check $x=-2$.

$\sqrt{x+2}=1-\sqrt{3x+7}$

$\sqrt{-2+2}=1-\sqrt{3(-2)+7}\,?$

$\sqrt{0}=1-\sqrt{-6+7}$

$0=1-\sqrt{1}$

$0=1-1 \Rightarrow 0=0$

This is a true statement.
-2 is a solution.

Check $x=-1$.

$\sqrt{x+2}=1-\sqrt{3x+7}$

$\sqrt{-1+2}=1-\sqrt{3(-1)+7}\,?$

$\sqrt{1}=1-\sqrt{-3+7}$

$1=1-\sqrt{4}$

$1=1-2 \Rightarrow 1=-1$

This is a false statement.
-1 is not a solution.

Solution set: $\{-2\}$

45. $\sqrt{2\sqrt{7x+2}}=\sqrt{3x+2}\Rightarrow\left(\sqrt{2\sqrt{7x+2}}\right)^2=\left(\sqrt{3x+2}\right)^2\Rightarrow 2\sqrt{7x+2}=3x+2\Rightarrow\left(2\sqrt{7x+2}\right)^2=(3x+2)^2$

$4(7x+2)=9x^2+12x+4\Rightarrow 28x+8=9x^2+12x+4\Rightarrow 0=9x^2-16x-4\Rightarrow 0=(9x+2)(x-2)$

$x=-\frac{2}{9}$ or $x=2$

Check $x=-\frac{2}{9}$.

$$\sqrt{2\sqrt{7x+2}}=\sqrt{3x+2}$$
$$\sqrt{2\sqrt{7\left(-\frac{2}{9}\right)+2}}=\sqrt{3\left(-\frac{2}{9}\right)+2}\ ?$$
$$\sqrt{2\sqrt{-\frac{14}{9}+2}}=\sqrt{-\frac{2}{3}+2}$$
$$\sqrt{2\sqrt{-\frac{14}{9}+\frac{18}{9}}}=\sqrt{-\frac{2}{3}+\frac{6}{3}}$$
$$\sqrt{2\sqrt{\frac{4}{9}}}=\sqrt{\frac{4}{3}}\Rightarrow\sqrt{2\left(\frac{2}{3}\right)}=\frac{\sqrt{4}}{\sqrt{3}}$$
$$\sqrt{\frac{4}{3}}=\frac{2}{\sqrt{3}}\cdot\frac{\sqrt{3}}{\sqrt{3}}\Rightarrow\frac{\sqrt{4}}{\sqrt{3}}=\frac{2\sqrt{3}}{3}$$
$$\frac{2}{\sqrt{3}}\cdot\frac{\sqrt{3}}{\sqrt{3}}=\frac{2\sqrt{3}}{3}\Rightarrow\frac{2\sqrt{3}}{3}=\frac{2\sqrt{3}}{3}$$

This is a true statement.

$-\frac{2}{9}$ is a solution.

Check $x=2$.

$$\sqrt{2\sqrt{7x+2}}=\sqrt{3x+2}$$
$$\sqrt{2\sqrt{7(2)+2}}=\sqrt{3(2)+2}\ ?$$
$$\sqrt{2\sqrt{14+2}}=\sqrt{6+2}$$
$$\sqrt{2\sqrt{16}}=\sqrt{8}$$
$$\sqrt{2(4)}=2\sqrt{2}$$
$$\sqrt{8}=2\sqrt{2}$$
$$2\sqrt{2}=2\sqrt{2}$$

This is a true statement.

2 is a solution.

Solution set: $\left\{-\frac{2}{9},2\right\}$

47. $3-\sqrt{x}=\sqrt{2\sqrt{x}-3}\Rightarrow\left(3-\sqrt{x}\right)^2=\left(\sqrt{2\sqrt{x}-3}\right)^2\Rightarrow 9-6\sqrt{x}+x=2\sqrt{x}-3\Rightarrow 12+x=8\sqrt{x}$

$(12+x)^2=\left(8\sqrt{x}\right)^2\Rightarrow 144+24x+x^2=64x\Rightarrow x^2-40x+144=0\Rightarrow(x-36)(x-4)=0$

$x=36$ or $x=4$

Check $x=36$.

$$3-\sqrt{x}=\sqrt{2\sqrt{x}-3}$$
$$3-\sqrt{36}=\sqrt{2\sqrt{36}-3}\ ?$$
$$3-6=\sqrt{2(6)-3}$$
$$-3=\sqrt{12-3}$$
$$-3=\sqrt{9}$$
$$-3=3$$

This is a false statement.
36 is not a solution.

Check $x=4$.

$$3-\sqrt{x}=\sqrt{2\sqrt{x}-3}$$
$$3-\sqrt{4}=\sqrt{2\sqrt{4}-3}\ ?$$
$$3-2=\sqrt{2(2)-3}$$
$$1=\sqrt{4-3}$$
$$1=\sqrt{1}$$
$$1=1$$

This is a true statement.
4 is a solution.

Solution set: $\{4\}$

49. $\sqrt[3]{4x+3}=\sqrt[3]{2x-1}\Rightarrow\left(\sqrt[3]{4x+3}\right)^3=\left(\sqrt[3]{2x-1}\right)^3\Rightarrow 4x+3=2x-1\Rightarrow 2x=-4\Rightarrow x=-2$

Check $x=-2$.

$$\sqrt[3]{4(-2)+3}=\sqrt[3]{2(-2)-1}$$
$$\sqrt[3]{-5}=\sqrt[3]{-5}\ ?$$
$$-\sqrt[3]{5}=-\sqrt[3]{5}$$

This is a true statement.

-2 is a solution. Thus, the solution set is $\{-2\}$.

51. $\sqrt[3]{5x^2-6x+2}-\sqrt[3]{x}=0 \Rightarrow \sqrt[3]{5x^2-6x+2}=\sqrt[3]{x}$

$\left(\sqrt[3]{5x^2-6x+2}\right)^3=\left(\sqrt[3]{x}\right)^3 \Rightarrow 5x^2-6x+2=x \Rightarrow 5x^2-7x+2=0 \Rightarrow (5x-2)(x-1)=0$

$x=\frac{2}{5}$ or $x=1$

Check $x=\frac{2}{5}$.

$$\begin{aligned}\sqrt[3]{5x^2-6x+2}-\sqrt[3]{x}&=0\\ \sqrt[3]{5\left(\frac{2}{5}\right)^2-6\left(\frac{2}{5}\right)+2}-\sqrt[3]{\frac{2}{5}}&=0\ ?\\ \sqrt[3]{5\left(\frac{4}{25}\right)-\frac{12}{5}+2}-\sqrt[3]{\frac{2}{5}}&=0\\ \sqrt[3]{\frac{4}{5}-\frac{12}{5}+\frac{10}{5}}-\sqrt[3]{\frac{2}{5}}&=0\\ \sqrt[3]{\frac{2}{5}}-\sqrt[3]{\frac{2}{5}}&=0\\ 0&=0\end{aligned}$$

This is a true statement.
$\frac{2}{5}$ is a solution.

Check $x=1$.

$$\begin{aligned}\sqrt[3]{5x^2-6x+2}-\sqrt[3]{x}&=0\\ \sqrt[3]{5(1)^2-6(1)+2}-\sqrt[3]{1}&=0\ ?\\ \sqrt[3]{5(1)-6+2}-1&=0\\ \sqrt[3]{5-6+2}-1&=0\\ \sqrt[3]{1}-1&=0\\ 1-1&=0\\ 0&=0\end{aligned}$$

This is a true statement.
1 is a solution.

Solution set: $\left\{\frac{2}{5},1\right\}$

53. $(2x+5)^{1/3}-(6x-1)^{1/3}=0 \Rightarrow (2x+5)^{1/3}=(6x-1)^{1/3} \Rightarrow \left[(2x+5)^{1/3}\right]^3=\left[(6x-1)^{1/3}\right]^3$

$2x+5=6x-1 \Rightarrow 5=4x-1 \Rightarrow 6=4x \Rightarrow \frac{6}{4}=x \Rightarrow x=\frac{3}{2}$

Check $x=\frac{3}{2}$.

$$\begin{aligned}(2x+5)^{1/3}-(6x-1)^{1/3}&=0\\ \left[2\left(\frac{3}{2}\right)+5\right]^{1/3}-\left[6\left(\frac{3}{2}\right)-1\right]^{1/3}&=0\ ?\\ (3+5)^{1/3}-(9-1)^{1/3}&=0\\ 8^{1/3}-8^{1/3}&=0\\ 2-2&=0\\ 0&=0\end{aligned}$$

This is a true statement.

Solution set: $\left\{\frac{3}{2}\right\}$

55. $\sqrt[4]{x-15}=2 \Rightarrow \left(\sqrt[4]{x-15}\right)^4=2^4 \Rightarrow x-15=16 \Rightarrow x=31$

Check $x=31$.

$$\begin{aligned}\sqrt[4]{x-15}&=2\\ \sqrt[4]{31-15}&=2\ ?\\ \sqrt[4]{16}&=2\\ 2&=2\end{aligned}$$

This is a true statement.

Solution set: $\{31\}$

57. $\sqrt[4]{x^2+2x}=\sqrt[4]{3} \Rightarrow \left(\sqrt[4]{x^2+2x}\right)^4=\left(\sqrt[4]{3}\right)^4 \Rightarrow x^2+2x=3 \Rightarrow x^2+2x-3=0 \Rightarrow (x+3)(x-1)=0$

$x=-3$ or $x=1$

Check $x=-3$.

$$\sqrt[4]{x^2+2x}=\sqrt[4]{3}$$
$$\sqrt[4]{(-3)^2+2(-3)}=\sqrt[4]{3}\ ?$$
$$\sqrt[4]{9-6}=\sqrt[4]{3}$$
$$\sqrt[4]{3}=\sqrt[4]{3}$$

This is a true statement.

-3 is a solution.

Check $x=1$.

$$\sqrt[4]{x^2+2x}=\sqrt[4]{3}$$
$$\sqrt[4]{1^2+2(1)}=\sqrt[4]{3}\ ?$$
$$\sqrt[4]{1+2}=\sqrt[4]{3}$$
$$\sqrt[4]{3}=\sqrt[4]{3}$$

This is a true statement.

1 is a solution.

Solution set: $\{-3,1\}$

59. $(x^2+24x)^{1/4}=3 \Rightarrow \left[\left(x^2+24x\right)^{1/4}\right]^4=3^4$

$$x^2+24x=81 \Rightarrow x^2+24x-81=0 \Rightarrow (x+27)(x-3)=0$$

$x=-27$ or $x=3$

Check $x=-27$.

$$(x^2+24x)^{1/4}=3$$
$$\left[(-27)^2+24(-27)\right]^{1/4}=3\ ?$$
$$(729-648)^{1/4}=3$$
$$81^{1/4}=3$$
$$3=3$$

This is a true statement.

-27 is a solution.

Check $x=3$.

$$(x^2+24x)^{1/4}=3$$
$$\left[3^2+24(3)\right]^{1/4}=3\ ?$$
$$(9+72)^{1/4}=3$$
$$81^{1/4}=3$$
$$3=3$$

This is a true statement.

3 is a solution.

Solution set: $\{-27, 3\}$

61. $2x^4-7x^2+5=0$

Let $u=x^2$; then $u^2=x^4$. With this substitution, the equation becomes $2u^2-7u+5=0$.

$2u^2-7u+5=0 \Rightarrow (u-1)(2u-5)=0$

$u=1$ or $u=\frac{5}{2}$

To find x, replace u with x^2.

$x^2=1$ or $x^2=\frac{5}{2}$

$x=\pm\sqrt{\frac{5}{2}}=\pm\frac{\sqrt{5}}{\sqrt{2}}\cdot\frac{\sqrt{2}}{\sqrt{2}}$

$x=\pm 1$ or $x=\pm\frac{\sqrt{10}}{2}$

Solution set: $\left\{\pm 1, \pm\frac{\sqrt{10}}{2}\right\}$

63. $x^4+2x^2-15=0$

Let $u=x^2$; then $u^2=x^4$.

$u^2+2u-15=0$

$(u-3)(u+5)=0$

$u=3$ or $u=-5$

To find x, replace x with x^2.

$x^2=3$ or $x^2=-5$

$x=\pm\sqrt{3}$ or $x=\pm\sqrt{-5}=\pm i\sqrt{5}$

Solution set: $\left\{\pm\sqrt{3}, \pm i\sqrt{5}\right\}$

65. $(2x-1)^{2/3} = x^{1/3}$

$[(2x-1)^{2/3}]^3 = (x^{1/3})^3$

$(2x-1)^2 = x$

$4x^2 - 4x + 1 = x$

$4x^2 - 5x + 1 = 0$

$(4x-1)(x-1) = 0$

$x = \frac{1}{4}$ or $x = 1$

Check $x = \frac{1}{4}$.

$(2x-1)^{2/3} = x^{1/3}$

$\left[2\left(\frac{1}{4}\right)-1\right]^{2/3} = \left(\frac{1}{4}\right)^{1/3}$?

$\left[\frac{1}{2}-1\right]^{2/3} = \frac{1}{\sqrt[3]{4}}\cdot\frac{\sqrt[3]{2}}{\sqrt[3]{2}}$

$\left[-\frac{1}{2}\right]^{2/3} = \frac{\sqrt[3]{2}}{2}$

$\left[\left(-\frac{1}{2}\right)^2\right]^{1/3} = \frac{\sqrt[3]{2}}{2}$

$\left(\frac{1}{4}\right)^{1/3} = \frac{\sqrt[3]{2}}{2}$

$\frac{1}{\sqrt[3]{4}}\cdot\frac{\sqrt[3]{2}}{\sqrt[3]{2}} = \frac{\sqrt[3]{2}}{2}$

$\frac{\sqrt[3]{2}}{2} = \frac{\sqrt[3]{2}}{2}$

This is a true statement.

$\frac{1}{4}$ is a solution.

Check $x = 1$.

$(2x-1)^{2/3} = x^{1/3}$

$[2(1)-1]^{2/3} = (1)^{1/3}$?

$[2-1]^{2/3} = 1$

$1^{2/3} = 1$

$1 = 1$

This is a true statement.

1 is a solution.

Solution set: $\left\{\frac{1}{4}, 1\right\}$

67. $x^{2/3} = 2x^{1/3}$

$\left(x^{2/3}\right)^3 = \left(2x^{1/3}\right)^3$

$x^2 = 8x$

$x^2 - 8x = 0 \Rightarrow x(x-8) = 0$

$x = 0$ or $x = 8$

Check $x = 0$.

$x^{2/3} = 2x^{1/3}$

$0^{2/3} = 2\left(0^{1/3}\right)$?

$0 = 2\cdot 0$

$0 = 0$

This is a true statement.

0 is a solution.

Check $x = 8$.

$x^{2/3} = 2x^{1/3}$

$8^{2/3} = 2\left(8^{1/3}\right)$?

$\left(8^2\right)^{1/3} = 2\cdot 2$

$64^{1/3} = 4$

$4 = 4$

This is a true statement.

8 is a solution.

Solution set: $\{0, 8\}$

69. $(x-1)^{2/3}+(x-1)^{1/3}-12=0$

Let $u=(x-1)^{1/3}$ then, $u^2=\left[(x-1)^{1/3}\right]^2=(x-1)^{2/3}$.

$u^2+u-12=0 \Rightarrow (u+4)(u-3)=0 \Rightarrow u=-4$ or $u=3$

To find x, replace u with $(x-1)^{1/3}$.

$(x-1)^{1/3}=-4 \Rightarrow \left[(x-1)^{1/3}\right]^3=(-4)^3 \Rightarrow x-1=-64 \Rightarrow x=-63$ or

$(x-1)^{1/3}=3 \Rightarrow \left[(x-1)^{1/3}\right]^3=3^3 \Rightarrow x-1=27 \Rightarrow x=28$

Check $x=-63$.

$$\begin{aligned}(x-1)^{2/3}+(x-1)^{1/3}-12&=0\\(-63-1)^{2/3}+(-63-1)^{1/3}-12&=0\ ?\\(-64)^{2/3}+(-64)^{1/3}-12&=0\\\left[(-64)^{1/3}\right]^2-4-12&=0\\(-4)^2-4-12&=0\\16-4-12&=0\\0&=0\end{aligned}$$

This is a true statement.

-63 is a solution.

Check $x=28$.

$$\begin{aligned}(x-1)^{2/3}+(x-1)^{1/3}-12&=0\\(28-1)^{2/3}+(28-1)^{1/3}-12&=0\ ?\\27^{2/3}+27^{1/3}-12&=0\\\left[27^{1/3}\right]^2+3-12&=0\\3^2+3-12&=0\\9+3-12&=0\\0&=0\end{aligned}$$

This is a true statement.

28 is a solution.

Solution set: $\{-63, 28\}$

71. $(x+1)^{2/5}-3(x+1)^{1/5}+2=0$

Let $u=(x+1)^{1/5}$ then, $u^2=\left[(x+1)^{1/5}\right]^2=(x+1)^{2/5}$.

$u^2-3u+2=0 \Rightarrow (u-1)(u-2)=0 \Rightarrow u=1$ or $u=2$

To find x, replace u with $(x+1)^{1/5}$.

$(x+1)^{1/5}=1 \Rightarrow \left[(x+1)^{1/5}\right]^5=1^5 \Rightarrow x+1=1 \Rightarrow x=0$ or

$(x+1)^{1/5}=2 \Rightarrow \left[(x+1)^{1/5}\right]^5=2^5 \Rightarrow x+1=32 \Rightarrow x=31$

Check $x=0$.

$$\begin{aligned}(x+1)^{2/5}-3(x+1)^{1/5}+2&=0\\(0+1)^{2/5}-3(0+1)^{1/5}+2&=0\ ?\\1^{2/5}-3(1)^{1/5}+2&=0\\1-3(1)+2&=0\\1-3+2&=0\end{aligned}$$

This is a true statement.

0 is a solution.

Check $x=31$.

$$\begin{aligned}(x+1)^{2/5}-3(x+1)^{1/5}+2&=0\\(31+1)^{2/5}-3(31+1)^{1/5}+2&=0\ ?\\32^{2/5}-3(32)^{1/5}+2&=0\\\left[(32)^{1/5}\right]^2-3(2)+2&=0\\2^2-6+2&=0\\4-6+2&=0\\0&=0\end{aligned}$$

This is a true statement.

31 is a solution.

Solution set: $\{0, 31\}$

73. $6(x+2)^4 - 11(x+2)^2 = -4 \Rightarrow 6(x+2)^4 - 11(x+2)^2 + 4 = 0$

Let $u = (x+2)^2$ then $u^2 = (x+2)^4$.

$6u^2 - 11u + 4 = 0 \Rightarrow (3u-4)(2u-1) = 0 \Rightarrow u = \frac{4}{3}$ or $u = \frac{1}{2}$

To find *x*, replace *u* with $(x+2)^2$.

$(x+2)^2 = \frac{4}{3} \Rightarrow x+2 = \pm\sqrt{\frac{4}{3}} = \pm\frac{2\sqrt{3}}{3} \Rightarrow x = -2 \pm \frac{2\sqrt{3}}{3} = -\frac{6}{3} \pm \frac{2\sqrt{3}}{3} = \frac{-6\pm 2\sqrt{3}}{3}$ or

$(x+2)^2 = \frac{1}{2} \Rightarrow x+2 = \pm\sqrt{\frac{1}{2}} = \pm\frac{\sqrt{2}}{2} \Rightarrow x = -2 \pm \frac{\sqrt{2}}{2} = -\frac{4}{2} \pm \frac{\sqrt{2}}{2} = \frac{-4\pm\sqrt{2}}{2}$

Solution set: $\left\{\frac{-6\pm 2\sqrt{3}}{3}, \frac{-4\pm\sqrt{2}}{2}\right\}$

75. $10x^{-2} + 33x^{-1} - 7 = 0$

Let $u = x^{-1}$; then $u^2 = x^{-2}$.

$10u^2 + 33u - 7 = 0 \Rightarrow (2u+7)(5u-1) = 0$

$u = -\frac{7}{2}$ or $u = \frac{1}{5}$

To find *x*, replace *u* with x^{-1}.

$x^{-1} = -\frac{7}{2}$ or $x^{-1} = \frac{1}{5}$

$x = -\frac{2}{7}$ or $x = 5$

Solution set: $\left\{-\frac{2}{7}, 5\right\}$

77. $x^{-2/3} + x^{-1/3} - 6 = 0$

Let $u = x^{-1/3}$; then $u^2 = \left(x^{-1/3}\right)^2 = x^{-2/3}$.

$u^2 + u - 6 = 0 \Rightarrow (u+3)(u-2) = 0$

$u = -3$ or $u = 2$

To find *x*, replace *u* with $x^{-1/3}$.

$x^{-1/3} = -3 \Rightarrow \left(x^{-1/3}\right)^{-3} = (-3)^{-3} \Rightarrow x = \frac{1}{(-3)^3} \Rightarrow x = -\frac{1}{27}$ or

$x^{-1/3} = 2 \Rightarrow \left(x^{-1/3}\right)^{-3} = 2^{-3} \Rightarrow x = \frac{1}{2^3} \Rightarrow x = \frac{1}{8}$

Check $x = -\frac{1}{27}$.

$$x^{-2/3} + x^{-1/3} - 6 = 0$$
$$\left(-\tfrac{1}{27}\right)^{-2/3} + \left(-\tfrac{1}{27}\right)^{-1/3} - 6 = 0\ ?$$
$$(-27)^{2/3} + (-27)^{1/3} - 6 = 0$$
$$\left[(-27)^{1/3}\right]^2 - 3 - 6 = 0$$
$$(-3)^2 - 3 - 6 = 0$$
$$9 - 3 - 6 = 0$$
$$0 = 0$$

This is a true statement

Check $x = \frac{1}{8}$.

$$x^{-2/3} + x^{-1/3} - 6 = 0$$
$$\left(\tfrac{1}{8}\right)^{-2/3} + \left(\tfrac{1}{8}\right)^{-1/3} - 6 = 0\ ?$$
$$8^{2/3} + 8^{1/3} - 6 = 0$$
$$\left(8^{1/3}\right)^2 + 2 - 6 = 0$$
$$2^2 + 2 - 6 = 0$$
$$4 + 2 - 6 = 0$$
$$0 = 0$$

This is a true statement.

Solution set: $\left\{-\frac{1}{27}, \frac{1}{8}\right\}$

79. Answers will vary

The student assumed that $(a-b)^2 = a^2 + b^2$.

This of course is a false assumption.

80. Answers will vary.

The first step should be squaring both sides of the equation.

$$\sqrt{x}+2=\sqrt{4+7\sqrt{x}}$$

$$\left(\sqrt{x}+2\right)^2=\left(\sqrt{4+7\sqrt{x}}\right)^2$$

81. $x-\sqrt{x}-12=0$

Let $u=\sqrt{x}$; then $u^2=x$. Solve the resulting equation by factoring.

$u^2-u-12=0 \Rightarrow (u-4)(u+3)=0$

$u=4$ or $u=-3$

To find x, replace u with $\sqrt{x}$.

$\sqrt{x}=4 \Rightarrow \left(\sqrt{x}\right)^2=4^2 \Rightarrow x=16$ or $\sqrt{x}=-3 \Rightarrow \left(\sqrt{x}\right)^2=(-3)^2 \Rightarrow x=9$

But $\sqrt{9} \neq -3$

So when $u=-3$, there is no solution for x.

Solution set: $\{16\}$

82. $x-\sqrt{x}-12=0$

Solve by isolating $\sqrt{x}$, then squaring both sides.

$x-12=\sqrt{x} \Rightarrow (x-12)^2=(\sqrt{x})^2 \Rightarrow x^2-24x+144=x \Rightarrow x^2-25x+144=0 \Rightarrow (x-16)(x-9)=0$

$x=16$ or $x=9$

Check $x = 16$.

$$x-\sqrt{x}-12=0$$
$$16-\sqrt{16}-12=0\ ?$$
$$16-4-12=0$$
$$0=0$$

This is a true statement.

Solution set: $\{16\}$

Check $x = 9$.

$$x-\sqrt{x}-12=0$$
$$9-\sqrt{9}-12=0\ ?$$
$$9-3-12=0$$
$$-6=0$$

This is a false statement.

9 does not satisfy the equation.

83. Answers will vary.

84. $3x-2\sqrt{x}-8=0$

Solve by substitution.

Let $u=\sqrt{x}$; then $u^2=x$. Solve the resulting equation by factoring.

$3u^2-2u-8=0 \Rightarrow (3u+4)(u-2)=0$

$u=-\frac{4}{3}$ or $u=2$

To find x, replace u with $\sqrt{x}$.

$\sqrt{x}=-\dfrac{4}{3}$ has no solution, because the result of a square root is never a negative real number.

$\sqrt{x}=2 \Rightarrow x=4$

Check $x = 4$.

$$3x-2\sqrt{x}-8=0$$
$$3(4)-2\sqrt{4}-8=0\ ?$$
$$3(4)-2(2)-8=0$$
$$12-4-8=0$$
$$0=0$$

This is a true statement.

Solution set: $\{4\}$

85. $d = k\sqrt{h}$ for h

$$\frac{d}{k} = \sqrt{h} \Rightarrow \frac{d^2}{k^2} = h$$

So, $h = \frac{d^2}{k^2}$.

87. $m^{3/4} + n^{3/4} = 1$ for m

$$m^{3/4} = 1 - n^{3/4}$$

Raise both sides to the $\frac{4}{3}$ power.

$$(m^{3/4})^{4/3} = (1 - n^{3/4})^{4/3}$$
$$m = (1 - n^{3/4})^{4/3}$$

89. $\frac{E}{e} = \frac{R+r}{r}$ for e

$$er\left(\frac{E}{e}\right) = er\left(\frac{R+r}{r}\right)$$

Multiply both sides by *er*.

$$Er = eR + er$$
$$Er = e(R+r)$$
$$\frac{Er}{R+r} = e$$

So, $e = \frac{Er}{R+r}$.

Summary Exercises on Solving Equations

1. $4x - 5 = 2x + 1 \Rightarrow 2x - 5 = 1 \Rightarrow 2x = 6 \Rightarrow x = 3$

Solution set: $\{3\}$

3. $x(x+6) = 9 \Rightarrow x^2 + 6x = 9 \Rightarrow x^2 + 6x - 9 = 0$

Solve by Completing the Square.

$$x^2 + 6x + 9 = 9 + 9$$

$$\text{Note:}\left[\tfrac{1}{2}\cdot 6\right]^2 = 3^2 = 9$$

$$(x+3)^2 = 18$$
$$x + 3 = \pm\sqrt{18}$$
$$x + 3 = \pm 3\sqrt{2}$$
$$x = -3 \pm 3\sqrt{2}$$

or

Solve by the Quadratic Formula.
Let $a = 1, b = 6,$ and $c = -9$.

$$x = \frac{-b \pm \sqrt{b^2 - 4ac}}{2a} = \frac{-6 \pm \sqrt{6^2 - 4(1)(-9)}}{2(1)} = \frac{-6 \pm \sqrt{36+36}}{2} = \frac{-6 \pm \sqrt{72}}{2} = \frac{-6 \pm 6\sqrt{2}}{2} = -3 \pm 3\sqrt{2}$$

Solution set: $\{-3 \pm \sqrt{2}\}$

5. $\sqrt{x+2} + 5 = \sqrt{x+15} \Rightarrow \left(\sqrt{x+2}+5\right)^2 = \left(\sqrt{x+15}\right)^2 \Rightarrow (x+2) + 10\sqrt{x+2} + 25 = x + 15 \Rightarrow$

$x + 27 + 10\sqrt{x+2} = x + 15 \Rightarrow 27 + 10\sqrt{x+2} = 15 \Rightarrow 10\sqrt{x+2} = -12 \Rightarrow 5\sqrt{x+2} = -6$

$\left(5\sqrt{x+2}\right)^2 = (-6)^2 \Rightarrow 25(x+2) = 36 \Rightarrow 25x + 50 = 36 \Rightarrow 25x = -14 \Rightarrow x = -\frac{14}{25}$

Check $x = -\frac{14}{25}$.

$$\sqrt{x+2} + 5 = \sqrt{x+15} \Rightarrow \sqrt{-\tfrac{14}{25} + 2} + 5 = \sqrt{-\tfrac{14}{25} + 15}\ ?$$

$$\sqrt{-\tfrac{14}{25} + \tfrac{50}{25}} + 5 = \sqrt{-\tfrac{14}{25} + \tfrac{375}{25}}$$

$$\sqrt{\tfrac{36}{25}} + 5 = \sqrt{\tfrac{361}{25}} \Rightarrow \tfrac{6}{5} + \tfrac{25}{5} = \tfrac{19}{5} \Rightarrow \tfrac{31}{5} = \tfrac{19}{5}$$

This is a false statement.
Solution set: $\varnothing$

7. $\dfrac{3x+4}{3}-\dfrac{2x}{x-3}=x$

The least common denominator is $3(x-3)$, which is equal to 0 if $x=3$. Therefore, 3 cannot possibly be a solution of this equation.

$$3(x-3)\left[\frac{3x+4}{3}-\frac{2x}{x-3}\right]=3(x-3)(x)\Rightarrow(x-3)(3x+4)-3(2x)=3x(x-3)$$
$$3x^2+4x-9x-12-6x=3x^2-9x\Rightarrow 3x^2-11x-12=3x^2-9x$$
$$-11x-12=-9x\Rightarrow -12=2x\Rightarrow -6=x$$

The restriction $x\neq 3$ does not affect the result. Therefore, the solution set is $\{-6\}$.

9. $5-\dfrac{2}{x}+\dfrac{1}{x^2}=0$; The least common denominator is x^2, which is equal to 0 if $x=0$. Therefore, 0 cannot possibly be a solution of this equation.

$$x^2\left[5-\frac{2}{x}+\frac{1}{x^2}\right]=x^2(0)\Rightarrow 5x^2-2x+1=0$$

Solve by Completing the Square.

$x^2-\frac{2}{5}x+\frac{1}{5}=0$ Multiply by $\frac{1}{5}$.

$x^2-\frac{2}{5}x+\frac{1}{25}=-\frac{1}{5}+\frac{1}{25}$

Note: $\left[\frac{1}{2}\cdot\left(-\frac{2}{5}\right)\right]^2=\left(-\frac{1}{5}\right)^2=\frac{1}{25}$

$\left(x-\frac{1}{5}\right)^2=-\frac{5}{25}+\frac{1}{25}=\frac{-4}{25}$

$x-\frac{1}{5}=\pm\sqrt{\frac{-4}{25}}$

$x-\frac{1}{5}=\pm\frac{2}{5}i$

$x=\frac{1}{5}\pm\frac{2}{5}i$

or

Solve by the Quadratic Formula.
Let $a=5$, $b=-2$, and $c=1$.

$$x=\frac{-b\pm\sqrt{b^2-4ac}}{2a}=\frac{-(-2)\pm\sqrt{(-2)^2-4(5)(1)}}{2(5)}=\frac{2\pm\sqrt{4-20}}{10}=\frac{2\pm\sqrt{-16}}{10}=\frac{2\pm 4i}{10}=\frac{2}{10}\pm\frac{4}{10}i=\frac{1}{5}\pm\frac{2}{5}i$$

The restriction $x\neq 0$ does not affect the result. Therefore, the solution set is $\left\{\frac{1}{5}\pm\frac{2}{5}i\right\}$.

11. $x^{-2/5}-2x^{-1/5}-15=0$

Let $u=x^{-1/5}$; then $u^2=\left(x^{-1/5}\right)^2=x^{-2/5}$. So, $u^2-2u-15=0\Rightarrow(u+3)(u-5)=0\Rightarrow u=-3$ or $u=5$

To find *x*, replace *u* with $x^{-1/5}$. We obtain $x^{-1/5}=-3\Rightarrow\left(x^{-1/5}\right)^{-5}=(-3)^{-5}\Rightarrow x=\frac{1}{(-3)^5}\Rightarrow x=-\frac{1}{243}$

or $x^{-1/5}=5\Rightarrow\left(x^{-1/5}\right)^{-5}=5^{-5}\Rightarrow x=\frac{1}{5^5}\Rightarrow x=\frac{1}{3125}$.

Check $x=-\frac{1}{243}$.

$x^{-2/5}-2x^{-1/5}-15=0$

$\left(-\frac{1}{243}\right)^{-2/5}-2\left(-\frac{1}{243}\right)^{-1/5}-15=0$?

$(-243)^{2/5}-2(-243)^{1/5}-15=0$

$\left[(-243)^{1/5}\right]^2-2(-3)-15=0$

$(-3)^2+6-15=0\Rightarrow 9+6-15=0\Rightarrow 0=0$

This is a true statement.

$-\frac{1}{243}$ is a solution.

Check $x=\frac{1}{3125}$.

$x^{-2/5}-2x^{-1/5}-15=0$

$\left(\frac{1}{3125}\right)^{-2/5}-2\left(\frac{1}{3125}\right)^{-1/5}-15=0$?

$(3125)^{2/5}-2(3125)^{1/5}-15=0$

$\left[(3125)^{1/5}\right]^2-2(5)-15=0$

$5^2-10-15=0\Rightarrow 25-10-15=0\Rightarrow 0=0$

This is a true statement.

$\frac{1}{3125}$ is a solution.

Solution set: $\left\{-\frac{1}{243},\frac{1}{3125}\right\}$

13. $x^4 - 3x^2 - 4 = 0$

Let $u = x^2$; then $u^2 = x^4$.

$u^2 - 3u - 4 = 0$

$(u+1)(u-4) = 0$

$u = -1$ or $u = 4$

To find x, replace x with x^2.

$x^2 = -1$ or $x^2 = 4$

$x = \pm\sqrt{-1} = \pm i$ or $x = \pm\sqrt{4} = \pm 2$

Solution set: $\{\pm i, \pm 2\}$

15. $\sqrt[4]{2x+1} = \sqrt[4]{9} \Rightarrow \left(\sqrt[4]{2x+1}\right)^4 = \left(\sqrt[4]{9}\right)^4$

$2x+1 = 9 \Rightarrow 2x = 8 \Rightarrow x = 4$

Check $x = 4$.

$$\sqrt[4]{2x+1} = \sqrt[4]{9}$$
$$\sqrt[4]{2(4)+1} = \sqrt[4]{9}\ ?$$
$$\sqrt[4]{8+1} = \sqrt[4]{9}$$
$$\sqrt[4]{9} = \sqrt[4]{9}$$

This is a true statement.

Solution set: $\{4\}$

Solution set: $\left\{\frac{1}{3} \pm \frac{\sqrt{2}}{3} i\right\}$.

17. $3[2x-(6-2x)+1] = 5x \Rightarrow 3(2x-6+2x+1) = 5x \Rightarrow 3(4x-5) = 5x \Rightarrow$

$$12x - 15 = 5 \Rightarrow x - 15 = -7x \Rightarrow \frac{-15}{-7} = x \Rightarrow x = \frac{15}{7}$$

Solution set: $\left\{\frac{15}{7}\right\}$

19. $(14-2x)^{2/3} = 4 \Rightarrow [(14-2x)^{2/3}]^3 = 4^3 \Rightarrow (14-2x)^2 = 64$

$196 - 56x + 4x^2 = 64 \Rightarrow 4x^2 - 56x + 132 = 0$

$4\left(x^2 - 14x + 33\right) = 0 \Rightarrow 4(x-3)(x-11) = 0$

$x = 3$ or $x = 11$

Check $x = 3$.

$$(14-2x)^{2/3} = 4$$
$$[14-2(3)]^{2/3} = 4\ ?$$
$$(14-6)^{2/3} = 4$$
$$8^{2/3} = 4$$
$$\left(8^{1/3}\right)^2 = 4$$
$$2^2 = 4$$
$$4 = 4$$

This is a true statement.

Check $x = 11$.

$$(14-2x)^{2/3} = 4$$
$$[14-2(11)]^{2/3} = 4\ ?$$
$$(14-22)^{2/3} = 4$$
$$(-8)^{2/3} = 4$$
$$\left[(-8)^{1/3}\right]^2 = 4$$
$$(-2)^2 = 4$$
$$4 = 4$$

This is a true statement.

Solution set: $\{3, 11\}$

Section 1.7: Inequalities

1. $x < -4$

The interval includes all real numbers less than –4, not including –4. The correct interval notation is $(-\infty, -4)$, so the correct choice is F.

3. $-2 < x \le 6$

The interval includes all real numbers from –2 to 6, not including –2, but including 6. The correct interval notation is (–2, 6], so the correct choice is A.

5. $x \geq -3$
The interval includes all real numbers greater than or equal to –3, so it includes –3. The correct interval notation is $[-3, \infty)$, so the correct choice is I.

7. The interval shown on the number line includes all real numbers between –2 and 6, including –2, but not including 6. The correct interval notation is [–2, 6), so the correct choice is B.

9. The interval shown on the number line includes all real numbers greater than 3, not including 3. The correct interval notation is $(3, \infty)$, so the correct choice is E.

11. Answers will vary.

13.
$$2x+1 \leq 9$$
$$2x+1-1 \leq 9-1$$
$$2x \leq 8$$
$$\frac{2x}{2} \leq \frac{8}{2}$$
$$x \leq 4$$
Solution set: $(-\infty, 4]$

Graph: 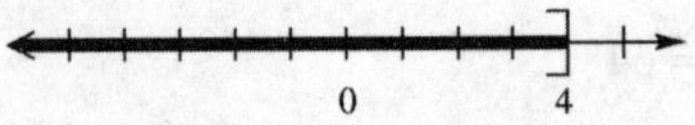

15.
$$-3x-2 \leq 1$$
$$-3x-2+2 \leq 1+2$$
$$-3x \leq 3$$
$$\frac{-3x}{-3} \geq \frac{3}{-3}$$
$$x \geq -1$$
Solution set: $[-1, \infty)$

Graph: 

17.
$$2(x+5)+1 \geq 5+3x$$
$$2x+10+1 \geq 5+3x$$
$$2x+11 \geq 5+3x$$
$$2x+11-3x \geq 5+3x-3x$$
$$-x+11 \geq 5$$
$$-x+11-11 \geq 5-11$$
$$\frac{-x}{-1} \leq \frac{-6}{-1}$$
$$x \leq 6$$
Solution set: $(-\infty, 6]$

Graph: 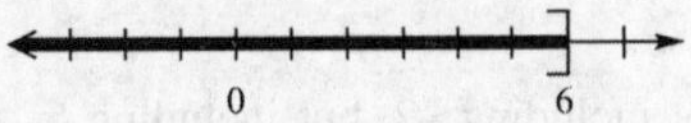

19.
$$8x-3x+2 < 2(x+7)$$
$$5x+2 < 2x+14$$
$$5x+2-2x < 2x+14-2x$$
$$3x+2 < 14$$
$$3x+2-2 < 14-2$$
$$3x < 12$$
$$\frac{3x}{3} < \frac{12}{3}$$
$$x < 4$$
Solution set: $(-\infty, 4)$

Graph: 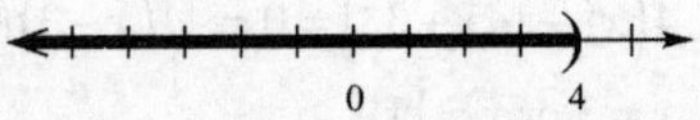

21.
$$\frac{4x+7}{-3} \leq 2x+5$$
$$(-3)\left(\frac{4x+7}{-3}\right) \geq (-3)(2x+5)$$
$$4x+7 \geq -6x-15$$
$$4x+7+6x \geq -6x-15+6x$$
$$10x+7 \geq -15$$
$$10x+7-7 \geq -15-7$$
$$10x \geq -22$$
$$\frac{10x}{10} \geq \frac{-22}{10}$$
$$x \geq -\tfrac{11}{5}$$
Solution set: $\left[-\tfrac{11}{5}, \infty\right)$

Graph: 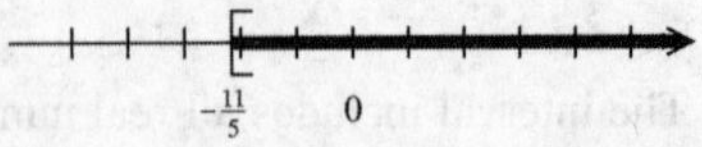

23. $$\frac{1}{3}x+\frac{2}{5}x-\frac{1}{2}(x+3)\le\frac{1}{10}$$
$$30\left[\frac{1}{3}x+\frac{2}{5}x-\frac{1}{2}(x+3)\right]\le 30\left[\frac{1}{10}\right]$$
$$10x+12x-15(x+3)\le 3$$
$$10x+12x-15x-45\le 3$$
$$7x-45\le 3$$
$$7x-45+45\le 3+45$$
$$7x\le 48$$
$$\frac{7x}{7}\le\frac{48}{7}$$
$$x\le\tfrac{48}{7}$$

Solution set: $\left(-\infty,\tfrac{48}{7}\right]$

Graph: 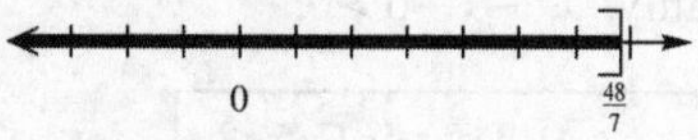

25. $$-3<7+2x<13$$
$$-3-7<7+2x-7<13-7$$
$$-10<2x<6$$
$$\frac{-10}{2}<\frac{2x}{2}<\frac{6}{2}$$
$$-5<x<3$$

Solution set: $(-5,3)$

Graph: 

27. $$10\le 2x+4\le 16$$
$$10-4\le 2x+4-4\le 16-4$$
$$6\le 2x\le 12$$
$$\frac{6}{2}\le\frac{2x}{2}\le\frac{12}{2}$$
$$3\le x\le 6$$

Solution set: $[3,6]$

Graph: 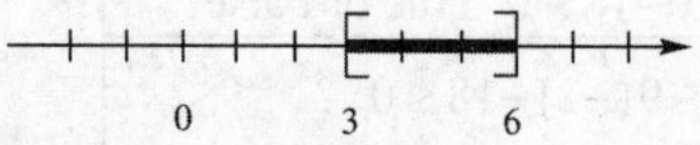

29. $$-10>-3x+2>-16$$
$$-10-2>-3x+2-2>-16-2$$
$$-12>-3x>-18$$
$$\frac{-12}{-3}<\frac{-3x}{-3}<\frac{-18}{-3}$$
$$4<x<6$$

Solution set: $(4,6)$

Graph: 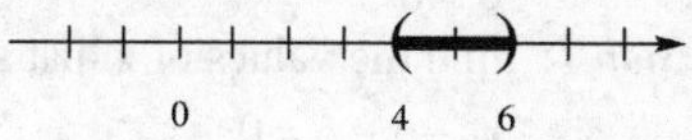

31. $$-4\le\frac{x+1}{2}\le 5$$
$$2(-4)\le 2\left(\frac{x+1}{2}\right)\le 2(5)$$
$$-8\le x+1\le 10$$
$$-8-1\le x+1-1\le 10-1$$
$$-9\le x\le 9$$

Solution set: $[-9,9]$

Graph: 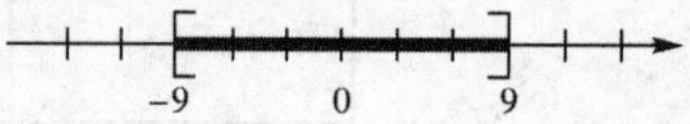

33. $$-3\le\frac{x-4}{-5}<4$$
$$(-5)(-3)\ge(-5)\left(\frac{x-4}{-5}\right)>(-5)(4)$$
$$15\ge x-4>-20$$
$$15+4\ge x-4+4>-20+4$$
$$19\ge x>-16$$
$$-16<x\le 19$$

Solution set: $(-16,19]$

Graph: 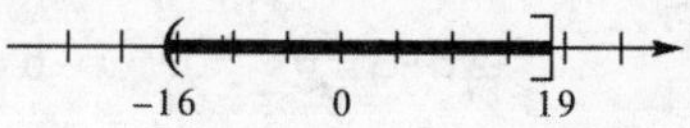

35. $C = 50x + 5000$; $R = 60x$
The product will at least break even when $R\ge C$.
Set $R\ge C$ and solve for x.
$60x\ge 50x+5000\Rightarrow 10x\ge 5000\Rightarrow x\ge 500$
The break-even point is at $x = 500$.
This product will at least break even if the number of units of picture frames produced is in interval $[500,\infty)$.

37. $C = 85x + 900$; $R = 105x$
The product will at least break even when $R \geq C$.
Set $R \geq C$ and solve for x.
$105x \geq 85x + 900 \Rightarrow 20x \geq 900 \Rightarrow x \geq 45$
The break-even point is $x = 45$.
The product will at least break even when the number of units of coffee cups produced is in the interval $[45, \infty)$.

39. $x^2 - x - 6 > 0$

Step 1: Find the values of x that satisfy $x^2 - x - 6 = 0$.

$$x^2 - x - 6 = 0 \Rightarrow (x+2)(x-3) = 0$$
$$x + 2 = 0 \quad \text{or} \quad x - 3 = 0$$
$$x = -2 \quad \text{or} \quad x = 3$$

Step 2: The two numbers divide a number line into three regions.

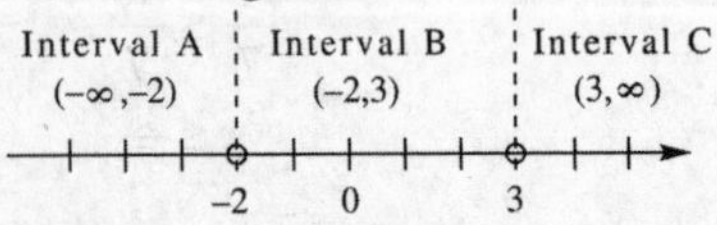

Step 3: Choose a test value to see if it satisfies the inequality, $x^2 - x - 6 > 0$.

Interval	Test Value	Is $x^2 - x - 6 > 0$ True or False?
A: $(-\infty, -2)$	−3	$(-3)^2 - (-3) - 6 > 0$? $6 > 0$ True
B: $(-2, 3)$	0	$0^2 - 0 - 6 > 0$? $-6 > 0$ False
C: $(3, \infty)$	4	$4^2 - 4 - 6 > 0$? $6 > 0$ True

Solution set: $(-\infty, -2) \cup (3, \infty)$

41. $2x^2 - 9x - 18 \leq 0$

Step 1: Find the values of x that satisfy $2x^2 - 9x - 18 = 0$.

$$2x^2 - 9x - 18 = 0$$
$$(2x+3)(x-6) = 0$$
$$2x + 3 = 0 \quad \text{or} \quad x - 6 = 0$$
$$x = -\tfrac{3}{2} \quad \text{or} \quad x = 6$$

Step 2: The two numbers divide a number line into three regions.

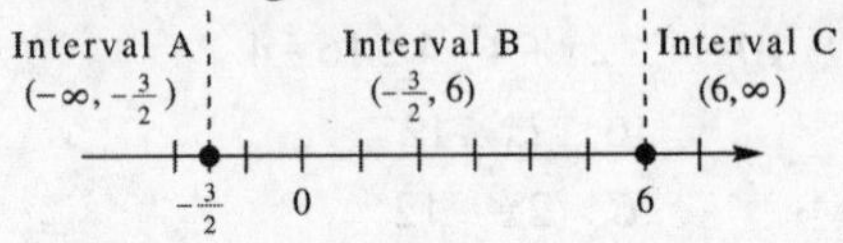

Step 3: Choose a test value to see if it satisfies the inequality, $2x^2 - 9x - 18 \leq 0$.

Interval	Test Value	Is $2x^2 - 9x - 18 \leq 0$ True or False?
A: $\left(-\infty, -\frac{3}{2}\right)$	−2	$2(-2)^2 - 9(-2) - 18 \leq 0$? $8 \leq 0$ False
B: $\left(-\frac{3}{2}, 6\right)$	0	$2(0)^2 - 9(0) - 18 \leq 0$? $-18 \leq 0$ True
C: $(6, \infty)$	7	$2(7)^2 - 9(7) - 18 \leq 0$? $17 \leq 0$ False

Solution set: $\left[-\frac{3}{2}, 6\right]$

43. $x^2+4x+6\ge 3 \Rightarrow x^2+4x+3\ge 0$

Step 1: Find the values of x that satisfy

$x^2+4x+3=0.$

$$x^2+4x+3=0$$
$$(x+3)(x+1)=0$$
$$x+3=0 \quad \text{or} \quad x+1=0$$
$$x=-3 \quad \text{or} \quad x=-1$$

Step 2: The two numbers divide a number line into three regions.

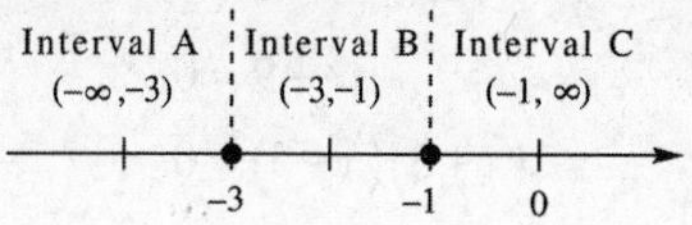

Step 3: Choose a test value to see if it satisfies the inequality, $x^2+4x+3\ge 0.$

Interval	Test Value	Is $x^2+4x+6\ge 3$ True or False?
A: $(-\infty,-3)$	-4	$(-4)^2+4(-4)+6\ge 3$? $6\ge 3$ True
B: $(-3,-1)$	-2	$(-2)^2+4(-2)+6\ge 3$? $2\ge 3$ False
C: $(-1,\infty)$	0	$0^2+4(0)+6\ge 3$? $6\ge 3$ True

Solution set: $(-\infty,-3]\cup[-1,\infty)$

45. $x(x-1)\le 6 \Rightarrow x^2-x\le 6 \Rightarrow x^2-x-6\le 0$

Step 1: Find the values of x that satisfy

$x^2-x-6=0.$

$$x^2-x-6=0$$
$$(x+2)(x-3)=0$$
$$x+2=0 \quad \text{or} \quad x-3=0$$
$$x=-2 \quad \text{or} \quad x=3$$

Step 2: The two numbers divide a number line into three regions.

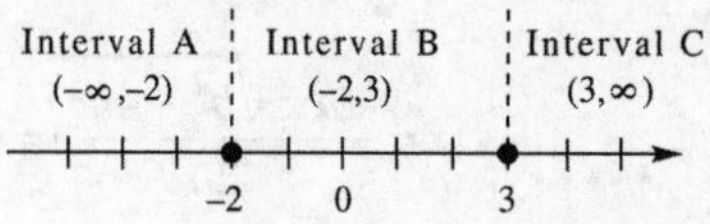

Step 3: Choose a test value to see if it satisfies the inequality, $x(x-1)\le 6.$

Interval	Test Value	Is $x(x-1)\le 6$ True or False?
A: $(-\infty,-2)$	-3	$-3(-3-1)\le 6$? $12\le 6$ False
B: $(-2,3)$	0	$0(0-1)\le 6$? $0\le 6$ True
C: $(3,\infty)$	4	$4(4-1)\le 6$? $12\le 6$ False

Solution set: $[-2,3]$

47. $x^2 \le 9 \Rightarrow x^2 - 9 \le 0$

Step 1: Find the values of x that satisfy $x^2 - 9 = 0$.

$$x^2 - 9 = 0$$
$$(x+3)(x-3) = 0$$
$$x+3=0 \quad \text{or} \quad x-3=0$$
$$x=-3 \quad \text{or} \quad x=3$$

Step 2: The two numbers divide a number line into three regions.

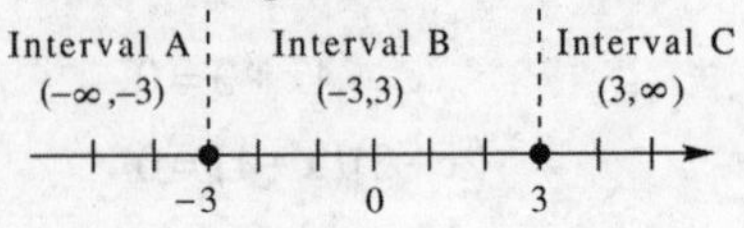

Step 3: Choose a test value to see if it satisfies the inequality, $x^2 \le 9$.

Interval	Test Value	Is $x^2 \le 9$ True or False?
A: $(-\infty,-3)$	−4	$(-4)^2 \le 9$? $16 \le 9$ False
B: $(-3,3)$	0	$0^2 \le 9$? $0 \le 9$ True
C: $(3,\infty)$	4	$4^2 \le 9$? $16 \le 9$ False

Solution set: [−3, 3]

49. $x^2 + 5x - 2 < 0$

Step 1: Find the values of x that satisfy $x^2 + 5x - 2 = 0$.
Use the quadratic formula to solve the equation.
Let $a = 1$, $b = 5$, and $c = -2$.

$$x = \frac{-b \pm \sqrt{b^2 - 4ac}}{2a} = \frac{-5 \pm \sqrt{5^2 - 4(1)(-2)}}{2(1)} = \frac{-5 \pm \sqrt{25+8}}{2} = \frac{-5 \pm \sqrt{33}}{2}$$

$$\frac{-5-\sqrt{33}}{2} \approx -5.4 \text{ or } \frac{-5+\sqrt{33}}{2} \approx .4$$

Step 2: The two numbers divide a number line into three regions.

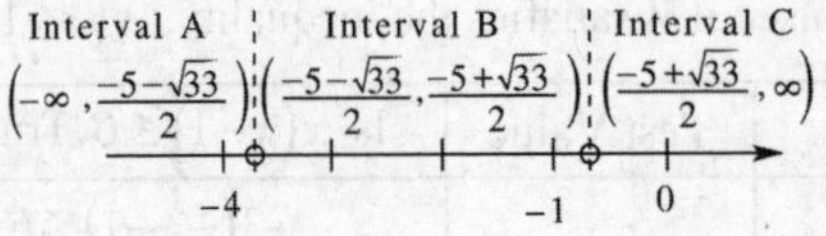

Step 3: Choose a test value to see if it satisfies the inequality, $x^2 + 5x - 2 < 0$.

Interval	Test Value	Is $x^2 + 5x - 2 < 0$ True or False?
A: $\left(-\infty, \frac{-5-\sqrt{33}}{2}\right)$	−6	$(-6)^2 + 5(-6) - 2 < 0$? $4 < 0$ False
B: $\left(\frac{-5-\sqrt{33}}{2}, \frac{-5+\sqrt{33}}{2}\right)$	0	$0^2 + 5(0) - 2 < 0$? $-2 < 0$ True
C: $\left(\frac{-5+\sqrt{33}}{2}, \infty\right)$	1	$(1)^2 + 5(1) - 2 < 0$? $4 < 0$ False

Solution set: $\left(\frac{-5-\sqrt{33}}{2}, \frac{-5+\sqrt{33}}{2}\right)$

51. $x^2-2x\le 1 \Rightarrow x^2-2x-1\le 0$

Step 1: Find the values of x that satisfy $x^2-2x-1=0$.
Use the quadratic formula to solve the equation.
Let $a=1$, $b=-2$, and $c=-1$.

$$x=\frac{-b\pm\sqrt{b^2-4ac}}{2a}=\frac{-(-2)\pm\sqrt{(-2)^2-4(1)(-1)}}{2(1)}=\frac{2\pm\sqrt{4+4}}{2}=\frac{2\pm\sqrt{8}}{2}=\frac{2\pm2\sqrt{2}}{2}=1\pm\sqrt{2}$$

$$1-\sqrt{2}\approx -.4 \text{ or } 1+\sqrt{2}\approx 2.4$$

Step 2: The two numbers divide a number line into three regions.

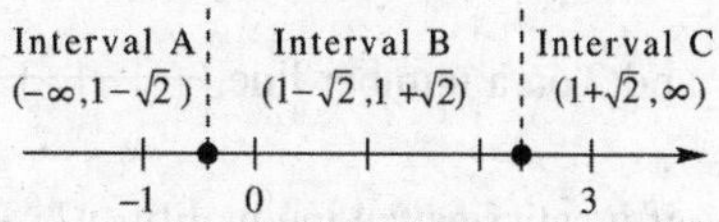

Step 3: Choose a test value to see if it satisfies the inequality, $x^2-2x\le 1$.

Interval	Test Value	Is $x^2-2x\le 1$ True or False?
A: $\left(-\infty,1-\sqrt{2}\right)$	-1	$(-1)^2-2(-1)\le 1$? $3\le 1$ False
B: $\left(1-\sqrt{2},1+\sqrt{2}\right)$	0	$0^2-2(0)\le 1$? $0\le 1$ True
C: $\left(1+\sqrt{2},\infty\right)$	3	$3^2-2(3)\le 1$? $3\le 1$ False

Solution set: $\left[1-\sqrt{2},1+\sqrt{2}\right]$

53. A; $(x+3)^2$ is equal to zero when $x=-3$. For any other real number, $(x+3)^2$ is positive. $(x+3)^2\ge 0$ has solution set $(-\infty,\infty)$.

55. $(3x-4)(x+2)(x+6)=0$
Set each factor to zero and solve.
$3x-4=0$ or $x+2=0$ or $x+6=0$
$x=\frac{4}{3}$ or $x=-2$ or $x=-6$
Solution set: $\left\{\frac{4}{3},-2,-6\right\}$

56. Plot the solutions –6, –2, and $\frac{4}{3}$ on a number line.

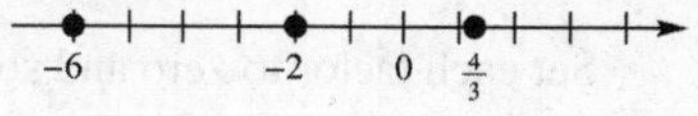

57.

Interval	Test Value	Is $(3x-4)(x+2)(x+6)\le 0$ True or False?
A: $(-\infty,-6)$	-10	$\left[3(-10)-4\right]\left[-10+2\right]\left[-10+6\right]\le 0$? $-1088\le 0$ True
B: $(-6,-2)$	-4	$\left[3(-4)-4\right]\left[-4+2\right]\left[-4+6\right]\le 0$? $64\le 0$ False
C: $\left(-2,\frac{4}{3}\right)$	0	$\left[3(0)-4\right]\left[0+2\right]\left[0+6\right]\le 0$? $-48\le 0$ True
D: $\left(\frac{4}{3},\infty\right)$	4	$\left[3(4)-4\right]\left[4+2\right]\left[4+6\right]\le 0$? $480\le 0$ False

58. 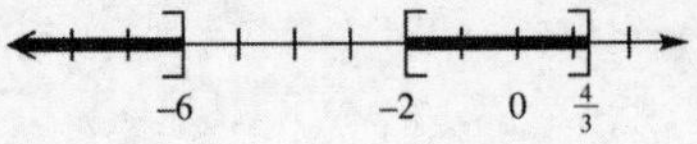

Solution set: $(-\infty,-6]\cup\left[-2,\frac{4}{3}\right]$

59. $(2x-3)(x+2)(x-3)\geq 0$

Step 1: Solve $(2x-3)(x+2)(x-3)=0$.

Set each factor to zero and solve.

$2x-3=0$ or $x+2=0$ or $x-3=0$

$x=\frac{3}{2}$ or $x=-2$ or $x=3$ $\Rightarrow$ Solution set: $\left\{-2,\frac{3}{2},3\right\}$

Step 2: Plot the solutions $-2, \frac{3}{2}$, and 3 on a number line. 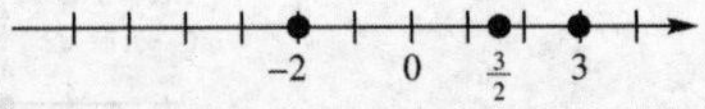

Step 3: Choose a test value to see if it satisfies the inequality, $(2x-3)(x+2)(x-3)\geq 0$.

Interval	Test Value	Is $(2x-3)(x+2)(x-3)\geq 0$ True or False?
A: $(-\infty,-2)$	-3	$[2(-3)-3][-3+2][-3-3]\geq 0$? $-54\geq 0$ False
B: $\left(-2,\frac{3}{2}\right)$	0	$[2(0)-3][0+2][0-3]\geq 0$? $18\geq 0$ True
C: $\left(\frac{3}{2},3\right)$	2	$[2(2)-3][2+2][2-3]\geq 0$? $-4\geq 0$ False
D: $(3,\infty)$	4	$[2(4)-3][4+2][4-3]\geq 0$? $30\geq 0$ True

Solution set: $\left[-2,\frac{3}{2}\right]\cup[3,\infty)$ 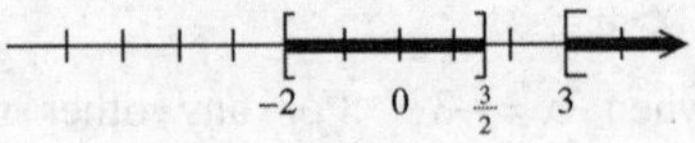

61. $4x-x^3\geq 0$

Step 1: Solve $4x-x^3=0$.

$$4x-x^3=0\Rightarrow x\left(4-x^2\right)=0\Rightarrow x(2+x)(2-x)=0$$

Set each factor to zero and solve.

$x=0$ or $2+x=0$ or $2-x=0$

$x=0$ or $x=-2$ or $2=x$ Solution set: $\{-2,0,2\}$

Step 2: The values -2, 0, and, 2 divide the number line into four intervals.

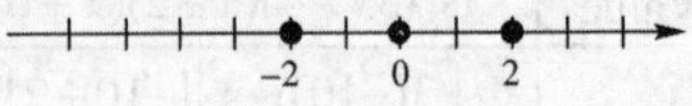

Continued on next page

61. (continued)

Step 3: Choose a test value to see if it satisfies the inequality, $4x - x^3 \ge 0$.

Interval	Test Value	Is $4x - x^3 \ge 0$ True or False?
A: $(-\infty, -2)$	-3	$4(-3) - (-3)^3 \ge 0$? $15 \ge 0$ True
B: $(-2, 0)$	-1	$4(-1) - (-1)^3 \ge 0$? $-3 \ge 0$ False
C: $(0, 2)$	1	$4(1) - 1^3 \ge 0$? $3 \ge 0$ True
D: $(2, \infty)$	3	$4(3) - 3^3 \ge 0$? $-15 \ge 0$ False

Solution set: $(-\infty, -2] \cup [0, 2]$ 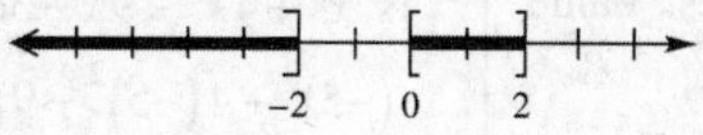

63. $(x+1)^2 (x-3) < 0$

Step 1: Solve $(x+1)^2 (x-3) = 0$.

Set each distinct factor to zero and solve.

$x + 1 = 0$ or $x - 3 = 0$

$x = -1$ or $x = 3$

Solution set: $\{-1, 3\}$

Step 2: The values -1 and 3 divide the number line into three intervals.

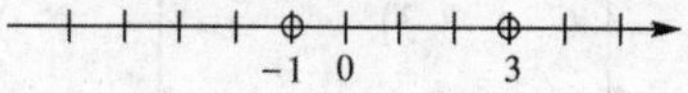

Step 3: Choose a test value to see if it satisfies the inequality, $(x+1)^2 (x-3) < 0$.

Interval	Test Value	Is $(x+1)^2 (x-3) < 0$ True or False?
A: $(-\infty, -1)$	-2	$(-2+1)^2 (-2-3) < 0$? $-5 < 0$ True
B: $(-1, 3)$	0	$(0+1)^2 (0-3) < 0$? $-3 < 0$ True
C: $(3, \infty)$	4	$(4+1)^2 (4-3) < 0$? $25 < 0$ False

Solution set: $(-\infty, -1) \cup (-1, 3)$ 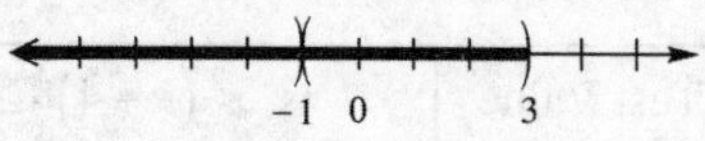

65. $x^3+4x^2-9x-36\geq 0$

Step 1: Solve $x^3+4x^2-9x-36=0 \Rightarrow x^2(x+4)-9(x+4)=0 \Rightarrow (x+4)(x^2-9)=0$

$$(x+4)(x+3)(x-3)=0$$

Set each factor to zero and solve.

$$x+4=0 \quad \text{or} \quad x+3=0 \quad \text{or} \quad x-3=0$$
$$x=-4 \quad \text{or} \quad x=-3 \quad \text{or} \quad x=3$$

Solution set: $\{-4,-3,3\}$

Step 2: The values $-4,-3$, and, 3 divide the number line into four intervals.

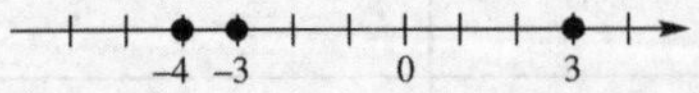

Step 3: Choose a test value to see if it satisfies the inequality, $x^3+4x^2-9x-36>0$.

Interval	Test Value	Is $x^3+4x^2-9x-36\geq 0$ True or False?
A: $(-\infty,-4)$	-5	$(-5)^3+4(-5)^2-9(-5)-36\geq 0$? $-16\geq 0$ False
B: $(-4,-3)$	-3.5	$(-3.5)^3+4(-3.5)^2-9(-3.5)-36\geq 0$? $1.625\geq 0$ True
C: $(-3,3)$	0	$0^3+4(0)^2-9(0)-36\geq 0$? $-36\geq 0$ False
D: $(3,\infty)$	4	$4^3+4(4)^2-9(4)-36\geq 0$? $56\geq 0$ True

Solution set: $[-4,-3]\cup[3,\infty)$

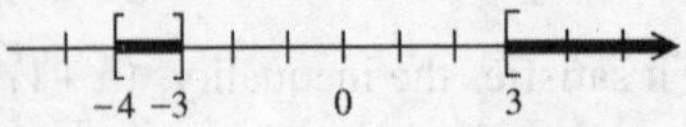

67. $x^2(x+4)^2\geq 0$

Step 1: Solve $x^2(x+4)^2\geq 0$.

Set each distinct factor to zero and solve.

$x=0$ or $x+4=0$

$x=0$ or $x=-4$

Solution set: $\{-4,0\}$

Step 2: The values -4 and 0 divide the number line into three intervals.

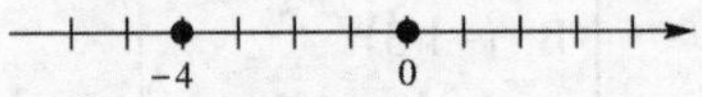

Step 3: Choose a test value to see if it satisfies the inequality, $x^2(x+4)^2\geq 0$.

Interval	Test Value	Is $x^2(x+4)^2\geq 0$ True or False?
A: $(-\infty,-4)$	-5	$(-5)^2(-5+4)^2\geq 0$? $25\geq 0$ True
B: $(-4,0)$	-1	$(-1)^2(-1+4)^2\geq 0$? $9\geq 0$ True
C: $(0,\infty)$	1	$1^2(1+4)^2\geq 0$? $25\geq 0$ True

Solution set: $(-\infty,\infty)$

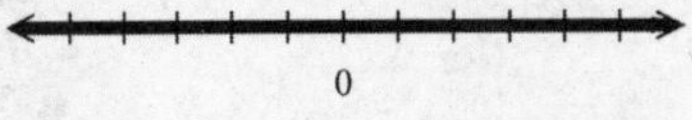

69. $\dfrac{x-3}{x+5} \le 0$

Since one side of the inequality is already 0, we start with Step 2.

Step 2: Determine the values that will cause either the numerator or denominator to equal 0.

$$x-3=0 \quad \text{or} \quad x+5=0$$
$$x=3 \quad \text{or} \quad x=-5$$

The values –5 and 3 to divide the number line into three regions. Use an open circle on –5 because it makes the denominator equal 0.

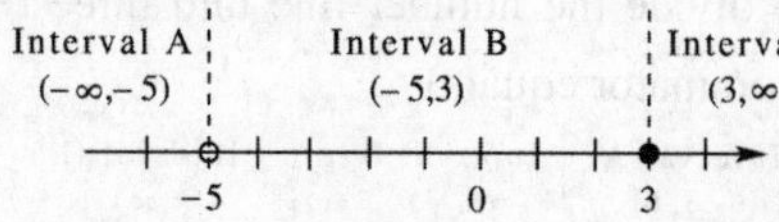

Step 3: Choose a test value to see if it satisfies the inequality, $\dfrac{x-3}{x+5} \le 0$.

Interval	Test Value	Is $\frac{x-3}{x+5} \le 0$ True or False?
A: $(-\infty,-5)$	–6	$\frac{-6-3}{-6+5} \le 0$? $9 \le 0$ False
B: $(-5,3)$	0	$\frac{0-3}{0+5} \le 0$? $-\frac{3}{5} \le 0$ True
C: $(3,\infty)$	4	$\frac{4-3}{4+5} \le 0$? $\frac{1}{9} \le 0$ False

Interval B satisfies the inequality. The endpoint –5 is not included because it makes the denominator 0.

Solution set: (–5, 3]

71. $\dfrac{x-1}{x+2} > 1$

Step 1: Rewrite the inequality so that 0 is on one side and there is a single fraction on the other side.

$$\frac{x-1}{x+2} - 1 > 0 \Rightarrow \frac{x-1}{x+2} - \frac{x+2}{x+2} > 0$$
$$\frac{x-1-(x+2)}{x+2} > 0 \Rightarrow \frac{x-1-x-2}{x+2} > 0$$
$$\frac{-3}{x+2} > 0$$

Step 2: Since the numerator is a constant, determine the values that will cause denominator to equal 0.

$$x+2=0 \Rightarrow x=-2$$

The value –2 divides the number line into two regions.

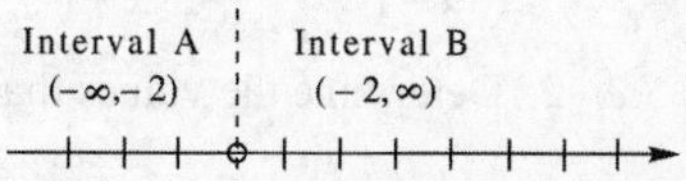

Step 3: Choose a test value to see if it satisfies the inequality, $\dfrac{x-1}{x+2} > 1$.

Interval	Test Value	Is $\frac{x-1}{x+2} > 1$ True or False?
A: $(-\infty,-2)$	–3	$\frac{-3-1}{-3+2} > 1$? $4 > 1$ True
B: $(-2,\infty)$	–1	$\frac{-1-1}{-1+2} > 1$? $-2 > 1$ False

Solution set: $(-\infty,-2)$

73. $\dfrac{3}{x-6} \le 2$

Step 1: Rewrite the inequality so that 0 is on one side and there is a single fraction on the other side.

$$\frac{3}{x-6}-2\le 0 \Rightarrow \frac{3}{x-6}-\frac{2(x-6)}{x-6}\le 0 \Rightarrow \frac{3-2(x-6)}{x-6}\le 0 \Rightarrow \frac{3-2x+12}{x-6}\le 0 \Rightarrow \frac{15-2x}{x-6}\le 0$$

Step 2: Determine the values that will cause either the numerator or denominator to equal 0.

$$15-2x=0 \quad \text{or} \quad x-6=0$$
$$x=\tfrac{15}{2} \quad \text{or} \quad x=6$$

The values 6 and $\frac{15}{2}$ to divide the number line into three regions. Use an open circle on 6 because it makes the denominator equal 0.

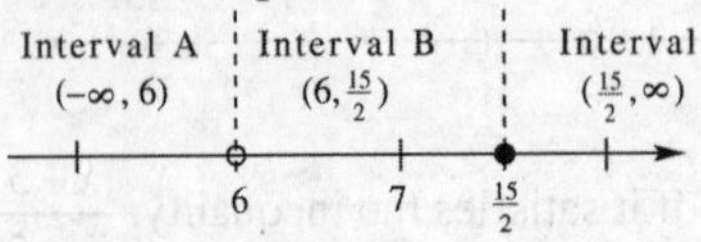

Step 3: Choose a test value to see if it satisfies the inequality, $\dfrac{3}{x-6} \le 2$.

Interval	Test Value	Is $\frac{3}{x-6} \le 2$ True or False?
A: $(-\infty, 6)$	0	$\frac{3}{0-6} \le 2$? $-\frac{1}{2} \le 2$ True
B: $\left(6, \frac{15}{2}\right)$	7	$\frac{3}{7-6} \le 2$? $3 \le 2$ False
C: $\left(\frac{15}{2}, \infty\right)$	8	$\frac{3}{8-6} \le 2$? $\frac{3}{2} \le 2$ True

Intervals A and C satisfiy the inequality. The endpoint 6 is not included because it makes the denominator 0.

Solution set: $(-\infty, 6) \cup \left[\frac{15}{2}, \infty\right)$

75. $\dfrac{4}{x-1} < 5$

Step 1: Rewrite the inequality so that 0 is on one side and there is a single fraction on the other side.

$$\frac{4}{x-1}-5<0 \Rightarrow \frac{4}{x-1}-\frac{5(x-1)}{x-1}<0 \Rightarrow \frac{4-5(x-1)}{x-1}<0 \Rightarrow \frac{4-5x+5}{x-1}<0 \Rightarrow \frac{9-5x}{x-1}<0$$

Step 2: Determine the values that will cause either the numerator or denominator to equal 0.

$$9-5x=0 \quad \text{or} \quad x-1=0$$
$$x=\tfrac{9}{5} \quad \text{or} \quad x=1$$

The values 1 and $\frac{9}{5}$ to divide the number line into three regions.

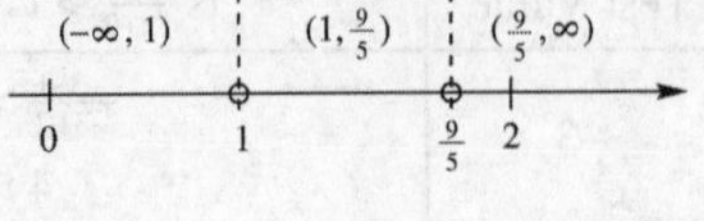

Continued on next page

75. (continued)

Step 3: Choose a test value to see if it satisfies the inequality, $\frac{4}{x-1}<5$.

Interval	Test Value	Is $\frac{4}{x-1}<5$ True or False?
A: $(-\infty,1)$	0	$\frac{4}{0-1}<5$? $-4<5$ True
B: $\left(1,\frac{9}{5}\right)$	$\frac{6}{5}$	$\frac{4}{\frac{6}{5}-1}<5$? $20<5$ False
C: $\left(\frac{9}{5},\infty\right)$	2	$\frac{4}{2-1}<5$? $4<5$ True

Solution set: $(-\infty,1)\cup\left(\frac{9}{5},\infty\right)$

77. $\frac{10}{3+2x}\le 5$

Step 1: Rewrite the inequality so that 0 is on one side and there is a single fraction on the other side.

$$\frac{10}{3+2x}-5\le 0 \Rightarrow \frac{10}{3+2x}-\frac{5(3+2x)}{3+2x}\le 0$$

$$\frac{10-5(3+2x)}{3+2x}\le 0 \Rightarrow \frac{10-15-10x}{3+2x}\le 0 \Rightarrow \frac{-10x-5}{3+2x}\le 0$$

Step 2: Determine the values that will cause either the numerator or denominator to equal 0.

$$-10x-5=0 \quad \text{or} \quad 3+2x=0$$

$$x=-\tfrac{1}{2} \quad \text{or} \quad x=-\tfrac{3}{2}$$

The values $-\frac{3}{2}$ and $-\frac{1}{2}$ to divide the number line into three regions. Use an open circle on $-\frac{3}{2}$ because it makes the denominator equal 0.

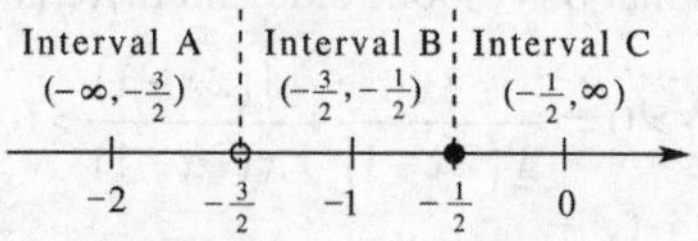

Step 3: Choose a test value to see if it satisfies the inequality, $\frac{10}{3+2x}\le 5$.

Interval	Test Value	Is $\frac{10}{3+2x}\le 5$ True or False?
A: $\left(-\infty,-\frac{3}{2}\right)$	−2	$\frac{10}{3+2(-2)}\le 5$? $-10\le 5$ True
B: $\left(-\frac{3}{2},-\frac{1}{2}\right)$	−1	$\frac{10}{3+2(-1)}\le 5$? $10\le 5$ False
C: $\left(-\frac{1}{2},\infty\right)$	0	$\frac{10}{3+2(0)}\le 5$? $\frac{10}{3}\le 5$ True

Intervals A and C satisfy the inequality. The endpoint $-\frac{3}{2}$ is not included because it makes the denominator 0.

Solution set: $\left(-\infty,-\frac{3}{2}\right)\cup\left[-\frac{1}{2},\infty\right)$

79. $\dfrac{7}{x+2} \geq \dfrac{1}{x+2}$

Step 1: Rewrite the inequality so that 0 is on one side and there is a single fraction on the other side.

$$\frac{7}{x+2} - \frac{1}{x+2} \geq 0 \Rightarrow \frac{6}{x+2} \geq 0$$

Step 2: Since the numerator is a constant, determine the value that will cause the denominator to equal 0.

$$x+2=0 \Rightarrow x=-2$$

The value −2 divides the number line into two regions. Use an open circle on −2 because it makes the denominator equal 0.

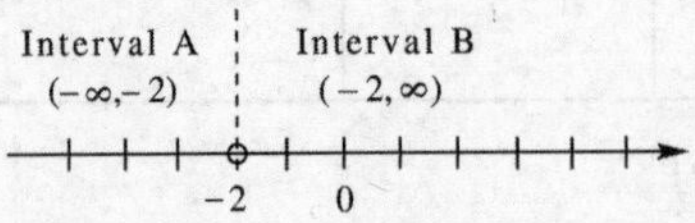

Step 3: Choose a test value to see if it satisfies the inequality, $\dfrac{7}{x+2} \geq \dfrac{1}{x+2}$.

Interval	Test Value	Is $\frac{7}{x+2} \geq \frac{1}{x+2}$ True or False?
A: $(-\infty,-2)$	−3	$\frac{7}{-3+2} \geq \frac{1}{-3+2}$? $-7 \geq -1$ False
B: $(-2,\infty)$	0	$\frac{7}{0+2} \geq \frac{1}{0+2}$? $\frac{7}{2} \geq \frac{1}{2}$ True

Interval B satisfies the inequality. The endpoint −2 is not included because it makes the denominator 0.

Solution set: $(-2,\infty)$

81. $\dfrac{3}{2x-1} > \dfrac{-4}{x}$

Step 1: Rewrite the inequality so that 0 is on one side and there is a single fraction on the other side.

$$\frac{3}{2x-1} + \frac{4}{x} > 0 \Rightarrow \frac{3x}{x(2x-1)} + \frac{4(2x-1)}{x(2x-1)} > 0$$

$$\frac{3x+4(2x-1)}{x(2x-1)} > 0 \Rightarrow \frac{3x+8x-4}{x(2x-1))} > 0 \Rightarrow \frac{11x-4}{x(2x-1)} > 0$$

Step 2: Determine the values that will cause either the numerator or denominator to equal 0.

$$11x-4=0 \quad \text{or} \quad x=0 \quad \text{or} \quad 2x-1=0$$
$$x=\tfrac{4}{11} \quad \text{or} \quad x=0 \quad \text{or} \quad x=\tfrac{1}{2}$$

The values 0, $\frac{4}{11}$, and $\frac{1}{2}$ divide the number line into four regions.

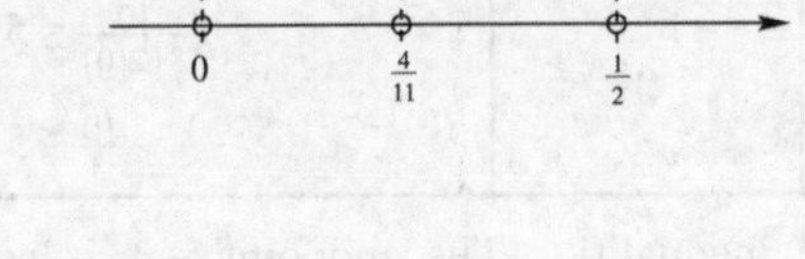

Continued on next page

81. (continued)

Step 3: Choose a test value to see if it satisfies the inequality, $\dfrac{3}{2x-1} > \dfrac{-4}{x}$.

Interval	Test Value	Is $\frac{3}{2x-1} > \frac{-4}{x}$ True or False?
A: $(-\infty, 0)$	-1	$\frac{3}{2(-1)-1} > \frac{-4}{-1}$? $-1 > 4$ False
B: $\left(0, \frac{4}{11}\right)$	$\frac{1}{11}$	$\frac{3}{2\left(\frac{1}{11}\right)-1} > \frac{-4}{\frac{1}{11}}$? or $-\frac{11}{3} > -44$ $-3\frac{2}{3} > -44$ True
C: $\left(\frac{4}{11}, \frac{1}{2}\right)$	$\frac{9}{22}$	$\frac{3}{2\left(\frac{9}{22}\right)-1} > \frac{-4}{\frac{9}{22}}$? or $-\frac{33}{2} > -\frac{88}{9}$ $-16\frac{1}{2} > -9\frac{7}{9}$ False
D: $\left(\frac{1}{2}, \infty\right)$	1	$\frac{3}{2(1)-1} > \frac{-4}{1}$? $3 > -4$ True

Solution set: $\left(0, \frac{4}{11}\right) \cup \left(\frac{1}{2}, \infty\right)$

83. $\dfrac{4}{x-2} \le \dfrac{3}{x-1}$

Step 1: Rewrite the inequality so that 0 is on one side and there is a single fraction on the other side.

$$\frac{4}{x-2} - \frac{3}{x-1} \le 0$$

$$\frac{4(x-1)}{(x-2)(x-1)} - \frac{3(x-2)}{(x-1)(x-2)} \le 0$$

$$\frac{4(x-1)-3(x-2)}{(x-2)(x-1)} \le 0$$

$$\frac{4x-4-3x+6}{(x-2)(x-1)} \le 0$$

$$\frac{x+2}{(x-2)(x-1)} \le 0$$

Step 2: Determine the values that will cause either the numerator or denominator to equal 0.

$$x+2=0 \quad \text{or} \quad x-2=0 \quad \text{or} \quad x-1=0$$

$$x=-2 \quad \text{or} \quad x=2 \quad \text{or} \quad x=1$$

The values –2, 1, and 2 divide the number line into four regions. Use an open circle on 1 and 2 because they make the denominator equal 0.

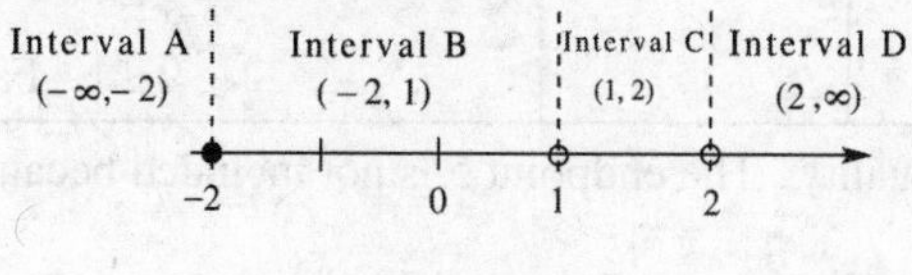

Continued on next page

83. (continued)

Step 3: Choose a test value to see if it satisfies the inequality, $\dfrac{4}{x-2} \le \dfrac{3}{x-1}$.

Interval	Test Value	Is $\frac{4}{x-2} \le \frac{3}{x-1}$ True or False?
A: $(-\infty,-2)$	-3	$\frac{4}{-3-2} \le \frac{3}{-3-1}$? or $-\frac{4}{5} \le -\frac{3}{4}$ $-\frac{16}{20} \le -\frac{15}{20}$ True
B: $(-2,1)$	0	$\frac{4}{0-2} \le \frac{3}{0-1}$? $-2 \le -3$ False
C: $(1,2)$	1.5	$\frac{4}{1.5-2} \le \frac{3}{1.5-1}$? $-8 \le 6$ True
D: $(2,\infty)$	3	$\frac{4}{3-2} \le \frac{3}{3-1}$? $4 \le \frac{3}{2}$ False

Interval A and C satisfy the inequality. The endpoints 1 and 2 are not included because they make the denominator 0.

Solution set: $(-\infty,-2] \cup (1,2)$

85. $\dfrac{x+3}{x-5} \le 1$

Step 1: Rewrite the inequality so that 0 is on one side and there is a single fraction on the other side.

$$\frac{x+3}{x-5} - 1 \le 0 \Rightarrow \frac{x+3}{x-5} - \frac{x-5}{x-5} \le 0 \Rightarrow \frac{x+3-(x-5)}{x-5} \le 0 \Rightarrow \frac{x+3-x+5}{x-5} \ge 0 \Rightarrow \frac{8}{x-5} \le 0$$

Step 2: Since the numerator is a constant, determine the value that will cause the denominator to equal 0.

$$x-5=0$$
$$x=5$$

The value 5 divides the number line into two regions. Use an open circle on 5 because it makes the denominator equal 0.

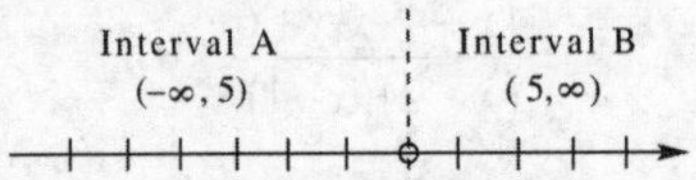

Step 3: Choose a test value to see if it satisfies the inequality, $\dfrac{x+3}{x-5} \le 1$.

Interval	Test Value	Is $\frac{x+3}{x-5} \le 1$ True or False?
A: $(-\infty,5)$	0	$\frac{0+3}{0-5} \le 1$? $-\frac{3}{5} \le 1$ True
B: $(5,\infty)$	6	$\frac{6+3}{6-5} \le 1$? $9 \le 1$ False

Interval A satisfies the inequality. The endpoint 5 is not included because it makes the denominator 0.

Solution set: $(-\infty,5)$

87. $\dfrac{2x-3}{x^2+1} \geq 0$

Since one side of the inequality is already 0, we start with Step 2.

Step 2: Determine the values that will cause either the numerator or denominator to equal 0.

$$2x-3=0 \quad \text{or} \quad x^2+1=0$$
$$x=\tfrac{3}{2} \qquad \text{has no real solutions}$$

$\frac{3}{2}$ divides the number line into two intervals.

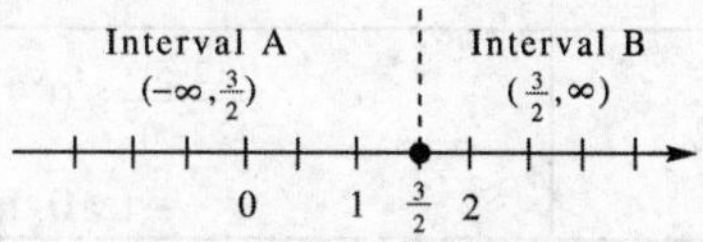

Step 3: Choose a test value to see if it satisfies the inequality, $\dfrac{2x-3}{x^2+1} \geq 0$.

Interval	Test Value	Is $\frac{2x-3}{x^2+1} \geq 0$ True or False?
A: $\left(-\infty, \frac{3}{2}\right)$	0	$\frac{2(0)-3}{0^2+1} \geq 0$? $-3 \geq 0$ False
B: $\left(\frac{3}{2}, \infty\right)$	2	$\frac{2(2)-3}{2^2+1} \geq 0$? $\frac{1}{5} \geq 0$ True

Solution set: $\left[\frac{3}{2}, \infty\right)$

89. $\dfrac{(3x-5)^2}{(2x-5)^3} > 0$

Since one side of the inequality is already 0, we start with Step 2.
Step 2: Determine the values that will cause either the numerator or denominator to equal 0.

$$3x-5=0 \quad \text{or} \quad 2x-5=0$$
$$x=\tfrac{5}{3} \quad \text{or} \quad x=\tfrac{5}{2}$$

The values $\frac{5}{3}$ and $\frac{5}{2}$ divide the number line into three intervals.

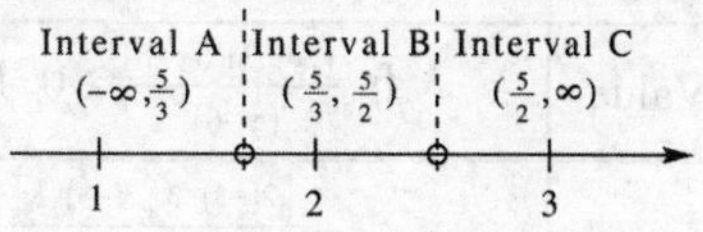

Continued on next page

89. (continued)

Step 3: Choose a test value to see if it satisfies the inequality, $\frac{(3x-5)^2}{(2x-5)^3} > 0$.

Interval	Test Value	Is $\frac{(3x-5)^2}{(2x-5)^3} > 0$ True or False?
A: $\left(-\infty, \frac{5}{3}\right)$	0	$\frac{(3\cdot 0-5)^2}{(2\cdot 0-5)^3} > 0$? $-\frac{1}{5} > 0$ False
B: $\left(\frac{5}{3}, \frac{5}{2}\right)$	2	$\frac{(3\cdot 2-5)^2}{(2\cdot 2-5)^3} > 0$? $-1 > 0$ False
C: $\left(\frac{5}{2}, \infty\right)$	3	$\frac{(3\cdot 3-5)^2}{(2\cdot 3-5)^3} > 0$? $16 > 0$ True

Solution set: $\left(\frac{5}{2}, \infty\right)$

91. $\frac{(2x-3)(3x+8)}{(x-6)^3} \geq 0$

Since one side of the inequality is already 0, we start with Step 2.

Step 2: Determine the values that will cause either the numerator or denominator to equal 0.

$$2x-3=0 \quad \text{or} \quad 3x+8=0 \quad \text{or} \quad x-6=0$$
$$x=\frac{3}{2} \quad \text{or} \quad x=-\frac{8}{3} \quad \text{or} \quad x=6$$

The values $-\frac{8}{3}$, $\frac{3}{2}$, and 6 divide the number line into four intervals. Use an open circle on 6 because it makes the denominator equal 0.

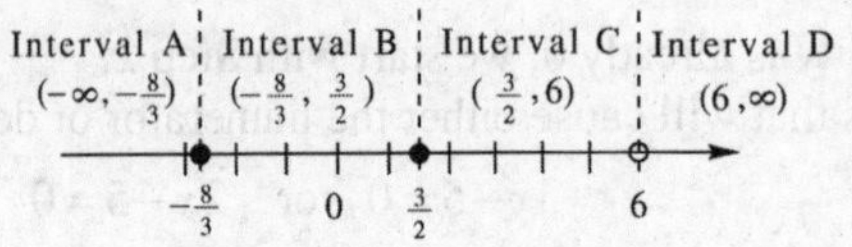

Step 3: Choose a test value to see if it satisfies the inequality, $\frac{(2x-3)(3x+8)}{(x-6)^3} \geq 0$.

Interval	Test Value	Is $\frac{(2x-3)(3x+8)}{(x-6)^3} \geq 0$ True or False?
A: $\left(-\infty, -\frac{8}{3}\right)$	−3	$\frac{[2(-3)-3][3(-3)+8]}{(-3-6)^3} \geq 0$? $-\frac{1}{81} \geq 0$ False
B: $\left(-\frac{8}{3}, \frac{3}{2}\right)$	0	$\frac{(2\cdot 0-3)(3\cdot 0+8)}{(0-6)^3} \geq 0$? $\frac{1}{9} \geq 0$ True
C: $\left(\frac{3}{2}, 6\right)$	2	$\frac{(2\cdot 2-3)(3\cdot 2+8)}{(2-6)^3} \geq 0$? $-\frac{7}{32} \geq 0$ False
D: $(6, \infty)$	7	$\frac{(2\cdot 7-3)(3\cdot 7+8)}{(7-6)^3} \geq 0$? $319 \geq 0$ True

Solution set: $\left[-\frac{8}{3}, \frac{3}{2}\right] \cup (6, \infty)$

93. $R = .56x + 6.8$

$$.56x + 6.8 < 7.5$$
$$.56x < .7$$
$$x < 1.25$$

This would imply in the years 1998 and 1999, the revenue would be below \$7.5 (billion). This correlates to the years 1998 and 1999.

$R = .56x + 6.8$

$$.56x + 6.8 > 8.5 \Rightarrow .56x > 1.7 \Rightarrow x > 3.04 \text{ (approximately)}$$

This would imply in the years 2001 and 2002, the revenue would exceed \$8.5 (billion).

Note, if $3 \le x < 4$ then this implies that the event occurs during the year 2001.

The linear model agrees favorably, except for the year 2001.

95. $-16t^2 + 220t \ge 624$

Step 1: Find the values of x that satisfy $-16t^2 + 220t = 624$.

$$-16t^2 + 220t = 624 \Rightarrow 0 = 16t^2 - 220t + 624 \Rightarrow 0 = 4t^2 - 55t + 156 \Rightarrow 0 = (t-4)(4t-39)$$

$$t - 4 = 0 \quad \text{or} \quad 4t - 39 = 0$$
$$t = 4 \quad \text{or} \quad t = \tfrac{39}{4} = 9.75$$

Step 2: The two numbers divide a number line into three regions, where $t \ge 0$.

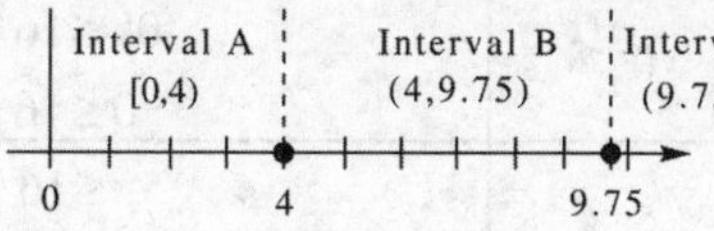

Step 3: Choose a test value to see if it satisfies the inequality, $-16t^2 + 220t \ge 624$.

Interval	Test Value	Is $-16t^2 + 220t \ge 624$ True or False?
A: $(0,4)$	1	$-16 \cdot 1^2 + 220 \cdot 1 \ge 624$? $204 \ge 624$ False
B: $(4,9.75)$	5	$-16 \cdot 5^2 + 220 \cdot 5 \ge 624$? $700 \ge 624$ True
C: $(9.75,\infty)$	10	$-16 \cdot 10^2 + 220 \cdot 10 \ge 624$? $600 \ge 624$ False

The projectile will be at least 624 feet above ground between 4 sec and 9.75 sec (inclusive).

97. **(a)** $1.5\times10^{-3} \le R \le 6.0\times10^{-3}$

$2.08\times10^{-5} \le \dfrac{R}{72} \le 8.33\times10^{-5}$ (Approximate values are given.)

(b) Let N be the number of additional lung cancer deaths each year. Then N would be determined by taking the annual individual risk times the total number of people. Thus, $N = (260\times10^6)\left(\dfrac{R}{72}\right)$.

The range for N would be approximately $(260\times10^6)(2.08\times10^{-5}) \le N \le (260\times10^6)(8.33\times10^{-5})$

$$5417 \le N \le 21{,}667.$$

Thus, radon gas exposure is expected by the EPA to cause approximately between 5400 and 21,700 cases of lung cancer each year in the United States.

99. Answers will vary.
The student's answer is not correct. Taking the square root of both sides (and including a $\pm$) can be done if one is examining an equation, not an inequality. The correct solution can be found using the methods described in this section.

$x^2 \le 16$

Step 1: Find the values of x that satisfy $x^2 = 16$.

$$x^2 = 16 \Rightarrow x^2 - 16 = 0 \Rightarrow (x+4)(x-4) = 0$$

$$x+4=0 \quad \text{or} \quad x-4=0$$

$$x=-4 \quad \text{or} \quad x=4$$

Step 2: The two numbers divide a number line into three regions.

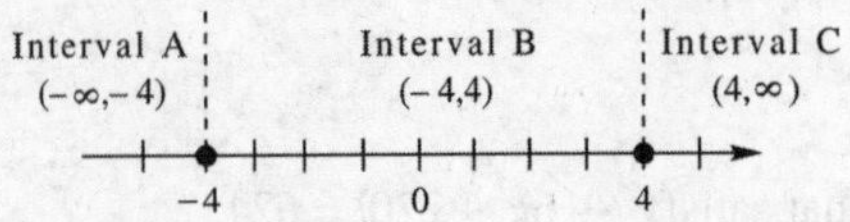

Step 3: Choose a test value to see if it satisfies the inequality, $x^2 \le 16$.

Interval	Test Value	Is $x^2 \le 16$ True or False?
A: $(-\infty,-4)$	-5	$(-5)^2 \le 16$? $25 \le 16$ False
B: $(-4,4)$	0	$0^2 \le 16$? $0 \le 16$ True
C: $(4,\infty)$	5	$5^2 \le 16$? $25 \le 16$ False

Solution set: $[-4,4]$

Section 1.8: Absolute Value Equations and Inequalities

1. $|x| = 4$
The solution set includes any value of x whose absolute value is 4; thus $x = 4$ or $x = -4$ are both solutions. The correct graph is F.

3. $|x| > -4$
The solution set is all real numbers, since the absolute value of any real number is always greater than -4. The correct graph is D, which shows the entire number line.

5. $|x| < 4$
The solution set includes any value of x whose absolute value is less than 4; thus x must be between -4 and 4, not including -4 or 4. The correct graph is G.

7. $|x| \le 4$
The solution set includes any value of x whose absolute value is less than or equal to 4; thus x must be between -4 and 4, including -4 and 4. The correct graph is C.

9. $|3x-1|=2$

$3x-1=2$ or $3x-1=-2$

$3x=3$ $\quad 3x=-1$

$x=1$ or $x=-\frac{1}{3}$

Solution set: $\left\{-\frac{1}{3}, 1\right\}$

11. $|5-3x|=3$

$5-3x=3$ or $5-3x=-3$

$2=3x$ $\quad 8=3x$

$\frac{2}{3}=x$ or $\frac{8}{3}=x$

Solution set: $\left\{\frac{2}{3}, \frac{8}{3}\right\}$

13. $\left|\frac{x-4}{2}\right|=5$

$\frac{x-4}{2}=5$ or $\frac{x-4}{2}=-5$

$x-4=10$ $\quad x-4=-10$

$x=14$ or $x=-6$

Solution set: $\{-6, 14\}$

15. $\left|\frac{5}{x-3}\right|=10$

$\frac{5}{x-3}=10$ or $\frac{5}{x-3}=-10$

$5=10(x-3)$ $\quad 5=-10(x-3)$

$5=10x-30$ $\quad 5=-10x+30$

$35=10x$ $\quad -25=-10x$

$\frac{35}{10}=x$ $\quad \frac{-25}{-10}=x$

$x=\frac{7}{2}$ or $x=\frac{5}{2}$

Solution set: $\left\{\frac{5}{2}, \frac{7}{2}\right\}$

17. $\left|\frac{6x+1}{x-1}\right|=3$

$\frac{6x+1}{x-1}=3$ or $\frac{6x+1}{x-1}=-3$

$6x+1=3(x-1)$ $\quad 6x+1=-3(x-1)$

$6x+1=3x-3$ $\quad 6x+1=-3x+3$

$3x=-4$ $\quad 9x=2$

$x=-\frac{4}{3}$ or $x=\frac{2}{9}$

Solution set: $\left\{-\frac{4}{3}, \frac{2}{9}\right\}$

19. $|2x-3|=|5x+4|$

$2x-3=5x+4$ or $2x-3=-(5x+4)$

$2x-3=-5x-4$

$-7=3x$

$7x=-1$

$-\frac{7}{3}=x$ or $x=\frac{-1}{7}=-\frac{1}{7}$

Solution set: $\left\{-\frac{7}{3}, -\frac{1}{7}\right\}$

21. $|4-3x|=|2-3x|$

$4-3x=2-3x$ or $4-3x=-(2-3x)$

$4=2$ False $\quad 4-3x=-2+3x$

$6=6x$

$1=x$

Solution set: $\{1\}$

23. $|5x-2|=|2-5x|$

$5x-2=2-5x$ or $5x-2=-(2-5x)$

$10x=4$ $\quad 5x-2=-2+5x$

$x=\frac{4}{10}$ $\quad 0=0$ True

$x=\frac{2}{5}$

Solution set: $(-\infty, \infty)$

25. Answers will vary.
If x is positive, then $-7x$ will be negative. Since the outcome of an absolute value can never be negative, a positive value of x is not possible.

27. $|2x+5|<3$

$-3<2x+5<3$

$-8<2x<-2$

$-4<x<-1$

Solution set: $(-4, -1)$

29. $|2x+5|\geq 3$

$2x+5\leq -3$ or $2x+5\geq 3$

$2x\leq -8$ $\quad 2x\geq -2$

$x\leq -4$ or $x\geq -1$

Solution set: $(-\infty, -4]\cup[-1, \infty)$

31 $\left|x-\frac{1}{2}\right|<2$

$-2<x-\frac{1}{2}<2$

$2(-2)<2\left(x-\frac{1}{2}\right)<2(2)$

$-4<2x-1<4$

$-3<2x<5$

$-\frac{3}{2}<x<\frac{5}{2}$

Solution set: $\left(-\frac{3}{2},\frac{5}{2}\right)$

33. $4|x-3|>12\Rightarrow|x-3|>3$

$x-3<-3$ or $x-3>3$

$x<0$ or $x>6$

Solution set: $(-\infty,0)\cup(6,\infty)$

35. $|5-3x|>7$

$5-3x<-7$ or $5-3x>7$

$-3x<-12$ $\quad$ $-3x>2$

$x>4$ or $x<-\frac{2}{3}$

Solution set: $\left(-\infty,-\frac{2}{3}\right)\cup(4,\infty)$

37. $|5-3x|\le 7$

$-7\le 5-3x\le 7$

$-12\le -3x\le 2$

$4\ge x\ge -\frac{2}{3}$

$-\frac{2}{3}\le x\le 4$

Solution set: $\left[-\frac{2}{3},4\right]$

39. $\left|\frac{2}{3}x+\frac{1}{2}\right|\le\frac{1}{6}$

$-\frac{1}{6}\le\frac{2}{3}x+\frac{1}{2}\le\frac{1}{6}$

$6\left(-\frac{1}{6}\right)\le 6\left(\frac{2}{3}x+\frac{1}{2}\right)\le 6\left(\frac{1}{6}\right)$

$-1\le 4x+3\le 1$

$-4\le 4x\le -2$

$-1\le x\le -\frac{1}{2}$

Solution set: $\left[-1,-\frac{1}{2}\right]$

41. $|4x+3|-2=-1\Rightarrow|4x+3|=1$

$4x+3=1$ or $4x+3=-1$

$4x=-2$ $\quad$ $4x=-4$

$x=\frac{-2}{4}=-\frac{1}{2}$ or $x=-1$

Solution set: $\left\{-\frac{1}{2},-1\right\}$

43. $|6-2x|+1=3\Rightarrow|6-2x|=2$

$6-2x=2$ or $6-2x=-2$

$-2x=-4$ $\quad$ $-2x=-8$

$x=2$ or $x=4$

Solution set: $\{2,4\}$

45. $|3x+1|-1<2\Rightarrow|3x+1|<3$

$-3<3x+1<3$

$-4<3x<2$

$-\frac{4}{3}<x<\frac{2}{3}$

Solution set: $\left(-\frac{4}{3},\frac{2}{3}\right)$

47. $\left|5x+\frac{1}{2}\right|-2<5\Rightarrow\left|5x+\frac{1}{2}\right|<7$

$-7<5x+\frac{1}{2}<7$

$2(-7)<2\left(5x+\frac{1}{2}\right)<2(7)$

$-14<10x+1<14$

$-15<10x<13$

$-\frac{15}{10}<x<\frac{13}{10}$

$-\frac{3}{2}<x<\frac{13}{10}$

Solution set: $\left(-\frac{3}{2},\frac{13}{10}\right)$

49. $|10-4x|+1\ge 5\Rightarrow|10-4x|\ge 4$

$10-4x\le -4$ or $10-4x\ge 4$

$-4x\le -14$ $\quad$ $-4x\ge -6$

$x\ge\frac{-14}{-4}$ $\quad$ $x\le\frac{-6}{-4}$

$x\ge\frac{7}{2}$ or $x\le\frac{3}{2}$

Solution set: $\left(-\infty,\frac{3}{2}\right]\cup\left[\frac{7}{2},\infty\right)$

51. Since the absolute value of a number is always nonnegative, the inequality $|10-4x|\ge -3$ is always true. The solution set is $(-\infty,\infty)$.

53. There is no number whose absolute value is less than any negative number. The solution set of $|6-3x|<-5$ is $\varnothing$.

55. The absolute value of a number will be 0 if that number is 0. Therefore $|8x+5|=0$ is equivalent to $8x+5=0$, which has solution set $\left\{-\frac{5}{8}\right\}$.

57. Any number less than zero will be negative. There is no number whose absolute value is a negative number. The solution set of $|4.3x+8.6|<0$ is $\varnothing$.

59. Since the absolute value of a number is always nonnegative, $|2x+1|<0$ is never true, so $|2x+1|\le 0$ is only true when $|2x+1|=0$.

$$|2x+1|=0 \Rightarrow 2x+1=0$$
$$2x=-1 \Rightarrow x=-\tfrac{1}{2}$$

Solution set: $\left\{-\frac{1}{2}\right\}$

61. $|3x+2|>0$ will be false only when $3x+2=0$, which occurs when $x=-\frac{2}{3}$. So the solution set for $|3x+2|>0$ is $\left(-\infty,-\frac{2}{3}\right)\cup\left(-\frac{2}{3},\infty\right)$.

63. 6 and the opposite of 6, namely -6.

64. $x^2-x=6 \Rightarrow x^2-x-6=0 \Rightarrow (x+2)(x-3)=0$

$x+2=0$ or $x-3=0$

$x=-2$ or $x=3$

Solution set: $\{-2,3\}$

65. $x^2-x=-6 \Rightarrow x^2-x+6=0$

The quadratic formula, $x=\dfrac{-b\pm\sqrt{b^2-4ac}}{2a}$, can be evaluated with $a=1, b=-1,$ and $c=6$.

$$x=\frac{-b\pm\sqrt{b^2-4ac}}{2a}=\frac{-(-1)\pm\sqrt{(-1)^2-4(1)(6)}}{2(1)}=\frac{1\pm\sqrt{1-24}}{2}=\frac{1\pm\sqrt{-23}}{2}=\frac{1\pm i\sqrt{23}}{2}=\frac{1}{2}\pm\frac{\sqrt{23}}{2}i$$

Solution set: $\left\{\frac{1}{2}\pm\frac{\sqrt{23}}{2}i\right\}$

66. $\left\{-2,3,\frac{1}{2}\pm\frac{\sqrt{23}}{2}i\right\}$

67. $|4x^2-23x-6|=0$

Because 0 and the opposite of 0 represent the same value, only one equation needs to be solved.

$$4x^2-23x-6=0 \Rightarrow (4x+1)(x-6)=0$$

$4x+1=0$ or $x-6=0$

$x=-\frac{1}{4}$ or $x=6$

Solution set: $\left\{-\frac{1}{4},6\right\}$

69. $|x^2+1| = |2x|$

$$x^2+1=2x \Rightarrow x^2-2x+1=0 \Rightarrow (x-1)^2=0 \Rightarrow x-1=0 \Rightarrow x=1$$

or

$$x^2+1=-2x \Rightarrow x^2+2x+1=0 \Rightarrow (x+1)^2=0 \Rightarrow x+1=0 \Rightarrow x=-1$$

Solution set: $\{-1,1\}$

71. Any number less than zero will be negative. There is no number whose absolute value is a negative number. The solution set of $|x^4+2x^2+1|<0$ is $\varnothing$.

73. $\left|\frac{3x+1}{x-4}\right| \geq 0$

This inequality will be true, except where $\frac{3x+1}{x-4}$ is undefined. This occurs when $x-4=0$, or $x=4$.
Solution set: $(-\infty,4)\cup(4,\infty)$

75. $|p-q|=5$, which is equivalent to $|q-p|=5$, indicates that the distance between p and q is 5 units.

77 "m is no more than 8 units from 9" means that m is 8 units or less from 9. Thus the distance between m and 9 is less than or equal to 8, or $|m-9|\leq 8$.

79. "p is within .0001 units of 9" means that p is less than .0001 units from 9. Thus the distance between p and 9 is less than .0001, or $|p-9|<.0001$.

81. "r is no less than 1 unit from 19" means that r is 1 unit or more from 19. Thus the distance between r and 19 is greater than or equal to 1, or $|r-19|\geq 1$.

83. Since we want y to be within .002 unit of 6, we have $|y-6|<.002$ or $|5x+1-6|<.002$.

$$|5x-5|<.002$$
$$-.002<5x-5<.002$$
$$4.998<5x<5.002$$
$$.9996<x<1.0004$$

Values of x in the interval $(.9996, 1.0004)$ would satisfy the condition.

85. $|y-8.0|\leq 1.5$

$$-1.5\leq y-8.0\leq 1.5 \Rightarrow 6.5\leq y\leq 9.5$$

The range of weights, in pounds, is [6.5, 9.5].

87. 780 is 50 more than 730 and 680 is 50 less than 730, so all of the temperatures in the acceptable range are within 50° of 730°. That is $|F-730|\leq 50$.

89. $|R_L-26.75|\leq 1.42 \Rightarrow -1.42\leq R_L-26.75\leq 1.42 \Rightarrow 25.33\leq R_L\leq 28.17$

$|R_E-38.75|\leq 2.17 \Rightarrow -2.17\leq R_E-38.75\leq 2.17 \Rightarrow 36.58\leq R_E\leq 40.92$

91. Answers will vary.

Chapter 1: Review Exercises

1. $2x+7=3x+1$

$7=x+1$

$6=x$

Solution set: $\{6\}$

3. $5x-2(x+4)=3(2x+1)$

$5x-2x-8=6x+3$

$3x-8=6x+3$

$-8=3x+3$

$-11=3x$

$-\frac{11}{3}=x$

Solution set: $\{-\frac{11}{3}\}$

5. $A=\dfrac{24f}{B(p+1)}$ for f (approximate annual interest rate)

$B(p+1)A=B(p+1)\left(\dfrac{24f}{B(p+1)}\right)$

$AB(p+1)=24f$

$\dfrac{AB(p+1)}{24}=f$

$f=\dfrac{AB(p+1)}{24}$

7. A and B cannot be equations used to find the number of pennies in a jar. The number of pennies must be a whole number.

A. $5x+3=9$

$5x=6$

$x=\frac{6}{5}$

B. $12x+3=-4$

$12x=-7$

$x=-\frac{7}{12}$

C. $100x=50(x+3)$

$100x=50x+150$

$50x=150\Rightarrow x=3$

D. $6(x+4)=x+24$

$6x+24=x+24$

$5x+24=24$

$5x=0\Rightarrow x=0$

9. Let x = the original length of the square (in inches).
Since the perimeter of a square is 4 times the length of one side, we have $4(x-4)=\frac{1}{2}(4x)+10$. Solve this equation for x to determine the length of each side of the original square.

$$4x-16=2x+10\Rightarrow 2x-16=10\Rightarrow 2x=26\Rightarrow x=13$$

The original square is 13 in. on each side.

11. Let x = the amount of 100% alcohol solution (in liters).

Strength	Liters of Solution	Liters of Pure Alcohol
100%	x	$1x=x$
10%	12	$.10\cdot 12=1.2$
30%	$x+12$	$.30(x+12)$

The number of liters of pure alcohol in the 100% solution plus the number of liters of pure alcohol in the 10% solution must equal the number of liters of pure alcohol in the 30% solution.

$$x+1.2=.30(x+12)\Rightarrow x+1.2=.30x+3.6\Rightarrow .7x+1.2=3.6\Rightarrow .7x=2.4\Rightarrow x=\frac{2.4}{.7}=\frac{24}{7}=3\tfrac{3}{7}\text{ L}$$

$3\frac{3}{7}$ L of the 100% solution should be added.

13. Let x = average speed upriver.
Then $x + 5$ = average speed on return trip.

	r	t	d
Upriver	x	1.2	$1.2x$
Downriver	$x+5$	.9	$.9(x+5)$

Since the distance upriver and downriver are the same, we solve the following.

$$1.2x = .9(x+5) \Rightarrow 1.2x = .9x + 4.5 \Rightarrow .3x = 4.5 \Rightarrow x = 15$$

The average speed of the boat upriver is 15 mph.

15. (a) In one year, the maximum amount of lead ingested would be

$$.05\ \frac{\text{mg}}{\text{liter}} \cdot 2\ \frac{\text{liters}}{\text{day}} \cdot 365.25\ \frac{\text{days}}{\text{year}} = 36.525\ \frac{\text{mg}}{\text{year}}.$$

The maximum amount A of lead (in milligrams) ingested in x years would be $A = 36.525x$.

(b) If $x = 72$, then $A = 36.525(72) = 2629.8$ mg.
The EPA maximum lead intake from water over a lifetime is 2629.8 mg.

17. (a) In 1985, $x = 1985$

$y = .100725x - 196.54$
$y = .100725(1985) - 196.54$
$y \approx 3.40$

The minimum wage in 1985 was \$3.40 according to the model. Compared to the table value of \$3.35, it is quite close; they differ by just \$.05.

(b) $y = .100725x - 196.54$
$3.80 = .100725x - 196.54$
$200.34 = .100725x$
$1989 \approx x$

In 1989, the model predicts the minimum wage to be \$3.80. It is fairly close to the table value of \$3.35. The table value for 1990 would be exact.

19. $(6-i)+(4-2i) = (6+4)+\left[-1+(-2)\right]i = 10+(-3)i = 10-3i$

21. $15i-(3+2i)-5 = (-3-5)+(15-2)i = -8+13i$

23. $(5-i)(3+4i) = 5(3)+5(4i)-i(3)-i(4i) = 15+20i-3i-4i^2 = 15+17i-4(-1) = 15+17i+4 = 19+17i$

25. $(5-11i)(5+11i) = 5^2-(11i)^2$ Product of the sum and difference of two terms

$$= 25-121i^2 = 25-121(-1) = 25+121 = 146$$

27. $-5i(3-i)^2 = -5i\left[3^2-2(3)(i)+i^2\right] = -5i\left[9-6i+(-1)\right]$

$$= -5i(8-6i) = -40i+30i^2 = -40i+30(-1) = -40i+(-30) = -30-40i$$

29. $\frac{12+i}{2+5i}=\frac{(12+i)(2-5i)}{(2+5i)(2-5i)}$

$=\frac{24-60i+2i-5i^2}{2^2-(5i)^2}=\frac{24-58i-5(-1)}{4-25i^2}=\frac{24-58i+5}{4-25(-1)}=\frac{29-58i}{4+25}=\frac{29-58i}{29}=\frac{29}{29}-\frac{58}{29}i=1-2i$

31. $i^7=i^4\cdot i^3=1\cdot(-i)=-i$

33. $i^{601}=i^{600}\cdot i=\left(i^4\right)^{150}\cdot i=1^{150}\cdot i=i$

35. $i^{-23}=i^{-24}\cdot i=\left(i^4\right)^{-8}\cdot i=1^{-8}\cdot i=i$

37. $(x+7)^2=5$

$x+7=\pm\sqrt{5}$

$x=-7\pm\sqrt{5}$

Solution set: $\{-7\pm\sqrt{5}\}$

39. $2x^2+x=15\Rightarrow 2x^2+x-15=0$

$(x+3)(2x-5)=0$

$x+3=0$ or $2x-5=0$

$x=-3$ or $x=\frac{5}{2}$

Solution set: $\left\{-3,\frac{5}{2}\right\}$

41. $-2x^2+11x+21=0$

$0=2x^2-11x-21$

$0=(2x+3)(x-7)$

$2x+3=0$ or $x-7=0$

$x=-\frac{3}{2}$ or $x=7$

Solution set: $\left\{-\frac{3}{2},7\right\}$

43. $(2x+1)(x-4)=x\Rightarrow 2x^2-8x+x-4=x\Rightarrow 2x^2-7x-4=x\Rightarrow 2x^2-8x-4=0\Rightarrow x^2-4x-2=0$

Solve by completing the square.

$x^2-4x-2=0$

$x^2-4x+4=2+4$

Note: $\left[\frac{1}{2}\cdot(-4)\right]^2=(-2)^2=2$

$(x-2)^2=6$

$x-2=\pm\sqrt{6}$

$x=2\pm\sqrt{6}$

Solution set: $\left\{2\pm\sqrt{6}\right\}$

Solve by the quadratic formula.
Let $a=1$, $b=-4$, and $c=-2$.

$x=\frac{-b\pm\sqrt{b^2-4ac}}{2a}$

$=\frac{-(-4)\pm\sqrt{(-4)^2-4(1)(-2)}}{2(1)}$

$=\frac{4\pm\sqrt{16+8}}{2}=\frac{4\pm\sqrt{24}}{2}$

$=\frac{4\pm 2\sqrt{6}}{2}=2\pm\sqrt{6}$

45. $x^2-\sqrt{5}x-1=0$

Using the quadratic formula would be the most direct approach.
$a=1, b=-\sqrt{5}$, and $c=-1$.

$x=\frac{-b\pm\sqrt{b^2-4ac}}{2a}=\frac{-(-\sqrt{5})\pm\sqrt{(-\sqrt{5})^2-4\cdot 1\cdot(-1)}}{2\cdot 1}=\frac{\sqrt{5}\pm\sqrt{5+4}}{2}=\frac{\sqrt{5}\pm\sqrt{9}}{2}=\frac{\sqrt{5}\pm 3}{2}$

Solution set: $\left\{\frac{\sqrt{5}\pm 3}{2}\right\}$

47. D $(7x+4)^2 = 11$

This equation has two real, distinct solutions since the positive number 11 has a positive square root and a negative square root.

49. A $(3x-4)^2 = -4$

This equation has two imaginary solutions since the negative number – 4 has two imaginary square roots.

51. $6x^2 - 2x = 3 \Rightarrow 6x^2 - 2x - 3 = 0$

$a = 6$, $b = -2$, and $c = -3$

$b^2 - 4ac = (-2)^2 - 4(6)(-3) = 4 + 72 = 76$

The equation has two distinct irrational solutions since the discriminant is positive but not a perfect square.

53. $-8x^2 - 10x = 7 \Rightarrow 0 = 8x^2 + 10x + 7$

$a = 8$, $b = 10$, and $c = 7$

$b^2 - 4ac = 10^2 - 4(8)(7) = 100 - 224 = -124$

The equation has two distinct nonreal complex solutions since the discriminant is negative.

55. $x(9x-6) = -1 \Rightarrow 9x^2 - 6x = -1 \Rightarrow 9x^2 - 6x + 1 = 0$

$a = 9$, $b = -6$, and $c = 1$

$b^2 - 4ac = (-6)^2 - 4(9)(1) = 36 - 36 = 0$

The equation has one rational solution (a double solution) since the discriminant is equal to zero.

57. The projectile will be 750 ft above the ground whenever $220t - 16t^2 = 750$.
Solve this equation for t.

$$220t - 16t^2 = 750 \Rightarrow 0 = 16t^2 - 220t + 750 \Rightarrow 0 = 8t^2 - 110t + 375 \Rightarrow 0 = (4t-25)(2t-15)$$

$$4t - 25 = 0 \quad \text{or} \quad 2t - 15 = 0$$

$$t = \tfrac{25}{4} = 6.25 \quad \text{or} \quad t = \tfrac{15}{2} = 7.5$$

The projectile will be 750 ft high at 6.25 sec and at 7.5 sec.

59. Let x = width of border.
Apply the formula $A = LW$ to both the outside and inside rectangles.
Inside area= Outside area – Border area

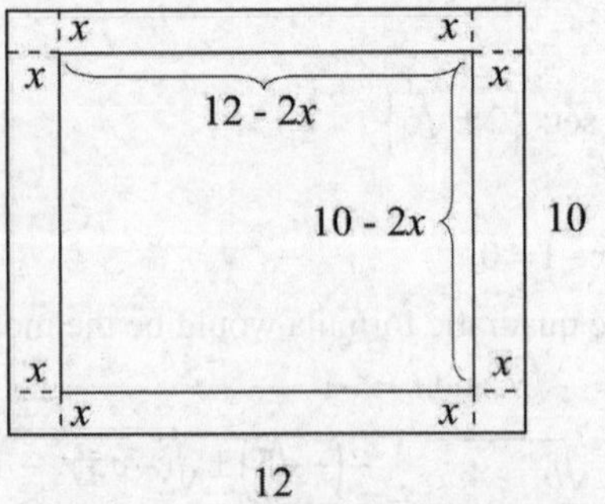

$(12-2x)(10-2x) = 12 \cdot 10 - 21$

$120 - 24x - 20x + 4x^2 = 120 - 21$

$120 - 44x + 4x^2 = 99$

$4x^2 - 44x + 120 = 99$

$4x^2 - 44x + 21 = 0$

$(2x-21)(2x-1) = 0$

$2x = 21 \quad \text{or} \quad 2x - 1 = 0$

$x = \tfrac{21}{2} = 10\tfrac{1}{2} \quad \text{or} \quad x = \tfrac{1}{2}$

The border width cannot be $10\tfrac{1}{2}$ since this exceeds the width of the outside rectangle, so reject this solution. The width of the border is $\tfrac{1}{2}$ ft.

61. In 1980, $x = 10$.

$$y = -6.77x^2 + 445.34x + 11{,}279.82$$
$$y = -6.77 \cdot 10^2 + 445.34 \cdot 10 + 11{,}279.82$$
$$y = -6.77 \cdot 100 + 4453.4 + 11{,}279.82$$
$$y = -677 + 4453.4 + 11{,}279.82$$
$$y = 15{,}056.22$$

Approximately 15,056 airports

63. $4x^4 + 3x^2 - 1 = 0$

Let $u = x^2$; then $u^2 = x^4$.

With this substitution, the equation becomes $4u^2 + 3u - 1 = 0$.

Solve this equation by factoring.

$$(u+1)(4u-1) = 0$$
$$u+1 = 0 \quad \text{or} \quad 4u - 1 = 0$$
$$u = -1 \quad \text{or} \quad u = \tfrac{1}{4}$$

To find x, replace u with x^2.

$$x^2 = -1 \quad \text{or} \quad x^2 = \tfrac{1}{4}$$
$$x = \pm\sqrt{-1} \quad \text{or} \quad x = \pm\sqrt{\tfrac{1}{4}}$$
$$x = \pm i \quad \text{or} \quad x = \pm\tfrac{1}{2}$$

Solution set: $\left\{\pm i, \pm\frac{1}{2}\right\}$

65. $\dfrac{2}{x} - \dfrac{4}{3x} = 8 + \dfrac{3}{x}$

$$3x\left(\frac{2}{x} - \frac{4}{3x}\right) = 3x\left(8 + \frac{3}{x}\right)$$
$$6 - 4 = 24x + 9$$
$$2 = 24x + 9$$
$$-7 = 24x$$
$$-\tfrac{7}{24} = x$$

Solution set: $\left\{-\frac{7}{24}\right\}$

67. $\dfrac{10}{4x-4} = \dfrac{1}{1-x}$ or $\dfrac{10}{4(x-1)} = \dfrac{1}{1-x}$ or $\dfrac{10}{4(x-1)} = \dfrac{(-1)\cdot 1}{(-1)(1-x)}$ or $\dfrac{10}{4(x-1)} = \dfrac{-1}{x-1}$

Multiply each term in the equation by the least common denominator, $4(x-1)$, assuming $x \neq 1$.

$$4(x-1)\left[\frac{10}{4(x-1)}\right] = 4(x-1)\left(\frac{-1}{x-1}\right) \Rightarrow 10 = -4 \Rightarrow 14 = 0$$

This is a false statement, the solution set is $\varnothing$.

or

$$\frac{10}{4x-4} = \frac{1}{1-x} \quad \text{or} \quad \frac{10}{4(x-1)} = \frac{1}{1-x}$$

Multiply each term in the equation by the least common denominator, $4(x-1)(1-x)$, assuming $x \neq 1$.

$$4(x-1)(1-x)\left[\frac{10}{4(x-1)}\right] = 4(x-1)(1-x)\left(\frac{1}{1-x}\right)$$
$$10(1-x) = 4(x-1) \Rightarrow 10 - 10x = 4x - 4 \Rightarrow 10 = 14x - 4 \Rightarrow 14 = 14x \Rightarrow 1 = x$$

Because of the restriction $x \neq 1$, the solution set is $\varnothing$.

69. $\frac{x}{x+2}+\frac{1}{x}+3=\frac{2}{x^2+2x}$ or $\frac{x}{x+2}+\frac{1}{x}+3=\frac{2}{x(x+2)}$

Multiply each term in the equation by the least common denominator, $x(x+2)$, assuming $x\neq 0,-2$.

$$x(x+2)\left[\frac{x}{x+2}+\frac{1}{x}+3\right]=x(x+2)\left(\frac{2}{x(x+2)}\right)\Rightarrow x^2+(x+2)+3x(x+2)=2$$

$$x^2+x+2+3x^2+6x=2\Rightarrow 4x^2+7x+2=2\Rightarrow 4x^2+7x=0\Rightarrow x(4x+7)=0$$

$$x=0 \quad\text{or}\quad 4x+7=0$$

$$x=0 \quad\text{or}\quad x=-\tfrac{7}{4}$$

Because of the restriction $x\neq 0$, the only valid solution is $-\frac{7}{4}$. The solution set is $\left\{-\frac{7}{4}\right\}$.

71. $(2x+3)^{2/3}+(2x+3)^{1/3}=6\Rightarrow(2x+3)^{2/3}+(2x+3)^{1/3}-6=0$

Let $u=(2x+3)^{1/3}$; then $u^2=[(2x+3)^{1/3}]^2=(2x+3)^{2/3}$.

With this substitution, the equation becomes $u^2+u-6=0$. Solve this equation by factoring.

$$(u+3)(u-2)=0$$

$$u+3=0 \quad\text{or}\quad u-2=0$$

$$u=-3 \quad\text{or}\quad u=2$$

To find x, replace u with $(2x+3)^{1/3}$.

$$(2x+3)^{1/3}=-3\Rightarrow\left[(2x+3)^{1/3}\right]^3=(-3)^3\Rightarrow 2x+3=-27\Rightarrow 2x=-30\Rightarrow x=-15$$

or

$$(2x+3)^{1/3}=2\Rightarrow\left[(2x+3)^{1/3}\right]^3=2^3\Rightarrow 2x+3=8\Rightarrow 2x=5\Rightarrow x=\tfrac{5}{2}$$

Check $x=-15$.

$$(2x+3)^{2/3}+(2x+3)^{1/3}=6$$
$$[2(-15)+3]^{2/3}+[2(-15)+3]^{1/3}=6\ ?$$
$$(-30+3)^{2/3}+(-30+3)^{1/3}=6$$
$$(-27)^{2/3}+(-27)^{1/3}=6$$
$$\left[(-27)^{1/3}\right]^2+(-3)=6$$
$$(-3)^2-3=6$$
$$9-3=6\Rightarrow 6=6$$

This is a true statement.

-15 is a solution.

Check $x=\frac{5}{2}$.

$$(2x+3)^{2/3}+(2x+3)^{1/3}=6$$
$$\left[2\left(\tfrac{5}{2}\right)+3\right]^{2/3}+\left[2\left(\tfrac{5}{2}\right)+3\right]^{1/3}=6\ ?$$
$$(5+3)^{2/3}+(5+3)^{1/3}=6$$
$$8^{2/3}+8^{1/3}=6$$
$$\left[8^{1/3}\right]^2+2=6$$
$$(2)^2+2=6$$
$$4+2=6\Rightarrow 6=6$$

This is a true statement.

$\frac{5}{2}$ is a solution.

Solution set: $\left\{-15,\frac{5}{2}\right\}$

73. $\sqrt{4x-2}=\sqrt{3x+1}\Rightarrow\left(\sqrt{4x-2}\right)^2=\left(\sqrt{3x+1}\right)^2\Rightarrow 4x-2=3x+1\Rightarrow x-2=1\Rightarrow x=3$

Check $x=3$.

$$\sqrt{4x-2}=\sqrt{3x+1}$$
$$\sqrt{4(3)-2}=\sqrt{3(3)+1}\ ?$$
$$\sqrt{12-2}=\sqrt{9+1}\Rightarrow\sqrt{10}=\sqrt{10}$$

This is a true statement. Thus, the solution set is $\{3\}$.

75. $\sqrt{x+2}=2+x$

$\left(\sqrt{x+2}\right)^2=(2+x)^2 \Rightarrow x+2=4+4x+x^2 \Rightarrow 0=x^2+3x+2 \Rightarrow 0=(x+2)(x+1)$

$x+2=0$ or $x+1=0$

$x=-2$ or $x=-1$

Check $x=-2$.

$\sqrt{x+2}=2+x$

$\sqrt{-2+2}=2+(-2)$?

$\sqrt{0}=0$

$0=0$

This is a true statement.

-2 is a solution.

Check $x=-1$.

$\sqrt{x+2}=2+x$

$\sqrt{-1+2}=2+(-1)$?

$\sqrt{1}=1$

$1=1$

This is a true statement.

-1 is a solution.

Solution set: $\{-2, -1\}$

77. $\sqrt{x+3}-\sqrt{3x+10}=1 \Rightarrow \sqrt{x+3}=1+\sqrt{3x+10} \Rightarrow \left(\sqrt{x+3}\right)^2=\left(1+\sqrt{3x+10}\right)^2$

$x+3=1+2\sqrt{3x+10}+(3x+10) \Rightarrow x+3=3x+11+2\sqrt{3x+10}$

$-2x-8=2\sqrt{3x+10} \Rightarrow x+4=-\sqrt{3x+10} \Rightarrow (x+4)^2=\left(-\sqrt{3x+10}\right)^2$

$x^2+8x+16=3x+10 \Rightarrow x^2+5x+6=0 \Rightarrow (x+2)(x+3)=0$

$x+3=0$ or $x+2=0$

$x=-3$ or $x=-2$

Check $x=-3$.

$\sqrt{x+3}-\sqrt{3x+10}=1$

$\sqrt{-3+3}-\sqrt{3(-3)+10}=1$?

$\sqrt{0}-\sqrt{-9+10}=1$

$0-\sqrt{1}=1$

$0-1=1$

$-1=1$

This is a false statement.

-3 is not a solution.

Check $x=-2$.

$\sqrt{x+3}-\sqrt{3x+10}=1$

$\sqrt{-2+3}-\sqrt{3(-2)+10}=1$?

$\sqrt{1}-\sqrt{-6+10}=1$

$1-\sqrt{4}=1$

$1-2=1$

$-1=1$

This is a false statement.

-2 is not a solution.

Since neither of the proposed solutions satisfies the original equation, the equation has no solution.
Solution set: $\varnothing$

79. $\sqrt{x^2+3x}-2=0$

$$\sqrt{x^2+3x}=2 \Rightarrow \left(\sqrt{x^2+3x}\right)^2=2^2 \Rightarrow x^2+3x=4 \Rightarrow x^2+3x-4=0 \Rightarrow (x-1)(x+4)=0$$

$$x-1=0 \quad \text{or} \quad x+4=0$$
$$x=1 \quad \text{or} \quad x=-4$$

Check $x=-4$.

$$\sqrt{x^2+3x}-2=0$$
$$\sqrt{(-4)^2+3(-4)}-2=0\ ?$$
$$\sqrt{16+(-12)}-2=0$$
$$\sqrt{4}-2=0$$
$$2-2=0 \Rightarrow 0=0$$

This is a true statement.
-4 is a solution.
Solution set: $\{-4,1\}$

Check $x=1$.

$$\sqrt{x^2+3x}-2=0$$
$$\sqrt{1^2+3(1)}-2=0\ ?$$
$$\sqrt{1+3}-2=0$$
$$\sqrt{4}-2=0$$
$$2-2=0 \Rightarrow 0=0$$

This is a true statement.
1 is a solution.

81. $\sqrt[3]{6x+2}-\sqrt[3]{4x}=0$

$$\sqrt[3]{6x+2}=\sqrt[3]{4x}$$
$$\left(\sqrt[3]{6x+2}\right)^3=\left(\sqrt[3]{4x}\right)^3$$
$$6x+2=4x$$
$$2=-2x$$
$$-1=x$$

Check $x=-1$.

$$\sqrt[3]{6x+2}-\sqrt[3]{4x}=0$$
$$\sqrt[3]{6(-1)+2}-\sqrt[3]{4(-1)}=0\ ?$$
$$\sqrt[3]{-6+2}-\sqrt[3]{-4}=0$$
$$\sqrt[3]{-4}-\left(-\sqrt[3]{4}\right)=0$$
$$-\sqrt[3]{4}+\sqrt[3]{4}=0 \Rightarrow 0=0$$

This is a true statement.
Solution set: $\{-1\}$

83. $-9x<4x+7$

$$-13x<7$$
$$x>-\frac{7}{13}$$

Solution set: $\left(-\frac{7}{13},\infty\right)$

85. $-5x-4\geq 3(2x-5)$

$$-5x-4\geq 6x-15$$
$$-11x-4\geq -15$$
$$-11x\geq -11$$
$$x\leq 1$$

Solution set: $(-\infty,1]$

87. $5\leq 2x-3\leq 7$

$$8\leq 2x\leq 10$$
$$4\leq x\leq 5$$

Solution set: $[4, 5]$

89. $x^2+3x-4\leq 0$

Step 1: Find the values of x that satisfy $x^2+3x-4=0$.

$$x^2+3x-4=0 \Rightarrow (x+4)(x-1)=0$$
$$x+4=0 \quad \text{or} \quad x-1=0$$
$$x=-4 \quad \text{or} \quad x=1$$

Step 2: The two numbers divide a number line into three regions.

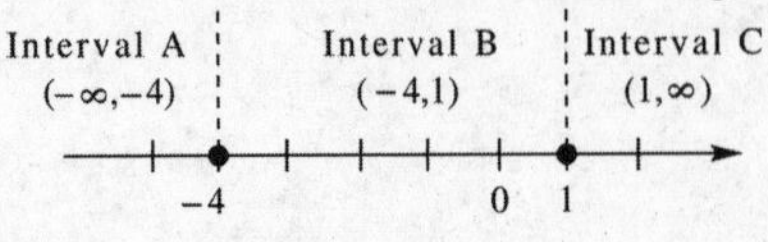

Continued on next page

89. (continued)

Step 3: Choose a test value to see if it satisfies the inequality, $x^2+3x-4\le 0$.

Interval	Test Value	Is $x^2+3x-4\le 0$ True or False?
A: $(-\infty,-4)$	-5	$(-5)^2+3(-5)-4\le 0$? $6\le 0$ False
B: $(-4,1)$	0	$0^2+3(0)-4\le 0$? $-4\le 0$ True
C: $(1,\infty)$	2	$2^2+3(2)-4\le 0$? $6\le 0$ False

Solution set: $[-4,1]$

91. $6x^2-11x-10<0$

Step 1: Find the values of x that satisfy $6x^2-11x-10=0$.

$$6x^2-11x-10=0$$
$$(3x+2)(2x-5)=0$$
$$3x+2=0 \quad \text{or} \quad 2x-5=0$$
$$x=-\tfrac{2}{3} \quad \text{or} \quad x=\tfrac{5}{2}$$

Step 2: The two numbers divide a number line into three regions.

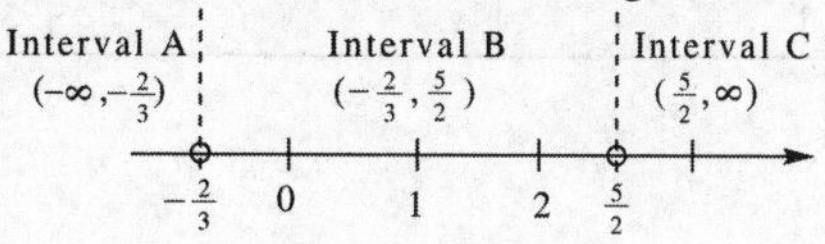

Step 3: Choose a test value to see if it satisfies the inequality, $6x^2-11x-10<0$.

Interval	Test Value	Is $6x^2-11x-10<0$ True or False?
A: $\left(-\infty,-\frac{2}{3}\right)$	-1	$6(-1)^2-11(-1)-10<0$? $7<0$ False
B: $\left(-\frac{2}{3},\frac{5}{2}\right)$	0	$6\cdot 0^2-11\cdot 0-10<0$? $-10<0$ True
C: $\left(\frac{5}{2},\infty\right)$	3	$6\cdot 3^2-11\cdot 3-10<0$? $11<0$ False

Solution set: $\left(-\frac{2}{3},\frac{5}{2}\right)$

93. $x^3 - 16x \le 0$

Step 1: Solve $x^3 - 16x = 0$.

$$x^3 - 16x = 0 \Rightarrow x(x^2 - 16) = 0 \Rightarrow x(x+4)(x-4) = 0$$

Set each factor to zero and solve.

$$x = 0 \quad \text{or} \quad x + 4 = 0 \quad \text{or} \quad x - 4 = 0$$
$$x = 0 \quad \text{or} \quad x = -4 \quad \text{or} \quad x = 4$$

Step 2: The values –4, 0, and, 4 divide the number line into four intervals.

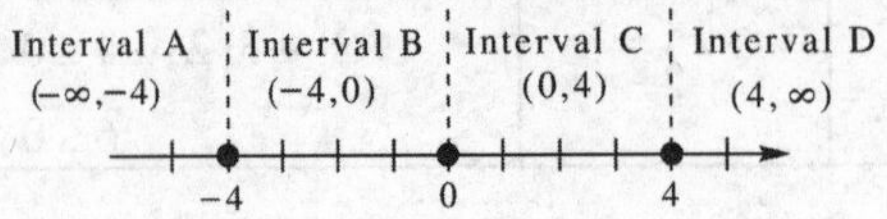

Step 3: Choose a test value to see if it satisfies the inequality, $x^3 - 16x \le 0$.

Interval	Test Value	Is $x^3 - 16x \le 0$ True or False?
A: $(-\infty, -4)$	-5	$(-5)^3 - 16(-5) \le 0$? $-45 \le 0$ True
B: $(-4, 0)$	-1	$(-1)^3 - 16(-1) \le 0$? $15 \le 0$ False
C: $(0, 4)$	1	$1^3 - 16 \cdot 1 \le 0$? $-15 \le 0$ True
D: $(4, \infty)$	5	$5^3 - 16 \cdot 5 \le 0$? $45 \le 0$ False

Solution set: $(-\infty, -4] \cup [0, 4]$

95. $\dfrac{3x+6}{x-5} > 0$

Since one side of the inequality is already 0, we start with Step 2.

Step 2: Determine the values that will cause either the numerator or denominator to equal 0.

$$3x + 6 = 0 \quad \text{or} \quad x - 5 = 0$$
$$x = -2 \quad \text{or} \quad x = 5$$

The values –2 and 5 to divide the number line into three regions.

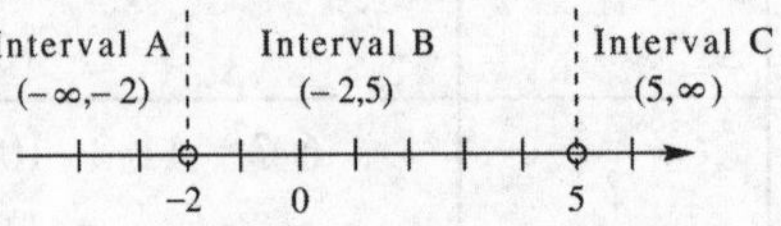

Step 3: Choose a test value to see if it satisfies the inequality, $\dfrac{3x+6}{x-5} > 0$.

Interval	Test Value	Is $\frac{3x+6}{x-5} > 0$ True or False?
A: $(-\infty, -2)$	-3	$\frac{3(-3)+6}{-3-5} > 0$? $\frac{3}{8} > 0$ True
B: $(-2, 5)$	0	$\frac{3(0)+6}{0-5} > 0$? $-\frac{6}{5} > 0$ False
C: $(5, \infty)$	6	$\frac{3(6)+6}{6-5} > 0$? $24 > 0$ True

Solution set: $(-\infty, -2) \cup (5, \infty)$

97. $\dfrac{3x-2}{x}>4$

Step 1: Rewrite the inequality so that 0 is on one side and there is a single fraction on the other side.

$$\frac{3x-2}{x}-4>0\Rightarrow\frac{3x-2}{x}-\frac{4x}{x}>0\Rightarrow\frac{3x-2-4x}{x}>0\Rightarrow\frac{-x-2}{x}>0$$

Step 2: Determine the values that will cause either the numerator or denominator to equal 0.

$$-x-2=0 \quad \text{or} \quad x=0$$
$$x=-2 \quad \text{or} \quad x=0$$

The values −2 and 0 divide the number line into three regions.

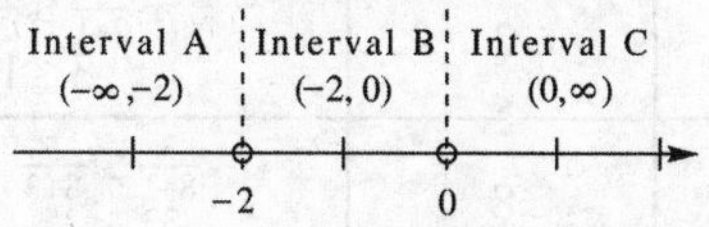

Step 3: Choose a test value to see if it satisfies the inequality, $\dfrac{3x-2}{x}>4.$

Interval	Test Value	Is $\frac{3x-2}{x}>4$ True or False?
A: $(-\infty,-2)$	−3	$\frac{3(-3)-2}{-3}>4$? $\frac{11}{3}>4$ False
B: $(-2,0)$	−1	$\frac{3(-1)-2}{-1}>4$? $5>4$ True
C: $(0,\infty)$	1	$\frac{3\cdot1-2}{1}>4$? $1>4$ False

Solution set: (−2, 0)

99. $\dfrac{3}{x-1}\le\dfrac{5}{x+3}$

Step 1: Rewrite the inequality so that 0 is on one side and there is a single fraction on the other side.

$$\frac{3}{x-1}-\frac{5}{x+3}\le0\Rightarrow\frac{3(x+3)}{(x-1)(x+3)}-\frac{5(x-1)}{(x+3)(x-1)}\le0$$

$$\frac{3(x+3)-5(x-1)}{(x-1)(x+3)}\le0\Rightarrow\frac{3x+9-5x+5}{(x-1)(x+3)}\le0\Rightarrow\frac{-2x+14}{(x-1)(x+3)}\le0$$

Step 2: Determine the values that will cause either the numerator or denominator to equal 0.

$$-2x+14=0 \quad \text{or} \quad x-1=0 \quad \text{or} \quad x+3=0$$
$$x=7 \quad \text{or} \quad x=1 \quad \text{or} \quad x=-3$$

The values −3, 1 and 7 divide the number line into four regions. Use an open circle on −3 and 1 because they make the denominator equal 0.

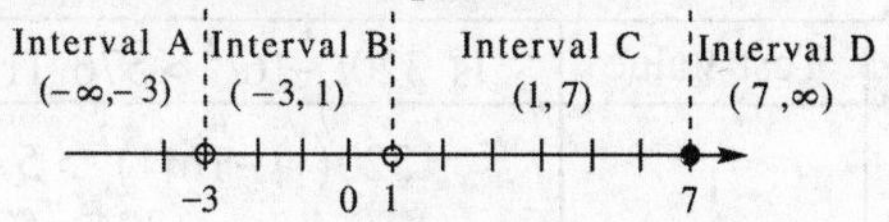

Continued on next page

99. (continued)

Step 3: Choose a test value to see if it satisfies the inequality, $\frac{3}{x-1} \le \frac{5}{x+3}$.

Interval	Test Value	Is $\frac{3}{x-1} \le \frac{5}{x+3}$ True or False?
A: $(-\infty,-3)$	-4	$\frac{3}{-4-1} \le \frac{5}{-4+3}$? $-\frac{3}{5} \le -5$ False
B: $(-3,1)$	0	$\frac{3}{0-1} \le \frac{5}{0+3}$? $-3 \le \frac{5}{3}$ True
C: $(1,7)$	2	$\frac{3}{2-1} \le \frac{5}{2+3}$? $3 \le 1$ False
D: $(7,\infty)$	8	$\frac{3}{8-1} \le \frac{5}{8+3}$? or $\frac{3}{7} \le \frac{5}{11}$ $\frac{33}{77} \le \frac{35}{77}$ True

Intervals B and D satisfy the inequality. The endpoints -3 and 1 are not included because they make the denominator 0.

Solution set: $(-3,1)\cup[7,\infty)$

101. **(a)** Answers will vary.

(b) Let x = the maximum initial concentration of ozone.

$x - .43x \le 50 \Rightarrow .57x \le 50 \Rightarrow x \le 87.7$ (approximately)

The filter will reduce ozone concentrations that don't exceed 87.7 ppb.

103. $s = 320 - 16t^2$

(a) When $s = 0$, the projectile will be at ground level.

$0 = 320t - 16t^2 \Rightarrow 16t^2 - 320t = 0 \Rightarrow t^2 - 20t = 0 \Rightarrow t(t-20) = 0 \Rightarrow t = 0$ or $t = 20$

The projectile will return to the ground after 20 sec.

(b) Solve $s > 576$ for t.

$320t - 16t^2 > 576 \Rightarrow 0 > 16t^2 - 320t + 576 \Rightarrow 0 > t^2 - 20t + 36$

Step 1: Find the values of x that satisfy $t^2 - 20t + 36 = 0$.

$$t^2 - 20t + 36 = 0 \Rightarrow (t-2)(t-18) = 0$$
$$t - 2 = 0 \quad \text{or} \quad t - 18 = 0$$
$$t = 2 \quad \text{or} \quad t = 18$$

Step 2: The two numbers divide a number line into three regions.

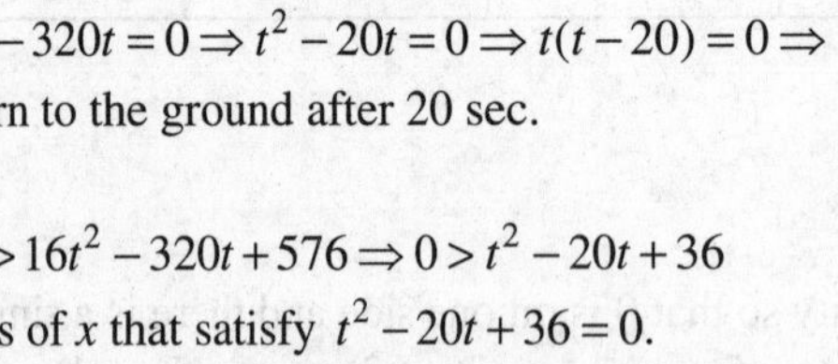

Step 3: Choose a test value to see if it satisfies the inequality, $320t - 16t^2 > 576$.

Interval	Test Value	Is $320t - 16t^2 > 576$ True or False?
A: $(0,2)$	1	$320(1) - 16(1)^2 > 576$? $304 > 576$ False
B: $(2,18)$	3	$320(3) - 16(3)^2 > 576$? $816 > 576$ True
C: $(18,\infty)$	20	$320(20) - 16(20)^2 > 576$? $0 > 576$ False

The projectile will be more than 576 ft above the ground between 2 and 18 sec.

105. Answers will vary.
3 cannot be in the solution set because when 3 is substituted into $\frac{2x+5}{x-3}$, division by zero occurs.

107. "at least 65" means that the number is 65 or greater; $W \geq 65$.

109. "as many as 100,000" means 100,000 or less; $a \leq 100{,}000$

111. $|x+4| = 7$

$x+4=7$ or $x+4=-7$

$x=3$ or $x=-11$

Solution set: $\{-11, 3\}$

113. $\left|\dfrac{7}{2-3x}\right| = 9$

$$\frac{7}{2-3x} = 9 \Rightarrow 7 = 9(2-3x) \Rightarrow 7 = 18-27x \Rightarrow -11 = -27x \Rightarrow \tfrac{-11}{-27} = x \Rightarrow x = \tfrac{11}{27}$$

or

$$\frac{7}{2-3x} = -9 \Rightarrow 7 = -9(2-3x) \Rightarrow 7 = -18+27x \Rightarrow 25 = 27x \Rightarrow \tfrac{25}{27} = x \Rightarrow x = \tfrac{25}{27}$$

Solution set: $\left\{\frac{11}{27}, \frac{25}{27}\right\}$

115. $|5x-1| = |2x+3|$

$5x-1 = 2x+3$ or $5x-1 = -(2x+3)$

$3x-1=3$ $\quad$ $5x-1=-2x-3$

$3x=4$ $\quad$ $7x-1=-3$

$7x=-2$

$x=\frac{4}{3}$ or $x=-\frac{2}{7}$

Solution set: $\left\{-\frac{2}{7}, \frac{4}{3}\right\}$

117. $|2z+9| \leq 3$

$-3 \leq 2z+9 \leq 3$

$-12 \leq 2z \leq -6$

$-6 \leq z \leq -3$

Solution set: $[-6,-3]$

119. $|7x-3| > 4$

$7x-3<-4$ or $7x-3>4$

$7x<-1$ $\quad$ $7x>7$

$x<-\frac{1}{7}$ or $x>1$

Solution set: $\left(-\infty,-\frac{1}{7}\right)\cup(1,\infty)$

121. $|3x+7|-5=0 \Rightarrow |3x+7|=5$

$3x+7=5$ or $3x+7=-5$

$3x=-2$ $\quad$ $3x=-12$

$x=-\frac{2}{3}$ or $x=-4$

Solution set: $\left\{-4, -\frac{2}{3}\right\}$

123. Since the absolute value of a number is always nonnegative, the inequality $|4x-12| \geq -2$ is always true. The solution set is $(-\infty,\infty)$.

125. Since the absolute value of a number is always nonnegative, $\left|x^2+4x\right|<0$ is never true, so $\left|x^2+4x\right| \leq 0$ is only true when $\left|x^2+4x\right| = 0$.

$$\left|x^2+4x\right| = 0 \Rightarrow x^2+4x=0 \Rightarrow x(x+4)=0$$

$x=0$ or $x+4=0$

$x-0$ or $x=-4$

Solution set: $\{-4,0\}$

127. "k is 12 units from 3 on the number line" means that the distance between k and 3 is 12 units, or $|k-3|=12$ (or $|3-k|=12$).

129. "t is no less than .01 unit from 4" means that t is .01 unit or more from 4. Thus, the distance between t and 4 is greater than or equal to .01, or $|t-4|\geq .01$ (or $|4-t|\geq .01$).

Chapter 1: Test

1.
$$\begin{aligned}3(x-4)-5(x+1)&=2-(x+24)\\3x-12-5x-10&=2-x-24\\-2x-22&=-x-22\\-22&=x-22\\0&=x\end{aligned}$$

Solution set: $\{0\}$

2.
$$\begin{aligned}\frac{2}{3}x+\frac{1}{2}(x-4)&=x-4\\6\left[\frac{2}{3}x+\frac{1}{2}(x-4)\right]&=6(x-4)\\4x+3(x-4)&=6x-24\\4x+3x-12&=6x-24\\7x-12&=6x-24\\x-12&=-24\\x&=-12\end{aligned}$$

Solution set: $\{-12\}$

3.
$$\begin{aligned}6x^2-11x&=7\\6x^2-11x-7&=0\\(2x+1)(3x-7)&=0\end{aligned}$$
$$2x+1=0 \quad\text{or}\quad 3x-7=0$$
$$x=-\tfrac{1}{2} \quad\text{or}\quad x=\tfrac{7}{3}$$

Solution set: $\left\{-\tfrac{1}{2},\tfrac{7}{3}\right\}$

4.
$$\begin{aligned}(3x+1)^2&=8\\3x+1&=\pm\sqrt{8}=\pm2\sqrt{2}\\3x&=-1\pm2\sqrt{2}\\x&=\frac{-1\pm2\sqrt{2}}{3}\end{aligned}$$

Solution set: $\left\{\frac{-1\pm2\sqrt{2}}{3}\right\}$

5. $3x^2+2x+2=0$

Solve by completing the square.

$$\begin{aligned}3x^2+2x+2&=0\\x^2+\tfrac{2}{3}x+\tfrac{2}{3}&=0\\x^2+\tfrac{2}{3}x+\tfrac{1}{9}&=-\tfrac{2}{3}+\tfrac{1}{9}\end{aligned}$$

$$\text{Note: }\left[\tfrac{1}{2}\cdot\left(-\tfrac{2}{3}\right)\right]^2=\left(-\tfrac{1}{3}\right)^2=\tfrac{1}{9}$$

$$\begin{aligned}\left(x+\tfrac{1}{3}\right)^2&=-\tfrac{5}{9}\\x+\tfrac{1}{3}&=\pm\sqrt{-\tfrac{5}{9}}\\x+\tfrac{1}{3}&=\pm\tfrac{\sqrt{5}}{3}i\\x&=-\tfrac{1}{3}\pm\tfrac{\sqrt{5}}{3}i\end{aligned}$$

Solution set: $\left\{-\tfrac{1}{3}\pm\tfrac{\sqrt{5}}{3}i\right\}$

Solve by the quadratic formula.

Let $a=3$, $b=2$, and $c=2$.

$$\begin{aligned}x&=\frac{-b\pm\sqrt{b^2-4ac}}{2a}\\&=\frac{-2\pm\sqrt{2^2-4(3)(2)}}{2(3)}\\&=\frac{-2\pm\sqrt{4-24}}{6}\\&=\frac{-2\pm\sqrt{-20}}{6}\\&=\frac{-2\pm2i\sqrt{5}}{6}\\&=-\tfrac{2}{6}\pm\tfrac{2\sqrt{5}}{6}i=-\tfrac{1}{3}\pm\tfrac{\sqrt{5}}{3}i\end{aligned}$$

6. $\frac{12}{x^2-9}+\frac{3}{x+3}=\frac{2}{x-3}$ or $\frac{12}{(x+3)(x-3)}+\frac{3}{x+3}=\frac{2}{x-3}$

Multiply each term in the equation by the least common denominator, $(x+3)(x-3)$ assuming $x \neq -3, 3$.

$$(x+3)(x-3)\left[\frac{12}{(x+3)(x-3)}+\frac{3}{x+3}\right]=(x+3)(x-3)\left(\frac{2}{x-3}\right)$$
$$12+3(x-3)=2(x+3)$$
$$12+3x-9=2x+6$$
$$3x+3=2x+6$$
$$x+3=6 \Rightarrow x=3$$

The only possible solution is 3. However, the variable is restricted to real numbers except -3 and 3. Therefore, the solution set is: $\varnothing$.

7. $\frac{4x}{x-2}+\frac{3}{x}=\frac{-6}{x^2-2x}$ or $\frac{4x}{x-2}+\frac{3}{x}=\frac{-6}{x(x-2)}$

Multiply each term in the equation by the least common denominator, $x(x-2)$, assuming $x \neq 0, 2$.

$$x(x-2)\left[\frac{4x}{x-2}+\frac{3}{x}\right]=x(x-2)\left(\frac{-6}{x(x-2)}\right)$$
$$4x^2+3(x-2)=-6 \Rightarrow 4x^2+3x-6=-6$$
$$4x^2+3x=0 \Rightarrow x(4x+3)=0$$
$$x=0 \quad \text{or} \quad 4x+3=0$$
$$x=0 \quad \text{or} \quad x=-\tfrac{3}{4}$$

Because of the restriction $x \neq 0$, the only valid solution is $-\frac{3}{4}$. The solution set is $\left\{-\frac{3}{4}\right\}$.

8. $\sqrt{3x+4}+4=2x \Rightarrow \sqrt{3x+4}=2x-4 \Rightarrow \left(\sqrt{3x+4}\right)^2=(2x-4)^2$

$$3x+4=4x^2-16x+16 \Rightarrow 0=4x^2-19x+12 \Rightarrow 0=(4x-3)(x-4)$$
$$4x-3=0 \quad \text{or} \quad x-4=0$$
$$x=\tfrac{3}{4} \quad \text{or} \quad x=4$$

Check $x=\frac{3}{4}$.

$$\sqrt{3x+4}+4=2x$$
$$\sqrt{3\left(\tfrac{3}{4}\right)+4}+4=2\left(\tfrac{3}{4}\right)\ ?$$
$$\sqrt{\tfrac{9}{4}+4}+4=\tfrac{3}{2}$$
$$\sqrt{\tfrac{25}{4}}+4=\tfrac{3}{2}$$
$$\tfrac{5}{2}+4=\tfrac{3}{2}$$
$$\tfrac{13}{2}=\tfrac{3}{2}$$

This is a false statement.

$\frac{3}{4}$ is a not solution.

Check $x=4$.

$$\sqrt{3x+4}+4=2x$$
$$\sqrt{3(4)+4}+4=2(4)\ ?$$
$$\sqrt{12+4}+4=8$$
$$\sqrt{16}+4=8$$
$$4+4=8$$
$$8=8$$

This is a true statement.

4 is a solution.

Solution set: $\{4\}$

9. $\sqrt{-2x+3}+\sqrt{x+3}=3 \Rightarrow \sqrt{-2x+3}=3-\sqrt{x+3} \Rightarrow \left(\sqrt{-2x+3}\right)^2=\left(3-\sqrt{x+3}\right)^2$

$-2x+3=9-6\sqrt{x+3}+(x+3) \Rightarrow -2x+3=12+x-6\sqrt{x+3} \Rightarrow -3x-9=-6\sqrt{x+3}$

$x+3=2\sqrt{x+3} \Rightarrow (x+3)^2=\left(2\sqrt{x+3}\right)^2 \Rightarrow x^2+6x+9=4(x+3)$

$x^2+6x+9=4x+12 \Rightarrow x^2+2x-3=0 \Rightarrow (x+3)(x-1)=0$

$$x+3=0 \quad \text{or} \quad x-1=0$$
$$x=-3 \quad \text{or} \quad x=1$$

Check $x=-3$.

$$\sqrt{-2x+3}+\sqrt{x+3}=3$$
$$\sqrt{-2(-3)+3}+\sqrt{-3+3}=3\ ?$$
$$\sqrt{6+3}+\sqrt{0}=3$$
$$\sqrt{9}+0=3$$
$$3+0=3 \Rightarrow 3=3$$

This is a true statement.
-3 is a solution.

Check $x=1$.

$$\sqrt{-2x+3}+\sqrt{x+3}=3$$
$$\sqrt{-2(1)+3}+\sqrt{1+3}=3\ ?$$
$$\sqrt{-2+3}+\sqrt{4}=3$$
$$\sqrt{1}+2=3$$
$$1+2=3$$
$$3=3$$

This is a true statement.
1 is a solution.

Solution set: $\{-3,1\}$

10. $\sqrt[3]{3x-8}=\sqrt[3]{9x+4} \Rightarrow \left(\sqrt[3]{3x-8}\right)^3=\left(\sqrt[3]{9x+4}\right)^3 \Rightarrow 3x-8=9x+4 \Rightarrow -8=6x+4 \Rightarrow -12=6x \Rightarrow -2=x$

Check $x=-2$.

$$\sqrt[3]{3x-8}=\sqrt[3]{9x+4}$$
$$\sqrt[3]{3(-2)-8}=\sqrt[3]{9(-2)+4}\ ?$$
$$\sqrt[3]{-6-8}=\sqrt[3]{-18+4}$$
$$\sqrt[3]{-14}=\sqrt[3]{-14}$$
$$-\sqrt[3]{14}=-\sqrt[3]{14}$$

This is a true statement.
Solution set: $\{-2\}$

11. $x^4-17x^2+16=0$
Let $u=x^2$; then $u^2=x^4$.
With this substitution, the equation becomes $u^2-17u+16=0$.
Solve this equation by factoring.

$$(u-1)(u-16)=0$$
$$u-1=0 \quad \text{or} \quad u-16=0$$
$$u=1 \quad \text{or} \quad u=16$$

To find x, replace u with x^2.

$$x^2=1 \quad \text{or} \quad x^2=16$$
$$x=\pm\sqrt{1} \quad \text{or} \quad x=\pm\sqrt{16}$$
$$x=\pm1 \quad \text{or} \quad x=\pm4$$

Solution set: $\{\pm1,\pm4\}$

12. $(x+3)^{2/3}+(x+3)^{1/3}-6=0$

Let $u=(x+3)^{1/3}$; then $u^2=\left[(x+3)^{1/3}\right]^2=(x+3)^{2/3}$.

$$u^2+u-6=0 \Rightarrow (u+3)(u-2)=0$$
$$u+3=0 \quad \text{or} \quad u-2=0$$
$$u=-3 \quad \text{or} \quad u=2$$

To find *x*, replace *u* with $(x+3)^{1/3}$.

$$(x+3)^{1/3}=-3 \quad \text{or} \quad (x+3)^{1/3}=2$$
$$\left[(x+3)^{1/3}\right]^3=(-3)^3 \qquad \left[(x+3)^{1/3}\right]^3=2^3$$
$$x+3=-27 \qquad x+3=8$$
$$x=-30 \quad \text{or} \quad x=5$$

Check $x=-30$.

$$(x+3)^{2/3}+(x+3)^{1/3}-6=0$$
$$(-30+3)^{2/3}+(-30+3)^{1/3}-6=0\ ?$$
$$(-27)^{2/3}+(-27)^{1/3}-6=0$$
$$\left[(-27)^{1/3}\right]^2+(-3)-6=0$$
$$(-3)^2-3-6=0$$
$$9-3-6=0$$
$$0=0$$

This is a true statement.
-30 is a solution.

Check $x=5$.

$$(x+3)^{2/3}+(x+3)^{1/3}-6=0$$
$$(5+3)^{2/3}+(5+3)^{1/3}-6=0\ ?$$
$$8^{2/3}+8^{1/3}-6=0$$
$$\left[8^{1/3}\right]^2+2-6=0$$
$$2^2+2-6=0$$
$$4+2-6=0$$
$$0=0$$

This is a true statement.
5 is a solution.

Solution set: $\{-30,5\}$

13. $|4x+3|=7$

$$4x+3=7 \quad \text{or} \quad 4x+3=-7$$
$$4x=4 \qquad 4x=-10$$
$$x=1 \quad \text{or} \quad x=-\tfrac{10}{4}=-\tfrac{5}{2}$$

Solution set: $\left\{-\frac{5}{2},1\right\}$

14. $|2x+1|=|x-5|$

$$2x+1=x-5 \quad \text{or} \quad 2x+1=-(x-5)$$
$$x+1=-5 \qquad 2x+1=-x+5$$
$$3x+1=5$$
$$3x=4$$
$$x=-6 \quad \text{or} \quad x=\tfrac{4}{3}$$

Solution set: $\left\{-6,\frac{4}{3}\right\}$

15. $S=2HW+2LW+2LH$

$$S-2LH=2HW+2LW$$
$$S-2LH=W(2H+2L)$$
$$\frac{S-2LH}{2H+2L}=W$$
$$W=\frac{S-2LH}{2H+2L}$$

16. (a) $(7-3i)-(2+5i)=(7-2)+(-3-5)i=5-8i$

(b) $(4+3i)(-5+3i)=-20+12i-15i+9i^2=-20-3i+9(-1)=-20-3i-9=-29-3i$

(c) $(8+3i)^2=8^2+2(8)(3i)+(3i)^2=64+48i+9i^2=64+48i+9(-1)=64+48i-9=55+48i$

(d) $\dfrac{3+19i}{1+3i}=\dfrac{(3+19i)(1-3i)}{(1+3i)(1-3i)}=\dfrac{3-9i+19i-57i^2}{1-(3i)^2}$

$$=\frac{3+10i-57(-1)}{1-9i^2}=\frac{3+10i+57}{1-9(-1)}=\frac{60+10i}{1+9}=\frac{60+10i}{10}=6+i$$

17. (a) $i^{18}=i^{16}\cdot i^2=\left(i^4\right)^4\cdot(-1)=1^4\cdot(-1)=-1$

(b) $i^{-27}=i^{-28}\cdot i=\left(i^4\right)^{-7}\cdot i=1^{-7}\cdot i=i$

(c) $\frac{1}{i^{15}}=i^{-15}=i^{-16}\cdot i=\left(i^4\right)^{-4}\cdot i=1^{-4}\cdot i=i$

18. (a) $1120\dfrac{\text{gal}}{\text{min}}\cdot 60\dfrac{\text{min}}{\text{hr}}\cdot 12\dfrac{\text{hr}}{\text{day}}=806{,}400\dfrac{\text{gal}}{\text{day}}$ minimum

The equation that will calculate the minimum amount of water pumped after x days would be $A=806{,}400x$.

(b) $A=806{,}400x$ when $x=30$ would be $A=806{,}400(30)=24{,}192{,}000$ gal.

(c) Since there would be $806{,}400\dfrac{\text{gal}}{\text{day}}$ minimum and each pool requires 20,000 gal, there would be a minimum of $\dfrac{806{,}400}{20{,}000}=40.32$ pools that could be filled each day. The equation that will calculate the minimum number of pools that could be filled after x days would be $P=40.32x$. Approximately 40 pools could be filled each day.

(d) Solve $P=40.32x$ where $P=1000$. $1000=40.32x\Rightarrow x=\frac{1000}{40.32}\approx 24.8$ days.

19. Let $w=$ width of rectangle.
Then $2w-10=$ length of rectangle.
Use the formula for the perimeter of a rectangle.

$$\begin{aligned}P&=2l+2w\\310&=2(2w-10)+2w\\310&=4w-20+2w\\310&=6w-20\\330&=6w\\55&=w\end{aligned}$$

The width is 55 m and the length is $2(55)-10=110-10=100$ m.

20. Let x = amount of cashews (in pounds).
Then $35 - x$ = amount of walnuts (in pounds).

	Cost per Pound	Amount of Nuts	
Cashews	7.00	x	$7.00x$
Walnuts	5.50	$35-x$	$5.50(35-x)$
Mixture	6.50	35	$35\cdot 6.50$

Solve the following equation.

$$7.00x+5.50(35-x)=35\cdot 6.50 \Rightarrow 7x+192.5-5.5x=227.5$$
$$1.5x+192.5=227.5 \Rightarrow 1.5x=35$$
$$x=\tfrac{35}{1.5}=\tfrac{350}{15}=\tfrac{70}{3}=23\tfrac{1}{3}$$

The fruit and nut stand owner should mix $23\frac{1}{3}$ lbs of cashews with $35-23\frac{1}{3}=11\frac{2}{3}$ lbs of walnuts.

21. Let x = time (in hours) the mother spent driving to meet plane.
Since Sheryl has been in the plane for 15 minutes, and 15 minutes is $\frac{1}{4}$ hr, Sheryl has been traveling by plane for $x+\frac{1}{4}$ hr.

	d	r	t
Sheryl by plane	420		$x+\frac{1}{4}$
Mother by car	20	40	x

The time driven by Sheryl's mother can be found by $20=40x \Rightarrow x=\frac{1}{2}$ hr. Sheryl, therefore, flew for $\frac{1}{2}+\frac{1}{4}=\frac{2}{4}+\frac{1}{4}=\frac{3}{4}$ hr. The rate of Sheryl's plane can be found by $r=\dfrac{d}{t}=\dfrac{420}{\frac{3}{4}}=420\cdot\frac{4}{3}=560$ kph.

22. $h=-16t^2+96t$

(a) Let h = 80 and solve for t.

$$80=-16t^2+96t \Rightarrow 16t^2-96t+80=0$$
$$t^2-6t+5=0 \Rightarrow (t-1)(t-5)=0$$
$$t-1=0 \quad \text{or} \quad t-5=0$$
$$t=1 \quad \text{or} \quad t=5$$

The projectile will reach a height of 80 ft at 1 sec and 5 sec.

(b) Let h = 0 and solve for t.

$$0=-16t^2+96t \Rightarrow 0=-16t(t-6)$$
$$t=0 \quad \text{or} \quad t-6=0$$
$$t=0 \quad \text{or} \quad t=6$$

The projectile will return to the ground at 6 sec.

23. The table shows each equation evaluated at the years 1975, 1994, and 2006. Equation B best models the data.

24. $-2(x-1)-10<2(x+2)$

$$-2x+2-10<2x+4$$
$$-2x-8<2x+4$$
$$-4x-8<4$$
$$-4x<12$$
$$x>-3$$

Solution set: $(-3,\infty)$

25. $-2\le\frac{1}{2}x+3\le 4$

$$2(-2)\le 2\left(\frac{1}{2}x+3\right)\le 2(4)$$
$$-4\le x+6\le 8$$
$$-10\le x\le 2$$

Solution set: $[-10, 2]$

26. $2x^2-x-3\ge 0$

Step 1: Find the values of x that satisfy $2x^2-x-3=0$.

$$2x^2-x-3=0$$
$$(x+1)(2x-3)=0$$
$$x+1=0 \quad\text{or}\quad 2x-3=0$$
$$x=-1 \quad\text{or}\quad x=\tfrac{3}{2}$$

Step 2: The two numbers divide a number line into three regions.

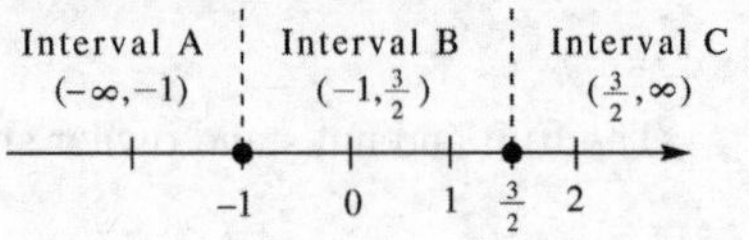

Step 3: Choose a test value to see if it satisfies the inequality, $2x^2-x-3\ge 0$.

Interval	Test Value	Is $2x^2-x-3\ge 0$ True or False?
A: $(-\infty,-1)$	-2	$2(-2)^2-(-2)-3\ge 0$? $7\ge 0$ True
B: $\left(-1,\frac{3}{2}\right)$	0	$2\cdot 0^2-0-3\ge 0$? $-3\ge 0$ False
C: $\left(\frac{3}{2},\infty\right)$	2	$2\cdot 2^2-2-3\ge 0$? $3\ge 0$ True

Solution set: $(-\infty,-1]\cup\left[\frac{3}{2},\infty\right)$

27. $\dfrac{x+1}{x-3}<5$

Step 1: Rewrite the inequality so that 0 is on one side and there is a single fraction on the other side.

$$\frac{x+1}{x-3}<5\Rightarrow\frac{x+1}{x-3}-5<0$$

$$\frac{x+1}{x-3}-\frac{5(x-3)}{x-3}<0\Rightarrow\frac{x+1-5(x-3)}{x-3}<0\Rightarrow\frac{x+1-5x+15}{x-3}<0\Rightarrow\frac{-4x+16}{x-3}<0$$

Step 2: Determine the values that will cause either the numerator or denominator to equal 0.

$$-4x+16=0 \quad\text{or}\quad x-3=0$$
$$x=4 \quad\text{or}\quad x=3$$

The values –2 and 2 to divide the number line into three regions.

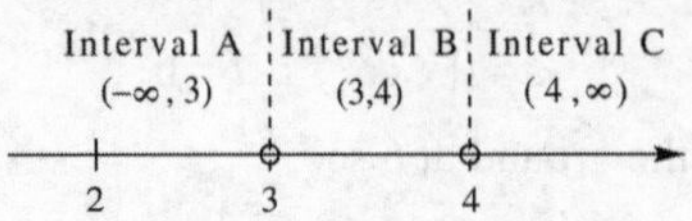

Continued on next page

27. (continued)

Step 3: Choose a test value to see if it satisfies the inequality, $\frac{x+1}{x-3} < 5$.

Interval	Test Value	Is $\frac{x+1}{x-3} < 5$ True or False?
A: $(-\infty, 3)$	0	$\frac{0+1}{0-3} < 5$? $-\frac{1}{3} < 5$ True
B: $(3, 4)$	3.5	$\frac{3.5+1}{3.5-3} < 5$? $9 < 5$ False
C: $(4, \infty)$	5	$\frac{5+1}{5-3} < 5$? $3 < 5$ True

Solution set: $(-\infty, 3) \cup (4, \infty)$

28. $|2x-5| < 9$

$-9 < 2x-5 < 9$

$-4 < 2x < 14$

$-2 < x < 7$

Solution set: $(-2, 7)$

29. $|2x+1| \geq 11$

$2x+1 \leq -11$ or $2x+1 \geq 11$

$2x \leq -12$ $\quad$ $2x \geq 10$

$x \leq -6$ or $x \geq 5$

Solution set: $(-\infty, -6] \cup [5, \infty)$

30. Any number less than zero will be negative. There is no number whose absolute value is a negative number. The solution set of $|3x+7| < 0$ is $\varnothing$.

Chapter 2
GRAPHS AND FUNCTIONS

Section 2.1: Graphs of Equations

Connections (page 192)

1. Answers will vary.

2. Answers will vary.
Latitude and longitude values pinpoint distances north or south of the equator and east or west of the prime meridian. Similarly on a Cartesian coordinate system, *x*- and *y*- coordinates give distances and directions from the *y*-axis and *x*-axis, respectively.

Exercises

1. true; The origin has coordinates $(0,0)$. So, the distance from $(0,0)$ to (a,b) is $d=\sqrt{(a-0)^2+(b-0)^2}=\sqrt{a^2+b^2}$.

3. false; The equation should be $x^2+y^2=4$ to satisfy these conditions.

5. any three of the following: $(2,-5),(-1,7),(3,-9),(5,-17),(6,-21)$

7. any three of the following: $(1993,31),(1995,35),(1997,37),(1999,35),(2001,28)$

9. $P(-5,-7)$, $Q(-13,1)$
   (a) $d(P,Q)=\sqrt{[-13-(-5)]^2+[1-(-7)]^2}=\sqrt{(-8)^2+8^2}=\sqrt{128}=8\sqrt{2}$
   (b) The midpoint *M* of the segment joining points *P* and *Q* has the following coordinates.
$$\left(\frac{-5+(-13)}{2},\frac{-7+1}{2}\right)=\left(\frac{-18}{2},\frac{-6}{2}\right)=(-9,-3)$$

11. $P(8,2)$, $Q(3,5)$
   (a) $d(P,Q)=\sqrt{(3-8)^2+(5-2)^2}=\sqrt{(-5)^2+3^2}=\sqrt{25+9}=\sqrt{34}$
   (b) The midpoint *M* of the segment joining points *P* and *Q* has coordinates $\left(\frac{8+3}{2},\frac{2+5}{2}\right)=\left(\frac{11}{2},\frac{7}{2}\right)$.

13. $P(-8,4)$, $Q(3,-5)$
   (a) $d(P,Q)=\sqrt{\left[3-(-8)\right]^2+(-5-4)^2}=\sqrt{11^2+(-9)^2}=\sqrt{121+81}=\sqrt{202}$
   (b) The midpoint *M* of the segment joining points *P* and *Q* has the following coordinates.
$$\left(\frac{-8+3}{2},\frac{4+(-5)}{2}\right)=\left(-\frac{5}{2},-\frac{1}{2}\right)$$

15. $P(3\sqrt{2},4\sqrt{5}),\ Q(\sqrt{2},-\sqrt{5})$

(a) $d(P,Q)=\sqrt{\left(\sqrt{2}-3\sqrt{2}\right)^2+\left(-\sqrt{5}-4\sqrt{5}\right)^2}=\sqrt{\left(-2\sqrt{2}\right)^2+\left(-5\sqrt{5}\right)^2}=\sqrt{8+125}=\sqrt{133}$

(b) The midpoint M of the segment joining points P and Q has the following coordinates .

$$\left(\frac{3\sqrt{2}+\sqrt{2}}{2},\frac{4\sqrt{5}+(-\sqrt{5})}{2}\right)=\left(\frac{4\sqrt{2}}{2},\frac{3\sqrt{5}}{2}\right)=\left(2\sqrt{2},\frac{3\sqrt{5}}{2}\right)$$

17. Label the points $A(-6,-4)$, $B(0,-2)$, and $C(-10,8)$. Use the distance formula to find the length of each side of the triangle.

$d(A,B)=\sqrt{[0-(-6)]^2+[-2-(-4)]^2}=\sqrt{6^2+2^2}=\sqrt{36+4}=\sqrt{40}$

$d(B,C)=\sqrt{(-10-0)^2+[8-(-2)]^2}=\sqrt{(-10)^2+10^2}=\sqrt{100+100}=\sqrt{200}$

$d(A,C)=\sqrt{[-10-(-6)]^2+[8-(-4)]^2}=\sqrt{(-4)^2+12^2}=\sqrt{16+144}=\sqrt{160}$

Since $\left(\sqrt{40}\right)^2+\left(\sqrt{160}\right)^2=\left(\sqrt{200}\right)^2$, triangle ABC is a right triangle.

19. Label the points $A(-4,1)$, $B(1,4)$, and $C(-6,-1)$.

$d(A,B)=\sqrt{[1-(-4)]^2+(4-1)^2}=\sqrt{5^2+3^2}=\sqrt{25+9}=\sqrt{34}$

$d(B,C)=\sqrt{(-6-1)^2+(-1-4)^2}=\sqrt{(-7)^2+(-5)^2}=\sqrt{49+25}=\sqrt{74}$

$d(A,C)=\sqrt{[-6-(-4)]^2+(-1-1)^2}=\sqrt{(-2)^2+(-2)^2}=\sqrt{4+4}=\sqrt{8}$

Since $(\sqrt{8})^2+(\sqrt{34})^2\neq(\sqrt{74})^2$ because $8+34=42\neq74$, triangle ABC is not a right triangle.

21. Label the points $A(-4,3)$, $B(2,5)$, and $C(-1,-6)$.

$d(A,B)=\sqrt{\left[2-(-4)\right]^2+(5-3)^2}=\sqrt{6^2+2^2}=\sqrt{36+4}=\sqrt{40}$

$d(B,C)=\sqrt{(-1-2)^2+(-6-5)^2}=\sqrt{(-3)^2+(-11)^2}=\sqrt{9+121}=\sqrt{130}$

$d(A,C)=\sqrt{\left[-1-(-4)\right]^2+(-6-3)^2}=\sqrt{3^2+(-9)^2}=\sqrt{9+81}=\sqrt{90}$

Since $\left(\sqrt{40}\right)^2+\left(\sqrt{90}\right)^2=\left(\sqrt{130}\right)^2$, triangle ABC is a right triangle.

23. Label the given points $A(0,-7)$, $B(-3,5)$, and $C(2,-15)$. Find the distance between each pair of points.

$d(A,B)=\sqrt{(-3-0)^2+\left[5-(-7)\right]^2}=\sqrt{(-3)^2+12^2}=\sqrt{9+144}=\sqrt{153}=3\sqrt{17}$

$d(B,C)=\sqrt{\left[2-(-3)\right]^2+(-15-5)^2}=\sqrt{5^2+(-20)^2}=\sqrt{25+400}=\sqrt{425}=5\sqrt{17}$

$d(A,C)=\sqrt{(2-0)^2+\left[-15-(-7)\right]^2}=\sqrt{2^2+(-8)^2}=\sqrt{68}=2\sqrt{17}$

Since $d(A,B)+d(A,C)=d(B,C)$ or $3\sqrt{17}+2\sqrt{17}=5\sqrt{17}$, the given points lie on a straight line.

25. Label the points $A(0, 9)$, $B(-3, -7)$, and $C(2, 19)$.

$d(A, B) = \sqrt{(-3-0)^2 + (-7-9)^2} = \sqrt{(-3)^2 + (-16)^2} = \sqrt{9+256} = \sqrt{265} \approx 16.279$

$d(B, C) = \sqrt{[2-(-3)]^2 + [19-(-7)]^2} = \sqrt{5^2 + 26^2} = \sqrt{25+676} = \sqrt{701} \approx 26.476$

$d(A, C) = \sqrt{(2-0)^2 + (19-9)^2} = \sqrt{2^2 + 10^2} = \sqrt{4+100} = \sqrt{104} \approx 10.198$

Since $d(A, B) + d(A, C) \neq d(B, C)$

or $\sqrt{265} + \sqrt{104} \neq \sqrt{701}$

$16.279 + 10.198 \neq 26.476,$

$26.477 \neq 26.476,$

the three given points are not collinear.

(Note, however, that these points are very close to lying on a straight line and may appear to lie on a straight line when graphed.)

27. Label the points $A(-7, 4)$, $B(6,-2)$, and $C(-1,1)$.

$d(A, B) = \sqrt{[6-(-7)]^2 + (-2-4)^2} = \sqrt{13^2 + (-6)^2} = \sqrt{169+36} = \sqrt{205} \approx 14.3178$

$d(B, C) = \sqrt{(-1-6)^2 + [1-(-2)]^2} = \sqrt{(-7)^2 + 3^2} = \sqrt{49+9} = \sqrt{58} \approx 7.6158$

$d(A, C) = \sqrt{[-1-(-7)]^2 + (1-4)^2} = \sqrt{6^2 + (-3)^2} = \sqrt{36+9} = \sqrt{45} \approx 6.7082$

Since $d(B, C) + d(A, C) \neq d(A, B)$

or $\sqrt{58} + \sqrt{45} \neq \sqrt{205}$

$7.6158 + 6.7082 \neq 14.3178$

$14.3240 \neq 14.3178,$

the three given points are not collinear.

(Note, however, that these points are very close to lying on a straight line and may appear to lie on a straight line when graphed.)

29. The points to use would be (1982, 79.1) and (2002, 69.3). Their midpoint is

$$\left(\frac{1982+2002}{2}, \frac{79.1+69.3}{2}\right) = \left(\frac{3984}{2}, \frac{148.4}{2}\right) = (1992, 74.2).$$

The estimate is 74.2%. This is 1.1% less than the actual percent of 75.3.

31. The points to use would be (1990, 13359) and (2000, 17603). Their midpoint is

$$\left(\frac{1990+2000}{2}, \frac{13359+17603}{2}\right) = \left(\frac{3990}{2}, \frac{30962}{2}\right) = (1995, 15481).$$

In 1995, it was approximately $15,481.

33. (a)

x	y	
0	−2	y-intercept: $x = 0 \Rightarrow 6y = 3(0) - 12 \Rightarrow 6y = -12 \Rightarrow y = -2$
4	0	x-intercept: $y = 0 \Rightarrow 6(0) = 3x - 12 \Rightarrow 0 = 3x - 12 \Rightarrow 12 = 3x \Rightarrow 4 = x$
2	−1	additional point

(b)

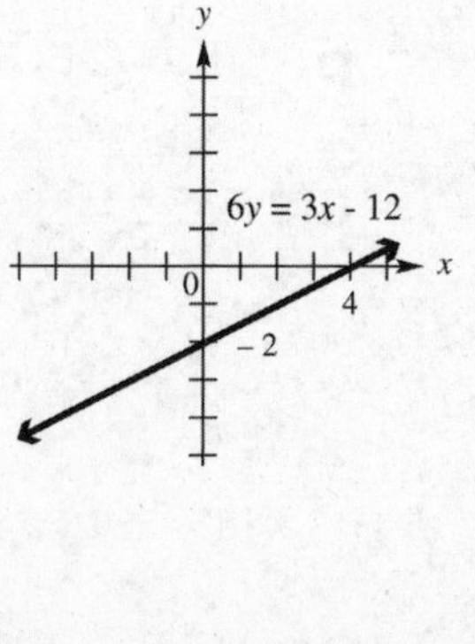

35. (a)

x	y	
0	$\frac{5}{3}$	y-intercept: $x=0 \Rightarrow 2(0)+3y=5 \Rightarrow 3y=5 \Rightarrow y=\frac{5}{3}$
$\frac{5}{2}$	0	x-intercept: $y=0 \Rightarrow 2x+3(0)=5 \Rightarrow 2x=5 \Rightarrow x=\frac{5}{2}$
4	-1	additional point

(b)

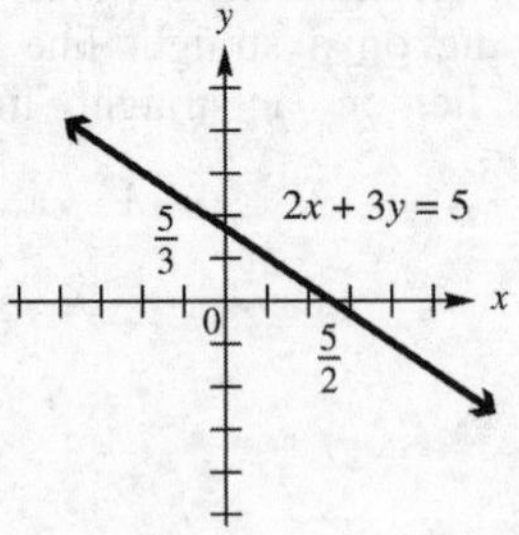

37. (a)

x	y	
0	0	x- and y-intercept: $0=0^2$
1	1	additional point
-2	4	additional point

(b)

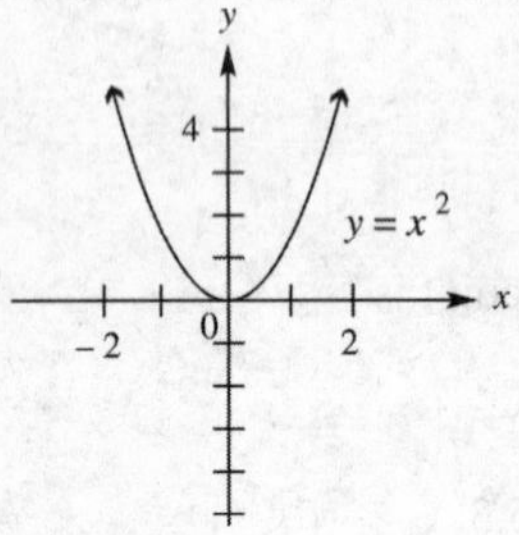

39. (a)

x	y	
3	0	x-intercept: $y=0 \Rightarrow 0=\sqrt{x-3} \Rightarrow 0=x-3 \Rightarrow 3=x$
4	1	additional point
7	2	additional point

no y-intercept: $x=0 \Rightarrow y=\sqrt{0-3} \Rightarrow y=\sqrt{-3}$

(b)

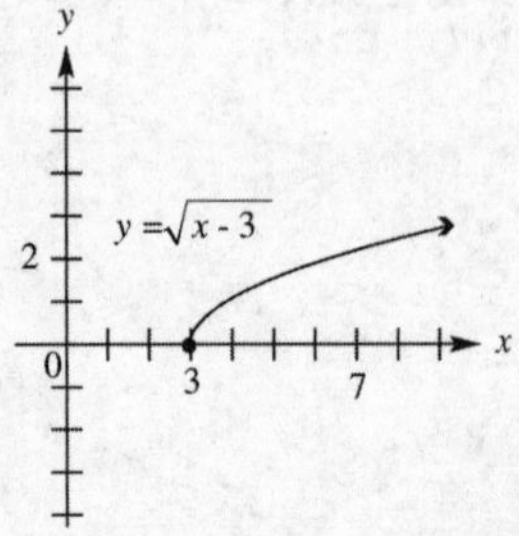

41. **(a)**

x	y	
0	2	y-intercept: $x=0 \Rightarrow y=\lvert 0-2\rvert \Rightarrow y=\lvert -2\rvert \Rightarrow y=2$
2	0	x-intercept: $y=0 \Rightarrow 0=\lvert x-2\rvert \Rightarrow 0=x-2 \Rightarrow 2=x$
−2	4	additional point
4	2	additional point

(b)

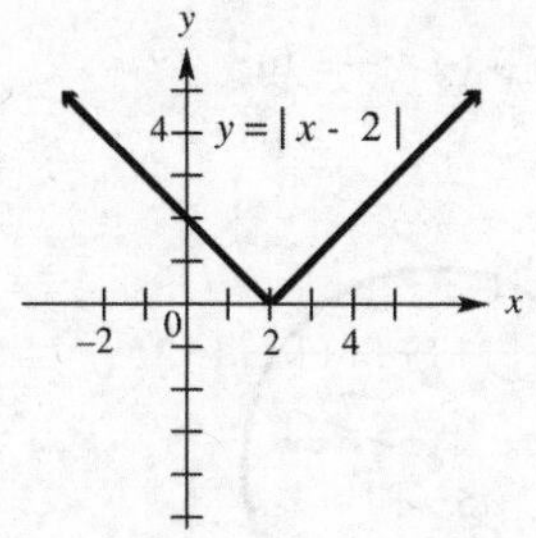

43. **(a)**

x	y	
0	0	x- and y-intercept: $0=0^3$
−1	−1	additional point
2	8	additional point

(b)

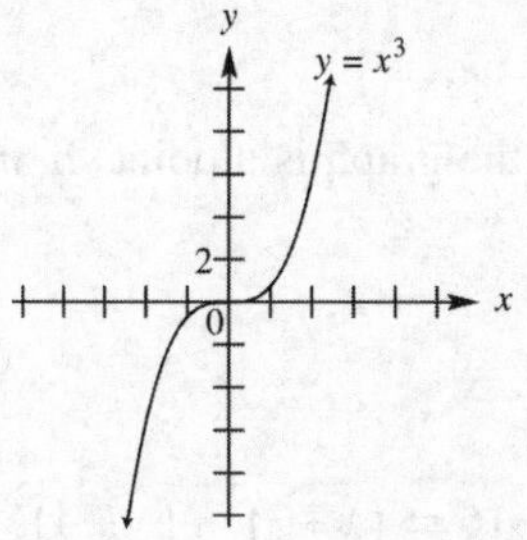

45. **(a)** Center (0, 0), radius 6

$$\sqrt{(x-0)^2+(y-0)^2}=6$$
$$(x-0)^2+(y-0)^2=6^2$$
$$x^2+y^2=36$$

(b)

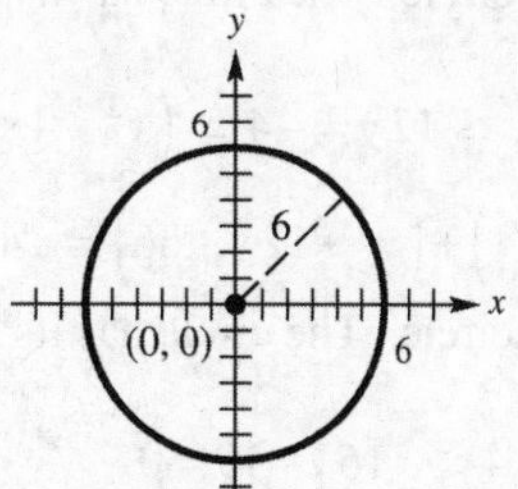

$x^2+y^2=36$

47. **(a)** Center (2, 0), radius 6

$$\sqrt{(x-2)^2+(y-0)^2}=6$$
$$(x-2)^2+(y-0)^2=6^2$$
$$(x-2)^2+y^2=36$$

(b)

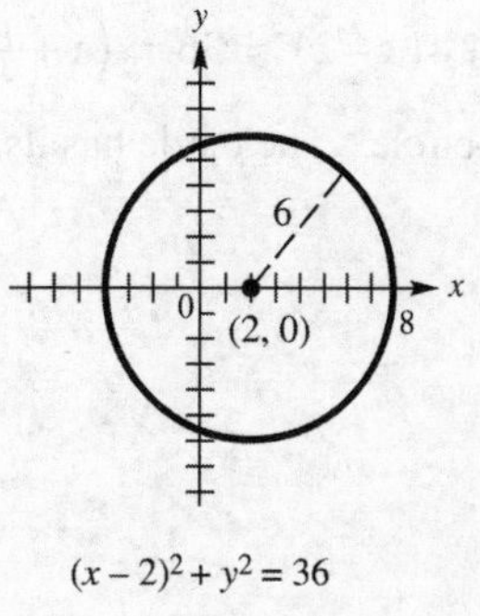

$(x-2)^2+y^2=36$

49. (a) Center (–2, 5), radius 4

$$\sqrt{[x-(-2)]^2+(y-5)^2}=4$$
$$[x-(-2)]^2+(y-5)^2=4^2$$
$$(x+2)^2+(y-5)^2=16$$

(b)

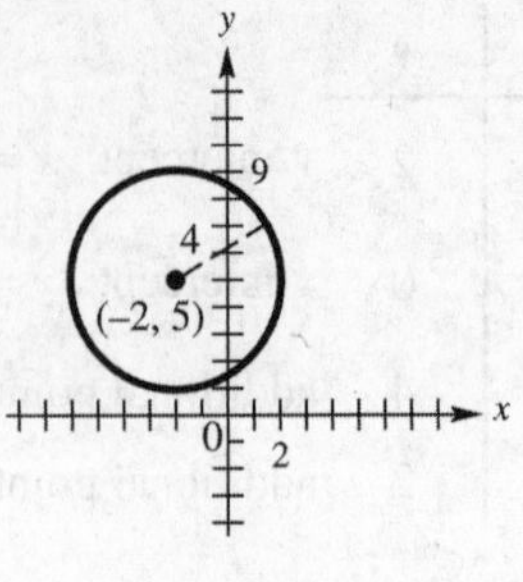

$(x+2)^2+(y-5)^2=16$

51. (a) Center (5, –4), radius 7

$$\sqrt{(x-5)^2+[y-(-4)]^2}=7$$
$$(x-5)^2+[y-(-4)]^2=7^2$$
$$(x-5)^2+(y+4)^2=49$$

(b)

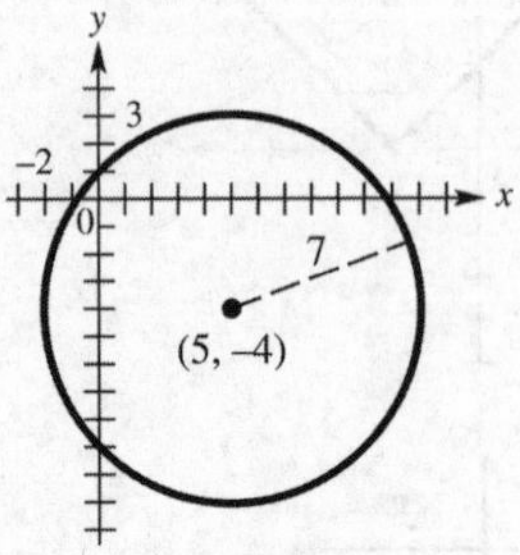

$(x-5)^2+(y+4)^2=49$

53. The radius of this circle is the distance from the center $C(3, 2)$ to the x-axis. This distance is 2, so $r = 2$.

$$(x-3)^2+(y-2)^2=2^2 \Rightarrow (x-3)^2+(y-2)^2=4$$

55. Answers will vary.
If $m>0$, this indicates the graph is a circle. If $m=0$, this indicates the graph is a point If $m<0$, this indicates the graph does not exist.

57. $x^2+6x+y^2+8y+9=0$
Complete the square on x and y separately.
$$\left(x^2+6x\right)+\left(y^2+8y\right)=-9 \Rightarrow \left(x^2+6x+9\right)+\left(y^2+8y+16\right)=-9+9+16 \Rightarrow (x+3)^2+(y+4)^2=16$$
Yes, it is a circle. The circle has its center at (–3, –4) and radius 4.

59. $x^2-4x+y^2+12y=-4 \Rightarrow \left(x^2-4x\right)+\left(y^2+12y\right)=-4$
$$\left(x^2-4x+4\right)+\left(y^2+12y+36\right)=-4+4+36 \Rightarrow (x-2)^2+(y+6)^2=36$$
Yes, it is a circle. The circle has its center at (2, –6) and radius 6.

61. $4x^2+4x+4y^2-16y-19=0$
$$4\left(x^2+x\right)+4\left(y^2-4y\right)=19 \Rightarrow 4\left(x^2+x+\tfrac{1}{4}\right)+4\left(y^2-4y+4\right)=19+4\left(\tfrac{1}{4}\right)+4(4)$$
$$4\left(x+\tfrac{1}{2}\right)^2+4(y-2)^2=36 \Rightarrow \left(x+\tfrac{1}{2}\right)^2+(y-2)^2=9$$
Yes, it is a circle. The circle has its center at $\left(-\frac{1}{2},2\right)$ and radius 3.

63.
$$x^2+2x+y^2-6y+14=0$$
$$\left(x^2+2x\right)+\left(y^2-6y\right)=-14$$
$$\left(x^2+2x+1\right)+\left(y^2-6y+9\right)=-14+1+9$$
$$(x+1)^2+(y-3)^2=-4$$
No, it is not a circle.

65. The midpoint M has coordinates $\left(\frac{-1+5}{2}, \frac{3+(-9)}{2}\right)=\left(\frac{4}{2}, \frac{-6}{2}\right)=(2,-3)$.

66. Use points $C(2, -3)$ and $P(-1, 3)$.
$$d(C, P)=\sqrt{(-1-2)^2+\left[3-(-3)\right]^2}=\sqrt{(-3)^2+6^2}=\sqrt{9+36}=\sqrt{45}=3\sqrt{5}$$
The radius is $3\sqrt{5}$.

67. Use points $C(2, -3)$ and $Q(5, -9)$.
$$d(C, Q)=\sqrt{(5-2)^2+\left[-9-(-3)\right]^2}=\sqrt{3^2+(-6)^2}=\sqrt{9+36}=\sqrt{45}=3\sqrt{5}$$
The radius is $3\sqrt{5}$.

68. Use the points $P(-1, 3)$ and $Q(5, -9)$. Since $d(P, Q)=\sqrt{\left[5-(-1)\right]^2+(-9-3)^2}=\sqrt{6^2+(-12)^2}$ $=\sqrt{36+144}=\sqrt{180}=6\sqrt{5}$, the radius is $\frac{1}{2}d(P, Q)$. Thus $r=\frac{1}{2}\left(6\sqrt{5}\right)=3\sqrt{5}$.

69. The center-radius form for this circle is $(x-2)^2+(y+3)^2=(3\sqrt{5})^2 \Rightarrow (x-2)^2+(y+3)^2=45$.

70. Label the endpoints of the diameter $P(3, -5)$ and $Q(-7, 3)$. The midpoint M of the segment joining P and Q has coordinates $\left(\frac{3+(-7)}{2}, \frac{-5+3}{2}\right)=\left(\frac{-4}{2}, \frac{-2}{2}\right)=(-2,-1)$. The center is $C(-2, -1)$.

To find the radius, we can use points $C(-2, -1)$.and $P(3, -5)$
$$d(C, P)=\sqrt{\left[3-(-2)\right]^2+\left[-5-(-1)\right]^2}=\sqrt{5^2+(-4)^2}=\sqrt{25+16}=\sqrt{41}$$
We could also use points $C(-2, -1)$.and $Q(-7, 3)$.
$$d(C, Q)=\sqrt{\left[-7-(-2)\right]^2+\left[3-(-1)\right]^2}=\sqrt{(-5)^2+4^2}=\sqrt{25+16}=\sqrt{41}$$
We could also use points $P(3, -5)$ and $Q(-7, 3)$.
$$d(C, Q)=\sqrt{(-7-3)^2+\left[3-(-5)\right]^2}=\sqrt{(-10)^2+8^2}=\sqrt{100+64}=\sqrt{164}=2\sqrt{41}$$
$$\frac{1}{2}d(P, Q)=\frac{1}{2}\left(2\sqrt{41}\right)=\sqrt{41}$$
The center-radius form of the equation of the circle is
$$[x-(-2)]^2+[y-(-1)]^2=(\sqrt{41})^2 \Rightarrow (x+2)^2+(y+1)^2=41.$$

71. Midpoint (5, 8), endpoint (13, 10)

$$\frac{13+x}{2}=5 \quad \text{and} \quad \frac{10+y}{2}=8$$

$$13+x=10 \quad \text{and} \quad 10+y=16$$

$$x=-3 \quad \text{and} \quad y=6.$$

The other endpoint has coordinates (–3, 6).

73. Midpoint (12, 6), endpoint (19, 16)

$$\frac{19+x}{2}=12 \quad \text{and} \quad \frac{16+y}{2}=6$$

$$19+x=24 \quad \text{and} \quad 16+y=12$$

$$x=5 \quad \text{and} \quad y=-4.$$

The other endpoint has coordinates (5, –4).

75. The midpoint M has coordinates $\left(\frac{x_1+x_2}{2}, \frac{y_1+y_2}{2}\right)$.

$$d(P,M)=\sqrt{\left(\frac{x_1+x_2}{2}-x_1\right)^2+\left(\frac{y_1+y_2}{2}-y_1\right)^2}=\sqrt{\left(\frac{x_1+x_2}{2}-\frac{2x_1}{2}\right)^2+\left(\frac{y_1+y_2}{2}-\frac{2y_1}{2}\right)^2}$$

$$=\sqrt{\left(\frac{x_2-x_1}{2}\right)^2+\left(\frac{y_2-y_1}{2}\right)^2}=\sqrt{\frac{(x_2-x_1)^2}{4}+\frac{(y_2-y_1)^2}{4}}=\sqrt{\frac{(x_2-x_1)^2+(y_2-y_1)^2}{4}}$$

$$=\tfrac{1}{2}\sqrt{(x_2-x_1)^2+(y_2-y_1)^2}$$

$$d(M,Q)=\sqrt{\left(x_2-\frac{x_1+x_2}{2}\right)^2+\left(y_2-\frac{y_1+y_2}{2}\right)^2}=\sqrt{\left(\frac{2x_2}{2}-\frac{x_1+x_2}{2}\right)^2+\left(\frac{2y_2}{2}-\frac{y_1+y_2}{2}\right)^2}$$

$$=\sqrt{\left(\frac{x_2-x_1}{2}\right)^2+\left(\frac{y_2-y_1}{2}\right)^2}=\sqrt{\frac{(x_2-x_1)^2}{4}+\frac{(y_2-y_1)^2}{4}}=\sqrt{\frac{(x_2-x_1)^2+(y_2-y_1)^2}{4}}$$

$$=\tfrac{1}{2}\sqrt{(x_2-x_1)^2+(y_2-y_1)^2}$$

$$d(P,Q)=\sqrt{(x_2-x_1)^2+(y_2-y_1)^2}$$

Since $\tfrac{1}{2}\sqrt{(x_2-x_1)^2+(y_2-y_1)^2}+\tfrac{1}{2}\sqrt{(x_2-x_1)^2+(y_2-y_1)^2}=\sqrt{(x_2-x_1)^2+(y_2-y_1)^2}$, this shows $d(P,M)+d(M,Q)=d(P,Q)$ and $d(P,M)=d(M,Q)$.

77. Points on the *x*-axis have *y*-coordinates equal to 0. The point on the *x*-axis will have the same *x*-coordinate as point (4, 3). Therefore, the line will intersect the *x*-axis at (4, 0).

79. Since (*a*, *b*) is in the second quadrant, *a* is negative and *b* is positive.
Therefore, (*a*, –*b*) will have a negative *x*-coordinate and a negative *y*-coordinate and will lie in quadrant III.
Also, (–*a*, *b*) will have a positive *x*-coordinate and a positive *y*-coordinate and will lie in quadrant I.
Also, (–*a*, –*b*) will have a positive *x*-coordinate and a negative *y*-coordinate and will lie in quadrant IV.
Finally, (*b*, *a*) will have a positive *x*-coordinate and a negative *y*-coordinate and will lie in quadrant IV.

81. To determine which points form sides of the quadrilateral (as opposed to diagonals), plot the points.

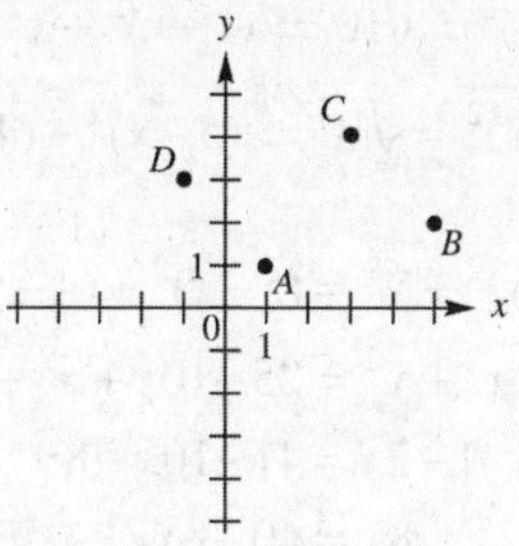

Use the distance formula to find the length of each side.

$$d(A, B) = \sqrt{(5-1)^2 + (2-1)^2} = \sqrt{4^2 + 1^2} = \sqrt{16+1} = \sqrt{17}$$

$$d(C, D) = \sqrt{(-1-3)^2 + (3-4)^2} = \sqrt{(-4)^2 + (-1)^2} = \sqrt{16+1} = \sqrt{17}$$

$$d(B, C) = \sqrt{(3-5)^2 + (4-2)^2} = \sqrt{(-2)^2 + 2^2} = \sqrt{4+4} = \sqrt{8}$$

$$d(D, A) = \sqrt{[1-(-1)]^2 + (1-3)^2} = \sqrt{2^2 + (-2)^2} = \sqrt{4+4} = \sqrt{8}$$

Since $d(A, B) = d(C, D)$ and $d(B, C) = d(D, A)$, the points are the vertices of a parallelogram. Since $d(A, B) \neq d(B, C)$, the points are not the vertices of a rhombus.

83. Label the points $P(x, y)$ and $Q(1, 3)$.

If $d(P,Q) = 4$, $\sqrt{(1-x)^2 + (3-y)^2} = 4 \Rightarrow (1-x)^2 + (3-y)^2 = 16.$

If $x = y$, then we can either substitute x for y or y for x. Substituting x for y we solve the following.

$$(1-x)^2 + (3-x)^2 = 16$$
$$1 - 2x + x^2 + 9 - 6x + x^2 = 16$$
$$2x^2 - 8x + 10 = 16$$
$$2x^2 - 8x - 6 = 0$$
$$x^2 - 4x - 3 = 0$$

To solve this equation, we can use the quadratic formula with $a = 1$, $b = -4$, and $c = -3$.

$$x = \frac{-(-4) \pm \sqrt{(-4)^2 - 4(1)(-3)}}{2(1)} = \frac{4 \pm \sqrt{16+12}}{2} = \frac{4 \pm \sqrt{28}}{2} = \frac{4 \pm 2\sqrt{7}}{2} = 2 \pm \sqrt{7}$$

Since $x = y$, the points are $\left(2+\sqrt{7}, 2+\sqrt{7}\right)$ and $\left(2-\sqrt{7}, 2-\sqrt{7}\right)$.

85. Let $P(x, y)$ be a point whose distance from $A(1, 0)$ is $\sqrt{10}$ and whose distance from $B(5, 4)$ is $\sqrt{10}$.

$d(P, A) = \sqrt{10}$, so $\sqrt{(1-x)^2+(0-y)^2} = \sqrt{10} \Rightarrow (1-x)^2 + y^2 = 10.$

$d(P, B) = \sqrt{10}$, so $\sqrt{(5-x)^2+(4-y)^2} = \sqrt{10} \Rightarrow (5-x)^2+(4-y)^2 = 10.$

Thus,

$$\begin{aligned}(1-x)^2 + y^2 &= (5-x)^2+(4-y)^2\\ 1-2x+x^2+y^2 &= 25-10x+x^2+16-8y+y^2\\ 1-2x &= 41-10x-8y\\ 8y &= 40-8x\\ y &= 5-x.\end{aligned}$$

Substitute $5 - x$ for y in the equation $(1-x)^2+y^2 = 10$ and solve for x.

$$\begin{aligned}(1-x)^2+(5-x)^2 = 10 &\Rightarrow 1-2x+x^2+25-10x+x^2 = 10\\ 2x^2-12x+26 = 10 &\Rightarrow 2x^2-12x+16 = 0\\ x^2-6x+8 = 0 &\Rightarrow (x-2)(x-4) = 0\\ x-2 = 0 \quad &\text{or} \quad x-4 = 0\\ x = 2 \quad &\text{or} \quad x = 4\end{aligned}$$

To find the corresponding values of y use the equation $y = 5 - x$.
If $x = 2$, then $y = 5 - 2 = 3$.
If $x = 4$, then $y = 5 - 4 = 1$.
The points satisfying the conditions are (2, 3) and (4, 1).

87. Label the points $A(3, y)$ and $B(-2, 9)$. If $d(A, B) = 12$,

$$\sqrt{(-2-3)^2+(9-y)^2} = 12 \Rightarrow \sqrt{(-5)^2+(9-y)^2} = 12 \Rightarrow (-5)^2+(9-y)^2 = 12^2$$

$$25+81-18y+y^2 = 144 \Rightarrow y^2-18y-38 = 0.$$

Solve this equation by using the quadratic formula with $a = 1$, $b = -18$, and $c = -38$.

$$y = \frac{-(-18)\pm\sqrt{(-18)^2-4(1)(-38)}}{2(1)} = \frac{18\pm\sqrt{324+152}}{2(1)}$$

$$= \frac{18\pm\sqrt{476}}{2} = \frac{18\pm\sqrt{4(119)}}{2} = \frac{18\pm2\sqrt{119}}{2} = 9\pm\sqrt{119}$$

The values of y are $9+\sqrt{119}$ and $9-\sqrt{119}$.

Section 2.2: Functions

1. Answers will vary.

3. independent variable

5. The relation is a function because for each different x-value there is exactly one y-value. This correspondence can be shown as follows.

$$\begin{array}{c}\{5, 3, 4, 9\}\ x\text{-values}\\ \downarrow\ \downarrow\ \downarrow\ \downarrow\\ \{1, 2, 9, 6\}\ y\text{-values}\end{array}$$

7. Two ordered pairs, namely $(2,4)$ and $(2,5)$, have the same x-value paired with different y-values, so the relation is not a function.

9. The relation is a function because for each different x-value there is exactly one y-value. This correspondence can be shown as follows.

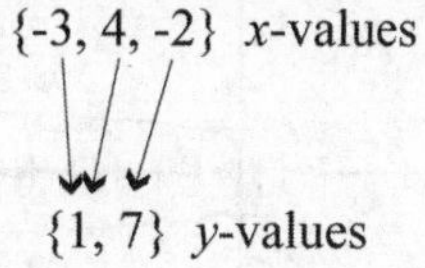

11. Two sets of ordered pairs, namely $(1,1)$ and $(1,-1)$ as well as $(2,4)$ and $(2,-4)$, have the same x-value paired with different y-values, so the relation is not a function.

domain: $\{0,1,2\}$; range: $\{-4,-1,0,1,4\}$

13. The relation is a function because for each different x-value there is exactly one y-value.
domain: $\{2,3,5,11,17\}$; range: $\{1,7,20\}$

15. The relation is a function because for each different year there is exactly one number of rounds played in the U.S.

domain: $\{1997,1998,1999,2000\}$; range: $\{547,200,000,\ 528,500,000,\ 564,100,000,\ 587,100,000\}$

17. This graph represents a function. If you pass a vertical line through the graph, one x-value corresponds to only one y-value.

domain: $(-\infty,\infty)$; range: $(-\infty,\infty)$

19. This graph does not represent a function. If you pass a vertical line through the graph, there are places where one value of x corresponds to two values of y.

domain: $[3,\infty)$; range: $(-\infty,\infty)$

21. This graph does not represent a function. If you pass a vertical line through the graph, there are places where one value of x corresponds to two values of y.

domain: $[-4,4]$; range: $[-3,3]$

23. $y = x^2$ represents a function since y is always found by squaring x. Thus, each value of x corresponds to just one value of y. x can be any real number. Since the square of any real number is not negative, the range would be zero or greater.

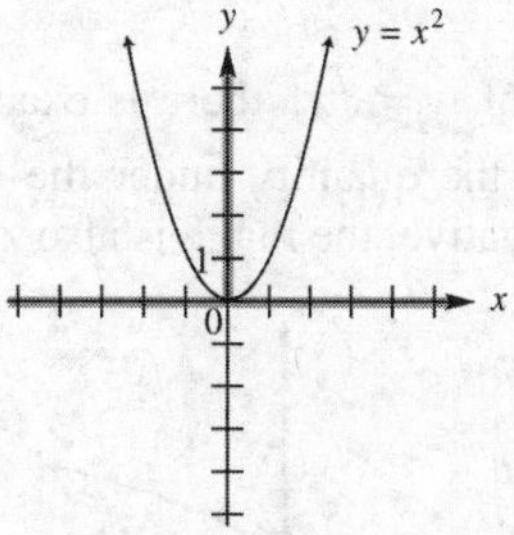

domain: $(-\infty,\infty)$; range: $[0,\infty)$

25. The ordered pairs $(1,1)$ and $(1,-1)$ both satisfy $x = y^6$. This equation does not represent a function. Because x is equal to the sixth power of y, the values of x are nonnegative. Any real number can be raised to the sixth power, so the range of the relation is all real numbers.

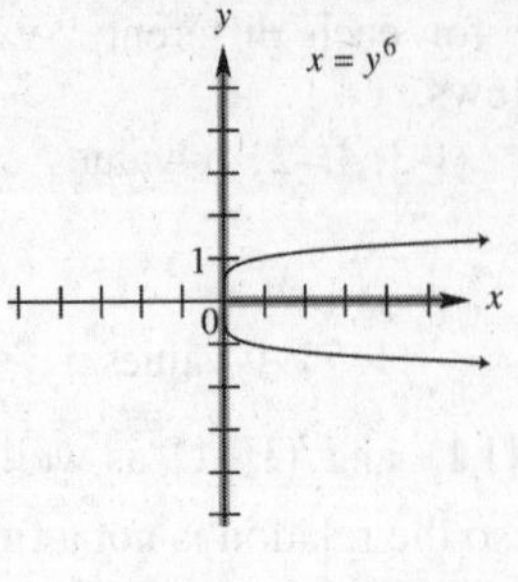

domain: $[0,\infty)$ range: $(-\infty,\infty)$

27. $y = 2x-6$ represents a function since y is found by multiplying x by 2 and subtracting 6. Each value of x corresponds to just one value of y. x can be any real number, so the domain is all real numbers. Since y is twice x, less 6, y also may be any real number, and so the range is also all real numbers.

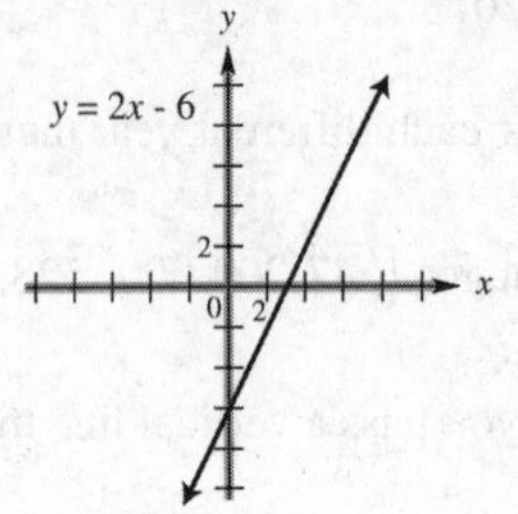

domain: $(-\infty,\infty)$; range: $(-\infty,\infty)$

29. By definition, y is a function of x if every value of x leads to exactly one value of y. Substituting a particular value of x, say 1, into $x+y<4$, corresponds to many values of y. The ordered pairs $(1,2)$, $(1,1)$, $(1,0)$, $(1,-1)$, and so on, all satisfy the inequality. This does not represent a function. Any number can be used for x or for y, so the domain and range of this relation are both all real numbers.

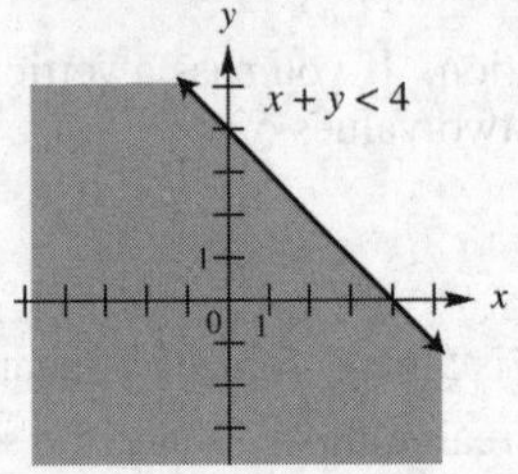

domain: $(-\infty,\infty)$; range: $(-\infty,\infty)$

31. For any choice of x in the domain of $y=\sqrt{x}$, there is exactly one corresponding value of y, so this equation defines a function. Since the quantity under the square root cannot be negative, we have $x \geq 0$. Because the radical is nonnegative, the range is also zero or greater.

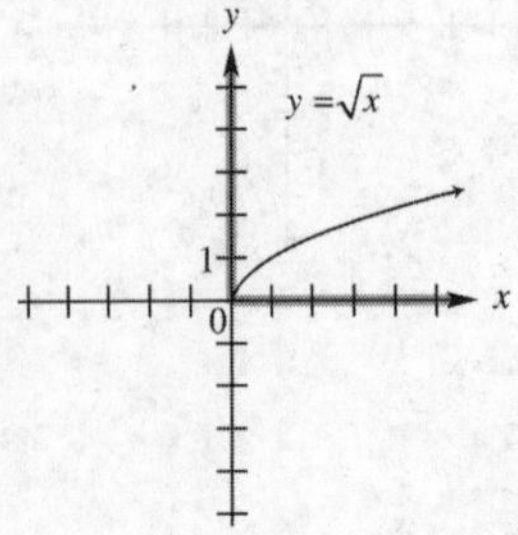

domain: $[0,\infty)$; range: $[0,\infty)$

33. Since $xy = 1$ can be rewritten as $y = \frac{1}{x}$, we can see that y can be found by dividing x into 1. This process produces one value of y for each value of x in the domain, so this equation is a function. The domain includes all real numbers except those that make the denominator equal to zero, namely $x = 0$. Values of y can be negative or positive, but never zero. Therefore, the range will be all real numbers except zero.

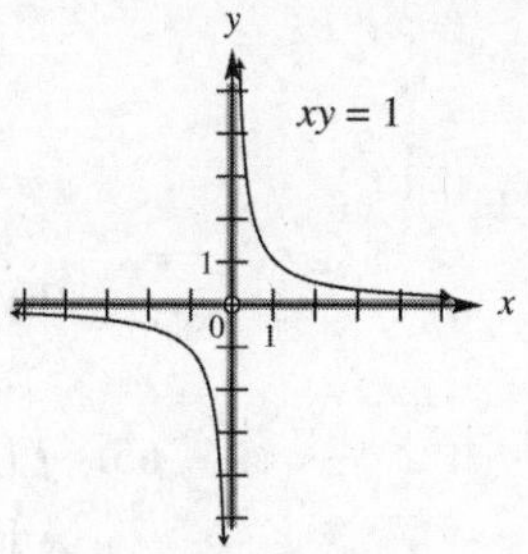

domain: $(-\infty,0)\cup(0,\infty)$; range: $(-\infty,0)\cup(0,\infty)$

35. For any choice of x in the domain of $y = \sqrt{4x+2}$ there is exactly one corresponding value of y, so this equation defines a function. Since the quantity under the square root cannot be negative, we have $4x+2 \ge 0 \Rightarrow 4x \ge -2 \Rightarrow x \ge \frac{-2}{4}$ or $x \ge -\frac{1}{2}$. Because the radical is nonnegative, the range is also zero or greater.

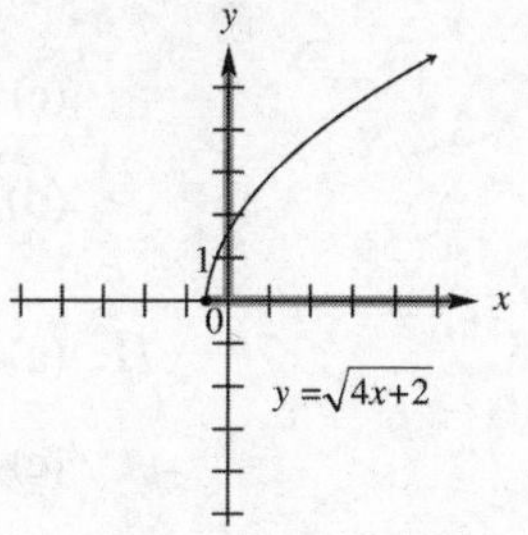

domain: $\left[-\frac{1}{2},\infty\right)$; range: $[0,\infty)$

37. Given any value in the domain of $y = \frac{2}{x-9}$, we find y by subtracting 9, then dividing into 2. This process produces one value of y for each value of x in the domain, so this equation is a function. The domain includes all real numbers except those that make the denominator equal to zero, namely $x = 9$. Values of y can be negative or positive, but never zero. Therefore, the range will be all real numbers except zero.

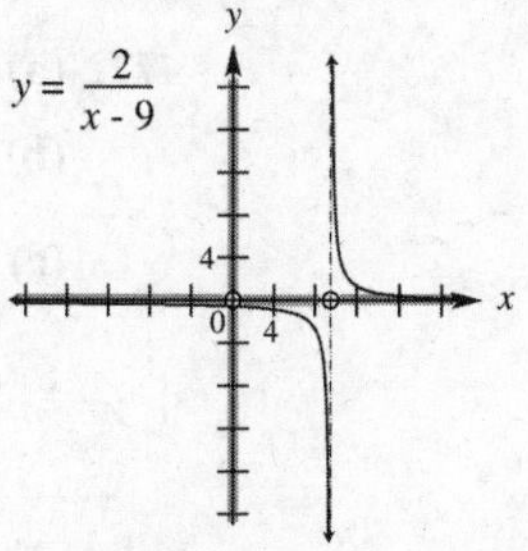

domain: $(-\infty,9)\cup(9,\infty)$; range: $(-\infty,0)\cup(0,\infty)$

39. B

41. $f(x) = -3x+4$

$f(0) = -3\cdot 0+4 = 0+4 = 4$

43. $g(x) = -x^2+4x+1$

$g(-2) = -(-2)^2+4(-2)+1$

$= -4+(-8)+1 = -11$

45. $f(x) = -3x + 4$
$f(p) = -3p + 4$

47. $f(x) = -3x + 4$
$f(-x) = -3(-x) + 4 = 3x + 4$

49. $f(x) = -3x + 4$
$f(x+2) = -3(x+2) + 4$
$= -3x - 6 + 4 = -3x - 2$

51. $f(x) = -3x + 4$
$f(2m-3) = -3(2m-3) + 4$
$= -6m + 9 + 4 = -6m + 13$

53. **(a)** $f(2) = 2$ **(b)** $f(-1) = 3$

55. **(a)** $f(2) = 15$ **(b)** $f(-1) = 10$

57. **(a)** $f(2) = 3$ **(b)** $f(-1) = -3$

59. **(a)** $x + 3y = 12$
$3y = -x + 12$
$y = \frac{-x+12}{3}$
$y = -\frac{1}{3}x + 4$
$f(x) = -\frac{1}{3}x + 4$

(b) $f(3) = -\frac{1}{3}(3) + 4 = -1 + 4 = 3$

61. **(a)** $y + 2x^2 = 3$
$y = -2x^2 + 3$
$f(x) = -2x^2 + 3$

(b) $f(3) = -2(3)^2 + 3 = -2 \cdot 9 + 3$
$= -18 + 3 = -15$

63. **(a)** $4x - 3y = 8$
$4x = 3y + 8$
$4x - 8 = 3y$
$\frac{4x-8}{3} = y$
$y = \frac{4}{3}x - \frac{8}{3}$
$f(x) = \frac{4}{3}x - \frac{8}{3}$

(b) $f(3) = \frac{4}{3}(3) - \frac{8}{3} = \frac{12}{3} - \frac{8}{3} = \frac{4}{3}$

65. $f(3) = 4$
Additional answers will vary.

67. $f(3)$ is the y-component of the coordinate, which is -4.

69. **(a)** $f(-2) = 0$
(b) $f(0) = 4$
(c) $f(1) = 2$
(d) $f(4) = 4$

71. **(a)** $f(-2) = -3$ **(b)** $f(0) = -2$
(c) $f(1) = 0$ **(d)** $f(4) = 2$

73. **(a)** $[4, \infty)$ **(b)** $(-\infty, -1]$
(c) $[-1, 4]$

75. **(a)** $(-\infty, 4]$ **(b)** $[4, \infty)$
(c) none

77. **(a)** none
(b) $(-\infty, -2]$; $[3, \infty)$
(c) $(-2, 3)$

79. **(a)** yes
(b) $[0, 24]$
(c) When $t = 8$, $y = 1200$ from the graph. At 8 A.M., approximately 1200 megawatts is being used.
(d) at 17 hr or 5 P.M.; at 4 A.M.
(e) $f(12) = 2000$; At 12 noon, electricity use is 2000 megawatts.
(f) increasing from 4 A.M. to 5 P.M.; decreasing from midnight to 4 A.M. and from 5 P.M. to midnight

81. **(a)** At $t = 12$ and $t = 20$, $y = 55$ from the graph. Therefore, after about 12 noon until about 8 P.M. the temperature was over 55°.

(b) At $t = 5$ and $t = 22$, $y = 40$ from the graph. Therefore, until about 6 A.M. and after 10 P.M. the temperature was below 40°.

(c) The temperature at noon in Bratenahl, Ohio was 55°. Since the temperature in Greenville is 7° higher, we are looking for the time at which Bratenahl, Ohio was 55° − 7°, or 48°. This occurred at approximately 10 A.M and 8:30 P.M.

Section 2.3: Linear Functions

1 B; $f(x) = 2x + 6$ is a linear function with y-intercept 6.

3. C; $f(x) = 7$ is a constant function.

5. A; $f(x) = 2x$ is a linear function whose graph passes through the origin, (0, 0).
$f(0) = 2(0) = 0$.

7. $f(x) = x - 4$; Use the intercepts.

$f(0) = 0 - 4 = -4$: y-intercept

$0 = x - 4 \Rightarrow x = 4$: x-intercept

Graph the line through (0, –4) and (4, 0).

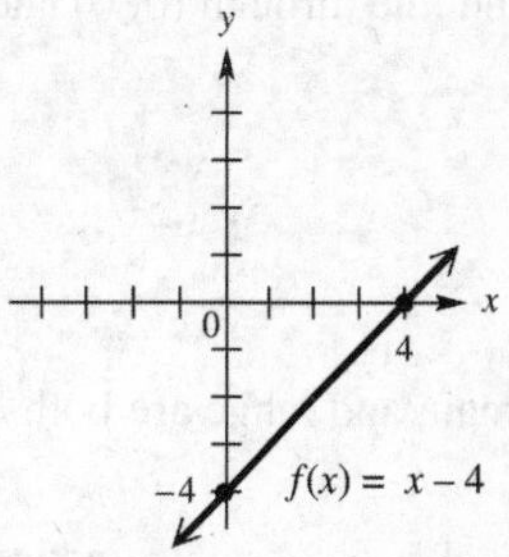

The domain and range are both $(-\infty, \infty)$.

9. $f(x) = \frac{1}{2}x - 6$; Use the intercepts.

$f(0) = \frac{1}{2}(0) - 6 = -6$: y-intercept

$0 = \frac{1}{2}x - 6 \Rightarrow 6 = \frac{1}{2}x \Rightarrow x = 12$: x-intercept

Graph the line through (0, –6) and (12, 0).

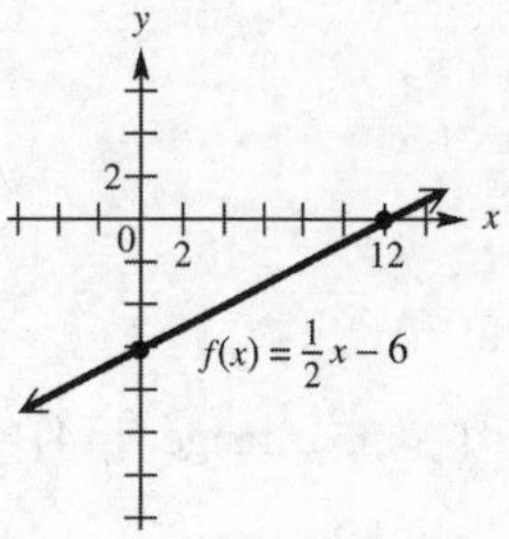

The domain and range are both $(-\infty, \infty)$.

11. $-4x + 3y = 9$; Use the intercepts.

$-4(0) + 3y = 9 \Rightarrow 3y = 9$

$y = 3$: y-intercept

$-4x + 3(0) = 9 \Rightarrow -4x = 9$

$x = -\frac{9}{4}$: x-intercept

Graph the line through $(0, 3)$ and $\left(-\frac{9}{4}, 0\right)$.

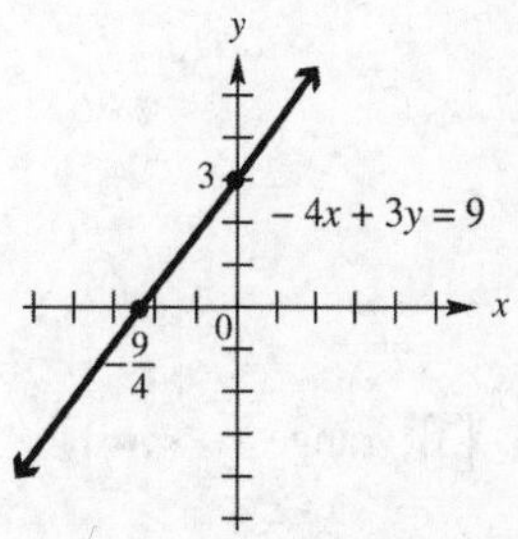

The domain and range are both $(-\infty, \infty)$.

13. $3y-4x=0$; Use the intercepts.

$$3y-4(0)=0 \Rightarrow 3y=0$$
$$y=0: y\text{-intercept}$$
$$3(0)-4x=0 \Rightarrow -4x=0$$
$$x=0: x\text{-intercept}$$

The graph has just one intercept. Choose an additional value, say 3, for x.

$$3y-4(3)=0 \Rightarrow 3y-12=0$$
$$3y=12 \Rightarrow y=4$$

Graph the line through $(0,0)$ and $(3,4)$.

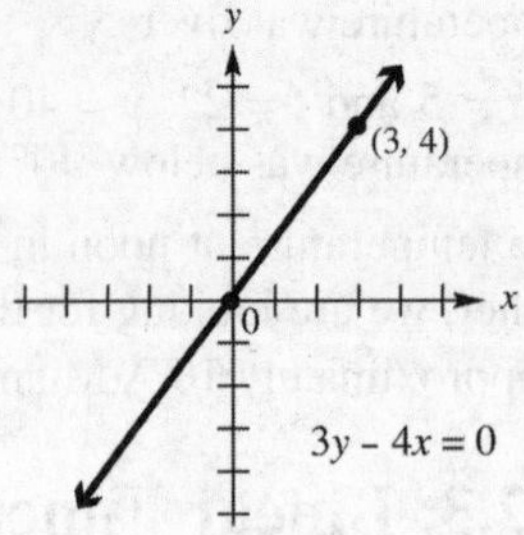

The domain and range are both $(-\infty,\infty)$.

15 $f(x)=3x$

The x-intercept and the y-intercept are both zero. This gives us only one point, (0, 0). If $x = 1$, $y = 3(1) = 3$. Another point is (1, 3). Graph the line through (0, 0) and (1, 3).

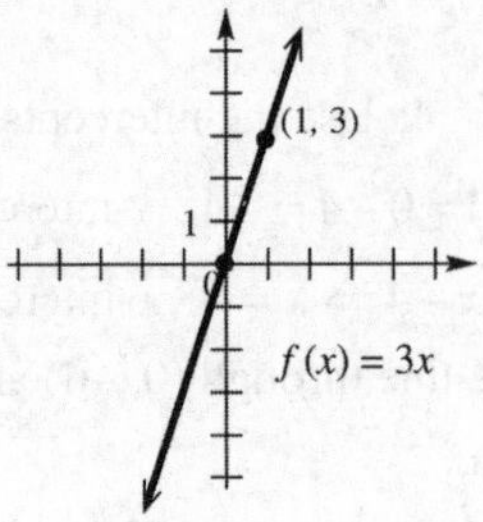

The domain and range are both $(-\infty,\infty)$.

17. $f(x)=-4$ is a constant function.

The graph of $f(x)=-4$ is a horizontal line with a y-intercept of -4.

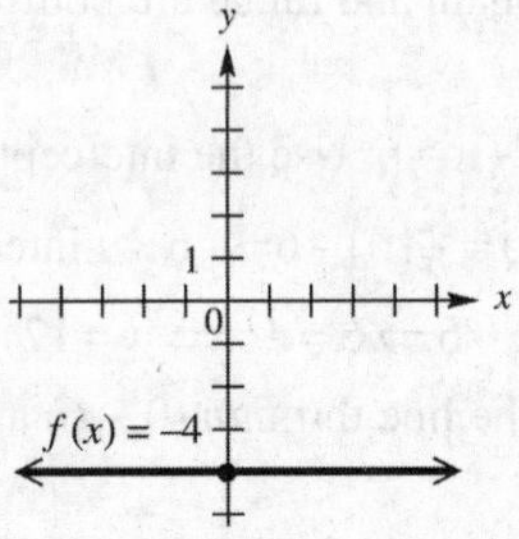

domain: $(-\infty,\infty)$; range: $\{-4\}$

19. $x = 3$ is a vertical line, intersecting the x-axis at (3, 0).

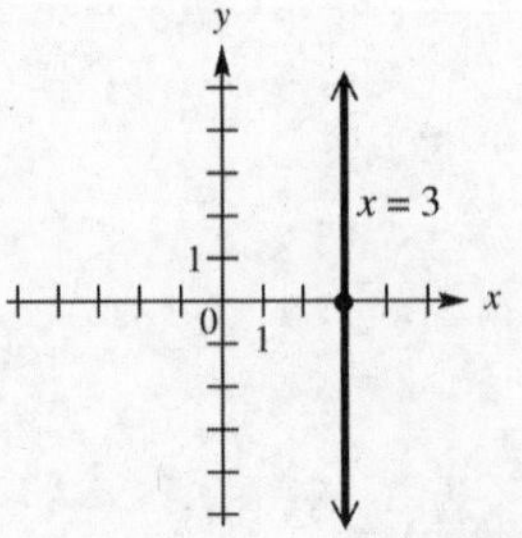

domain: $\{3\}$; range: $(-\infty,\infty)$

21. $2x + 4 = 0 \Rightarrow 2x = -4 \Rightarrow x = -2$ is a vertical line intersecting the x-axis at $(-2, 0)$.

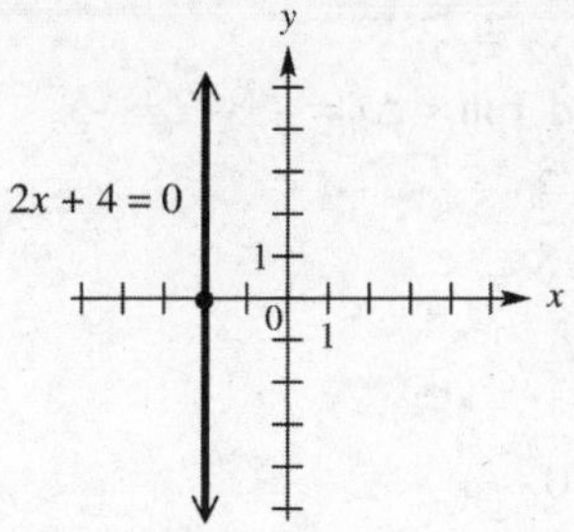

domain: $\{-2\}$; range: $(-\infty, \infty)$

23. $-x + 5 = 0 \Rightarrow x = 5$ is a vertical line intersecting the x-axis at $(5, 0)$.

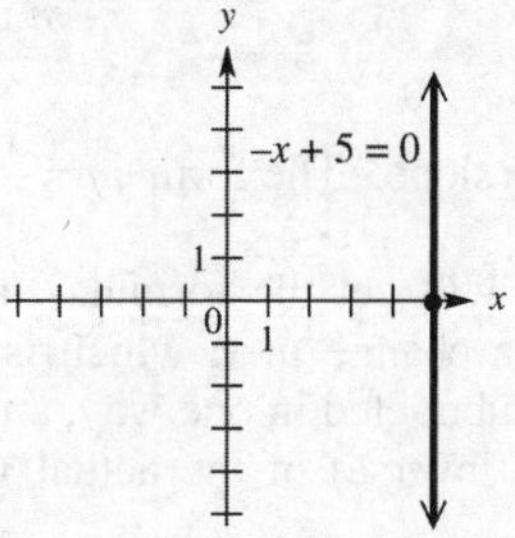

domain: $\{5\}$; range: $(-\infty, \infty)$

25. $y = 2$ is a horizontal line with y-intercept 2. Choice A resembles this.

27. $x = 2$ is a vertical line with x-intercept 2. Choice D resembles this.

29. $y = 3x + 4$; Use $Y_1 = 3X + 4$.

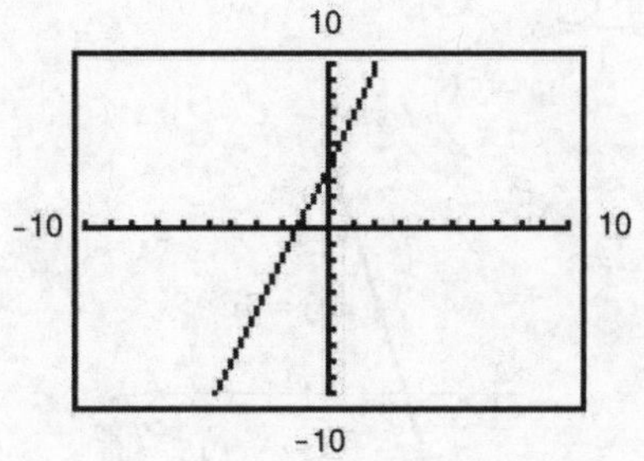

31. $3x + 4y = 6$; Solve for y.

$$3x + 4y = 6$$
$$4y = -3x + 6$$
$$y = -\tfrac{3}{4}x + \tfrac{3}{2}$$

Use $Y_1 = (-3/4)X + (3/2)$ or $Y_1 = -3/4X + 3/2$.

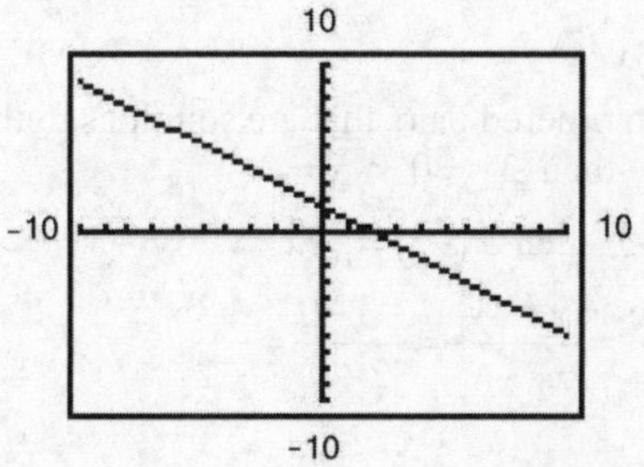

33. The rise is 2.5 feet while the run is 10 feet so the slope is $\frac{2.5}{10} = .25 = 25\% = \frac{1}{4}$. So A = .25, $C = \frac{2.5}{10}$, D = 25%, and $E = \frac{1}{4}$ are all expressions of the slope.

35. through (2, –1) and (–3, –3)
Let $x_1 = 2,\ y_1 = -1,\ x_2 = -3,$ and $y_2 = -3.$
Then rise $= \Delta y = -3 - (-1) = -2$ and run $= \Delta x = -3 - 2 = -5.$

The slope is $m = \frac{\text{rise}}{\text{run}} = \frac{\Delta y}{\Delta x} = \frac{-2}{-5} = \frac{2}{5}.$

37. Through (5, 9) and (–2, 9)
$$m = \frac{\Delta y}{\Delta x} = \frac{y_2 - y_1}{x_2 - x_1} = \frac{9-9}{-2-5} = \frac{0}{-7} = 0$$

39. Horizontal, through (3, –7)
The slope of every horizontal line is zero, so $m = 0$.

41. Vertical, through (3, –7)
The slope of every vertical line is undefined; m is undefined.

43. Both B and C can be used to find the slope. The form $m = \frac{y_2 - y_1}{x_2 - x_1}$ is the form that is standardly used.

If you rename points 1 and 2, you will get the formula stated in choice B. Choice D is incorrect because it shows a change in x to a change in y, which is not how slope is defined. Choice A is incorrect because the y - values are subtracted in one way, and the x - values in the opposite way. This will result in the opposite (additive inverse) of the actual value of the slope of the line that passes between the two points.

45. $y = 3x + 5$
Find two ordered pairs that are solutions to the equation.
If $x = 0$, then $y = 3(0) + 5 \Rightarrow y = 5.$

If $x = -1$ then $y = 3(-1) + 5 \Rightarrow y = -3 + 5 \Rightarrow y = 2.$ Thus two ordered pairs are $(0,5)$ and $(-1,2)$.

$$m = \frac{\text{rise}}{\text{run}} = \frac{y_2 - y_1}{x_2 - x_1} = \frac{2-5}{-1-0} = \frac{-3}{-1} = 3.$$

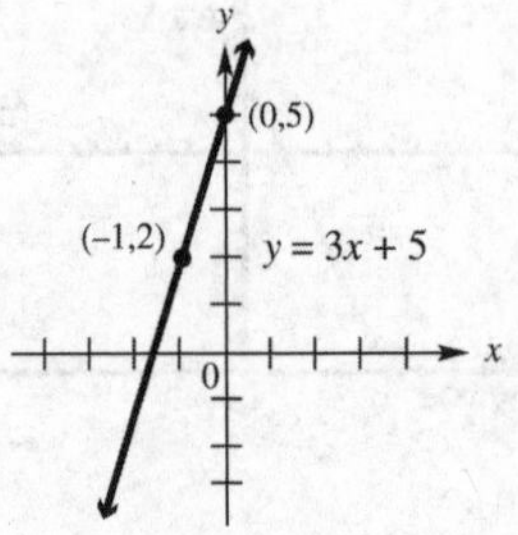

47. $2y = -3x$
Find two ordered pairs that are solutions to the equation.
If $x = 0$, then $2y = 0 \Rightarrow y = 0.$

If $y = -3$, then $2(-3) = -3x \Rightarrow -6 = -3x \Rightarrow x = 2.$ Thus two ordered pairs are $(0,0)$ and $(2,-3)$.

$$m = \frac{\text{rise}}{\text{run}} = \frac{y_2 - y_1}{x_2 - x_1} = \frac{-3-0}{2-0} = -\frac{3}{2}.$$

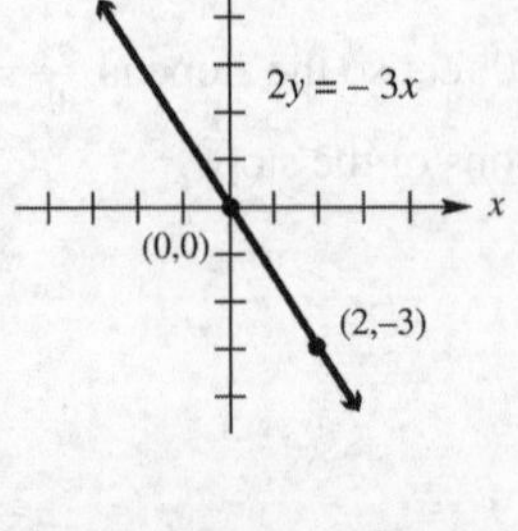

49. $5x-2y=10$

Find two ordered pairs that are solutions to the equation.

If $x=0$, then $5(0)-2y=10 \Rightarrow -2y=10 \Rightarrow y=-5$.

If $y=0$, then $5x-2(0)=10 \Rightarrow 5x=10 \Rightarrow x=2$. Thus two ordered pairs are $(0,-5)$ and $(2,0)$.

$$m=\frac{\text{rise}}{\text{run}}=\frac{y_2-y_1}{x_2-x_1}=\frac{0-(-5)}{2-0}=\frac{5}{2}.$$

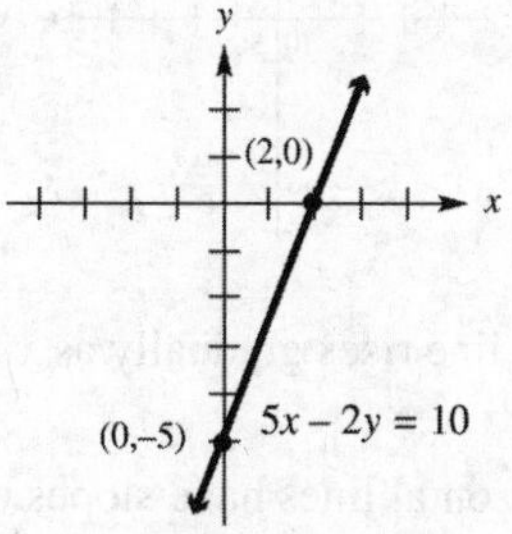

51. Answers will vary.

53. Through (–1, 3), $m=\frac{3}{2}$

First locate the point (–1, 3).

Since the slope is $\frac{3}{2}$, a change of 2 units horizontally (2 units to the right) produces a change of 3 units vertically (3 units up). This gives a second point, (1, 6), which can be used to complete the graph.

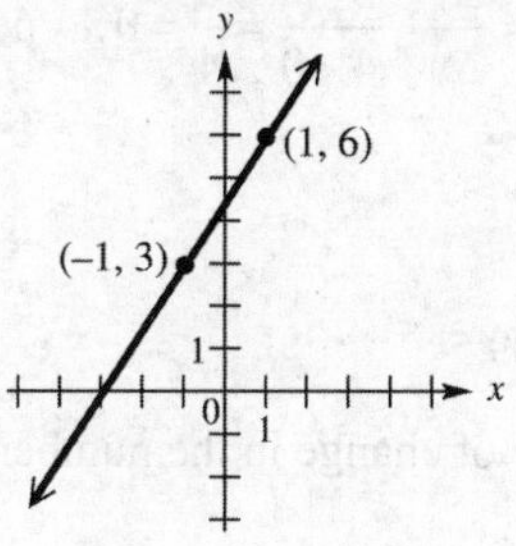

55. Through (3, –4), $m=-\frac{1}{3}$

First locate the point (3, –4).

Since the slope is $-\frac{1}{3}$, a change of 3 units horizontally (3 units to the right) produces a change of –1 unit vertically (1 unit down). This gives a second point, (6, –5), which can be used to complete the graph.

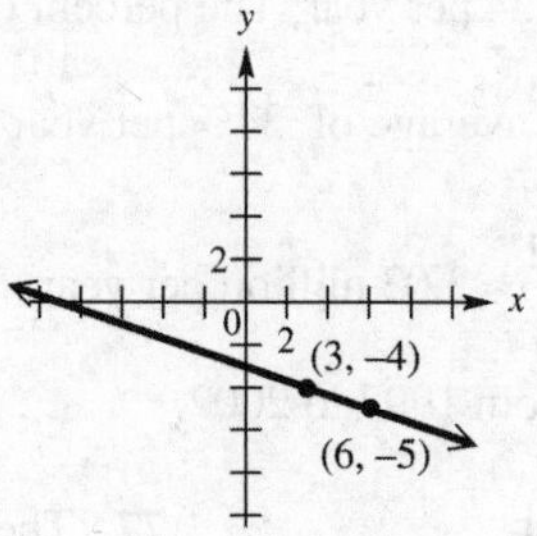

57. Through $\left(-\frac{1}{2}, 4\right)$, $m = 0$

The graph is the horizontal line through $\left(-\frac{1}{2}, 4\right)$.

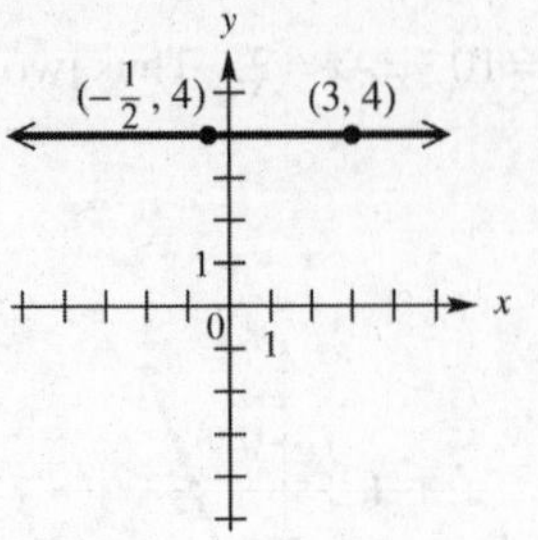

59. $m = \frac{1}{2}$ matches graph D because the line rises gradually as x increases.

61. $m = 0$ matches graph A because horizontal lines have slopes of 0.

63. $m = 2$ matches graph E because the line rises rapidly as x increases.

65. The average rate of change is $m = \frac{\Delta y}{\Delta x} = \frac{20-4}{4-0} = \frac{-16}{4} = -\$4$ (thousand) per year; The value of the machine is decreasing \$4000 each year during these years.

67. The average rate of change is $m = \frac{\Delta y}{\Delta x} = \frac{3-3}{4-0} = \frac{0}{4} = 0\%$ per year; The percent of pay raise is not changing - it is 3% each year.

69. **(a)** Answers will vary.

(b) $m = \frac{12{,}057 - 2773}{1999 - 1950} = \frac{9284}{49} \approx 189.5$

This means that the average rate of change in the number of radio stations per year is an increase of about 189.5 stations.

71. **(a)** $m = \frac{y_2 - y_1}{x_2 - x_1} = \frac{20.8 - 25.9}{1998 - 1995} = \frac{-5.1}{3} = -1.7$ million recipients per year

(b) The negative slope means the numbers of recipients *decreased* by 1.7 million each year.

73. $m = \frac{y_2 - y_1}{x_2 - x_1} = \frac{16.7 - 15}{2000 - 1995} = \frac{1.7}{5} = .34$ per year; The percent of freshman listing business as their probable field of study increased an average of .34% per year from 1995 to 2000.

75. $m = \frac{y_2 - y_1}{x_2 - x_1} = \frac{15.5 - .349}{2002 - 1997} = \frac{15.151}{5} \approx 3.03$ million per year; Sales of DVD players increased an average of 3.03 million each year from 1997 to 2002.

76. The first two points are $A(0, -6)$ and $B(1, -3)$.

$m = \frac{-3-(-6)}{1-0} = \frac{3}{1} = 3$

77. The second and third points are B(1, –3) and C(2, 0).

$m = \frac{0-(-3)}{2-1} = \frac{3}{1} = 3$

78. If we use any two points on a line to find its slope, we find that the slope is <u>the same</u> in all cases.

79. The first two points are $A(0, -6)$ and $B(1, -3)$.
$d(A, B) = \sqrt{[-3-(-6)]^2 + (1-0)^2} = \sqrt{3^2 + 1^2} = \sqrt{9+1} = \sqrt{10}$

80. The second and fourth points are $B(1, -3)$ and $D(3, 3)$.
$d(B, D) = \sqrt{[3-(-3)]^2 + (3-1)^2} = \sqrt{6^2 + 2^2} = \sqrt{36+4} = \sqrt{40} = 2\sqrt{10}$

81. The first and fourth points are $A(0, -6)$ and $D(3, 3)$.
$d(A, D) = \sqrt{[3-(-6)]^2 + (3-0)^2} = \sqrt{9^2 + 3^2} = \sqrt{81+9} = \sqrt{90} = 3\sqrt{10}$

82. $\sqrt{10} + 2\sqrt{10} = 3\sqrt{10}$; The sum is $3\sqrt{10}$, which is equal to the answer in Exercise 81.

83. If points *A*, *B*, and *C* lie on a line in that order, then the distance between *A* and *B* added to the distance between B and C is equal to the distance between A and C. (The order of the last two may be reversed.)

84. The midpoint of the segment joining $A(0, -6)$ and $G(6, 12)$ has coordinates $\left(\frac{0+6}{2}, \frac{-6+12}{2}\right) = \left(\frac{6}{2}, \frac{6}{2}\right)$ $= (3,3)$. The midpoint is $M(3, 3)$, which is the same as the middle entry in the table.

85. The midpoint of the segment joining $E(4, 6)$ and $F(5, 9)$ has coordinates $\left(\frac{4+5}{2}, \frac{6+9}{2}\right) = \left(\frac{9}{2}, \frac{15}{2}\right)$ = (4.5, 7.5). If the *x*-value 4.5 were in the table, the corresponding *y*-value would be 7.5.

87. **(a)** $C(x) = 11x + 180$

(b) $R(x) = 20x$

(c) $P(x) = R(x) - C(x)$
$= 20x - (11x + 180)$
$= 20x - 11x - 180 = 9x - 180$

(d) $C(x) = R(x)$
$11x + 180 = 20x$
$180 = 9x$
$20 = x$
20 units; produce

89. **(a)** $C(x) = 400x + 1650$

(b) $R(x) = 305x$

(c) $P(x) = R(x) - C(x) = 305x - (400x + 1650) = 305x - 400x - 1650 = -95x - 1650$

(d) $C(x) = R(x)$
$400x + 1650 = 305x \Rightarrow 95x + 1650 = 0 \Rightarrow 95x = -1650 \Rightarrow x \approx -17.37$ units

This result indicates a negative "break-even point," but the number of units produced must be a positive number. A calculator graph of the lines $Y_1 = 400X + 1650$ and $Y_2 = 305X$ on the same screen or solving the inequality $305x < 400x + 1650$ will show that $R(x) < C(x)$ for all positive values of *x* (in fact whenever *x* is greater than -17.4). Do not produce the product since it is impossible to make a profit.

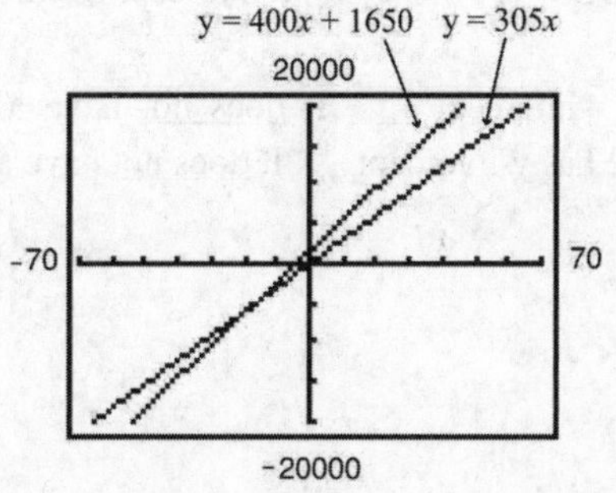

Section 2.4: Equations of Lines; Curve Fitting

1. $y = \frac{1}{4}x + 2$ is graphed in D.
The slope is $\frac{1}{4}$ and the y-intercept is 2.

3. $y - (-1) = \frac{3}{2}(x - 1)$ is graphed in C.
The slope is $\frac{3}{2}$ and a point on the graph is (1, –1).

5. Through (1, 3), $m = -2$
Write the equation in point-slope form.
$y - y_1 = m(x - x_1) \Rightarrow y - 3 = -2(x - 1)$
Then, change to standard form.
$$y - 3 = -2x + 2 \Rightarrow 2x + y = 5$$

7. Through (–5, 4), $m = -\frac{3}{2}$
Write the equation in point-slope form.
$$y - 4 = -\frac{3}{2}[x - (-5)]$$
Change to standard form.
$$2(y - 4) = -3(x + 5)$$
$$2y - 8 = -3x - 15$$
$$3x + 2y = -7$$

9. Through (–8, 4), undefined slope
Since undefined slope indicates a vertical line, the equation will have the form $x = a$. The equation of the line is $x = -8$.

11. Through (–1, 3) and (3, 4)
First find m.
$$m = \frac{4 - 3}{3 - (-1)} = \frac{1}{4}$$
Use either point and the point-slope form.
$$y - 4 = \frac{1}{4}(x - 3)$$
Change to slope-intercept form.
$$4(y - 4) = x - 3$$
$$4y - 16 = x - 3$$
$$4y = x + 13$$
$$y = \frac{1}{4}x + \frac{13}{4}$$

13. x-intercept 3, y-intercept –2
The line passes through (3, 0) and (0, –2). Use these points to find m.
$$m = \frac{-2 - 0}{0 - 3} = \frac{2}{3}$$
Using slope-intercept form we have $y = \frac{2}{3}x - 2$.

15. Vertical, through (–6, 4)
The equation of a vertical line has an equation of the form $x = a$. Since the line passes through (–6, 4), the equation is $x = -6$. (Since this slope of a vertical line is undefined, this equation cannot be written in slope-intercept form.)

17. $m = 5, b = 15$
Using slope-intercept form, we have $y = 5x + 15$.

19. $m = -\frac{2}{3}, b = -\frac{4}{5}$
Using slope-intercept form, we have $y = -\frac{2}{3}x - \frac{4}{5}$.

21. slope 0, y-intercept $\frac{3}{2}$
These represent $m = 0$ and $b = \frac{3}{2}$. Using slope-intercept form we have $y = (0)x + \frac{3}{2} \Rightarrow y = \frac{3}{2}$.

23. The line $x + 2 = 0$ has x-intercept <u>–2</u>. It <u>does not</u> have a y-intercept. The slope of this line is <u>undefined</u>. The line $4y = 2$ has y-intercept $\frac{1}{2}$. It <u>does not</u> have an x-intercept. The slope of this line is <u>0</u>.

25. **(a)** The graph of $y = 2x + 3$ has a positive slope and a positive y-intercept. These conditions match graph B.

(b) The graph of $y = -2x + 3$ has a negative slope and a positive y-intercept. These conditions match graph D.

(c) The graph of $y = 2x - 3$ has a positive slope and a negative y-intercept. These conditions match graph A.

(d) The graph of $y = -2x - 3$ has a negative slope and a negative y-intercept. These conditions match graph C.

27. $y = 3x - 1$
This equation is in the slope-intercept form, $y = mx + b$.
slope: 3; y-intercept: -1

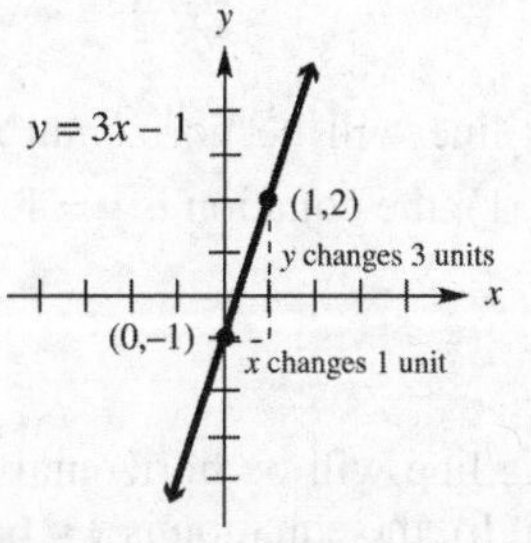

29. $4x - y = 7$
Solve for y to write the equation in slope-intercept form.
$-y = -4x + 7 \Rightarrow y = 4x - 7$
slope: 4; y-intercept: -7

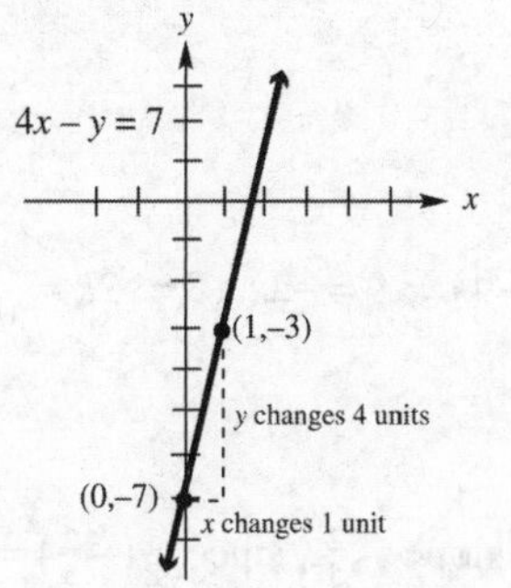

31. $4y = -3x$
$$y = -\tfrac{3}{4}x \text{ or } y = -\tfrac{3}{4}x + 0$$
slope: $-\frac{3}{4}$; y-intercept 0

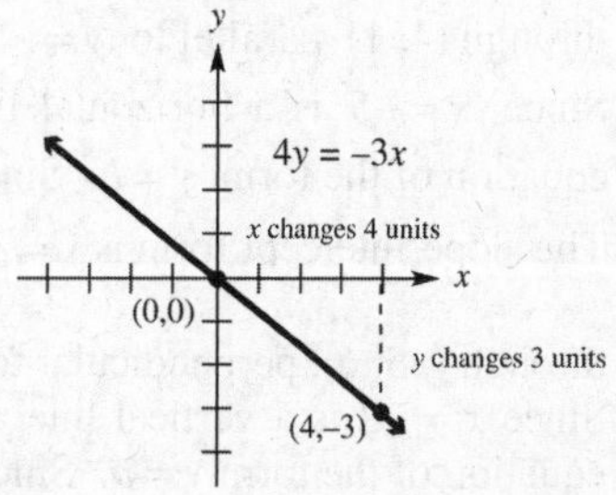

33. $x + 2y = -4$
Solve the equation for y to write the equation in slope-intercept form.
$2y = -x - 4 \Rightarrow y = -\frac{1}{2}x - 2$
slope: $-\frac{1}{2}$; y-intercept: -2

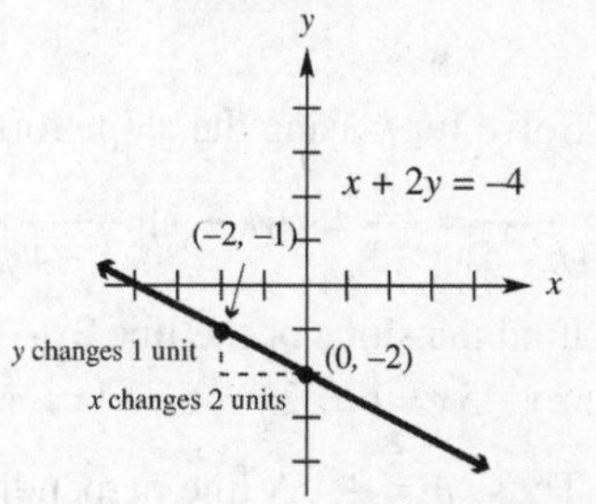

35. **(a)** through $(-1, 4)$, parallel to $x + 3y = 5$
First, find the slope of the line $x + 3y = 5$ by writing this equation in slope-intercept form.
$$x + 3y = 5 \Rightarrow 3y = -x + 5 \Rightarrow y = -\tfrac{1}{3}x + \tfrac{5}{3}$$
The slope is $-\frac{1}{3}$. Since the lines are parallel, $-\frac{1}{3}$ is also the slope of the line whose equation is to be found. Substitute $m = -\frac{1}{3}$, $x_1 = -1$, and $y_1 = 4$ into the point-slope form.
$$y - y_1 = m(x - x_1) \Rightarrow y - 4 = -\tfrac{1}{3}[x - (-1)] \Rightarrow y - 4 = -\tfrac{1}{3}(x + 1)$$
$$3(y - 4) = -1(x + 1) \Rightarrow 3y - 12 = -x - 1 \Rightarrow x + 3y = 11$$

(b) Solve for y. $3y = -x + 11 \Rightarrow y = -\frac{1}{3}x + \frac{11}{3}$

37. (a) through (1, 6), perpendicular to $3x + 5y = 1$
First, find the slope of the line $3x + 5y = 1$ by writing this equation in slope-intercept form.

$$3x+5y=1 \Rightarrow 5y=-3x+1 \Rightarrow y=-\tfrac{3}{5}x+\tfrac{1}{5}$$

This line has a slope of $-\frac{3}{5}$. The slope of any line perpendicular to this line is $\frac{5}{3}$, since $-\frac{3}{5}\left(\frac{5}{3}\right)=-1$.

Substitute $m=\frac{5}{3}$, $x_1=1$, and $y_1=6$ into the point-slope form.

$$y-6=\tfrac{5}{3}(x-1) \Rightarrow 3(y-6)=5(x-1) \Rightarrow 3y-18=5x-5$$
$$-13=5x-3y \text{ or } 5x-3y=-13$$

(b) Solve for y. $3y=5x+13 \Rightarrow y=\frac{5}{3}x+\frac{13}{3}$

39. (a) through (4, 1), parallel to $y=-5$
Since $y=-5$ is a horizontal line, any line parallel to this line will be horizontal and have an equation of the form $y=b$. Since the line passes through (4, 1), the equation is $y = 1$.

(b) The slope-intercept form is $y = 1$.

41. (a) through (–5, 6), perpendicular to $x = -2$.
Since $x = -2$ is a vertical line, any line perpendicular to this line will be horizontal and have an equation of the form $y = b$. Since the line passes through (–5, 6), the equation is $y = 6$.

(b) The slope-intercept form is $y = 6$.

43. (a) Find the slope of the line $3y + 2x = 6$.

$$3y+2x=6 \Rightarrow 3y=-2x+6 \Rightarrow y=-\tfrac{2}{3}x+2$$

Thus, $m=-\frac{2}{3}$. A line parallel to $3y + 2x = 6$ also has slope $-\frac{2}{3}$.

$$\frac{2-(-1)}{k-4}=-\frac{2}{3}$$

Solve for k using the slope formula.

$$\frac{3}{k-4}=-\frac{2}{3} \Rightarrow 3(k-4)\left(\frac{3}{k-4}\right)=3(k-4)\left(-\frac{2}{3}\right) \Rightarrow 9=-2(k-4) \Rightarrow 9=-2k+8 \Rightarrow 2k=-1 \Rightarrow k=-\tfrac{1}{2}$$

(b) Find the slope of the line $2y - 5x = 1$.
$2y-5x=1 \Rightarrow 2y=5x+1 \Rightarrow y=\frac{5}{2}x+\frac{1}{2}$

Thus, $m=\frac{5}{2}$. A line perpendicular to $2y - 5x = 1$ will have slope $-\frac{2}{5}$, since $\frac{5}{2}\left(-\frac{2}{5}\right)=-1$.
Solve this equation for k.

$$\frac{3}{k-4}=-\frac{2}{5} \Rightarrow 5(k-4)\left(\frac{3}{k-4}\right)=5(k-4)\left(-\frac{2}{5}\right) \Rightarrow 15=-2(k-4) \Rightarrow 15=-2k+8 \Rightarrow 2k=-7 \Rightarrow k=-\tfrac{7}{2}$$

45. (1970, 43.3), (1995, 58.9)

$$m=\frac{58.9-43.3}{1995-1970}=\frac{15.6}{25}=.624$$

Now use either point, say (1970, 43.3), and the point-slope form to find the equation.

$$y-43.3=.624(x-1970)$$
$$y-43.3=.624x-1229.28$$
$$y=.624x-1185.98$$

Let $x = 1996$. We have $y = .624\,(1996) - 1185.98 \approx 59.5$. The percent of women in the civilian labor force is predicted to be 59.5%. This figure is very close to the actual figure.

47. **(a)** (0, 9340), (12, 18,116)

$$m = \frac{18{,}116 - 9340}{12 - 0} = \frac{8776}{12} \approx 731.3$$

From the point (0, 9340), the value of b is 9340. Therefore we have the following.

$$f(x) \approx 731.3x + 9340$$

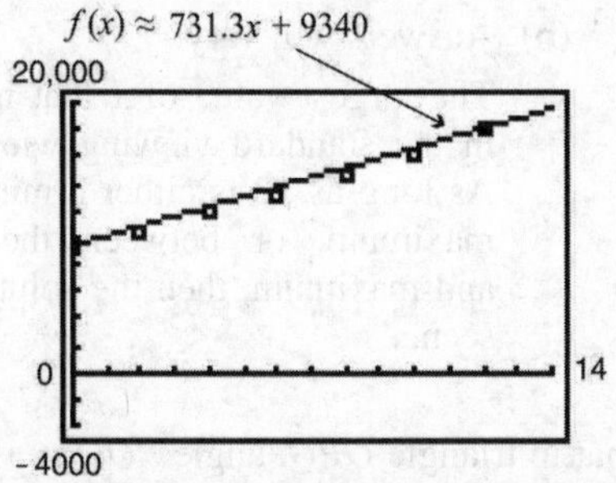

The average tuition increase is about \$731 per year for the period, because this is the slope of the line.

(b) 1995 corresponds to $x = 5$.

$$f(5) \approx 731.3(5) + 9340 = 12{,}996.50$$

This is a fairly good approximation.

(c) From the calculator,
$f(x) \approx 730.14x + 8984.71$

49. **(a)** The ordered pairs are (0, 32) and (100, 212).

The slope is $m = \frac{212 - 32}{100 - 0} = \frac{180}{100} = \frac{9}{5}$.

Use $(x_1, y_1) = (0, 32)$ and $m = \frac{9}{5}$ in the point-slope form.

$$y - y_1 = m(x - x_1)$$
$$y - 32 = \tfrac{9}{5}(x - 0)$$
$$y - 32 = \tfrac{9}{5}x$$
$$y = \tfrac{9}{5}x + 32$$
$$\text{or } F = \tfrac{9}{5}C + 32$$

(b) $F = \frac{9}{5}C + 32$

$$5F = 9(C + 32)$$
$$5F = 9C + 160$$
$$9C = 5F - 160$$
$$9C = 5(F - 32)$$
$$C = \tfrac{5}{9}(F - 32)$$

(c) If $F = C$,

$$F = \tfrac{5}{9}(F - 32)$$
$$9F = 5(F - 32)$$
$$9F = 5F - 160$$
$$4F = -160$$
$$F = -40.$$

$F = C$ when F is $-40°$.

51. **(a)** Since we are wanting to find C as a function of I, use the points (6650, 3839) and (4215, 5494), where the first component represents the independent variable, I. First find the slope of the line.

$$m = \frac{5494 - 3839}{4215 - 6650} = \frac{1655}{-2435} \approx -.6797$$

Now use either point, say (6650, 3839), and the point-slope form to find the equation.

$$y - 3839 = -.6797(x - 6650)$$
$$y - 3839 = -.6797x + 4520.005$$
$$y \approx -.6797x + 8359$$
$$\text{or } C = -.6797I + 8359$$

(b) Since the slope is $-.6797$, the marginal propensity to consume is $-.6797$.

53. $7x - 2x + 4 - 5 = 3x + 1$

(a) $7x - 2x + 4 - 5 - 3x - 1 = 0$

$$2x - 2 = 0$$

$y = 2x - 2$

(b) 1

(c) $7x - 2x + 4 - 5 = 3x + 1$

$$5x - 1 = 3x + 1$$
$$2x - 1 = 1$$
$$2x = 2$$
$$x = 1$$

Solution set: $\{1\}$

55. $4x-3(4-2x)=2(x-3)+6x+2$

(a) $4x-3(4-2x)-2(x-3)-6x-2=0$

$4x-12+6x-2x+6-6x-2=0$

$2x-8=0$

$y=2x-8$

(b) 4

(c) $4x-3(4-2x)=2(x-3)+6x+2$

$4x-12+6x=2x-6+6x+2$

$10x-12=8x-4 \Rightarrow 2x-12=-4$

$2x=8 \Rightarrow x=4$

Solution set: $\{4\}$

57. (a) $-2(x-5)=-x-2$

$-2x+10=-x-2$

$10=x-2$

$12=x$

Solution set: $\{12\}$

(b) Answers will vary.
The largest value of x that is displayed in the standard viewing window is 10. As long as 12 is either a minimum or a maximum, or between the minimum and maximum, then the solution will be seen.

58. The Pythagorean Theorem and its converse assure us that in triangle OPQ, angle POQ is a right angle if and only if $[d(O, P)]^2+[d(O, Q)]^2=[d(P, Q)]^2$.

59. $d(O, P)=\sqrt{(x_1-0)^2+(m_1x_1-0)^2}$

$=\sqrt{x_1^{\,2}+m_1^{\,2}x_1^{\,2}}$

60. $d(O, Q)=\sqrt{(x_2-0)^2+(m_2x_2-0)^2}$

$=\sqrt{x_2^{\,2}+m_2^{\,2}x_2^{\,2}}$

61. $d(P, Q)=\sqrt{(x_2-x_1)^2+(m_2x_2-m_1x_1)^2}$

62.

$$[d(O, P)]^2+[d(O, Q)]^2=[d(P, Q)]^2$$

$$\left[\sqrt{x_1^{\,2}+m_1^{\,2}x_1^{\,2}}\right]^2+\left[\sqrt{x_2^{\,2}+m_2^{\,2}x_2^{\,2}}\right]^2=\left[\sqrt{(x_2-x_1)^2+(m_2x_2-m_1x_1)^2}\right]^2$$

$$\left(x_1^{\,2}+m_1^{\,2}x_1^{\,2}\right)+\left(x_2^{\,2}+m_2^{\,2}x_2^{\,2}\right)=(x_2-x_1)^2+(m_2x_2-m_1x_1)^2$$

$$x_1^{\,2}+m_1^{\,2}x_1^{\,2}+x_2^{\,2}+m_2^{\,2}x_2^{\,2}=x_2^{\,2}-2x_2x_1+x_1^{\,2}+m_2^{\,2}x_2^{\,2}-2m_1m_2x_1x_2+m_1^{\,2}x_1^{\,2}$$

$$0=-2x_2x_1-2m_1m_2x_1x_2$$

$$-2m_1m_2x_1x-2x_2x_1=0$$

63. $-2m_1m_2x_1x_2-2x_1x_2=0$

$-2x_1x_2(m_1m_2+1)=0$

64. $-2x_1x_2(m_1m_2+1)=0$

Since $x_1 \neq 0$ and $x_2 \neq 0$, we have $m_1m_2+1=0$ implying that $m_1m_2=-1$.

65. If two nonvertical lines are perpendicular, then the product of the slopes of these lines is –1.

67. Label the points as follows: $A(-1,5)$, $B(2,-4)$, and $C(4,-10)$.

For A and B: $m=\dfrac{-4-5}{2-(-1)}=\dfrac{-9}{3}=-3$

For B and C, $m=\dfrac{-10-(-4)}{4-2}=\dfrac{-6}{2}=-3$

For A and C, $m=\dfrac{-10-5}{4-(-1)}=\dfrac{-15}{5}=-3$

Since all three slopes are the same, the points are collinear.

69. $A(-1, 4), B(-2, -1), C(1, 14)$

For A and B, $m = \dfrac{-1-4}{-2-(-1)} = \dfrac{-5}{-1} = 5$

For B and C, $m = \dfrac{14-(-1)}{1-(-2)} = \dfrac{15}{3} = 5$

For A and C, $m = \dfrac{14-4}{1-(-1)} = \dfrac{10}{2} = 5$

Since all three slopes are the same, the points are collinear.

Summary Exercises on Graphs, Functions, and Equations

1. $P(3, 5), Q(2, -3)$

(a) $d(P, Q) = \sqrt{(2-3)^2 + (-3-5)^2}$

$= \sqrt{(-1)^2 + (-8)^2}$

$= \sqrt{1+64} = \sqrt{65}$

(b) The midpoint M of the segment joining points P and Q has coordinates

$$\left(\frac{3+2}{2}, \frac{5+(-3)}{2}\right) = \left(\frac{5}{2}, \frac{2}{2}\right) = \left(\frac{5}{2}, 1\right).$$

(c) First find m: $m = \dfrac{-3-5}{2-3} = \dfrac{-8}{-1} = 8$

Use either point and the point-slope form.

$$y - 5 = 8(x-3)$$

Change to slope-intercept form.

$$y - 5 = 8x - 24$$
$$y = 8x - 19$$

3. $P(-2, 2), Q(3, 2)$

(a) $d(P, Q) = \sqrt{[3-(-2)]^2 + (2-2)^2} = \sqrt{5^2 + 0^2} = \sqrt{25+0} = \sqrt{25} = 5$

(b) The midpoint M of the segment joining points P and Q has the following coordinates.

$$\left(\frac{-2+3}{2}, \frac{2+2}{2}\right) = \left(\frac{1}{2}, \frac{4}{2}\right) = \left(\frac{1}{2}, 2\right)$$

(c) First find m: $m = \dfrac{2-2}{3-(-2)} = \dfrac{0}{5} = 0$

All lines that have a slope of 0 are horizontal lines. The equation of a horizontal line has an equation of the form $y = b$. Since the line passes through $(3, 2)$, the equation is $y = 2$.

5. $P(5, -1), Q(5, 1)$

(a) $d(P, Q) = \sqrt{(5-5)^2 + [1-(-1)]^2}$

$= \sqrt{0^2 + 2^2} = \sqrt{0+4} = \sqrt{4} = 2$

(b) The midpoint M of the segment joining points P and Q has the following coordinates.

$$\left(\frac{5+5}{2}, \frac{-1+1}{2}\right) = \left(\frac{10}{2}, \frac{0}{2}\right) = (5, 0)$$

(c) First find m.

$$m = \frac{1-(-1)}{5-5} = \frac{2}{0} = \text{undefined}$$

All lines that have an undefined slope are vertical lines. The equation of a vertical line has an equation of the form $x = a$. Since the line passes through $(5, 1)$, the equation is $x = 5$. (Since this slope of a vertical line is undefined, this equation cannot be written in slope-intercept form.)

7. $P\left(2\sqrt{3},3\sqrt{5}\right),\ Q\left(6\sqrt{3},3\sqrt{5}\right)$

(a) $d(P,Q)=\sqrt{\left(6\sqrt{3}-2\sqrt{3}\right)^2+\left(3\sqrt{5}-3\sqrt{5}\right)^2}=\sqrt{\left(4\sqrt{3}\right)^2+0^2}=\sqrt{48}=4\sqrt{3}$

(b) The midpoint M of the segment joining points P and Q has coordinates

$$\left(\frac{2\sqrt{3}+6\sqrt{3}}{2},\frac{3\sqrt{5}+3\sqrt{5}}{2}\right)=\left(\frac{8\sqrt{3}}{2},\frac{6\sqrt{5}}{2}\right)=\left(4\sqrt{3},\ 3\sqrt{5}\right).$$

(c) First find m: $m=\dfrac{3\sqrt{5}-3\sqrt{5}}{6\sqrt{3}-2\sqrt{3}}=\dfrac{0}{4\sqrt{3}}=0$

All lines that have a slope of 0 are horizontal lines. The equation of a horizontal line has an equation of the form $y=b$. Since the line passes through $\left(2\sqrt{3},3\sqrt{5}\right)$, the equation is $y=3\sqrt{5}$.

9. Through $(-2,1)$ and $(4,-1)$

First find m: $m=\dfrac{-1-1}{4-(-2)}=\dfrac{-2}{6}=-\dfrac{1}{3}$

Use either point and the point-slope form.

$$y-(-1)=-\tfrac{1}{3}(x-4)$$

Change to slope-intercept form.

$$3(y+1)=-(x-4)$$
$$3y+3=-x+4$$
$$3y=-x+1$$
$$y=-\tfrac{1}{3}x+\tfrac{1}{3}$$

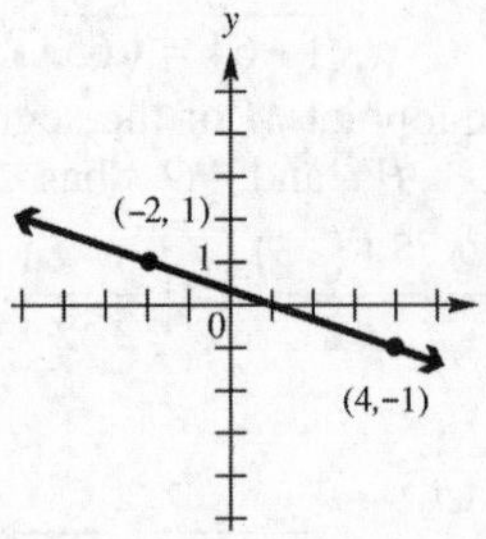

11. the circle with center $(2,-1)$ and radius 3

$$(x-2)^2+[y-(-1)]^2=3^2$$
$$(x-2)^2+(y+1)^2=9$$

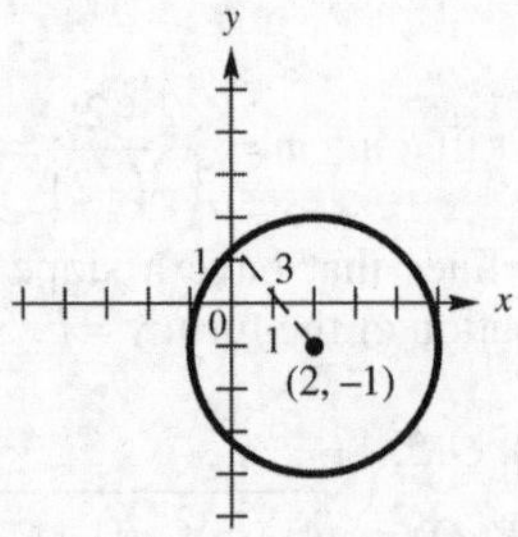

13. the line through $(3,-5)$ with slope $-\frac{5}{6}$

Write the equation in point-slope form.

$$y-(-5)=-\tfrac{5}{6}(x-3)$$

Change to standard form.

$$6(y+5)=-5(x-3)\Rightarrow 6y+30=-5x+15$$
$$6y=-5x-15\Rightarrow y=-\tfrac{5}{6}x-\tfrac{15}{6}$$
$$y=-\tfrac{5}{6}x-\tfrac{5}{2}$$

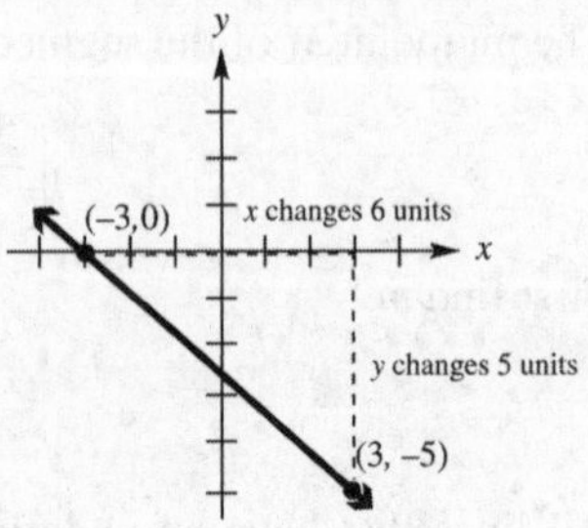

15. a line through (–3, 2) and parallel to the line $2x+3y=6$

First, find the slope of the line $2x+3y=6$ by writing this equation in slope-intercept form.

$$2x+3y=6 \Rightarrow 3y=-2x+6 \Rightarrow y=-\tfrac{2}{3}x+2$$

The slope is $-\frac{2}{3}$. Since the lines are parallel, $-\frac{2}{3}$ is also the slope of the line whose equation is to be found. Substitute $m=-\frac{2}{3}$, $x_1=-3$, and $y_1=2$ into the point-slope form.

$$y-y_1=m(x-x_1) \Rightarrow y-2=-\tfrac{2}{3}[x-(-3)] \Rightarrow 3(y-2)=-2(x+3)$$

$$3y-6=-2x-6 \Rightarrow 3y=-2x \Rightarrow y=-\tfrac{2}{3}x$$

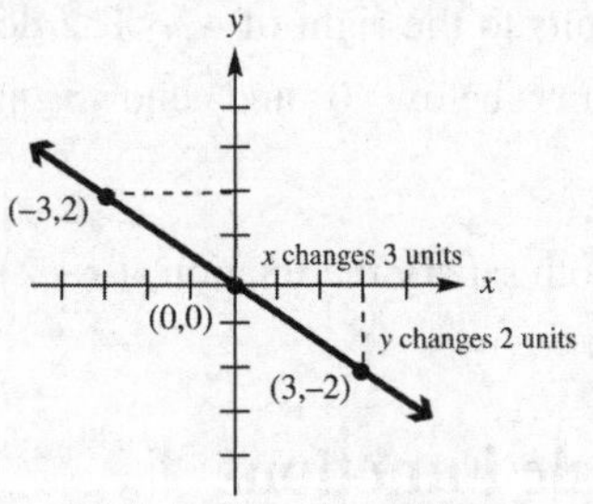

17. $x^2-4x+y^2+2y=4$

Complete the square on *x* and *y* separately.

$$(x^2-4x)+(y^2+2y)=4$$

$$(x^2-4x+4)+(y^2+2y+1)=4+4+1$$

$$(x-2)^2+(y+1)^2=9$$

Yes, it is a circle. The circle has its center at $(2,-1)$ and radius 3.

19. $x^2-12x+y^2+20=0$

Complete the square on *x* and *y* separately.

$$(x^2-12x)+y^2=-20 \Rightarrow (x^2-12x+36)+y^2=-20+36 \Rightarrow (x-6)^2+y^2=16$$

Yes, it is a circle. The circle has its center at (6, 0) and radius 4.

21. $x^2-2x+y^2+10=0$

Complete the square on *x* and *y* separately.

$$(x^2-2x)+y^2=-10$$

$$(x^2-2x+1)+y^2=-10+1$$

$$(x-1)^2+y^2=-9$$

No, it is not a circle.

23. **(a)** The equation can be rewritten as $-2y=-3x+1 \Rightarrow y=\frac{3}{2}x-\frac{1}{2}$. x can be any real number, so the domain is all real numbers and the range is also all real numbers.

domain: $(-\infty,\infty)$; range: $(-\infty,\infty)$

(b) Each value of *x* corresponds to just one value of *y*. $3x-2y=1$ represents a function.

$$y=\tfrac{3}{2}x-\tfrac{1}{2} \Rightarrow f(x)=\tfrac{3}{2}x-\tfrac{1}{2}$$

$$f(-2)=\tfrac{3}{2}(-2)-\tfrac{1}{2}=\tfrac{-6}{2}-\tfrac{1}{2}=-\tfrac{7}{2}$$

25. (a) The equation can be rewritten as $-4y=-x-6 \Rightarrow y=\frac{1}{4}x+\frac{6}{4} \Rightarrow y=\frac{1}{4}x+\frac{3}{2}$. x can be any real number, so the domain is all real numbers and the range is also all real numbers.

domain: $(-\infty,\infty)$; range: $(-\infty,\infty)$

(b) Each value of x corresponds to just one value of y. $x-4y=-6$ represents a function.

$$y=\tfrac{1}{4}x+\tfrac{3}{2} \Rightarrow f(x)=\tfrac{1}{4}x+\tfrac{3}{2} \Rightarrow f(-2)=\tfrac{1}{4}(-2)+\tfrac{3}{2}=-\tfrac{1}{2}+\tfrac{3}{2}=\tfrac{2}{2}=1$$

27. (a) $(x+2)^2+y^2=25$ is a circle centered at $(-2,0)$ with a radius of 5. The domain will start 5 units to the left of –2 and end 5 units to the right of –2. The domain will be $[-2-5,-2+5]=[-7,3]$. The range will start 5 units below 0 and end 5 units above 0. The range will be $[0-5,0+5]=[-5,5]$.

(b) Since $(-2,5)$ and $(-2,-5)$ both satisfy the relation, $(x+2)^2+y^2=25$ does not represent a function.

Section 2.5: Graphs of Basic Functions

1. The function is continuous over the entire domain of real numbers $(-\infty,\infty)$.

3. The function is continuous over the interval $[0,\infty)$.

5. The function has a point of discontinuity at $x=1$. It is continuous over the interval $(-\infty,1)$ and the interval $[1,\infty)$.

7. The equation $y=x^2$ matches graph E. The domain is $(-\infty,\infty)$.

9. The equation $y=x^3$ matches graph A. The range is $(-\infty,\infty)$.

11. Graph F is the graph of the identity function. Its equation is $y=x$.

13. The equation $y=\sqrt[3]{x}$ matches graph H. No, there is no interval over which the function is decreasing.

15. The graph in B is discontinuous at many points. Assuming the graph continues, the range would be $\{\ldots,-3,-2,-1,0,1,2,3,\ldots\}$.

17. $f(x)=\begin{cases}2x & \text{if } x\le -1\\ x-1 & \text{if } x>-1\end{cases}$

(a) $f(-5)=2(-5)=-10$

(b) $f(-1)=2(-1)=-2$

(c) $f(0)=0-1=-1$

(d) $f(3)=3-1=2$

19. $f(x)=\begin{cases}2+x & \text{if } x<-4\\ -x & \text{if } -4\le x\le 2\\ 3x & \text{if } x>2\end{cases}$

(a) $f(-5)=2+(-5)=-3$

(b) $f(-1)=-(-1)=1$

(c) $f(0)=-0=0$

(d) $f(3)=3\cdot 3=9$

21. $f(x)=\begin{cases}x-1 & \text{if } x\le 3\\ 2 & \text{if } x>3\end{cases}$

Draw the graph of $y = x - 1$ to the left of $x = 3$, including the endpoint at $x = 3$. Draw the graph of $y = 2$ to the right of $x = 3$, and note that the endpoint at $x = 3$ coincides with the endpoint of the other ray.

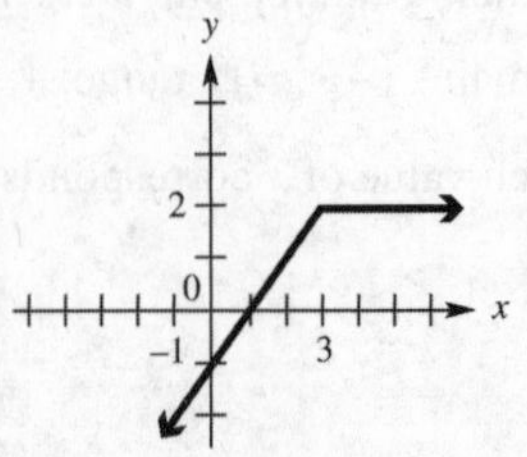

23. $f(x)=\begin{cases}4-x & \text{if } x<2\\ 1+2x & \text{if } x\geq 2\end{cases}$

Draw the graph of $y=4-x$ to the left of $x = 2$, but do not include the endpoint. Draw the graph of $y=1+2x$ to the right of $x = 2$, including the endpoint.

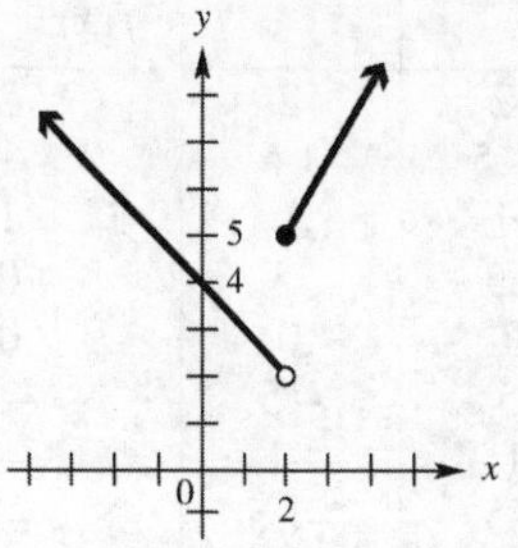

25. $f(x)=\begin{cases}5x-4 & \text{if } x\leq 1\\ x & \text{if } x>1\end{cases}$

Graph the line $y=5x-4$ to the left of $x=1$, including the endpoint. Draw $y=x$ to the right of $x=1$, and note that the endpoint at $x=1$ coincides with the endpoint of the other ray.

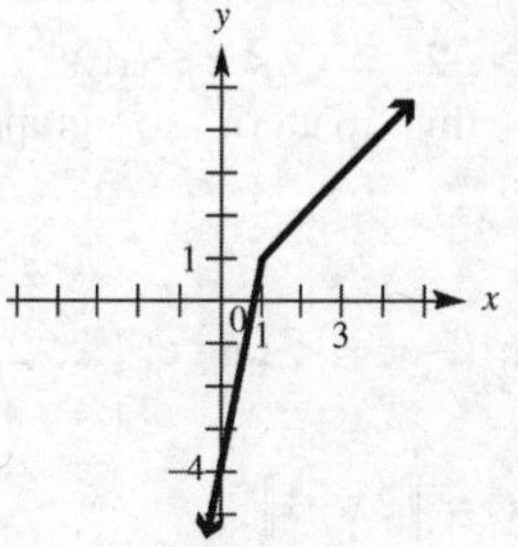

27. $f(x)=\begin{cases}2+x & \text{if } x<-4\\ -x & \text{if } -4\leq x\leq 5\\ 3x & \text{if } x>5\end{cases}$

Draw the graph of $y = 2 + x$ to the left of -4, but do not include the endpoint at $x = 4$. Draw the graph of $y = -x$ between -4 and 5, including both endpoints. Draw the graph of $y = 3x$ to the right of 5, but do not include the endpoint at $x = 5$.

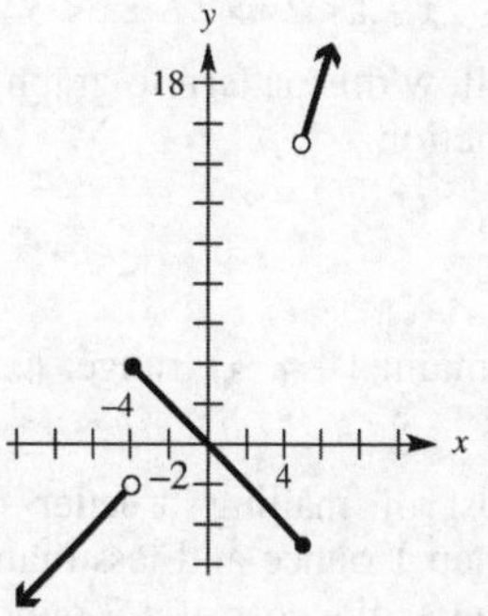

29. The solid circle on the graph shows that the endpoint (0, –1) is part of the graph, while the open circle shows that the endpoint (0, 1) is not part of the graph. The graph is made up of parts of two horizontal lines. The function which fits this graph is

$f(x)=\begin{cases}-1 & \text{if } x\leq 0\\ 1 & \text{if } x>0.\end{cases}$

domain: $(-\infty,\infty)$; range: $\{-1, 1\}$

31. The graph is made up of parts of two horizontal lines. The solid circle shows that the endpoint (0, 2) of the one on the left belongs to the graph, while the open circle shows that the endpoint (0, –1) of the one on the right does not belong to the graph. The function that fits this graph is

$f(x)=\begin{cases}2 & \text{if } x\leq 0\\ -1 & \text{if } x>1.\end{cases}$

domain: $(-\infty,0]\cup(1,\infty)$; range: $\{-1, 2\}$

33. $f(x) = [\![-x]\!]$

Plot points.

x	$-x$	$f(x) = [\![-x]\!]$
−2	2	2
−1.5	1.5	1
−1	1	1
−.5	.5	0
0	0	0
.5	−.5	−1
1	−1	−1
1.5	−1.5	−2
2	−2	−2

More generally, to get $y = 0$, we need $0 \le -x < 1 \Rightarrow 0 \ge x > -1 \Rightarrow -1 < x \le 0$.

To get $y = 1$, we need $1 \le -x < 2 \Rightarrow -1 \ge x > -2 \Rightarrow -2 < x \le -1$.

Follow this pattern to graph the step function.

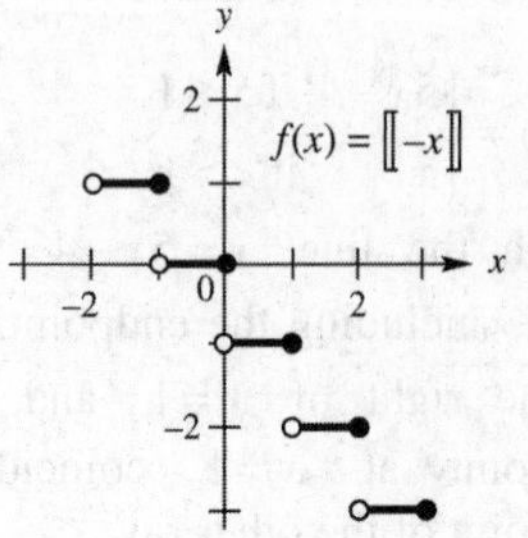

domain: $(-\infty, \infty)$; range: $\{\ldots,-2,-1,0,1,2,\ldots\}$

35. $g(x) = [\![2x-1]\!]$

To get $y = 0$, we need

$0 \le 2x-1 < 1 \Rightarrow 1 \le 2x < 2 \Rightarrow \frac{1}{2} \le x < 1.$

To get $y = 1$, we need

$1 \le 2x-1 < 2 \Rightarrow 2 \le 2x < 3 \Rightarrow 1 \le x < \frac{3}{2}.$

Follow this pattern to graph the step function.

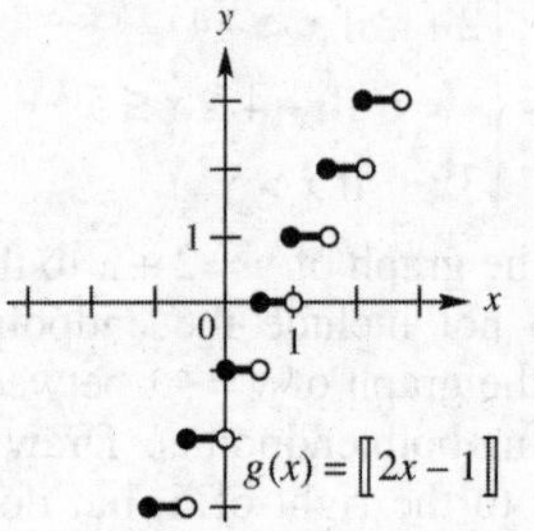

domain: $(-\infty, \infty)$; range: $\{\ldots, 2,-1,0,1,2,\ldots\}$

37. The cost of mailing a letter that weights more than 1 ounce and less than 2 ounces is the same as the cost of a 2-ounce letter, and the cost of mailing a letter that weighs more than 2 ounces and less than 3 ounces is the same as the cost of a 3-ounce letter, etc.

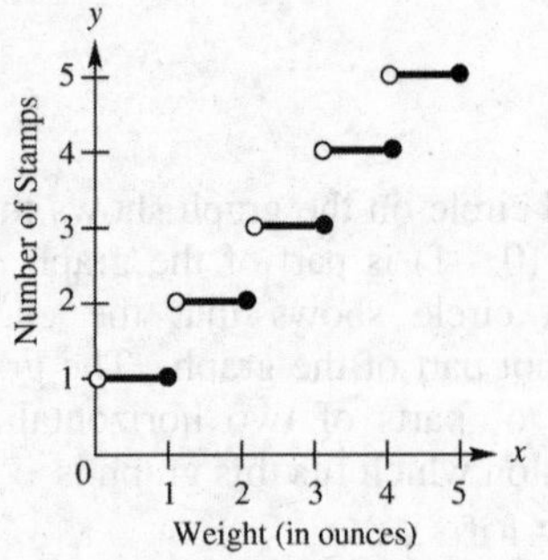

39. $f(x) = \begin{cases} x^2 - 4 \text{ if } x \ge 0 \\ -x+5 \text{ if } x < 0 \end{cases}$

The graph is a line with negative slope for $x < 0$ and a parabola opening upward for $x \ge 0$. This matches graph B.

41. $f(x) = \begin{cases} 6 \text{ if } x \ge 0 \\ -6 \text{ if } x < 0 \end{cases}$

The graph is the horizontal line $y = -6$ for $x < 0$ and the horizontal line $y = 6$ for $x \ge 0$. This matches graph D.

43. (a) For the interval $[3,6]$ we must consider the points $(3,73)$ and $(6,72)$.

First find m: $m=\dfrac{72-73}{6-3}=\dfrac{-1}{3}=-\dfrac{1}{3}$

Use either point and the point-slope form.

$$\begin{aligned} y-72&=-\tfrac{1}{3}(x-6)\\ 3(y-72)&=-(x-6)\\ 3y-216&=-x+6\\ 3y&=-x+222\\ y&=-\tfrac{1}{3}x+74 \end{aligned}$$

For the interval $(6,9]$ we must consider the points $(6,72)$ and $(9,69)$.

First find m: $m=\dfrac{69-72}{9-6}=\dfrac{-3}{3}=-1$

Use either point and the point-slope form.

$$\begin{aligned} y-72&=-1(x-6)\\ y-72&=-x+6\\ y&=-x+78 \end{aligned}$$

(b) $f(x)=\begin{cases} -\frac{1}{3}x+74 & \text{if } 3\le x\le 6\\ -x+78 & \text{if } 6<x\le 9 \end{cases}$

45. $i(t)=\begin{cases} 40t+100 & \text{if } 0\le t\le 3\\ 220 & \text{if } 3<t\le 8\\ -80t+860 & \text{if } 8<t\le 10\\ 60 & \text{if } 10<t\le 24 \end{cases}$

(a) 6 A.M. is the starting time, so 7 A.M. corresponds to $t = 1$.
Use $i(t) = 40(t) + 100$.
Since $t = 1$,
$i(1)=40(1)+100=40+100=140.$

(b) 9 A.M. corresponds to $t = 3$.
$i(3)=40(3)+100=120+100=220$

(c) 10 A.M. corresponds to $t = 4$.
Use $i(t) = 220$.
$i(4) = 220$

(d) Noon corresponds to $t = 6$.
Use $i(t) = 220$.
$i(6) = 220$

(e) 3 P.M. corresponds to $t = 9$.
Use $i(t)=-80t+860$.
$i(9)=-80(9)+860=-720+860=140$

(f) 5 P.M. corresponds to $t = 11$.
Use $i(t) = 60$.
$i(11) = 60$

(g) Midnight corresponds to $t = 18$.
Use $i(t) = 60$.
$i(18) = 60$

(h)

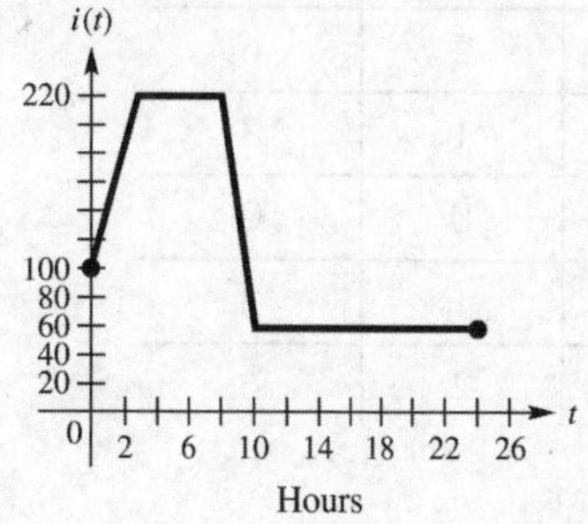

47. Since $x=y^2$ implies $y=\pm\sqrt{x}$, we have $y_1=\sqrt{x}$ and $y_2=-\sqrt{x}$.

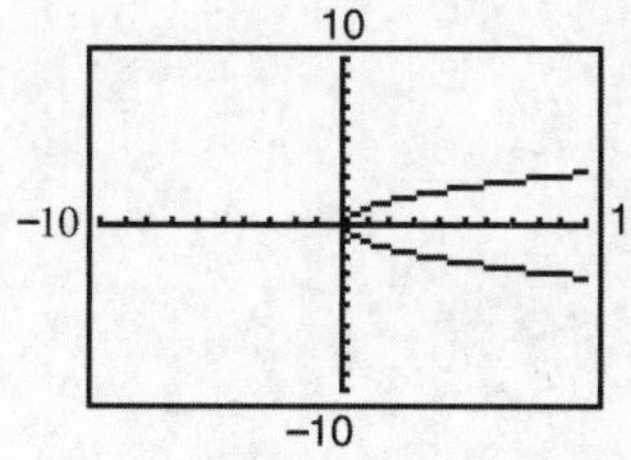

Section 2.6: Graphing Techniques

Connections (page 263)
Answers will vary.

Exercises

1. **(a)** B; $y=(x-7)^2$ is a shift of $y=x^2$, 7 units to the right.

(b) D; $y=x^2-7$ is a shift of $y=x^2$, 7 units downward.

(c) E; $y=7x^2$ is a vertical stretch of $y=x^2$, by a factor of 7.

(d) A; $y=(x+7)^2$ is a shift of $y=x^2$, 7 units to the left.

(e) C; $y=x^2+7$ is a shift of $y=x^2$, 7 units upward.

3. **(a)** B; $y=x^2+2$ is a shift of $y=x^2$, 2 units upward.

(b) A; $y=x^2-2$ is a shift of $y=x^2$, 2 units downward.

(c) G; $y=(x+2)^2$ is a shift of $y=x^2$, 2 units to the left.

(d) C; $y=(x-2)^2$ is a shift of $y=x^2$, 2 units to the right.

(e) F; $y=2x^2$ is a vertical stretch of $y=x^2$, by a factor of 2.

(f) D; $y=-x^2$ is a reflection of $y=x^2$, across the x-axis.

(g) H; $y=(x-2)^2+1$ is a shift of $y=x^2$, 2 units to the right and 1 unit upward.

(h) E; $y=(x+2)^2+1$ is a shift of $y=x^2$, 2 units to the left and 1 unit upward.

5. $y=3|x|$

x	$y=\|x\|$	$y=3\|x\|$
−2	2	6
−1	1	3
0	0	0
1	1	3
2	2	6

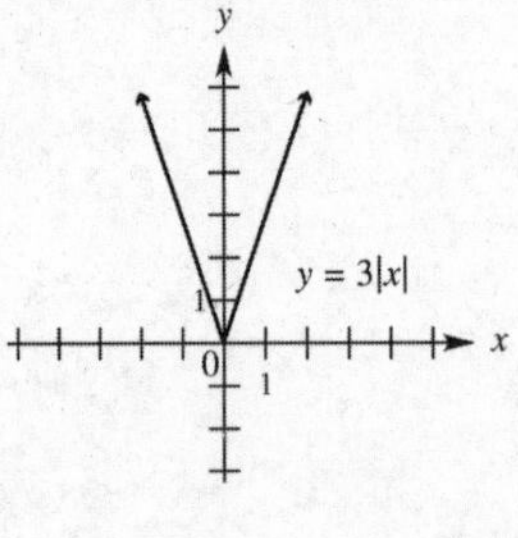

7. $y=\frac{2}{3}|x|$

x	$y=\|x\|$	$y=\frac{2}{3}\|x\|$
−3	3	2
−2	2	$\frac{4}{3}$
−1	1	$\frac{2}{3}$
0	0	0
1	1	$\frac{2}{3}$
2	2	$\frac{4}{3}$
3	3	2

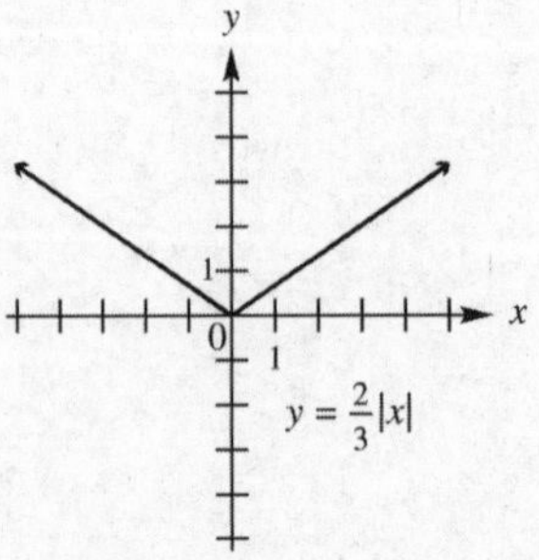

9. $y = -3|x|$

x	$y = \|x\|$	$y = -3\|x\|$
−2	2	−6
−1	1	−3
0	0	0
1	1	−3
2	2	−6

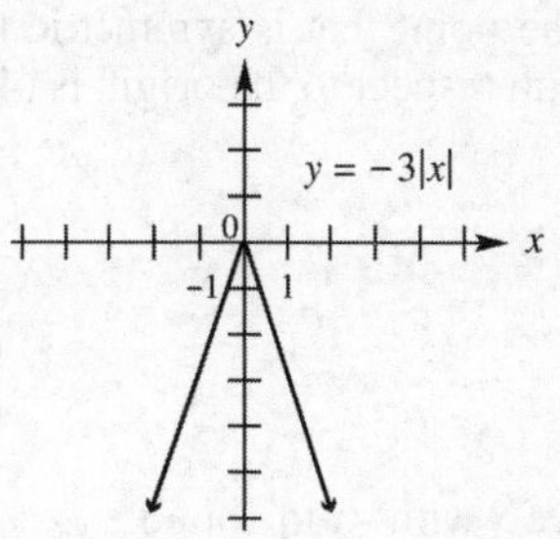

11. $y = \left|-\frac{1}{2}x\right|$

x	$y = \|x\|$	$y = \left\|-\frac{1}{2}x\right\| = \left\|-\frac{1}{2}\right\|\|x\| = \frac{1}{2}\|x\|$
−4	4	2
−3	3	$\frac{3}{2}$
−2	2	1
−1	1	$\frac{1}{2}$
0	0	0
1	1	$\frac{1}{2}$
2	2	1
3	3	$\frac{3}{2}$
4	4	2

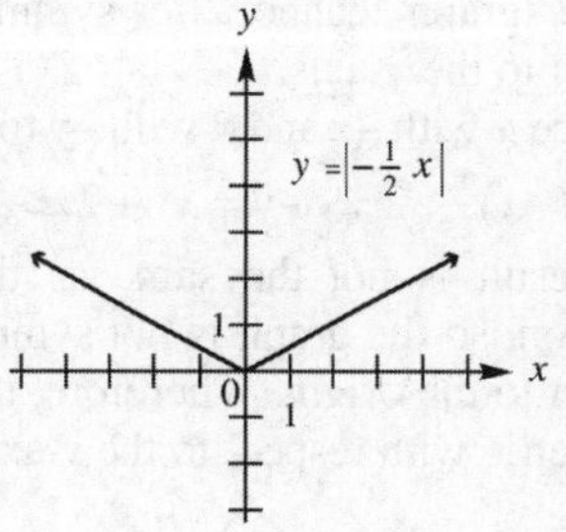

13. (a) $y = \frac{1}{4}f(x)$ is a vertical shrinking of *f*, by a factor of $\frac{1}{4}$. The point that corresponds to $(8,12)$ on this translated function would be $\left(8, \frac{1}{4}\cdot 12\right) = (8,3)$.

(b) $y = 4f(x)$ is a vertical stretching of *f*, by a factor of 4. The point that corresponds to $(8,12)$ on this translated function would be $(8, 4\cdot 12) = (8,48)$.

15. (a) The point that is symmetric to (5, –3) with respect to the *x*-axis is (5, 3).

(b) The point that is symmetric to (5, –3) with respect to the *y*-axis is (–5, –3).

(c) The point that is symmetric to (5, –3) with respect to the origin is (–5, 3).

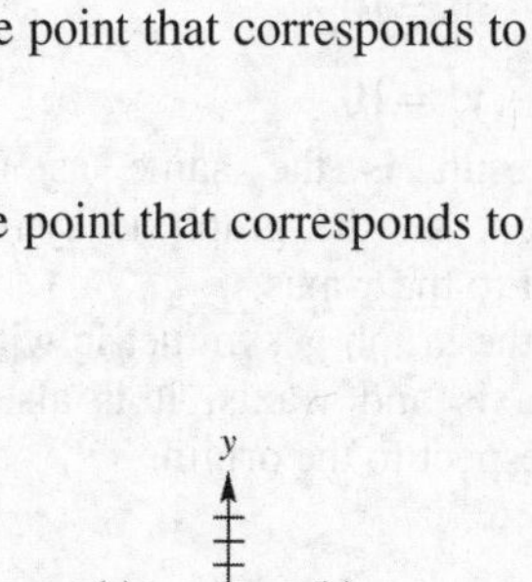

17. **(a)** The point that is symmetric to (–4, –2) with respect to the x-axis is (–4, 2).

(b) The point that is symmetric to (–4, –2) with respect to the y-axis is (4, –2).

(c) The point that is symmetric to (–4, –2) with respect to the origin is (4, 2).

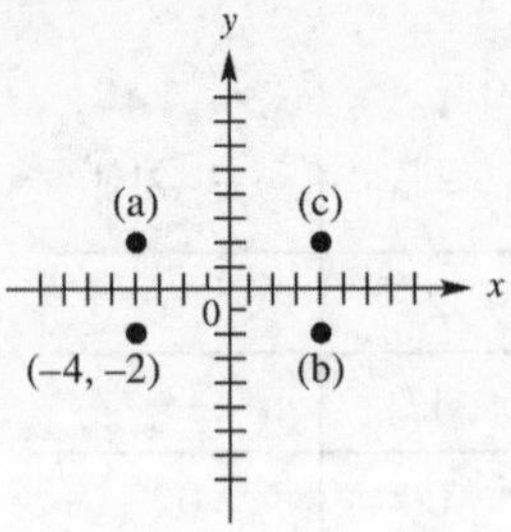

19. $y = x^2 + 2$

Replace x with $-x$ to obtain

$y = (-x)^2 + 2 = x^2 + 2.$

The result is the same as the original equation, so the graph is symmetric with respect to the y-axis. Since y is a function of x, the graph cannot be symmetric with respect to the x-axis.

Replace x with $-x$ and y with $-y$ to obtain

$-y = (-x)^2 + 2 \Rightarrow -y = x^2 + 2 \Rightarrow y = -x^2 - 2.$

The result is not the same as the original equation, so the graph is not symmetric with respect to the origin. Therefore, the graph is symmetric with respect to the y-axis only.

21. $x^2 + y^2 = 10$

Replace x with $-x$ to obtain

$(-x)^2 + y^2 = 10$

$x^2 + y^2 = 10.$

The result is the same as the original equation, so the graph is symmetric with respect to the y-axis.

Replace y with $-y$ to obtain

$x^2 + (-y)^2 = 10$

$x^2 + y^2 = 10.$

The result is the same as the original equation, so the graph is symmetric with respect to the x-axis.

Since the graph is symmetric with respect to the x-axis and y-axis, it is also symmetric with respect to the origin.

23. $y = -3x^3$

Replace x with $-x$ to obtain

$y = -3(-x)^3 \Rightarrow y = -3(-x^3) \Rightarrow y = 3x^3.$

The result is not the same as the original equation, so the graph is not symmetric with respect to the y-axis.

Replace y with $-y$ to obtain

$-y = -3x^3$

$y = 3x^3.$

The result is not the same as the original equation, so the graph is not symmetric with respect to the x-axis.

Replace x with $-x$ and y with $-y$ to obtain

$-y = -3(-x)^3$

$-y = -3(-x^3)$

$-y = 3x^3$

$y = -3x^3.$

The result is the same as the original equation, so the graph is symmetric with respect to the origin. Therefore, the graph is symmetric with respect to the origin only.

25. $y = x^2 - x + 7$

Replace x with $-x$ to obtain

$y = (-x)^2 - (-x) + 7 = x^2 + x + 7.$

The result is not the same as the original equation, so the graph is not symmetric with respect to the y-axis.

Since y is a function of x, the graph cannot be symmetric with respect to the x-axis.

Replace x with $-x$ and y with $-y$ to obtain

$-y = (-x)^2 - (-x) + 7$

$-y = x^2 + x + 7$

$y = -x^2 - x - 7.$

The result is not the same as the original equation, so the graph is not symmetric with respect to the origin.

Therefore, the graph has none of the listed symmetries.

27. $f(x) = -x^3 + 2x$

$f(-x) = -(-x)^3 + 2(-x)$

$= x^3 - 2x = -\left(-x^3 + 2x\right) = -f(x)$

The function is odd.

29. $f(x) = .5x^4 - 2x^2 + 1$

$f(-x) = .5(-x)^4 - 2(-x)^2 + 1$

$= .5x^4 - 2x^2 + 1 = f(x)$

The function is even.

31. $f(x) = x^3 - x + 3$

$f(x) = (-x)^3 - (-x) + 3$

$= -x^3 + x + 3 = -\left(x^3 - x - 3\right) \neq -f(x)$

The function is neither.

33. $y = x^2 - 1$

This graph may be obtained by translating the graph of $y = x^2$, 1 unit downward.

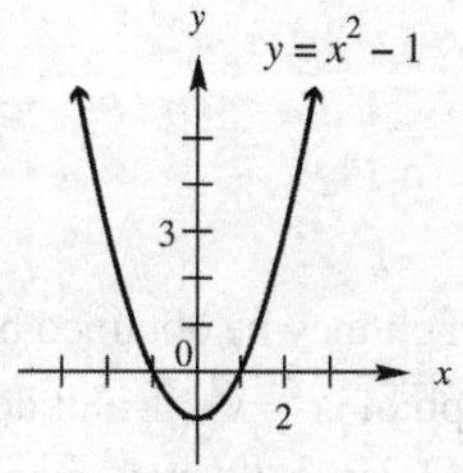

35. $y = x^2 + 2$

This graph may be obtained by translating the graph of $y = x^2$, 2 units upward.

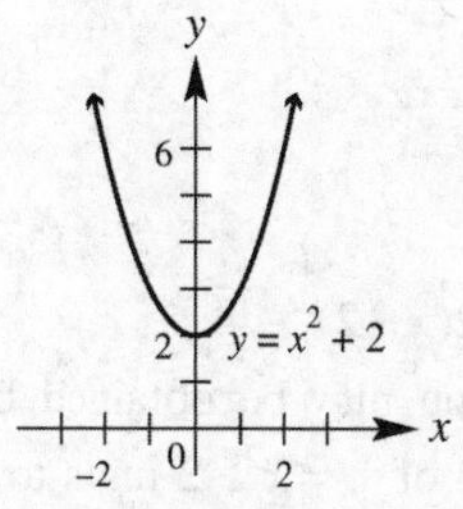

37. $y = (x - 4)^2$

This graph may be obtained by translating the graph of $y = x^2$, 4 units to the right.

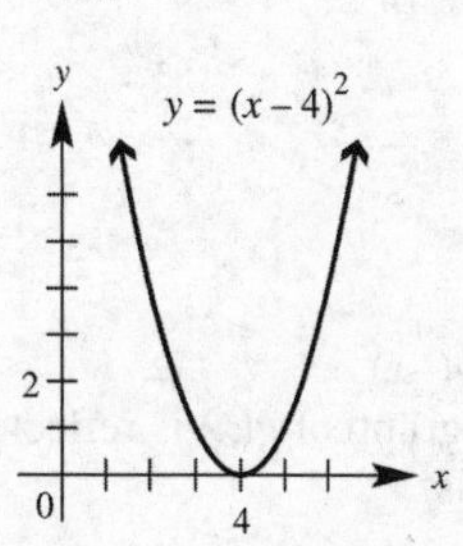

39. $y = (x + 2)^2$

This graph may be obtained by translating the graph of $y = x^2$, 2 units to the left.

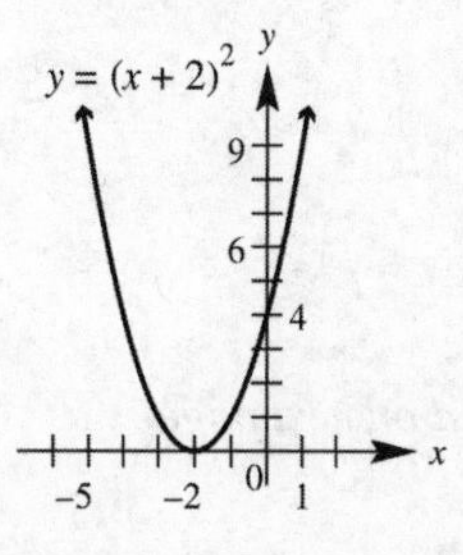

41. $y = |x| - 1$

The graph is obtained by translating the graph of $y = |x|$, 1 unit downward.

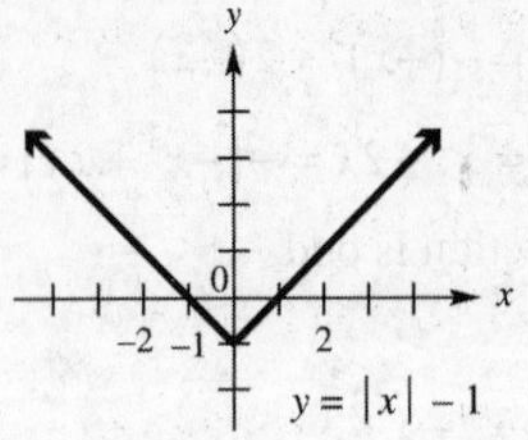

43. $y = -(x+1)^3$

This graph may be obtained by translating the graph of $y = x^3$, 1 unit to the left. It is then reflected about the x-axis.

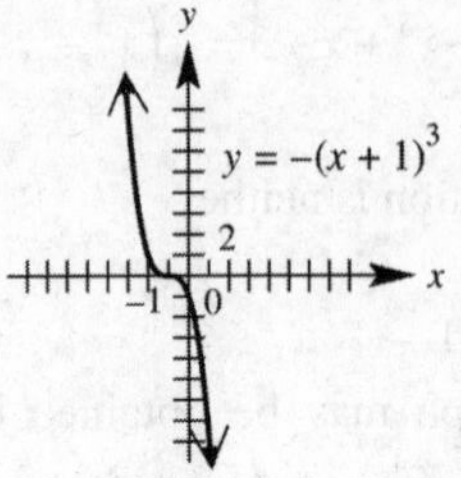

45. $y = 2x^2 - 1$

This graph may be obtained by translating the graph of $y = x^2$, 1 unit down. It is then stretched vertically by a factor of 2.

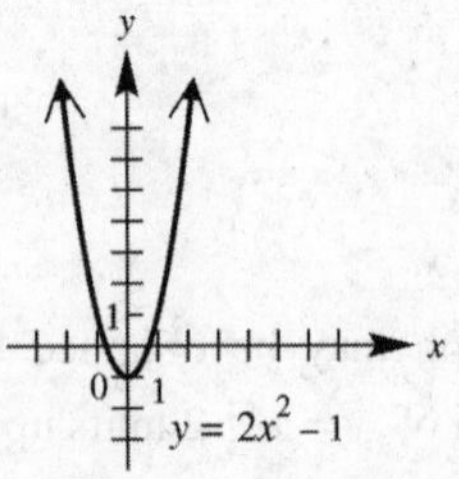

47. $f(x) = 2(x-2)^2 - 4$

This graph may be obtained by translating the graph of $y = x^2$, 2 units to the right and 4 units down. It is then stretched vertically by a factor of 2.

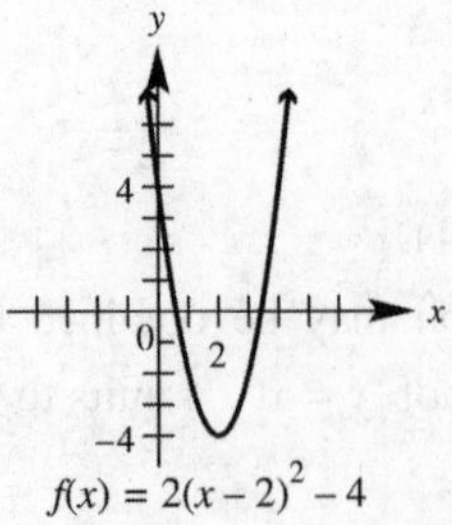

49. **(a)** $y = g(-x)$

The graph of $g(x)$ is reflected across the y-axis.

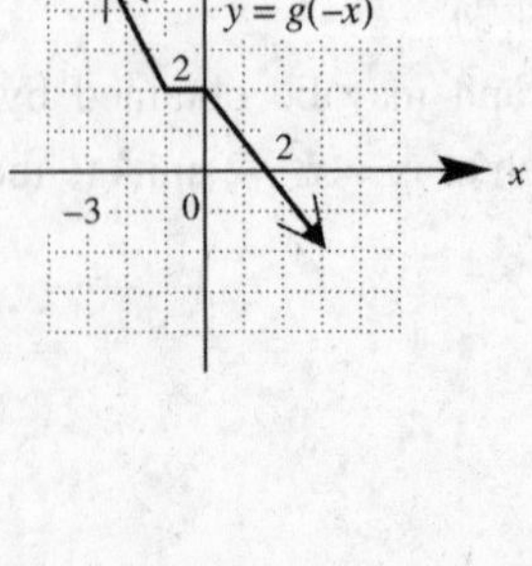

Continued on next page

49. (continued)

(b) $y = g(x-2)$

The graph of $g(x)$ is translated to the right 2 units.

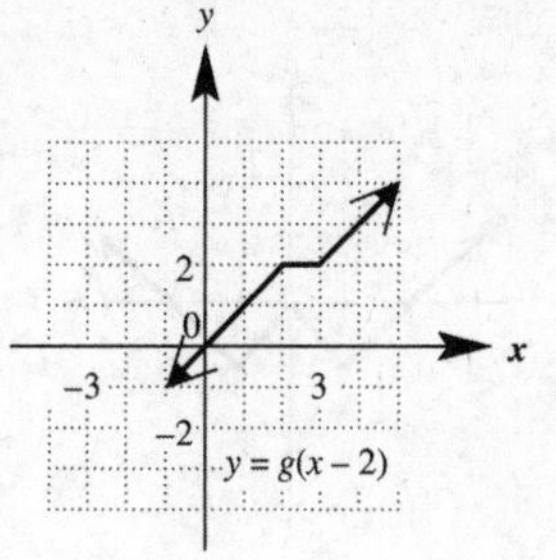

(c) $y = -g(x) + 2$

The graph of $g(x)$ is reflected across the x-axis and translated 2 units up.

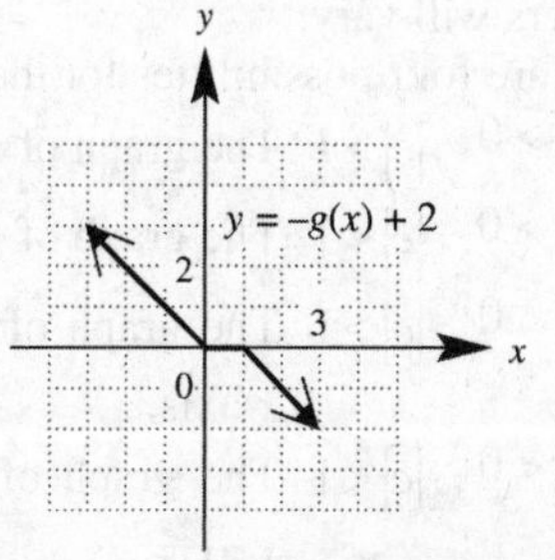

51. It is the graph of $f(x) = |x|$ translated 1 unit to the left, reflected across the x-axis, and translated 3 units up. The equation is $y = -|x+1| + 3$.

53. It is the graph of $g(x) = \sqrt{x}$ translated 4 units to the left, stretched vertically by a factor of 2, and translated 4 units down. The equation is $y = 2\sqrt{x+4} - 4$.

55. Since $f(3) = 6$, the point (3, 6) is on the graph. Since the graph is symmetric with respect to the origin, the point (–3, –6) is on the graph. Therefore, $f(-3) = -6$.

57. Since $f(3) = 6$, the point (3, 6) is on the graph. Since the graph is symmetric with respect to the line $x = 6$ and since the point (3, 6) is 3 units to the left of the line $x = 6$, the image point of (3, 6), 3 units to the right of the line $x = 6$, is (9, 6). Therefore, $f(9) = 6$.

59. An odd function is a function whose graph is symmetric with respect to the origin. Since (3, 6) is on the graph, (–3, –6) must also be on the graph. Therefore, $f(-3) = -6$.

61. $f(x) = 2x + 5$

Translate the graph of $f(x)$ up 2 units to obtain the graph of $t(x) = (2x+5)+2 = 2x+7$.

Now translate the graph of $t(x) = 2x + 7$ left 3 units to obtain the graph of $g(x) = 2(x+3)+7 = 2x+6+7 = 2x+13$. (Note that if the original graph is first translated to the left 3 units and then up 2 units, the final result will be the same.)

63 (a) Since $f(-x) = f(x)$, the graph is symmetric with respect to the y-axis.

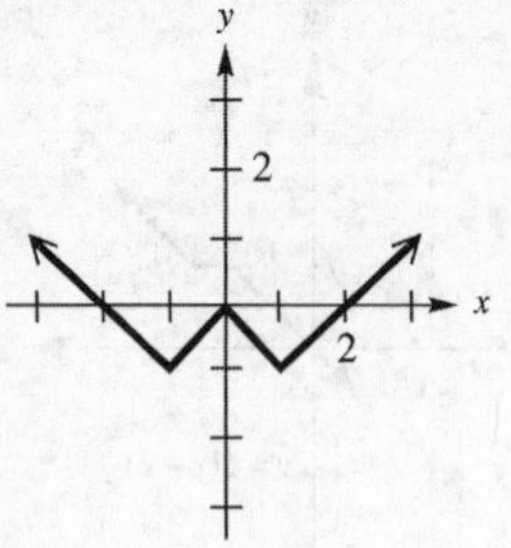

(b) Since $f(-x) = -f(x)$, the graph is symmetric with respect to the origin.

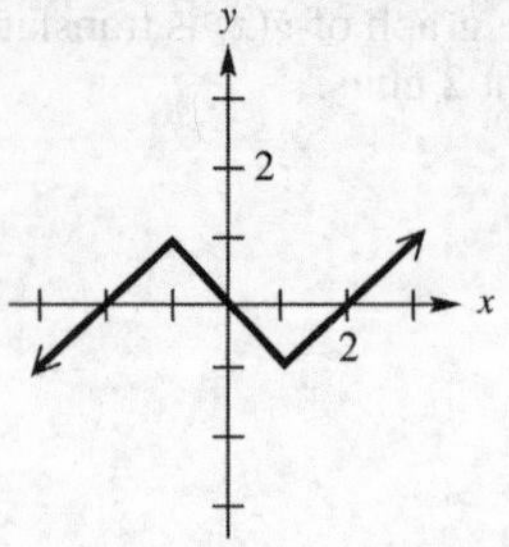

65. Answers will vary.
There are four possibilities for the constant, c.

i) $c>0$ $|c|>1$ The graph of $F(x)$ is stretched vertically by a factor of c.

ii) $c>0$ $|c|<1$ The graph of $F(x)$ is shrunk vertically by a factor of c.

iii) $c<0$ $|c|>1$ The graph of $F(x)$ is stretched vertically by a factor of $-c$ and reflected over the x-axis.

iv) $c<0$ $|c|<1$ The graph of $F(x)$ is shrunk vertically by a factor of $-c$ and reflected over the x-axis.

67. The graph of $F(x)=x^2+6$ is translated 6 units up from the graph of $f(x)=x^2$.

68. $G(x)=x+6$

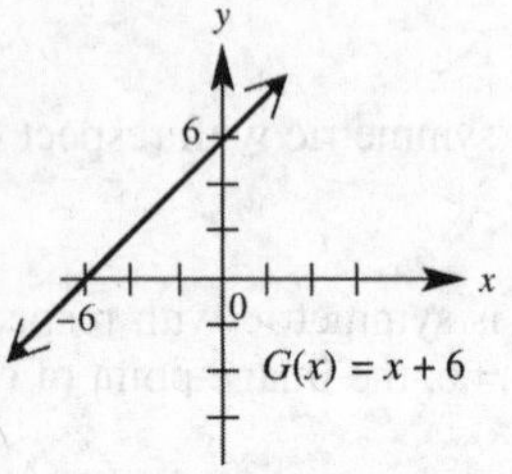

69. The graph of $G(x)=x+6$ is translated 6 units up from the graph of $g(x)=x$.

70. The graph of $F(x)=(x-6)^2$ is translated 6 units to the right from the graph of $f(x)=x^2$.

71. $G(x)=x-6$

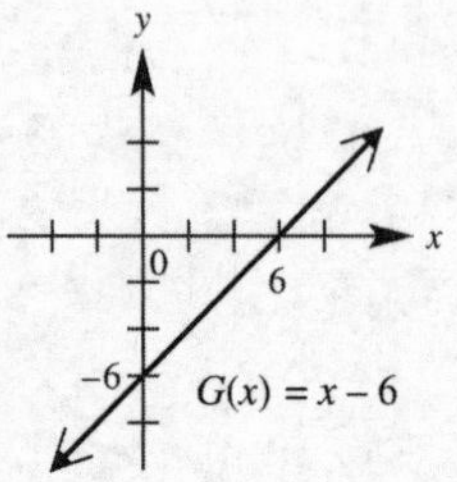

72. The graph of $G(x)=x-6$ is translated 6 units to the right from the graph of $g(x)=x$.

73. (a) Choose any value x. Find the corresponding value of y on both graphs and compare these values. For example, choose $x=2$. From the graph, $f(2)=1$ and $g(2)=3$. For any value x, the y-value for $g(x)$ is 2 greater than the y-value for $f(x)$, so the graph of $g(x)$ is a vertical translation of the graph of $f(x)$ up 2 units. Therefore $g(x)=f(x)+2$, that is $c=2$.

(b) Choose any value y. Find the corresponding value of x on both graphs and compare these values. For example, choose $y=3$. From the graph, $f(6)=3$ and $g(2)=3$. For any value y, the x-value for $g(x)$ is 4 less than the x-value for $f(x)$, so the graph of $g(x)$ is a horizontal translation of the graph of $f(x)$ to the left 4 units. Therefore $g(x)=f(x+4)$, that is $c=4$.

Section 2.7: Function Operations and Composition

In Exercises 1–7, $f(x) = 5x^2 - 2x$ and $g(x) = 6x + 4$.

1. $(f+g)(3) = f(3) + g(3)$

$$= \left[5(3)^2 - 2(3)\right] + [6(3)+4]$$
$$= (45-6) + (18+4)$$
$$= 39 + 22 = 61$$

3. $(fg)(4) = f(4) \cdot g(4)$

$$= [5(4)^2 - 2(4)] \cdot [6(4)+4]$$
$$= [5(16) - 2(4)] \cdot [24+4]$$
$$= (80-8) \cdot (28) = 72(28) = 2016$$

5. $\left(\dfrac{f}{g}\right)(-1) = \dfrac{f(-1)}{g(-1)} = \dfrac{5(-1)^2 - 2(-1)}{6(-1)+4}$

$$= \frac{5+2}{-6+4} = -\frac{7}{2}$$

7. $(f-g)(m) = f(m) - g(m)$

$$= (5m^2 - 2m) - (6m+4)$$
$$= 5m^2 - 2m - 6m - 4$$
$$= 5m^2 - 8m - 4$$

9. $f(x) = 3x+4,\ g(x) = 2x-5$

i) $(f+g)(x) = f(x) + g(x) = (3x+4) + (2x-5) = 5x - 1$

ii) $(f-g)(x) = f(x) - g(x) = (3x+4) - (2x-5) = x + 9$

iii) $(fg)(x) = f(x) \cdot g(x) = (3x+4)(2x-5) = 6x^2 - 15x + 8x - 20 = 6x^2 - 7x - 20$

iv) $\left(\dfrac{f}{g}\right)(x) = \dfrac{f(x)}{g(x)} = \dfrac{3x+4}{2x-5}$

The domains of both f and g are the set of all real numbers, so the domains of $f+g$, $f-g$, and fg are all $(-\infty, \infty)$. The domain of $\frac{f}{g}$ is the set of all real numbers for which $g(x) \neq 0$. This is the set of all real numbers except $\frac{5}{2}$, which is written in interval notation as $\left(-\infty, \frac{5}{2}\right) \cup \left(\frac{5}{2}, \infty\right)$.

11. $f(x) = 2x^2 - 3x,\ g(x) = x^2 - x + 3$

i) $(f+g)(x) = f(x) + g(x) = (2x^2 - 3x) + (x^2 - x + 3) = 3x^2 - 4x + 3$

ii) $(f-g)(x) = f(x) - g(x) = (2x^2 - 3x) - (x^2 - x + 3) = 2x^2 - 3x - x^2 + x - 3 = x^2 - 2x - 3$

iii) $(fg)(x) = f(x) \cdot g(x) = (2x^2 - 3x)(x^2 - x + 3)$

$$= 2x^4 - 2x^3 + 6x^2 - 3x^3 + 3x^2 - 9x = 2x^4 - 5x^3 + 9x^2 - 9x$$

iv) $\left(\dfrac{f}{g}\right)(x) = \dfrac{f(x)}{g(x)} = \dfrac{2x^2 - 3x}{x^2 - x + 3}$

The domains of both f and g are the set of all real numbers, so the domains of $f+g$, $f-g$, and fg are all $(-\infty, \infty)$. The domain of $\frac{f}{g}$ is the set of all real numbers for which $g(x) \neq 0$.

This is the set of all real numbers except $\frac{1}{4}$, which is written in interval notation as $\left(-\infty, \frac{1}{4}\right) \cup \left(\frac{1}{4}, \infty\right)$.

If $x^2 - x + 3 = 0$, then by the quadratic formula $x = \frac{1 \pm i\sqrt{11}}{2}$. The equation has no real solutions. There are no real numbers which make the denominator zero. Thus, the domain of $\frac{f}{g}$ is also $(-\infty, \infty)$.

13. $f(x)=\sqrt{4x-1},\ g(x)=\dfrac{1}{x}$

i) $(f+g)(x)=f(x)+g(x)=\sqrt{4x-1}+\dfrac{1}{x}$

ii) $(f-g)(x)=f(x)-g(x)=\sqrt{4x-1}-\dfrac{1}{x}$

iii) $(fg)(x)=f(x)\cdot g(x)=\sqrt{4x-1}\left(\dfrac{1}{x}\right)=\dfrac{\sqrt{4x-1}}{x}$

iv) $\left(\dfrac{f}{g}\right)(x)=\dfrac{f(x)}{g(x)}=\dfrac{\sqrt{4x-1}}{\frac{1}{x}}=x\sqrt{4x-1}$

Since $4x-1\ge 0 \Rightarrow 4x\ge 1 \Rightarrow x\ge \frac{1}{4}$, the domain of f is $\left[\frac{1}{4},\infty\right)$. The domain of g is $(-\infty,0)\cup(0,\infty)$. Considering the intersection of the domains of f and g, the domains of $f+g$, $f-g$, and fg are all $\left[\frac{1}{4},\infty\right)$. Since $\frac{1}{x}\ne 0$ for any value of x, the domain of $\frac{f}{g}$ is also $\left[\frac{1}{4},\infty\right)$.

In the response to Exercise 15, numerical answers may vary.

15. $G(1996)\approx 7.7$ and $B(1996)\approx 11.8$, thus $T(1996)=G(1996)+B(1996)=7.7+11.8=19.5$.

17. Looking at the graphs of the functions, the slopes of the line segments for the period 1991-1996 are much steeper than the slopes of the corresponding line segments for the period 1978-1991. Thus, the number of sodas increased more rapidly during the period 1991-1996.

In the response to Exercise 19, numerical answers may vary.

19. $(T-S)(2000)=T(2000)-S(2000)=19-13=6$; It represents the dollars in billions spent for general science in 2000.

21. In space and other technologies spending was almost static in the years 1995 – 2000.

23. (a) $(f+g)(2)=f(2)+g(2)$
$=4+(-2)=2$

(b) $(f-g)(1)=f(1)-g(1)=1-(-3)=4$

(c) $(fg)(0)=f(0)\cdot g(0)=0(-4)=0$

(d) $\left(\dfrac{f}{g}\right)(1)=\dfrac{f(1)}{g(1)}=\dfrac{1}{-3}=-\dfrac{1}{3}$

25. (a) $(f+g)(-1)=f(-1)+g(-1)=0+3=3$

(b) $(f-g)(-2)=f(-2)-g(-2)$
$=-1-4=-5$

(c) $(fg)(0)=f(0)\cdot g(0)=1\cdot 2=2$

(d) $\left(\dfrac{f}{g}\right)(2)=\dfrac{f(2)}{g(2)}=\dfrac{3}{0}=$ undefined

27. (a) $(f+g)(2)=f(2)+g(2)$
$=7+(-2)=5$

(b) $(f-g)(4)=f(4)-g(4)=10-5=5$

(c) $(fg)(-2)=f(-2)\cdot g(-2)=0\cdot 6=0$

(d) $\left(\dfrac{f}{g}\right)(0)=\dfrac{f(0)}{g(0)}=\dfrac{5}{0}=$ undefined

29.

x	$f(x)$	$g(x)$	$(f+g)(x)$	$(f-g)(x)$	$(fg)(x)$	$\left(\frac{f}{g}\right)(x)$
-2	0	6	$0+6=6$	$0-6=-6$	$0\cdot 6=0$	$\frac{0}{6}=0$
0	5	0	$5+0=5$	$5-0=5$	$5\cdot 0=0$	$\frac{5}{0}=$ undefined
2	7	-2	$7+(-2)=5$	$7-(-2)=9$	$7(-2)=-14$	$\frac{7}{-2}=-3.5$
4	10	5	$10+5=15$	$10-5=5$	$10\cdot 5=50$	$\frac{10}{5}=2$

31. Answers will vary.

The difference quotient, $\frac{f(x+h)-f(x)}{h}$, represents the slope of the secant line which passes through points $(x, f(x))$ and $(x+h, f(x+h))$. The formula is derived by applying the rule that slope represents a change in y to a change in x.

33. $f(x)=2-x$

(a) $f(x+h)=2-(x+h)=2-x-h$

(b) $f(x+h)-f(x)=(2-x-h)-(2-x)$
$=2-x-h-2+x=-h$

(c) $\frac{f(x+h)-f(x)}{h}=\frac{-h}{h}=-1$

35. $f(x)=6x+2$

(a) $f(x+h)=6(x+h)+2=6x+6h+2$

(b) $f(x+h)-f(x)$
$=(6x+6h+2)-(6x+2)$
$=6x+6h+2-6x-2=6h$

(c) $\frac{f(x+h)-f(x)}{h}=\frac{6h}{h}=6$

37. $f(x)=-2x+5$

(a) $f(x+h)=-2(x+h)+5$
$=-2x-2h+5$

(b) $f(x+h)-f(x)$
$=(-2x-2h+5)-(-2x+5)$
$=-2x-2h+5+2x-5$
$=-2h$

(c) $\frac{f(x+h)-f(x)}{h}=\frac{-2h}{h}=-2$

39. $f(x)=x^2-4$

(a) $f(x+h)=(x+h)^2-4$
$=x^2+2xh+h^2-4$

(b) $f(x+h)-f(x)$
$=(x^2+2xh+h^2-4)-(x^2-4)$
$=x^2+2xh+h^2-4-x^2+4$
$=2xh+h^2$

(c) $\frac{f(x+h)-f(x)}{h}=\frac{2xh+h^2}{h}$
$=\frac{h(2x+h)}{h}=2x+h$

41. Since $g(x)=-x+3$, $g(4)=-4+3=-1$.

Therefore, $(f\circ g)(4)=f[g(4)]=f(-1)=2(-1)-3=-2-3=-5$.

43. Since $g(x)=-x+3$, $g(-2)=-(-2)+3=5$.

Therefore, $(f\circ g)(-2)=f[g(-2)]=f(5)=2(5)-3=10-3=7$.

45. Since $f(x)=2x-3$, $f(0)=2(0)-3=0-3=-3$.
Therefore, $(g\circ f)(0)=g\left[f(0)\right]=g(-3)=-(-3)+3=3+3=6$.

47. Since $f(x)=2x-3$, $f(2)=2(2)-3=4-3=1$.
Therefore, $(f\circ f)(2)=f\left[f(2)\right]=f(1)=2(1)-3=2-3=-1$.

49. $(f\circ g)(2)=f[g(2)]=f(3)=1$

51. $(g\circ f)(3)=g[f(3)]=g(1)=9$

53. $(f\circ f)(4)=f[f(4)]=f(3)=1$

55. $(f\circ g)(1)=f[g(1)]=f(9)$
However, $f(9)$ cannot be determined from the table given.

57. $f(x)=-6x+9$, $g(x)=5x+7$
$(f\circ g)(x)=f[g(x)]=f(5x+7)=-6(5x+7)+9=-30x-42+9=-30x-33$
$(g\circ f)(x)=g[f(x)]=g(-6x+9)=5(-6x+9)+7=-30x+45+7=-30x+52$

59. $f(x)=4x^2+2x+8$, $g(x)=x+5$
$(f\circ g)(x)=f[g(x)]=f(x+5)$
$=4(x+5)^2+2(x+5)+8=4(x^2+10x+25)+2x+10+8$
$=4x^2+40x+100+2x+18=4x^2+42x+118$
$(g\circ f)(x)=g[f(x)]=g(4x^2+2x+8)=(4x^2+2x+8)+5=4x^2+2x+13$

61. $f(x)=\dfrac{2}{x^4}$, $g(x)=2-x$
$(f\circ g)(x)=f[g(x)]=f(2-x)=\dfrac{2}{(2-x)^4}$
Domain: $(-\infty,2)\cup(2,\infty)$
$(g\circ f)(x)=g[f(x)]=g\left(\dfrac{2}{x^4}\right)=2-\dfrac{2}{x^4}$
Domain: $(-\infty,0)\cup(0,\infty)$

63. $f(x)=9x^2-11x$, $g(x)=2\sqrt{x+2}$
$(f\circ g)(x)=f[g(x)]=f(2\sqrt{x+2})$
$=9(2\sqrt{x+2})^2-11(2\sqrt{x+2})$
$=9[4(x+2)]-22\sqrt{x+2}$
$=9(4x+8)-22\sqrt{x+2}$
$=36x+72-22\sqrt{x+2}$
$(g\circ f)(x)=g[f(x)]=g(9x^2-11x)$
$=2\sqrt{(9x^2-11x)+2}$
$=2\sqrt{9x^2-11x+2}$

65. $g\left[f(2)\right]=g(1)=2$ and $g\left[f(3)\right]=g(2)=5$
Since $g\left[f(1)\right]=7$ and $f(1)=3$, $g(3)=7$.

x	$f(x)$	$g(x)$	$g[f(x)]$
1	3	2	7
2	1	5	**2**
3	2	**7**	**5**

67. Answers will vary.
In general, composition of functions is not commutative.

69. $(f\circ g)(x)=f\left[g(x)\right]=4\left[\frac{1}{4}(x-2)\right]+2=\left(4\cdot\frac{1}{4}\right)(x-2)+2=(x-2)+2=x-2+2=x$

$(g\circ f)(x)=g\left[f(x)\right]=\frac{1}{4}\left[(4x+2)-2\right]=\frac{1}{4}(4x+2-2)=\frac{1}{4}(4x)=x$

71. $(f\circ g)(x)=f\left[g(x)\right]=\sqrt[3]{5\left(\frac{1}{5}x^3-\frac{4}{5}\right)+4}=\sqrt[3]{x^3-4+4}=\sqrt[3]{x^3}=x$

$(g\circ f)(x)=g\left[f(x)\right]=\frac{1}{5}\left(\sqrt[3]{5x+4}\right)^3-\frac{4}{5}=\frac{1}{5}(5x+4)-\frac{4}{5}=\frac{5x}{5}+\frac{4}{5}-\frac{4}{5}=\frac{5x}{5}=x$

In Exercises 73–77, we give only one of many possible ways.

73. $h(x)=(6x-2)^2$

Let $g(x) = 6x - 2$ and $f(x)=x^2$.

$(f\circ g)(x)=f(6x-2)=(6x-2)^2=h(x)$

75. $h(x)=\sqrt{x^2-1}$

Let $g(x)=x^2-1$ and $f(x)=\sqrt{x}$.

$(f\circ g)(x)=f(x^2-1)=\sqrt{x^2-1}=h(x)$.

77. $h(x)=\sqrt{6x}+12$

Let $g(x)=6x$ and $f(x)=\sqrt{x}+12$.

$(f\circ g)(x)=f(6x)=\sqrt{6x}+12=h(x)$

79. $f(x) = 12x$, $g(x) = 5280x$

$(f\circ g)(x)=f[g(x)]=f(5280x)$

$=12(5280x)=63,360x$

The function $f\circ g$ computes the number of inches in x miles.

81. $A(x)=\frac{\sqrt{3}}{4}x^2$

(a) $A(2x)=\frac{\sqrt{3}}{4}(2x)^2=\frac{\sqrt{3}}{4}(4x^2)=\sqrt{3}x^2$

(b) $A(16)=A(2\cdot 8)=\sqrt{3}(8)^2$

$=64\sqrt{3}$ square units

83. **(a)** $r(t)=4t$ and $A(r)=\pi r^2$

$(A\circ r)(t)=A[r(t)]$

$=A(4t)=\pi(4t)^2=16\pi t^2$

(b) $(A\circ r)(t)$ defines the area of the leak in terms of the time t, in minutes.

(c) $A(3)=16\pi(3)^2=144\pi\text{ ft}^2$

85. Let x = the number of people less than 100 people that attend.

(a) x people fewer than 100 attend, so $100 - x$ people do attend $N(x) = 100 - x$

(b) The cost per person starts at \$20 and increases by \$5 for each of the x people that do not attend. The total increase is \$5x, and the cost per person increases to \$20 + \$5x. Thus, $G(x) = 20 + 5x$.

(c) $C(x)=N(x)\cdot G(x)=(100-x)(20+5x)$

(d) If 80 people attend, $x = 100 - 80 = 20$.

$C(20)=(100-20)\left[20+5(20)\right]=(80)(20+100)=(80)(120)=\$9600$

Chapter 2: Review Exercises

1. $P(3, -1)$, $Q(-4, 5)$

$d(P, Q)=\sqrt{(-4-3)^2+[5-(-1)]^2}=\sqrt{(-7)^2+6^2}=\sqrt{49+36}=\sqrt{85}$

Midpoint: $\left(\frac{3+(-4)}{2}, \frac{-1+5}{2}\right)=\left(\frac{-1}{2}, \frac{4}{2}\right)=\left(-\frac{1}{2}, 2\right)$

3. $A(-6, 3)$, $B(-6, 8)$

$d(A, B)=\sqrt{[-6-(-6)]^2+(8-3)^2}=\sqrt{0+5^2}=\sqrt{25}=5$

Midpoint: $\left(\frac{-6+(-6)}{2}, \frac{3+8}{2}\right)=\left(\frac{-12}{2}, \frac{11}{2}\right)=\left(-6, \frac{11}{2}\right)$

5. Label the points $A(-1, 2)$, $B(-10, 5)$, and $C(-4, k)$.

$d(A, B)=\sqrt{[-1-(-10)]^2+(2-5)^2}=\sqrt{9^2+(-3)^2}=\sqrt{81+9}=\sqrt{90}$

$d(A, C)=\sqrt{[-4-(-1)]^2+(k-2)^2}=\sqrt{9+(k-2)^2}$

$d(B, C)=\sqrt{[-10-(-4)]^2+(5-k)^2}=\sqrt{36+(k-5)^2}$

If segment AB is the hypotenuse, then $\left(\sqrt{90}\right)^2=\left[\sqrt{9+(k-2)^2}\right]^2+\left[\sqrt{36+(k-5)^2}\right]^2$.

$$\left(\sqrt{90}\right)^2=\left[\sqrt{9+(k-2)^2}\right]^2+\left[\sqrt{36+(k-5)^2}\right]^2 \Rightarrow 90=9+(k-2)^2+36+(k-5)^2$$

$$90=9+k^2-4k+4+36+k^2-10k+25 \Rightarrow 0=2k^2-14k-16$$

$$0=k^2-7k-8 \Rightarrow 0=(k-8)(k+1) \Rightarrow k=8 \text{ or } k=-1$$

Another approach is if segment AB is the hypotenuse, the product of the slopes of lines AC and BC is -1 since the product of slopes of perpendicular lines is -1.

$$\left(\frac{k-2}{-4-(-1)}\right)\cdot\left(\frac{k-5}{-4-(-10)}\right)=-1 \Rightarrow \left(\frac{k-2}{-3}\right)\cdot\left(\frac{k-5}{6}\right)=-1 \Rightarrow \frac{(k-2)(k-5)}{-18}=-1$$

$$\frac{k^2-5k-2k+10}{-18}=-1 \Rightarrow k^2-7k+10=18 \Rightarrow k^2-7k-8=0 \Rightarrow (k+8)(k-1)=0 \Rightarrow k=8 \text{ or } k=-1$$

We will use the second approach for investigating the other two sides of the triangle.

If segment AC is the hypotenuse, the product of the slopes of lines AB and BC is -1 since the product of slopes of perpendicular lines is -1.

$$\left(\frac{5-2}{-10-(-1)}\right)\cdot\left(\frac{k-5}{-4-(-10)}\right)=-1 \Rightarrow \left(\frac{3}{-9}\right)\cdot\left(\frac{k-5}{6}\right)=-1 \Rightarrow \frac{k-5}{-18}=-1 \Rightarrow k-5=18 \Rightarrow k=23$$

If segment BC is the hypotenuse, the product of the slopes of lines AB and AC is -1.

$$\left(\frac{3}{-9}\right)\cdot\left(\frac{k-2}{-4-(-1)}\right)=-1 \Rightarrow \left(\frac{-1}{3}\right)\cdot\left(\frac{k-2}{-3}\right)=-1 \Rightarrow \frac{k-2}{9}=-1 \Rightarrow k-2=-9 \Rightarrow k=-7$$

The possible values of k are -7, 23, 8, and -1.

7. Center (–2, 3), radius 15

$$(x-h)^2+(y-k)^2=r^2$$
$$[x-(-2)]^2+(y-3)^2=15^2$$
$$(x+2)^2+(y-3)^2=225$$

9. Center (–8, 1), passing through (0, 16)
The radius is the distance from the center to any point on the circle. The distance between (–8, 1) and (0, 16) is $r=\sqrt{(-8-0)^2+(1-16)^2}=\sqrt{8^2+15^2}=\sqrt{64+225}=\sqrt{289}=17$.

The equation of the circle is $[x-(-8)]^2+(y-1)^2=17^2 \Rightarrow (x+8)^2+(y-1)^2=289$.

11. $x^2-4x+y^2+6y+12=0$
Complete the square on x and y to put the equation in center-radius form.

$$\left(x^2-4x\right)+\left(y^2+6y\right)=-12$$
$$\left(x^2-4x+4\right)+\left(y^2+6y+9\right)=-12+4+9$$
$$(x-2)^2+(y+3)^2=1$$

The circle has center (2, –3) and radius 1.

13.

$$2x^2+14x+2y^2+6y+2=0$$
$$x^2+7x+y^2+3y+1=0$$
$$\left(x^2+7x\right)+\left(y^2+3y\right)=-1$$
$$\left(x^2+7x+\tfrac{49}{4}\right)+\left(y^2+3y+\tfrac{9}{4}\right)=-1+\tfrac{49}{4}+\tfrac{9}{4}$$
$$\left(x+\tfrac{7}{2}\right)^2+\left(y+\tfrac{3}{2}\right)^2=-\tfrac{4}{4}+\tfrac{49}{4}+\tfrac{9}{4}$$
$$\left(x+\tfrac{7}{2}\right)^2+\left(y+\tfrac{3}{2}\right)^2=\tfrac{54}{4}$$

The circle has center $\left(-\frac{7}{2},-\frac{3}{2}\right)$ and radius $\sqrt{\frac{54}{4}}=\frac{\sqrt{54}}{\sqrt{4}}=\frac{\sqrt{9\cdot 6}}{\sqrt{4}}=\frac{3\sqrt{6}}{2}$.

15. Find all possible values of x so that the distance between $(x, -9)$ and $(3, -5)$ is 6.

$$\sqrt{(3-x)^2+(-5+9)^2}=6$$
$$\sqrt{9-6x+x^2+16}=6$$
$$\sqrt{x^2-6x+25}=6$$
$$x^2-6x+25=36$$
$$x^2-6x-11=0$$

Apply the quadratic formula where $a=1, b=-6$, and $c=-11$.

$$x=\frac{6\pm\sqrt{36-4(1)(-11)}}{2}=\frac{6\pm\sqrt{36+44}}{2}=\frac{6\pm\sqrt{80}}{2}=\frac{6\pm 4\sqrt{5}}{2}=\frac{2(3\pm 2\sqrt{5})}{2}$$
$$x=3+2\sqrt{5} \text{ or } x=3-2\sqrt{5}$$

17. The graph of $(x-4)^2+(y+5)^2=0$ is the single point (4, –5). (One could think of it as a circle with center (4, –5) and radius zero.)

19. This is not the graph of a function because a vertical line can intersect it in two points.
domain: $[-6,6]$; range: $[-6,6]$

21. This is not the graph of a function because a vertical line can intersect it in two points.
domain: $(-\infty,\infty)$; range: $(-\infty,-1]\cup[1,\infty)$

23. This is not the graph of a function because a vertical line can intersect it in two points.
domain: $[0,\infty)$; range: $(-\infty,\infty)$

25. $y=3-x^2$
Each value of x corresponds to exactly one value of y, so this equation defines a function.

27. $y=\sqrt{x-7}$
For each value of x in the domain, which is $[7,\infty)$, there is exactly one value of y. Thus, this equation defines a function.

29. $y=\dfrac{8+x}{8-x}$
x can be any real number except 8, since this will give a denominator of zero. Thus, the domain is $(-\infty,8)\cup(8,\infty)$.

31. $y=\sqrt{49-x^2}$

In the function $y=\sqrt{49-x^2}$, we must have $49-x^2\geq 0$.

Step 1: Find the values of x that satisfy $49-x^2=0$.

$$49-x^2=0$$
$$(7+x)(7-x)=0$$
$$7+x=0 \quad \text{or} \quad 7-x=0$$
$$x=-7 \quad \text{or} \quad 7=x$$

Step 2: The two numbers divide a number line into three regions.

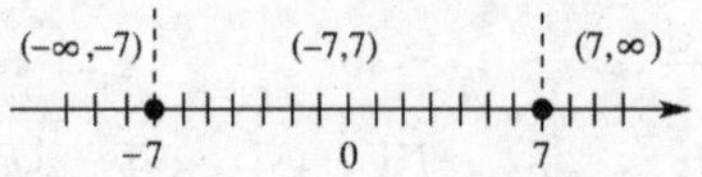

Step 3: Choose a test value to see if it satisfies the inequality, $49-x^2\geq 0$.

Interval	Test Value	Is $49-x^2\geq 0$ True or False?
$(-\infty,-7)$	–8	$49-(-8)^2\geq 0$? $-15\geq 0$ False
$(-7,7)$	0	$49-0^2\geq 0$? $49\geq 0$ True
$(7,\infty)$	8	$49-8^2\geq 0$? $-15\geq 0$ False

Solving this inequality, we obtain a solution interval of [–7, 7].

33. We need to consider the solid dot. Thus, $f(0)=0$.

35. $f(x)=-2x^2+3x-6\Rightarrow f(2.1)=-2\cdot 2.1^2+3\cdot 2.1-6=-2\cdot 4.41+3\cdot 2.1-6=-8.82+6.3-6=-8.52$

37. $f(x)=-2x^2+3x-6\Rightarrow f(k)=-2k^2+3k-6$

39. $2x-5y=5$

$$-5y=-2x+5$$
$$y=\frac{2}{5}x-1$$

The graph is the line with slope $\frac{2}{5}$ and y-intercept -1.

It may also be graphed using intercepts. To do this, locate the x-intercept.

x-intercept: $y=0$

$$2x-5(0)=5 \Rightarrow 2x=5 \Rightarrow x=\frac{5}{2}$$

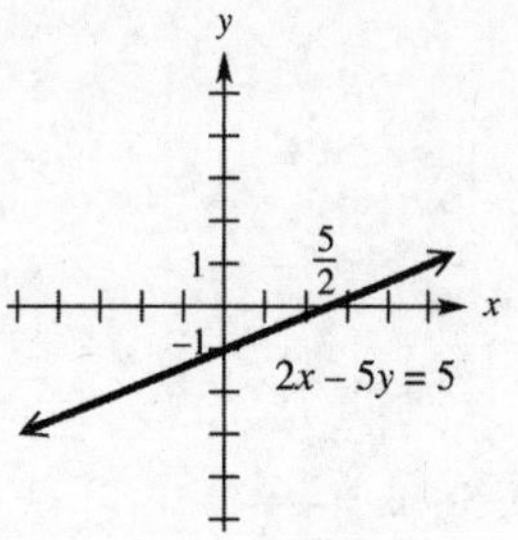

41. $2x+5y=20$

$$5y=-2x+20$$
$$y=-\frac{2}{5}x+4$$

The graph is the line with slope of $-\frac{2}{5}$ and y-intercept 4.

It may also be graphed using intercepts. To do this, locate the x-intercept.

x-intercept: $y=0$

$$2x+5(0)=20 \Rightarrow 2x=20 \Rightarrow x=10$$

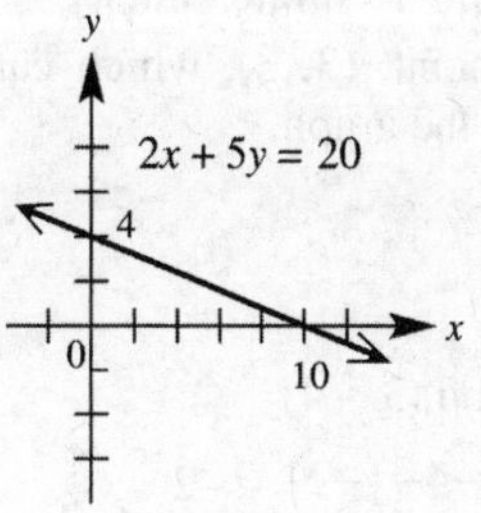

43. $f(x)=x$

The graph is the line with slope 1 and y-intercept 0, which means that it passes through the origin. Use another point such as (1, 1) to complete the graph.

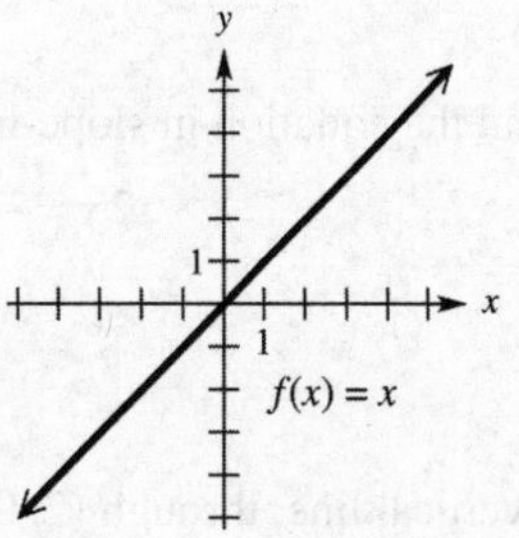

45. $x=-5$

The graph is the vertical line through $(-5, 0)$.

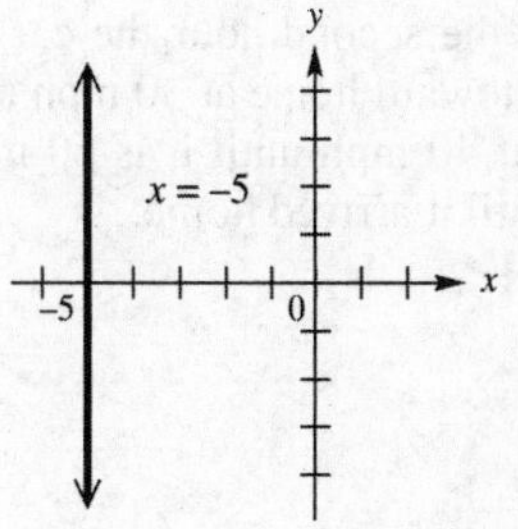

47. $y+2=0 \Rightarrow y=-2$

The graph is the horizontal line through $(0,-2)$.

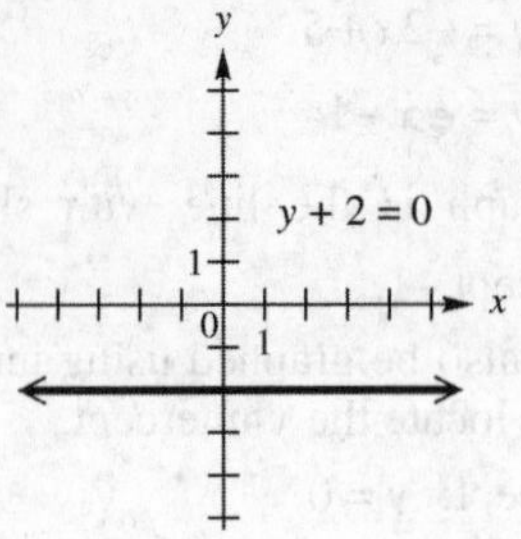

49. Line through (0, 5), $m=-\frac{2}{3}$

Note that $m=-\frac{2}{3}=\frac{-2}{3}$.

Begin by locating the point (0, 5). Since the slope is $\frac{-2}{3}$, a change of 3 units horizontally (3 units to the right) produces a change of –2 units vertically (2 units down). This gives a second point, (3, 3), which can be used to complete the graph.

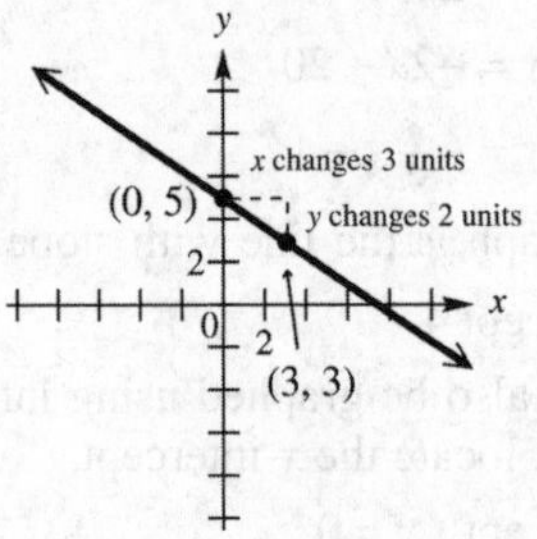

51. through (2, –2) and (3, –4)

$$m=\frac{y_2-y_1}{x_2-x_1}=\frac{-4-(-2)}{3-2}=\frac{-2}{1}=-2$$

53. through (0, –7) and (3, –7)

$$m=\frac{-7-(-7)}{3-0}=\frac{0}{3}=0$$

55. $11x+2y=3$

Solve for y to put the equation in slope-intercept form.

$$2y=-11x+3 \Rightarrow y=-\frac{11}{2}x+\frac{3}{2}$$

Thus, the slope is $-\frac{11}{2}$.

57. $x-2=0 \Rightarrow x=2$

The graph is a vertical line, through (2, 0). The slope is undefined.

59. Initially, the car is at home. After traveling for 30 mph for 1 hr, the car is 30 mi away from home. During the second hour the car travels 20 mph until it is 50 mi away. During the third hour the car travels toward home at 30 mph until it is 20 mi away. During the fourth hour the car travels away from home at 40 mph until it is 60 mi away from home. During the last hour, the car travels 60 mi at 60 mph until it arrived home.

61. (a) We need to first find the slope of a line that passes between points $(6, 12.6)$ and $(11, 30.7)$.

$$m = \frac{y_2 - y_1}{x_2 - x_1} = \frac{30.7 - 12.6}{11 - 6} = \frac{18.1}{5} = 3.62$$

Now use the point-slope form with $(x_1, y_1) = (6, 12.6)$ and $m = 3.62$. (The other point, (11,30.7), could also have been used.)

$$y - 12.6 = 3.62(x - 6) \Rightarrow y - 12.6 = 3.62x - 21.72 \Rightarrow y = 3.62x - 9.12$$

The slope, 3.62, indicates that the number of e-filing taxpayers increased by 3.62% each year from 1996 to 2001.

(b) For 2005, we evaluate the function for $x = 15$.

$$y = 3.62(15) - 9.12 = 54.3 - 9.12 = 45.18$$

45.18% of the tax returns are predicted to be filed electronically.

63. through (3, –5) with slope –2
Use the point-slope form.

$$y - y_1 = m(x - x_1)$$
$$y - (-5) = -2(x - 3)$$
$$y + 5 = -2(x - 3)$$
$$y + 5 = -2x + 6$$
$$y = -2x + 1$$

65. through (2, –1) parallel to $3x - y = 1$
Find the slope of $3x - y = 1$.

$$3x - y = 1$$
$$-y = -3x + 1$$
$$y = 3x - 1$$

The slope of this line is 3. Since parallel lines have the same slope, 3 is also the slope of the line whose equation is to be found.
Now use the point-slope form with $(x_1, y_1) = (2, -1)$ and $m = 3$.

$$y - y_1 = m(x - x_1)$$
$$y - (-1) = 3(x - 2)$$
$$y + 1 = 3x - 6$$
$$y = 3x - 7$$

67. through (2, –10), perpendicular to a line with an undefined slope
A line with an undefined slope is a vertical line. Any line perpendicular to a vertical line is a horizontal line, with an equation of the form $y = b$. Since the line passes through (2, –10), the equation of the line is $y = -10$.

69. through (–7, 4), perpendicular to $y = 8$
The line $y = 8$ is a horizontal line, so any line perpendicular to it will be a vertical line. Since x has the same value at all points on the line, the equation is $x = -7$.

71. $f(x) = |x| - 3$
The graph is the same as that of $y = |x|$, except that it is translated 3 units downward.

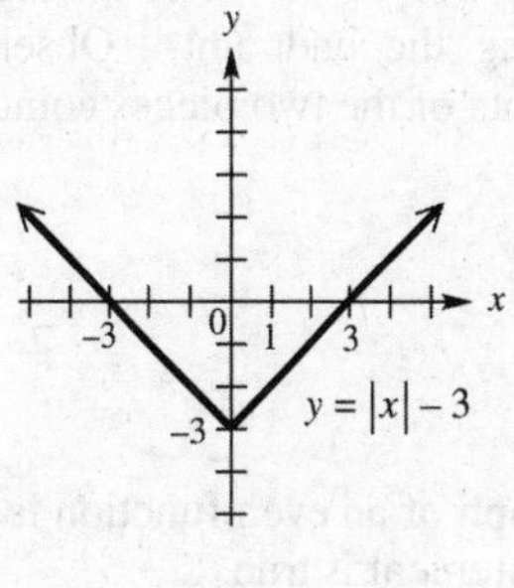

73. $f(x) = -|x+1| + 3 = -|x-(-1)| + 3$

The graph of $f(x) = -|x+1| + 3$ is a translation of the graph of $y = |x|$ to the left 1 unit, reflected over the x-axis and translated up 3 units.

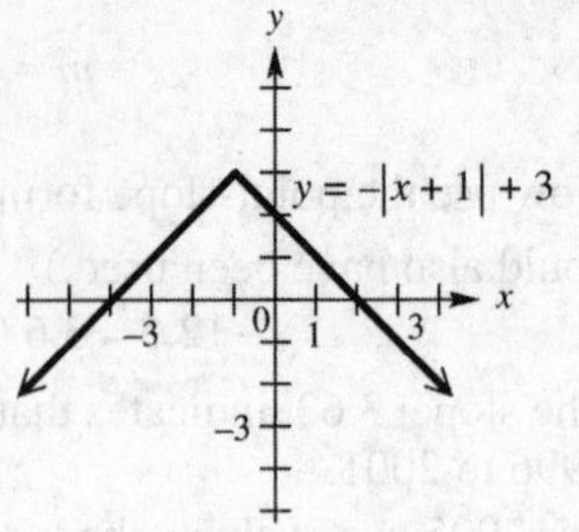

75. $f(x) = [\![x-3]\!]$

To get $y = 0$, we need $0 \le x-3 < 1 \Rightarrow$
$3 \le x < 4$.
To get $y = 1$, we need $1 \le x-3 < 2 \Rightarrow$
$4 \le x < 5$.
Follow this pattern to graph the step function.

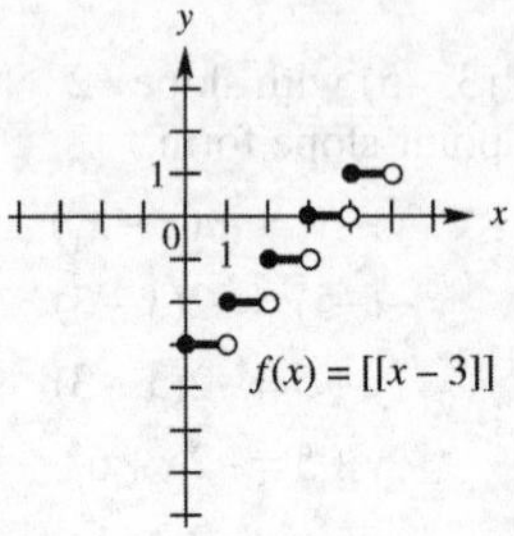

77. $f(x) = \begin{cases} -4x+2 & \text{if } x \le 1 \\ 3x-5 & \text{if } x > 1 \end{cases}$

Draw the graph of $y = -4x + 2$ to the left of $x = 1$, including the endpoint at $x = 1$. Draw the graph of $y = 3x - 5$ to the right of $x = 1$, but do not include the endpoint at $x = 1$. Observe that the endpoints of the two pieces coincide.

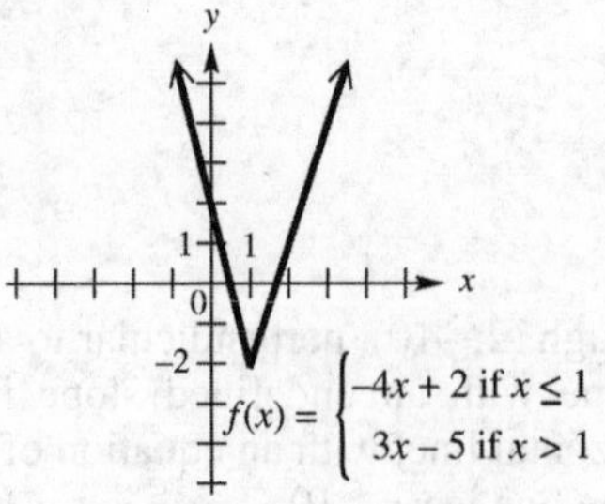

79. $f(x) = \begin{cases} |x| & \text{if } x < 3 \\ 6-x & \text{if } x \ge 3 \end{cases}$

Draw the graph of $y = |x|$ to the left of $x = 3$, but do not include the endpoint. Draw the graph of $y = 6 - x$ to the right of $x = 3$, including the endpoint. Observe that the endpoints of the two pieces coincide.

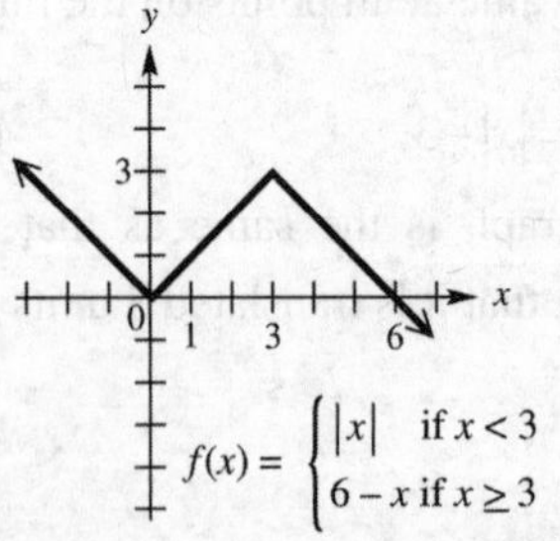

81. The graph of an even function is symmetric with respect to the y-axis. This statement is true.

83. If (a, b) is on the graph of an even function, so is $(a, -b)$.
The statement is false. For example, $f(x) = x^2$ is even, and (2, 4) is on the graph but (2, –4) is not.

85. The constant function $f(x) = 0$ is both even and odd.
Since $f(-x) = 0 = f(x)$, the function is even. Also since $f(-x) = 0 = -0 = -f(x)$, the function is odd.
This statement is true.

87. $x + y^2 = 8$
Replace x with $-x$ to obtain $(-x) + y^2 = 8$.
The result is not the same as the original equation, so the graph is not symmetric with respect to the y-axis.

Replace y with $-y$ to obtain $x + (-y)^2 = 8 \Rightarrow x + y^2 = 8$.
The result is the same as the original equation, so the graph is symmetric with respect to the x-axis.

Replace x with $-x$ and y with $-y$ to obtain $(-x) + (-y)^2 = 8 \Rightarrow (-x) + y^2 = 8$.
The result is not the same as the original equation, so the graph is not symmetric with respect to the origin.

The graph is symmetric with respect to the x-axis only.

89. $x^2 = y^3$
Replace x with $-x$ to obtain $(-x)^2 = y^3 \Rightarrow x^2 = y^3$.
The result is the same as the original equation, so the graph is symmetric with respect to the y-axis.

Replace y with $-y$ to obtain $x^2 = (-y)^3 \Rightarrow x^2 = -y^3$.
The result is not the same as the original equation, so the graph is not symmetric with respect to the x-axis.

Replace x with $-x$ and y with $-y$ to obtain $(-x)^2 = (-y)^3 \Rightarrow x^2 = -y^3$.
The result is not the same as the original equation, so the graph is not symmetric with respect to the origin.

Therefore, the graph is symmetric with respect to the y-axis only.

91. $|x + 2| = |y - 3|$
Replace x with $-x$ to obtain $|-x + 2| = |y - 3|$
Since $|-x + 2| \neq |x + 2|$, the graph is not symmetric with respect to the y-axis.

Replace y with $-y$ to obtain $|x + 2| = |-y - 3|$.
Since $|-y - 3| \neq |y - 3|$, the graph is not symmetric with respect to the x-axis.

Replace x with $-x$ and y with $-y$ to obtain $|-x + 2| = |-y - 3|$.
This equation is not equivalent to the original one, so the graph is not symmetric with respect to the origin.

Therefore, the graph has none of the listed symmetries.

93. To obtain the graph of $g(x) = -|x|$, reflect the graph of $f(x) = |x|$ across the x-axis.

95. To obtain the graph of $k(x) = 2|x-4|$, translate the graph of $f(x) = |x|$ to the right 4 units and stretch vertically by a factor of 2.

97. If the graph of $f(x) = 3x - 4$ is reflected about the *y*-axis, we obtain a graph whose equation is $y = f(-x) = 3(-x) - 4 = -3x - 4$.

99. **(a)** To graph $y = f(x) + 3$, translate the graph of $y = f(x)$, 3 units up.

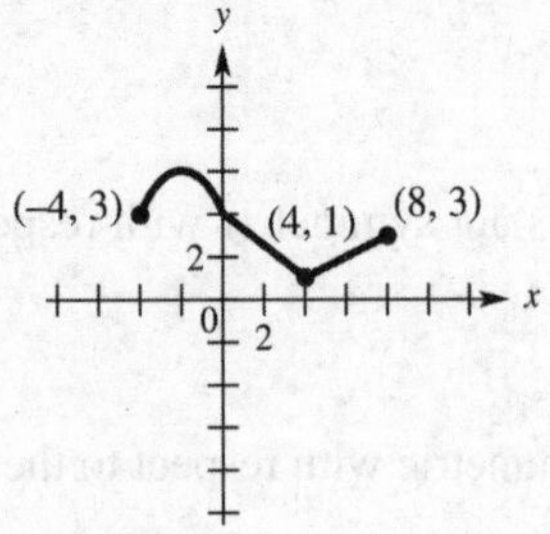

(b) To graph $y = f(x-2)$, translate the graph of $y = f(x)$, 2 units to the right.

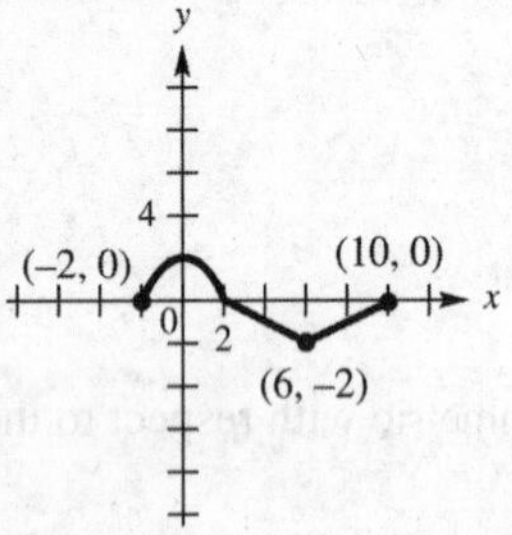

(c) To graph $y = f(x+3) - 2$, translate the graph of $y = f(x)$, 3 units to the left and 2 units down.

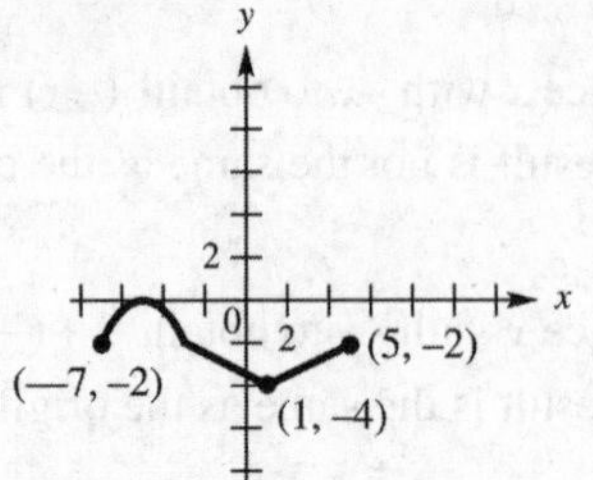

(d) To graph $y = |f(x)|$, keep the graph of $y = f(x)$ as it is where $y \geq 0$ and reflect the graph about the *x*-axis where $y < 0$.

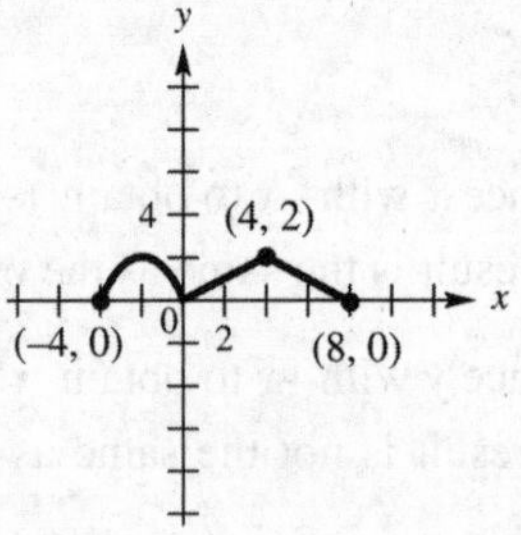

For Exercises 101–107, $f(x) = 3x^2 - 4$ and $g(x) = x^2 - 3x - 4$.

101.
$$\begin{aligned}(fg)(x) &= f(x)\cdot g(x)\\ &= (3x^2-4)(x^2-3x-4)\\ &= 3x^4 - 9x^3 - 12x^2 - 4x^2 + 12x + 16\\ &= 3x^4 - 9x^3 - 16x^2 + 12x + 16\end{aligned}$$

103.
$$\begin{aligned}(f+g)(-4) &= f(-4) + g(-4) = [3(-4)^2 - 4] + [(-4)^2 - 3(-4) - 4]\\ &= [3(16) - 4] + [16 - 3(-4) - 4] = [48 - 4] + [16 + 12 - 4] = 44 + 24 = 68\end{aligned}$$

105. $\left(\dfrac{f}{g}\right)(3) = \dfrac{f(3)}{g(3)} = \dfrac{3\cdot 3^2 - 4}{3^2 - 3\cdot 3 - 4} = \dfrac{3\cdot 9 - 4}{9 - 3\cdot 3 - 4} = \dfrac{27-4}{9-9-4} = \dfrac{23}{-4} = -\dfrac{23}{4}$

107. The domain of $(fg)(x)$ is the intersection of the domain of $f(x)$ and the domain of $g(x)$. Both have domain $(-\infty, \infty)$, so the domain of $(fg)(x)$ is $(-\infty, \infty)$.

109. $f(x)=\frac{1}{x},\ g(x)=x^2+1$

Since $(f\circ g)(x)=f[g(x)]$ and $(f\circ g)(x)=\frac{1}{x^2+1}$, choices (C) and (D) are not equal to $(f\circ g)(x)$.

111. $f(x)=x^2-5x+3$

$f(x+h)=(x+h)^2-5(x+h)+3=x^2+2xh+h^2-5x-5h+3$

$f(x+h)-f(x)=(x^2+2xh+h^2-5x-5h+3)-(x^2-5x+3)$

$=x^2+2xh+h^2-5x-5h+3-x^2+5x-3=2xh+h^2-5h$

$$\frac{f(x+h)-f(x)}{h}=\frac{2xh+h^2-5h}{h}=\frac{h(2x+h-5)}{h}=2x+h-5$$

For Exercises 113–115, $f(x)=\sqrt{x-2}$ and $g(x)=x^2$.

113. $(g\circ f)(x)=g[f(x)]=g\left(\sqrt{x-2}\right)=\left(\sqrt{x-2}\right)^2=x-2$

115. Since $f(x)=\sqrt{x-2},\ f(3)=\sqrt{3-2}=\sqrt{1}=1$.

Therefore, $(g\circ f)(3)=g\left[f(3)\right]=g(1)=1^2=1$.

117. $(f+g)(1)=f(1)+g(1)=7+1=8$

119. $(fg)(-1)=f(-1)\cdot g(-1)=3(-2)=-6$

121. $(g\circ f)(-2)=g[f(-2)]=g(1)=2$

123. $(f\circ g)(2)=f[g(2)]=f(2)=1$

125. Let x = number of yards.
$f(x)=36x$, where $f(x)$ is the number of inches.
$g(x)=1760x$, where $g(x)$ is the number of miles.
Then $(g\circ f)(x)=g\left[f(x)\right]=1760(36x)=63{,}360x$.
There are $63{,}360x$ inches in x miles.

127. If $V(r)=\frac{4}{3}\pi r^3$ and if the radius is increased by 3 inches, then the amount of volume gained is given by $V_g(r)=V(r+3)-V(r)=\frac{4}{3}\pi(r+3)^3-\frac{4}{3}\pi r^3$.

Chapter 2: Test

1. **(a)** The domain of $f(x)=\sqrt{x}+3$ occurs when $x\geq 0$. In interval notation, this correlates to the interval in D, $[0,\infty)$.

(b) The range of $f(x)=\sqrt{x-3}$ is all real numbers greater than or equal to 0. In interval notation, this correlates to the interval in D, $[0,\infty)$.

(c) The domain of $f(x)=x^2-3$ is all real numbers. In interval notation, this correlates to the interval in C, $(-\infty,\infty)$.

(d) The range of $f(x)=x^2+3$ is all real numbers greater than or equal to 3. In interval notation, this correlates to the interval in B, $[3,\infty)$.

(e) The domain of $f(x)=\sqrt[3]{x-3}$ is all real numbers. In interval notation, this correlates to the interval in C, $(-\infty,\infty)$.

(f) The range of $f(x)=\sqrt[3]{x}+3$ is all real numbers. In interval notation, this correlates to the interval in C, $(-\infty,\infty)$.

(g) The domain of $f(x)=|x|-3$ is all real numbers. In interval notation, this correlates to the interval in C, $(-\infty,\infty)$.

(h) The range of $f(x)=|x+3|$ is all real numbers greater than or equal to 0. In interval notation, this correlates to the interval in D, $[0,\infty)$.

(i) The domain of $x=y^2$ is $x\geq 0$ since when you square any value of y, the outcome will be nonnegative. In interval notation, this correlates to the interval in D, $[0,\infty)$.

(j) The range of $x=y^2$ is all real numbers. In interval notation, this correlates to the interval in C, $(-\infty,\infty)$.

2. Consider the points $(-2,1)$ and $(3,4)$.

$$m=\frac{4-1}{3-(-2)}=\frac{3}{5}$$

3. We label the points $A(-2,1)$ and $B(3,4)$.

$$\begin{aligned} d(A,B)&=\sqrt{[3-(-2)]^2+(4-1)^2}\\ &=\sqrt{5^2+3^2}\\ &=\sqrt{25+9}\\ &=\sqrt{34} \end{aligned}$$

4. The midpoint has coordinates

$$\left(\frac{-2+3}{2},\frac{1+4}{2}\right)=\left(\frac{1}{2},\frac{5}{2}\right).$$

5. Use the point-slope form with $(x_1, y_1)=(-2,1)$ and $m=\frac{3}{5}$.

$$\begin{aligned} y-y_1&=m(x-x_1)\\ y-1&=\tfrac{3}{5}[x-(-2)]\\ y-1&=\tfrac{3}{5}(x+2)\\ 5(y-1)&=3(x+2)\\ 5y-5&=3x+6\\ 5y&=3x+11\\ -3x+5y&=11\Rightarrow 3x-5y=-11 \end{aligned}$$

6. Solve $3x-5y=-11$ for y.

$$\begin{aligned} 3x-5y&=-11\\ -5y&=-3x-11\\ y&=\tfrac{3}{5}x+\tfrac{11}{5} \end{aligned}$$

Therefore, the linear function is $f(x)=\frac{3}{5}x+\frac{11}{5}$.

7. **(a)** This is not the graph of a function because some vertical lines intersect it in more than one point. The domain of the relation is [0, 4]. The range is [–4, 4].

(b) This is the graph of a function because no vertical line intersects the graph in more than one point. The domain of the function is $(-\infty, -1)\cup(-1, \infty)$. The range is $(-\infty, 0)\cup(0, \infty)$. As x is getting larger on the intervals $(-\infty,-1)$ and $(-1,\infty)$, the value of y is decreasing, so the function is decreasing on these intervals. (The function is never increasing or constant.)

8. Point A has coordinates (5, –3).

(a) The equation of a vertical line through A is $x = 5$.

(b) The equation of a horizontal line through A is $y = -3$.

9. The slope of the graph of $y=-3x+2$ is –3.

(a) A line parallel to the graph of $y=-3x+2$ has a slope of –3.
Use the point-slope form with $(x_1, y_1)=(2,3)$ and $m=-3$.

$$\begin{aligned} y-y_1 &= m(x-x_1) \\ y-3 &= -3(x-2) \\ y-3 &= -3x+6 \\ y &= -3x+9 \end{aligned}$$

(b) A line perpendicular to the graph of $y=-3x+2$ has a slope of $\frac{1}{3}$ since $-3\left(\frac{1}{3}\right)=-1$.

$$\begin{aligned} y-3 &= \tfrac{1}{3}(x-2) \\ 3(y-3) &= x-2 \\ 3y-9 &= x-2 \\ 3y &= x+7 \\ y &= \tfrac{1}{3}x+\tfrac{7}{3} \end{aligned}$$

10. **(a)** $(-\infty,-3)$

(b) $(4,\infty)$

(c) $[-3,4]$

(d) $(-\infty,-3)$; $[-3,4]$; $(4,\infty)$

(e) $(-\infty,\infty)$

(f) $(-\infty,2)$

11. To graph $y=|x-2|-1$, we translate the graph of $y=|x|$, 2 units to the right and 1 unit down.

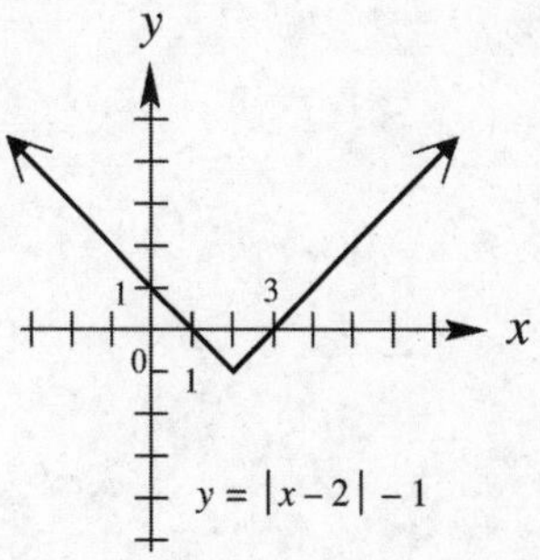

12. $f(x) = [\![x+1]\!]$

To get $y = 0$, we need $0 \le x+1 < 1 \Rightarrow -1 \le x < 0$.

To get $y = 1$, we need $1 \le x+1 < 2 \Rightarrow 0 \le x < 1$.

Follow this pattern to graph the step function.

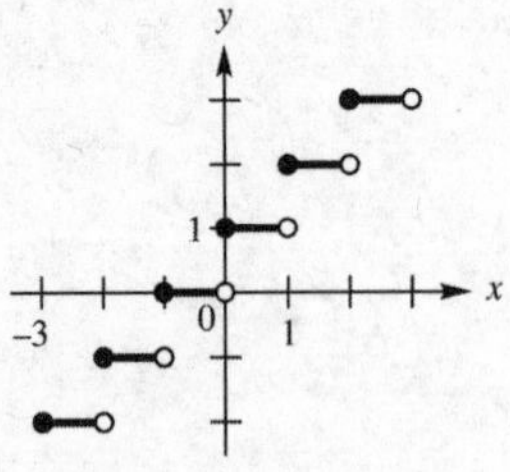

$f(x) = [\![x + 1]\!]$

13. $f(x) = \begin{cases} 3 & \text{if } x < -2 \\ 2 - \frac{1}{2}x & \text{if } x \ge -2 \end{cases}$

For values of x with $x < -2$, we graph the horizontal line $y = 3$. For values of x with $x \ge -2$, we graph the line with a slope of $-\frac{1}{2}$ and a y-intercept of 2. Two points on this line are (–2, 3) and (0, 2).

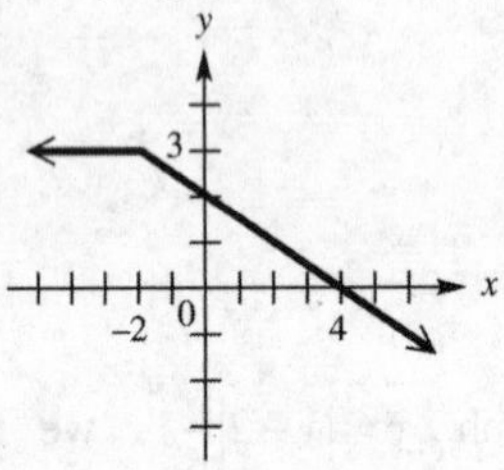

$f(x) = \begin{cases} 3 & \text{if } x < -2 \\ 2 - \frac{1}{2}x & \text{if } x \ge -2 \end{cases}$

14. **(a)** Shift $f(x)$, 2 units vertically upward.

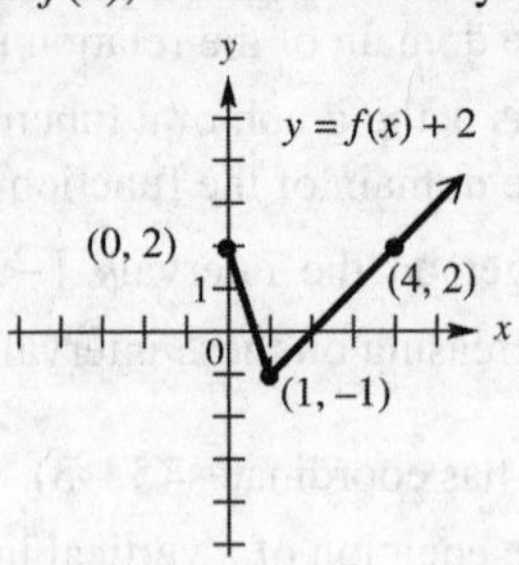

(b) Shift $f(x)$, 2 units horizontally to the left.

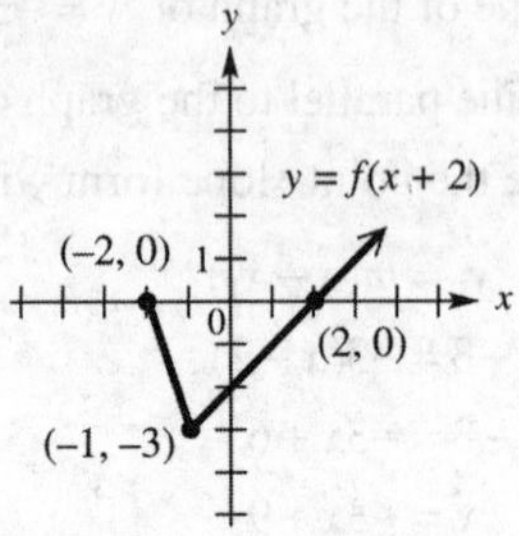

(c) Reflect $f(x)$, across the x-axis.

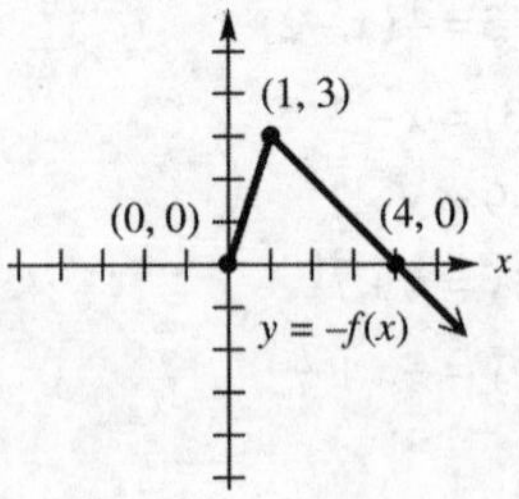

(d) Reflect $f(x)$, across the y-axis.

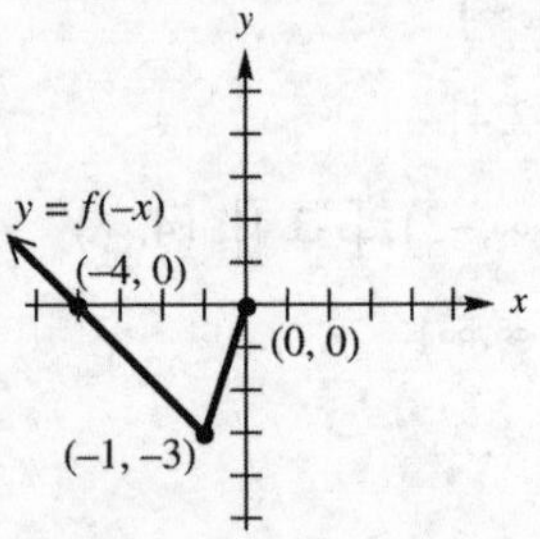

(e) Stretch $f(x)$, vertically by a factor of 2.

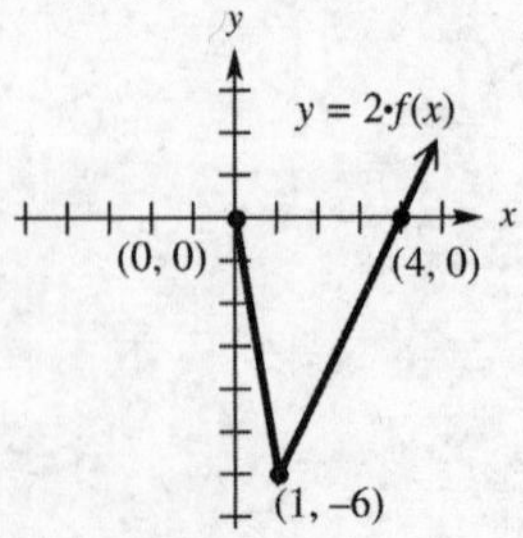

15. Answers will vary.

Starting with $y = \sqrt{x}$, we shift it to the left 2 units and stretch it vertically by a factor of 2. The graph is then reflected over the x-axis and then shifted down 3 units.

16. $3x^2 - y^2 = 3$

(a) Replace y with $-y$ to obtain $3x^2 - (-y)^2 = 3 \Rightarrow 3x^2 - y^2 = 3$.

The result is the same as the original equation, so the graph is symmetric with respect to the x-axis.

(b) Replace x with $-x$ to obtain $3(-x)^2 - y^2 = 3 \Rightarrow 3x^2 - y^2 = 3$.

The result is the same as the original equation, so the graph is symmetric with respect to the y-axis.

(c) Since the graph is symmetric with respect to the x-axis and with respect to the y-axis, it must also be symmetric with respect to the origin.

17. $f(x) = 2x^2 - 3x + 2,\ g(x) = -2x + 1$

(a) $(f - g)(x) = f(x) - g(x) = \left(2x^2 - 3x + 2\right) - (-2x + 1) = 2x^2 - 3x + 2 + 2x - 1 = 2x^2 - x + 1$

(b) $\left(\dfrac{f}{g}\right)(x) = \dfrac{f(x)}{g(x)} = \dfrac{2x^2 - 3x + 2}{-2x + 1}$

(c) We must determine which values solve the equation $-2x + 1 = 0$.

$$-2x + 1 = 0 \Rightarrow -2x = -1 \Rightarrow x = \tfrac{1}{2}$$

Thus, $\frac{1}{2}$ is excluded from the domain, and the domain is $\left(-\infty, \frac{1}{2}\right) \cup \left(\frac{1}{2}, \infty\right)$..

(d) $f(x) = 2x^2 - 3x + 2$

$$f(x+h) = 2(x+h)^2 - 3(x+h) + 2$$
$$= 2\left(x^2 + 2xh + h^2\right) - 3x - 3h + 2 = 2x^2 + 4xh + 2h^2 - 3x - 3h + 2$$

$$f(x+h) - f(x) = (2x^2 + 4xh + 2h^2 - 3x - 3h + 2) - (2x^2 - 3x + 2)$$
$$= 2x^2 + 4xh + 2h^2 - 3x - 3h + 2 - 2x^2 + 3x - 2 = 4xh + 2h^2 - 3h$$

$$\frac{f(x+h) - f(x)}{h} = \frac{4xh + 2h^2 - 3h}{h} = \frac{h(4x + 2h - 3)}{h} = 4x + 2h - 3$$

18. (a) $(f + g)(1) = f(1) + g(1) = (2 \cdot 1^2 - 3 \cdot 1 + 2) + (-2 \cdot 1 + 1)$

$$= (2 \cdot 1 - 3 \cdot 1 + 2) + (-2 \cdot 1 + 1) = (2 - 3 + 2) + (-2 + 1) = 1 + (-1) = 0$$

(b) $(fg)(2) = f(2) \cdot g(2) = (2 \cdot 2^2 - 3 \cdot 2 + 2) \cdot (-2 \cdot 2 + 1)$

$$= (2 \cdot 4 - 3 \cdot 2 + 2) \cdot (-2 \cdot 2 + 1) = (8 - 6 + 2) \cdot (-4 + 1) = 4(-3) = -12$$

(c) Since $g(x) = -2x + 1,\ g(0) = -2(0) + 1 = 0 + 1 = 1$.

Therefore, $(f \circ g)(0) = f\left[g(0)\right] = f(1) = 2 \cdot 1^2 - 3 \cdot 1 + 2 = 2 \cdot 1 - 3 \cdot 1 + 2 = 2 - 3 + 2 = 1$.

19. $f(x) = .4[\![x]\!] + .75 \Rightarrow f(5.5) = .4[\![5.5]\!] + .75 = .4(5) + .75 = 2 + .75 = \$2.75$

20. **(a)** $C(x) = 3300 + 4.50x$

(b) $R(x) = 10.50x$

(c) $P(x) = R(x) - C(x) = 10.50x - (3300 + 4.50x) = 6.00x - 3300$

(d)

$$\begin{aligned} P(x) &> 0 \\ 6.00x - 3300 &> 0 \\ 6.00x &> 3300 \\ x &> 550 \end{aligned}$$

He must produce and sell 551 items before he earns a profit.

Chapter 3
POLYNOMIAL AND RATIONAL FUNCTIONS

Section 3.1: Quadratic Functions and Models

1. $f(x)=(x+3)^2-4$

(a) domain: $(-\infty, \infty)$; range: $[-4, \infty)$

(b) vertex: $(h, k)=(-3, -4)$

(c) axis: $x=-3$

(d) To find the y-intercept, let $x=0$.

$y=(0+3)^2-4=3^2-4=9-4=5$

y-intercept: 5

(e) To find the x-intercepts, let $f(x)=0$.

$$0=(x+3)^2-4$$
$$(x+3)^2=4$$
$$x+3=\pm\sqrt{4}=\pm 2$$
$$x=-3\pm 2$$
$$x=-3-2=-5 \text{ or } x=-3+2=-1$$

x-intercepts: -5 and -1

3. $f(x)=-2(x+3)^2+2$

(a) domain: $(-\infty, \infty)$; range: $(-\infty, 2]$

(b) vertex: $(h, k)=(-3, 2)$

(c) axis: $x=-3$

(d) To find the y-intercept, let $x=0$.

$$y=-2(0+3)^2+2=-2\cdot 3^2+2$$
$$=-2\cdot 9+2=-18+2=-16$$

y-intercept: -16

(e) To find the x-intercepts, let $f(x)=0$.

$$0=-2(x+3)^2+2$$
$$(x+3)^2=1$$
$$x+3=\pm\sqrt{1}=\pm 1$$
$$x=-3\pm 1$$
$$x=-3-1=-4 \text{ or } x=-3+1=-2$$

x-intercepts: -4 and -2

5. $f(x)=(x-4)^2-3$

Since $a>0$, the parabola opens upward. The vertex is at $(4, -3)$. The correct graph, therefore, is B.

7. $f(x)=(x+4)^2-3$

Since $a>0$, the parabola opens upward. The vertex is at $(-4, -3)$. The correct graph, therefore, is D.

9. For parts (a), (b), (c), and (d), see the following graph.

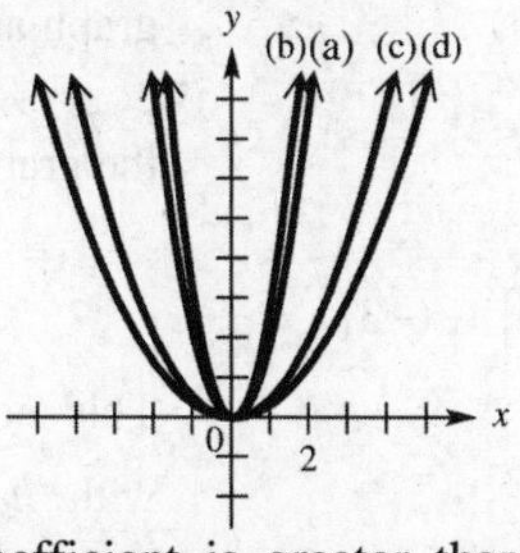

(e) If the absolute value of the coefficient is greater than 1, it causes the graph to be stretched vertically, so it is narrower. If the absolute value of the coefficient is between 0 and 1, it causes the graph to shrink vertically, so it is broader.

11. For parts (a), (b), (c), and (d), see the following graph.

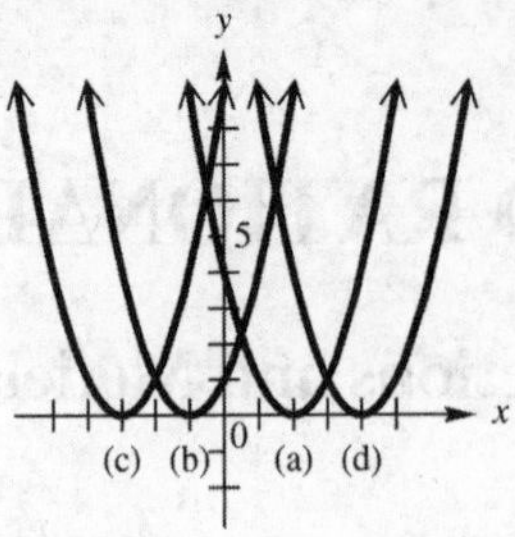

(e) The graph of $(x-h)^2$ is translated h units to the right if h is positive and $|h|$ units to the left if h is negative.

13. $f(x)=(x-2)^2$

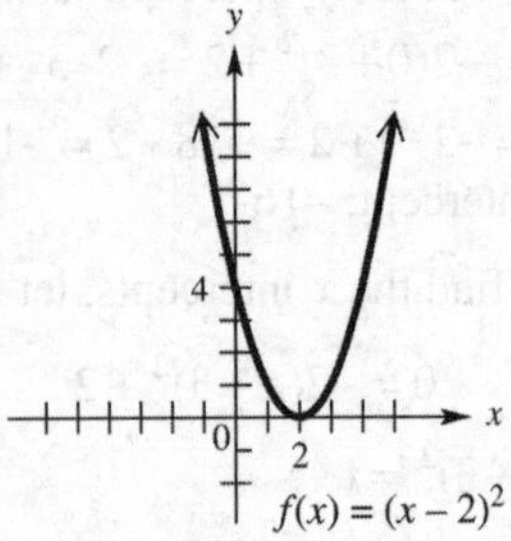

This equation is of the form $y=(x-h)^2$, with $h = 2$. The graph opens upward and has the same shape as that of $y=x^2$. It is a horizontal translation of the graph of $y=x^2$, 2 units to the right. The vertex is (2, 0) and the axis is the vertical line $x = 2$. Additional points on the graph are $(1,1)$ and $(3,1)$. The domain is $(-\infty, \infty)$. Since the smallest value of y is 0 and the graph opens upward, the range is $[0, \infty)$.

15. $f(x)=(x+3)^2-4=[x-(-3)]^2+(-4)$

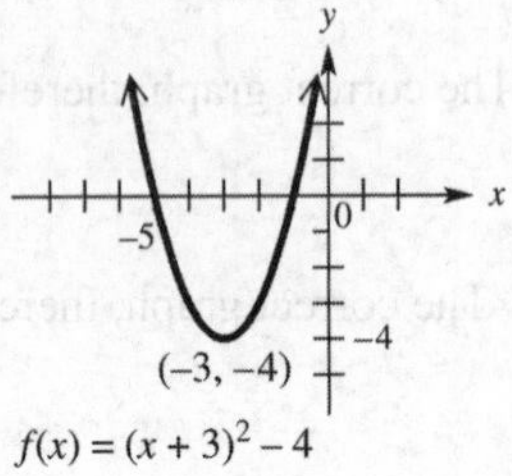

This equation is of the form $y=(x-h)^2+k$, with $h = -3$ and $k = -4$. The graph opens upward and has the same shape as $y=x^2$. The vertex is $(-3, -4)$. It is a translation of $y=x^2$, 3 units to the left and 4 units down. The axis is the vertical line $x = -3$. Additional points on the graph are $(-4,-3)$ and $(-2,-3)$. The domain is $(-\infty, \infty)$. Since the smallest value of y is -4 and the graph opens upward, the range is $[-4, \infty)$.

17. $f(x)=-\frac{1}{2}(x+1)^2-3=-\frac{1}{2}[x-(-1)]^2+(-3)$

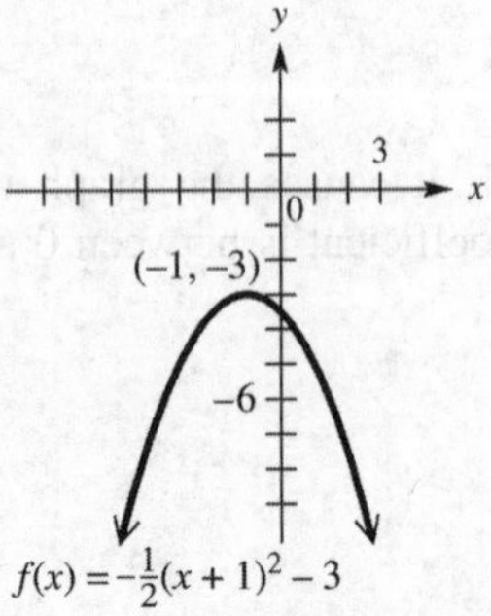

This equation is of the form $y=a(x-h)^2+k$, with $h=-1$, $k=-3$, and $a=-\frac{1}{2}$. The graph opens downward and is wider than $y=x^2$. The vertex is $(-1, -3)$. It is a translation of the graph $y=-\frac{1}{2}x^2$, 1 unit to the left and 3 units down. The axis is the vertical line $x = -1$. Additional points on the graph are $\left(-2,-3\frac{1}{2}\right)$ and $\left(0,-3\frac{1}{2}\right)$. The domain is $(-\infty, \infty)$. Since the largest value of y is -3 and the graph opens downward, the range is $(-\infty, -3]$.

19. $f(x) = x^2 - 2x + 3$; Rewrite by completing the square on x.

$f(x) = x^2 - 2x + 3 = (x^2 - 2x + 1 - 1) + 3$ Note: $\left[\frac{1}{2}(-2)\right]^2 = (-1)^2 = 1$

$= (x^2 - 2x + 1) - 1 + 3 = (x - 1)^2 + 2$

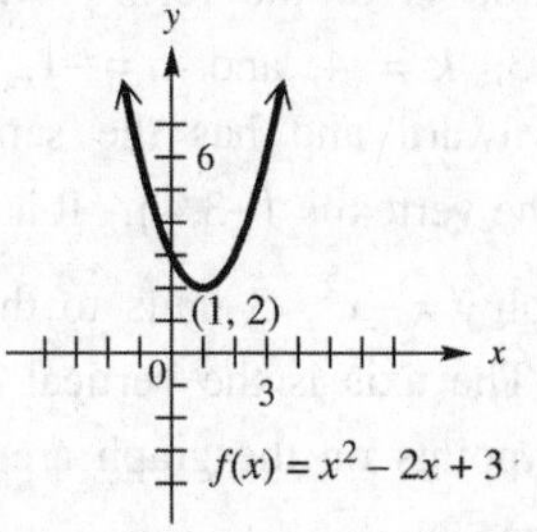

This equation is of the form $y = (x - h)^2 + k$, with $h = 1$ and $k = 2$. The graph opens upward and has the same shape as $y = x^2$. The vertex is (1, 2). It is a translation of the graph $y = x^2$, 1 unit to the right and 2 units up. The axis is the vertical line $x = 1$. Additional points on the graph are $(0, 3)$ and $(2, 3)$. The domain is $(-\infty, \infty)$. Since the smallest value of y is 2 and the graph opens upward, the range is $[2, \infty)$.

21. $f(x) = x^2 - 10x + 21$; Rewrite by completing the square on x.

$f(x) = x^2 - 10x + 21 = (x^2 - 10x + 25 - 25) + 21$ Note: $\left[\frac{1}{2}(-10)\right]^2 = (-5)^2 = 25$

$= (x^2 - 10x + 25) - 25 + 21 = (x - 5)^2 - 4 = (x - 5)^2 + (-4)$

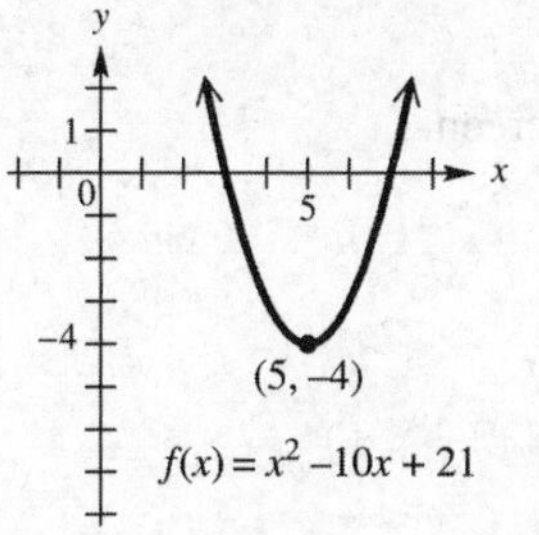

This equation is of the form $y = (x - h)^2 + k$, with $h = 5$ and $k = -4$. The graph opens upward and has the same shape as $y = x^2$. The vertex is (5, –4). It is a translation of the graph $y = x^2$, 5 units to the right and 4 units down. The axis is the vertical line $x = 5$. Additional points on the graph are $(4, -3)$ and $(6, -3)$. The domain is $(-\infty, \infty)$. Since the smallest value of y is – 4 and the graph opens upward, the range is $[-4, \infty)$.

23. $f(x) = -2x^2 - 12x - 16$; Rewrite by completing the square on x.

$f(x) = -2x^2 - 12x - 16 = -2(x^2 + 6x) - 16 = -2(x^2 + 6x + 9 - 9) - 16$ Note: $\left[\frac{1}{2}(6)\right]^2 = 3^2 = 9$

$= -2(x^2 + 6x + 9) + 18 - 16 = -2(x + 3)^2 + 2 = -2[x - (-3)]^2 + 2$

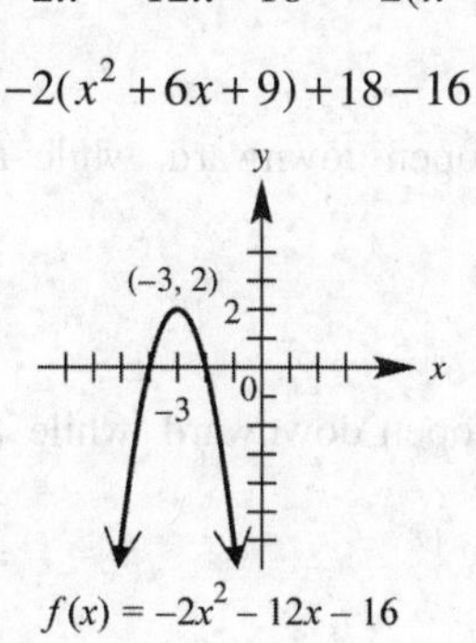

This equation is of the form $y = a(x - h)^2 + k$, with $h = -3$, $k = 2$, and $a = -2$. The graph opens downward and is narrower than $y = x^2$. The vertex is $(-3, 2)$. It is a translation of the graph $y = -2x^2$, 3 units to the left and 2 units up. The axis is the vertical line $x = -3$. Additional points on the graph are $(-4, 0)$ and $(-2, 0)$. The domain is $(-\infty, \infty)$. Since the largest value of y is 2 and the graph opens downward, the range is $(-\infty, 2]$.

25. $f(x)=-x^2-6x-5$; Rewrite by completing the square on x.

$f(x)=-x^2-6x-5=-(x^2+6x+9-9)-5$ Note: $\left[\frac{1}{2}(6)\right]^2=3^2=9$

$=-(x^2+6x+9)+9-5=-(x+3)^2+4=-1\cdot[x-(-3)]^2+4$

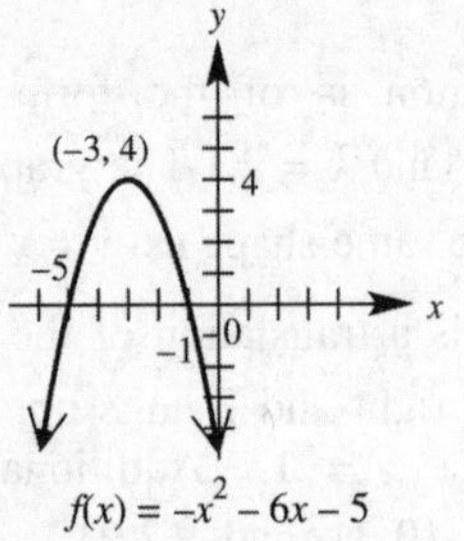

This equation is of the form $y=a(x-h)^2+k$, with $h=-3$, $k=4$, and $a=-1$. The graph opens downward and has the same shape as $y=x^2$. The vertex is $(-3,4)$. It is a translation of the graph $y=-x^2$, 3 units to the left and 4 units up. The axis is the vertical line $x=-3$. Additional points on the graph are $(-2,3)$ and $(-1,0)$. The domain is $(-\infty,\infty)$. Since the largest value of y is 4 and the graph opens downward, the range is $(-\infty,4]$.

27. The minimum value of $f(x)$ is $f(-3)=3$.

29. There are no real solutions to the equation $f(x)=1$ since the value of $f(x)$ is never less than 3.

31. Graph the functions $y=3x^2-2$ and $y=3(x^2-2)$ on the same screen.

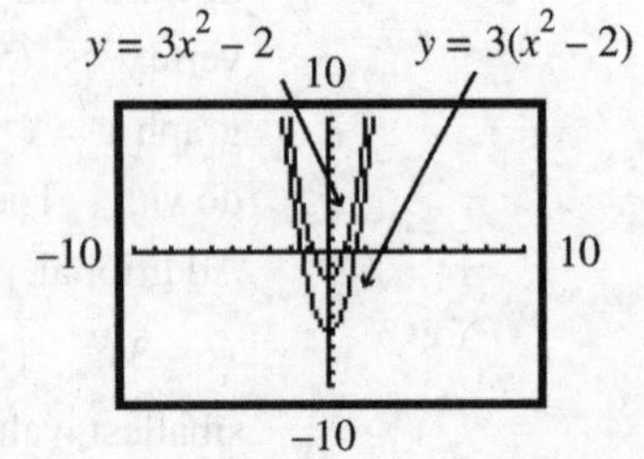

We see that the graphs are two different parabolas. Since the graphs are not the same, the expressions $3x^2-2$ and $3(x^2-2)$ are not equivalent. This result can be confirmed algebraically since $3(x^2-2)=3x^2-6\neq 3x^2-2$.

33. $a<0,\ b^2-4ac=0$

The correct choice is E. $a<0$ indicates that the parabola will open downward, while $b^2-4ac=0$ indicates that the graph will have exactly one x-intercept.

35. $a<0,\ b^2-4ac<0$

The correct choice is D. $a<0$ indicates that the parabola will open downward, while $b^2-4ac<0$ indicates that the graph will have no x-intercepts.

37. $a>0,\ b^2-4ac>0$

The correct choice is C. $a>0$ indicates that the parabola will open upward, while $b^2-4ac>0$ indicates that the graph will have two x-intercepts.

39. The vertex of the parabola in the figure is (1, 4) and the y-intercept is 2. The equation takes the form $f(x) = a(x-1)^2 + 4$. When $x = 0, f(x) = 2$, so $2 = a(0-1)^2 + 4 \Rightarrow 2 = a + 4 \Rightarrow a = -2$.

The equation is $f(x) = -2(x-1)^2 + 4$.

This function may also be written as $f(x) = -2(x^2 - 2x + 1) + 4 = -2x^2 + 4x - 2 + 4 = -2x^2 + 4x + 2$.

Graphing this function on a graphing calculator shows that the graph matches the equation.

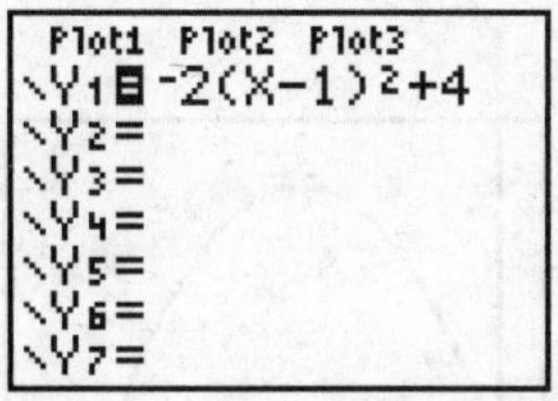

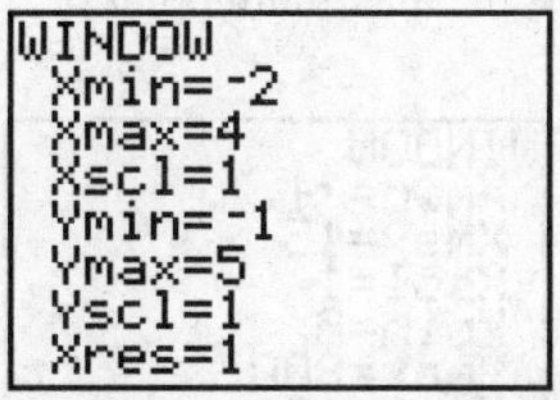

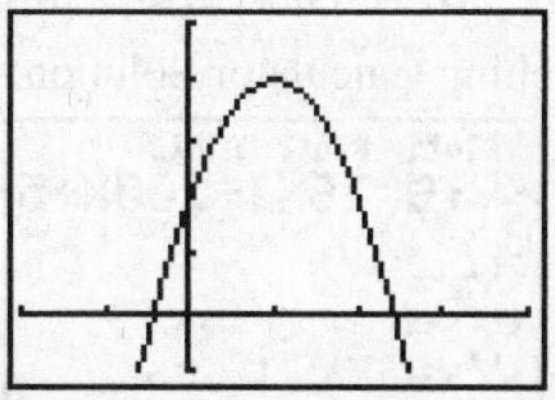

This graph can be displayed in other modes. If you press the MODE button, the following screen will appear. Toggle down to the last row and change FULL to Horiz.

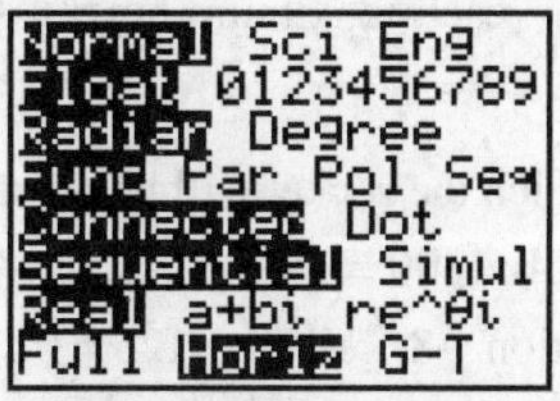

Hit 2nd then GRAPH (TABLE) to get the table to display below the graph.

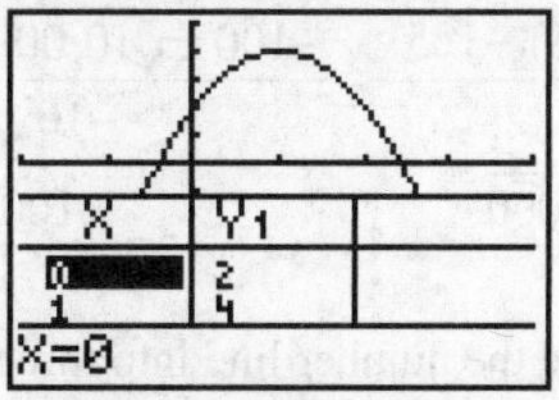

If you press the MODE button again, you can change to G-T mode (Graph-Table).

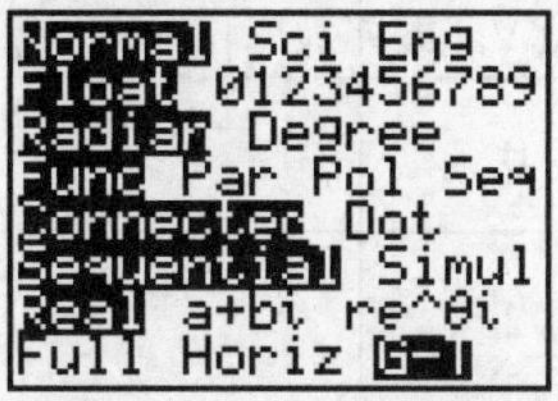

When you press the Graph button, the following screen will appear.

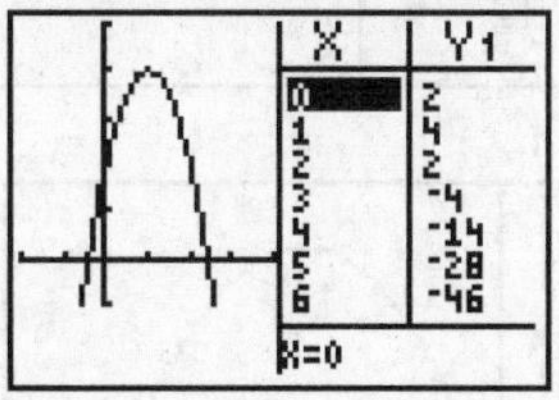

41. Quadratic; the points lie in a pattern that suggests a parabola opening downward, so a < 0.

43. Quadratic; the points lie in a pattern suggesting a parabola opening upward, so $a > 0$.

45. Linear; The points lie in pattern that suggesting a positive slope.

47. (a) Since $v_0 = 200$, and $s_0 = 50$, and $s(t) = -16t^2 + v_0 t + s_0$ we have $s(t)$ or $f(t) = -16t^2 + 200t + 50$.

(b) Algebraic Solution:

Find the coordinates of the vertex of the parabola. Using the vertex formula with $a = -16$ and $b = 200$, $x = -\frac{b}{2a} = -\frac{200}{2(-16)} = 6.25$ and $y = -16(6.25)^2 + 200(6.25) + 50 = 675$. The vertex is $(6.25, 675)$. Since $a < 0$, this is the maximum point.

Graphing Calculator Solution:

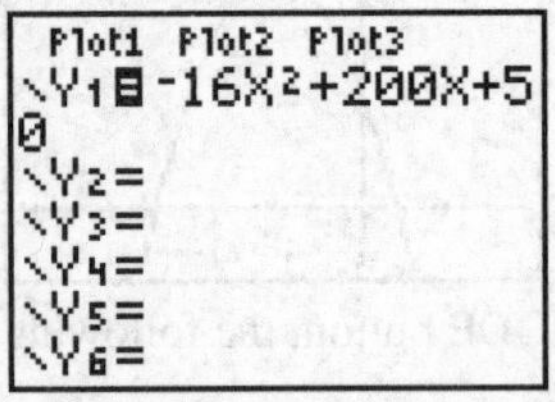

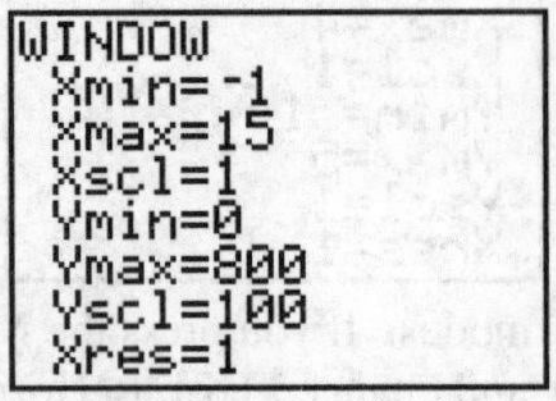

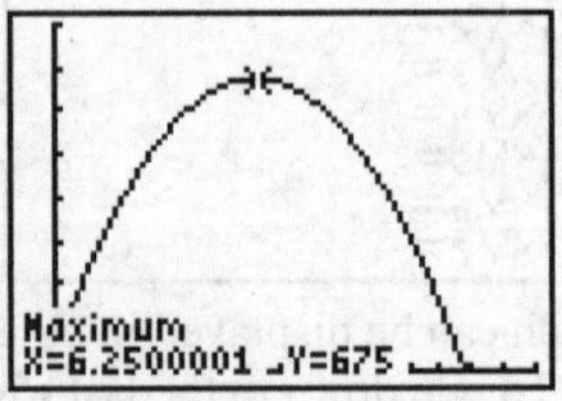

Thus, the number of seconds to reach maximum height is 6.25 seconds. The maximum height is 675 ft.

(c) Algebraic Solution:

To find the time interval in which the rocket will be more than 300 ft above ground level, solve the inequality $-16t^2 + 200t + 50 > 300 \Rightarrow -16t^2 + 200t - 250 > 0 \Rightarrow -8t^2 + 100t - 125 > 0$.

Solve the corresponding equation $-8t^2 + 100t - 125 = 0$.

Use the quadratic formula with $a = -8$, $b = 100$, and $c = -125$.

$$t = \frac{-100 \pm \sqrt{100^2 - 4(-8)(-125)}}{2(-8)} = \frac{-100 \pm \sqrt{10{,}000 - 4000}}{-16} = \frac{-100 \pm \sqrt{6000}}{-16}$$

$$t = \frac{-100 + \sqrt{6000}}{-16} \approx 1.4 \quad \text{or} \quad t = \frac{-100 - \sqrt{6000}}{-16} \approx 11.1$$

The values 1.4 and 11.1 divide the number line into three intervals: $(-\infty, 1.4)$, $(1.4, 11.1)$, and $(11.1, \infty)$. Use a test point in each interval to determine where the inequality is satisfied.

Interval	Test Value	Is $-16t^2 + 200t + 50 > 300$ True or False?
$(-\infty, 1.4)$	0	$-16 \cdot 0^2 + 200 \cdot 0 + 50 > 300$? $50 > 300$ False
$(1.4, 11.1)$	2	$-16 \cdot 2^2 + 200 \cdot 2 + 50 > 300$? $386 > 300$ True
$(11.1, \infty)$	12	$-16 \cdot 12^2 + 200 \cdot 12 + 50 > 300$? $146 > 300$ False

Graphing Calculator Solution:

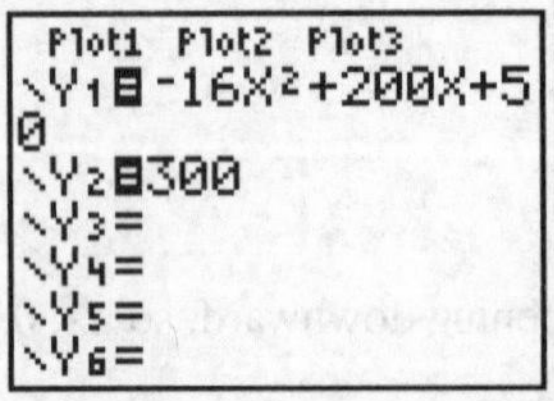

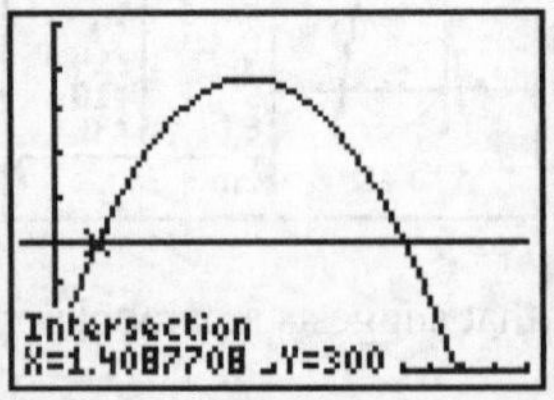

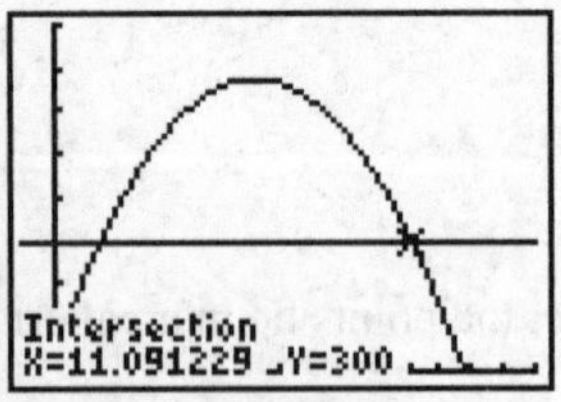

The rocket will be more than 300 ft above the ground between 1.4 sec and 1.1 sec.

Continued on next page

47. (continued)

(d) Algebraic Solution:

To find the number of seconds for the toy rocket to hit the ground, let $f(t) = 0$ and solve for t.

$$-16t^2 + 200t + 50 = 0$$

Use the quadratic formula with $a = -16$, $b = 200$, and $c = 50$.

$$t = \frac{-200 \pm \sqrt{200^2 - 4(-16)(50)}}{2(-16)} = \frac{-200 \pm \sqrt{40{,}000 + 3200}}{-32} = \frac{-200 \pm \sqrt{43{,}200}}{-32}$$

$$t = \frac{-200 + \sqrt{43{,}200}}{-32} \approx -.25 \quad \text{or} \quad t = \frac{-200 - \sqrt{43{,}200}}{-32} \approx 12.75$$

We reject the negative solution.

Graphing Calculator Solution:

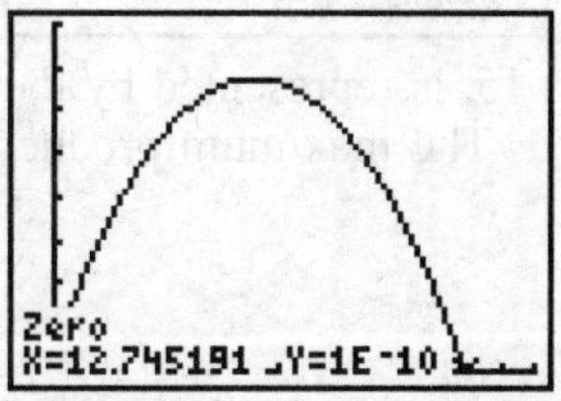

It will take approximately 12.75 seconds for the toy rocket to hit the ground.

49. Since $v_0 = 150$, and $s_0 = 0$, and $s(t) = -16t^2 + v_0 t + s_0$ we have $s(t) = -16t^2 + 150t$.

Algebraic Solution:

To find if the ball will reach a height of 400 ft above ground level, solve the inequality

$-16t^2 + 150t \geq 400 \Rightarrow -16t^2 + 150t - 400 \geq 0 \Rightarrow -8t^2 + 75t - 200 \geq 0.$

Solve the corresponding equation $-8t^2 + 75t - 200 = 0.$

Use the quadratic formula with $a = -8$, $b = 75$, and $c = -200$.

$$t = \frac{-75 \pm \sqrt{75^2 - 4(-8)(-200)}}{2(-8)} = \frac{-75 \pm \sqrt{5625 - 6400}}{-16} = \frac{-75 \pm \sqrt{-775}}{-16} = \frac{-75 \pm 5i\sqrt{31}}{-16}$$

The solution to the equation does not represent real values.

Graphing Calculator Solution:

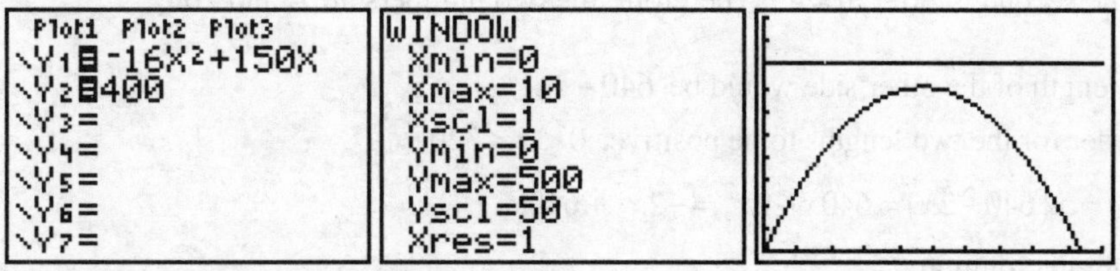

The line and the curve do not intersect.

The ball will not reach a height of 400 ft.

51. **(a)** The other positive number would be $30 - x$.

(b) In order for the two numbers to be positive, $0 < x < 30$.

(c) $f(x) = x(30 - x) = 30x - x^2 = -x^2 + 30x$

Continued on next page

51. (continued)

(d) Algebraic Solution:

Find the coordinates of the vertex of the parabola. Using the vertex formula with $a=-1$ and $b=30$, $x=-\frac{b}{2a}=-\frac{30}{2(-1)}=-\frac{30}{-2}=15$ and $y=-1(15)^2+30(15)=-225+450=225$. Since $a<0$, this is the maximum point.

Graphing Calculator Solution:

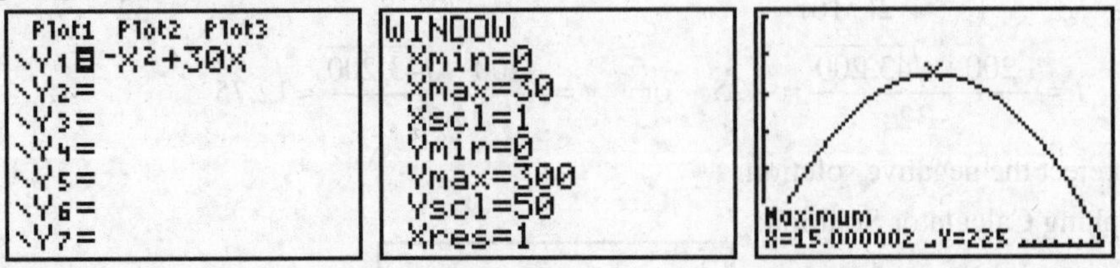

Thus, the first positive number, 15, is represented by the x-coordinate of the vertex. The second positive number is $30-15=15$. The maximum product of 225 is given by the y-coordinate of the vertex.

(e) Algebraic Solution:

Solve the equation $-x^2+30x=104$.

$$-x^2+30x=104 \Rightarrow x^2-30x+104=0 \Rightarrow (x-4)(x-26)=0$$

$$x-4=0 \quad \text{or} \quad x-26=0$$

$$x=4 \qquad\qquad x=26$$

Graphing Calculator Solution:

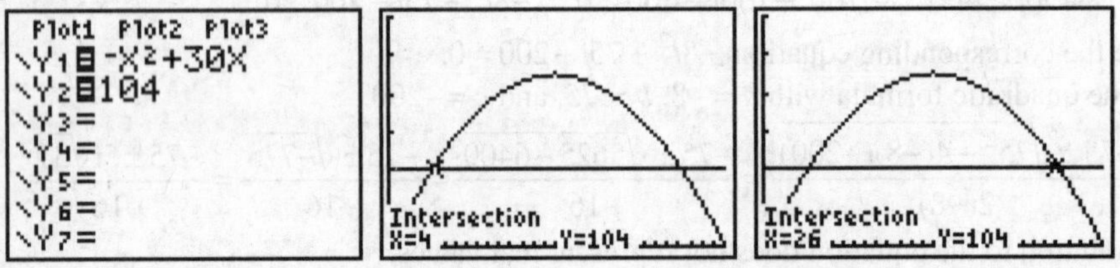

When the first positive number is 4, the second is $30-4=26$. When the first positive number is 26, the second is $30-26=4$. Therefore, the two numbers are 4 and 26.

53. (a) The length of the other side would be $640-2x$.

(b) In order for the two lengths to be positive, $0<x<320$.

(c) $A(x)=x(640-2x)=640x-2x^2=-2x^2+640x$

(d) Algebraic Solution:

Solve the inequality $30{,}000<-2x^2+640x<40{,}000$. Treat this as two inequalities, $-2x^2+640x>30{,}000$ and $-2x^2+640x<40{,}000$.

For $-2x^2+640x>30{,}000$, we solve the corresponding equation $-2x^2+640x=30{,}000$.

This equation is equivalent to $-2x^2+640x-30{,}000=0$ or $x^2-320x+15{,}000=0$.

Use the quadratic formula with $a=1$, $b=-320$, and $c=15{,}000$.

$$x=\frac{-(-320)\pm\sqrt{(-320)^2-4(1)(15{,}000)}}{2(1)}=\frac{320\pm\sqrt{102{,}400-60{,}000}}{2}=\frac{320\pm\sqrt{42{,}400}}{2}$$

$$x=\frac{320-\sqrt{42{,}400}}{2}\approx 57.04 \quad \text{or} \quad x=\frac{320+\sqrt{42{,}400}}{2}\approx 262.96$$

Continued on next page

53. (d) (continued)

The values 57.04 and 262.96 divide the number line into three intervals: $(-\infty, 57.04)$, $(57.04, 262.96)$, and $(262.96, \infty)$. Use a test point in each interval to determine where the inequality is satisfied.

Interval	Test Value	Is $-2x^2 + 640x > 30,000$ True or False?
$(-\infty, 57.04)$	0	$-2 \cdot 0^2 + 640 \cdot 0 > 30,000$? $0 > 30,000$ False
$(57.04, 262.96)$	60	$-2 \cdot 60^2 + 640 \cdot 60 > 30,000$? $31,200 > 30,000$ True
$(262.96, \infty)$	300	$-2 \cdot 300^2 + 640 \cdot 300 > 30,000$? $12,000 > 30,000$ False

Thus, the first inequality is satisfied when the measure of x is in the interval $(57.04, 262.96)$.

For $-2x^2 + 640x < 40,000$, we solve the corresponding equation $-2x^2 + 640x = 40,000$.

This equation is equivalent to $-2x^2 + 640x - 40,000 = 0$ or $x^2 - 320x + 20,000 = 0$

Use the quadratic formula with $a = 1$, $b = -320$, and $c = 20,000$.

$$x = \frac{-(-320) \pm \sqrt{(-320)^2 - 4(1)(20,000)}}{2(1)} = \frac{320 \pm \sqrt{102,400 - 80,000}}{2} = \frac{320 \pm \sqrt{22,400}}{2}$$

$$x = \frac{320 - \sqrt{22,400}}{2} \approx 85.17 \quad \text{or} \quad x = \frac{320 + \sqrt{22,400}}{2} \approx 234.83$$

The values 85.17 and 234.83 divide the number line into three intervals: $(-\infty, 85.17)$, $(85.17, 234.83)$, and $(234.83, \infty)$. Use a test point in each interval to determine where the inequality is satisfied.

Interval	Test Value	Is $-2x^2 + 640x < 40,000$ True or False?
$(-\infty, 85.17)$	0	$-2 \cdot 0^2 + 640 \cdot 0 < 40,000$? $0 < 40,000$ True
$(85.17, 234.83)$	90	$-2 \cdot 90^2 + 640 \cdot 90 < 40,000$? $41,400 < 40,000$ False
$(234.83, \infty)$	300	$-2 \cdot 300^2 + 640 \cdot 300 < 40,000$? $12,000 < 40,000$ True

Thus, the second inequality is satisfied when the measure of x is in the interval $(-\infty, 85.17)$ or $(234.83, \infty)$. We must now seek the intersection of the intervals $(57.04, 262.96)$, and $(-\infty, 85.17)$ or $(234.83, \infty)$. If we use the real number line as an aid, we can see that the solution would be between 57.04 ft and 85.17 ft or 234.83 ft and 262.96 ft.

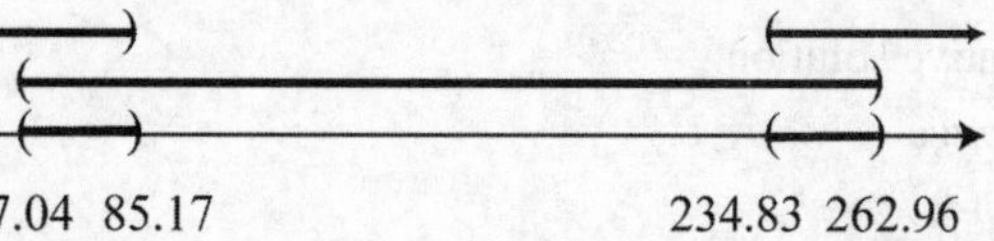

Continued on next page

53. **(d)** (continued)

Graphing Calculator Solution:

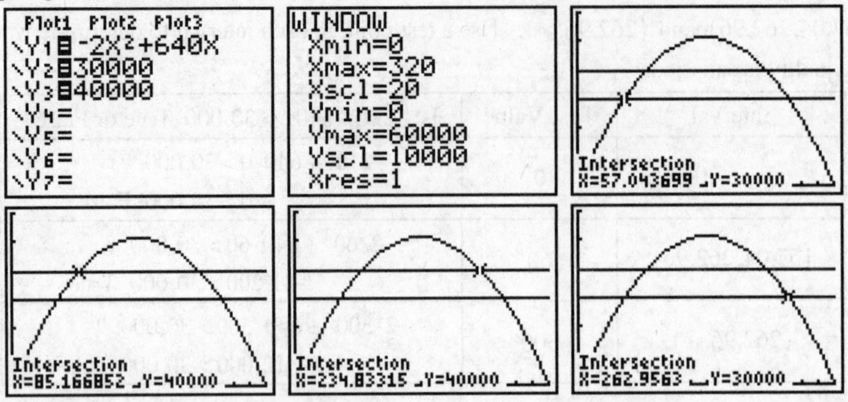

We can see from the graphs that the quadratic function lies between the lines when x is between 57.04 ft and 85.17 ft or 234.83 ft and 262.96 ft.

(e) Algebraic Solution:

Find the coordinates of the vertex of the parabola, $A(x) = -2x^2 + 640x$. Using the vertex formula with $a = -2$ and $b = 640$. We have $x = -\frac{b}{2a} = -\frac{640}{2(-2)} = 160$ and

$y = -2(160)^2 + 640(160) = 51,200$. Since $a < 0$, this is the maximum point.

Graphing Calculator Solution:

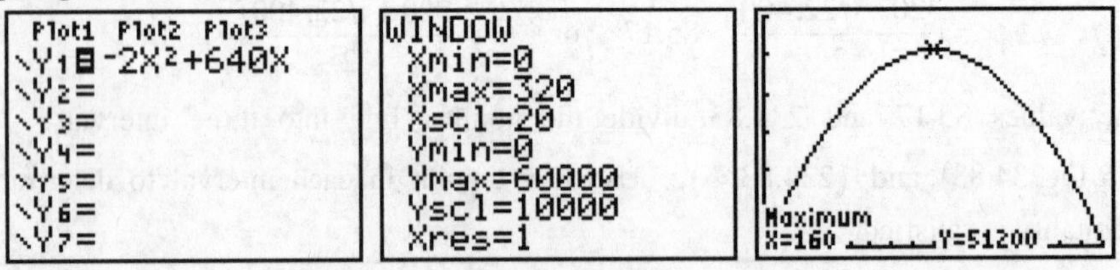

Thus, the length of the two parallel sides would be 160 ft and the third side would be $640 - 2(160) = 620 - 320 = 320$ ft. The maximum area would be 512,000 ft^2.

55. **(a)** The length of the original piece of cardboard would be $2x$.

(b) The length of the rectangular box would be $2x - 4$ and the width would be $x - 4$, where $x > 4$.

(c) $V(x) = (2x-4)(x-4)(2) = (2x^2 - 12x + 16)(2) = 4x^2 - 24x + 32$

(d) Algebraic Solution:

Solve the equation $4x^2 - 24x + 32 = 320$.

$$4x^2 - 24x + 32 = 320 \Rightarrow 4x^2 - 24x - 288 = 0 \Rightarrow x^2 - 6x - 72 = 0 = (x+6)(x-12) = 0$$

$$x + 6 = 0 \quad \text{or} \quad x - 12 = 0$$

$$x = -6 \qquad\qquad x = 12$$

We discard the negative solution.

Continued on next page

55. (d) (continued)

Graphing Calculator Solution:

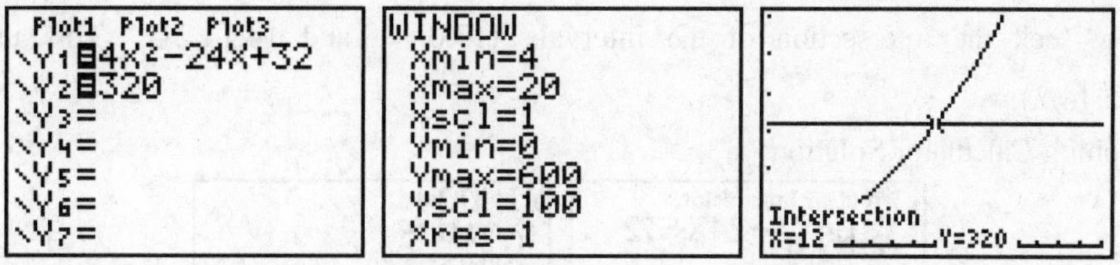

If $x = 12$, then the dimensions of the bottom of the box will be $12 - 4 = 8$ in by $2(12) - 4 = 24 - 4 = 20$ in.

(e) Algebraic Solution:

Solve the inequality $400 < 4x^2 - 24x + 32 < 500$. Treat this as two inequalities, $4x^2 - 24x + 32 > 400$ and $4x^2 - 24x + 32 < 500$.

For $4x^2 - 24x + 32 > 400$, we solve the corresponding equation $4x^2 - 24x + 32 = 400$.

This equation is equivalent to $4x^2 - 24x - 368 = 0$ or $x^2 - 6x - 92 = 0$

Use the quadratic formula with $a = 1$, $b = -6$, and $c = -92$.

$$x = \frac{-(-6) \pm \sqrt{(-6)^2 - 4(1)(-92)}}{2(1)} = \frac{6 \pm \sqrt{36 + 368}}{2} = \frac{6 \pm \sqrt{404}}{2} = \frac{6 \pm 2\sqrt{101}}{2} = 3 \pm \sqrt{101}$$

$$x = 3 - \sqrt{101} \approx -7.0 \quad \text{or} \quad x = 3 + \sqrt{101} \approx 13.0$$

Since $x > 4$, we need only check the intervals: $(4, 13.0)$ and $(13.0, \infty)$. Use a test point in each interval to determine where the inequality is satisfied.

Interval	Test Value	Is $4x^2 - 24x + 32 > 400$ True or False?
$(4, 13.0)$	5	$4 \cdot 5^2 - 24 \cdot 5 + 32 > 400$? $12 > 400$ False
$(13.0, \infty)$	14	$4 \cdot 14^2 - 24 \cdot 14 + 32 > 400$? $480 > 400$ True

Thus, the first inequality is satisfied when the length, *x*, is in the interval $(13.0, \infty)$.

For $4x^2 - 24x + 32 < 500$, we solve the corresponding equation $4x^2 - 24x + 32 = 500$.

This equation is equivalent to $4x^2 - 24x - 468 = 0$ or $x^2 - 6x - 117 = 0$

Use the quadratic formula with $a = 1$, $b = -6$, and $c = -117$.

$$x = \frac{-(-6) \pm \sqrt{(-6)^2 - 4(1)(-117)}}{2(1)} = \frac{6 \pm \sqrt{36 + 468}}{2} = \frac{6 \pm \sqrt{504}}{2} = \frac{6 \pm 2\sqrt{126}}{2} = 3 \pm \sqrt{126}$$

$$x = 3 - \sqrt{126} \approx -8.2 \quad \text{or} \quad x = 3 + \sqrt{126} \approx 14.2$$

Since $x > 4$, we need only check the intervals: $(4, 14.2)$ and $(14.2, \infty)$. Use a test point in each interval to determine where the inequality is satisfied.

Interval	Test Value	Is $4x^2 - 24x + 32 < 500$ True or False?
$(4, 14.2)$	5	$4 \cdot 5^2 - 24 \cdot 5 + 32 < 500$? $12 < 500$ True
$(14.2, \infty)$	15	$4 \cdot 15^2 - 24 \cdot 15 + 32 < 500$? $572 < 500$ False

Continued on next page

55. (e) (continued)

Thus, the second inequality is satisfied when the length, x, is in the interval $(4, 14.2)$. We must now seek the intersection of the intervals $(13.0, \infty)$ and $(4, 14.2)$. This intersection is $(13, 14.2)$.

Graphing Calculator Solution:

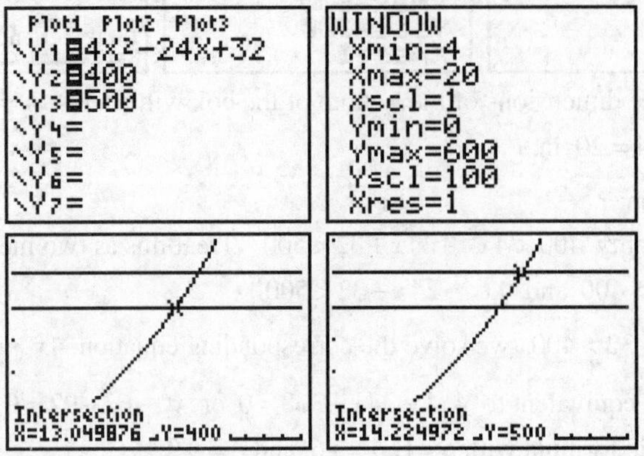

We can see from the graphs that the quadratic function lies between the lines when x is between 13.0 in and 14.2 in.

Thus, when the original width is between 13.0 in and 14.2 in, the volume will be between 400 in^3 and 500 in^3.

57. $h(x) = -.5x^2 + 1.25x + 3$

(a) Find $h(x)$ when $x = 2$.

$$h(2) = -.5(2)^2 + 1.25(2) + 3 = -.5(4) + 1.25(2) + 3 = -2 + 2.5 + 3 = 3.5.$$

When the distance from the base of the stump was 2 ft, the frog was 3.5 ft high.

(b) Algebraic Solution:

Find x when $h(x) = 3.25$.

$3.25 = -0.5x^2 + 1.25x + 3 \Rightarrow 0.5x^2 - 1.25x + 0.25 = 0 \Rightarrow 2x^2 - 5x + 1 = 0$

Use the quadratic formula with $a = 2$, $b = -5$, and $c = 1$.

$$x = \frac{-(-5) \pm \sqrt{(-5)^2 - 4(2)(1)}}{2(2)} = \frac{5 \pm \sqrt{25-8}}{4} = \frac{5 \pm \sqrt{17}}{4}$$

$$x = \frac{5-\sqrt{17}}{4} \approx .2 \text{ or } x = \frac{5+\sqrt{17}}{4} \approx 2.3$$

Graphing Calculator Solution:

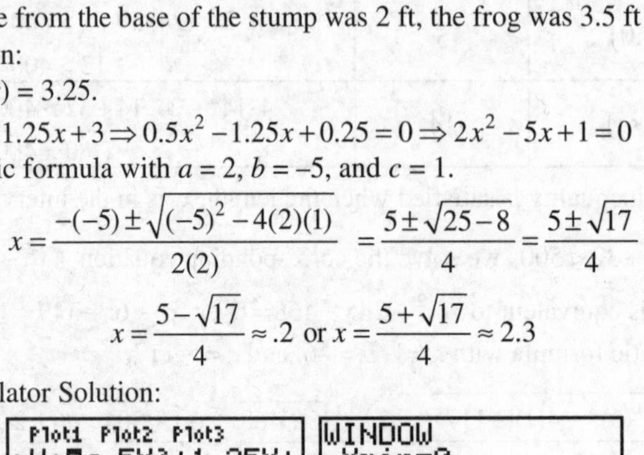

Continued on next page

57. (b) (continued)

The frog was 3.25 ft above the ground when he was approximately .2 ft from the stump (on the way up) and 2.3 ft from the stump (on the way down).

(c) Algebraic Solution:

Since the parabola opens downward, the vertex is the maximum point. Use the vertex formula to find the x-coordinate of the vertex of $h(x) = -0.5x^2 + 1.25x + 3$.

$$x = -\frac{b}{2a} = -\frac{1.25}{2(-0.5)} = -\frac{1.25}{-1} = 1.25$$

Graphing Calculator Solution:

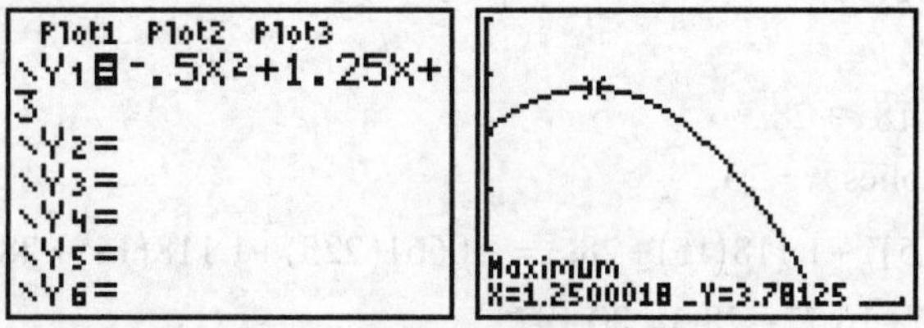

The frog reached its highest point at 1.25 ft from the stump.

(d) The maximum height is the y-coordinate of the vertex.

$$y = h(1.25) = -.5(1.25)^2 + 1.25(1.25) + 3 = 3.78125$$

The maximum height reached by the frog was approximately 3.78 ft. This agrees with the graphing calculator solution by interpreting the y-coordinate of the vertex as the maximum height.

59. $y = \dfrac{-16x^2}{.434v^2} + 1.15x + 8$

(a) Let $y = 10$ and $x = 15$.

$$10 = \frac{-16(15)^2}{.434v^2} + 1.15(15) + 8 \Rightarrow 10 = \frac{-16(225)}{.434v^2} + 1.15(15) + 8 \Rightarrow 10 = \frac{-3600}{.434v^2} + 17.25 + 8$$

$$10 = \frac{-3600}{.434v^2} + 25.25 \Rightarrow \frac{3600}{.434v^2} = 15.25 \Rightarrow 3600 = 6.6185v^2 \Rightarrow \frac{3600}{6.6185} = v^2$$

$$\pm\sqrt{\frac{3600}{6.6185}} = v \Rightarrow v \approx \pm 23.32$$

Since v represents a velocity, only the positive square root is meaningful. The basketball should have an initial velocity of 23.32 ft per sec.

(b) $y = \dfrac{-16x^2}{.434(23.32)^2} + 1.15x + 8$

Algebraic Solution:

Since the parabola opens downward, the vertex is the maximum point. Use the vertex formula to find the x-coordinate of the vertex.

$$x = -\frac{b}{2a} = -\frac{1.15}{2\left(\frac{-16}{.434(23.32)^2}\right)} \approx 8.482$$

To find the y-coordinate of the vertex, evaluate the quadratic function when $x = 8.482$.

$$y = \frac{-16(8.482)^2}{.434(23.32)^2} + 1.15(8.482) + 8 \approx 12.88$$

Continued on next page

59. (b) (continued)

Graphing Calculator Solution:

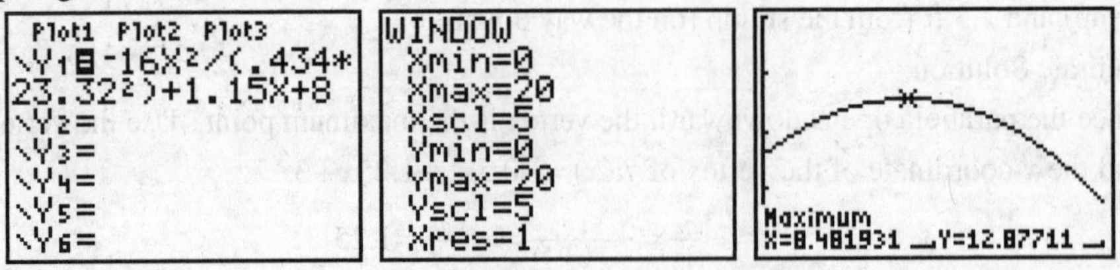

The y-coordinate of the vertex represents the maximum height of the basketball, which is approximately 12.88 ft.

61. $f(x) = -.0661x^2 + 1.118x + 28.3$

(a) The year 2005 implies $x = 15$.

$$f(15) = -.0661(15)^2 + 1.118(15) + 28.3 = -.0661(225) + 1.118(15) + 28.3$$
$$= -14.8725 + 16.77 + 28.3 = 30.1975$$

Approximately 30.2 (percent) is predicted for 2005.

(b) Answers will vary.
It is not realistic to assume they will decrease, based on the trend seen in the period 1990-2000.

63. $f(x) = .071x^2 - .426x + 8.05$

We seek the x-coordinate of the vertex.

Algebraic Solution:

Since the parabola opens upward, the vertex is the minimum point. Use the vertex formula to find the x-coordinate of the vertex.

$$x = -\frac{b}{2a} = -\frac{-.426}{2(.071)} = -\frac{-.426}{.142} = 3$$

Graphing Calculator Solution:

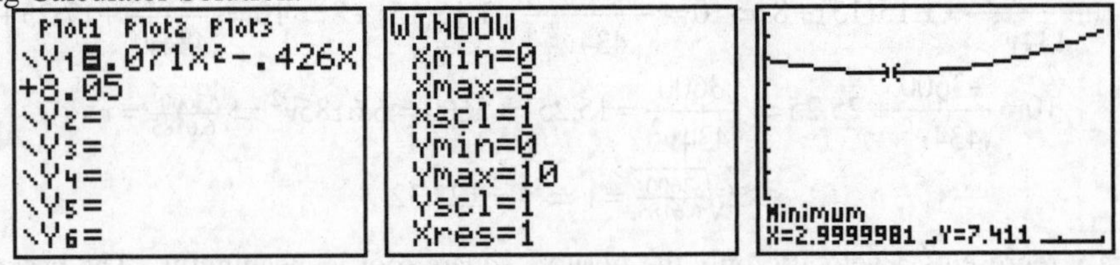

Since $x = 3$ corresponds to 1992, in 1992 the percent of affluent households reached a minimum.

65. (a) Plot the 12 points (2, 1563), (3, 4647), …(16, 584,394).

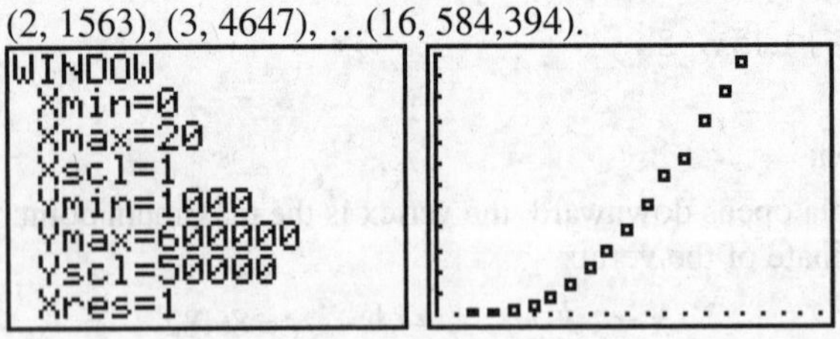

(b) Answers will vary.

(c) Let the point (2, 1563) be the vertex. Then, $f(x) = a(x-2)^2 + 1563$.
Next let the point (13, 361,509) lie on the graph of the function and solve for a.

$$f(13) = a(13-2)^2 + 1563 = 361{,}509 \Rightarrow a(11)^2 + 1563 = 361{,}509 \Rightarrow 121a + 1563 = 361{,}509$$
$$121a = 359{,}946 \Rightarrow a = \frac{359{,}946}{121} \approx 2974.76.$$

Thus, $f(x) = 2974.76(x-2)^2 + 1563$.

Continued on next page

65. (continued)

(d) Plotting the points together with $f(x)$, we see that there is a relatively good fit.

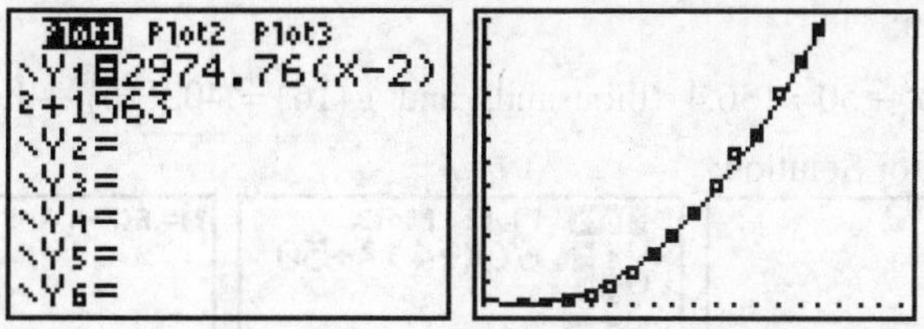

(e) $x = 19$ corresponds to the year 1999, and $x = 20$ corresponds to the year 2000.

Algebraic Solution:

$f(19) = 2974.76(19-2)^2 + 1563 \approx 861{,}269$ and $f(20) = 2974.76(20-2)^2 + 1563 \approx 965{,}385.$

Graphing Calculator Solution:

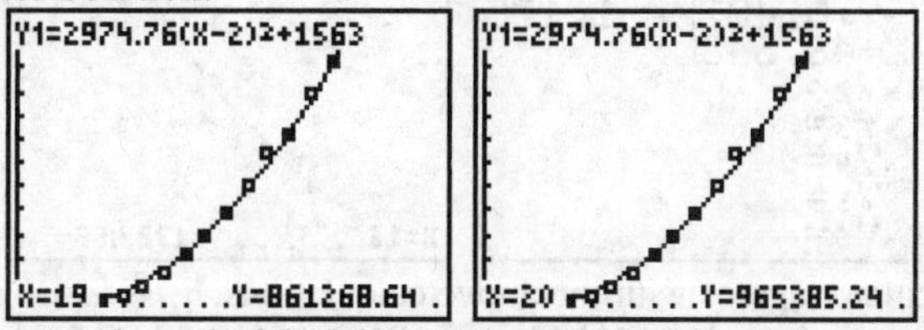

In the year 1999, approximately 861,269 people will have been diagnosed with AIDS since 1981.
In the year 2000, approximately 965,385 people will have been diagnosed with AIDS since 1981.

(f) The number of new cases in the year 2000 will be approximately
$f(20) - f(19) \approx 965{,}385 - 861{,}269 = 104{,}116.$

67. **(a)** Plot the 12 points (4, 50), (6, 56), …(14, 110).

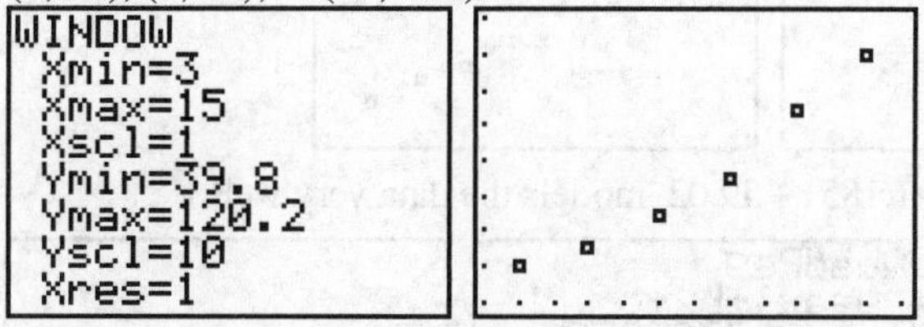

(b) Let the point (4, 50), be the vertex. Then, $f(x) = a(x-4)^2 + 50.$.

Next let the point (14, 110) lie on the graph of the function and solve for a.

$$f(14) = a(14-4)^2 + 50 = 110 \Rightarrow a(10)^2 + 50 = 110 \Rightarrow 100a + 50 = 110$$

$$100a = 60 \Rightarrow a = \tfrac{60}{100} = .6.$$

Thus, $f(x) = .6(x-4)^2 + 50.$

(c) Plotting the points together with $f(x)$, we see that there is a relatively good fit.

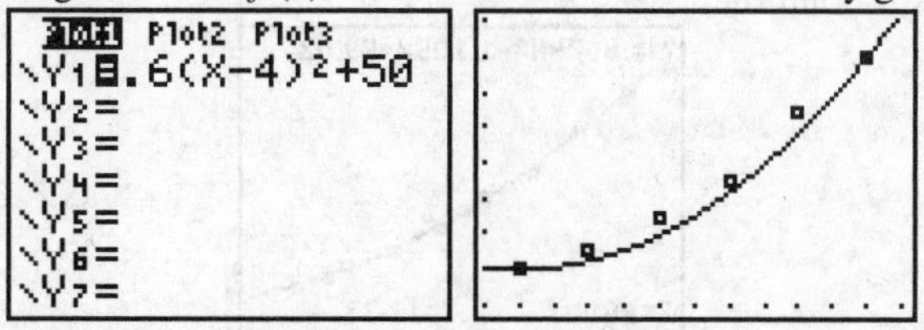

(d) The quadratic regression curve is $g(x) = .402x^2 - 1.175x + 48.343$ (thousand).

Continued on next page

67. (continued)

(e) $x = 16$ corresponds to the year 2006.

Algebraic Solution:

$f(16) = .6(16-4)^2 + 50 = 136.4$ (thousand) and $g(16) = .402(16)^2 - 1.175(16) + 48.343 \approx 132.5$

Graphing Calculator Solution:

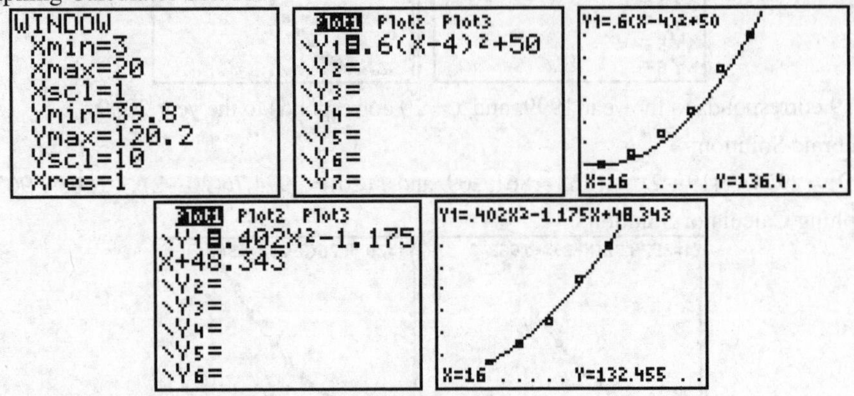

The graphing calculator agrees with the above calculations.

In the year 2006, approximately 136.4 (thousand) are predicted by f to be over 100 in 2006.

In the year 2006, approximately 132.5 (thousand) are predicted by g to be over 100 in 2006.

69. (a)

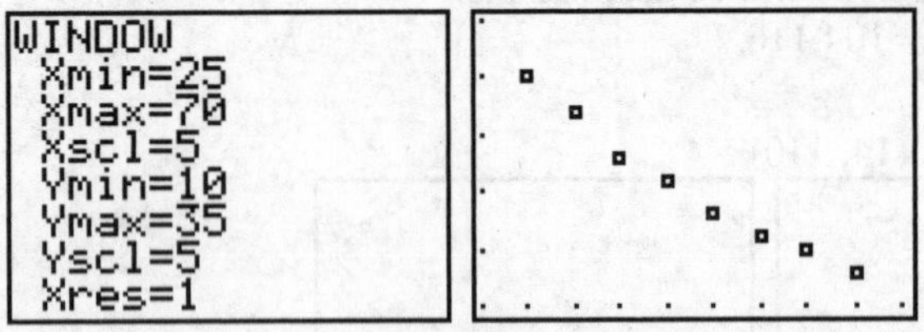

(b) $g(x) = .0074x^2 - 1.185x + 59.02$ models the data very well.

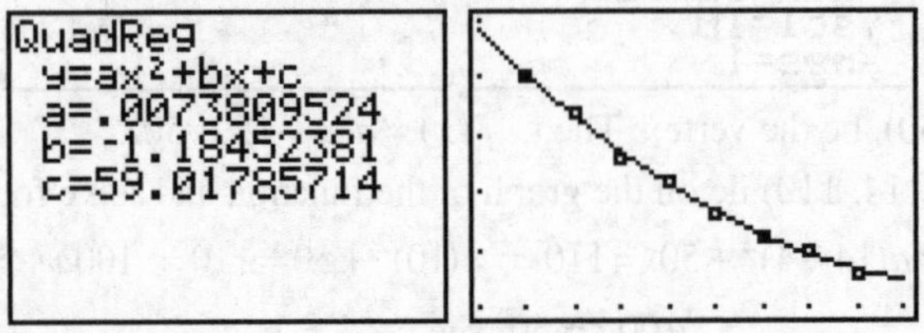

(c) Algebraic Solution:

$g(70) = .0074(70)^2 - 1.185(70) + 59.02 = 12.33$

Graphing Calculator Solution:

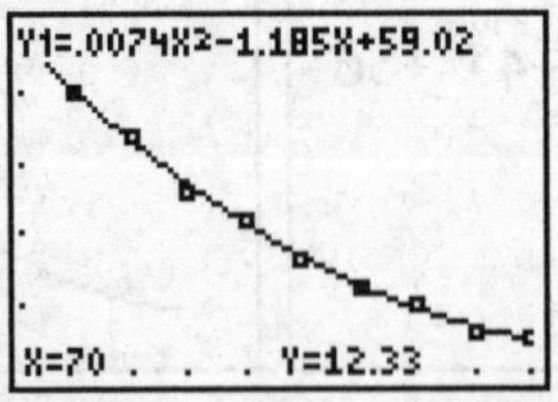

With an initial speed of 70 mph, the coast-down time would be 12.33 sec.

(d) A speed of approximately 39.1 mph corresponds to a coast-down time of 24 sec.

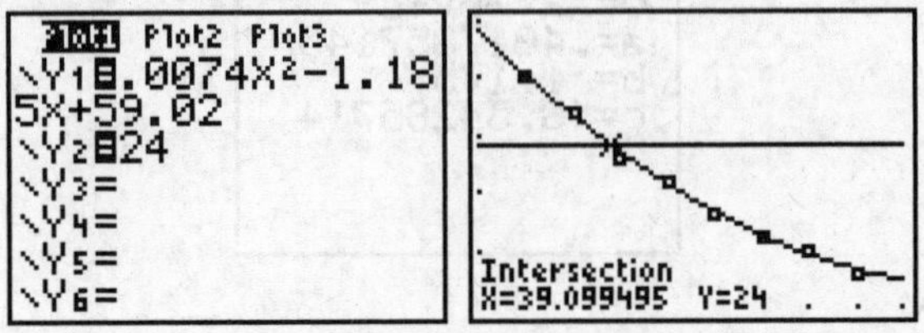

71. $y = x^2 - 10x + c$

An x-intercept occurs where $y = 0$, or $0 = x^2 - 10x + c$. There will be exactly one x-intercept if this equation has exactly one solution, or if the discriminant is zero.

$$b^2 - 4ac = 0 \Rightarrow (-10)^2 - 4(1)c = 0 \Rightarrow\Rightarrow 100 - 4c = 0 \Rightarrow 100 = 4c \Rightarrow c = 25$$

73. x-intercepts 2 and 5, and y-intercept 5

Since we have x-intercepts 2 and 5, f has linear factors of $x-2$ and $x-5$.

$$f(x) = a(x-2)(x-5) = a(x^2 - 7x + 10)$$

Since the y-intercept is 5, $f(0) = 5$.

$$f(x) = a(0^2 - 7(0) + 10) = 5 \Rightarrow 10a = 5 \Rightarrow a = \tfrac{1}{2}$$

The required quadratic function is $f(x) = \frac{1}{2}(x^2 - 7x + 10) = \frac{1}{2}x^2 - \frac{7}{2}x + 5.$

75. $y = -(x-2)^2 + 9$

The graph of this equation is a parabola with vertex (2, 9) that opens downward. The largest possible value of y is the value of y at the vertex, or $y = 9$.

(a) As a number increases, its square root increases. Since the largest possible value of $-(x-2)^2 + 9$ is 9, the largest possible value of $\sqrt{-(x-2)^2 + 9}$ is $\sqrt{9} = 3$.

(b) As a number increases, its reciprocal decreases. Since the largest possible value of $-(x-2)^2 + 9$ is 9, the smallest *positive* value of $\frac{1}{-(x-2)^2+9}$ is $\frac{1}{9}$.

77. Use the distance formula, $d(P, R) = \sqrt{(x_1 - x_2)^2 + (y_1 - y_2)^2}$, to find the distance between the points $P(x, 2x)$ and $R(1, 7)$, where P is any point on the line $y = 2x$.

$$d(P, R) = \sqrt{(x-1)^2 + (2x-7)^2} = \sqrt{(x^2 - 2x + 1) + (4x^2 - 28x + 49)} = \sqrt{5x^2 - 30x + 50}$$

Consider the equation $y = 5x^2 - 30x + 50$. This is the equation of a parabola opening upward, so the expression $5x^2 - 30x + 50$ has a minimum value, which is the y-value of the vertex. Complete the square to find the vertex.

$$y = 5x^2 - 30x + 50 = 5(x^2 - 6x) + 50 = 5(x^2 - 6x + 9 - 9) + 50 = 5(x^2 - 6x + 9) - 45 + 50 = 5(x-3)^2 + 5$$

The vertex is (3, 5), so the minimum value of $5x^2 - 30x + 50$ is 5 when $x = 3$. Thus, the minimum value of $\sqrt{5x^2 - 30x + 50}$ is $\sqrt{5}$ when $x = 3$. The point on the line $y = 2x$ for which $x = 3$ is (3, 6). Thus, the closest point on the line $y = 2x$ to the point (1, 7) is the point (3, 6).

79. $f(x) = 3x^2 + 9x + 5$ has a zero when $3x^2 + 9x + 5 = 0$. Applying the quadratic formula with $a = 3$, $b = 9$, and $c = 5$, we have $x = \frac{-9 \pm \sqrt{9^2 - 4 \cdot 3 \cdot 5}}{2 \cdot 3}$. Thus, if we evaluate f with $\frac{-9 + \sqrt{9^2 - 4 \cdot 3 \cdot 5}}{2 \cdot 3}$, the outcome would be zero.

81. Graph the function $f(x) = x^2 + 2x - 8$.
Complete the square to find the vertex, (–1, –9).

$$y = x^2 - 2x - 8$$
$$= (x^2 - 2x) - 8$$
$$= (x^2 - 2x + 1 - 1) - 8$$
$$= (x^2 - 2x + 1) - 1 - 8$$
$$= (x - 1)^2 - 9$$

From the graph (and table), we see that the x-intercepts are – 4 and 2.
Use a table of values to find points on the graph.

x	y
–5	7
–4	0
–3	–5
–2	–8
–1	–9
0	–8
1	–5
2	0
3	7

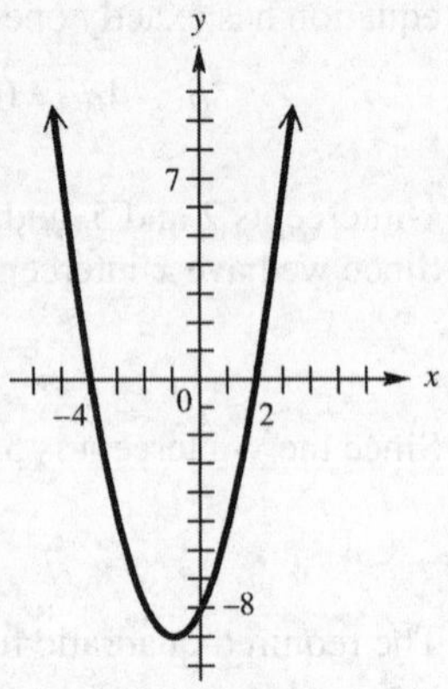

$f(x) = x^2 + 2x - 8$

82. The solution set of the inequality $x^2 + 2x - 8 < 0$ consists of all x-values for which the graph of f lies below the x-axis. By examining the graph of the function $f(x) = x^2 + 2x - 8$ from Exercise 81, we see that the graph lies below the x-axis when x is between the – 4 and 2. Thus, the solution set is the open interval (– 4, 2).

83. Graph $g(x) = -f(x) = -x^2 - 2x + 8$. The graph of g is obtained by reflecting the graph of f across the x-axis.

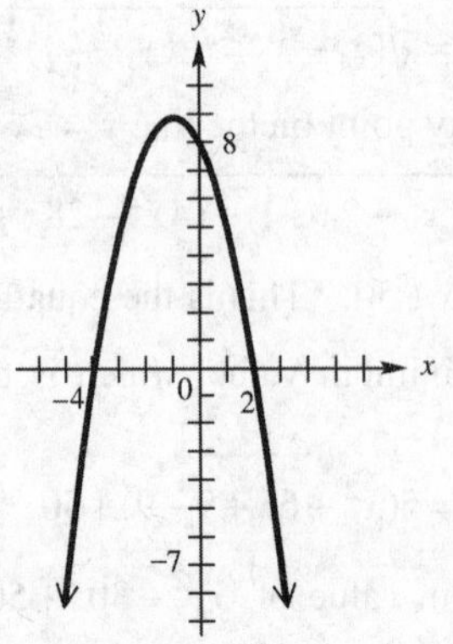

$g(x) = -f(x) = -x^2 - 2x + 8$

84. The solution set of the inequality $-x^2 - 2x - 8 > 0$ consists of all x values for which the graph of g lies above the x-axis. By examining the graph of $g(x) = -x^2 - 2x + 8$ from Exercise 83, we see that the graph lies above the x-axis when x is between –4 and 2. Thus, the solution set is the open interval (– 4, 2).

85. The two solution sets are the same, the open interval (– 4, 2).

86. Answers will vary.

Section 3.2: Synthetic Division

Connections (page 318)

1. To find $f(-2+i)$ use synthetic division with $f(x)=x^3-4x^2+2x-29i.$

$$\begin{array}{r|rrrr} -2+i & 1 & -4 & 2 & -29i \\ & & -2+i & 11-8i & -18+29i \\ \hline & 1 & -6+i & 13-8i & -18 \end{array}$$

The remainder is –18 so by the remainder theorem $f(-2+i)=-18$.

2. Use synthetic division to check if i is a zero of $f(x)=x^3+2ix^2+2x+i.$

$$\begin{array}{r|rrrr} i & 1 & 2i & 2 & i \\ & & i & -3 & -i \\ \hline & 1 & 3i & -1 & 0 \end{array}$$

Since the remainder is 0, $f(i)=0$ and i is a zero of $f(x)$. To check $-i$, perform synthetic division.

$$\begin{array}{r|rrrr} -i & 1 & 2i & 2 & i \\ & & -i & 1 & -3i \\ \hline & 1 & i & 3 & -2i \end{array}$$

Since the remainder is $-2i$, $f(-i)=-2i$ and $-i$ is not a zero of $f(x)$.

3. Answers will vary.

One example is the function $f(x)=x^2+1$.

Exercises

1. Express $x+5$ in the form $x-k$ by writing it as $x-(-5)$. Thus $k=-5$.

$$\begin{array}{r|rrrr} -5 & 1 & 2 & -17 & -12 \\ & & -5 & 15 & 10 \\ \hline & 1 & -3 & -2 & -2 \end{array} \qquad \frac{x^3+2x^2-17x-12}{x+5}=x^2-3x-2+\frac{-2}{x+5}$$

3. Express $x+1$ in the form $x-k$ by writing it as $x-(-1)$. Thus $k=-1$.

Since the x^2 – term is missing, include a 0 as its coefficient.

$$\begin{array}{r|rrrr} -1 & 4 & 0 & -3 & -2 \\ & & -4 & 4 & -1 \\ \hline & 4 & -4 & 1 & -3 \end{array} \qquad \frac{4x^3-3x-2}{x+1}=4x^2-4x+1+\frac{-3}{x+1}$$

5. Express $x+4$ in the form $x-k$ by writing it as $x-(-4)$. Thus $k=-4$.

$$\begin{array}{r|rrrrr} -4 & 1 & 4 & 2 & 9 & 4 \\ & & -4 & 0 & -8 & -4 \\ \hline & 1 & 0 & 2 & 1 & 0 \end{array} \qquad \frac{x^4+4x^3+2x^2+9x+4}{x+4}=x^3+2x+1$$

7. Express $x+2$ in the form $x-k$ by writing it as $x-(-2)$. Thus $k=-2$.

$$\begin{array}{r|rrrrrr} -2 & 1 & 3 & 2 & 2 & 3 & 1 \\ & & -2 & -2 & 0 & -4 & 2 \\ \hline & 1 & 1 & 0 & 2 & -1 & 3 \end{array} \qquad \frac{x^5+3x^4+2x^3+2x^2+3x+1}{x+2}=x^4+x^3+2x-1+\frac{3}{x+2}$$

9. Since $x-2$ is in the form $x-k$, $k=2$.

$$\begin{array}{r|rrrr} 2 & -9 & 8 & -7 & 2 \\ & & -18 & -20 & -54 \\ \hline & -9 & -10 & -27 & -52 \end{array} \qquad \frac{-9x^3+8x^2-7x+2}{x-2}=-9x^2-10x-27+\frac{-52}{x-2}$$

11. Since $x-\frac{1}{3}$ is in the form $x-k$, $k=\frac{1}{3}$.

$$\begin{array}{r|rrrr} \frac{1}{3} & \frac{1}{3} & -\frac{2}{9} & \frac{1}{27} & 1 \\ & & \frac{1}{9} & -\frac{1}{27} & 0 \\ \hline & \frac{1}{3} & -\frac{1}{9} & 0 & 1 \end{array} \qquad \frac{\frac{1}{3}x^3-\frac{2}{9}x^2+\frac{1}{27}x+1}{x-\frac{1}{3}}=\frac{1}{3}x^2-\frac{1}{9}x+\frac{1}{x-\frac{1}{3}}$$

13. Since $x-2$ is in the form $x-k$, $k=2$. Since the constant term is missing, include a 0.

$$\begin{array}{r|rrrrr} 2 & 1 & -3 & -4 & 12 & 0 \\ & & 2 & -2 & -12 & 0 \\ \hline & 1 & -1 & -6 & 0 & 0 \end{array} \qquad \frac{x^4-3x^3-4x^2+12x}{x-2}=x^3-x^2-6x$$

15. Since $x-1$ is in the form $x-k$, $k=1$. Since the x^2 and $x-$ terms are missing, include 0's as their coefficients.

$$\begin{array}{r|rrrr} 1 & 1 & 0 & 0 & -1 \\ & & 1 & 1 & 1 \\ \hline & 1 & 1 & 1 & 0 \end{array} \qquad \frac{x^3-1}{x-1}=x^2+x+1$$

17. Express $x+1$ in the form $x-k$ by writing it as $x-(-1)$. Thus $k=-1$.

Since the x^4, x^3, x^2 and $x-$ terms are missing, include 0's as their coefficients.

$$\begin{array}{r|rrrrrr} -1 & 1 & 0 & 0 & 0 & 0 & 1 \\ & & -1 & 1 & -1 & 1 & -1 \\ \hline & 1 & -1 & 1 & -1 & 1 & 0 \end{array} \qquad \frac{x^5+1}{x+1}=x^4-x^3+x^2-x+1$$

19. $f(x)=2x^3+x^2+x-8;\ k=-1$

Use synthetic division to write the polynomial in the form $f(x)=(x-k)q(x)+r$.

$$\begin{array}{r|rrrr} -1 & 2 & 1 & 1 & -8 \\ & & -2 & 1 & -2 \\ \hline & 2 & -1 & 2 & -10 \end{array} \qquad f(x)=[x-(-1)](2x^2-x+2)-10=(x+1)(2x^2-x+2)-10$$

21. $f(x) = -x^3 + 2x^2 + 4;\ k = -2$

$$\begin{array}{r|rrrr} -2 & -1 & 2 & 0 & 4 \\ & & 2 & -8 & 16 \\ \hline & -1 & 4 & -8 & 20 \end{array}$$

$f(x) = [x-(-2)](-x^2 + 4x - 8) + 20 = (x+2)(-x^2 + 4x - 8) + 20$

23. $f(x) = 4x^4 - 3x^3 - 20x^2 - x;\ k = 3$

$$\begin{array}{r|rrrrr} 3 & 4 & -3 & -20 & -1 & 0 \\ & & 12 & 27 & 21 & 60 \\ \hline & 4 & 9 & 7 & 20 & 60 \end{array}$$

$f(x) = (x-3)(4x^3 + 9x^2 + 7x + 20) + 60$

25. $f(x) = 3x^4 + 4x^3 - 10x^2 + 15;\ k = -1$

$$\begin{array}{r|rrrrr} -1 & 3 & 4 & -10 & 0 & 15 \\ & & -3 & -1 & 11 & -11 \\ \hline & 3 & 1 & -11 & 11 & 4 \end{array}$$

$f(x) = [x-(-1)](3x^3 + x^2 - 11x + 11) + 4 = (x+1)(3x^3 + x^2 - 11x + 11) + 4$

27. $f(x) = x^2 + 5x + 6;\ k = -2$

$$\begin{array}{r|rrr} -2 & 1 & 5 & 6 \\ & & -2 & -6 \\ \hline & 1 & 3 & 0 \end{array}$$

$f(-2) = 0$

29. $f(x) = 2x^2 - 3x - 3;\ k = 2$

$$\begin{array}{r|rrr} 2 & 2 & -3 & -3 \\ & & 4 & 2 \\ \hline & 2 & 1 & -1 \end{array}$$

$f(2) = -1$

31. $f(x) = x^3 - 4x^2 + 2x + 1;\ k = -1$

$$\begin{array}{r|rrrr} -1 & 1 & -4 & 2 & 1 \\ & & -1 & 5 & -7 \\ \hline & 1 & -5 & 7 & -6 \end{array}$$

$f(-1) = -6$

33. $f(x) = 2x^5 - 10x^3 - 19x^2 - 45;\ k = 3$

$$\begin{array}{r|rrrrrr} 3 & 2 & 0 & -10 & -19 & 0 & -50 \\ & & 6 & 18 & 24 & 15 & 45 \\ \hline & 2 & 6 & 8 & 5 & 15 & -5 \end{array}$$

$f(3) = -5$

35. $f(x) = 6x^4 + x^3 - 8x^2 + 5x + 6;\ k = \frac{1}{2}$

$$\begin{array}{r|rrrrr} \frac{1}{2} & 6 & 1 & -8 & 5 & 6 \\ & & 3 & 2 & -3 & 1 \\ \hline & 6 & 4 & -6 & 2 & 7 \end{array}$$

$f\left(\frac{1}{2}\right) = 7$

37. $f(x) = x^2 - 5x + 1;\ k = 2+i$

$$\begin{array}{r|rrr} 2+i & 1 & -5 & 1 \\ & & 2+i & -7-i \\ \hline & 1 & -3+i & -6-i \end{array}$$

$f(2+i) = -6-i$

39. To determine if $k = 2$ is a zero of $f(x) = x^2 + 2x - 8$, divide synthetically.

$$\begin{array}{r|rrr} 2 & 1 & 2 & -8 \\ & & 2 & 8 \\ \hline & 1 & 4 & 0 \end{array}$$

Yes, 2 is a zero of $f(x)$ because $f(2) = 0$.

41. To determine if $k = 2$ is a zero of $f(x) = x^3 - 3x^2 + 4x - 4$, divide synthetically.

$$\begin{array}{r|rrrr} 2 & 1 & -3 & 4 & -4 \\ & & 2 & -2 & 4 \\ \hline & 1 & -1 & 2 & 0 \end{array}$$

Yes, 2 is a zero of $f(x)$ because $f(2) = 0$.

43. To determine if $k = 1$ is a zero of $f(x) = 2x^3 - 6x^2 - 9x + 4$, divide synthetically.

$$\begin{array}{r|rrrr} 1 & 2 & -6 & -9 & 4 \\ & & 2 & -4 & -13 \\ \hline & 2 & -4 & -13 & -9 \end{array}$$

No, 1 is not a zero of $f(x)$ because $f(1) = -9$.

45. To determine if $k = 0$ is a zero of $f(x) = x^3 + 7x^2 + 10x$, divide synthetically.

$$\begin{array}{r|rrrr} 0 & 1 & 7 & 10 & 0 \\ & & 0 & 0 & 0 \\ \hline & 1 & 7 & 2 & 0 \end{array}$$

Yes, 0 is a zero of $f(x)$ because $f(0) = 0$.

47. To determine if $k = -\frac{3}{2}$ is a zero of $f(x) = 2x^4 + 3x^3 - 8x^2 - 2x + 15$, divide synthetically.

$$\begin{array}{r|rrrrr} -\frac{3}{2} & 2 & 3 & -8 & -2 & 15 \\ & & -3 & 0 & 12 & -15 \\ \hline & 2 & 0 & -8 & 10 & 0 \end{array}$$

Yes, $-\frac{3}{2}$ is a zero of $f(x)$ because $f\left(-\frac{3}{2}\right) = 0$.

49. To determine if $k = \frac{2}{5}$ is a zero of $f(x) = 5x^4 + 2x^3 - x + 3$, divide synthetically.

$$\begin{array}{r|rrrrr} \frac{2}{5} & 5 & 2 & 0 & -1 & 3 \\ & & 2 & \frac{8}{5} & \frac{16}{25} & -\frac{18}{125} \\ \hline & 5 & 4 & \frac{8}{5} & -\frac{9}{25} & \frac{357}{125} \end{array}$$

No, $\frac{2}{5}$ is not a zero of $f(x)$ because $f\left(\frac{2}{5}\right) = \frac{357}{125}$.

51. To determine if $k = 1 - i$ is a zero of $f(x) = x^2 - 2x + 2$, divide synthetically.

$$\begin{array}{r|rrr} 1-i & 1 & -2 & 2 \\ & & 1-i & -2 \\ \hline & 1 & -1-i & 0 \end{array}$$

Yes, $1 - i$ is a zero of $f(x)$ because $f(1-i) = 0$.

53. To determine if $k = 2 + i$ is a zero of $f(x) = x^2 + 3x + 4$, divide synthetically.

$$\begin{array}{r|rrr} 2+i & 1 & 3 & 4 \\ & & 2+i & 9+7i \\ \hline & 1 & 5+i & 13+7i \end{array}$$

No, $2 + i$ is not a zero of $f(x)$ because $f(2+i) = 13 + 7i$.

55. To determine if $k = 1 + i$ is a zero of $f(x) = x^3 + 3x^2 - x + 1$, divide synthetically.

$$\begin{array}{r|rrrr} 1+i & 1 & 3 & -1 & 1 \\ & & 1+i & 3+5i & -3+7i \\ \hline & 1 & 4+i & 2+5i & -2+7i \end{array}$$

No, $1 + i$ is not a zero of $f(x)$ because $f(1+i) = -2 + 7i$.

57. 1 raised to *any* power is 1.

58. The result from Exercise 57 is 1. If we multiply 1 by a real number, the result is the real number. It is equal to the real number because 1 is the identity element for multiplication.

59. We can evaluate $f(1)$ by adding the coefficients of *f*.

60. $f(x) = x^3 - 4x^2 + 9x - 6$

$f(1) = 1^3 - 4\cdot 1^2 + 9\cdot 1 - 6 = 1 - 4 + 9 - 6 = 0$

The sum of the coefficients of f is $1 + (-4) + 9 + (-6) = 0$.

The answers agree.

61. $f(x) = x^3 - 4x^2 + 9x - 6$

$f(-x) = (-x)^3 - 4(-x)^2 + 9(-x) - 6 = -x^3 - 4x^2 - 9x - 6$

$f(-1) = (-1)^3 - 4(-1)^2 + 9(-1) - 6 = -1 - 4 - 9 - 6 = -20$

62. $f(-x) = -x^3 - 4x^2 - 9x - 6$

The sum of the coefficients of $f(-x)$ is $-1 + (-4) + (-9) + (-6) = -20$.

$f(-1) = -20$

They are both –20. Our conjecture is, to find $f(-1)$, add the coefficients of $f(-x)$.

Section 3.3: Zeros of Polynomial Functions

Connections (page 328)

1. $x = \sqrt[3]{\frac{n}{2} + \sqrt{\left(\frac{n}{2}\right)^2 + \left(\frac{m}{3}\right)^3}} - \sqrt[3]{\frac{-n}{2} + \sqrt{\left(\frac{n}{2}\right)^2 + \left(\frac{m}{3}\right)^3}}$ can be used to solve a cubic equation $x^3 + mx = n$.

For $x^3 + 9x = 26$, $m = 9$ and $n = 26$.
Substitute

$$x = \sqrt[3]{\frac{26}{2} + \sqrt{\left(\frac{26}{2}\right)^2 + \left(\frac{9}{3}\right)^3}} - \sqrt[3]{-\frac{26}{2} + \sqrt{\left(\frac{26}{2}\right)^2 + \left(\frac{9}{3}\right)^3}} = \sqrt[3]{13 + \sqrt{13^2 + 3^3}} - \sqrt[3]{-13 + \sqrt{13^2 + 3^3}}$$

$$= \sqrt[3]{13 + \sqrt{169 + 27}} - \sqrt[3]{-13 + \sqrt{169 + 27}} = \sqrt[3]{13 + 14} - \sqrt[3]{-13 + 14} = \sqrt[3]{27} - \sqrt[3]{1} = 3 - 1 = 2$$

Exercises

1. Since $x - 1$ is a factor of $f(x) = x^6 - x^4 + 2x^2 - 2$, we are assured that $f(1) = 0$. This statement is justified by the factor theorem; therefore, it is true.

3. For the function $f(x) = (x + 2)^4(x - 3)$, 2 is a zero of multiplicity 4. To find the zero, set the factor equal to 0.

$$x + 2 = 0 \Rightarrow x = -2$$

2 is not a zero of the function; therefore, the statement is false. (It would be true to say that –2 is a zero of multiplicity 4.)

5. $x^3 - 5x^2 + 3x + 1;\ x - 1$

Let $f(x) = x^3 - 5x^2 + 3x + 1$. By the factor theorem, $x - 1$ will be a factor of $f(x)$ if and only if $f(1) = 0$. Use synthetic division and the remainder theorem.

$$\begin{array}{r|rrrr} 1 & 1 & -5 & 3 & 1 \\ & & 1 & -4 & -1 \\ \hline & 1 & -4 & -1 & 0 \end{array}$$

Since $f(1) = 0$, $x - 1$ is a factor of $f(x)$.

7. $2x^4 + 5x^3 - 8x^2 + 3x + 13;\ x + 1$

Let $f(x) = 2x^4 + 5x^3 - 8x^2 + 3x + 13$. By the factor theorem, $x + 1$ will be a factor of $f(x)$ if and only if $f(-1) = 0$. Use synthetic division and the remainder theorem.

$$\begin{array}{r|rrrrr} -1 & 2 & 5 & -8 & 3 & 13 \\ & & -2 & -3 & 11 & -14 \\ \hline & 2 & 3 & -11 & 14 & -1 \end{array}$$

Since the $f(-1) = -1$, $x + 1$ is <u>not</u> a factor of $f(x)$.

9. $-x^3+3x-2;\ x+2$

Let $f(x)=-x^3+3x-2$. By the factor theorem, x + 2 will be a factor of $f(x)$ if and only if $f(-2)=0$. Use synthetic division and the remainder theorem.

$$\begin{array}{r|rrrr} -2 & -1 & 0 & 3 & -2 \\ & & 2 & -4 & 2 \\ \hline & -1 & 2 & -1 & 0 \end{array}$$

Since $f(-2)=0$, $x+2$ is a factor of $f(x)$.

11. $4x^2+2x+54;\ x-4$

Let $f(x)=4x^2+2x+54$. By the factor theorem, x – 4 will be a factor of $f(x)$ if and only if $f(4)=0$. Use synthetic division and the remainder theorem.

$$\begin{array}{r|rrr} 4 & 4 & 2 & 54 \\ & & 16 & 72 \\ \hline & 4 & 18 & 126 \end{array}$$

Since the remainder is 126, $f(4)=126$, so $x-4$ is not a factor of $f(x)$.

13. $x^3+2x^2-3;\ x-1$

Let $f(x)=x^3+2x^2-1$. By the factor theorem, x – 1 will be a factor of $f(x)$ if and only if $f(1)=0$. Use synthetic division and the remainder theorem.

$$\begin{array}{r|rrrr} 1 & 1 & 2 & 0 & -3 \\ & & 1 & 3 & 3 \\ \hline & 1 & 3 & 3 & 0 \end{array}$$

Since $f(1)=0$, $x-1$ is a factor of $f(x)$.

15. $2x^4+5x^3-2x^2+5x+6;\ x+3$

Let $f(x)=2x^4+5x^3-2x^2+5x+6$. By the factor theorem, x + 3 will be a factor of $f(x)$ if and only if $f(-3)=0$. Use synthetic division and the remainder theorem.

$$\begin{array}{r|rrrrr} -3 & 2 & 5 & -2 & 5 & 6 \\ & & -6 & 3 & -3 & -6 \\ \hline & 2 & -1 & 1 & 2 & 0 \end{array}$$

Since $f(-3)=0$, $x+3$ is a factor of $f(x)$.

17. $f(x)=2x^3-3x^2-17x+30;\ k=2$

Since 2 is a zero of $f(x)$, $x-2$ is a factor. Divide $f(x)$ by $x-2$.

$$\begin{array}{r|rrrr} 2 & 2 & -3 & -17 & 30 \\ & & 4 & 2 & -30 \\ \hline & 2 & 1 & -15 & 0 \end{array}$$

Thus, $f(x)=(x-2)(2x^2+x-15)=(x-2)(2x-5)(x+3)$.

19. $f(x)=6x^3+13x^2-14x+3;\ k=-3$

Since –3 is a zero of $f(x)$, $x+3$ is a factor. Divide $f(x)$ by $x+3$.

$$\begin{array}{r|rrrr} -3 & 6 & 13 & -14 & 3 \\ & & -18 & 15 & -3 \\ \hline & 6 & -5 & 1 & 0 \end{array}$$

Thus, $f(x)=(x+3)(6x^2-5x+1)=(x+3)(3x-1)(2x-1)$.

21. $f(x)=6x^3+25x^2+3x-4;\ k=-4$

Since –4 is a zero of $f(x)$, $x+4$ is a factor. Divide $f(x)$ by $x+4$.

$$\begin{array}{r|rrrr} -4 & 6 & 25 & 3 & -4 \\ & & -24 & -4 & 4 \\ \hline & 6 & 1 & -1 & 0 \end{array}$$

Thus, $f(x)=(x+4)(6x^2+x-1)=(x+4)(3x-1)(2x+1)$.

23. $f(x)=x^3+(7-3i)x^2+(12-21i)x-36i;\ k=3i$

Since $3i$ is a zero of $f(x)$, $x-3i$ is a factor. Divide $f(x)$ by $x-3i$.

$$\begin{array}{r|rrrr} 3i & 1 & 7-3i & 12-21i & -36i \\ & & 3i & 21i & 36i \\ \hline & 1 & 7 & 12 & 0 \end{array}$$

Thus, $f(x)=(x-3i)(x^2+7x+12)=(x-3i)(x+4)(x+3)$.

25. $f(x)=2x^3+(3-2i)x^2+(-8-5i)x+(3+3i);\ k=1+i$

Since $1+i$ is a zero of $f(x)$, $x-(1+i)$ is a factor. Divide $f(x)$ by $x-(1+i)$.

$$\begin{array}{r|rrrr} 1+i & 2 & 3-2i & -8-5i & 3+3i \\ & & 2+2i & 5+5i & -3-3i \\ \hline & 2 & 5 & -3 & 0 \end{array}$$

Thus, $f(x)=\left[x-(1+i)\right](2x^2+5x-3)=\left[x-(1+i)\right](2x-1)(x+3)$.

27. $f(x)=x^4+2x^3-7x^2-20x-12;\ k=-2$ (multiplicity 2)

Since -2 is a zero of $f(x)$, $x+2$ is a factor. Divide $f(x)$ by $x+2$.

$$\begin{array}{r|rrrrr} -2 & 1 & 2 & -7 & -20 & -12 \\ & & -2 & 0 & 14 & 12 \\ \hline & 1 & 0 & -7 & -6 & 0 \end{array}$$

Thus, $f(x)=x^4+2x^3-7x^2-20x-12=(x+2)\left(x^3-7x-6\right)$

Since -2 has multiplicity 2, divide the quotient polynomial by $x+2$.

$$\begin{array}{r|rrrr} -2 & 1 & 0 & -7 & -6 \\ & & -2 & 4 & 6 \\ \hline & 1 & -2 & -3 & 0 \end{array}$$

Thus, $f(x)=(x+2)\left(x^3-7x-6\right)=(x+2)^2\left(x^2-2x-3\right)=(x+2)^2(x+1)(x-3)$

29. $f(x)=x^3-x^2-4x-6;\ 3$

Since 3 is a zero, first divide $f(x)$ by $x-3$.

$$\begin{array}{r|rrrr} 3 & 1 & -1 & -4 & -6 \\ & & 3 & 6 & 6 \\ \hline & 1 & 2 & 2 & 0 \end{array}$$

This gives $f(x)=(x-3)(x^2+2x+2)$. Since x^2+2x+2 cannot be factored, use the quadratic formula with $a=1$, $b=2$, and $c=2$ to find the remaining two zeros.

$$x=\frac{-2\pm\sqrt{4-4(1)(2)}}{2(1)}=\frac{-2\pm\sqrt{4-8}}{2}=\frac{-2\pm\sqrt{-4}}{2}=\frac{-2\pm 2i}{2}=-1\pm i$$

The remaining zeros are $-1\pm i$.

31. $f(x)=x^3-7x^2+17x-15;\ 2-i$

Since $2-i$ is also a zero, first divide $f(x)$ by $x-(2-i)$.

$$\begin{array}{r|rrrr} 2-i & 1 & -7 & 17 & -15 \\ & & 2-i & -11+3i & 15 \\ \hline & 1 & -5-i & 6+3i & 0 \end{array}$$

By the conjugate zeros theorem, $2+i$ is also a zero, so divide the quotient polynomial from the first synthetic division by $x-(2+i)$.

$$\begin{array}{r|rrr} 2+i & 1 & -5-i & 6+3i \\ & & 2+i & -6-3i \\ \hline & 1 & -3 & 0 \end{array}$$

This gives $f(x)=[x-(2-i)][x-(2+i)](x-3)$. The remaining zeros are $2+i$ and 3.

33. $f(x) = x^4 + 5x^2 + 4;\ -i$

Since $-i$ is a zero, first divide $f(x)$ by $x + i$.

$$\begin{array}{r|rrrrr} -i & 1 & 0 & 5 & 0 & 4 \\ & & -i & -1 & -4i & -4 \\ \hline & 1 & -i & 4 & -4i & 0 \end{array}$$

By the conjugate zeros theorem, i is also a zero, so divide the quotient polynomial from the first synthetic division by $x - i$.

$$\begin{array}{r|rrrr} i & 1 & -i & 4 & -4i \\ & & i & 0 & 4i \\ \hline & 1 & 0 & 4 & 0 \end{array}$$

The remaining zeros will be zeros of the new quotient polynomial, $x^2 + 4$. Find the remaining zeros by using the square root property.

$x^2 + 4 = 0 \Rightarrow x^2 = -4 \Rightarrow x = \pm\sqrt{-4} \Rightarrow x = \pm 2i$. The other zeros are i and $\pm 2i$.

35. (a) $f(x) = x^3 - 2x^2 - 13x - 10$

p must be a factor of $a_0 = -10$ and q must be a factor of $a_3 = 1$. Thus, p can be ±1, ±2, ±5, ±10 and q can be ±1. The possible rational zeros, $\frac{p}{q}$, are ±1, ±2, ±5, ±10.

(b) The remainder theorem shows that –1 is a zero.

$$\begin{array}{r|rrrr} -1 & 1 & -2 & -13 & -10 \\ & & -1 & 3 & 10 \\ \hline & 1 & -3 & -10 & 0 \end{array}$$

The new quotient polynomial will be $x^2 - 3x - 10$.

$$x^2 - 3x - 10 = 0$$
$$(x+2)(x-5) = 0$$
$$x + 2 = 0 \quad \text{or} \quad x - 5 = 0$$
$$x = -2 \qquad\qquad x = 5$$

The rational zeros are –1, –2, and 5.

(c) Since the three zeros are –1, –2, and 5, the factors are $x + 1$, $x + 2$, and $x - 5$.

$f(x) = (x+1)(x+2)(x-5)$

37. (a) $f(x) = x^3 + 6x^2 - x - 30$

p must be a factor of $a_0 = -30$ and q must be a factor of $a_3 = 1$. Thus, p can be ±1, ±2, ±3, ±5, ±6, ±10, ±15, ±30 and q can be ±1. The possible zeros, $\frac{p}{q}$, are ±1, ±2, ±3, ±5, ±6, ±10, ±15, ±30.

(b) The remainder theorem shows that –5 is a zero.

$$\begin{array}{r|rrrr} -5 & 1 & 6 & -1 & -30 \\ & & -5 & -5 & 30 \\ \hline & 1 & 1 & -6 & 0 \end{array}$$

The new quotient polynomial will be $x^2 + x - 6$.

$$x^2 + x - 6 = 0$$
$$(x+3)(x-2) = 0$$
$$x + 3 = 0 \quad \text{or} \quad x - 2 = 0$$
$$x = -3 \qquad\qquad x = 2$$

The rational zeros are –5, –3, and 2.

(c) Since the three zeros are –5, –3, and 2, the factors are $x + 5$, $x + 3$, and $x - 2$.

$f(x) = (x+5)(x+3)(x-2)$

39. (a) $f(x) = 6x^3 + 17x^2 - 31x - 12$

p must be a factor of $a_0 = -12$ and q must be a factor of $a_3 = 6$. Thus, p can be ± 1, ± 2, ± 3, ± 4, ± 6, ± 12 and q can be ± 1, ± 2, ± 3, ± 6. The possible zeros, $\frac{p}{q}$, are ± 1, ± 2, ± 3, ± 4, ± 6, ± 12, $\pm\frac{1}{2}$, $\pm\frac{3}{2}$, $\pm\frac{1}{3}$, $\pm\frac{2}{3}$, $\pm\frac{4}{3}$, $\pm\frac{1}{6}$.

Continued on next page

39. (continued)

(b) The remainder theorem shows that – 4 is a zero.

$$\begin{array}{r|rrrr} -4 & 6 & 17 & -31 & -12 \\ & & -24 & 28 & 12 \\ \hline & 6 & -7 & -3 & 0 \end{array}$$

The new quotient polynomial will be $6x^2 - 7x - 3$.

$$6x^2 - 7x - 3 = 0 \Rightarrow (3x+1)(2x-3) = 0$$

$$3x + 1 = 0 \quad \text{or} \quad 2x - 3 = 0$$

$$x = -\tfrac{1}{3} \qquad\qquad x = \tfrac{3}{2}$$

The rational zeros are $-4, -\frac{1}{3}$, and $\frac{3}{2}$.

(c) Since the three zeros are $-4, -\frac{1}{3}$, and $\frac{3}{2}$, the factors are $x + 4$, $3x + 1$, and $2x - 3$.

$f(x) = (x+4)(3x+1)(2x-3)$

41. (a) $f(x) = 24x^3 + 40x^2 - 2x - 12$

p must be a factor of $a_0 = -12$ and q must be a factor of $a_3 = 24$. Thus, p can be $\pm 1, \pm 2, \pm 3, \pm 4, \pm 6, \pm 12$ and q can be $\pm 1, \pm 2, \pm 3, \pm 4, \pm 6, \pm 8, \pm 12, \pm 24$. The possible zeros, $\frac{p}{q}$, are $\pm 1, \pm 2, \pm 3, \pm 4, \pm 6, \pm 12, \pm\frac{1}{2}, \pm\frac{3}{2}, \pm\frac{1}{3}, \pm\frac{2}{3}, \pm\frac{4}{3}, \pm\frac{1}{4}, \pm\frac{3}{4}, \pm\frac{1}{6}, \pm\frac{1}{8}, \pm\frac{3}{8}, \pm\frac{1}{12}, \pm\frac{1}{24}$.

(b) The remainder theorem shows that $-\frac{3}{2}$ is a zero. The new quotient polynomial is $24x^2 + 4x - 8$.

$$\begin{array}{r|rrrr} -\frac{3}{2} & 24 & 40 & -2 & -12 \\ & & -36 & -6 & 12 \\ \hline & 24 & 4 & -8 & 0 \end{array}$$

$$24x^2 + 4x - 8 = 0 \Rightarrow 4(6x^2 + x - 2) = 0 \Rightarrow 4(3x+2)(2x-1) = 0$$

$$3x + 2 = 0 \quad \text{or} \quad 2x - 1 = 0$$

$$x = -\tfrac{2}{3} \qquad\qquad x = \tfrac{1}{2}$$

The rational zeros are $-\frac{3}{2}, -\frac{2}{3}$, and $\frac{1}{2}$.

(c) Since the three rational zeros are $-\frac{3}{2}, -\frac{2}{3}$, and $\frac{1}{2}$, the factors are $3x + 2$, $2x + 3$, and $2x - 1$.

$$f(x) = 2(2x+3)(3x+2)(2x-1)$$

Note: Since $-\frac{3}{2}$ is a zero,

$$f(x) = 24x^3 + 40x^2 - 2x - 12 = \left[x - \left(-\tfrac{3}{2}\right)\right]\left(24x^2 + 4x - 8\right) = \left(x + \tfrac{3}{2}\right)\left[4(6x^2 + x + 2)\right]$$

$$= 4\left(x + \tfrac{3}{2}\right)(3x+2)(2x-1) = 2\left[2\left(x + \tfrac{3}{2}\right)\right](3x+2)(2x-1) = 2(2x+3)(3x+2)(2x-1).$$

43. $f(x) = 7x^3 + x$

To find the zeros, let $f(x)=0$ and factor the binomial.

$$7x^3 + x = 0 \Rightarrow x(7x^2 + 1) = 0$$

Set each factor equal to zero and solve for x.

$$x = 0 \quad \text{or} \quad 7x^2 + 1 = 0 \Rightarrow 7x^2 = -1 \Rightarrow x^2 = -\tfrac{1}{7} \Rightarrow x = \pm\sqrt{-\tfrac{1}{7}} = \pm\tfrac{\sqrt{7}}{7}$$

The zeros are 0 and $\pm\frac{\sqrt{7}}{7}i$.

45. $f(x)=3(x-2)(x+3)(x^2-1)$
To find the zeros, let $f(x) = 0$.
Set each factor equal to zero and solve for x.

$$x-2=0 \Rightarrow x=2 \text{ and } x+3=0 \Rightarrow x=-3 \text{ and } x^2-1=0 \Rightarrow x^2=1 \Rightarrow x=\pm 1$$

The zeros are 2, –3, 1, and –1.

47. $f(x)=(x^2+x-2)^5(x-1+\sqrt{3})^2$
To find the zeros, let $f(x)=0$.
Set each factor equal to zero and solve for x.
$(x^2+x-2)^5=0 \Rightarrow x^2+x-2=0 \Rightarrow (x+2)(x-1)=0 \Rightarrow x=-2$, multiplicity 5 or $x=1$, multiplicity 5
$(x-1+\sqrt{3})^2=0 \Rightarrow x-1+\sqrt{3}=0 \Rightarrow x=1-\sqrt{3}$, multiplicity 2
The zeros are –2 (multiplicity 5), 1 (multiplicity 5) and $1-\sqrt{3}$ (multiplicity 2).

49. Zeros of –3, 1, and 4, $f(2)=30$
These three zeros give $x-(-3)=x+3$, $x-1$, and $x-4$ as factors of $f(x)$. Since $f(x)$ is to be degree 3, these are the only possible factors by the number of zeros theorem. Therefore, $f(x)$ has the form $f(x)=a(x+3)(x-1)(x-4)$ for some real number a. To find a, use the fact that $f(2)=30$.

$$f(2)=a(2+3)(2-1)(2-4)=30 \Rightarrow a(5)(1)(-2)=30 \Rightarrow -10a=30 \Rightarrow a=-3$$

Thus, $f(x)=-3(x+3)(x-1)(x-4)=-3(x^2+2x-3)(x-4)=-3(x^3-2x^2-11x+12)=-3x^3+6x^2+33x-36.$

51. Zeros of – 2, 1, and 0; $f(-1)=-1$
These three zeros give $x-(-2)=x+2$, $x-1$, and $x-0=x$ as factors of $f(x)$. Since $f(x)$ is to be degree 3, these are the only possible factors by the number of zeros theorem. Therefore, $f(x)$ has the form $f(x)=a(x+2)(x-1)x$ for some real number a. To find a, use the fact that $f(-1)=-1$.

$$f(-1)=a(-1+2)(-1-1)(-1)=-1 \Rightarrow a(1)(-2)(-1)=-1 \Rightarrow 2a=-1 \Rightarrow a=-\tfrac{1}{2}$$

Thus, $f(x)=-\frac{1}{2}(x+2)(x-1)x=-\frac{1}{2}(x^2+x-2)x=-\frac{1}{2}x^3-\frac{1}{2}x^2+x.$

53. Zero of –3 having multiplicity 3; $f(3)=36$
These three zeros give $x-(-3)=x+3$, $x-(-3)=x+3$, and $x-(-3)=x+3$ as factors of $f(x)$. Since $f(x)$ is to be degree 3, these are the only possible factors by the number of zeros theorem. Therefore, $f(x)$ has the form $f(x)=a(x+3)(x+3)(x+3)=a(x+3)^3$ for some real number a. To find a, use the fact that $f(3)=36$.

$$f(3)=a(3+3)^3=36 \Rightarrow a(6)^3=36 \Rightarrow 216a=36 \Rightarrow a=\tfrac{1}{6}$$

Thus, $f(x)=\frac{1}{6}(x+3)^3=\frac{1}{6}(x+3)^2(x+3)=\frac{1}{6}(x^2+6x+9)(x+3)$
$=\frac{1}{6}(x^3+9x^2+27x+27)=\frac{1}{6}x^3+\frac{3}{2}x^2+\frac{9}{2}x+\frac{9}{2}.$

In Exercises 55 - 71, we must find a polynomial of least degree with real coefficients having the given zeros. For each of these exercises, other answers are possible.

55. $5+i$ and $5-i$

$$f(x)=[x-(5+i)][x-(5-i)]=(x-5-i)(x-5+i)=[(x-5)-i][(x-5)+i]=(x-5)^2-i^2$$
$$=(x^2-10x+25)-i^2=x^2-10x+25+1=x^2-10x+26$$

57. 2 and $1+i$
By the conjugate zeros theorem, $1-i$ must also be a zero.
$$f(x)=(x-2)\left[x-(1+i)\right]\left[x-(1-i)\right]=(x-2)(x-1-i)(x-1+i)=(x-2)\left[(x-1)-i\right]\left[(x-1)+i\right]$$
$$=(x-2)\left[(x-1)^2-i^2\right]=(x-2)\left[\left(x^2-2x+1\right)-i^2\right]=(x-2)\left(x^2-2x+1+1\right)$$
$$=(x-2)\left(x^2-2x+2\right)=x^3-4x^2+6x-4$$

59. $1+\sqrt{2}, 1-\sqrt{2}$, and 1
$$f(x)=\left[x-\left(1+\sqrt{2}\right)\right]\left[x-\left(1-\sqrt{2}\right)\right](x-1)=\left(x-1-\sqrt{2}\right)\left(x-1+\sqrt{2}\right)(x-1)$$
$$=\left[(x-1)-\sqrt{2}\right]\left[(x-1)+\sqrt{2}\right](x-1)=\left[(x-1)^2-\left(\sqrt{2}\right)^2\right](x-1)$$
$$=\left(x^2-2x+1-2\right)(x-1)=\left(x^2-2x-1\right)(x-1)=x^3-3x^2+x+1$$

61. $2+i, 2-i$, 3, and -1
$$f(x)=\left[x-(2+i)\right]\left[x-(2-i)\right](x-3)(x+1)=\left[(x-2-i)(x-2+i)\right]\left[(x-3)(x+1)\right]$$
$$=\left[(x-2)-i\right]\left[(x-2)+i\right]\left(x^2-2x-3\right)=\left[(x-2)^2-i^2\right]\left(x^2-2x-3\right)$$
$$=\left[\left(x^2-4x+4\right)-i^2\right]\left(x^2-2x-3\right)=\left(x^2-4x+4+1\right)\left(x^2-2x-3\right)$$
$$=\left(x^2-4x+5\right)\left(x^2-2x-3\right)=x^4-6x^3+10x^2+2x-15$$

63. 2 and 3 + *i*
By the conjugate zeros theorem, 3 – *i* must also be a zero.
$$f(x)=(x-2)\left[x-(3+i)\right]\left[x-(3-i)\right]=(x-2)\left[(x-3)-i\right]\left[(x-3)+i\right]$$
$$=(x-2)\left[(x-3)^2-i^2\right]=(x-2)\left(x^2-6x+9+1\right)=(x-2)\left(x^2-6x+10\right)=x^3-8x^2+22x-20$$

65. $1-\sqrt{2}, 1+\sqrt{2}$, and $1-i$
By the conjugate zeros theorem, $1+i$ must also be a zero.
$$f(x)=\left[x-\left(1-\sqrt{2}\right)\right]\left[x-\left(1+\sqrt{2}\right)\right]\left[x-(1-i)\right]\left[x-(1+i)\right]$$
$$=\left(x-1+\sqrt{2}\right)\left(x-1-\sqrt{2}\right)(x-1+i)(x-1-i)$$
$$=\left[(x-1)+\sqrt{2}\right]\left[(x-1)-\sqrt{2}\right]\left[(x-1)+i\right]\left[(x-1)-i\right]$$
$$=\left[(x-1)^2-\left(\sqrt{2}\right)^2\right]\left[(x-1)^2-i^2\right]$$
$$=\left(x^2-2x+1-2\right)\left[\left(x^2-2x+1\right)-i^2\right]=\left(x^2-2x-1\right)\left(x^2-2x+1+1\right)$$
$$=\left(x^2-2x-1\right)\left(x^2-2x+2\right)$$
$$=x^4-4x^3+5x^2-2x-2$$

67. $2-i$ and $6-3i$

By the conjugate zeros theorem, $2+i$ and $6+3i$ must also be zeros.

$$\begin{aligned}f(x)&=[x-(2-i)][x-(2+i)][x-(6-3i)][x-(6+3i)]\\&=[(x-2+i)(x-2-i)][(x-6+3i)(x-6-3i)]\\&=[(x-2)+i][(x-2)-i][(x-6)+3i][(x-6)-3i]=\left[(x-2)^2-i^2\right]\left[(x-6)^2-(3i)^2\right]\\&=\left[(x^2-4x+4)-i^2\right]\left[(x^2-12x+36)-9i^2\right]=(x^2-4x+4+1)(x^2-12x+36+9)\\&=(x^2-4x+5)(x^2-12x+45)=x^4-16x^3+98x^2-240x+225\end{aligned}$$

69. 4, $1-2i$, and $3+4i$

By the conjugate zeros theorem, $1+i$ and $3-4i$ must also be zeros.

$$\begin{aligned}f(x)&=(x-4)[x-(1-2i)][x-(1+2i)][x-(3+4i)][x-(3-4i)]\\&=(x-4)(x-1+2i)(x-1-2i)(x-3-4i)(x-3+4i)\\&=(x-4)[(x-1)+2i][(x-1)-2i][(x-3)-4i][(x-3)+4i]\\&=(x-4)\left[(x-1)^2-(2i)^2\right]\left[(x-3)^2-(4i)^2\right]=(x-4)(x^2-2x+1-4i^2)(x^2-6x+9-16i^2)\\&=(x-4)(x^2-2x+1+4)(x^2-6x+9+16)=(x-4)(x^2-2x+5)(x^2-6x+25)\\&=(x-4)(x^4-8x^3+42x^2-80x+125)=x^5-12x^4+74x^3-248x^2+445x-500\end{aligned}$$

71. $1 + 2i$, 2 (multiplicity 2).

By the conjugate zeros theorem, $1 - 2i$ must also be a zero.

$$\begin{aligned}f(x)&=(x-2)^2[x-(1+2i)][x-(1-2i)]=(x^2-4x+4)[(x-1)-2i][(x-1)+2i]\\&=(x^2-4x+4)\left[(x-1)^2-(2i)^2\right]=(x^2-4x+4)(x^2-2x+1-4i^2)\\&=(x^2-4x+4)(x^2-2x+1+4)\\&=(x^2-4x+4)(x^2-2x+5)=x^4-6x^3+17x^2-28x+20\end{aligned}$$

73. $f(x)=2x^3-4x^2+2x+7$

$f(x)=\underbrace{2x^3-4x^2}_{1}\underbrace{\;+2x}_{2}+7$ has 2 variations in sign. f has either 2 or 2 – 2 = 0 positive real zeros.

$f(-x)=-2x^3-4x^2\underbrace{-2x+7}_{1}$ has 1 variation in sign. f has 1 negative real zero.

75. $f(x)=5x^4+3x^2+2x-9$

$f(x)=5x^4+3x^2\underbrace{+2x-9}_{1}$ has 1 variation in sign. f has 1 positive real zero.

$f(-x)=5x^4\underbrace{+3x^2-2x}_{1}-9$ has 1 variation in sign. f has 1 negative real zero.

77. $f(x)=x^5+3x^4-x^3+2x+3$

$f(x)=x^5\underbrace{+3x^4-x^3}_{1}\underbrace{\;+2x}_{2}+3$ has 2 variations in sign. f has 2 or 2 – 2 = 0 positive real zeros.

$f(-x)=\underbrace{-x^5+3x^4}_{1}\underbrace{+x^3-2x}_{2}\underbrace{\;+3}_{3}$ has 3 variations in sign. f has 3 or 3 – 2 = 1 negative real zeros.

For exercises 79 – 81, let $c = a + bi$ and $d = m + ni$.

79. $\overline{c+d} = \overline{c} + \overline{d}$

Since $\overline{c+d} = \overline{(a+bi)+(m+ni)} = \overline{(a+m)+(b+n)i} = (a+m)-(b+n)i$

$= a+m-bi-ni = (a-bi)+(m-ni) = \overline{c}+\overline{d}$, the statement is true.

81. $\overline{a} = a$ for any real number a

If a is a real number then a is of the form $a + 0 \cdot i$. Since $\overline{a} = \overline{a+0\cdot i} = a - 0i = a$, the statement is true.

Section 3.4: Polynomial Functions: Graphs, Applications, and Models

1. $y = x^3 - 3x^2 - 6x + 8$

The range of an odd-degree polynomial is $(-\infty, \infty)$. The y-intercept of the graph is 8. The graph fitting these criteria is A.

3. Since graph C crosses the x-axis at one point, the graph has one real zero.

5. A polynomial of degree 3 can have at most 2 turning points. Graphs B and D have more than 2 turning points, so they cannot be graphs of cubic polynomial functions.

7. Since graph B touches the x-axis at –5, the function has 2 real zeros of –5. The two other real zeros are where the graph crosses the x-axis, at 0 and 3.

$f(x) = x^4 + 7x^3 - 5x^2 - 75x = x(x+5)^2(x-3)$

9. $f(x) = 2x^4$ is in the form $f(x) = ax^n$.

$|a| = 2 > 1$, so the graph is narrower than $f(x) = x^4$. It includes the points $(-2, 32)$, $(-1, 2)$, $(0, 0)$, $(1, 2)$, and $(2, 32)$. Connect these points with a smooth curve.

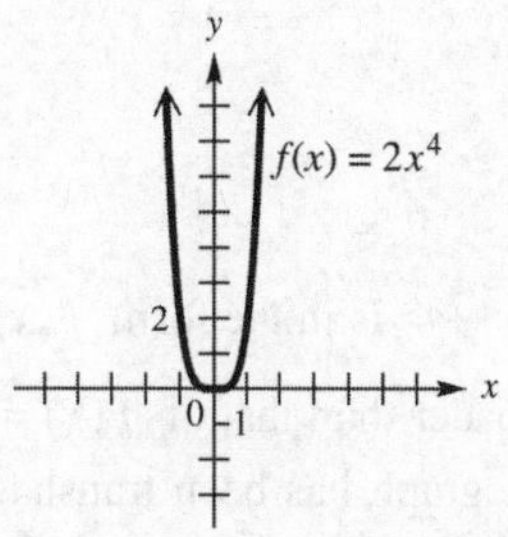

11. $f(x) = -\frac{2}{3}x^5$ is in the form $f(x) = ax^n$.

$|a| = \frac{2}{3} < 1$, so the graph is broader than that of $f(x) = x^5$. Since $a = -\frac{2}{3}$ is a negative, the graph is the reflection of $f(x) = \frac{2}{3}x^5$ about the x-axis. It includes the points $\left(-2, \frac{64}{3}\right)$, $\left(-1, \frac{2}{3}\right)$, $(0, 0)$, $\left(1, -\frac{2}{3}\right)$, and $\left(2, -\frac{64}{3}\right)$. Connect these points with a smooth curve.

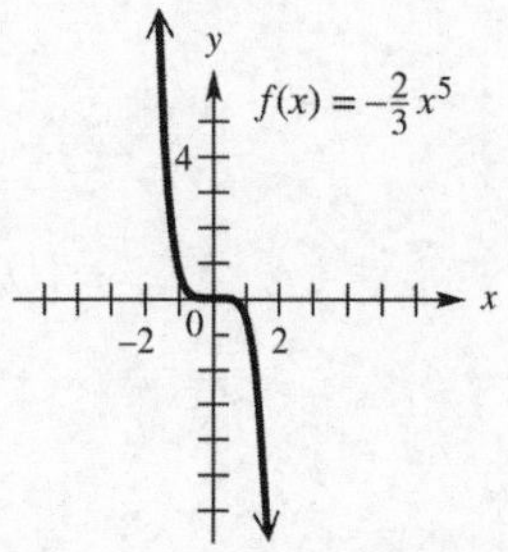

13. $f(x)=\frac{1}{2}x^3+1$ is in the form $f(x)=ax^n+k$, with $|a|=\frac{1}{2}<0$ and $k=1$.

The graph of $f(x)=\frac{1}{2}x^3+1$ looks like $y=x^3$ but is broader and is translated 1 unit up. The graph includes the points $(-2,-3)$, $\left(-1,\frac{1}{2}\right)$, $(0,1)$, $\left(1,\frac{3}{2}\right)$, and $(2,5)$.

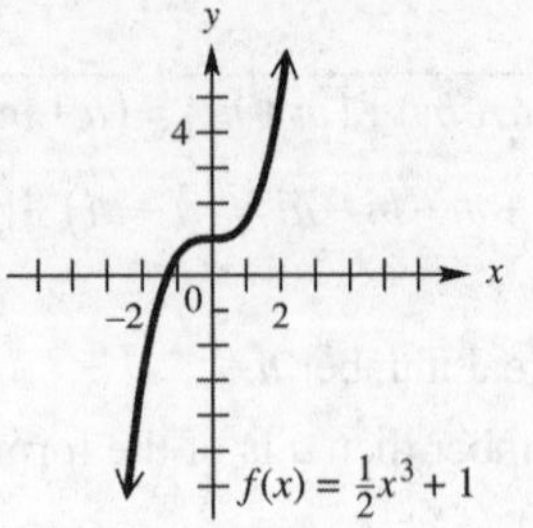

15. $f(x)=-(x+1)^3=-[x-(-1)]^3$

The graph can be obtained by reflecting the graph of $f(x)=x^3$ about the x-axis and then translating it 1 unit to the left.

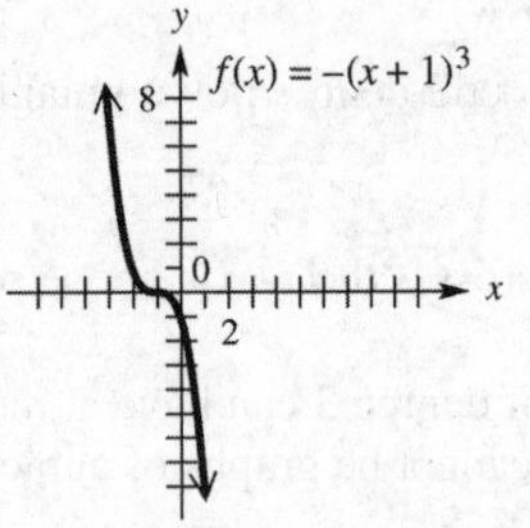

17. $f(x)=(x-1)^4+2$

This graph has the same shape as $y=x^4$, but is translated 1 unit to the right and 2 units up.

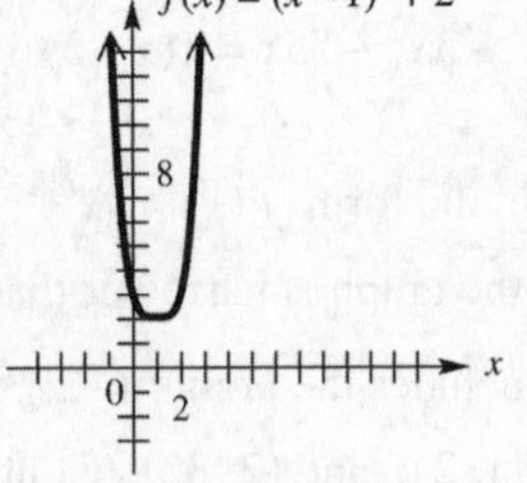

19. $f(x)=\frac{1}{2}(x-2)^2+4$ is in the form $f(x)=a(x-h)^n+k$, with $|a|=\frac{1}{2}<1$.

The graph is broader than that of $f(x)=x^2$. Since $h=2$, the graph has been translated 2 units to the right. Also, since $k=4$, the graph has been translated 4 units up.

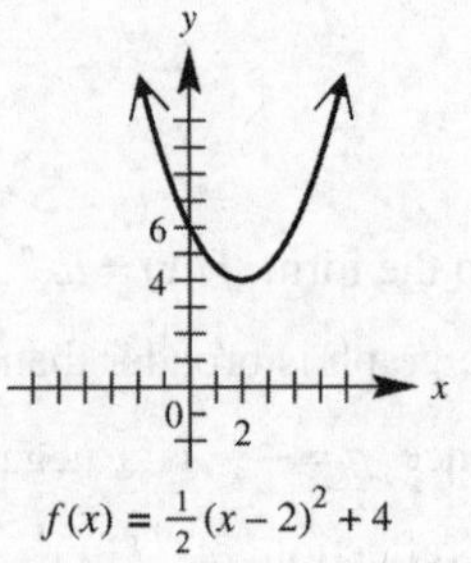

21.

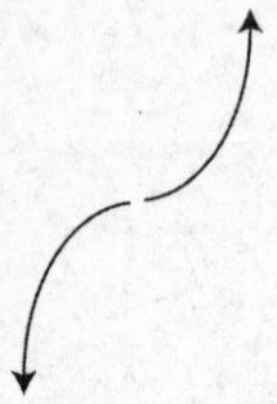

23.

25.

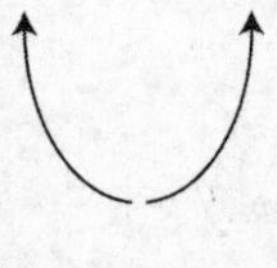

27.

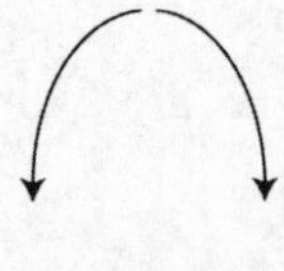

29. $f(x) = x^3 + 5x^2 + 2x - 8$

Step 1 p must be a factor of $a_0 = -8$ and q must be a factor of $a_3 = 1$. Thus, p can be ±1, ±2, ±4, ±8 and q can be ±1. The possible rational zeros, $\frac{p}{q}$, are ±1, ±2, ±4, and ±8. The remainder theorem shows that – 4 is a zero.

$$\begin{array}{r|rrrr} -4 & 1 & 5 & 2 & -8 \\ & & -4 & -4 & 8 \\ \hline & 1 & 1 & -2 & 0 \end{array}$$

The new quotient polynomial is $x^2 + x - 2$.

$$x^2 + x - 2 = 0$$
$$(x+2)(x-1) = 0$$
$$x+2 = 0 \quad \text{or} \quad x-1 = 0$$
$$x = -2 \qquad\qquad x = 1$$

The rational zeros are – 4, –2, and 1. Since the three zeros are – 4, –2, and 1, the factors are $x + 4$, $x + 2$, and $x - 1$ and thus $f(x) = (x+4)(x+2)(x-1)$.

Step 2 $f(0) = -8$, so plot $(0, -8)$.

Step 3 The x-intercepts divide the x-axis into four intervals:

Interval	Test Point	Value of $f(x)$	Sign of $f(x)$	Graph Above or Below x-Axis
(–∞, –4)	–5	–18	Negative	Below
(–4, –2)	–3	4	Positive	Above
(–2, 1)	0	–8	Negative	Below
(1, ∞)	2	24	Positive	Above

Plot the x-intercepts, y-intercept and test points (the y-intercept is one of the test points) with a smooth curve to get the graph.

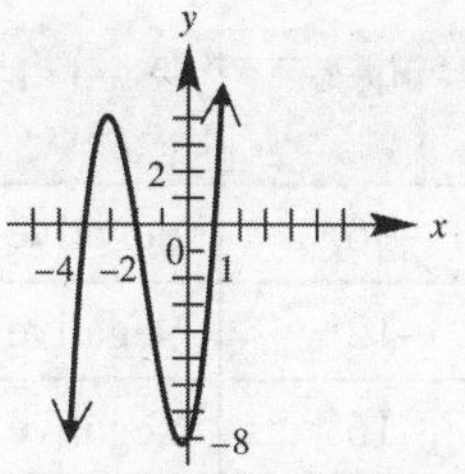

$f(x) = x^3 + 5x^2 + 2x - 8$

31. $f(x) = 2x(x-3)(x+2)$

Step 1 Set each factor equal to 0 and solve the resulting equations to find the zeros of the function.

$$2x = 0 \text{ or } x - 3 = 0 \text{ or } x + 2 = 0$$
$$x = 0 \qquad x = 3 \qquad x = -2$$

The three zeros, –2, 0, and 3, divide the x-axis into four regions. Test a point in each region to find the sign of $f(x)$ in that region.

Step 2 $f(0) = 0$, so plot $(0, 0)$.

Continued on next page

31. (continued)

Step 3 The x-intercepts divide the x-axis into four intervals.

Interval	Test Point	Value of $f(x)$	Sign of $f(x)$	Graph Above or Below x-Axis
$(-\infty, -2)$	-3	-36	Negative	Below
$(-2, 0)$	-1	8	Positive	Above
$(0, 3)$	1	-12	Negative	Below
$(3, \infty)$	4	48	Positive	Above

Plot the x-intercepts, y-intercept (which is also an x-intercept in this exercise), and test points with a smooth curve to get the graph.

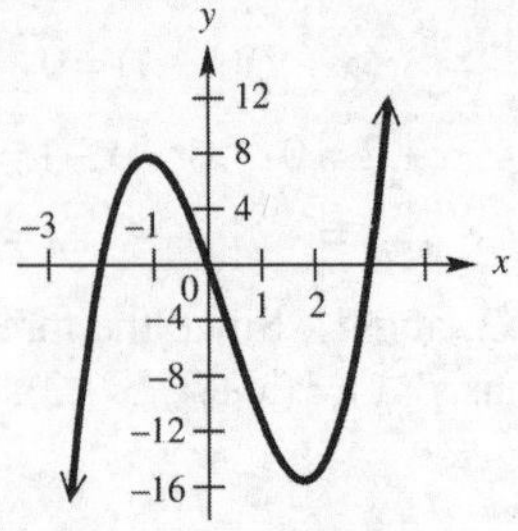

$f(x) = 2x(x-3)(x+2)$

33. $f(x) = x^2(x-2)(x+3)^2$

Step 1 Set each factor equal to 0 and solve the resulting equations to find the zeros of the function.

$$x^2 = 0 \text{ or } x-2=0 \quad \text{or} \quad (x+3)^2 = 0$$

$$x = 0 \qquad x = 2 \qquad\qquad x = -3$$

The zeros are –3, 0, and 2, divide the x-axis into four regions. Test a point in each region to find the sign of $f(x)$ in that region.

Step 2 $f(0) = 0$, so plot $(0,0)$.

Step 3 The x-intercepts divide the x-axis into four intervals.

Interval	Test Point	Value of $f(x)$	Sign of $f(x)$	Graph Above or Below x-Axis
$(-\infty, -3)$	-4	-96	Negative	Below
$(-3, 0)$	-1	-12	Negative	Below
$(0, 2)$	1	-16	Negative	Below
$(2, \infty)$	3	324	Positive	Above

Plot the x-intercepts, y-intercept (which is also an x-intercept in this exercise), and test points with a smooth curve to get the graph.

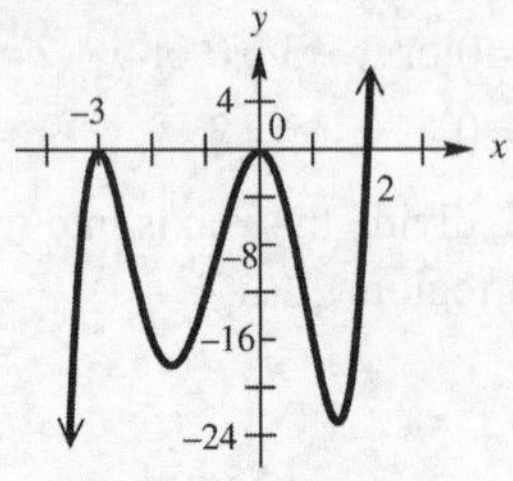

$f(x) = x^2(x-2)(x+3)^2$

35. $f(x) = (3x-1)(x+2)^2$

Step 1 Set each factor equal to 0 and solve the resulting equations to find the zeros of the function.

$$3x-1=0 \text{ or } x+2=0$$
$$x=\tfrac{1}{3} \qquad x=-2$$

The zeros are -2 and $\frac{1}{3}$, which divide the x-axis into three regions. Test a point in each region to find the sign of $f(x)$ in that region.

Step 2 $f(0)=-4$, so plot $(0,-4)$.

Step 3 The x-intercepts divide the x-axis into three intervals.

Interval	Test Point	Value of $f(x)$	Sign of $f(x)$	Graph Above or Below x-Axis
$(-\infty,-2)$	-3	-10	Negative	Below
$\left(-2,\frac{1}{3}\right)$	0	-4	Negative	Below
$\left(\frac{1}{3},\infty\right)$	1	18	Positive	Above

Plot the x-intercepts, y-intercept, and test points (the y-intercept is one of the test points) with a smooth curve to get the graph.

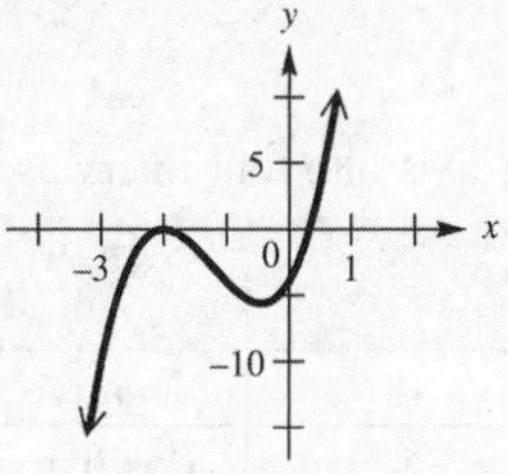

$f(x) = (3x-1)(x+2)^2$

37. $f(x) = x^3+5x^2-x-5$

Step 1 Find the zeros of the function by factoring by grouping.

$$f(x) = x^3+5x^2-x-5 = x^2(x+5)-1(x+5) = (x+5)(x^2-1) = (x+5)(x+1)(x-1)$$

$$x+5=0 \quad \text{or} \quad x+1=0 \quad \text{or} \quad x-1=0$$
$$x=-5 \qquad x=-1 \qquad x=1$$

The zeros are -5, -1, and 1, which divide the x-axis into four regions. Test a point in each region to find the sign of $f(x)$ in that region.

Step 2 $f(0)=-5$, so plot $(0,-5)$.

Step 3 The x-intercepts divide the x-axis into four intervals.

Interval	Test Point	Value of $f(x)$	Sign of $f(x)$	Graph Above or Below x-Axis
$(-\infty,-5)$	-6	-35	Negative	Below
$(-5,-1)$	-2	9	Positive	Above
$(-1,1)$	0	-5	Negative	Below
$(1,\infty)$	2	21	Positive	Above

Continued on next page

37. *Step 3* (continued)

Plot the x-intercepts, y-intercept, and test points (the y-intercept is one of the test points) with a smooth curve to get the graph.

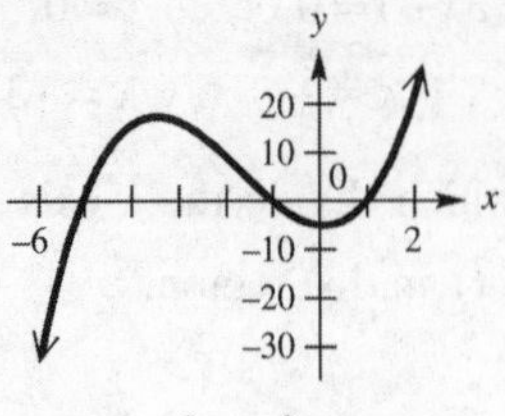

$f(x) = x^3 + 5x^2 - x - 5$

39. $f(x) = x^3 - x^2 - 2x$

Step 1 Find the zeros of the function by factoring out the common factor, x, and then factoring the resulting quadratic factor. Set each factor equal to 0 and solve the resulting equations.

$$f(x) = x^3 - x^2 - 2x = x(x^2 - x - 2) = x(x+1)(x-2)$$

$$x = 0 \quad \text{or} \quad x+1=0 \quad \text{or} \quad x-2=0$$

$$x=-1 \qquad x=2$$

The zeros are –1, 0, and 2, which divide the x-axis into four regions. Test a point in each region to find the sign of $f(x)$ in that region.

Step 2 $f(0) = 0$, so plot $(0,0)$.

Step 3 The x-intercepts divide the x-axis into four intervals.

Interval	Test Point	Value of $f(x)$	Sign of $f(x)$	Graph Above or Below x-Axis
$(-\infty, -1)$	-2	-8	Negative	Below
$(-1, 0)$	$-\frac{1}{2}$	$\frac{5}{8}$	Positive	Above
$(0, 2)$	1	-2	Negative	Below
$(2, \infty)$	3	12	Positive	Above

Plot the x-intercepts, y-intercept (which is also an x-intercept in this exercise), and test points with a smooth curve to get the graph.

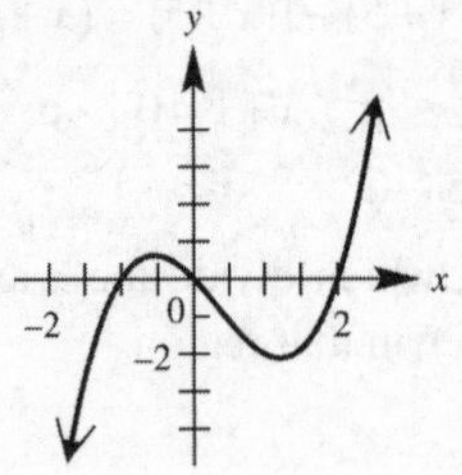

$f(x) = x^3 - x^2 - 2x$

41. $f(x)=2x^3(x^2-4)(x-1)$

Step 1 Find the zeros of the function by factoring the difference of two squares in the polynomial. Set each factor equal to 0 and solve the resulting equations.

$$f(x)=2x^3(x^2-4)(x-1)=2x^3(x+2)(x-2)(x-1)$$

$$2x^3=0 \quad \text{or } x+2=0 \quad \text{or} \quad x-2=0 \quad \text{or } x-1=0$$

$$x=0 \qquad x=-2 \qquad x=2 \qquad x=1$$

The zeros are –2, 0, 1, and 2, which divide the *x*-axis into five regions. Test a point in each region to find the sign of $f(x)$ in that region.

Step 2 $f(0)=0$, so plot $(0,0)$.

Step 3 The *x*-intercepts divide the *x*-axis into four intervals.

Interval	Test Point	Value of $f(x)$	Sign of $f(x)$	Graph Above or Below *x*-Axis
$(-\infty,-2)$	-3	1080	Positive	Above
$(-2, 0)$	-1	-12	Negative	Below
$(0, 1)$	$\frac{1}{2}$	$\frac{15}{32}\approx .5$	Positive	Above
$(1, 2)$	$\frac{3}{2}$	$-\frac{189}{32}\approx -5.9$	Negative	Below
$(2, \infty)$	3	540	Positive	Above

Plot the *x*-intercepts, *y*-intercept (which is also an *x*-intercept in this exercise), and test points with a smooth curve to get the graph.

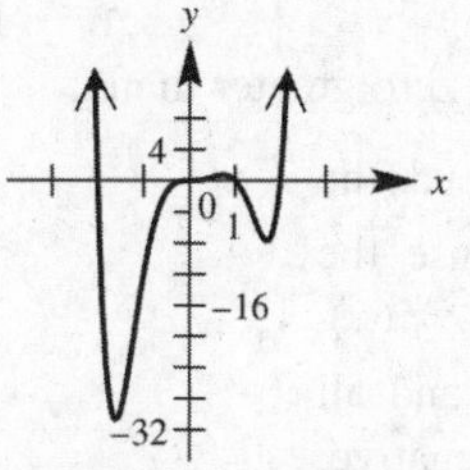

$f(x)=2x^3(x^2-4)(x-1)$

43. $f(x)=2x^2-7x+4$; 2 and 3

Use synthetic division to find *f*(2) and *f*(3).

```
2)2 -7  4     3)2 -7  4
     4 -6          6 -3
  2 -3 -2       2 -1  1
```

Since $f(2)=-2$ is negative and $f(3)=1$ is positive, there is a zero between 2 and 3.

45. $f(x)=2x^3-5x^2-5x+7$; 0 and 1

Since $f(0)=7$ can easily be determined, use synthetic division only to find *f*(1).

```
1)2 -5 -5  7
     2 -3 -8
  2 -3 -8 -1
```

Since $f(0)=7$ is positive and $f(1)=-1$ is negative, there is a zero between 0 and 1.

47. $f(x) = 2x^4 - 4x^2 + 4x - 8$; 1 and 2

Use synthetic division to find $f(1)$ and $f(2)$.

$$\begin{array}{r|rrrrr} 1 & 2 & 0 & -4 & 4 & -8 \\ & & 2 & 2 & -2 & 2 \\ \hline & 2 & 2 & -2 & 2 & -6 \end{array} \qquad \begin{array}{r|rrrrr} 2 & 2 & 0 & -4 & 4 & -8 \\ & & 4 & 8 & 8 & 24 \\ \hline & 2 & 4 & 4 & 12 & 16 \end{array}$$

Since $f(1) = -6$ is negative and $f(2) = 16$ is positive, there is a zero between 1 and 2.

49. $f(x) = x^4 + x^3 - 6x^2 - 20x - 16$; 3.2 and 3.3

Use synthetic division to find $f(3.2)$ and $f(3.3)$.

$$\begin{array}{r|rrrrr} 3.2 & 1 & 1 & -6 & -20 & -16 \\ & & 3.2 & 13.44 & 23.808 & 12.1856 \\ \hline & 1 & 4.2 & 7.44 & 3.808 & -3.8144 \end{array} \qquad \begin{array}{r|rrrrr} 3.3 & 1 & 1 & -6 & -20 & -16 \\ & & 3.3 & 14.19 & 27.027 & 23.1891 \\ \hline & 1 & 4.3 & 8.19 & 7.027 & 7.1891 \end{array}$$

Since $f(3.2) = -3.8144$ is negative and $f(3.3) = 7.1892$ is positive, there is a zero between 3.2 and 3.3.

51. $f(x) = x^4 - 4x^3 - 20x^2 + 32x + 12$; -1 and 0

Since $f(0) = 12$ can easily be determined, use synthetic division only to find $f(-1)$.

$$\begin{array}{r|rrrrr} -1 & 1 & -4 & -20 & 32 & 12 \\ & & -1 & 5 & 15 & -47 \\ \hline & 1 & -5 & -15 & 47 & -35 \end{array}$$

Since $f(-1) = -35$ is negative and $f(0) = 12$ is positive, there is a zero between -1 and 0.

53. $f(x) = x^4 - x^3 + 3x^2 - 8x + 8$; no real zero greater than 2

Since $f(x)$ has real coefficients and the leading coefficient, 1, is positive, use the boundedness theorem. Divide $f(x)$ synthetically by $x - 2$. Since $2 > 0$ and all numbers in the last row are nonnegative, $f(x)$ has no zero greater than 2.

$$\begin{array}{r|rrrrr} 2 & 1 & -1 & 3 & -8 & 8 \\ & & 2 & 2 & 10 & 4 \\ \hline & 1 & 1 & 5 & 2 & 12 \end{array}$$

55. $f(x) = x^4 + x^3 - x^2 + 3$; no real zero less than -2

Since $f(x)$ has real coefficients, use the boundedness theorem. Divide $f(x)$ synthetically by $x + 2 = x - (-2)$. Since $-2 < 0$ and the numbers in the last row alternate in sign, $f(x)$ has no zero less than -2.

$$\begin{array}{r|rrrrr} -2 & 1 & 1 & -1 & 0 & 3 \\ & & -2 & 2 & -2 & 4 \\ \hline & 1 & -1 & 1 & -2 & 7 \end{array}$$

57. $f(x)=3x^4+2x^3-4x^2+x-1$; no real zero greater than 1

Since $f(x)$ has real coefficients and the leading coefficient, 3, is positive, use the boundedness theorem. Divide $f(x)$ synthetically by $x-1$. Since $1>0$ and all numbers in the last row are nonnegative, $f(x)$ has no zero greater than 1.

$$\begin{array}{r|rrrrr} 1 & 3 & 2 & -4 & 1 & -1 \\ & & 3 & 5 & 1 & 2 \\ \hline & 3 & 5 & 1 & 2 & 1 \end{array}$$

59. $f(x)=x^5-3x^3+x+2$; no real zero greater than 2

Since $f(x)$ has real coefficients and the leading coefficient, 1, is positive, use the boundedness theorem. Divide $f(x)$ synthetically by $x-2$. Since $2>0$ and all numbers in the last row are nonnegative, $f(x)$ has no zero greater than 2.

$$\begin{array}{r|rrrrrr} 2 & 1 & 0 & -3 & 0 & 1 & 2 \\ & & 2 & 4 & 2 & 4 & 10 \\ \hline & 1 & 2 & 1 & 2 & 5 & 12 \end{array}$$

61. The graph shows that the zeros are –6, 2, and 5. The polynomial function has the form $f(x)=a(x+6)(x-2)(x-5)$. Since (0, 30) is on the graph, $f(0) = 30$.

$$f(0)=a(0+6)(0-2)(0-5) \Rightarrow 30=60a \Rightarrow \tfrac{1}{2}=a$$

A cubic polynomial that has the graph shown is $f(x)=\frac{1}{2}(x+6)(x-2)(x-5)$ or $f(x)=\frac{1}{2}x^3-\frac{1}{2}x^2-16x+30$.

63. $f(1.25)\approx -14.21875$

In order to have the calculator give the third screen, enter your function and the window, then press the GRAPH button. Press the TRACE button, then type in 1.25 then hit the ENTER key.

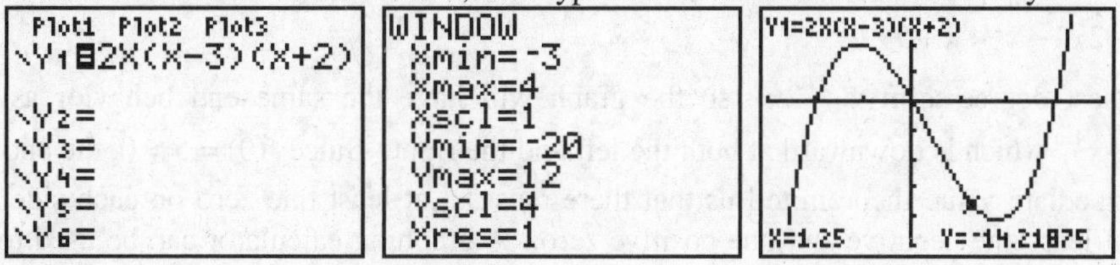

65. $f(1.25)\approx 29.046875$

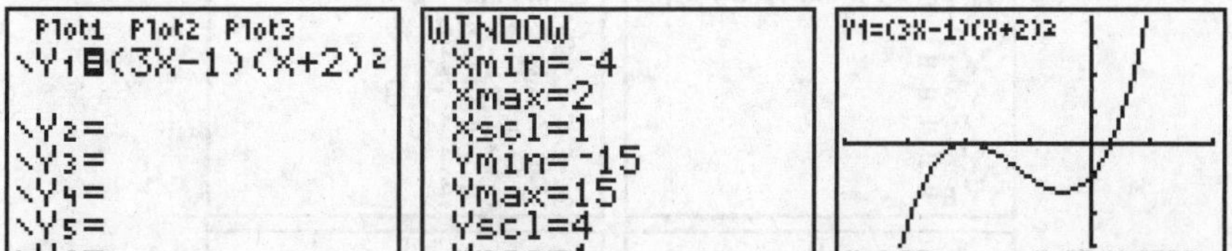

67. $f(x)=2x^2-7x+4$; 2 and 3

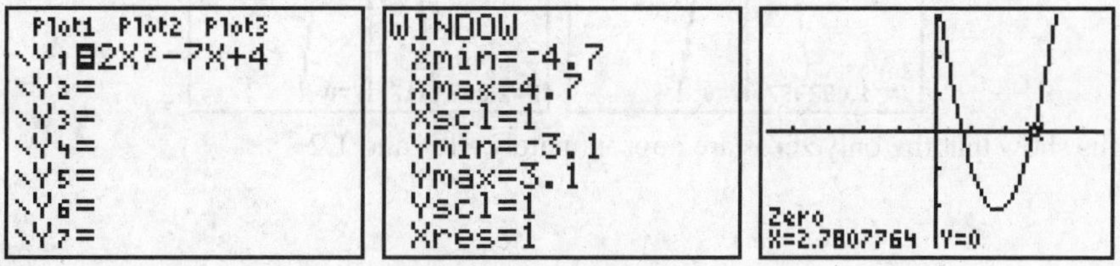

The real zero between 2 and 3 is approximately 2.7807764.

69. $f(x) = 2x^4 - 4x^2 + 4x - 8$; 1 and 2

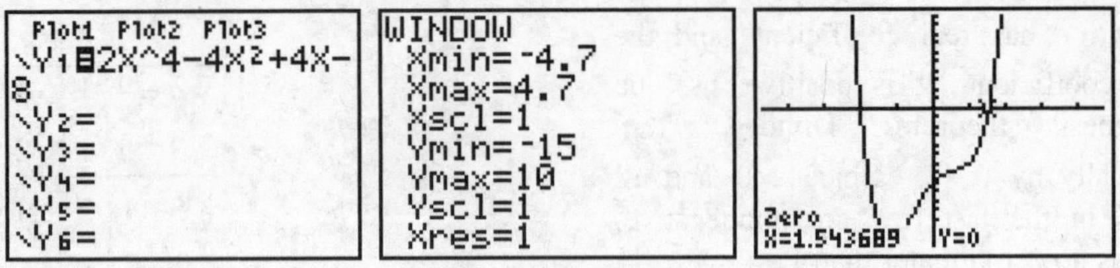

The real zero between 1 and 2 is approximately 1.543689.

71. $f(x) = x^3 + 3x^2 - 2x - 6$

The highest degree term is x^3, so the graph will have end behavior similar to the graph of $f(x) = x^3$, which is downward at the left and upward at the right. T here is at least one real zero because the polynomial is of odd degree. There are at most three real zeros because the polynomial is third-degree. A graphing calculator can be used to approximate each zero.

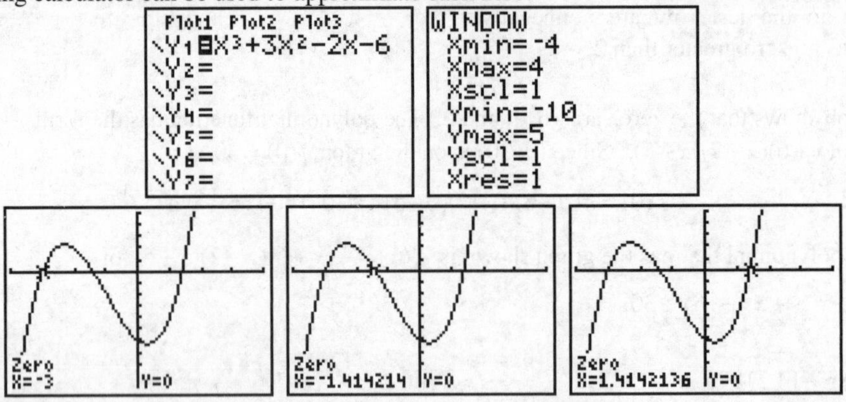

The graphs show that the zeros are approximately –3.0, –1.4 and 1.4.

73. $f(x) = -2x^4 - x^2 + x + 5$

The highest degree term is $-2x^4$ so the graph will have the same end behavior as the graph of $f(x) = -x^4$, which is downward at both the left and the right. Since $f(0) = 5 > 0$, the end behavior and the intermediate value theorem tell us that there must be at least one zero on each side of the *y*-axis, that is, at least one negative and one positive zero. A graphing calculator can be used to approximate each zero.

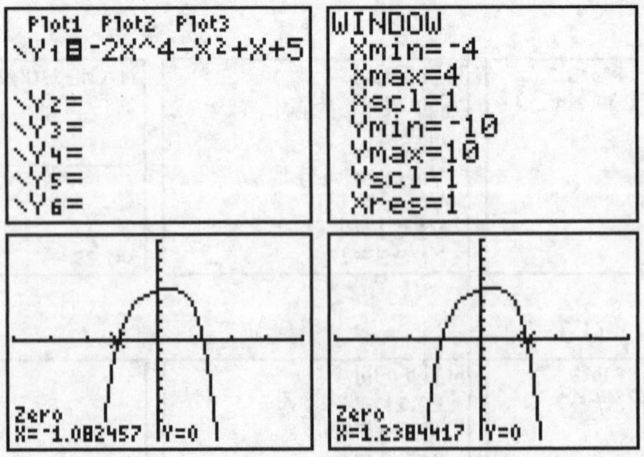

The graphs show that the only zeros are approximately –1.1 and 1.2

75. $f(x) = x^3 + 4x^2 - 8x - 8; [-3.8, -3]$

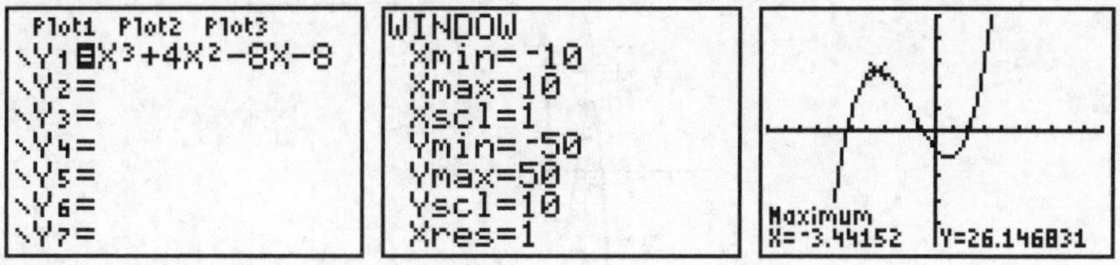

The turning point is (–3.44, 26.15).

77. $f(x) = 2x^3 - 5x^2 - x + 1; [-1, 0]$

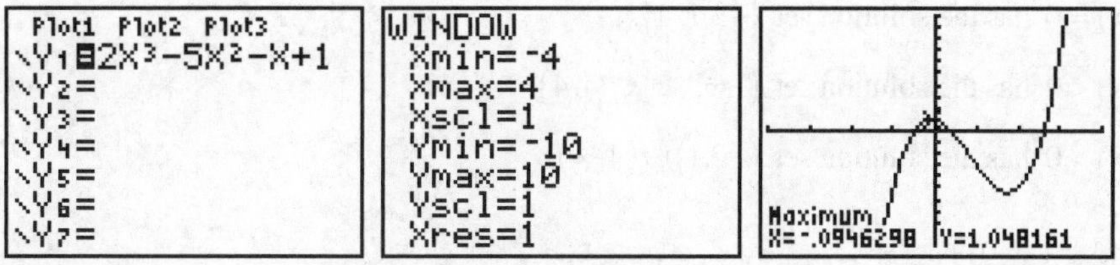

The turning point is (–.09, 1.05).

79. $f(x) = x^4 - 7x^3 + 13x^2 + 6x - 28; [-1, 0]$

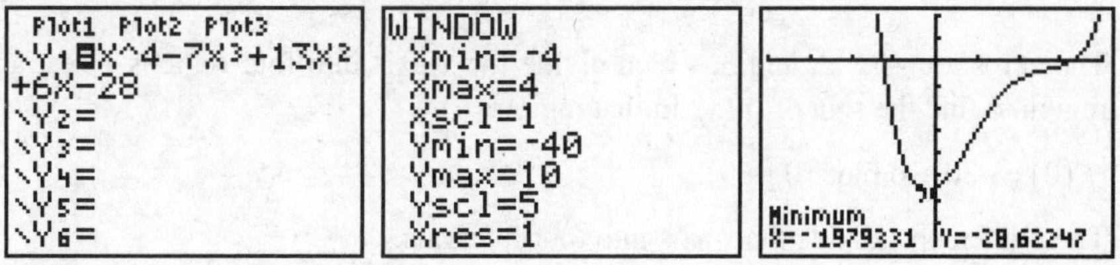

The turning point is (–.20, –28.62).

81. Answers will vary.

83. $f(x) = x^3 - 3x^2 - 6x + 8 = (x-4)(x-1)(x+2)$

Step 1 Set each factor equal to 0 and solve the resulting equations to find the zeros of the function.

$$x - 4 = 0 \quad \text{or} \quad x - 1 = 0 \quad \text{or} \quad x + 2 = 0$$
$$x = 4 \qquad\qquad x = 1 \qquad\qquad x = -2$$

The zeros are –2, 1, and 4, which divide the x-axis into four regions. Test a point in each region to find the sign of $f(x)$ in that region.

Step 2 $f(0) = 8$, so plot $(0, 8)$.

Step 3 The x-intercepts divide the x-axis into four intervals.

Interval	Test Point	Value of $f(x)$	Sign of $f(x)$	Graph Above or Below x-Axis
$(-\infty, -2)$	–3	–28	Negative	Below
$(-2, 1)$	0	8	Positive	Above
$(1, 4)$	2	–8	Negative	Below
$(4, \infty)$	5	28	Positive	Above

Plot the x-intercepts, y-intercept, and test points (the y-intercept is one of the test points) with a smooth curve to get the graph.

Continued on next page

83. *Step 3* (continued)

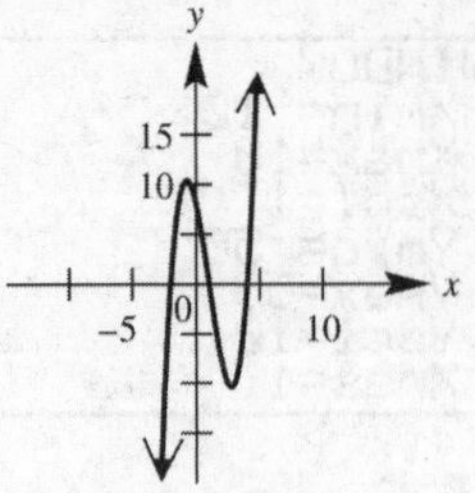

$f(x) = x^3 - 3x^2 - 6x + 8$
$= (x - 4)(x - 1)(x + 2)$

(a) $f(x) = 0$ has the solution set $\{-2, 1, 4\}$.

(b) $f(x) < 0$ has the solution set $(-\infty, -2) \cup (1, 4)$.

(c) $f(x) > 0$ has the solution set $(-2, 1) \cup (4, \infty)$.

84. $f(x) = x^3 + 4x^2 - 11x - 30 = (x-3)(x+2)(x+5)$

Step 1 Set each factor equal to 0 and solve the resulting equations to find the zeros of the function.

$$x - 3 = 0 \quad \text{or} \quad x + 2 = 0 \quad \text{or} \quad x + 5 = 0$$
$$x = 3 \qquad x = -2 \qquad x = -5$$

The zeros are –5, –2, and 3, which divide the *x*-axis into four regions. Test a point in each region to find the sign of $f(x)$ in that region.

Step 2 $f(0) = -30$, so plot $(0, -30)$.

Step 3 The *x*-intercepts divide the *x*-axis into four intervals.

Interval	Test Point	Value of $f(x)$	Sign of $f(x)$	Graph Above or Below *x*-Axis
$(-\infty, -5)$	–6	–36	Negative	Below
$(-5, -2)$	–3	12	Positive	Above
$(-2, 3)$	0	–30	Negative	Below
$(3, \infty)$	4	54	Positive	Above

Plot the *x*-intercepts, *y*-intercept, and test points (the *y*-intercept is one of the test points) with a smooth curve to get the graph.

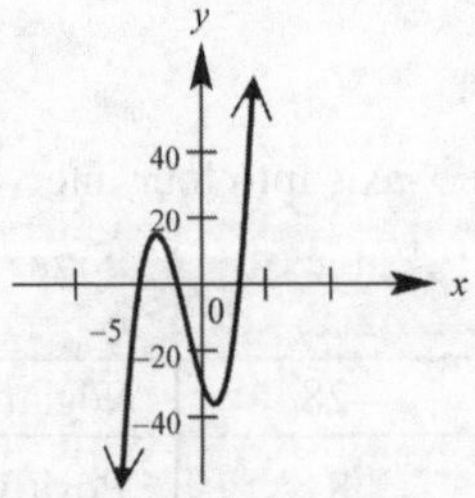

$f(x) = x^3 + 4x^2 - 11x - 30$
$= (x - 3)(x + 2)(x + 5)$

(a) $f(x) = 0$ has the solution set $\{-5, -2, 3\}$.

(b) $f(x) < 0$ has the solution set $(-\infty, -5) \cup (-2, 3)$.

(c) $f(x) > 0$ has the solution set $(-5, -2) \cup (3, \infty)$.

85. $f(x)=2x^4-9x^3-5x^2+57x-45=(x-3)^2(2x+5)(x-1)$

Step 1 Set each factor equal to 0 and solve the resulting equations to find the zeros of the function.

$$(x-3)^2=0 \quad \text{or} \quad 2x+5=0 \quad \text{or} \quad x-1=0$$
$$x=3 \qquad x=-\tfrac{5}{2} \qquad x=1$$

The zeros are $-\frac{5}{2}=-2.5$, 1, and 3, which divide the x-axis into four regions. Test a point in each region to find the sign of $f(x)$ in that region.

Step 2 $f(0)=-45$, so plot $(0,-45)$.

Step 3 The x-intercepts divide the x-axis into four intervals.

Interval	Test Point	Value of $f(x)$	Sign of $f(x)$	Graph Above or Below x-Axis
$(-\infty,-2.5)$	−3	144	Positive	Above
$(-2.5, 1)$	0	−45	Negative	Below
$(1, 3)$	2	9	Positive	Above
$(3, \infty)$	4	39	Positive	Above

Plot the x-intercepts, y-intercept, and test points (the y-intercept is one of the test points) with a smooth curve to get the graph.

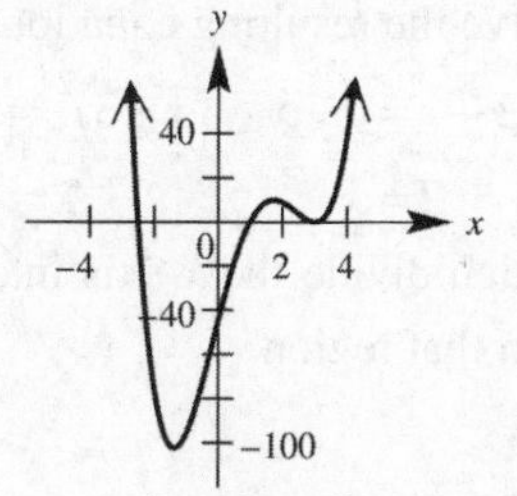

$f(x)=2x^4-9x^3-5x^2+57x-45$
$=(x-3)^2(2x+5)(x-1)$

(a) $f(x)=0$ has the solution set $\{-2.5, 1, 3 \text{ (multiplicity 2)}\}$.

(b) $f(x)<0$ has the solution set $(-2.5,1)$.

(c) $f(x)>0$ has the solution set $(-\infty,-2.5)\cup(1,3)\cup(3,\infty)$.

86. $f(x)=4x^4+27x^3-42x^2-445x-300=(x+5)^2(4x+3)(x-4)$

Step 1 Set each factor equal to 0 and solve the resulting equations to find the zeros of the function.

$$(x+5)^2=0 \quad \text{or} \quad 4x+3=0 \quad \text{or} \quad x-4=0$$
$$x=-5 \qquad x=-\tfrac{3}{4} \qquad x=4$$

The zeros are −5, $-\frac{3}{4}=-.75$, and 4, which divide the x-axis into four regions. Test a point in each region to find the sign of $f(x)$ in that region.

Step 2 $f(0)=-300$, so plot $(0,-300)$.

Continued on next page

87. (continued)

Step 3 The x-intercepts divide the x-axis into four intervals.

Interval	Test Point	Value of $f(x)$	Sign of $f(x)$	Graph Above or Below x-Axis
$(-\infty, -5)$	-6	210	Positive	Above
$(-5, -.75)$	-1	80	Positive	Above
$(-.75, 4)$	0	-300	Negative	Below
$(4, \infty)$	5	2300	Positive	Above

Plot the x-intercepts, y-intercept, and test points (the y-intercept is one of the test points) with a smooth curve to get the graph.

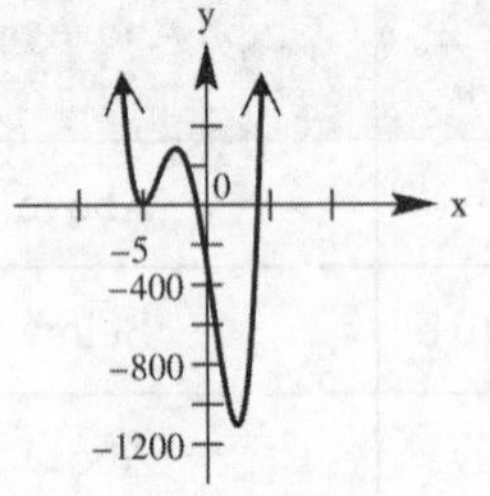

$f(x) = 4x^4 + 27x^3 - 42x^2 - 445x - 300$
$= (x+5)^2(4x+3)(x-4)$

(a) $f(x) = 0$ has the solution set $\{-5 \text{ (muliplicity 2)}, -.75, 4\}$.

(b) $f(x) < 0$ has the solution set $(-.75, 4)$.

(c) $f(x) > 0$ has the solution set $(-\infty, -5) \cup (-5, -.75) \cup (4, \infty)$.

87. $f(x) = -x^4 - 4x^3 + 3x^2 + 18x = x(2-x)(x+3)^2$

Step 1 Set each factor equal to 0 and solve the resulting equations to find the zeros of the function.

$$x = 0 \quad \text{or} \quad 2 - x = 0 \quad \text{or} \quad (x+3)^2 = 0$$
$$2 = x \qquad\qquad x = -3$$

The zeros are 0, 2, and -3, which divide the x-axis into four regions. Test a point in each region to find the sign of $f(x)$ in that region.

Step 2 $f(0) = 0$, so plot $(0, 0)$.

Step 3 The x-intercepts divide the x-axis into four intervals.

Interval	Test Point	Value of $f(x)$	Sign of $f(x)$	Graph Above or Below x-Axis
$(-\infty, -3)$	-4	-24	Negative	Below
$(-3, 0)$	-1	-12	Negative	Below
$(0, 2)$	1	16	Positive	Above
$(2, \infty)$	3	-108	Negative	Below

Plot the x-intercepts, y-intercept (which is also an x-intercept in this exercise), and test points with a smooth curve to get the graph.

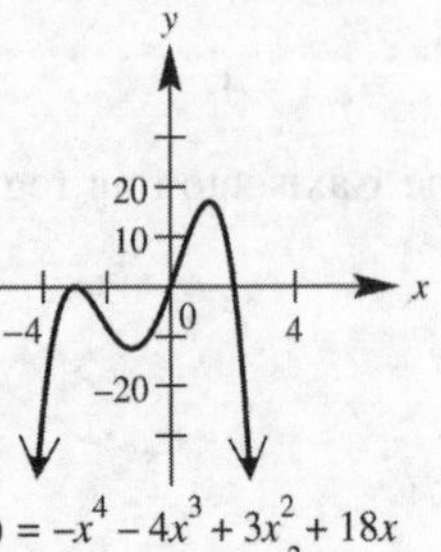

$f(x) = -x^4 - 4x^3 + 3x^2 + 18x$
$= x(2-x)(x+3)^2$

(a) $f(x) = 0$ has the solution set $\{-3 \text{ (multiplicity 2)}, 0, 2\}$.

(b) $f(x) \geq 0$ has the solution set $\{-3\} \cup [0, 2]$.

(c) $f(x) \leq 0$ has the solution set $(-\infty, 0] \cup [2, \infty)$.

88. $f(x)=-x^4+2x^3+8x^2=x^2(4-x)(x+2)$

Step 1 Set each factor equal to 0 and solve the resulting equations to find the zeros of the function.

$$x^2=0 \quad \text{or} \quad 4-x=0 \quad \text{or} \quad x+2=0$$
$$x=0 \qquad\qquad 4=x \qquad\qquad x=-2$$

The zeros are –2, 0, and 4, which divide the x-axis into four regions. Test a point in each region to find the sign of $f(x)$ in that region.

Step 2 $f(0)=0$, so plot $(0,0)$.

Step 3 The x-intercepts divide the x-axis into four intervals.

Interval	Test Point	Value of $f(x)$	Sign of $f(x)$	Graph Above or Below x-Axis
$(-\infty,-2)$	–3	–63	Negative	Below
$(-2, 0)$	–1	5	Positive	Above
$(0, 4)$	1	9	Positive	Above
$(4, \infty)$	5	–175	Negative	Below

Plot the x-intercepts, y-intercept (which is also an x-intercept in this exercise), and test points with a smooth curve to get the graph.

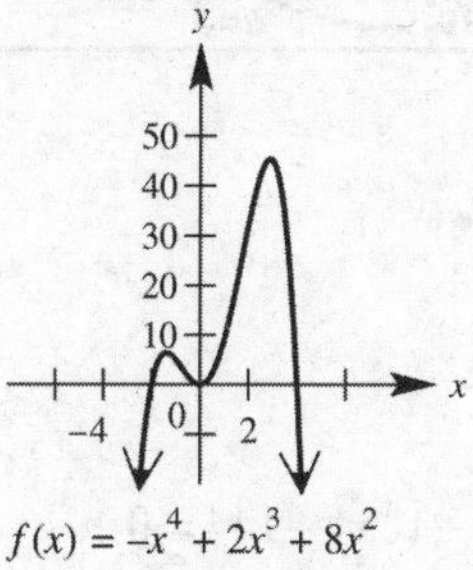

$f(x)=-x^4+2x^3+8x^2$
$=x^2(4-x)(x+2)$

(a) $f(x)=0$ has the solution set $\{-2,0\text{ (multiplicity 2)}, 4\}$.

(b) $f(x)\ge 0$ has the solution set $[-2,4]$.

(c) $f(x)\le 0$ has the solution set $(-\infty,-2]\cup\{0\}\cup[4,\infty)$.

89. (a) In order for the length, width and height of the box to be positive quantities, $0<x<6$.

(b) The width of the rectangular base of the box would be $12-2x$. The length would be $18-2x$ and the height would be x. The volume would be the product of these three measures; therefore, $V(x)=x(18-2x)(12-2x)=4x^3-60x^2+216x$.

(c) When x is approximately 2.35 in. the maximum volume will be approximately 228.16 in.^{3}.

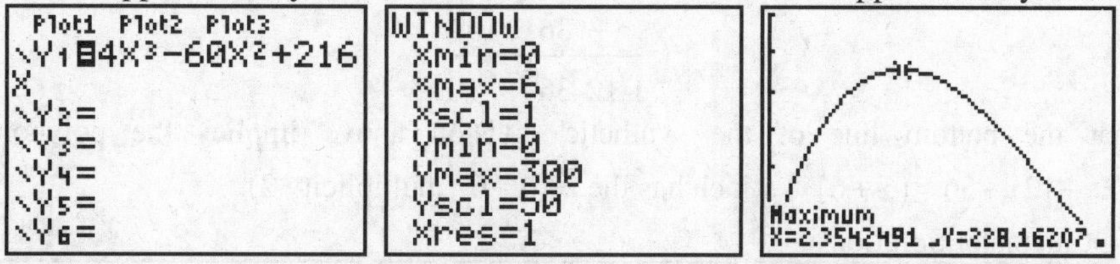

(d) When x is between .42 in. (approximately) and 5 in., the volume will be greater than 80 in.^{3}.

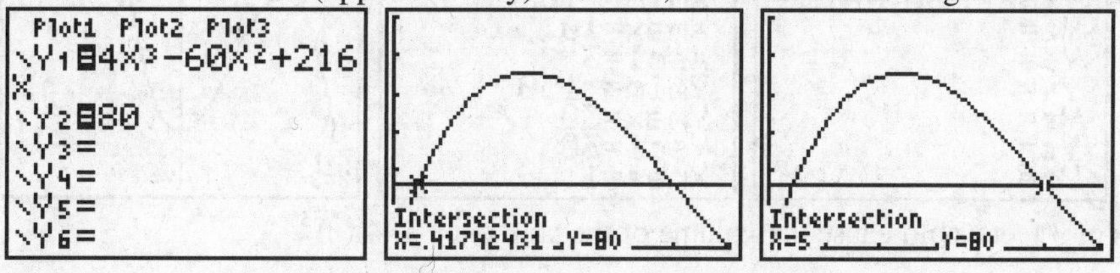

91. (a) length of the leg = $x-1$. The domain is $x>1$ or $(1,\infty)$.

(b) By the Pythagorean theorem,

$$a^2+b^2=c^2 \Rightarrow a^2+(x-1)^2=x^2 \Rightarrow a^2=x^2-(x-1)^2 \Rightarrow a=\sqrt{x^2-(x-1)^2}$$

Thus, the length of other leg is $\sqrt{x^2-(x-1)^2}$.

(c) $A=\frac{1}{2}bh \Rightarrow 84=\frac{1}{2}(x-1)\left(\sqrt{x^2-(x-1)^2}\right)$

Multiply by 2: $168=(x-1)\left(\sqrt{x^2-(x-1)^2}\right)$

Square both sides.

$$28,224=(x-1)^2\left[x^2-(x-1)^2\right] \Rightarrow 28,224=(x^2-2x+1)\cdot\left[x^2-(x^2-2x+1)\right]$$

$$28,224=(x^2-2x+1)(2x-1) \Rightarrow 28,224=2x^3-5x^2+4x-1$$

$$2x^3-5x^2+4x-28,225=0$$

(d) Solving this cubic equation graphically, we obtain $x=25$. If $x=25$, $x-1=24$, and $\sqrt{x^2-(x-1)^2}=\sqrt{625-576}=\sqrt{49}=7$. The hypotenuse is 25 in.; the legs are 24 in. and 7 in.

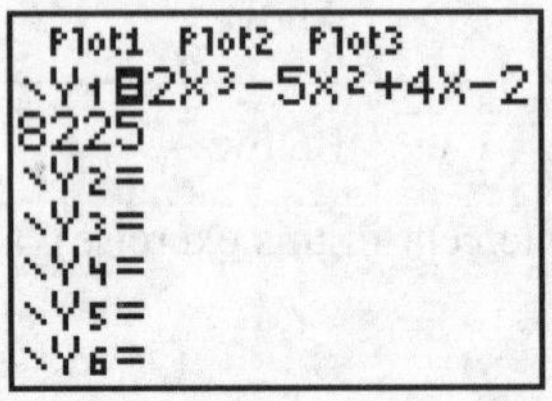

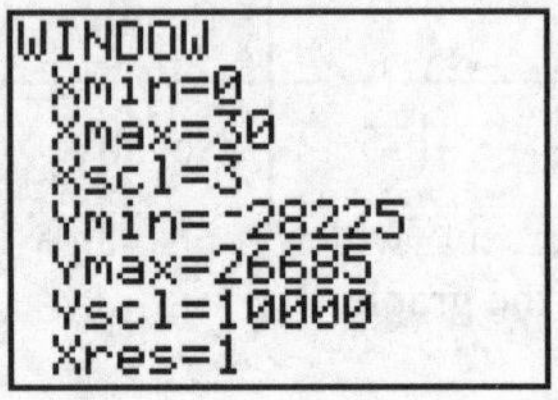

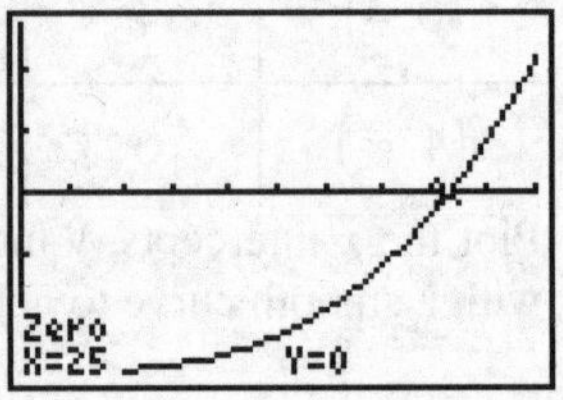

93. Use the following volume formulas:

$V_{\text{cylinder}}=\pi r^2 h$ and $V_{\text{hemisphere}}=\frac{1}{2}V_{\text{sphere}}=\frac{1}{2}\left(\frac{4}{3}\pi r^3\right)=\frac{2}{3}\pi r^3$

$\pi r^2 h+2\left(\frac{2}{3}\pi r^3\right)=$ Total volume of tank (V)

Let $V=144\pi$, $h=12$, and $r=x$.

$$\pi x^2(12)+\frac{4}{3}\pi x^3=144\pi \Rightarrow \frac{4}{3}x^3+12x^2=144 \Rightarrow \frac{4}{3}x^3+12x^2-144=0$$

$$4x^3+36x^2-432=0 \Rightarrow x^3+9x^2-108=0$$

The end behavior of the graph of $f(x)=x^3+9x^2-108$, together with the negative y-intercept, tells us that this cubic polynomial must have one positive zero. (We are not interested in negative zeros because x represents the radius.)

Algebraic Solution:

Use synthetic division or a graphing calculator to locate this zero.

$$\begin{array}{r|rrrr} 3 & 1 & 9 & 0 & -108 \\ & & 3 & 36 & 108 \\ \hline & 1 & 12 & 36 & 0 \end{array}$$

Note that the bottom line of the synthetic division above implies the polynomial function $g(x)=x^2+12x+36=(x+6)^2$, which has the zero -6 (multiplicity 2).

Graphing Calculator Solution:

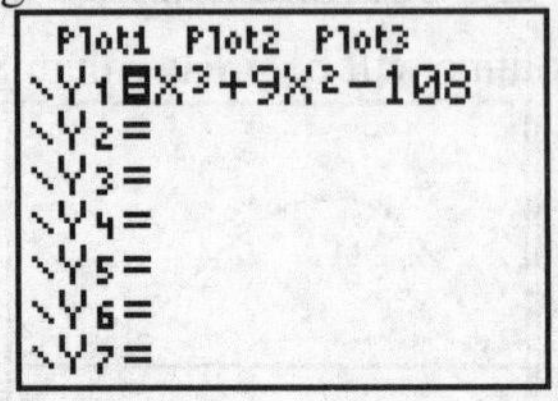

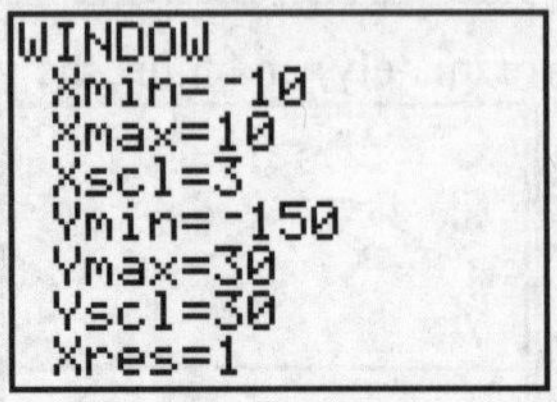

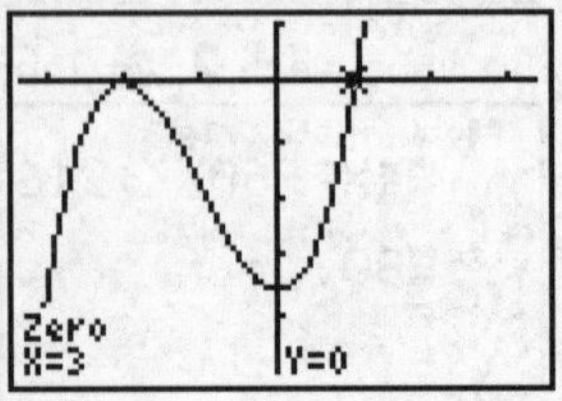

A radius of 3 feet would cause the volume of the tank to be 144π ft^3.

95. $f(x)=\frac{\pi}{3}x^3-5\pi x^2+\frac{500\pi d}{3}$

Use a graphing calculator for the three parts of this exercise.

(a) When $d=.8$ we have $f(x)=\frac{\pi}{3}x^3-5\pi x^2+\frac{500\pi(.8)}{3}$.

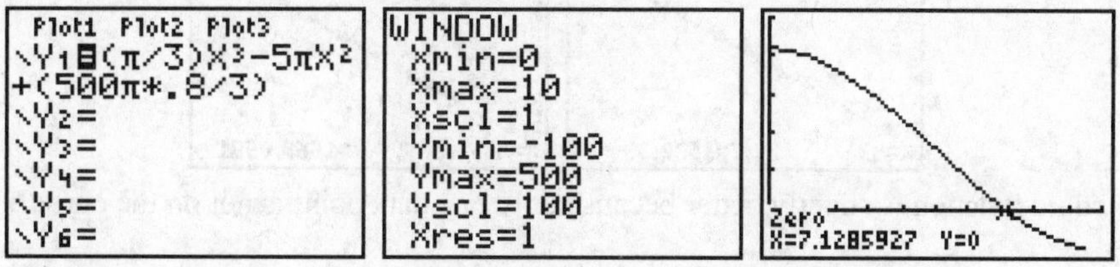

The approximate depth is 7.13 cm. The ball floats partly above the surface.

(b) When $d=2.7$ we have $f(x)=\frac{\pi}{3}x^3-5\pi x^2+\frac{500\pi(2.7)}{3}$.

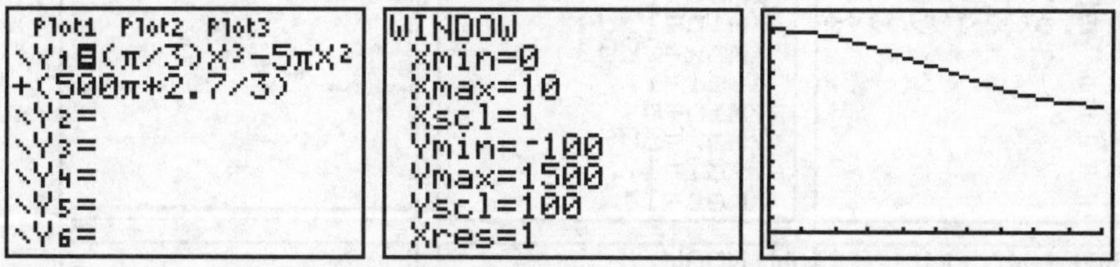

There is no x-intercept in this window. The sphere is more dense than water and sinks below the surface.

(c) When $d=1$ we have $f(x)=\frac{\pi}{3}x^3-5\pi x^2+\frac{500\pi}{3}$.

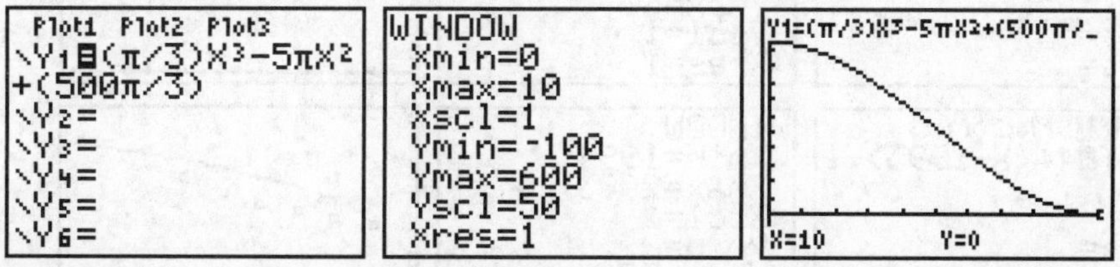

By tracing on the curve we see that the approximate depth is 10 cm. The balloon is submerged with its top even with the surface.

97. (a)

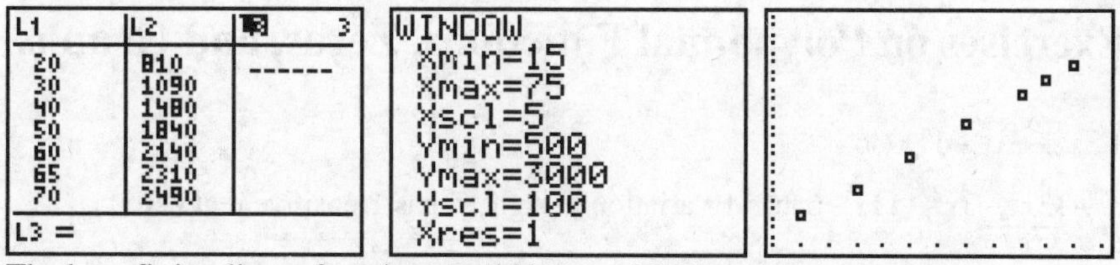

(b) The best-fitting linear function would be $y=33.93x+113.4$.

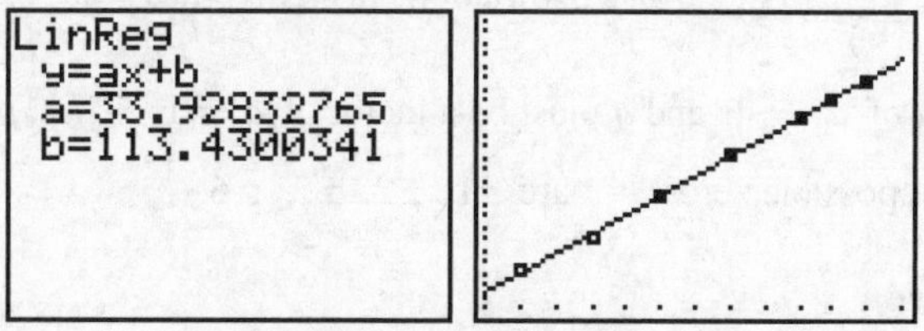

(c) The best-fitting cubic function would be $y=-.0032x^3+.4245x^2+16.64x+323.1$.

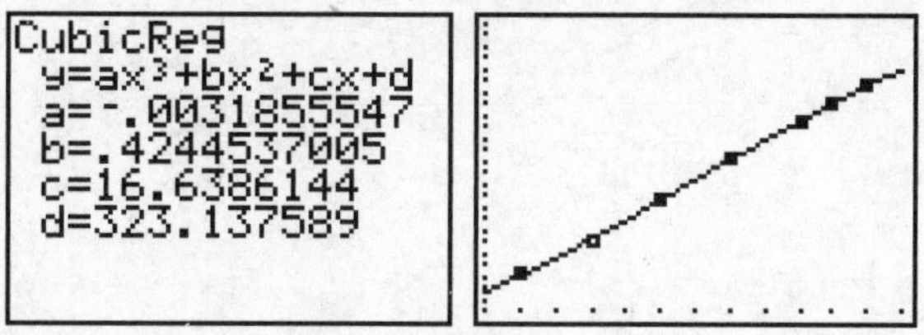

Continued on next page

97. (continued)

(d) linear: approximately 1572 ft; cubic: approximately 1570 ft

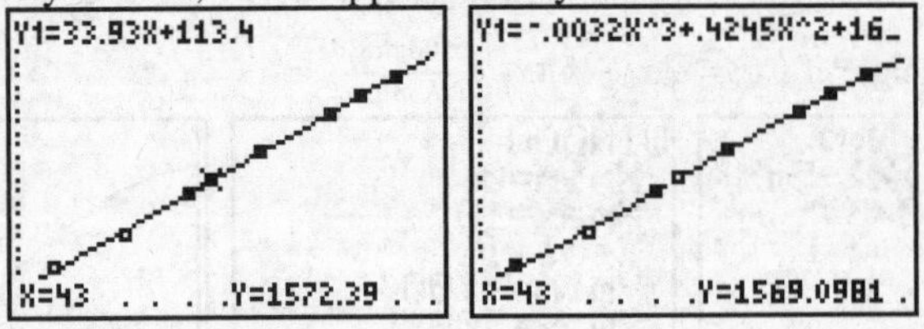

(e) The cubic function is slightly better because only one data point is not on the curve.

99. The function in B, $g(x)=1.6(x-1995)+15$ provides the best model.

A.

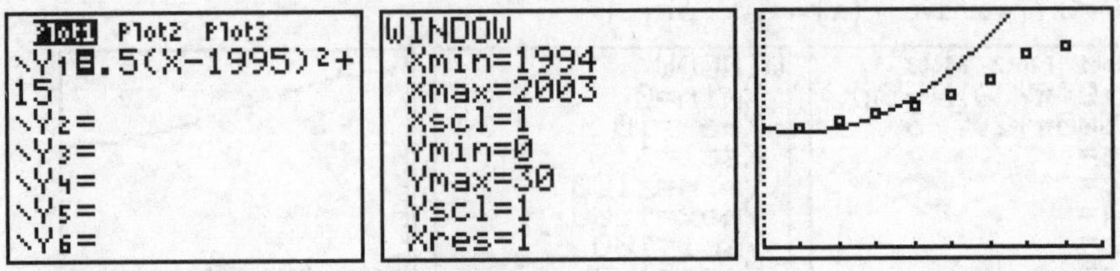

B.

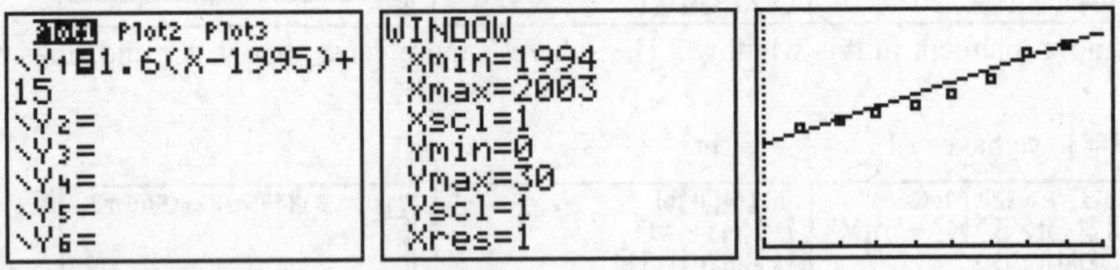

C.

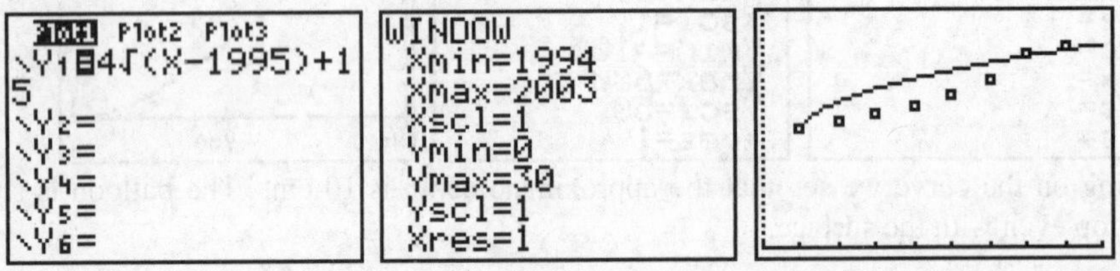

Summary Exercises on Polynomial Functions, Zeros, and Graphs

1. $f(x)=x^4+3x^3-3x^2-11x-6$

(a) $f(x)=x^4\underbrace{+3x^3-3x^2}_{1}-11x-6$ has 1 variation in sign. f has 1 positive real zero.

$f(-x)=\underbrace{x^4-3x^3}_{1}\underbrace{-3x^2+11x}_{2}\underbrace{+11x-6}_{3}$ has 3 variations in sign. f has 3 or 3 – 2 = 1 negative real zeros.

(b) p must be a factor of $a_0=-6$ and q must be a factor of $a_4=1$. Thus, p can be ±1, ±2, ±3, ±6 and q can be ±1. The possible zeros, $\frac{p}{q}$, are ±1, ±2, ±3, ±6.

Continued on next page

1. (continued)

(c) The remainder theorem shows that 2 is zero.

$$\begin{array}{r|rrrrr} 2 & 1 & 3 & -3 & -11 & -6 \\ & & 2 & 10 & 14 & 6 \\ \hline & 1 & 5 & 7 & 3 & 0 \end{array}$$

The new quotient polynomial is x^3+5x^2+7x+3. Since f has 1 positive real zero, try negative values. The remainder theorem shows that -3 is zero.

$$\begin{array}{r|rrrr} -3 & 1 & 5 & 7 & 3 \\ & & -3 & -6 & -3 \\ \hline & 1 & 2 & 1 & 0 \end{array}$$

The new quotient polynomial is x^2+2x+1. Factor this polynomial and set equal to zero to find the remaining zeros.

$$x^2+2x+1=0 \Rightarrow (x+1)^2=0 \Rightarrow x+1=0 \Rightarrow x=-1$$

The rational zeros are -3, -1 (multiplicity 2), and 2.

(d) All zeros have been found, and they are all rational.

(e) All zeros have been found, and they are all real.

(f) The x-intercepts occur when $x=-3,-1,$ and 2.

(g) $f(0)=-6$

(h)

$$\begin{array}{r|rrrrr} 4 & 1 & 3 & -3 & -11 & -6 \\ & & 4 & 28 & 100 & 356 \\ \hline & 1 & 7 & 25 & 89 & 350 \end{array}$$

The corresponding point on the graph is $(4,350)$.

(i)

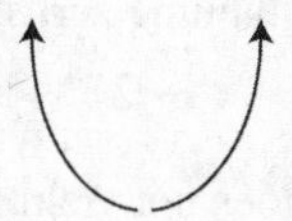

(j) The x-intercepts divide the x-axis into four intervals:

Interval	Test Point	Value of $f(x)$	Sign of $f(x)$	Graph Above or Below x-Axis
$(-\infty,-3)$	-4	54	Positive	Above
$(-3,-1)$	-2	-4	Negative	Below
$(-1,2)$	0	-6	Negative	Below
$(2,\infty)$	3	96	Positive	Above

Plot the x-intercepts, y-intercept and test points with a smooth curve to get the graph.

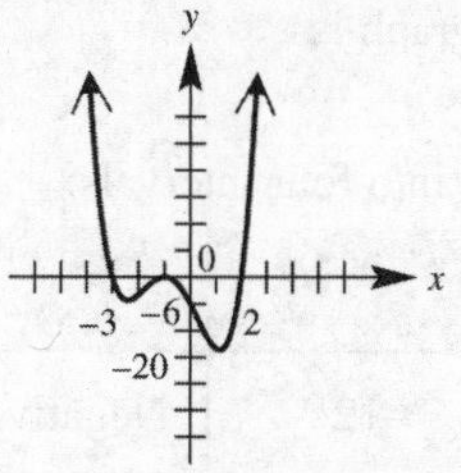

$f(x)=x^4+3x^3-3x^2-11x-6$

3. $f(x) = 2x^5 - 10x^4 + x^3 - 5x^2 - x + 5$

(a) $f(x) = \underbrace{2x^5 - 10x^4}_{1} \underbrace{+ x^3}_{2} \underbrace{- 5x^2}_{3} \underbrace{- x + 5}_{4}$ has 4 variations in sign. f has 4 or $4 - 2 = 2$ or $2 - 2 = 0$ positive real zeros.

$f(-x) = -2x^5 - 10x^4 - x^3 \underbrace{-5x^2 + x}_{1} + 5$ has 1 variation in sign. f has 1 negative real zero.

(b) p must be a factor of $a_0 = 5$ and q must be a factor of $a_5 = 2$. Thus, p can be $\pm 1, \pm 5$ and q can be $\pm 1, \pm 2$. The possible zeros, $\frac{p}{q}$, are $\pm 1, \pm 5, \pm \frac{1}{2}, \pm \frac{5}{2}$.

(c) The remainder theorem shows that 5 is zero.

$$\begin{array}{r|rrrrrr} 5 & 2 & -10 & 1 & -5 & -1 & 5 \\ & & 10 & 0 & 5 & 0 & -5 \\ \hline & 2 & 0 & 1 & 0 & -1 & 0 \end{array}$$

The rational zero is 5.

The new quotient polynomial will be $2x^4 + x^2 - 1$. At this point, if we try to determine which of the possible rational zero will result in a remainder of zero, we will find that none of them work. We have found the only rational zero of our polynomial function.

(d) Since the new quotient polynomial is $2x^4 + x^2 - 1$, we can factor this polynomial and set equal to zero to find the remaining zeros.

$$2x^4 + x^2 - 1 = 0 \Rightarrow (x^2 + 1)(2x^2 - 1) = 0$$

Since $x^2 + 1 = 0$ does not yield any real solutions, we will examine $2x^2 - 1 = 0$ first.

$$2x^2 - 1 = 0 \Rightarrow 2x^2 = 1 \Rightarrow x^2 = \tfrac{1}{2} \Rightarrow x = \pm\sqrt{\tfrac{1}{2}} = \pm\tfrac{\sqrt{2}}{2}$$

The other real zeros are $-\frac{\sqrt{2}}{2}$ and $\frac{\sqrt{2}}{2}$.

(e) Examining $x^2 + 1 = 0$, we have $x^2 = -1 \Rightarrow x = \pm\sqrt{-1} = \pm i$. Thus, the complex zeros are $-i$ and i.

(f) The x-intercepts occur when $x = -\frac{\sqrt{2}}{2} \approx -.71$, $\frac{\sqrt{2}}{2} \approx .71$, and 5.

(g) $f(0) = 5$

(h)

$$\begin{array}{r|rrrrrr} 4 & 2 & -10 & 1 & -5 & -1 & 5 \\ & & 8 & -8 & -28 & -132 & -532 \\ \hline & 2 & -2 & -7 & -33 & -133 & -527 \end{array}$$

The corresponding point on the graph is $(4, -527)$.

(i)

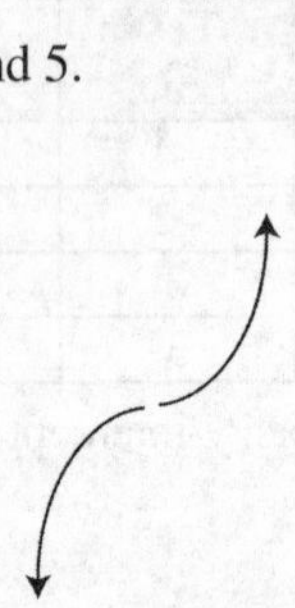

(j) The x-intercepts divide the x-axis into four intervals:

Interval	Test Point	Value of $f(x)$	Sign of $f(x)$	Graph Above or Below x-Axis
$\left(-\infty, -\frac{\sqrt{2}}{2}\right)$	–1	–12	Negative	Below
$\left(-\frac{\sqrt{2}}{2}, \frac{\sqrt{2}}{2}\right)$	0	5	Positive	Above
$\left(\frac{\sqrt{2}}{2}, 5\right)$	1	–8	Negative	Below
$(5, \infty)$	6	2627	Positive	Above

Plot the x-intercepts, y-intercept and test points (the y-intercept is also a test point) with a smooth curve to get the graph.

Continued on next page

3. (continued)

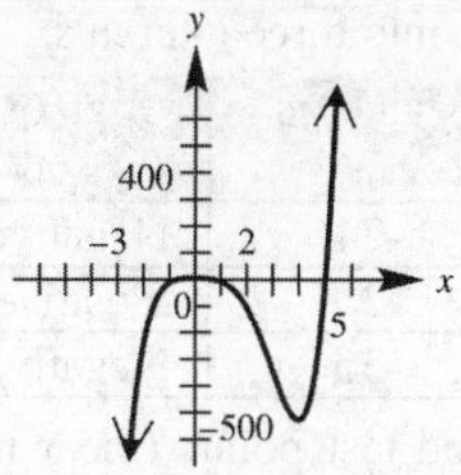

$f(x) = 2x^5 - 10x^4 + x^3 - 5x^2 - x + 5$

5. $f(x) = -2x^4 - x^3 + x + 2$

(a) $f(x) = -2x^4 \underbrace{-x^3 +}_{1} x + 2$ has 1 variation in sign. f has 1 positive real zero.

$f(x) = \underbrace{-2x^4 +}_{1} \underbrace{x^3 -}_{2} \underbrace{x +}_{3} 2$ has 3 variations in sign. f has 3 or $3 - 2 = 1$ negative real zeros.

(b) p must be a factor of $a_0 = 2$ and q must be a factor of $a_4 = -2$. Thus, p can be $\pm 1, \pm 2$ and q can be $\pm 1, \pm 2$. The possible zeros, $\frac{p}{q}$, are $\pm 1, \pm 2, \pm \frac{1}{2}$.

(c) The remainder theorem shows that -1 is zero.

$-1)$	-2	-1	0	1	2
		2	-1	1	-2
	-2	1	-1	2	0

The new quotient polynomial will be $-2x^3 + x^2 - x + 2$. Since the signs are alternating in the bottom row of the synthetic division, we know that -1 is a lower bound. The remainder theorem shows that 1 is zero.

$1)$	-2	1	-1	2
		-2	-1	-2
	-2	-1	-2	0

The new quotient polynomial is $-2x^2 - x - 2 = -(2x^2 + x + 2)$. At this point, if we try to determine which of the possible rational zeros will result in a remainder of zero, we will find that none of them work. We have found the only rational zeros of our polynomial function. The rational zeros are -1 and 1.

(d) If we examine the discriminant of $2x^2 + x + 2$, namely $1^2 - 4(2)(2) = 1 - 16 = -15$, we see that it is negative, which implies there are no other real zeros.

(e) To find the remaining complex zeros, we must solve $2x^2 + x + 2 = 0$. To solve this equation, we use the quadratic formula with $a = 2, b = 1$, and $c = 2$.

$$x = \frac{-1 \pm \sqrt{1^2 - 4(2)(2)}}{2(2)} = \frac{-1 \pm \sqrt{1-16}}{4} = \frac{-1 \pm \sqrt{-15}}{4} = \frac{-1 \pm i\sqrt{15}}{4}$$

Thus, the other complex zeros are $-\frac{1}{4} + i\frac{\sqrt{15}}{4}$ and $-\frac{1}{4} - i\frac{\sqrt{15}}{4}$

(f) The x-intercepts occur when $x = -1$ and 1.

(g) $f(0) = 2$

(h)

$4)$	-2	-1	0	1	2
		-8	-36	-144	-572
	-2	-9	-36	-143	-570

The corresponding point on the graph is $(4, -570)$.

(i)

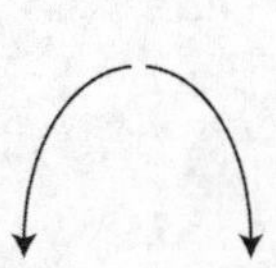

Continued on next page

5. (continued)

(j) The x-intercepts divide the x-axis into three intervals:

Interval	Test Point	Value of $f(x)$	Sign of $f(x)$	Graph Above or Below x-Axis
$(-\infty, -1)$	-2	-24	Negative	Below
$(-1, 1)$	0	2	Positive	Above
$(1, \infty)$	2	-36	Negative	Below

Plot the x-intercepts, y-intercept and test points (the y-intercept is also a test point) with a smooth curve to get the graph.

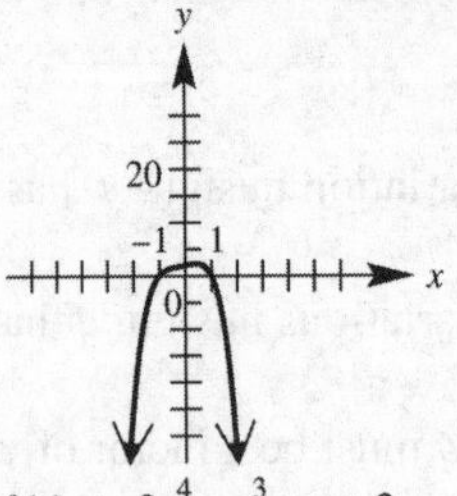

$f(x) = -2x^4 - x^3 + x + 2$

7. $f(x) = 3x^4 - 14x^2 - 5$

(a) $f(x) = \underbrace{3x^4 - 14x^2}_{1} - 5$ has 1 variation in sign. f has 1 positive real zero.

$f(-x) = \underbrace{3x^4 - 14x^2}_{1} - 5$ has 1 variation in sign. f has 1 negative real zeros.

(b) p must be a factor of $a_0 = -5$ and q must be a factor of $a_4 = 3$. Thus, p can be $\pm1, \pm5$ and q can be $\pm1, \pm3$. The possible zeros, $\frac{p}{q}$, are ±1, ±5, $\pm\frac{1}{3}$, $\pm\frac{5}{3}$.

(c) If we try to determine which of the possible rational zeros will result in a remainder of zero, we will find that none of them work.
There are no rational zeros.

(d) We can factor the polynomial, $3x^4 - 14x^2 - 5$, and set equal to zero to the remaining zeros.

$$3x^4 - 14x^2 - 5 = 0 \Rightarrow \left(3x^2 + 1\right)\left(x^2 - 5\right) = 0$$

Since $3x^2 + 1 = 0$ does not yield any real solutions, we will examine $x^2 - 5 = 0$ first.

$$x^2 - 5 = 0 \Rightarrow x^2 = 5 \Rightarrow x = \pm\sqrt{5}$$

The real zeros are $-\sqrt{5}$ and $\sqrt{5}$.

(e) Examining $3x^2 + 1 = 0$, we have $3x^2 = -1 \Rightarrow x^2 = -\frac{1}{3} \Rightarrow x = \pm\sqrt{-\frac{1}{3}} = \pm i\frac{\sqrt{3}}{3}$. Thus, the complex zeros are $-i\frac{\sqrt{3}}{3}$ and $i\frac{\sqrt{3}}{3}$.

(f) The x-intercepts occur when $x = -\sqrt{5} \approx -2.24$ and $\sqrt{5} \approx 2.24$.

(g) $f(0) = -5$

Continued on next page

7. (continued)

(h)

$$\begin{array}{r|rrrrr} 4 & 3 & 0 & -14 & 0 & -5 \\ & & 12 & 48 & 136 & 544 \\ \hline & 3 & 12 & 34 & 136 & 539 \end{array}$$

The corresponding point on the graph is $(4, 539)$.

(i)

(j) The *x*-intercepts divide the *x*-axis into three intervals:

Interval	Test Point	Value of $f(x)$	Sign of $f(x)$	Graph Above or Below *x*-Axis
$\left(-\infty, -\sqrt{5}\right)$	–3	112	Positive	Above
$\left(-\sqrt{5}, \sqrt{5}\right)$	0	–5	Negative	Below
$\left(\sqrt{5}, \infty\right)$	3	112	Positive	Above

Plot the *x*-intercepts, *y*-intercept and test points (the *y*-intercept is also a test point) with a smooth curve to get the graph.

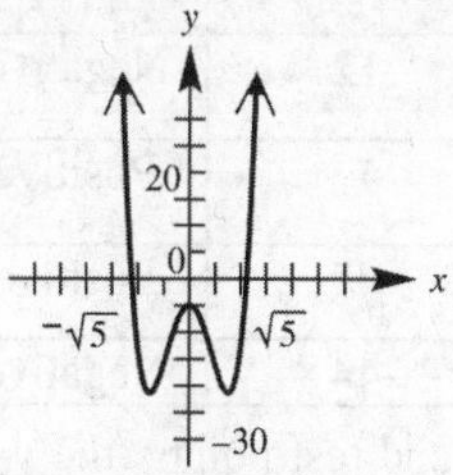

$f(x) = 3x^4 - 14x^2 - 5$

9. $f(x) = -3x^4 + 22x^3 - 55x^2 + 52x - 12$

(a) $f(x) = \underbrace{-3x^4 + 22x^3}_{1}\underbrace{}_{2}\underbrace{-55x^2}_{3} \underbrace{+52x}_{4} - 12$ has 4 variations in sign. f has 4 or $4 - 2 = 2$ or $2 - 2 = 0$ positive real zeros.

$f(-x) = -3x^4 - 22x^3 - 55x^2 - 52x - 12$ has 0 variations in sign. f has 0 negative real zeros.

(b) p must be a factor of $a_0 = -12$ and q must be a factor of $a_4 = -3$. Thus, p can be ±1, ±2, ±3, ±4, ±6, ±12 and q can be $\pm 1, \pm 3$. The possible zeros, $\frac{p}{q}$, are $\pm 1, \pm 2, \pm 3, \pm 4, \pm 6, \pm 12, \pm \frac{1}{3}, \pm \frac{2}{3}, \pm \frac{4}{3}$.

(c) The remainder theorem shows that 2 is a zero.

$$\begin{array}{r|rrrrr} 2 & -3 & 22 & -55 & 52 & -12 \\ & & -6 & 32 & -46 & 12 \\ \hline & -3 & 16 & -23 & 6 & 0 \end{array}$$

The new quotient polynomial will be $-3x^3 + 15x^2 - 23x + 6$. The remainder theorem shows that 3 is zero.

$$\begin{array}{r|rrrr} 3 & -3 & 16 & -23 & 6 \\ & & -9 & 21 & -6 \\ \hline & -3 & 7 & -2 & 0 \end{array}$$

Continued on next page

9. **(c)** (continued)

The new quotient polynomial is $-3x^2+7x-2=-\left(3x^2-7x+2\right)$. Factor $3x^2-7x+2$ and set equal to zero to find the remaining zeros.

$$3x^2-7x+2=0 \Rightarrow (3x-1)(x-2)=0$$
$$3x-1=0 \Rightarrow x=\tfrac{1}{3} \text{ or } x-2=0 \Rightarrow x=2$$

The rational zeros are $\frac{1}{3}$, 2 (multiplicity 2), and 3.

(d) All zeros have been found, and they are all rational.

(e) All zeros have been found, and they are all real.

(f) The x-intercepts occur when $x=\frac{1}{3}$, 2, and 3.

(g) $f(0)=-12$

(h)
$$\begin{array}{r|rrrrr} 4 & -3 & 22 & -55 & 52 & -12 \\ & & -12 & 40 & -60 & -32 \\ \hline & -3 & 10 & -15 & -8 & -44 \end{array}$$

The corresponding point on the graph is $(4,-44)$.

(i)

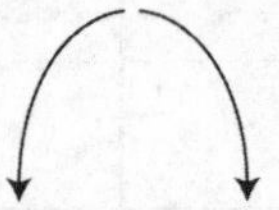

(j) The x-intercepts divide the x-axis into four intervals:

Interval	Test Point	Value of $f(x)$	Sign of $f(x)$	Graph Above or Below x-Axis
$\left(-\infty,\frac{1}{3}\right)$	0	-12	Negative	Below
$\left(\frac{1}{3},2\right)$	1	4	Positive	Above
(2, 3)	$\frac{5}{2}$	$\frac{13}{16}$	Positive	Above
$(3,\infty)$	4	-44	Negative	Below

Plot the x-intercepts, y-intercept and test points (the y-intercept is also a test point) with a smooth curve to get the graph.

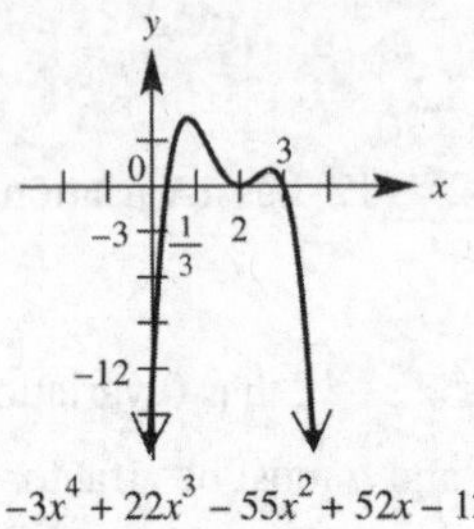

$f(x)=-3x^4+22x^3-55x^2+52x-12$

Section 3.5: Rational Functions: Graphs, Applications, and Models

1. $f(x)=\frac{1}{x}$
Domain: $(-\infty,0)\cup(0,\infty)$
Range: $(-\infty,0)\cup(0,\infty)$

3. $f(x)=\frac{1}{x}$
Increasing: nowhere
Decreasing: $(-\infty,0)\cup(0,\infty)$
Constant: nowhere

5. $y=\frac{1}{x-3}+2$
Vertical Asymptote: $x=3$
Horizontal Asymptote: $y=2$

7. $f(x)=\frac{1}{x^2}$ is an even function. It exhibits symmetry with respect to y-axis.

9. Graphs A, B, and C have a domain of $(-\infty,3)\cup(3,\infty)$.

11. Graph A has a range of $(-\infty,0)\cup(0,\infty)$.

13. Graph A has a single solution to the equation $f(x)=3$.

15. Graphs A, C, and D have the x-axis as a horizontal asymptote.

17. $f(x)=\frac{2}{x}$

Since $\frac{2}{x}=2\cdot\frac{1}{x}$, the graph of $f(x)=\frac{2}{x}$ will be similar to the graph of $f(x)=\frac{1}{x}$, except that each point will be twice as far from the x-axis. Just as with the graph of $f(x)=\frac{1}{x}$, $y=0$ is the horizontal asymptote and $x=0$ is the vertical asymptote.

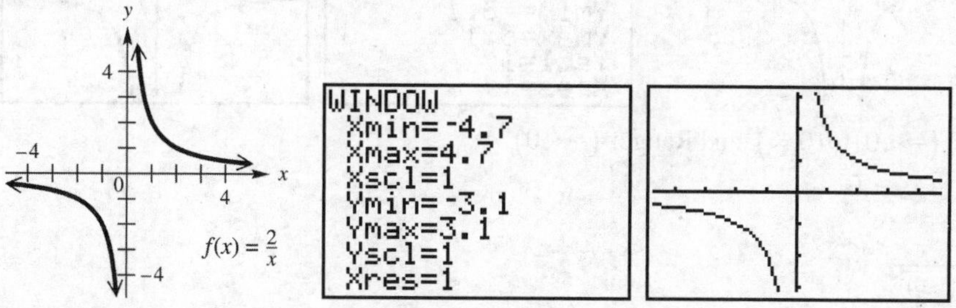

Domain: $(-\infty,0)\cup(0,\infty)$ and Range: $(-\infty,0)\cup(0,\infty)$

19. $f(x)=\frac{1}{x+2}$

Since $\frac{1}{x+2}=\frac{1}{x-(2)}$, the graph of $f(x)=\frac{1}{x+2}$ will be similar to the graph of $f(x)=\frac{1}{x}$, except that each point will be translated 2 units to the left. Just as with $f(x)=\frac{1}{x}$, $y=0$ is the horizontal asymptote, but this graph has $x=-2$ as its vertical asymptote (this affects the domain).

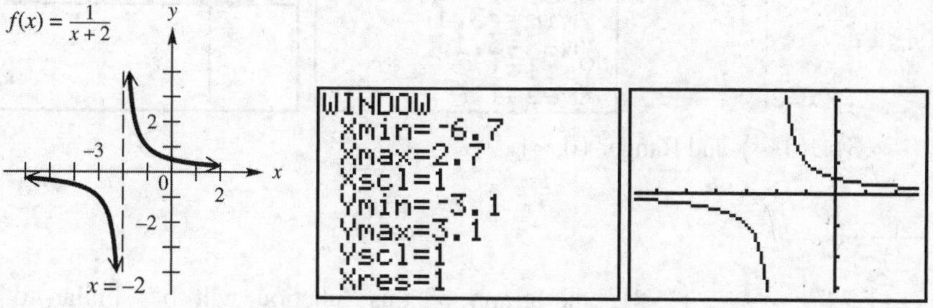

Domain: $(-\infty,-2)\cup(-2,\infty)$ and Range: $(-\infty,0)\cup(0,\infty)$

21. $f(x)=\frac{1}{x}+1$

The graph of this function will be similar to the graph of $f(x)=\frac{1}{x}$, except that each point will be translated 1 unit upward. Just as with $f(x)=\frac{1}{x}$, $x=0$ is the vertical asymptote, but this graph has $y=1$ as its horizontal asymptote (this affects the range).

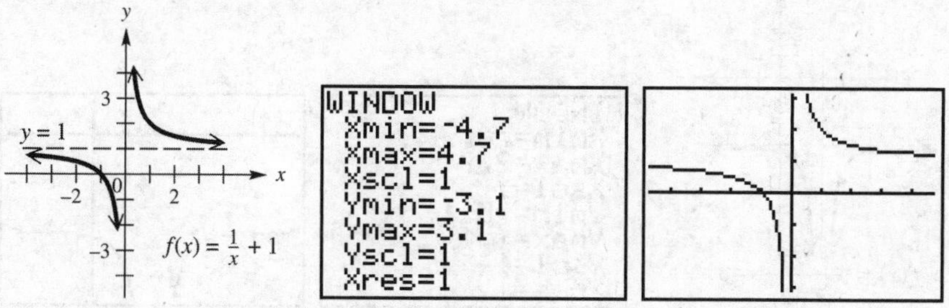

Domain: $(-\infty,0)\cup(0,\infty)$ and Range: $(-\infty,1)\cup(1,\infty)$

23. $f(x) = -\frac{2}{x^2}$

Since $-\frac{2}{x^2} = -2 \cdot \frac{1}{x^2}$, the graph of $f(x) = -\frac{2}{x^2}$ is similar to the graph of $f(x) = \frac{1}{x^2}$, except each point will be 2 times as far from the x-axis. Because of the negative sign, the graph will be reflected about the x-axis (this affects the range).

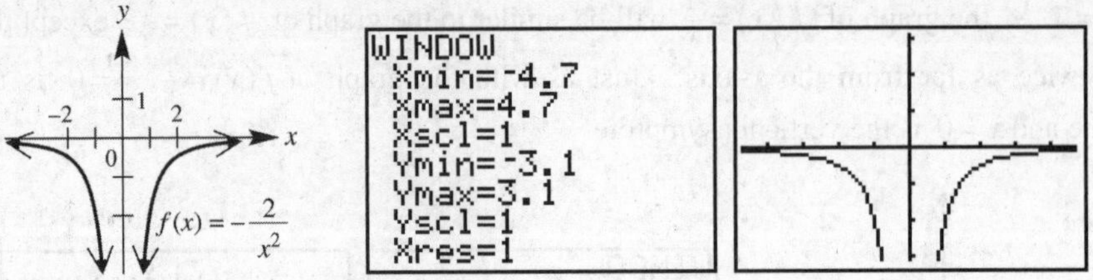

Domain: $(-\infty, 0) \cup (0, \infty)$ and Range: $(-\infty, 0)$

25. $f(x) = \frac{1}{(x-3)^2}$

The graph of $f(x) = \frac{1}{(x-3)^2}$ will be similar to the graph of $f(x) = \frac{1}{x^2}$, except that each point will be translated 3 units to the right. Just as with $f(x) = \frac{1}{x^2}$, $y = 0$ is the horizontal asymptote, but this graph has $x = 3$ as its vertical asymptote (this affects the domain).

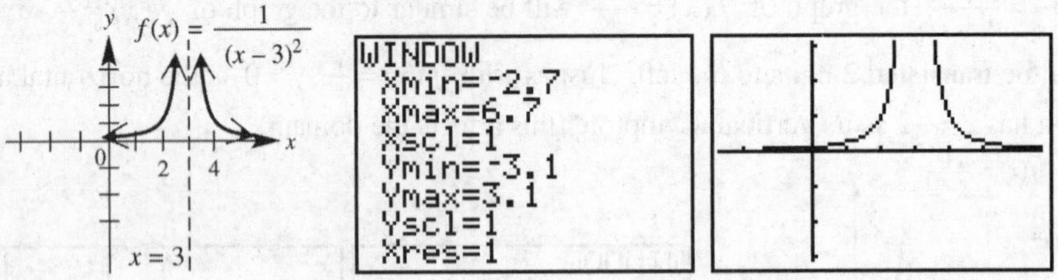

Domain: $(-\infty, 3) \cup (3, \infty)$ and Range: $(0, \infty)$

27. $f(x) = \frac{-1}{(x+2)^2} - 3$

Since $\frac{-1}{(x+2)^2} - 3 = -\frac{1}{[x-(-2)]^2} + (-3)$, the graph of this function will be similar to the graph of $f(x) = \frac{1}{x^2}$, except that each point will be translated 3 units downward and two units to the left. Unlike the graph of $f(x) = \frac{1}{x^2}$, the vertical asymptote of $f(x) = \frac{-1}{(x+2)^2} - 3$ will be $x = -2$ (this affects the domain). Also the negative affects the range by reflecting the graph about a horizontal axis and the horizontal asymptote, which is $y = -3$, also affects the range.

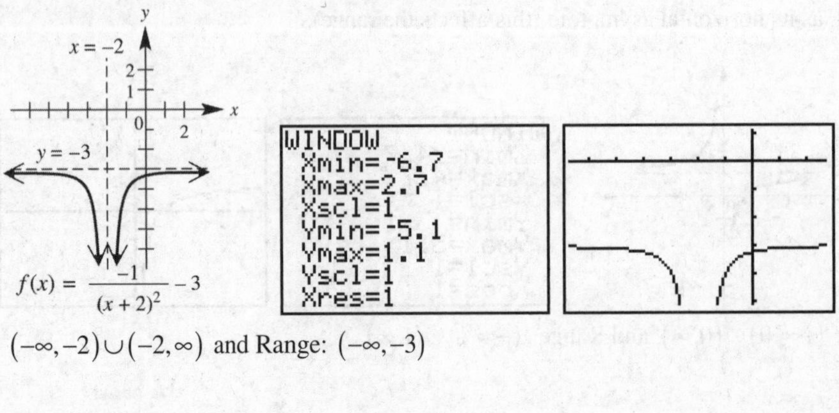

Domain: $(-\infty, -2) \cup (-2, \infty)$ and Range: $(-\infty, -3)$

29. D; The graph of $f(x)=\frac{x+7}{x+1}$ has the vertical asymptote at $x=-1$.

31. G; The graph of $f(x)=\frac{1}{x+4}$ has the *x*-axis as its horizontal asymptote, and the *y*-axis is not its vertical asymptote. The line $x=-4$ is its vertical asymptote.

33. E; The graph of $f(x)=\frac{x^2-16}{x+4}$ has a "hole" in its graph located at $x=-4$ since $f(x)=\frac{x^2-16}{x+4}=\frac{(x+4)(x-4)}{x+4}=x-4,\ x\neq-4$.

35. F; The graph of $f(x)=\frac{x^2+3x+4}{x-5}$ has an oblique asymptote since $f(x)=x+8+\frac{44}{x-5}$.

37. $f(x)=\frac{3}{x-5}$

To find the vertical asymptote, set the denominator equal to zero.

$$x-5=0\Rightarrow x=5$$

The equation of the vertical asymptote is $x=5$. To find the horizontal asymptote, divide each term by the largest power of *x* in the expression.

$$f(x)=\frac{\frac{3}{x}}{\frac{x}{x}-\frac{5}{x}}=\frac{\frac{3}{x}}{1-\frac{5}{x}}$$

As $|x|\to\infty$, $\frac{1}{x}$ approaches 0, thus $f(x)$ approaches $\frac{0}{1-0}=\frac{0}{1}=0$. The line $y=0$ (that is, the *x*-axis) is the horizontal asymptote.

39. $f(x)=\frac{4-3x}{2x+1}$

To find the vertical asymptote, set the denominator equal to zero.

$$2x+1=0\Rightarrow x=-\frac{1}{2}$$

The equation of the vertical asymptote is $x=-\frac{1}{2}$. To find the horizontal asymptote, divide each term by the largest power of *x* in the expression.

$$f(x)=\frac{\frac{4}{x}-\frac{3x}{x}}{\frac{2x}{x}+\frac{1}{x}}=\frac{\frac{4}{x}-3}{2+\frac{1}{x}}$$

As $|x|\to\infty$, $\frac{1}{x}$ approaches 0, so $f(x)$ approaches $\frac{0-3}{2+0}=-\frac{3}{2}$. The equation of the horizontal asymptote is $y=-\frac{3}{2}$.

41. $f(x)=\frac{x^2-1}{x+3}$

The vertical asymptote is $x=-3$, found by solving $x+3=0$. Since the numerator is of degree exactly one more than the denominator, there is no horizontal asymptote, but there may be an oblique asymptote. To find it, divide the numerator by the denominator.

$$\begin{array}{r|rrr} -3 & 1 & 0 & -1 \\ & & -3 & 9 \\ \hline & 1 & -3 & 8 \end{array}$$

Thus, $f(x)=\frac{x^2-1}{x+3}=x-3+\frac{8}{x+3}$.

For very large values of $|x|$, $\frac{8}{x+3}$ is close to 0, and the graph approaches the line $y=x-3$.

43. $f(x)=\frac{(x-3)(x+1)}{(x+2)(2x-5)}$

To find the vertical asymptotes, set the denominator equal to zero and solve.

$$x+2=0\Rightarrow x=-2 \text{ and } 2x-5=0\Rightarrow x=\frac{5}{2}$$

Thus, the vertical asymptotes are $x=-2$ and $x=\frac{5}{2}$.

To determine the horizontal asymptote, first multiply the factors in the numerator and denominator to get $f(x)=\frac{x^2-2x-3}{2x^2-x-10}$. Divide the numerator and denominator by x^2.

$$f(x)=\frac{\frac{x^2}{x^2}-\frac{2x}{x^2}-\frac{3}{x^2}}{\frac{2x^2}{x^2}-\frac{x}{x^2}-\frac{10}{x^2}}=\frac{1-\frac{2}{x}-\frac{3}{x^2}}{2-\frac{1}{x}-\frac{10}{x^2}}$$

As $|x|\to\infty$, $\frac{1}{x}$ and $\frac{1}{x^2}$ approach 0, so $f(x)$ approaches $\frac{1-0-0}{2-0-0}=\frac{1}{2}$. Thus, the equation of the horizontal asymptote is $y=\frac{1}{2}$.

45. $f(x)=\frac{x^2+1}{x^2+9}$

To find the vertical asymptotes, set the denominator equal to zero and solve.

$$x^2+9=0\Rightarrow x^2=-9\Rightarrow x=\pm\sqrt{-9}=\pm3i$$

Thus, there are no vertical asymptotes.

To determine the horizontal asymptote, divide the numerator and denominator by x^2.

$$f(x)=\frac{\frac{x^2}{x^2}+\frac{1}{x^2}}{\frac{x^2}{x^2}+\frac{9}{x^2}}=\frac{1+\frac{1}{x^2}}{1+\frac{9}{x^2}}$$

As $|x|\to\infty$, $\frac{1}{x^2}$ approaches 0, so $f(x)$ approaches $\frac{1+0}{1+0}=\frac{1}{1}=1$. Thus, the equation of the horizontal asymptote is $y=1$.

47. (a) Translating $y=\frac{1}{x}$ three units to the right gives $y=\frac{1}{x-3}$. Translating $y=\frac{1}{x-3}$ two units up yields $y=\frac{1}{x-3}+2=\frac{1}{x-3}+\frac{2x-6}{x-3}=\frac{2x-5}{x-3}$. So $f(x)=\frac{2x-5}{x-3}$.

(b) $f(x)=\frac{2x-5}{x-3}$ has a zero when $2x-5=0$ or $x=\frac{5}{2}$.

(c) $f(x)=\frac{2x-5}{x-3}$ has a horizontal asymptote at $y=2$ and a vertical asymptote at $x=3$.

49. (a) $f(x)=x+1+\frac{x^2-x}{x^4+1}$ has an oblique asymptote of $y=x+1$.

(b) In order to determine when the function intersects the oblique asymptote, we must determine the values of that that make $\frac{x^2-x}{x^4+1}=0$. Since $\frac{x^2-x}{x^4+1}=\frac{x(x-1)}{x^4+1}$, and $x(x-1)=0$ when $x=0$ or $x=1$, the function crosses its asymptote at $x=0$ and $x=1$.

(c) For large values of x, $\frac{x^2-x}{x^4+1}>0$. Thus as $x\to\infty$, the function approaches its asymptote from above.

51. $f(x) = \frac{x+1}{x-4}$

Step 1 The graph has a vertical asymptote where $x - 4 = 0$.

$$x - 4 = 0 \Rightarrow x = 4$$

Step 2 Since the degree of the numerator equals the degree of the denominator, the graph has a horizontal asymptote at $y = \frac{1}{1} = 1$.

Step 3 The y-intercept is $f(0) = -\frac{1}{4}$.

Step 4 Any x-intercepts are found by solving $f(x) = 0$.

$$\frac{x+1}{x-4} = 0 \Rightarrow x + 1 = 0 \Rightarrow x = -1$$

The only x-intercept is –1.

Step 5 The graph will intersect the horizontal asymptote when $\frac{x+1}{x-4} = 1$.

$$\frac{x+1}{x-4} = 1 \Rightarrow x + 1 = 1(x - 4) \Rightarrow x + 1 = x - 4 \Rightarrow 1 = -4$$

This is a false statement, so the graph does not intersect the horizontal asymptote.

Step 6 Since the vertical asymptote is $x = 4$ and the x-intercept occurs at -1, we must determine values in three intervals.

Interval	Test Point	Value of $f(x)$	Sign of $f(x)$	Graph Above or Below x-Axis
$(-\infty, -1)$	–2	$\frac{1}{6}$	Positive	Above
$(-1, 4)$	3	–4	Negative	Below
$(4, \infty)$	5	6	Positive	Above

Step 7 Use the asymptotes, intercepts, and these points to sketch the graph.

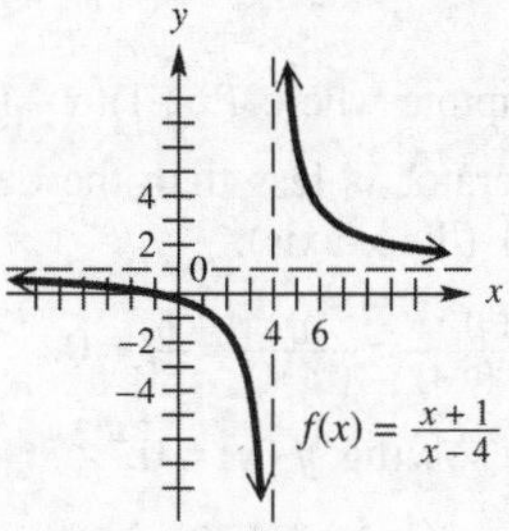

53. $f(x) = \frac{3x}{x^2-x-2} \Rightarrow f(x) = \frac{3x}{(x+1)(x-2)}$

Step 1 The graph has a vertical asymptote where $(x+1)(x-2) = 0$, that is, when $x = -1$ and $x = 2$.

Step 2 Since the degree of the numerator is less than the degree of the denominator, the graph has a horizontal asymptote at $y = 0$ (the x-axis).

Step 3 The y-intercept is $f(0) = \frac{3(0)}{(0+1)(0-2)} = \frac{0}{(1)(-2)} = \frac{0}{-2} = 0$.

Step 4 Any x-intercepts are found by solving $f(x) = 0$.

$$\frac{3x}{(x+1)(x-2)} = 0 \Rightarrow 3x = 0 \Rightarrow x = 0$$

The only x-intercept is 0.

Step 5 The graph will intersect the horizontal asymptote when $\frac{3x}{(x+1)(x-2)} = 0$.

$$\frac{3x}{(x+1)(x-2)} = 0 \Rightarrow 3x = 0 \Rightarrow x = 0$$

Continued on next page

53. (continued)

Step 6 Since the vertical asymptotes are $x=-1$ and $x=2$ and the x-intercept occurs at 0, we must determine values in four intervals.

Interval	Test Point	Value of $f(x)$	Sign of $f(x)$	Graph Above or Below x-Axis
$(-\infty,-1)$	-2	$-\frac{3}{2}$	Negative	Below
$(-1, 0)$	$-\frac{1}{2}$	$\frac{6}{5}$	Positive	Above
$(0, 2)$	1	$-\frac{3}{2}$	Negative	Below
$(2, \infty)$	3	$\frac{9}{4}$	Positive	Above

Step 7 Use the asymptotes, intercepts, and these points to sketch the graph.

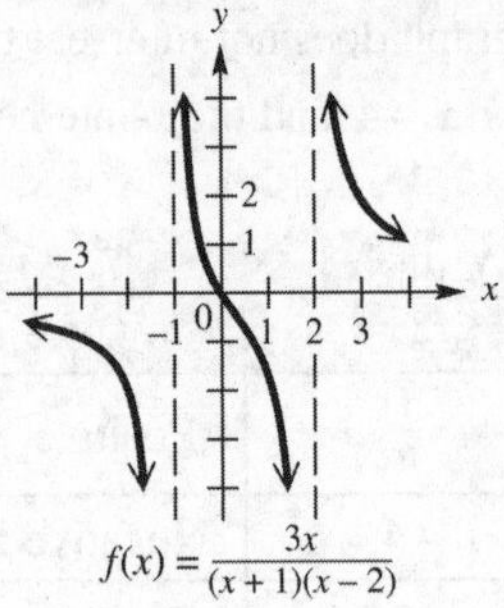

55. $f(x)=\frac{5x}{x^2-1}=\frac{5x}{(x+1)(x-1)}$

Step 1 The graph has a vertical asymptote where $(x+1)(x-1)=0$, that is, when $x=-1$ and $x=1$.

Step 2 Since the degree of the numerator is less than the degree of the denominator, the graph has a horizontal asymptote at $y=0$ (the x-axis).

Step 3 The y-intercept is $f(0)=\frac{5(0)}{(0+1)(0-1)}=\frac{0}{(1)(-1)}=\frac{0}{-1}=0.$

Step 4 Any x-intercepts are found by solving $f(x)=0$.

$$\frac{5x}{(x+1)(x-1)}=0 \Rightarrow 5x=0 \Rightarrow x=0$$

The only x-intercept is 0.

Step 5 The graph will intersect the horizontal asymptote when $\frac{5x}{(x+1)(x-1)}=0.$

$$\frac{5x}{(x+1)(x-1)}=0 \Rightarrow 5x=0 \Rightarrow x=0$$

Step 6 Since the vertical asymptotes are $x=-1$ and $x=1$ and the x-intercept occurs at 0, we must determine values in four intervals.

Interval	Test Point	Value of $f(x)$	Sign of $f(x)$	Graph Above or Below x-Axis
$(-\infty,-1)$	-2	$-\frac{10}{3}$	Negative	Below
$(-1,0)$	$-\frac{1}{2}$	$\frac{10}{3}$	Positive	Above
$(0,1)$	$\frac{1}{2}$	$-\frac{10}{3}$	Negative	Below
$(1,\infty)$	2	$\frac{10}{3}$	Positive	Above

Continued on next page

55. (continued)

Step 7 Use the asymptotes, intercepts, and these points to sketch the graph.

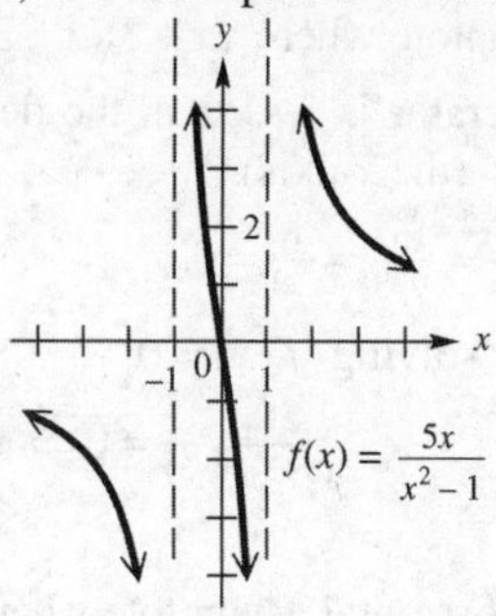

57. $f(x)=\frac{x^2-2x}{x^2+6x+9}=\frac{x(x-2)}{(x+3)^2}$

Step 1 The graph has a vertical asymptote where $(x+3)^2=0,$ that is, when $x=-3.$

Step 2 Since the degree of the numerator equals the degree of the denominator, the graph has a horizontal asymptote at $y=\frac{1}{1}=1.$

Step 3 The *y*-intercept is $f(0)=\frac{0^2-2(0)}{0^2+6(0)+9}=\frac{0-0}{0+0+9}=\frac{0}{9}=0.$

Step 4 Any *x*-intercepts are found by solving $f(x)=0.$

$$\frac{x(x-2)}{(x+3)^2}=0\Rightarrow x(x-2)=0$$

$$x=0 \text{ or } x-2=0$$

$$x=2$$

The *x*-intercepts are 0 and 2.

Step 5 The graph will intersect the horizontal asymptote when $\frac{x(x-2)}{(x+3)^2}=1.$

$$\frac{x(x-2)}{(x+3)^2}=1\Rightarrow x(x-2)=(x+3)^2\Rightarrow x^2-2x=x^2+6x+9\Rightarrow -2x=6x+9\Rightarrow -8x=9\Rightarrow x=-\frac{9}{8}$$

Step 6 Since the vertical asymptote is $x=-3$ and the *x*-intercepts occur at 0 and 2, we must determine values in four intervals.

Interval	Test Point	Value of $f(x)$	Sign of $f(x)$	Graph Above or Below *x*-Axis
$(-\infty,-3)$	−4	24	Positive	Above
$(-3,0)$	−1	$\frac{3}{4}$	Positive	Above
$(0,2)$	1	$-\frac{1}{16}$	Negative	Below
$(2,\infty)$	3	$\frac{1}{12}$	Positive	Above

Step 7 Use the asymptotes, intercepts, and these points to sketch the graph.

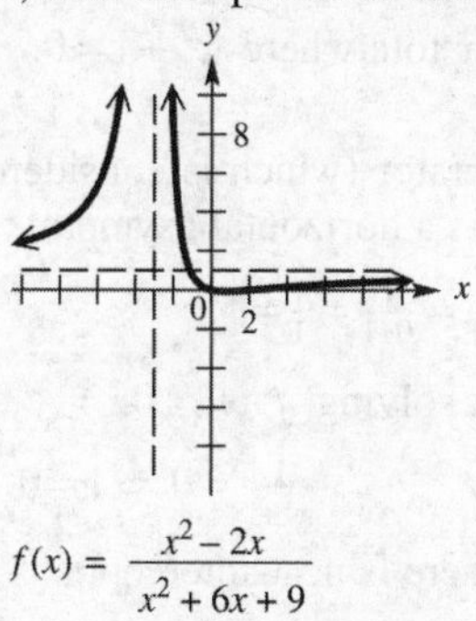

59. $f(x) = \frac{x}{x^2-9} = \frac{x}{(x+3)(x-3)}$

Step 1 The graph has a vertical asymptote where $(x+3)(x-3) = 0$, that is, when $x = -3$ and $x = 3$.

Step 2 Since the degree of the numerator is less than the degree of the denominator, the graph has a horizontal asymptote at $y = 0$ (the x-axis).

Step 3 The y-intercept is $f(0) = \frac{0}{0^2-9} = \frac{0}{0-9} = \frac{0}{-9} = 0.$

Step 4 Any x-intercepts are found by solving $f(x) = 0.$

$$\frac{x}{(x+3)(x-3)} = 0 \Rightarrow x = 0$$

The only x-intercept is 0.

Step 5 The graph will intersect the horizontal asymptote when $\frac{x}{(x+3)(x-3)} = 0.$

$$\frac{x}{(x+3)(x-3)} = 0 \Rightarrow x = 0$$

Step 6 Since the vertical asymptotes are $x = -3$ and $x = 3$ and the x-intercept occurs at 0, we must determine values in four intervals.

Interval	Test Point	Value of $f(x)$	Sign of $f(x)$	Graph Above or Below x-Axis
$(-\infty, -3)$	-4	$-\frac{4}{7}$	Negative	Below
$(-3, 0)$	-2	$\frac{2}{5}$	Positive	Above
$(0, 3)$	2	$-\frac{2}{5}$	Negative	Below
$(3, \infty)$	4	$\frac{4}{7}$	Positive	Above

Step 7 Use the asymptotes, intercepts, and these points to sketch the graph.

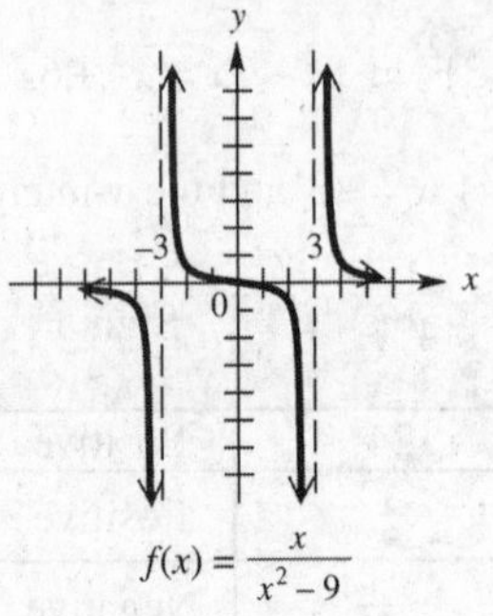

61. $f(x) = \frac{1}{x^2+1}$

Step 1 The graph has a vertical asymptote where $x^2+1 = 0$. Since we have $x^2+1 = 0 \Rightarrow x = \pm i$, there are no vertical asymptotes.

Step 2 Since the degree of the numerator (which is considered degree zero) is less than the degree of the denominator, the graph has a horizontal asymptote at $y = 0$ (the x-axis).

Step 3 The y-intercept is $f(0) = \frac{1}{0^2+1} = \frac{1}{0+1} = \frac{1}{1} = 1.$

Step 4 Any x-intercepts are found by solving $f(x) = 0.$

$$\frac{1}{x^2+1} = 0 \Rightarrow 1 = 0$$

This is a false statement, so there is no x-intercept.

Continued on next page

61. (continued)

Step 5 The graph will intersect the horizontal asymptote when $\frac{1}{x^2+1}=0.$

$$\frac{1}{x^2+1}=0 \Rightarrow 1=0$$

This is a false statement, so the graph does not intersect the horizontal asymptote.

Step 6 Since there are no vertical asymptotes and no x-intercepts, we can see from the y-intercept that the function is always positive and, therefore, above the x-axis. Because of the limited information we have, we should explore symmetry and calculate a few more points on the graph.

x	y
-3	$\frac{1}{10}$
$\frac{1}{2}$	$\frac{4}{5}$
1	$\frac{1}{2}$

Since $f(-x)=\frac{1}{(-x)^2+1}=\frac{1}{x^2+1}=f(x)$, the graph is symmetric about the y-axis.

Step 7 Use the asymptote, y-intercept, these points, and symmetry to sketch the graph.

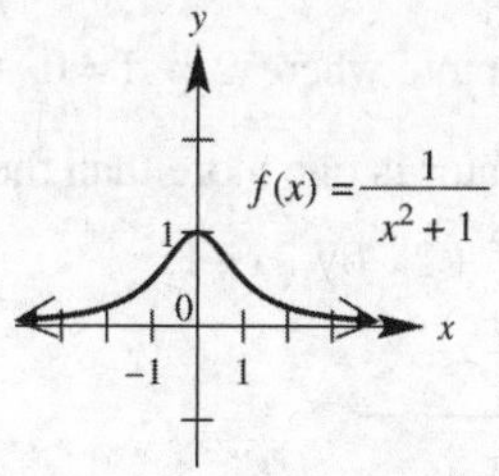

63. $f(x)=\frac{x^2+1}{x+3}$

Step 1 The graph has a vertical asymptote where $x+3=0$, that is, when $x=-3$.

Step 2 Since the degree of the numerator is one more than the degree of the denominator, the graph has an oblique asymptote. Divide x^2+1 by $x+3$.

$$\begin{array}{r|rrr} -3 & 1 & 0 & 1 \\ & & -3 & 9 \\ \hline & 1 & -3 & 10 \end{array}$$

$$f(x)=\frac{x^2+1}{x+3}=x-3+\frac{10}{x+3}$$

The oblique asymptote is the line $y=x-3$.

Step 3 The y-intercept is $f(0)=\frac{0^2+1}{0+3}=\frac{0+1}{3}=\frac{1}{3}.$

Step 4 Any x-intercepts are found by solving $f(x)=0$.

$$\frac{x^2+1}{x+3}=0 \Rightarrow x^2+1=0 \Rightarrow x=\pm i$$

There are no x-intercepts.

Step 5 The graph will intersect the oblique asymptote when $\frac{x^2+1}{x+3}=x-3.$

$$\frac{x^2+1}{x+3}=x-3 \Rightarrow x^2+1=(x+3)(x-3) \Rightarrow x^2+1=x^2-9 \Rightarrow 1=-9$$

This is a false statement, so the graph does not intersect the oblique asymptote.

Continued on next page

63. (continued)

Step 6 Since the vertical asymptote is $x = -3$ and there are no x-intercepts, we must determine values in two intervals.

Interval	Test Point	Value of $f(x)$	Sign of $f(x)$	Graph Above or Below x-Axis
$(-\infty, -3)$	-4	-17	Negative	Below
$(-3, \infty)$	4	$\frac{17}{7}$	Positive	Above

Step 7 Use the asymptotes, y-intercept, and these points to sketch the graph.

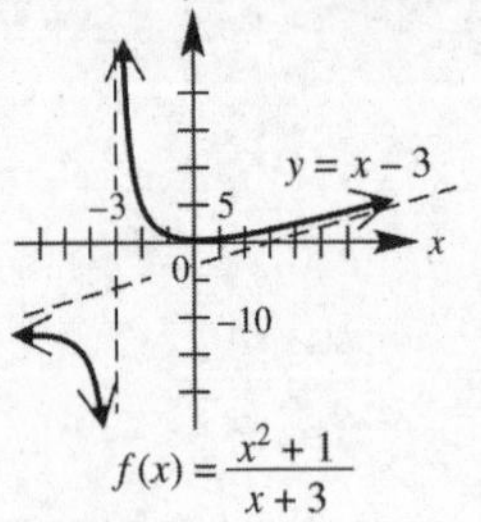

65. $f(x) = \frac{x^2+2x}{2x-1} = \frac{x(x+2)}{2x-1}$

Step 1 The graph has a vertical asymptote where $2x - 1 = 0$, that is, when $x = \frac{1}{2}$.

Step 2 Since the degree of the numerator is one more than the degree of the denominator, $f(x)$ has an oblique asymptote. Divide $x^2 + 2x$ by $2x - 1$.

$$\begin{array}{r} \frac{1}{2}x + \frac{5}{4} \\ 2x-1\overline{)x^2 + 2x} \\ \underline{x^2 - \frac{1}{2}x} \\ \frac{5}{2}x \\ \underline{\frac{5}{2}x - \frac{5}{4}} \\ \frac{5}{4} \end{array}$$

$$f(x) = \frac{x^2+2x}{2x-1} = \frac{1}{2}x + \frac{5}{4} + \frac{\frac{5}{4}}{2x-1}$$

The oblique asymptote is $y = \frac{1}{2}x + \frac{5}{4}$.

Note: Since the denominator is linear, we could also perform synthetic division. However in order to perform synthetic division, we must make the denominator in the form of $x - c$ by multiplying the numerator and denominator by $\frac{1}{2}$ (or dividing numerator and denominator by 2).

Step 3 The y-intercept is $f(0) = \frac{0^2+2(0)}{2(0)-1} = \frac{0+0}{0-1} = \frac{0}{-1} = 0.$

Step 4 Any x-intercepts are found by solving $f(x) = 0$.

$$\frac{x(x+2)}{2x-1} = 0 \Rightarrow x(x+2) = 0$$
$$x = 0 \text{ or } x + 2 = 0$$
$$x = -2$$

Continued on next page

65. (continued)

Step 5 The graph will intersect the oblique asymptote when $\frac{x^2+2x}{2x-1}=\frac{1}{2}x+\frac{5}{4}$.

$$\frac{x^2+2x}{2x-1}=\frac{1}{2}x+\frac{5}{4}\Rightarrow\frac{x^2+2x}{2x-1}=\frac{1}{4}(2x+5)\Rightarrow x^2+2x=\frac{1}{4}(2x-1)(2x+5)$$
$$x^2+2x=\frac{1}{4}(4x^2+8x-5)\Rightarrow x^2+2x=x^2+2x-\frac{5}{4}\Rightarrow 0=-\frac{5}{4}$$

This is a false statement, so the graph does not intersect the oblique asymptote.

Step 6 Since the vertical asymptote is $x=\frac{1}{2}$ and x-intercepts are 0 and −2, we must determine values in four intervals.

Interval	Test Point	Value of $f(x)$	Sign of $f(x)$	Graph Above or Below x-Axis
$(-\infty,-2)$	−3	$-\frac{3}{7}$	Negative	Below
$(-2,0)$	−1	$\frac{1}{3}$	Positive	Above
$(0,\frac{1}{2})$	$\frac{1}{4}$	$-\frac{9}{8}$	Negative	Below
$(\frac{1}{2},\infty)$	1	3	Positive	Above

Step 7 Use the asymptotes, intercepts, and these points to sketch the graph.

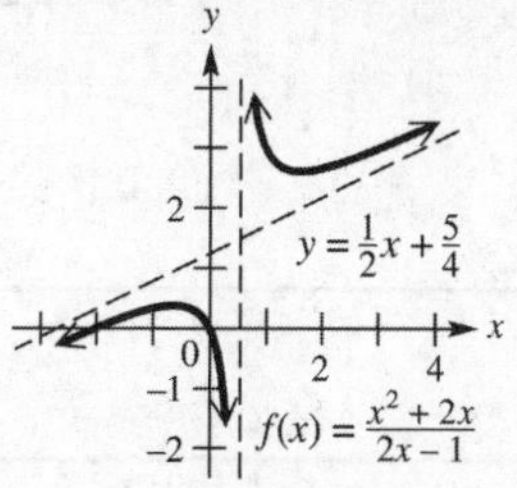

67. $f(x)=\frac{x^2-9}{x+3}$

Since reduction can occur after factoring, $f(x)=\frac{x^2-9}{x+3}=\frac{(x+3)(x-3)}{x+3}=x-3\ (x\neq-3)$, the graph of this function will be the same as the graph of $y=x-3$ (a straight line), with the exception of the point with x-value −3. A "hole" appears in the graph at (−3, −6).

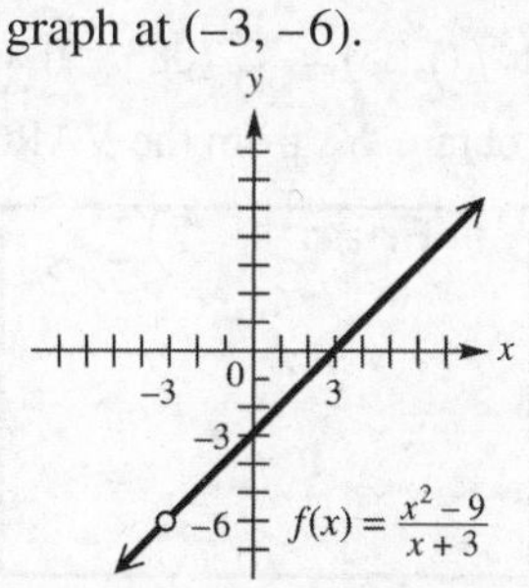

69. The graph has a vertical asymptote, $x=2$, so $x-2$ is the denominator of the function. There is a "hole" in the graph at $x=-2$, so $x+2$ is in the denominator and numerator also. The x-intercept is 3, so that when $f(x)=0$, $x=3$. This condition exists if $x-3$ is a factor of the numerator. Putting these conditions together, we have a possible function $f(x)=\frac{(x-3)(x+2)}{(x-2)(x+2)}$ or $f(x)=\frac{x^2-x-6}{x^2-4}$.

71. The graph has vertical asymptotes at $x = 4$ and $x = 0$, so $x - 4$ and x are factors in the denominator of the function. The only x-intercept is 2, so that when $f(x) = 0$, $x = 2$. This condition exists if $x - 2$ is a factor of the numerator. The graph has a horizontal asymptote $y = 0$, so the degree of the denominator is larger than the degree of the numerator. Putting these conditions together, we have a possible function $f(x) = \frac{x-2}{x(x-4)}$ or $f(x) = \frac{x-2}{x^2-4x}$.

73. Several answers are possible. One answer is $f(x) = \frac{(x-3)(x+1)}{(x-1)^2}$.

75. $f(x) = \frac{x+1}{x-4}$

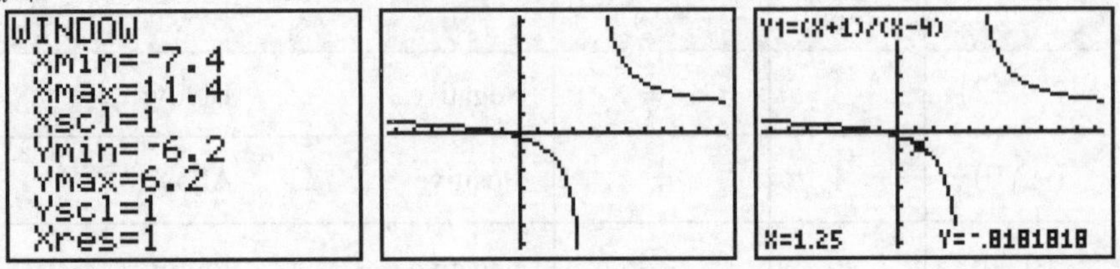

From the last screen we can see that $f(1.25) = -.\overline{81}$. If you wanted the fractional equivalent, you can go back to your homescreen and obtain Y_1 from the VARS menu. Thus $f(1.25) = -\frac{9}{11}$.

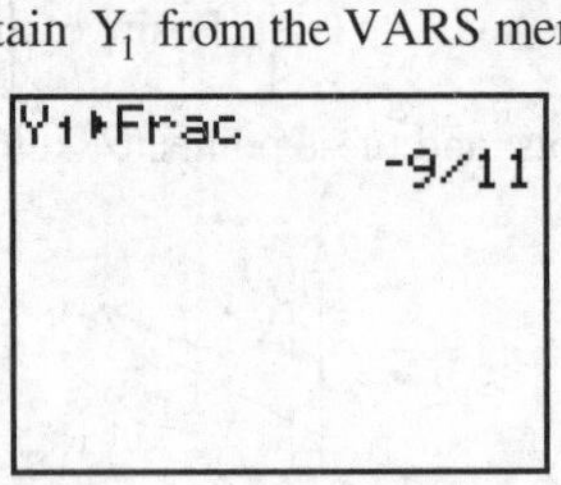

77. $f(x) = \frac{x^2+2x}{2x-1}$

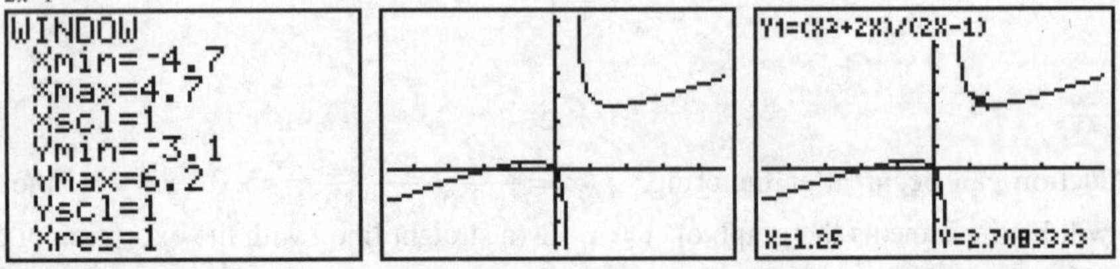

From the last screen we can see that $f(1.25) = -2.708\overline{3}$. If you wanted the fractional equivalent, you can go back to your homescreen and obtain Y_1 from the VARS menu. Thus $f(1.25) = \frac{65}{24}$.

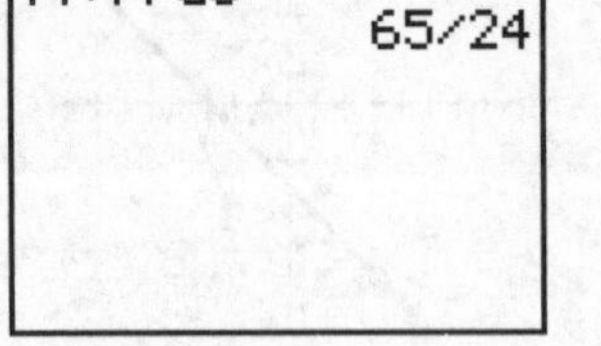

79. (a) $T(r)=\frac{2r-k}{2r^2-2kr}; k-25 \Rightarrow T(r)=\frac{2r-25}{2r^2-2(25)r}=\frac{2r-25}{2r^2-50r}$

Graph $Y_1=\frac{2x-25}{2x^2-50x}$ and $Y_2=.5$ (since 30 sec = .5 min) on the same screen.

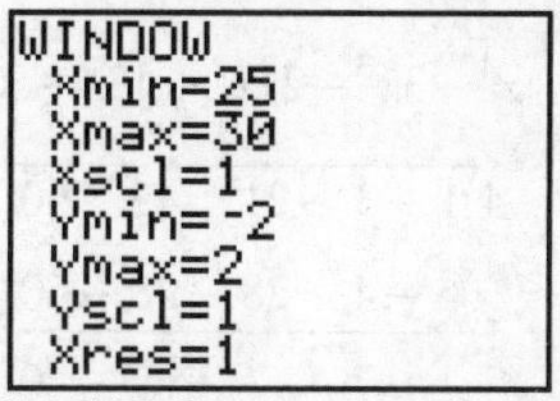

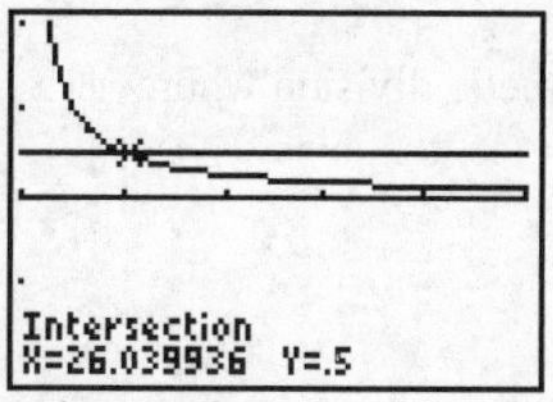

Using the "intersect" option in the CALC menu, we find that the graphs intersect at $x \approx 26$, which represents $r \approx 26$ in the given function. Therefore, there must be an average admittance rate of 26 vehicles per minute.

(b) $\frac{26}{5.3} \approx 4.9$ or 5 parking attendants must be on duty to keep the wait less than 30 seconds.

81. (a) Graph $y=d(x)=\frac{8710x^2-69{,}400x+470{,}000}{1.08x^2-324x+82{,}200}$ and $y=300$ on the same calculator screen.

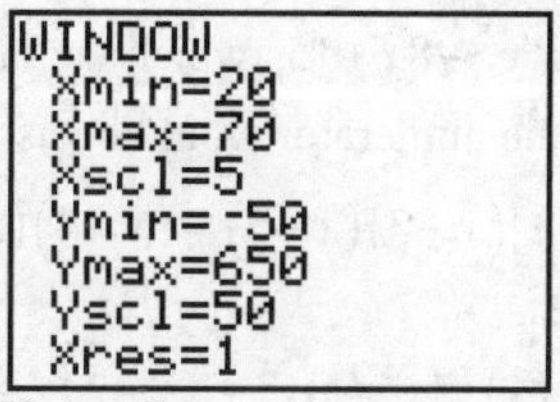

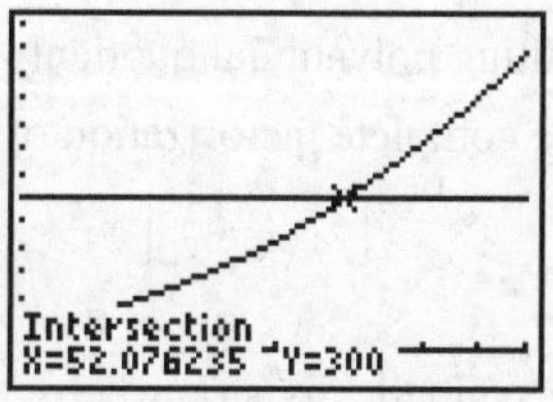

The graphs intersect when $x \approx 52.1$ miles per hour.

(b)

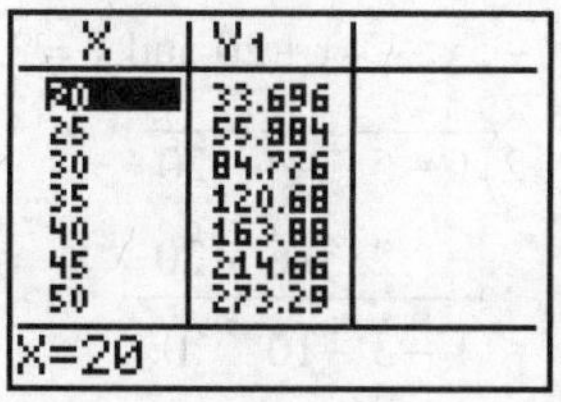

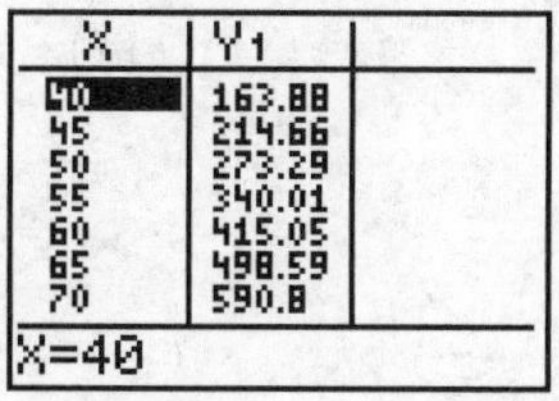

x	$d(x)$	x	$d(x)$
20	**34**	50	**273**
25	**56**	55	**340**
30	**85**	60	**415**
35	**121**	65	**499**
40	**164**	70	**591**
45	**215**		

(c) By comparing values in the table generated in part b, it appears that when the speed is doubled, the stopping distance is more than doubled.

(d) If the stopping distance doubled whenever the speed doubled, then there would be a linear relationship between the speed and the stopping distance.

83. $R(x)=\frac{80x-8000}{x-110}$

(a) $x=55 \Rightarrow R(55)=\frac{80(55)-8000}{55-110} \approx \$65.5$ tens of millions

(b) $x=60 \Rightarrow R(60)=\frac{80(60)-8000}{60-110}=\$64$ tens of millions

(c) $x=70 \Rightarrow R(70)=\frac{80(70)-8000}{70-110}=\$60$ tens of millions

(d) $x=90 \Rightarrow R(90)=\frac{80(90)-8000}{90-110}=\$40$ tens of millions

(e) $x=100 \Rightarrow R(100)=\frac{80(100)-8000}{100-110}=\$0$

(f)

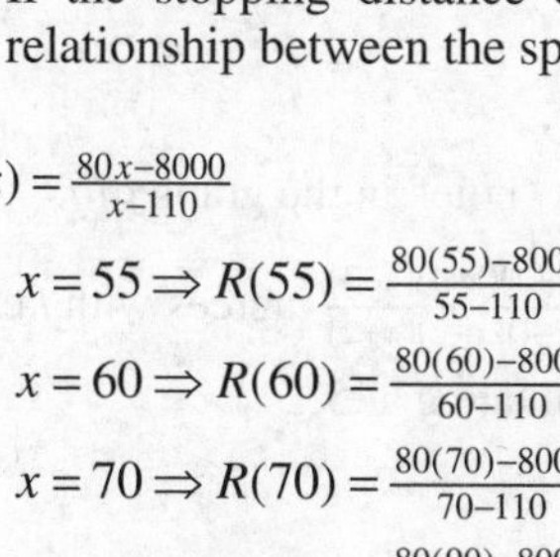

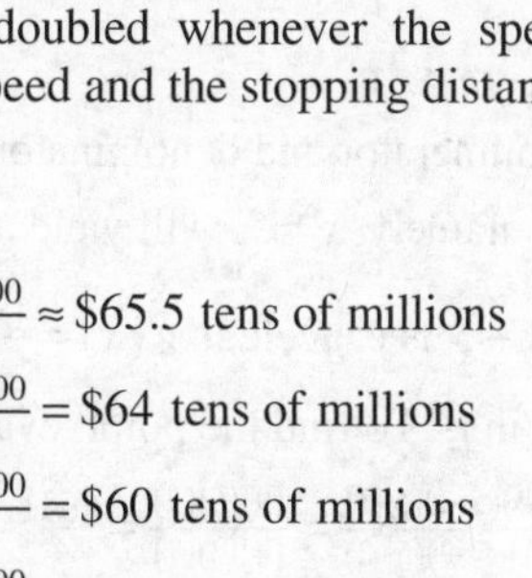

85. Since the degree of the numerator equals the degree of the denominator in $f(x)=\frac{x^4-3x^3-21x^2+43x+60}{x^4-6x^3+x^2+24x-20}$, the graph has a horizontal asymptote at $y=\frac{1}{1}=1$.

86. Use synthetic division where $g(x)=x^4-3x^3-21x^2+43x+60$ and $k=-4$.

$$\begin{array}{r|rrrrr} -4 & 1 & -3 & -21 & 43 & 60 \\ & & -4 & 28 & -28 & -60 \\ \hline & 1 & -7 & 7 & 15 & 0 \end{array}$$

Now use synthetic division where $h(x)=x^3-7x^2+7x+15$ and $k=-1$.

$$\begin{array}{r|rrrr} -1 & 1 & -7 & 7 & 15 \\ & & -1 & 8 & -15 \\ \hline & 1 & -8 & 15 & 0 \end{array}$$

The resulting polynomial quotient is $x^2-8x+15$, which factors to $(x-3)(x-5)$. Thus, the complete factorization of the numerator would be as follows.

$$[x-(-4)][x-(-1)](x-3)(x-5)=(x+4)(x+1)(x-3)(x-5)$$

87. (a) Use synthetic division where $g(x)=x^4-6x^3+x^2+24x-20$ and $k=1$.

$$\begin{array}{r|rrrrr} 1 & 1 & -6 & 1 & 24 & -20 \\ & & 1 & -5 & -4 & 20 \\ \hline & 1 & -5 & -4 & 20 & 0 \end{array}$$

Now use synthetic division where $h(x)=x^3-5x^2-4x+20$ and $k=2$.

$$\begin{array}{r|rrrr} 2 & 1 & -5 & -4 & 20 \\ & & 2 & -6 & -20 \\ \hline & 1 & -3 & -10 & 0 \end{array}$$

The resulting polynomial quotient is $x^2-3x-10$, which factors to $(x+2)(x-5)$. Thus, the complete factorization of the denominator would be $(x-1)(x-2)(x+2)(x-5)$.

(b) $f(x)=\frac{(x+4)(x+1)(x-3)(x-5)}{(x-1)(x-2)(x+2)(x-5)}$

88. (a) $x-5$ is common factor to both the numerator and denominator.

(b) The value of x that makes $x-5=0$, namely $x=5$, will yield a "hole" in the graph of *f*.

Note: When the common factor of $x-5$ is canceled, $g(x)=\frac{(x+4)(x+1)(x-3)}{(x-1)(x-2)(x+2)}$ agrees with *f* except at one point, which is the "hole" in *f*. To find the point, evaluate *g* at 5.

$$g(5)=\frac{(5+4)(5+1)(5-3)}{(5-1)(5-2)(5+2)}=\frac{(9)(6)(2)}{(4)(3)(7)}=\frac{108}{84}=\frac{9}{7}$$

89. Although $x-5$ is a factor of the numerator, it will not yield an *x*-intercept because it is also a factor of the denominator. The other three factors of the numerator (namely $(x+4)$, $(x+1)$, and $(x-3)$) will yield *x*-intercepts of -4, -1, and 3 because any of these will yield $f(x)=0$.

90. The *y*-intercept occurs at $f(0)=\frac{0^4-3(0^3)-21(0^2)+43(0)+60}{0^4-6(0^3)+0^2+24(0)-20}=\frac{60}{-20}=-3$.

91. Although $x-5$ is a factor of the denominator, it will not yield a vertical asymptote because it is also a factor of the numerator. The other three factors of the denominator $\left(\text{namely } (x-1), (x-2), \text{ and } (x+2)\right)$ will yield vertical asymptotes of $x=1$, $x=2$, and $x=-2$ because any of these will yield a denominator of zero.

92. To determine where the function intersects the horizontal asymptote, we must solve the equation $\frac{x^4-3x^3-21x^2+43x+60}{x^4-6x^3+x^2+24x-20}=1$. However, since we know that the numerator and denominator have a common factor of $x-5$, it would be easier to solve the equation $\frac{(x+4)(x+1)(x-3)}{(x-1)(x-2)(x+2)}=1$.

$$\frac{(x+4)(x+1)(x-3)}{(x-1)(x-2)(x+2)}=1 \Rightarrow \frac{x^3+2x^2-11x-12}{x^3-x^2-4x+4}=1 \Rightarrow x^3+2x^2-11x-12=x^3-x^2-4x+4 \Rightarrow 3x^2-7x-16=0$$

Solve for x using the quadratic formula where $a=3$, $b=-7$, and $c=-16$.

$$x=\frac{-(-7)\pm\sqrt{(-7)^2-4(3)(-16)}}{2(3)}=\frac{7\pm\sqrt{49+192}}{6}=\frac{7\pm\sqrt{241}}{6} \Rightarrow x=\frac{7-\sqrt{241}}{6}\approx -1.42 \text{ or } x=\frac{7+\sqrt{241}}{6}\approx 3.75$$

Thus the points of intersection are $\left(\frac{7-\sqrt{241}}{6},1\right)$ and $\left(\frac{7+\sqrt{241}}{6},1\right)$.

93. The vertical asymptotes are $x=1$, $x=2$, and $x=-2$ and the x-intercepts occur at -4, -1, and 3. We should also consider the "hole" in the graph which occurs at $x=5$. This divides the real number line into eight intervals.

Interval	Test Point	Value of $f(x)$	Sign of $f(x)$	Graph Above or Below x-Axis
$(-\infty,-4)$	-5	$\frac{16}{63}$	Positive	Above
$(-4,-2)$	-3	$-\frac{3}{5}$	Negative	Below
$(-2,-1)$	$-\frac{3}{2}$	$\frac{9}{7}$	Positive	Above
$(-1,1)$	0	-3	Negative	Below
$(1,2)$	$\frac{3}{2}$	$\frac{165}{7}$	Positive	Above
$(2,3)$	$\frac{5}{2}$	$-\frac{91}{27}$	Negative	Below
$(3,5)$	4	$\frac{10}{9}$	Positive	Above
$(5,\infty)$	6	$\frac{21}{16}$	Positive	Above

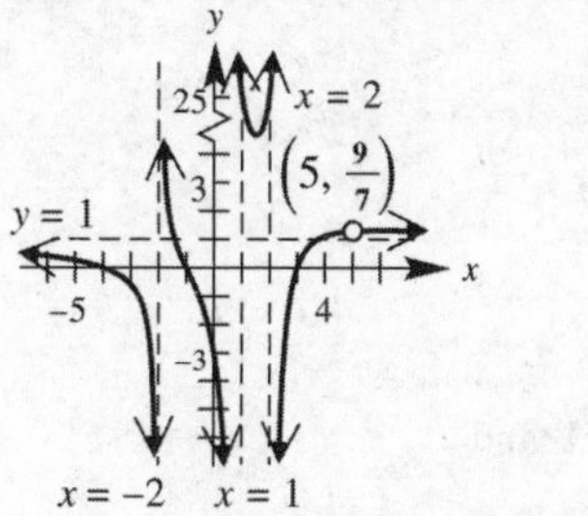

$$f(x)=\frac{x^4-3x^3-21x^2+43x+60}{x^4-6x^3+x^2+24x-20}$$

94. **(a)** $(-4,-2)\cup(-1,1)\cup(2,3)$

(b) $(-\infty,-4)\cup(-2,-1)\cup(1,2)\cup(3,5)\cup(5,\infty)$

Section 3.6: Variation

1. $C = 2\pi r$, where C is the circumference of a circle of radius r

   The circumference of a circle varies directly as (or is proportional to) its radius.

3. $v = \frac{d}{t}$, where v is the average speed when traveling d miles in t hours

   The average speed varies directly as (or is proportional to) the distance traveled and inversely as the time.

5. $s = kx^3$, where s is the strength of a muscle of length x

   The strength of a muscle varies directly as (or is proportional to) the cube of its length.

7. y varies directly as x, $y = kx$, is a straight-line model. It matches graph C.

9. y varies directly as the second power of x, $y = kx^2$, matches graph A.

11. *Step 1* $y = kx$

    Step 2 Substitute $x = 2$ & $y = 10$ to find k.

    $$10 = k(2)$$
    $$k = 5$$

    Step 3 $y = 5x$

    Step 4 Now find y when $x = -6$.

    $$y = 5(-6) = -30$$

13. *Step 1* $m = kxy$

    Step 2 Substitute $m = 10$, $x = 4$, and $y = 7$ to find k.

    $$10 = k(4)(7)$$
    $$10 = 28k$$
    $$k = \frac{5}{14}$$

    Step 3 $m = \frac{5}{14}xy$

    Step 4 Now find m when $x = 11$ and $y = 8$.

    $$m = \frac{5}{14}(11)(8) = \frac{440}{14} = \frac{220}{7}$$

15. *Step 1* $y = \frac{k}{x}$

    Step 2 Substitute $x = 3$ & $y = 10$ to find k.

    $$10 = \frac{k}{3}$$
    $$k = 30$$

    Step 3 $y = \frac{30}{x}$

    Step 4 Now find y when $x = 12$.

    $$y = \frac{30}{12} = \frac{5}{2}$$

17. *Step 1* $r = \frac{km^2}{s}$

    Step 2 Substitute $r = 12$, $m = 6$, and $s = 4$ to find k.

    $$12 = \frac{k \cdot 6^2}{4} \Rightarrow 12 = \frac{36k}{4}$$
    $$12 = 9k \Rightarrow k = \frac{4}{3}$$

    Step 3 $r = \frac{4}{3} \cdot \frac{m^2}{s} = \frac{4m^2}{3s}$

    Step 4 Now find r when $m = 4$ & $s = 10$.

    $$r = \frac{4(4^2)}{3(10)} = \frac{4(16)}{30} = \frac{64}{30} = \frac{32}{15}$$

19. *Step 1* $a = \frac{kmn^2}{y^3}$

    Step 2 Substitute $a = 9$, $m = 4$, $n = 9$, and $y = 3$ to find k.

    $$9 = \frac{k(4)(9^2)}{3^3} \Rightarrow 9 = \frac{k(4)(81)}{27}$$
    $$9 = \frac{324k}{27} \Rightarrow 9 = 12k$$
    $$k = \frac{3}{4}$$

    Step 3 $a = \frac{3}{4} \cdot \frac{mn^2}{y^3} = \frac{3mn^2}{4y^3}$

    Step 4 Now find a when $m = 6$, $n = 2$, and $y = 5$.

    $$a = \frac{3(6)(2^2)}{4(5^3)} = \frac{3(6)(4)}{4(125)} = \frac{18}{125}$$

21. *Step 1* Let C be the circumference of the circle (in inches).
r is the radius of the circle (in inches).

$$C = kr$$

Step 2 Substitute $C = 43.96$ and $r = 7$ to find k.

$$43.96 = k(7)$$
$$k = 6.28$$

Step 3 $C = 6.28r$

Step 4 Now find C when $r = 11$.

$$C = 6.28(11) = 69.08$$

A radius of 11 in. yields a circumference of 69.08 in.

23. *Step 1* Let R be the resistance (in ohms).
t is the temperature (in degrees Kelvin, K).

$$R = kt$$

Step 2 Substitute $R = 646$ and $t = 190$ to find k.

$$646 = k(190)$$
$$k = \tfrac{646}{190} = \tfrac{17}{5}$$

Step 3 $R = \tfrac{17}{5}t$

Step 4 Now find R when $t = 250$.

$$R = \tfrac{17}{5}(250) = 850$$

A resistance of 850 ohms occurs at 250K.

25. *Step 1* Let e be weight on earth (in lbs).
m is weight on moon (in lbs).

$$e = km$$

Step 2 Substitute $e = 200$ and $m = 32$ to find k.

$$200 = k(32)$$
$$k = \tfrac{200}{32} = 6.25$$

Step 3 $e = 6.25m$

Step 4 Now find m when $e = 50$.

$$60 = 6.25m$$
$$m = \tfrac{50}{6.25} = 8$$

The dog would weigh 8 lbs on the moon.

27. *Step 1* Let d be the distance the spring stretches (in inches).
f is the force applied (in lbs).

$$d = kf$$

Step 2 Substitute $d = 8$ & $f = 15$ to find k.

$$8 = k(15)$$
$$k = \tfrac{8}{15}$$

Step 3 $d = \tfrac{8}{15}f$

Step 4 Now find d when $f = 30$.

$$d = \tfrac{8}{15}(30) = 16$$

The spring will stretch 16 in.

29. *Step 1* Let v be the speed of the pulley (in rpm).
D is the diameter of the pulley (in inches).

$$v = \tfrac{k}{D}$$

Step 2 Substitute $v = 150$ and $D = 3$ to find k.

$$150 = \tfrac{k}{3}$$
$$k = 450$$

Step 3 $v = \tfrac{450}{d}$

Step 4 Now find v when $D = 5$.

$$v = \tfrac{450}{5} = 90$$

The 5-in. diameter pulley will have a speed of 90 revolutions per minute.

31. *Step 1* Let R be the resistance (in ohms).
D be the diameter (in inches).

$$R = \tfrac{k}{D^2}$$

Step 2 Substitute $D = .01$ and $R = .4$ to find k.

$$.4 = \tfrac{k}{.01^2}$$
$$.4 = \tfrac{k}{.0001}$$
$$k = .00004$$

Step 3 $R = \tfrac{.00004}{D^2}$

Step 4 Now find R when $D = .03$.

$$R = \tfrac{.00004}{.03^2} = \tfrac{.00004}{.0009} \approx .0444$$

The resistance is approximately .0444 ohm.

33. *Step 1* Let i be the interest (in dollars). p is the principal (in dollars). t is the time (in years).

$$i = kpt$$

Step 2 Substitute $i = 110$, $p = 1000$, and $t = 2$ to find k.

$$110 = k(1000)(2)$$
$$110 = 2000k$$
$$k = \frac{110}{2000} = .055\ (5.5\%)$$

Step 3 $i = .055pt$

Step 4 Now find i when $p = 5000$ and $t = 5$.

$$i = .055(5000)(5) = 1375$$

The amount of interest is \$1375.

35. *Step 1* Let F be the force of the wind (in lbs). A is the area (in ft^2). v is the velocity of the wind (in mph).

$$F = kAv^2$$

Step 2 Substitute $F = 50$, $A = \frac{1}{2}$, and $v = 40$ to find k.

$$50 = k\left(\tfrac{1}{2}\right)\left(40^2\right)$$
$$50 = k\left(\tfrac{1}{2}\right)(1600)$$
$$50 = 800k$$
$$k = \frac{50}{800} = \frac{1}{16}$$

Step 3 $F = \frac{1}{16}Av^2$

Step 4 Now find F when $v = 80$, and $A = 2$.

$$F = \tfrac{1}{16}(2)\left(80^2\right)$$
$$F = \tfrac{1}{16}(2)(6400) = 800$$

The force would be 800 pounds.

37. *Step 1* Let L be the load (in metric tons). D is the diameter (in meters). h is the height (in meters).

$$L = \frac{kD^4}{h^2}$$

Step 2 Substitute $h = 9$, $D = 1$, and $L = 8$ to find k.

$$8 = \frac{k\left(1^4\right)}{9^2}$$
$$8 = \frac{k}{81}$$
$$k = 648$$

Step 3 $L = \frac{648D^4}{h^2}$

Step 4 Now find L when $D = \frac{2}{3}$ and $h = 12$.

$$L = \frac{648\left(\frac{2}{3}\right)^4}{12^2}$$
$$L = \frac{648\left(\frac{16}{81}\right)}{144}$$
$$L = \frac{128}{144} = \frac{8}{9}$$

A column 12 m high and $\frac{2}{3}$ m in diameter will support $\frac{8}{9}$ metric ton.

39. *Step 1* Let p be the period of pendulum (in sec). l is the length of pendulum (in cm). a is the acceleration due to gravity $\left(\text{in } \frac{\text{cm}}{\text{sec}^2}\right)$.

$$p = \frac{k\sqrt{l}}{\sqrt{a}}$$

Step 2 Substitute $p = 6\pi$, $l = 289$, and $a = 980$ to find k.

$$6\pi = \frac{k\sqrt{289}}{\sqrt{980}}$$
$$6\pi = \frac{17k}{14\sqrt{5}}$$
$$84\sqrt{5}\pi = 17k$$
$$k = \frac{84\sqrt{5}\pi}{17}$$

Step 3 $p = \frac{84\sqrt{5}\pi}{17} \cdot \frac{\sqrt{l}}{\sqrt{a}} = \frac{84\sqrt{5}\pi\sqrt{l}}{17\sqrt{a}}$

Step 4 Now find p when $l = 121$ and $a = 980$.

$$p = \frac{84\pi\sqrt{5}\sqrt{121}}{17\sqrt{980}}$$
$$p = \frac{84\pi\sqrt{5}(11)}{17\left(14\sqrt{5}\right)} = \frac{924\pi\sqrt{5}}{238\sqrt{5}} = \frac{66\pi}{17}$$

The period is $\frac{66\pi}{17}$ sec.

41. *Step 1* Let B be the BMI. w is the weight (in lbs). h is the height (in inches).

$$B = \frac{kw}{h^2}$$

Step 2 Substitute $w = 177$, $B = 24$, and $h = 72$ (6 feet) to find k.

$$24 = \frac{k(177)}{72^2}$$

$$24 = \frac{177k}{5184}$$

$$124,416 = 177k$$

$$k = \frac{124,416}{177} = \frac{41,472}{59}$$

Step 3 $B = \frac{41,472}{59} \cdot \frac{w}{h^2} = \frac{41,472w}{59h^2}$

Step 4 Now find B when $w = 130$ and $h = 66$.

$$B = \frac{41,472(130)}{59(66^2)}$$

$$B = \frac{5,391,360}{59(4356)}$$

$$B = \frac{5,391,360}{257,004} \approx 20.98$$

The BMI would be approximately 21.

43. *Step 1* Let R be the radiation. t is the temperature (in degrees Kelvin, K).

$$R = kt^4$$

Step 2 Substitute $R = 213.73$ and $t = 293$ to find k.

$$213.73 = k(293^4)$$

$$k = \frac{213.73}{293^4} \approx 2.9 \times 10^{-8}$$

Step 3 $R = (2.9 \times 10^{-8})t^4$

Step 4 Now find R when $t = 335$.

$$R = (2.9 \times 10^{-8}) \cdot 335^4 \approx 365.24$$

The radiation of heat would be 365.24.

45. *Step 1* Let p be the person's pelidisi. w is the person's weight (in g). h is the person's sitting height (in cm).

$$p = \frac{k\sqrt[3]{w}}{h}$$

Step 2 Substitute $w = 48,820$, $h = 78.7$, and $p = 100$ to find k.

$$100 = \frac{k\sqrt[3]{48,820}}{78.7}$$

$$7870 = \sqrt[3]{48,820}k$$

$$k = \frac{7870}{\sqrt[3]{48,820}}$$

$$k \approx 215.33$$

Step 3 $p = \frac{215.33\sqrt[3]{w}}{h}$

Step 4 Now find p when $w = 54,430$ and $h = 88.9$.

$$p = \frac{215.33\sqrt[3]{54,430}}{88.9} \approx 92$$

This person's pelidisi is 92. The individual is undernourished since his pelidisi is below 100.

47. For $k > 0$, if y varies directly as x, when x increases, y <u>increases</u>, and when x decreases, y <u>decreases</u>.

49. $y = \frac{k}{x}$

If x is doubled, then $y_1 = \frac{k}{2x} = \frac{1}{2} \cdot \frac{k}{x} = \frac{1}{2}y$. Thus, y is half as large as it was before.

51. $y = kx$

If x is replaced by $\frac{1}{3}x$, then we have $y_1 = k\left(\frac{1}{3}x\right) = \frac{1}{3} \cdot kx = \frac{1}{3}y$. Thus, y is one-third as large as it was before.

53. $p = \frac{kr^3}{t^2}$

If r is replaced by $\frac{1}{2}r$ and t is replaced by $2t$, then we have the following.

$$p_1 = \frac{k\left(\frac{1}{2}r\right)^3}{(2t)^2} = \frac{k\left(\frac{1}{8}r^3\right)}{4t^2} = \frac{1}{8} \cdot \frac{kr^3}{4t^2} = \frac{kr^3}{32t^2} = \frac{1}{32} \cdot \frac{kr^3}{t^2}$$

Thus, so p is $\frac{1}{32}$ as large as it was before.

Chapter 3: Review Exercises

1. $f(x)=3(x+4)^2-5$

Since $f(x)=3(x+4)^2-5=3[x-(-4)]^2+(-5)$, the function has the form $f(x)=a(x-h)^2+k$ with $a=3$, $h=-4$, and $k=-5$. The graph is a parabola that opens upward with vertex $(h,k)=(-4,-5)$. The axis is $x=h \Rightarrow x=-4$. To find the x-intercepts, let $f(x)=0$.

$3(x+4)^2-5=0 \Rightarrow 3(x+4)^2=5 \Rightarrow (x+4)^2=\frac{5}{3} \Rightarrow x+4=\pm\sqrt{\frac{5}{3}} \Rightarrow x=-4\pm\sqrt{\frac{5}{3}}=-4\pm\frac{\sqrt{15}}{3}=\frac{-12\pm\sqrt{15}}{3}$

Thus, the x-intercepts are $\frac{-12\pm\sqrt{15}}{3}$ or approximately –5.3 and –2.7. To find the y-intercept, let $x=0$.

$$f(0)=3(0+4)^2-5=3(16)-5=48-5=43$$

The y-intercept is 43.

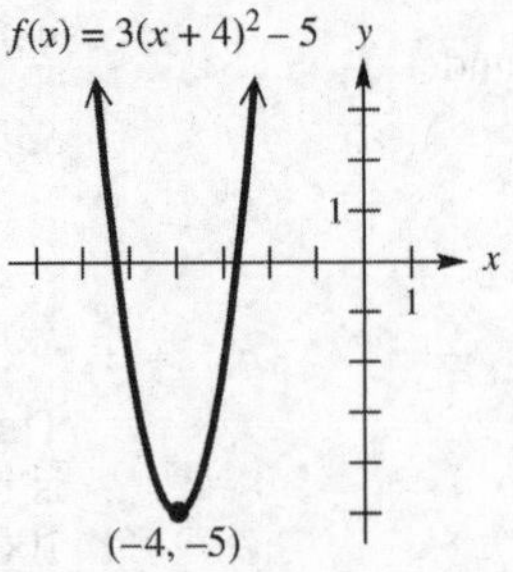

The domain is $(-\infty,\infty)$. Since the lowest point on the graph is $(-4,-5)$, the range is $[-5,\infty)$.

3. $f(x)=-3x^2-12x-1$

Complete the square so the function has the form $f(x)=a(x-h)^2+k$.

$$f(x)=-3x^2-12x-1=-3(x^2+4x)-1=-3(x^2+4x+4-4)-1$$
$$f(x)=-3(x+2)^2+12-1=-3[x-(-2)]^2+11$$

This parabola is in now in standard form with $a=-3$, $h=-2$, and $k=11$. It opens downward with vertex $(h,k)=(-2,11)$. The axis is $x=h \Rightarrow x=-2$. To find the x-intercepts, let $f(x)=0$.

$$-3(x+2)^2+11=0 \Rightarrow -3(x+2)^2=-11 \Rightarrow (x+2)^2=\frac{11}{3} \Rightarrow x+2=\pm\sqrt{\frac{11}{3}}$$
$$x=-2\pm\sqrt{\frac{11}{3}}=-2\pm\frac{\sqrt{33}}{3}=\frac{-6\pm\sqrt{33}}{3}$$

Thus, the x-intercepts are $\frac{-6\pm\sqrt{33}}{3}$ or approximately -3.9 and $-.1$. To find the y-intercept, let $x=0$.

$$f(0)=-3(0^2)-12(0)-1=-1$$

The y-intercept is -1.

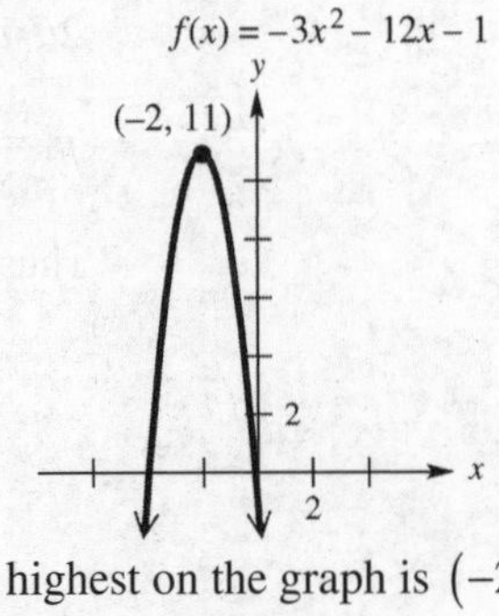

The domain is $(-\infty,\infty)$. Since the highest on the graph is $(-2,11)$, the range is $(-\infty,11]$.

5. $f(x)=a(x-h)^2+k;\ a>0$

The graph is a parabola that opens upward. The coordinates of the lowest point of the graph are represented by the vertex, (h, k).

7. For the graph to have one or more x-intercepts, $f(x)=0$ must have real number solutions.

$$a(x-h)^2+k=0 \Rightarrow a(x-h)^2=-k \Rightarrow (x-h)^2=\tfrac{-k}{a} \Rightarrow x-h=\pm\sqrt{\tfrac{-k}{a}} \Rightarrow x=h\pm\sqrt{\tfrac{-k}{a}}$$

These solutions are real only if $\frac{-k}{a}\ge 0$. Since a > 0, this condition is equivalent to $-k\ge 0$ or $k\le 0$.

The x-intercepts for these conditions are given by $h\pm\sqrt{\frac{-k}{a}}$.

9. Let x = the width of the rectangular region.
$180-2x$ = the length of the region.

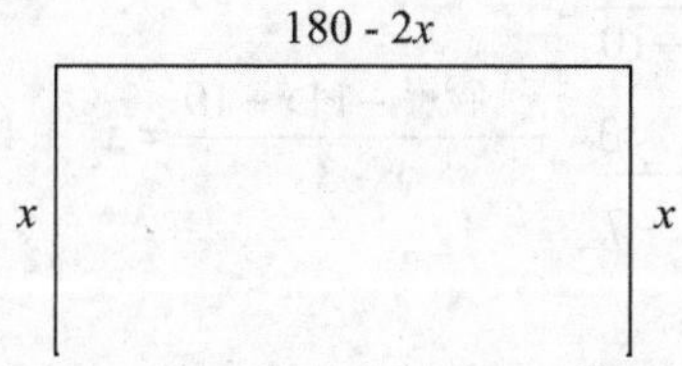

Since $A=LW$, we have $A(x)=(180-2x)x=-2x^2+180x$. Since the graph of $A(x)$ is a parabola that opens downward, the maximum area is the y-coordinate of the vertex.

$$A(x)=-2x^2+180x=-2(x^2-90x)=-2(x^2-90x+2025)+4050=-2(x-45)^2+4050$$

The x-coordinate of the vertex, $x=45$, is the width that gives the maximum area. The length will be $L=180-2(45)=90$. Thus, the dimensions of the region are 90 m × 45 m.

11. Because $V(x)$ has different equations on two different intervals, it is a piecewise-defined function.

$$V(x)=\begin{cases}2x^2-32x+150 & \text{if } 1\le x<8\\ 31x-226 & \text{if } 8\le x\le 12\end{cases}$$

Note: Since $2\cdot 8^2-32\cdot 8+150=22$ and $31\cdot 8-226=22$, the point (8, 22) can be found using either rule, and the graph will have no breaks.

(a) In January, $x=1$.
$V(x)=2x^2-32x+150$
$V(1)=2(1)^2-32(1)+150=120$

(b) In May, $x=5$.
$V(x)=2x^2-32x+150$
$V(5)=2(5)^2-32(5)+150=40$

(c) In August, $x=8$.
$V(x)=31x-226$
$V(8)=31(8)-226=22$

(d) In October, $x=10$.
$V(x)=31x-226$
$V(10)=31(10)-226=84$

(e) In December, $x=12$.
$V(x)=31x-226$
$V(12)=31(12)-226=146$

(f)

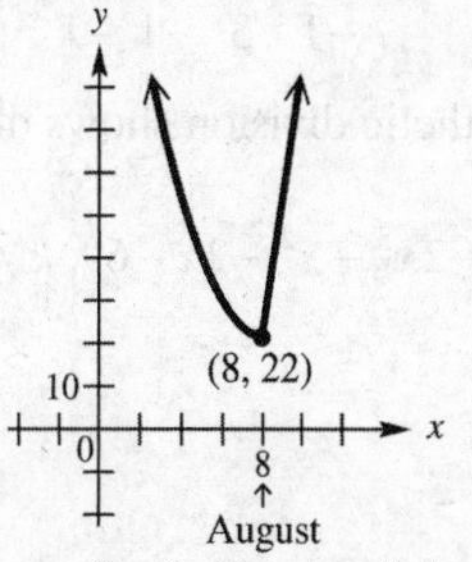

The graph shows a minimum point at (8, 22). Thus, in August $(x=8)$ the fewest volunteers are available.

13. $f(x) = -2.64x^2 + 5.47x + 3.54$

The discriminant is $b^2 - 4ac$ in the standard quadratic equation $y = ax^2 + bx + c$. Here we have $a = -2.64$, $b = 5.47$, and $c = 3.54$. Thus, $b^2 - 4ac = (5.47)^2 - 4(-2.64)(3.54) = 67.3033$. Because the discriminant is 67.3033, a positive number, there are two x-intercepts.

15. (a) $f(x) > 0$ on the open interval $(-.52, 2.59)$.

(b) $f(x) < 0$ on $(-\infty, -.52) \cup (2.59, \infty)$.

17. $\dfrac{x^3 + x^2 - 11x - 10}{x - 3}$

Since $x - 3$ is in the form $x - k$, $k = 3$.

$$\begin{array}{r|rrrr} 3 & 1 & 1 & -11 & -10 \\ & & 3 & 12 & 3 \\ \hline & 1 & 4 & 1 & -7 \end{array} \qquad \frac{x^3 + x^2 - 11x - 10}{x - 3} = x^2 + 4x + 1 + \frac{-7}{x - 3}$$

19. $\dfrac{2x^3 - x + 6}{x + 4}$

Express $x + 4$ in the form $x - k$ by writing it as $x - (-4)$. Thus we have $k = -4$. Since the x^2 – term is missing, include a 0 as its coefficient.

$$\begin{array}{r|rrrr} -4 & 2 & 0 & -1 & 6 \\ & & -8 & 32 & -124 \\ \hline & 2 & -8 & 31 & -118 \end{array} \qquad \frac{2x^3 - x + 6}{x + 4} = 2x^2 - 8x + 31 + \frac{-118}{x + 4}$$

21. $f(x) = 5x^3 - 3x^2 + 2x - 6$; $k = 2$

Use synthetic division to write the polynomial in the form $f(x) = (x - k)q(x) + r$.

$$\begin{array}{r|rrrr} 2 & 5 & -3 & 2 & -6 \\ & & 10 & 14 & 32 \\ \hline & 5 & 7 & 16 & 26 \end{array} \qquad f(x) = (x - 2)(5x^2 + 7x + 16) + 26$$

23. $f(x) = -x^3 + 5x^2 - 7x + 1$; find $f(2)$.

$$\begin{array}{r|rrrr} 2 & -1 & 5 & -7 & 1 \\ & & -2 & 6 & -2 \\ \hline & -1 & 3 & -1 & -1 \end{array}$$

The synthetic division shows that $f(2) = -1$.

25. $f(x) = 5x^4 - 12x^2 + 2x - 8$; find $f(2)$.

$$\begin{array}{r|rrrrr} 2 & 5 & 0 & -12 & 2 & -8 \\ & & 10 & 20 & 16 & 36 \\ \hline & 5 & 10 & 8 & 18 & 28 \end{array}$$

The synthetic division shows that $f(2) = 28$.

27. $f(x) = -2x^3 + x^2 - 2x - 69$; $k = -3$

$$\begin{array}{r|rrrr} -3 & -2 & 1 & -2 & -69 \\ & & 6 & -21 & 69 \\ \hline & -2 & 7 & -23 & 0 \end{array}$$

Since $f(-3) = 0$, we have that -3 is a zero of the function.

29. By the conjugate zeros theorem, $7 - 2i$ is also a zero.

In Exercises 31 through 33, other answers are possible.

31. Zeros: –1, 4, 7

$$f(x)=[x-(-1)](x-4)(x-7)=(x+1)(x-4)(x-7)=(x+1)[(x-4)(x-7)]$$
$$=(x+1)(x^2-11x+28)=x^3-10x^2+17x+28$$

33. Zeros: $\sqrt{3}, -\sqrt{3}$, 2, 3.

$$f(x)=(x-\sqrt{3})(x+\sqrt{3})(x-2)(x-3)=[(x-\sqrt{3})(x+\sqrt{3})][(x-2)(x-3)]$$
$$=(x^2-3)(x^2-5x+6)=x^4-5x^3+3x^2+15x-18$$

35. $f(x)=2x^3-9x^2-6x+5$

p must be a factor of $a_0=5$ and q must be a factor of $a_3=2$. Thus, p can be $\pm1, \pm5$, and q can be $\pm1, \pm2$. The possible zeros, $\frac{p}{q}$, are $\pm1, \pm5, \pm\frac{1}{2}, \pm\frac{5}{2}$. The remainder theorem shows that $\frac{1}{2}$ is a zero.

$$\begin{array}{r|rrrr} \frac{1}{2} & 2 & -9 & -6 & 5 \\ & & 1 & -4 & -5 \\ \hline & 2 & -8 & -10 & 0 \end{array}$$

The new quotient polynomial is therefore $2x^2-8x-10$.

$$2x^2-8x-10=0$$
$$x^2-4x-5=0$$
$$(x+1)(x-5)=0$$
$$x+1=0 \quad \text{or} \quad x-5=0$$
$$x=-1 \qquad x=5$$

The rational zeros are $\frac{1}{2}$, –1, and 5.

37. $f(x)=3x^3-8x^2+x+2$

(a) To show there is a zero between –1 and 0, we need to find $f(-1)$ and $f(0)$. Find $f(-1)$ by synthetic division and $f(0)$ by evaluating the function.

$$\begin{array}{r|rrrr} -1 & 3 & -8 & 1 & 2 \\ & & -3 & 11 & -12 \\ \hline & 3 & -11 & 12 & -10 \end{array}$$

$$f(0)=3(0^3)-8(0^2)+(0)+2=2$$

Since $f(-1)=-10<0$ and $f(0)=2>0$, there must be a zero between –1 and 0.

(b) To show there is a zero between 2 and 3, we need to find $f(2)$ and $f(3)$. Find these by synthetic division.

$$\begin{array}{r|rrrr} 2 & 3 & -8 & 1 & 2 \\ & & 6 & -4 & -6 \\ \hline & 3 & -2 & -3 & -4 \end{array} \qquad \begin{array}{r|rrrr} 3 & 3 & -8 & 1 & 2 \\ & & 9 & 3 & 12 \\ \hline & 3 & 1 & 4 & 14 \end{array}$$

Since $f(2)=-4<0$ and $f(3)=14>0$, there must be a zero between 2 and 3.

39. $f(x)=6x^4+13x^3-11x^2-3x+5$

(a) To show that there is no zero greater than 1, we must show that 1 is an upper bound.

$$\begin{array}{r|rrrrr} 1 & 6 & 13 & -11 & -3 & 5 \\ & & 6 & 19 & 8 & 5 \\ \hline & 6 & 19 & 8 & 5 & 10 \end{array}$$

Since the 1 is positive and the bottom row has all positive numbers, there is no zero greater than 1.

(b) To show that there is no zero less than -3, we must show that -3 is an lower bound.

$$\begin{array}{r|rrrrr} -3 & 6 & 13 & -11 & -3 & 5 \\ & & -18 & 15 & -12 & 45 \\ \hline & 6 & -5 & 4 & -15 & 50 \end{array}$$

Since the -3 is negative and the bottom row alternates in sign, there is no zero less than -3.

41. To determine if $x+1$ is a factor of $f(x)=x^3+2x^2+3x+2$, we can find $f(-1)$ by synthetic division.

$$\begin{array}{r|rrrr} -1 & 1 & 2 & 3 & 2 \\ & & -1 & -1 & -2 \\ \hline & 1 & 1 & 2 & 0 \end{array}$$

Since $f(-1)=0$, $x+1$ is a factor of $f(x)$.

43. Since $f(x)=a[x-(-2)](x-1)(x-4)=a(x+2)(x-1)(x-4)$, we can solve for a.

$$16=a(2+2)(2-1)(2-4)\Rightarrow 16=-8a\Rightarrow a=-2$$

The polynomial function is $f(x)=-2(x+2)(x-1)(x-4)$. It can be expanded as follows.

$$\begin{aligned} f(x)&=-2(x+2)(x-1)(x-4)=-2[(x+2)(x-1)](x-4) \\ &=-2(x^2+x-2)(x-4)=-2(x^3-3x^2-6x+8)=-2x^3+6x^2+12x-16 \end{aligned}$$

45. $f(x)=2x^4-x^3+7x^2-4x-4$; 1 and $2i$ are zeros.

Use synthetic division where $k=1$.

$$\begin{array}{r|rrrrr} 1 & 2 & -1 & 7 & -4 & -4 \\ & & 2 & 1 & 8 & 4 \\ \hline & 2 & 1 & 8 & 4 & 0 \end{array}$$

Synthetically divide $2i$ into the quotient polynomial.

$$\begin{array}{r|rrrr} 2i & 2 & 1 & 8 & 4 \\ & & 4i & -8+2i & -4 \\ \hline & 2 & 1+4i & 2i & 0 \end{array}$$

Since $2i$ is a zero, $-2i$ is also a zero. Synthetically divide $-2i$ into the quotient polynomial.

$$\begin{array}{r|rrr} -2i & 2 & 1+4i & 2i \\ & & -4i & -2i \\ \hline & 2 & 1 & 0 \end{array}$$

Since the quotient polynomial represented is $2x+1$, we can set it equal to zero to find the remaining zero.

$$2x+1=0\Rightarrow x=-\tfrac{1}{2}$$

Thus, all the zeros are 1, $-\frac{1}{2}$ and $\pm 2i$.

47. To determine the value of s such that when the polynomial x^3-3x^2+sx-4 is divided by $x-2$, the remainder is 5, we perform synthetic division.

$$\begin{array}{r|rrrr} 2) & 1 & -3 & s & -4 \\ & & 2 & -2 & 2s-4 \\ \hline & 1 & -1 & s-2 & 2s-8 \end{array}$$

To ensure that 5 is the remainder set $2s-8$ equal to 5 and solve.

$$2s-8=5 \Rightarrow 2s=13 \Rightarrow s=\tfrac{13}{2}$$

Thus, the value of s is $\frac{13}{2}$.

49. Any polynomial that can be factored as $a(x-b)^3$, where a and b are real numbers, will be a cubic polynomial function having exactly one real zero. One example is $f(x)=2(x-1)^3$.

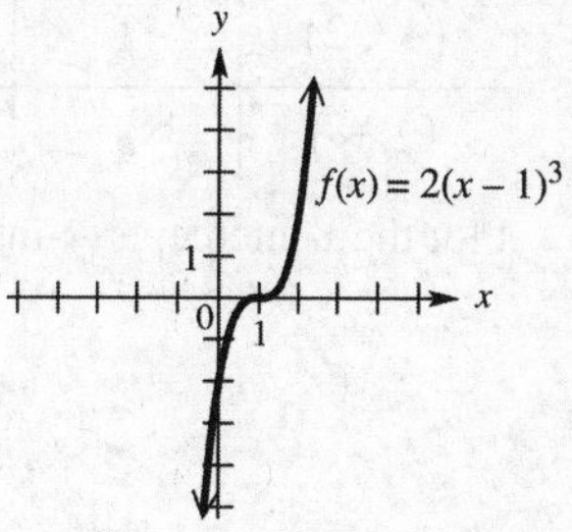

51. The polynomial has a leading coefficient of $6x^7$.

(a) The domain is $(-\infty,\infty)$.

(b) The range is $(-\infty,\infty)$.

(c) As $x\to\infty$, $f(x)\to\infty$ and as $x\to-\infty$, $f(x)\to-\infty$.

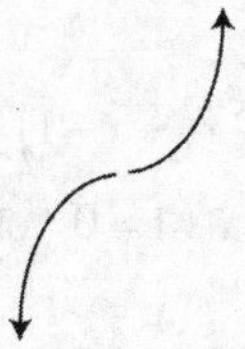

(d) There are at most 7 zeros.
(e) There are at most 6 turning points.

53. $f(x)=(x-2)^2(x-5)$ is a cubic polynomial with positive y-values for $x>5$, so it matches graph C.

55. $f(x)=(x-2)^2(x-5)^2$ is a quartic polynomial that is always greater than or equal to 0, so it matches graph E.

57. $f(x)=-(x-2)(x-5)$ is a quadratic polynomial that opens down, so it matches graph B.

59. $f(x)=(x-2)^2(x+3)$

Step 1 Set each factor equal to 0 and solve the resulting equations to find the zeros of the function.

$$(x-2)^2=0 \quad \text{or} \quad x+3=0$$
$$x=2 \qquad\qquad x=-3$$

The zeros are –3 and 2, which divide the x-axis into three regions. Test a point in each region to find the sign of $f(x)$ in that region.

Step 2 $f(0)=(0-2)^2(0+3)=4\cdot 3=12$, so plot $(0,12)$.

Continued on next page

59. (continued)

Step 3 The x-intercepts divide the x-axis into three intervals.

Interval	Test Point	Value of $f(x)$	Sign of $f(x)$	Graph Above or Below x-Axis
$(-\infty, -3)$	−4	−36	Negative	Below
$(-3, 2)$	1	4	Positive	Above
$(2, \infty)$	3	6	Positive	Above

Plot the x-intercepts, y-intercept, and test points with a smooth curve to get the graph.

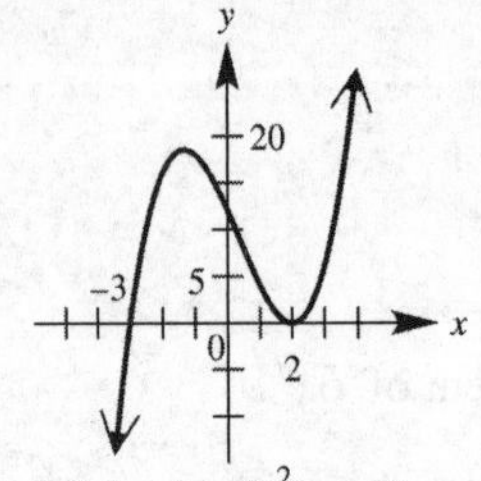

$f(x) = (x-2)^2(x+3)$

61. $f(x) = 2x^3 + x^2 - x$

Step 1 Factor the polynomial function and set each factor equal to 0 and solve the resulting equations to find the zeros of the function.

$$2x^3 + x^2 - x = x(2x^2 + x - 1) = x(x+1)(2x-1)$$

$$x = 0 \quad \text{or} \quad x+1=0 \quad \text{or} \quad 2x-1=0$$

$$x=-1 \qquad\qquad x=\tfrac{1}{2}$$

The zeros are −1, 0, and $\frac{1}{2}$, which divide the x-axis into four regions. Test a point in each region to find the sign of $f(x)$ in that region.

Step 2 $f(0)=0$, so plot $(0,0)$.

Step 3 The x-intercepts divide the x-axis into four intervals.

Interval	Test Point	Value of $f(x)$	Sign of $f(x)$	Graph Above or Below x-Axis
$(-\infty, -1)$	−2	−10	Negative	Below
$(-1, 0)$	$-\frac{1}{2}$	$\frac{1}{2}$	Positive	Above
$(0, \frac{1}{2})$	$\frac{1}{4}$	$-\frac{5}{32}$	Negative	Below
$(\frac{1}{2}, \infty)$	1	2	Positive	Above

Plot the x-intercepts, y-intercept (the y-intercept is also an x-intercept), and test points with a smooth curve to get the graph.

$f(x) = 2x^3 + x^2 - x$

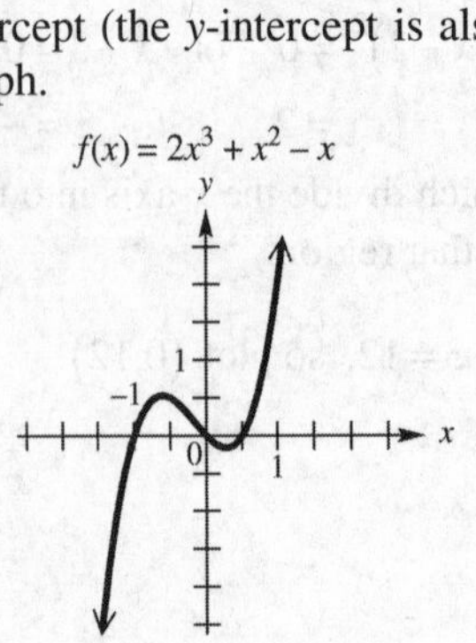

63. Using the calculator, we find that the real zeros are 7.6533119, 1, and −.6533119. For the two approximations of the zeros, a higher accuracy can be found by going to the home screen and displaying the stored x-value.

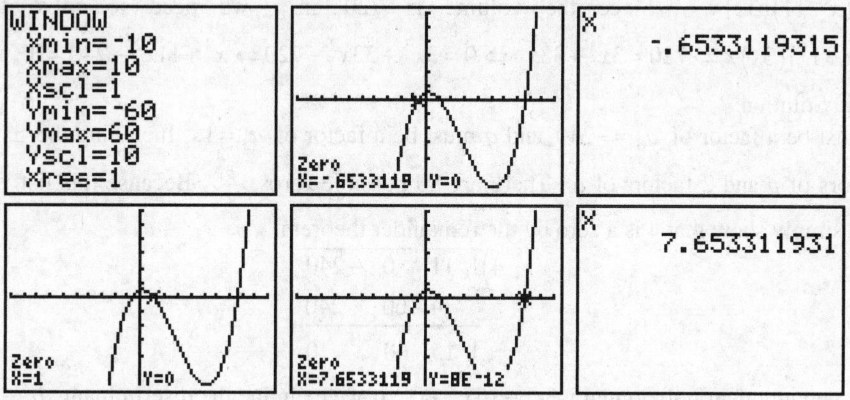

65. (a)

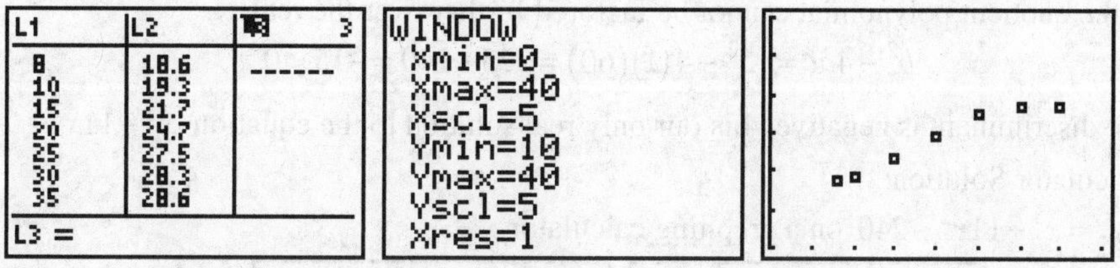

(b) $f(x) = -.011x^2 + .869x + 11.9$

(c) $f(x) = -.00087x^3 + .0456x^2 - .219x + 17.8$

(d)

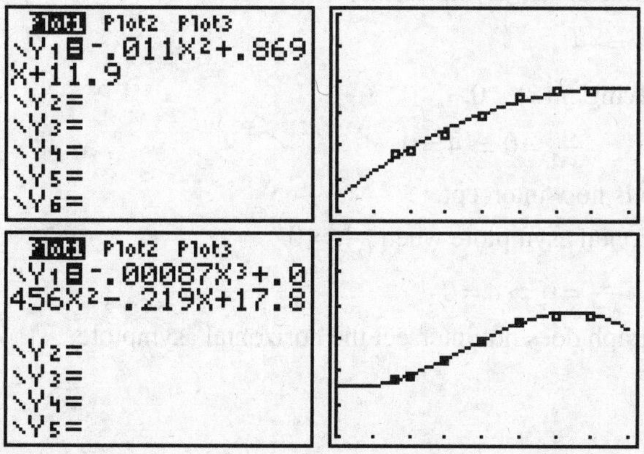

(e) Both functions approximate the data well. The quadratic function is probably better for prediction, because it is unlikely that the percent of out-of-pocket spending would decrease after 2025 (as the cubic function shows) unless changes were made in Medicare law.

67. $V_{\text{box}} = LWH$

If we let $L = x+11$, $W = 3x$, and $H = x$, we have the volume of the rectangular box is $V(x) = (x+11)(3x)x$. Since the volume is 720 in.^{3}, we need to solve the equation $720 = (x+11)(3x)x \Rightarrow 720 = 3x^3 + 33x^2 \Rightarrow 0 = 3x^3 + 33x^2 - 720 \Rightarrow x^3 + 11x^2 - 240 = 0.$

Algebraic Solution:

p must be a factor of $a_0 = -240$ and q must be a factor of $a_3 = 1$. Including the $\pm$, there are 40 factors of p and 2 factors of q. There are 80 possible zeros, $\frac{p}{q}$. Because this list is so long, we will simply show that 4 is a zero by the remainder theorem.

$$\begin{array}{r|rrrr} 4 & 1 & 11 & 0 & -240 \\ & & 4 & 60 & 240 \\ \hline & 1 & 15 & 60 & 0 \end{array}$$

The new quotient polynomial is $x^2 + 15x + 60$. If we examine the discriminant, $b^2 - 4ac$, we will see that the quotient polynomial cannot be factored further over the reals.

$$b^2 - 4ac = 15^2 - 4(1)(60) = 225 - 240 = -15 < 0$$

Since the discriminant is negative, 4 is our only real solution to the equation $x^3 + 11x^2 - 240 = 0$.

Graphing Calculator Solution:

Graph $Y_1 = x^3 + 11x^2 - 240$ on a graphing calculator.

```
WINDOW
 Xmin=-15
 Xmax=10
 Xscl=1
 Ymin=-250
 Ymax=50
 Yscl=50
 Xres=1
```

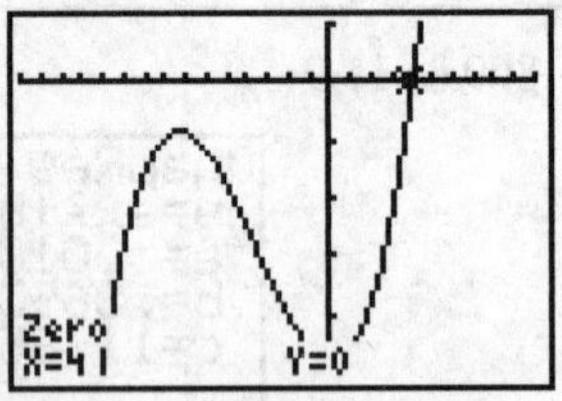

The graph will show that 4 is the only real zero.

Since the only real solution is 4, the dimensions of the rectangular box are 4 in. by 3(4) = 12 in. by $4+11=15$ in. or 12 in. $\times$ 4 in. $\times$ 15 in.

69. $f(x) = \frac{4}{x-1}$

Step 1 The graph has a vertical asymptote where $x - 1 = 0$.

$$x - 1 = 0 \Rightarrow x = 1$$

Step 2 Since the degree of the numerator (which is considered degree zero) is less than the degree of the denominator, the graph has a horizontal asymptote at $y = 0$ (the x-axis).

Step 3 The y-intercept is $f(0) = \frac{4}{0-1} = \frac{4}{-1} = -4.$

Step 4 Any x-intercepts are found by solving $f(x) = 0$.

$$\frac{4}{x-1} = 0 \Rightarrow 4 = 0$$

This is a false statement, so there is no x-intercept.

Step 5 The graph will intersect the horizontal asymptote when $\frac{4}{x-1} = 0$.

$$\frac{4}{x-1} = 0 \Rightarrow 4 = 0$$

This is a false statement, so the graph does not intersect the horizontal asymptote.

Continued on next page

69. (continued)

Step 6 Since the vertical asymptote is $x = 1$ and there is no x-intercept, we must determine values in two intervals.

Interval	Test Point	Value of $f(x)$	Sign of $f(x)$	Graph Above or Below x-Axis
$(-\infty, 1)$	-2	$-\frac{4}{3}$	Negative	Below
$(1, \infty)$	2	4	Positive	Above

Step 7 Use the asymptotes, intercepts, and these points to sketch the graph.

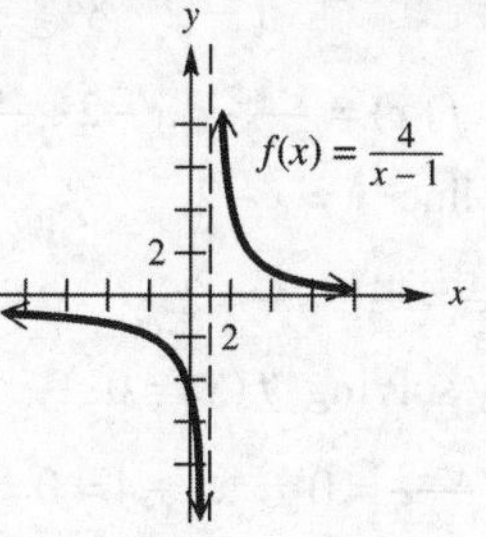

71. $f(x) = \frac{6x}{x^2+x-2} = \frac{6x}{(x+2)(x-1)}$

Step 1 The graph has a vertical asymptote where $(x+2)(x-1) = 0$, that is, when $x = -2$ and $x = 1$.

Step 2 Since the degree of the numerator is less than the degree of the denominator, the graph has a horizontal asymptote at $y = 0$ (the x-axis).

Step 3 The y-intercept is $f(0) = \frac{6(0)}{0^2+0-2} = \frac{0}{0+0-2} = \frac{0}{-2} = 0.$

Step 4 Any x-intercepts are found by solving $f(x) = 0.$

$$\frac{6x}{x^2+x-2} = 0 \Rightarrow 6x = 0 \Rightarrow x = 0$$

The only x-intercept is 0.

Step 5 The graph will intersect the horizontal asymptote when $\frac{6x}{x^2+x-2} = 0.$

$$\frac{6x}{x^2+x-2} = 0 \Rightarrow 6x = 0 \Rightarrow x = 0$$

Step 6 Since the vertical asymptotes are $x = -2$ and $x = 1$ and the x-intercept occurs at 0, we must determine values in four intervals.

Interval	Test Point	Value of $f(x)$	Sign of $f(x)$	Graph Above or Below x-Axis
$(-\infty, -2)$	-3	$-\frac{9}{2}$	Negative	Below
$(-2, 0)$	-1	3	Positive	Above
$(0, 1)$	$\frac{1}{2}$	$-\frac{12}{5}$	Negative	Below
$(1, \infty)$	2	3	Positive	Above

Step 7 Use the asymptotes, intercepts, and these points to sketch the graph.

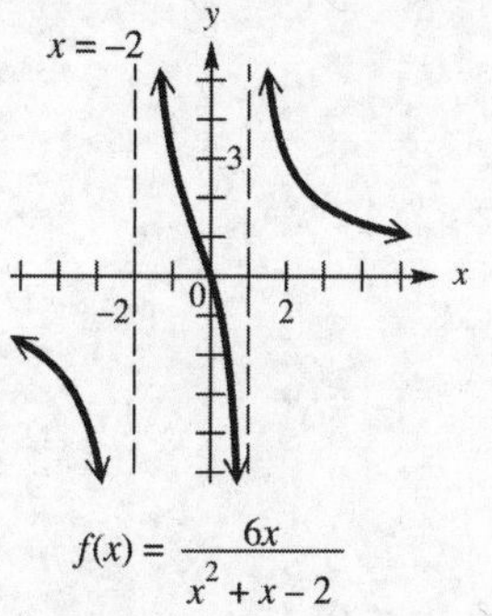

73. $f(x) = \frac{x^2+4}{x+2}$

Step 1 The graph has a vertical asymptote where $x+2=0 \Rightarrow x=-2$.

Step 2 Since the degree of the numerator is one more than the degree of the denominator, the graph has an oblique asymptote. Divide x^2+4 by $x+2$.

$$\begin{array}{r|rrr} -2 & 1 & 0 & 4 \\ & & -2 & 4 \\ \hline & 1 & -2 & 8 \end{array}$$

$$f(x) = \frac{x^2+4}{x+2} = x-2+\frac{8}{x+3}$$

The oblique asymptote is the line $y = x-2$.

Step 3 The y-intercept is $f(0) = \frac{0^2+4}{0+2} = \frac{0+4}{2} = \frac{4}{2} = 2$.

Step 4 Any x-intercepts are found by solving $f(x) = 0$.

$$\frac{x^2+4}{x+2} = 0 \Rightarrow x^2+4=0 \Rightarrow x = \pm 2i$$

There are no x-intercepts.

Step 5 The graph will intersect the oblique asymptote when $\frac{x^2+4}{x+2} = x-2$.

$$\frac{x^2+4}{x+2} = x-2 \Rightarrow x^2+4 = (x+2)(x-2) \Rightarrow x^2+4 = x^2-4 \Rightarrow 4 = -4$$

This is a false statement, so the graph does not intersect the oblique asymptote.

Step 6 Since the vertical asymptote is $x=-2$ and there are no x-intercepts, we must determine values in two intervals.

Interval	Test Point	Value of $f(x)$	Sign of $f(x)$	Graph Above or Below x-Axis
$(-\infty, -2)$	-3	-13	Negative	Below
$(-2, \infty)$	3	$\frac{13}{5}$	Positive	Above

Step 7 Use the asymptotes, y-intercept, and these points to sketch the graph.

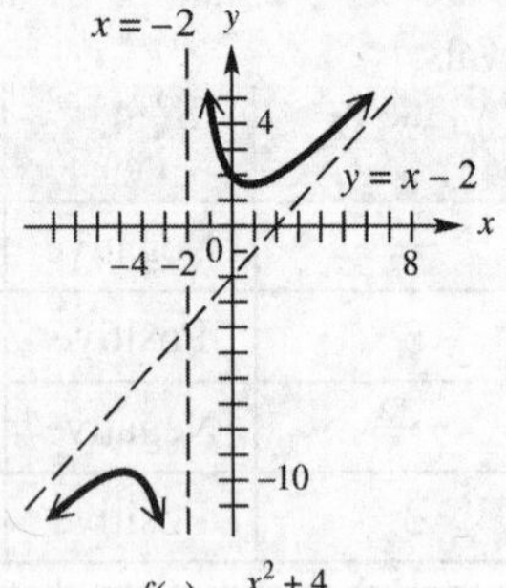

$f(x) = \frac{x^2+4}{x+2}$

75. $f(x)=\frac{-2}{x^2+1}$

Step 1 The graph has a vertical asymptote where $x^2+1=0$. Since we have $x^2+1=0 \Rightarrow x=\pm i$, there are no vertical asymptotes.

Step 2 Since the degree of the numerator (which is considered degree zero) is less than the degree of the denominator, the graph has a horizontal asymptote at $y=0$ (the x-axis).

Step 3 The y-intercept is $f(0)=\frac{-2}{0^2+1}=\frac{-2}{0+1}=\frac{-2}{1}=-2$.

Step 4 Any x-intercepts are found by solving $f(x)=0$.

$$\frac{-2}{x^2+1}=0 \Rightarrow -2=0$$

This is a false statement, so there is no x-intercept.

Step 5 The graph will intersect the horizontal asymptote when $\frac{-2}{x^2+1}=0$.

$$\frac{-2}{x^2+1}=0 \Rightarrow -2=0$$

This is a false statement, so the graph does not intersect the horizontal asymptote.

Step 6 Since there are no vertical asymptotes and no x-intercept, we can see from the y-intercept that the function is always negative and, therefore, below the x-axis. Because of the limited information we have, we should explore symmetry and calculate a few more points on the graph.

x	y
-3	$-\frac{1}{5}$
$\frac{1}{2}$	$-\frac{8}{5}$
1	-1

Since $f(-x)=\frac{-2}{(-x)^2+1}=\frac{-2}{x^2+1}=f(x)$, the graph is symmetric about the y-axis.

Step 7 Use the asymptote, y-intercept, these points, and symmetry to sketch the graph.

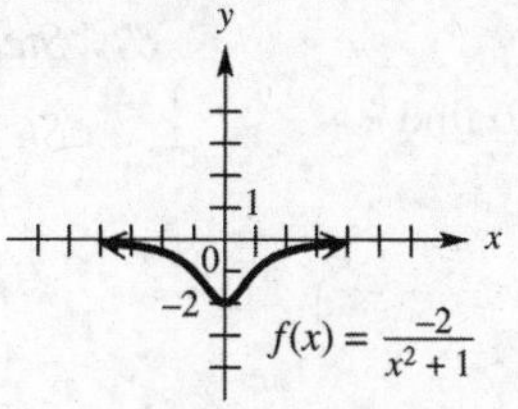

77. (a)

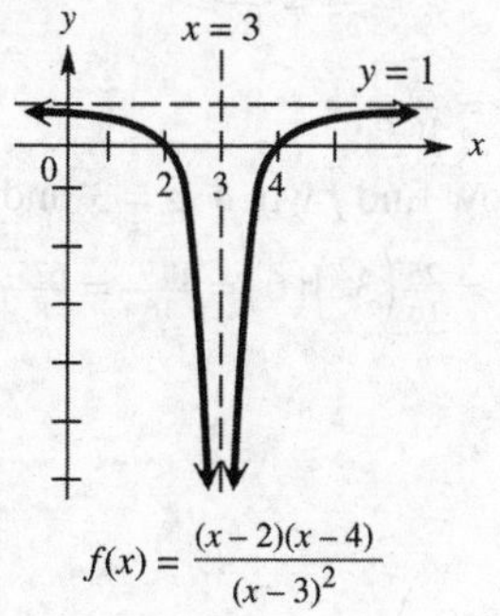

(b) The graph has a vertical asymptote $x=3$, so $x-3$ is in the denominator of the function. The x-intercepts are 2 and 4, so that when $f(x)=0$, $x=2$ or $x=4$. This would exist if $x-2$ and $x-4$ were factors of the numerator. The horizontal asymptote is $y=1$, so the numerator and denominator have the same degree. Since the numerator will have degree 2, we must make the denominator also have degree 2. Putting these conditions together, we get a possible function $f(x)=\frac{(x-2)(x-4)}{(x-3)^2}$.

79. The graph has a vertical asymptote $x=1$, so $x-1$ is in the denominator of the function. The x-intercept is 2, so that when $f(x)=0$, $x=2$. This would exist if $x-2$ was a factor of the numerator. The horizontal asymptote is $y=-3$, so the numerator and denominator have the same degree. They both have degree 1. Also, from the horizontal asymptote, we have $y=-3=\frac{a_n}{b_n}=\frac{-3}{1}$. Putting these conditions together, we have a possible function $f(x)=\frac{-3(x-2)}{x-1}$ or $f(x)=\frac{-3x+6}{x-1}$

81. $C(x)=\frac{6.7x}{100-x}$

(a) 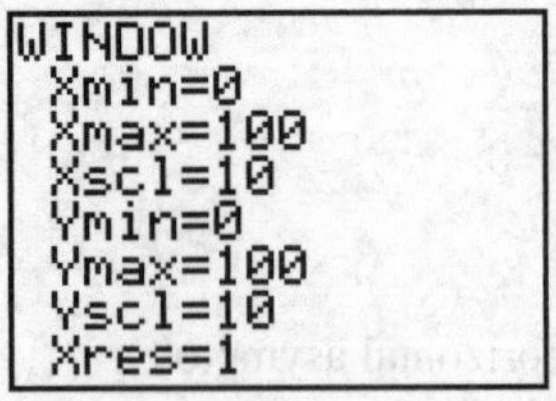

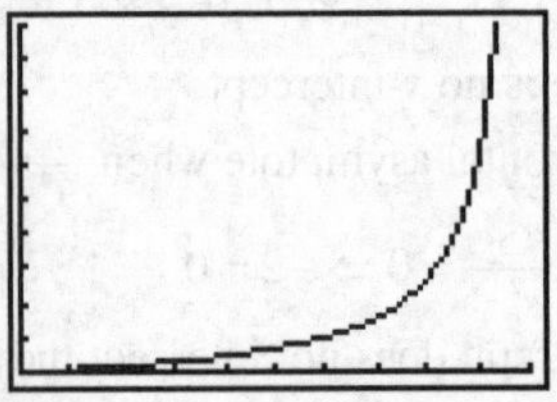

(b) To find the cost to remove 95% of the pollutant, find $C(95)$.

$C(95)=\frac{6.7(95)}{100-95}=127.3$

This can also be found using the graphing calculator.

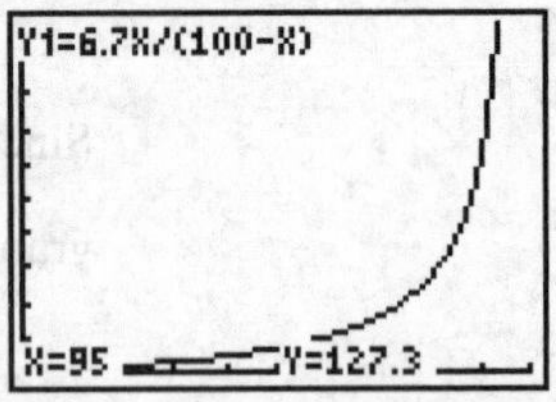

It would cost $127.3 thousand to remove 95% of the pollutant.

83. *Step 1* $x=ky$

Step 2 Substitute $x=10$ & $y=7$ to find k.

$10=k(7)$

$k=\frac{10}{7}$

Step 3 $x=\frac{10}{7}y$

Step 4 Now find y when $x=50$.

$50=\frac{10}{7}y$

$350=10y$

$y=35$

85. *Step 1* $t=\frac{k}{s}$

Step 2 Substitute $t=3$ & $s=5$ to find k.

$3=\frac{k}{5}$

$k=15$

Step 3 $t=\frac{15}{s}$

Step 4 Now find s when $t=5$.

$5=\frac{15}{s}\Rightarrow 5s=15\Rightarrow s=3$

87. *Step 1* $f=kg^2h$

Step 2 Substitute $f=50$, $g=4$, and $h=2$ to find k.

$50=k\left(4^2\right)(2)$

$50=32k$

$k=\frac{50}{32}=\frac{25}{16}$

Step 3 $f=\frac{25}{16}g^2h$

Step 4 Now find f when $g=3$ and $h=6$.

$f=\frac{25}{16}\left(3^2\right)(6)=\frac{1350}{16}=\frac{675}{8}=84\frac{3}{8}$

89. *Step 1* Let f be the force to keep car from skidding (in lbs).
r is the radius of curve (in ft).
w is the weight of car (in lbs).
s is the speed of the car (in mph).

$$f = \frac{kws^2}{r}$$

Step 2 $f = 3000$, $w = 2000$, $r = 500$, and $s = 30$ to find k.

$$3000 = \frac{k(2000)(30^2)}{500} \Rightarrow 3000 = \frac{1{,}800{,}000k}{500} \Rightarrow 3000 = 3600k \Rightarrow k = \frac{3000}{3600} = \frac{5}{6}$$

Step 3 $f = \frac{5}{6} \cdot \frac{ws^2}{r} = \frac{5ws^2}{6r}$

Step 4 Now find f when $w = 2000$, $r = 800$, and $s = 60$

$$f = \frac{5(2000)(60^2)}{6(800)} = 7500$$

A force of 7500 lb is needed.

Chapter 3: Test

1. $f(x) = -2x^2 + 6x - 3$

Complete the square so the function has the form $f(x) = a(x-h)^2 + k$.

$$f(x) = -2x^2 + 6x - 3 = -2(x^2 - 3x) - 3 = -2\left(x^2 - 3x + \tfrac{9}{4} - \tfrac{9}{4}\right) - 3 \quad \text{Note: } \left[\tfrac{1}{2}(-3)\right]^2 = \tfrac{9}{4}$$
$$= -2\left(x - \tfrac{3}{2}\right)^2 + \tfrac{9}{2} - 3 = -2\left(x - \tfrac{3}{2}\right)^2 + \tfrac{3}{2}$$

This parabola is in now in standard form with $a = -2$, $h = \frac{3}{2}$, and $k = \frac{3}{2}$. It opens downward with vertex $(h, k) = \left(\frac{3}{2}, \frac{3}{2}\right)$. The axis is $x = h \Rightarrow x = \frac{3}{2}$. To find the x-intercepts, let $f(x) = 0$.

$$-2\left(x - \tfrac{3}{2}\right)^2 + \tfrac{3}{2} = 0 \Rightarrow -2\left(x - \tfrac{3}{2}\right)^2 = -\tfrac{3}{2} \Rightarrow \left(x - \tfrac{3}{2}\right)^2 = \tfrac{3}{4} \Rightarrow x - \tfrac{3}{2} = \pm\sqrt{\tfrac{3}{4}}$$
$$x = \tfrac{3}{2} \pm \sqrt{\tfrac{3}{4}} = \tfrac{3}{2} \pm \tfrac{\sqrt{3}}{2} = \tfrac{3 \pm \sqrt{3}}{2}$$

Thus the x-intercepts are $\frac{3 \pm \sqrt{3}}{2}$ or approximately .63 and 2.37.

Note: If you use the quadratic formula to solve $-2x^2 + 6x - 3 = 0$ where $a = -2, b = 6,$ and $c = -3$, you will arrive at the equivalent answer of x-intercepts: $\frac{-3 \pm \sqrt{3}}{-2}$.

To find the y-intercept, let $x = 0$.

$$f(0) = -2(0^2) + 6(0) - 3 = -3$$

The y-intercept is–3.

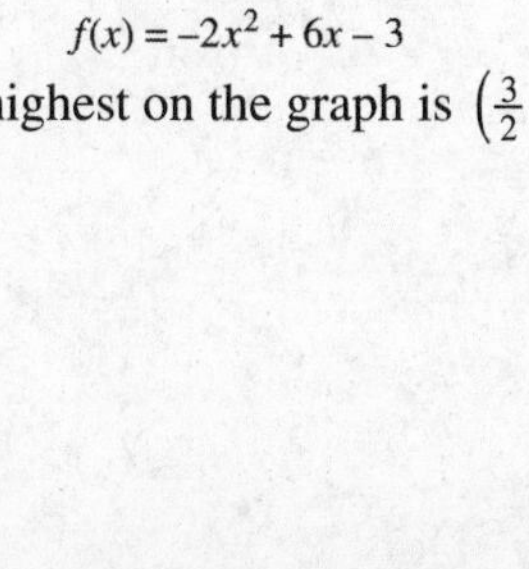

$f(x) = -2x^2 + 6x - 3$

The domain is $(-\infty, \infty)$. Since the highest on the graph is $\left(\frac{3}{2}, \frac{3}{2}\right)$, the range is $\left(-\infty, \frac{3}{2}\right]$.

2. $f(x) = -.3857x^2 + 1.2829x + 11.329$

The year 2003 corresponds to $x = 5$ in this model.

$$f(5) = -.3857(5^2) + 1.2829(5) + 11.329 = 8.101$$

Approximately 8.1 million tickets would have been sold in 2003 according to the model.

3. $\dfrac{3x^3 + 4x^2 - 9x + 6}{x + 2}$

Express $x + 2$ in the form $x - k$ by writing it as $x - (-2)$. Thus $k = -2$.

$$\begin{array}{r|rrrr} -2 & 3 & 4 & -9 & 6 \\ & & -6 & 4 & 10 \\ \hline & 3 & -2 & -5 & 16 \end{array}$$

$$\frac{3x^3 + 4x^2 - 9x + 6}{x + 2} = 3x^2 - 2x - 5 + \frac{16}{x + 2}$$

4. $\dfrac{2x^3 - 11x^2 + 28}{x - 5}$

Since $x - 5$ is in the form $x - k$, $k = 5$.

$$\begin{array}{r|rrrr} 5 & 2 & -11 & 0 & 28 \\ & & 10 & -5 & -25 \\ \hline & 2 & -1 & -5 & 3 \end{array}$$

$$\frac{2x^3 - 11x^2 + 28}{x - 5} = 2x^2 - x - 5 + \frac{3}{x - 5}$$

5. $f(x) = 2x^3 - 9x^2 + 4x + 8;\ k = 5$

$$\begin{array}{r|rrrr} 5 & 2 & -9 & 4 & 8 \\ & & 10 & 5 & 45 \\ \hline & 2 & 1 & 9 & 53 \end{array}$$

Thus, $f(5) = 53$.

6. $6x^4 - 11x^3 - 35x^2 + 34x + 24;\ x - 3$

Let $f(x) = 6x^4 - 11x^3 - 35x^2 + 34x + 24$. By the factor theorem, $x - 3$ will be a factor of $f(x)$ only if $f(3) = 0$.

$$\begin{array}{r|rrrrr} 3 & 6 & -11 & -35 & 34 & 24 \\ & & 18 & 21 & -42 & -24 \\ \hline & 6 & 7 & -14 & -8 & 0 \end{array}$$

Since $f(3) = 0$, $x - 3$ is a factor of $f(x)$.

The other factor is $6x^3 + 7x^2 - 14x - 8$.

7. $f(x) = x^3 + 8x^2 + 25x + 26;\ -2$

Since -2 is a zero, first divide $f(x)$ by $x + 2$.

$$\begin{array}{r|rrrr} -2 & 1 & 8 & 25 & 26 \\ & & -2 & -12 & -26 \\ \hline & 1 & 6 & 13 & 0 \end{array}$$

This gives $f(x) = (x + 2)(x^2 + 6x + 13)$. Since $x^2 + 6x + 13$ cannot be factored, use the quadratic formula with $a = 1$, $b = 6$, and $c = 13$ to find the remaining two zeros.

$$x = \frac{-6 \pm \sqrt{6^2 - 4(1)(13)}}{2(1)} = \frac{-6 \pm \sqrt{36 - 52}}{2} = \frac{-6 \pm \sqrt{-16}}{2} = \frac{-6 \pm 4i}{2} = -3 \pm 2i$$

The zeros are -2, $-3 - 2i$, and $-3 + 2i$.

8. Zeros of –1, 2 and i; $f(3)=80$

By the conjugate zeros theorem, $-i$ is also a zero. The polynomial has the following form.

$$f(x)=a(x+1)(x-2)(x-i)(x+i)$$

Use the condition $f(3)=80$ to find a.

$$80=a(3+1)(3-2)(3-i)(3+i)\Rightarrow 80=a(4)(1)\left[(3-i)(3+i)\right]\Rightarrow 80=a\left[(4)(1)\right]\left[3^2-i^2\right]$$

$$80=a(4)\left[9-(-1)\right]\Rightarrow 80=a(4)(10)\Rightarrow 80=40a\Rightarrow a=2$$

Thus we have the following.

$$f(x)=2(x+1)(x-2)(x-i)(x+i)=2\left[(x+1)(x-2)\right]\left[(x-i)(x+i)\right]$$

$$=2\left(x^2-x-2\right)\left(x^2+1\right)=2\left(x^4-x^3-x^2-x-2\right)=2x^4-2x^3-2x^2-2x-4$$

9. Since $f(x)=x^4+8x^2+12=\left(x^2+6\right)\left(x^2+2\right)$, the zeros are $\pm i\sqrt{6}$ and $\pm i\sqrt{2}$. Moreover, $f(x)>0$ for all x; the graph never crosses or touches the x-axis, so $f(x)$ has no real zeros.

10. (a) $f(x)=x^3-5x^2+2x+7$; find $f(1)$ and $f(2)$ synthetically.

$$1\overline{)\begin{array}{rrrr}1 & -5 & 2 & 7\\ & 1 & -4 & -2\\ \hline 1 & -4 & -2 & 5\end{array}} \qquad 2\overline{)\begin{array}{rrrr}1 & -5 & 2 & 7\\ & 2 & -6 & -8\\ \hline 1 & -3 & -4 & -1\end{array}}$$

By the intermediate value theorem, since $f(1)=5>0$ and $f(2)=-1<0$, there must be at least one real zero between 1 and 2.

(b) $f(x)=\underbrace{x^3-5x^2}_{1}\underbrace{+2x}_{2}+7$ has 2 variations in sign. f has 2 or $2-2=0$ positive real zeros.

$f(-x)=-x^3-5x^2\underbrace{-2x+7}_{1}$ has 1 variation in sign. f has 1 negative real zero.

(c) Using the calculator, we find that the real zeros are 4.0937635, 1.8370381, and –.9308016. For these approximations, a higher accuracy can be found by going to the home screen and displaying the stored x-value.

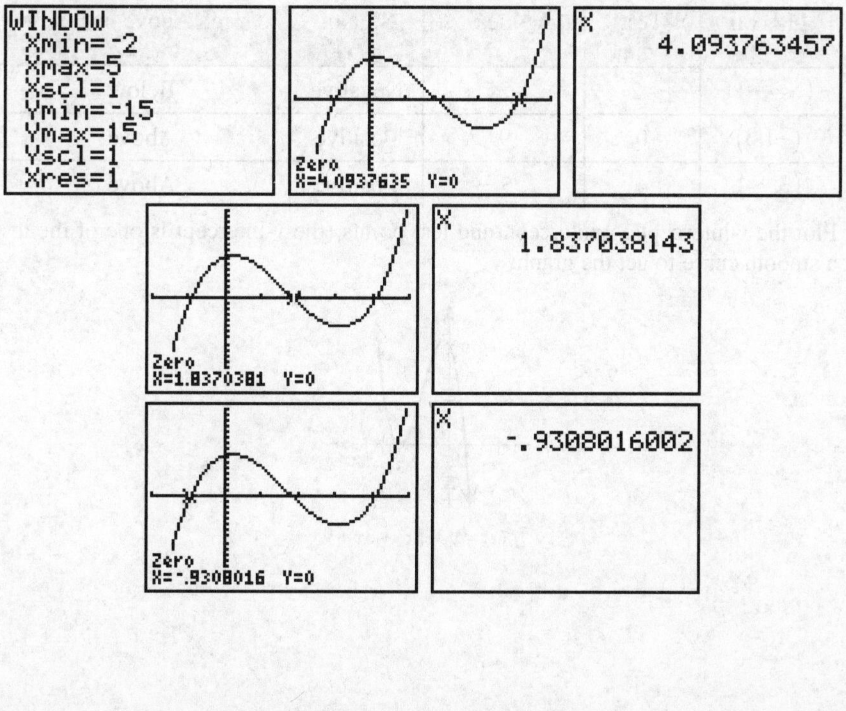

11.

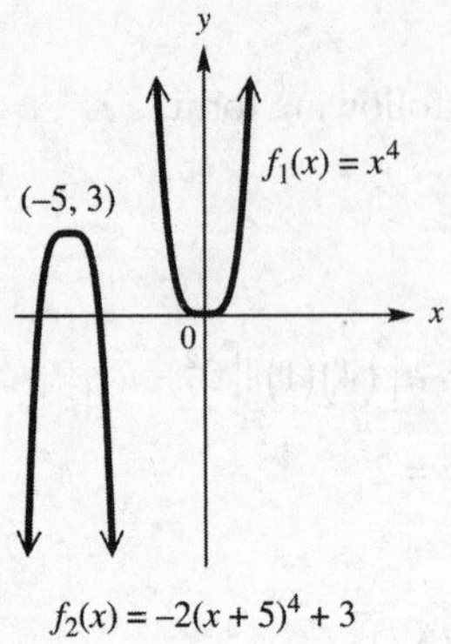

To obtain the graph of f_2, shift the graph of f_1 5 units to the left, stretch by a factor of 2, reflect across the x-axis, and shift 3 units up.

12. $f(x) = -x^7 + x - 4$

Since $f(x)$ is of odd degree and the sign of a_n is negative, the end behavior is ↖↘. The correct graph is C.

13. $f(x) = x^3 - 5x^2 + 3x + 9$

Step 1 The first step is to find the zeros of the polynomial function. p must be a factor of $a_0 = 9$ and q must be a factor of $a_3 = 1$. Thus, p can be $\pm1, \pm3, \pm9$ and q can be ±1. The possible zeros, $\frac{p}{q}$, are $\pm1, \pm3, \pm9$. The remainder theorem shows that 3 is a zero.

$$\begin{array}{r|rrrr} 3 & 1 & -5 & 3 & 9 \\ & & 3 & -6 & -9 \\ \hline & 1 & -2 & -3 & 0 \end{array}$$

The new quotient polynomial is $x^2 - 2x - 3$.

$x^2 - 2x - 3 = 0 \Rightarrow (x+1)(x-3) = 0$

$x + 1 = 0$ or $x - 3 = 0$

$x = -1$ $\quad$ $x = 3$

The rational zeros are -1 and 3 (multiplicity 2), which divide the x-axis into three regions. Test a point in each region to find the sign of $f(x)$ in that region.

Step 2 $f(0) = 9$, so plot $(0, 9)$.

Step 3 The x-intercepts divide the x-axis into three intervals.

Interval	Test Point	Value of $f(x)$	Sign of $f(x)$	Graph Above or Below x-Axis
$(-\infty, -1)$	−2	−25	Negative	Below
$(-1, 3)$	0	9	Positive	Above
$(3, \infty)$	4	5	Positive	Above

Plot the x-intercepts, y-intercept, and test points (the y-intercept is one of the test points) with a smooth curve to get the graph.

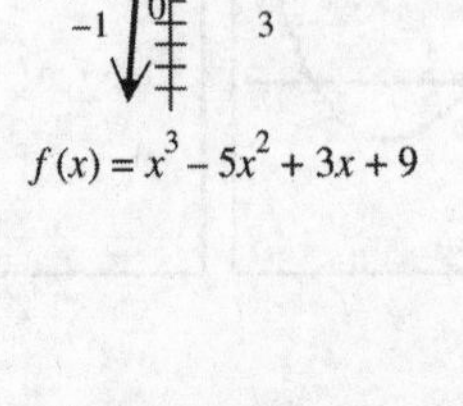

14. $f(x)=2x^2(x-2)^2$

Step 1 Set each factor equal to 0 and solve the resulting equations to find the zeros of the function.

$$2x^2=0 \quad \text{or} \quad (x-2)^2=0$$
$$x=0 \qquad\qquad x=2$$

The zeros are 0 (multiplicity 2) and 2 (multiplicity 2), which divide the x-axis into three regions. Test a point in each region to find the sign of $f(x)$ in that region.

Step 2 $f(0)=0$, so plot $(0,0)$.

Step 3 The x-intercepts divide the x-axis into three intervals.

Interval	Test Point	Value of $f(x)$	Sign of $f(x)$	Graph Above or Below x-Axis
$(-\infty,0)$	-1	18	Positive	Above
$(0,2)$	1	2	Positive	Above
$(2,\infty)$	3	18	Positive	Above

Plot the x-intercepts, y-intercept (the y-intercept is an x-intercept), and test points with a smooth curve to get the graph.

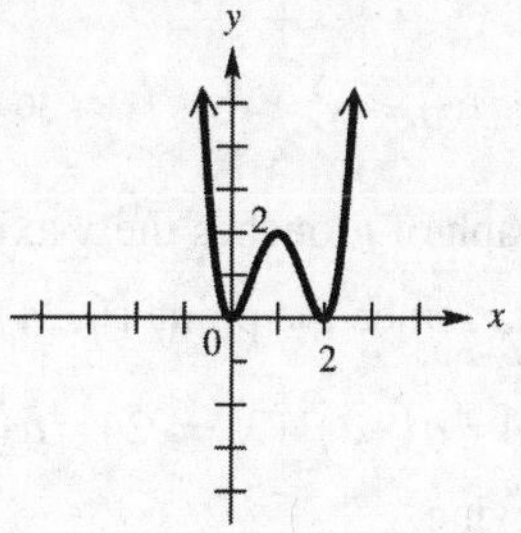

$f(x) = 2x^2(x-2)^2$

15. $f(x)=-x^3-4x^2+11x+30$

Step 1 The first step is to find the zeros of the polynomial function.

p must be a factor of $a_0=30$ and q must be a factor of $a_3=-1$. Thus, p can be $\pm1, \pm2, \pm3, \pm5, \pm6, \pm10, \pm15, \pm30$ and q can be ±1. The possible zeros, $\frac{p}{q}$, are $\pm1, \pm2, \pm3, \pm5, \pm6, \pm10, \pm15, \pm30$. The remainder theorem shows that 3 is a zero.

$$\begin{array}{r|rrrr} 3 & -1 & -4 & 11 & 30 \\ & & -3 & -21 & -30 \\ \hline & -1 & -7 & -10 & 0 \end{array}$$

The new quotient polynomial is $-x^2-7x-10$.

$$-x^2-7x-10=0 \Rightarrow x^2+7x+10=0 \Rightarrow (x+5)(x+2)=0$$
$$x+5=0 \quad \text{or} \quad x+2=0$$
$$x=-5 \qquad\qquad x=-2$$

The rational zeros are -5, -2, and 3, which divide the x-axis into four regions. Test a point in each region to find the sign of $f(x)$ in that region.

Step 2 $f(0)=30$, so plot $(0,30)$.

Continued on next page

15. (continued)

Step 3 The x-intercepts divide the x-axis into four intervals.

Interval	Test Point	Value of $f(x)$	Sign of $f(x)$	Graph Above or Below x-Axis
$(-\infty,-5)$	-6	36	Positive	Above
$(-5,-2)$	-3	-12	Negative	Below
$(-2,3)$	0	30	Positive	Above
$(3,\infty)$	4	-54	Negative	Below

Plot the x-intercepts, y-intercept, and test points (the y-intercept is one of the test points) with a smooth curve to get the graph.

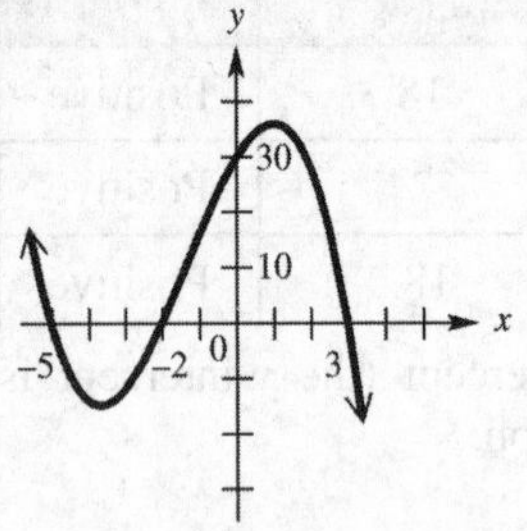

$f(x) = -x^3 - 4x^2 + 11x + 30$

16. The zeros are -3 and 2. Since the graph of f touches the x-axis at 2, the zero 2 has multiplicity 2. Thus, $f(x) = a(x-2)^2(x+3)$. Also, since the point $(0,24)$ is on the graph, we have $f(0) = 24$.

$$24 = a(0-2)^2(0+3) \Rightarrow 24 = a(-2)^2(3) \Rightarrow 24 = a(4)(3) \Rightarrow 24 = 12a \Rightarrow a = 2$$

The polynomial function is the following.

$$f(x) = 2(x-2)^2(x+3) = 2(x^2-4x+4)(x+3) = 2(x^3-x^2-8x+12) = 2x^3-2x^2-16x+24$$

17. $f(t) = 1.06t^3 - 24.6t^2 + 180t$

(a) $f(2) = 1.06(2^3) - 24.6(2)^2 + 180(2) = 270.08$

This can also be found using the graphing calculator.

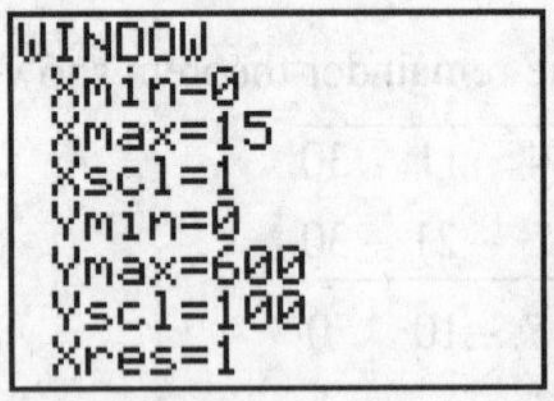

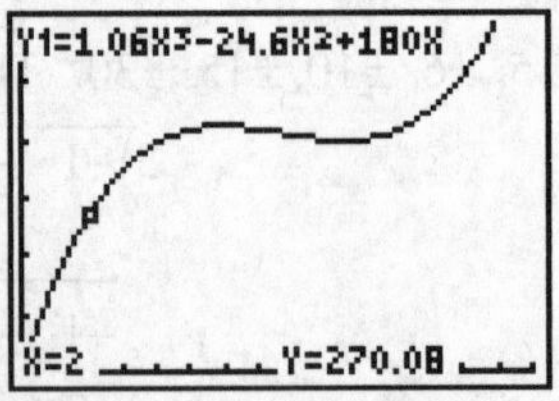

(b) From the graph we see that the amount of change is increasing from $t = 0$ to $t = 5.9$ and from $t = 9.5$ to $t = 15$ and decreasing from $t = 5.9$ to $t = 9.5$.

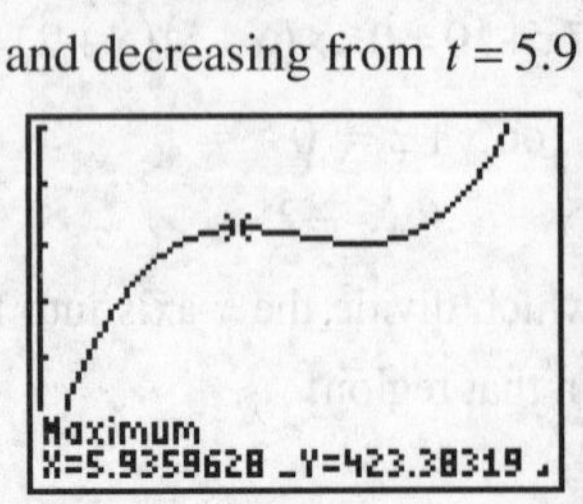

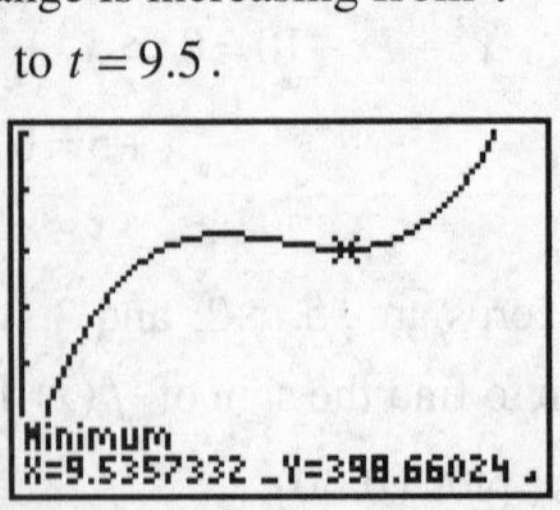

18. $f(x)=\frac{3x-1}{x-2}$

Step 1 The graph has a vertical asymptote where $x-2=0$, that is, when $x=2$.

Step 2 Since the degree of the numerator equals the degree of the denominator, the graph has a horizontal asymptote at $y=\frac{3}{1}=3$.

Step 3 The *y*-intercept is $f(0)=\frac{3(0)-1}{0-2}=\frac{0-1}{-2}=\frac{-1}{-2}=\frac{1}{2}$.

Step 4 Any *x*-intercepts are found by solving $f(x)=0$.

$$\frac{3x-1}{x-2}=0\Rightarrow 3x-1=0$$
$$3x=1\Rightarrow x=\frac{1}{3}$$

The only *x*-intercept is $\frac{1}{3}$.

Step 5 The graph will intersect the horizontal asymptote when $\frac{3x-1}{x-2}=3$.

$$\frac{3x-1}{x-2}=3\Rightarrow 3x-1=3(x-2)\Rightarrow 3x-1=3x-6\Rightarrow -1=-6$$

This is a false statement, so the graph does not intersect the horizontal asymptote.

Step 6 Since the vertical asymptote is $x=2$ and the *x*-intercept occurs at $\frac{1}{3}$, we must determine values in three intervals.

Interval	Test Point	Value of $f(x)$	Sign of $f(x)$	Graph Above or Below *x*-Axis
$\left(-\infty,\frac{1}{3}\right)$	0	$\frac{1}{2}$	Positive	Above
$\left(\frac{1}{3},2\right)$	1	-2	Negative	Below
$(2,\infty)$	3	8	Positive	Above

Step 7 Use the asymptotes, intercepts, and test points (the *y*-intercept is one of the test points) to sketch the graph.

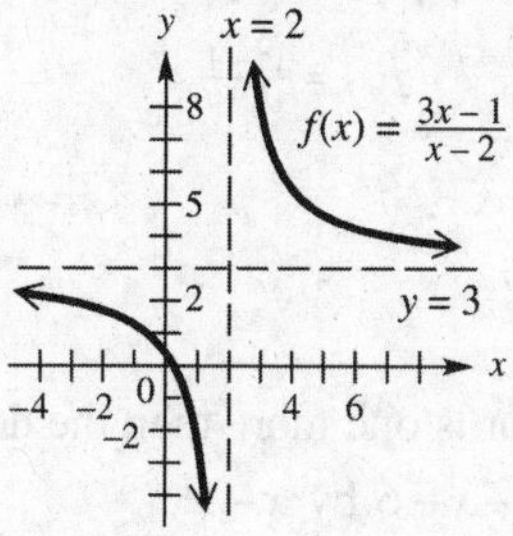

19. $f(x)=\frac{x^2-1}{x^2-9}=\frac{(x+1)(x-1)}{(x+3)(x-3)}$

Step 1 The graph has a vertical asymptote where $(x+3)(x-3)=0$, that is, when $x=-3$ and $x=3$.

Step 2 Since the degree of the numerator equals the degree of the denominator, the graph has a horizontal asymptote at $y=\frac{1}{1}=1$.

Step 3 The *y*-intercept is $f(0)=\frac{0^2-1}{0^2-9}=\frac{-1}{-9}=\frac{1}{9}$.

Step 4 Any *x*-intercepts are found by solving $f(x)=0$.

$$\frac{(x+1)(x-1)}{(x+3)(x-3)}=0\Rightarrow (x+1)(x-1)=0$$
$$x=-1 \text{ or } x=1$$

The *x*-intercepts are -1 and 1.

Continued on next page

19. (continued)

Step 5 The graph will intersect the horizontal asymptote when $\frac{x^2-1}{x^2-9}=1.$

$$\frac{x^2-1}{x^2-9}=1 \Rightarrow x^2-1=x^2-9 \Rightarrow -1=-9$$

This is a false statement, so the graph does not intersect the horizontal asymptote.

Step 6 Since the vertical asymptotes are $x=-3$ and $x=3$, and the x-intercepts occur at -1 and 1, we must determine values in five intervals.

Interval	Test Point	Value of $f(x)$	Sign of $f(x)$	Graph Above or Below x-Axis
$(-\infty,-3)$	-4	$\frac{15}{7}$	Positive	Above
$(-3,-1)$	-2	$-\frac{3}{5}$	Negative	Below
$(-1,1)$	0	$\frac{1}{9}$	Positive	Above
$(1,3)$	2	$-\frac{3}{5}$	Negative	Below
$(3,\infty)$	4	$\frac{15}{7}$	Positive	Above

Step 7 Use the asymptotes, intercepts, and test points (the y-intercept is one of the test points) to sketch the graph. Note: This function is an even function, thus the graph is symmetric with respect to the y-axis.

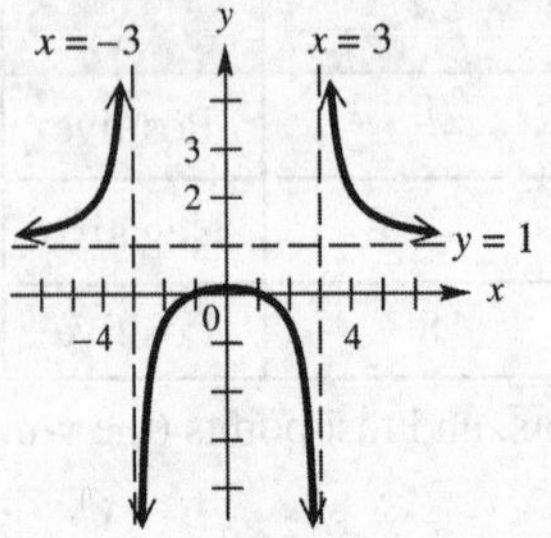

$f(x)=\frac{x^2-1}{x^2-9}$

20. $f(x)=\dfrac{2x^2+x-6}{x-1}$

(a) Since the degree of the numerator is one more than the degree of the denominator, the graph has an oblique asymptote. Divide $2x^2+x-6$ by $x-1$.

$$\begin{array}{r|rrr} 1 & 2 & 1 & -6 \\ & & 2 & 3 \\ \hline & 2 & 3 & -3 \end{array}$$

$$f(x)=\frac{2x^2+x-6}{x-1}=2x+3-\frac{3}{x-1}$$

The oblique asymptote is the line $y=2x+3$.

(b) To find the x-intercepts, let $f(x)=0$.

$$\frac{2x^2+x-6}{x-1}=0 \Rightarrow 2x^2+x-6=0$$

$$(x+2)(2x-3)=0$$

$$x=-2 \text{ or } x=\frac{3}{2}$$

The x-intercepts are -2 and $\frac{3}{2}$.

Continued on next page

20. (continued)

(c) The y-intercept is $f(0)=\frac{2(0^2)+0-6}{0-1}=\frac{2(0)+0-6}{-1}=\frac{0+0-6}{-1}=\frac{-6}{-1}=6.$

(d) To find the vertical asymptote, set the denominator equal to zero and solve for x.

$$x-1=0 \Rightarrow x=1$$

The equation of the vertical asymptote is $x=1$.

(e) Use the information from (a)–(d) and a few additional points to graph the function. Since the vertical asymptote is $x=1$, and the x-intercepts occur at -2 and $\frac{3}{2}$, we must determine values in four intervals.

Interval	Test Point	Value of $f(x)$	Sign of $f(x)$	Graph Above or Below x-Axis
$(-\infty,-2)$	-3	$-\frac{9}{4}$	Negative	Below
$(-2,1)$	0	6	Positive	Above
$\left(1,\frac{3}{2}\right)$	$1\frac{1}{4}=\frac{5}{4}$	$-\frac{13}{2}$	Negative	Below
$\left(\frac{3}{2},\infty\right)$	2	4	Positive	Above

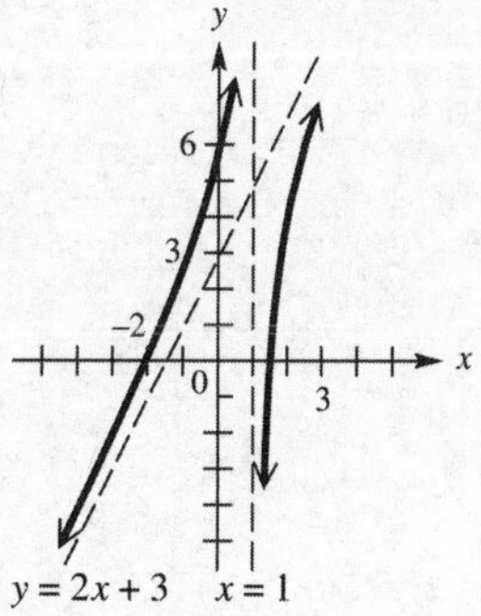

$f(x)=\frac{2x^2+x-6}{x-1}$

21. *Step 1* $y=k\sqrt{x}$

Step 2 Substitute $y=12$ and $x=4$ to find k.

$$12=k\sqrt{4}$$
$$12=2k$$
$$k=6$$

Step 3 $y=6\sqrt{x}$

Step 4 Now find y when $x=100$.

$$y=6\sqrt{100}=6\cdot 10=60$$

22. *Step 1* Let w be the weight of the object (in kg). d is the distance from the center of Earth (in km).

$$w=\frac{k}{d^2}$$

Step 2 Substitute $w=90$ and $d=6400$ to find k.

$$90=\frac{k}{6400^2}$$
$$90=\frac{k}{40{,}960{,}000}$$
$$k=3{,}686{,}400{,}000$$

Step 3 $w=\frac{3{,}686{,}400{,}000}{d^2}$

Step 4 Now find w when $d=800+6400=7200$.

$$w=\frac{3{,}686{,}400{,}000}{7200^2}$$
$$w=\frac{3{,}686{,}400{,}000}{51{,}840{,}000}=\frac{640}{9}\approx 71.1$$

The man weighs $\frac{640}{9}$ kg or approximately 71.1 kg.

Chapter 4

EXPONENTIAL AND LOGARITHMIC FUNCTIONS

Section 4.1: Inverse Functions

1. It is not one-to-one because both Illinois and Wisconsin are paired with the same range element, 40.

3. This is a one-to-one function since every horizontal line intersects the graph in no more than one point.

5. This is a one-to-one function since every horizontal line intersects the graph in no more than one point.

7. This is not a one-to-one function since there is a horizontal line that intersects the graph in more than one point. (Here a horizontal line intersects the curve at an infinite number of points.)

9. $y=(x-2)^2$

If $x=0,\ y=(0-2)^2=(-2)^2=4$. If $x=4,\ y=(4-2)^2=2^2=4$.

Since two different values of x lead to the same value of y, the function is not one-to-one.

11. $y=\sqrt{36-x^2}$

If $x=6,\ y=\sqrt{36-6^2}=\sqrt{36-36}=\sqrt{0}=0$.

If $x=-6,\ y=\sqrt{36-(-6)^2}=\sqrt{36-36}=\sqrt{0}=0$.

Since two different values of x lead to the same value of y, the function is not one-to-one.

13. $y=2x^3+1$

Looking at this function graphed on a TI-83, we can see that it appears that any horizontal line passed through the function will intersect the graph in at most one place.

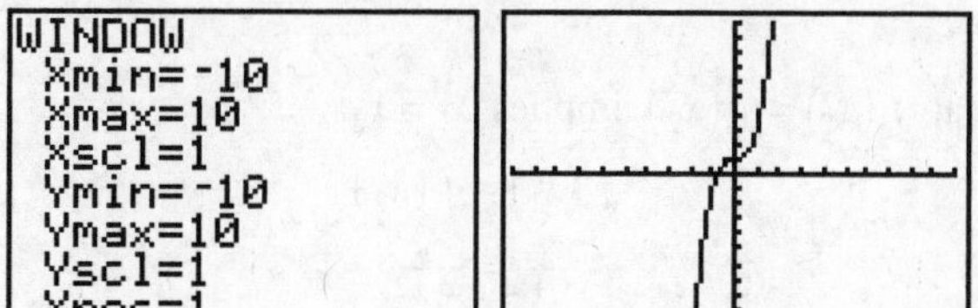

If we attempt to find the inverse function, we see that this function can be found.

Step 1 Interchange x and y.

$$x=2y^3+1$$

Step 2 Solve for y.

$$x=2y^3+1\Rightarrow x-1=2y^3\Rightarrow \tfrac{x-1}{2}=y^3\Rightarrow y=\sqrt[3]{\tfrac{x-1}{2}}$$

Step 3 Replace y with $f^{-1}(x)$.

$$f^{-1}(x)=\sqrt[3]{\tfrac{x-1}{2}}$$

Continued on next page

13. (continued)

Also, an acceptable way of showing that a function is one-to-one is to assume that you have two equal y-values $\left(f(x_1)=f(x_2)\right)$ and show that they must have come from the same x-value $(x_1=x_2)$.

$$f(x_1)=f(x_2)$$
$$2(x_1)^3+1=2(x_2)^3+1$$
$$2(x_1)^3=2(x_2)^3$$
$$(x_1)^3=(x_2)^3$$
$$\sqrt[3]{(x_1)^3}=\sqrt[3]{(x_2)^3}$$
$$x_1=x_2$$

So, the function is one-to-one.

15. $y=\frac{1}{x+2}$

Looking at this function graphed on a TI-83, we can see that it appears that any horizontal line passed through the function will intersect the graph in at most one place.

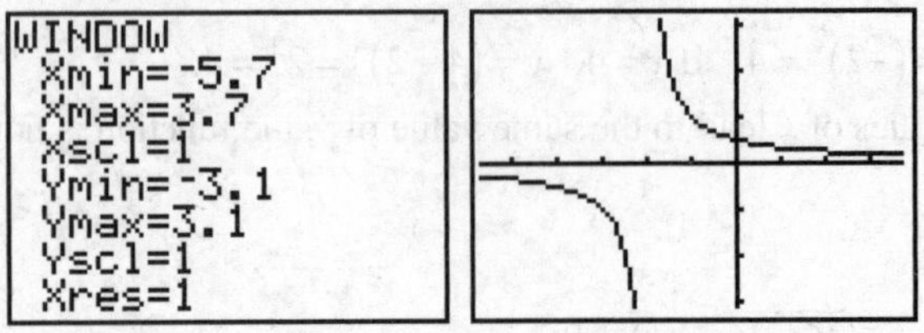

If we attempt to find the inverse function, we see that this function can be found.

Step 1 Interchange x and y.

$x=\frac{1}{y+2}$

Step 2 Solve for y.

$x=\frac{1}{y+2}\Rightarrow x(y+2)=1\Rightarrow xy+2x=1\Rightarrow xy=1-2x\Rightarrow y=\frac{1-2x}{x}$

Step 3 Replace y with $f^{-1}(x)$.

$f^{-1}(x)=\frac{1-2x}{x}$

We could also show that $f(x_1)=f(x_2)$ implies $x_1=x_2$.

$$f(x_1)=f(x_2)$$
$$\frac{1}{x_1+2}=\frac{1}{x_2+2}$$
$$x_2+2=x_1+2$$
$$x_2=x_1$$

So, the function is one-to-one.

17. In order for a function to have an inverse, it must be one-to-one.

19. The domain of f is equal to the range of f^{-1}, and the range of f is equal to the domain of f^{-1}.

21. It is false that if $f(x)=x^2$, then $f^{-1}(x)=\sqrt{x}$ because f is not a one-to-one function and, hence, does not have an inverse.

23. If a function f has an inverse and $f(-3)=6$, then $f^{-1}(6)=-3$.

25. Answers will vary.
A polynomial of even degree has end behavior pointing in the same direction. This would indicate that the function would not pass the horizontal line test and cannot have an inverse.

27. The inverse operation of tying your shoelaces would be untying your shoelaces, since untying "undoes" tying.

29. The inverse operation of entering a room would be leaving a room, since leaving "undoes" entering.

31. The inverse operation of fast-forwarding a tape would be rewinding a tape, since rewinding "undoes" fast-forwarding.

33. For each point (x, y) for the first function, there is a point (y, x) for the second function, so $f(x)$ and $g(x)$ are inverses of each other.

35. The point $(3,5)$ is on $f(x)$, but the point $(5,3)$ is not on $g(x)$ (there is another example), so the functions are not inverses of each other.

37. These functions are inverses since their graphs are symmetric with respect to the line $y = x$.

39. $f(x)=2x+4,\ g(x)=\frac{1}{2}x-2$

$(f\circ g)(x)=f[g(x)]=2(\tfrac{1}{2}x-2)+4=x-4+4=x$

$(g\circ f)(x)=g[f(x)]=\tfrac{1}{2}(2x+4)-2=x+2-2=x$

Since $(f\circ g)(x)=x$ and $(g\circ f)(x)=x$, these functions are inverses.

41. $f(x)=\frac{2}{x+6},\ g(x)=\frac{6x+2}{x}$

$$(f\circ g)(x)=f[g(x)]=\frac{2}{\frac{6x+2}{x}+6}=\frac{2}{\frac{6x+2+6x}{x}}=\frac{2}{1}\cdot\frac{x}{12x+2}=\frac{2x}{12x+2}=\frac{x}{6x+1}\neq x$$

Since $(f\circ g)(x)\neq x$, the functions are not inverses. It is not necessary to check $(g\circ f)(x)$.

43. $f(x)=x^2+3$, domain $[0,\infty)$; $g(x)=\sqrt{x-3}$, domain $[3,\infty)$

$(f\circ g)(x)=f[g(x)]=f\left(\sqrt{x-3}\right)=\left(\sqrt{x-3}\right)^2+3=x$

$(g\circ f)(x)=g[f(x)]=g\left(x^2+3\right)=\sqrt{x^2+3-3}=\sqrt{x^2}=|x|=x$ for $[0,\infty)$

Since $(f\circ g)(x)=x$ and $(g\circ f)(x)=x$, these functions are inverses.

45. Since each y-value corresponds to only one x-value, this function is one-to one and has an inverse. The inverse is: $\{(6,-3),(1,2),(8,5)\}$.

47. Since the y-value -3 corresponds to two different x-values, this function is not one-to-one.

49. $y = 3x - 4$

The function, $f(x) = 3x - 4$, is one-to-one.

(a) *Step 1* Interchange x and y.

$x = 3y - 4$

Step 2 Solve for y.

$x = 3y - 4 \Rightarrow x + 4 = 3y \Rightarrow \frac{x+4}{3} = y \Rightarrow y = \frac{x+4}{3} = \frac{1}{3}x + \frac{4}{3}$

Step 3 Replace y with $f^{-1}(x)$.

$f^{-1}(x) = \frac{1}{3}x + \frac{4}{3}$

(b) The graph of the original function, $f(x) = 3x - 4$, is a line with slope 3 and y-intercept -4. Since $f^{-1}(x) = \frac{1}{3}x + \frac{4}{3}$, the graph of the inverse function is a line with slope $\frac{1}{3}$ and y-intercept $\frac{4}{3}$.

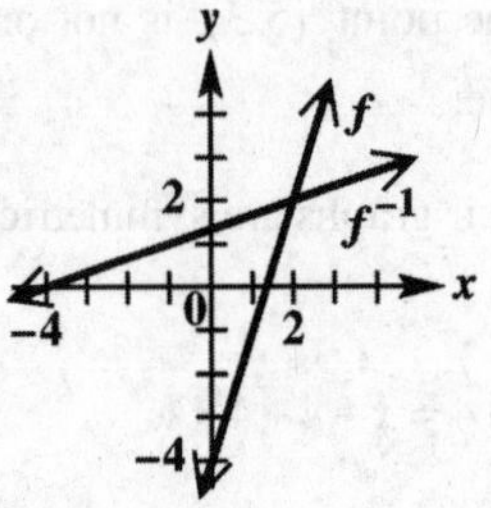

(c) For both $f(x)$ and $f^{-1}(x)$, the domain is $(-\infty, \infty)$ and the range is $(-\infty, \infty)$.

51. $f(x) = -4x + 3$

This function is one-to-one.

(a) *Step 1* Replace $f(x)$ with y and interchange x and y.

$y = -4x + 3$

$x = -4y + 3$

Step 2 Solve for y.

$x = -4y + 3 \Rightarrow x - 3 = -4y \Rightarrow \frac{x-3}{-4} = y \Rightarrow y = \frac{x-3}{-4} = -\frac{1}{4}x + \frac{3}{4}$

Step 3 Replace y with $f^{-1}(x)$.

$f^{-1}(x) = -\frac{1}{4}x + \frac{3}{4}$

(b) The graph of the original function, $f(x) = -4x + 3$, is a line with slope -4 and y-intercept 3. Since $f^{-1}(x) = -\frac{1}{4}x + \frac{3}{4}$, the graph of the inverse function is a line with slope $-\frac{1}{4}$ and y-intercept $\frac{3}{4}$.

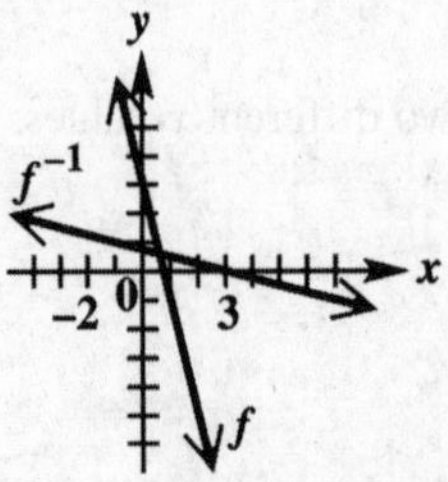

(c) For both $f(x)$ and $f^{-1}(x)$, the domain is $(-\infty, \infty)$ and the range is $(-\infty, \infty)$.

53. $f(x) = x^3 + 1$

This function is one-to-one.

(a) *Step 1* Replace $f(x)$ with y and interchange x and y.

$y = x^3 + 1$

$x = y^3 + 1$

Step 2 Solve for y.

$x = y^3 + 1 \Rightarrow x - 1 = y^3$

$\sqrt[3]{x-1} = y$

$y = \sqrt[3]{x-1}$

Step 3 Replace y with $f^{-1}(x)$.

$f^{-1}(x) = \sqrt[3]{x-1}$

(b) Tables of ordered pairs will be helpful in drawing the graphs of these functions.

x	$f(x)$	x	$f^{-1}(x)$
–2	–7	–7	–2
–1	0	0	–1
0	1	1	0
1	2	2	1
2	9	9	2

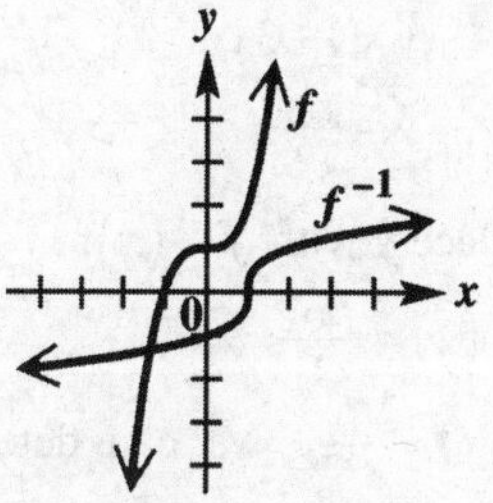

(c) For both $f(x)$ and $f^{-1}(x)$, the domain is $(-\infty, \infty)$ and the range is $(-\infty, \infty)$.

55. $y = x^2$

This is not a one-to-one function since two different x-values can correspond to the same y-value ($2^2 = 4$ and $(-2)^2 = 4$, for example), so this function is not one-to-one. Thus, the function has no inverse function.

57. $y = \frac{1}{x}$

The function, $f(x) = \frac{1}{x}$, is one-to-one.

(a) *Step 1* Interchange x and y.

$y = \frac{1}{x}$

$x = \frac{1}{y}$

Step 2 Solve for y.

$x = \frac{1}{y} \Rightarrow xy = 1 \Rightarrow y = \frac{1}{x}$

Step 3 Replace y with $f^{-1}(x)$.

$f^{-1}(x) = \frac{1}{x}$

(b) Tables of ordered pairs will be helpful in drawing the graph of this function (in this case, $f(x) = f^{-1}(x)$).

x	$f(x) = f^{-1}(x)$
–2	$-\frac{1}{2}$
–1	–1
$-\frac{1}{2}$	–2
$\frac{1}{2}$	2
1	1
2	$\frac{1}{2}$

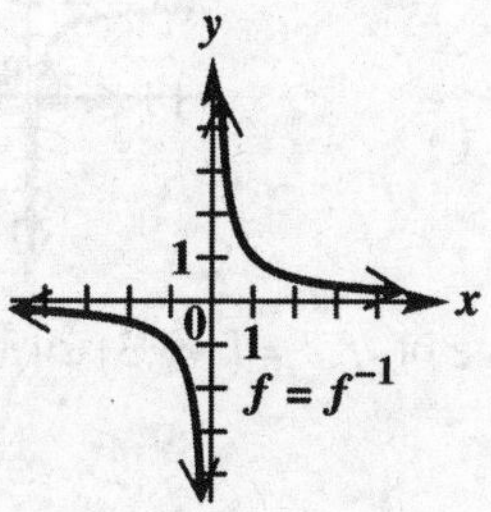

(c) For both $f(x)$ and $f^{-1}(x)$, the domain and range are both $(-\infty, 0) \cup (0, \infty)$.

59. $f(x)=\frac{1}{x-3}$

This function is one-to-one.

(a) *Step 1* Replace $f(x)$ with y and interchange x and y.

$$y=\frac{1}{x-3}$$
$$x=\frac{1}{y-3}$$

Step 2 Solve for y.

$$x=\frac{1}{y-3}$$
$$x(y-3)=1$$
$$xy-3x=1$$
$$xy=1+3x$$
$$y=\frac{1+3x}{x}$$

Step 3 Replace y with $f^{-1}(x)$.

$$f^{-1}(x)=\frac{1+3x}{x}$$

(b) To graph $f(x)=\frac{1}{x-3}$, we can determine that there are no x-intercepts. The y-intercept is $f(0)=\frac{1}{0-3}=-\frac{1}{3}$. There is a vertical aymptote when the denominator is zero, $x-3=0$, which implies $x=3$ is the vertical asymptote. Also, the horizontal asymptote is $y=0$ since the degree of the numerator is less than the denominator. Examining the following intervals, we have test points which will be helpful in drawing the graph of f as well as f^{-1}.

Interval	Test Point	Value of $f(x)$	Sign of $f(x)$	Graph Above or Below x-Axis
$(-\infty, 3)$	2	-1	Negative	Below
$(3, \infty)$	4	1	Positive	Above

Plot the vertical asymptote, y-intercept, and test points with a smooth curve to get the graph of f. To graph $f^{-1}(x)=\frac{1+3x}{x}$, we can determine that the x-intercept occurs when $1+3x=0 \Rightarrow x=-\frac{1}{3}$. There is no y-intercept since 0 is not in the domain f^{-1}. There is a vertical aymptote when the denominator is zero, namely $x=0$. Also, since the degree of the numerator is the same as the denominator, the horizontal asymptote is $y=\frac{3}{1}=3$. Using this information along with the points $(-1,2)$ and $(1,4)$, we can sketch f^{-1}.

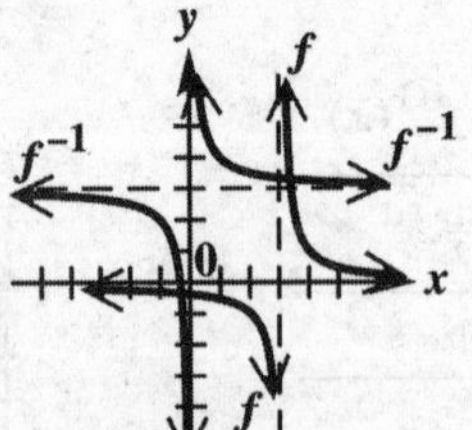

(c) Domain of f = range of $f^{-1}=(-\infty,3)\cup(3,\infty)$; Domain of f^{-1} = range of $f=(-\infty,0)\cup(0,\infty)$

61. $f(x)=\sqrt{6+x}$

This function is one-to-one.

(a) *Step 1* Replace $f(x)$ with *y* and interchange *x* and *y*.

$$y=\sqrt{6+x}$$
$$x=\sqrt{6+y}$$

Step 2 Solve for *y*. In this problem we must consider that the range of *f* will be the domain of f^{-1}.

$$x=\sqrt{6+y}$$
$$x^2=\left(\sqrt{6+y}\right)^2,\text{ for } x\ge 0$$
$$x^2=6+y,\text{ for } x\ge 0$$
$$x^2-6=y,\text{ for } x\ge 0$$

Step 3 Replace *y* with $f^{-1}(x)$.

$$f^{-1}(x)=x^2-6,\text{ for } x\ge 0$$

(b) Tables of ordered pairs will be helpful in drawing the graphs of these functions.

x	$f(x)$	x	$f^{-1}(x)$
–6	0	0	–6
–5	1	1	–5
–2	2	2	–2
3	3	3	3

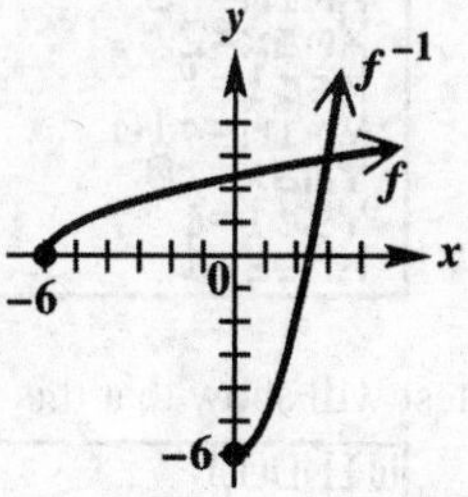

(c) Domain of *f* = range of f^{-1} = $[-6,\infty)$; Range of *f* = domain of f^{-1} = $[0,\infty)$

63. Draw the mirror image of the original graph across the line $y=x$.

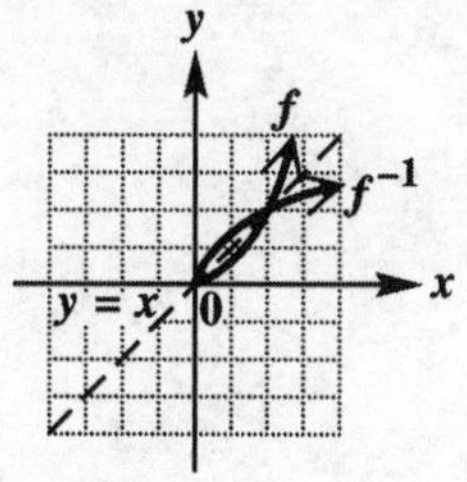

65. Carefully draw the mirror image of the original graph across the line $y=x$.

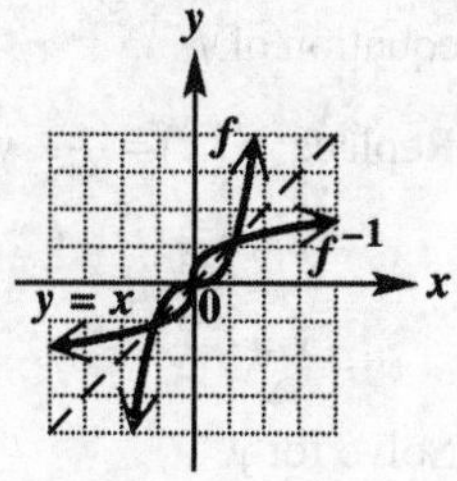

67. Draw the mirror image of the original graph across the line $y=x$.

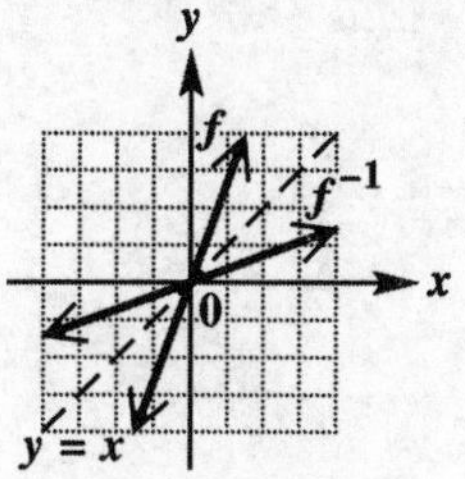

69. To find $f^{-1}(4)$, find the point with *y*-coordinate equal to 4. That point is (4, 4). The graph of f^{-1} contains (4, 4). Hence $f^{-1}(4)=4$.

71. To find $f^{-1}(0)$, find the point with *y*-coordinate equal to 0. That point is $(2,0)$. The graph of f^{-1} contains $(0,2)$. Hence $f^{-1}(0)=2$.

73. To find $f^{-1}(-3)$, find the point with *y*-coordinate equal to −3. That point is $(-2,-3)$. The graph of f^{-1} contains $(-3,-2)$. Hence $f^{-1}(-3)=-2$.

75. $f^{-1}(1000)$ represents the number of dollars required to build 1000 cars.

77. If a line has slope *a*, the slope of its reflection in the line $y=x$ will be reciprocal of *a*, which is $\frac{1}{a}$.

79. The horizontal line test will show that this function is not one-to-one.

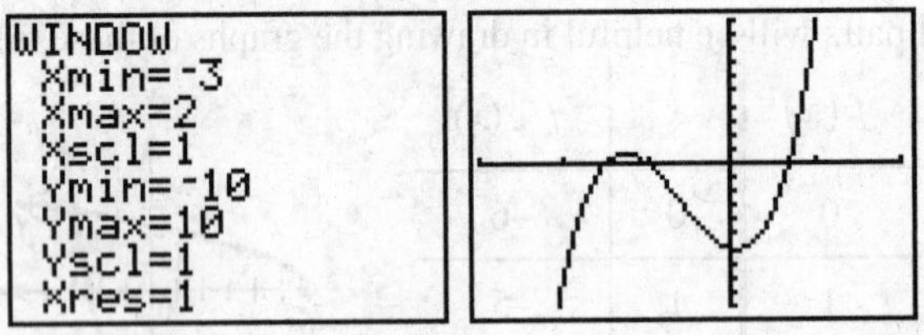

81. The horizontal line test will show that this function is one-to-one.

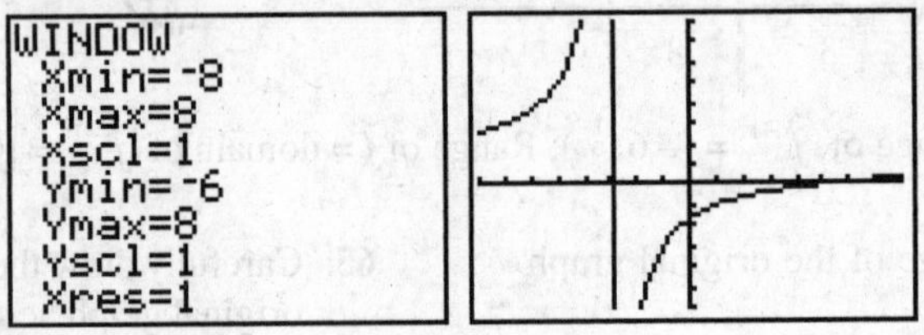

Find the equation of f^{-1}.

Step 1 Replace $f(x)=\frac{x-5}{x+3}$ with *y* and interchange *x* and *y*.

$$y=\frac{x-5}{x+3}$$

$$x=\frac{y-5}{y+3}$$

Step 2 Solve for *y*.

$$x=\frac{y-5}{y+3}\Rightarrow x(y+3)=y-5\Rightarrow xy+3x=y-5$$

$$xy-y=-5-3x\Rightarrow y(x-1)=-5-3x\Rightarrow y=\frac{-5-3x}{x-1}$$

Step 3 Replace *y* with $f^{-1}(x)$.

$$f^{-1}(x)=\frac{-5-3x}{x-1}$$

83. Given $f(x)=3x-2$, find $f^{-1}(x)$.

Step 1 Replace $f(x)=3x-2$ with *y* and interchange *x* and *y*.

$$y=3x-2$$
$$x=3y-2$$

Step 2 Solve for *y*.

$$x=3y-2 \Rightarrow x+2=3y \Rightarrow \frac{x+2}{3}=y$$

Step 3 Replace *y* with $f^{-1}(x)$.

$$f^{-1}(x)=\frac{x+2}{3}$$

37; $f^{-1}(37)=\frac{37+2}{3}=\frac{39}{3}=13$; M	25; $f^{-1}(25)=\frac{25+2}{3}=\frac{27}{3}=9$; I	19; $f^{-1}(9)=\frac{19+2}{3}=\frac{21}{3}=7$; G
61; $f^{-1}(61)=\frac{61+2}{3}=\frac{63}{3}=21$; U	13; $f^{-1}(13)=\frac{13+2}{3}=\frac{15}{3}=5$; E	34; $f^{-1}(34)=\frac{34+2}{3}=\frac{36}{3}=12$; L
22; $f^{-1}(22)=\frac{22+2}{3}=\frac{24}{3}=8$; H	1; $f^{-1}(1)=\frac{1+2}{3}=\frac{3}{3}=1$; A	55; $f^{-1}(55)=\frac{55+2}{3}=\frac{57}{3}=19$; S
1; $f^{-1}(1)=\frac{1+2}{3}=\frac{3}{3}=1$; A	52; $f^{-1}(52)=\frac{52+2}{3}=\frac{54}{3}=18$; R	52; $f^{-1}(52)=\frac{52+2}{3}=\frac{54}{3}=18$; R
25; $f^{-1}(25)=\frac{25+2}{3}=\frac{27}{3}=9$; I	64; $f^{-1}(64)=\frac{64+2}{3}=\frac{66}{3}=22$; V	13; $f^{-1}(13)=\frac{13+2}{3}=\frac{15}{3}=5$; E
10; $f^{-1}(10)=\frac{10+2}{3}=\frac{12}{3}=4$; D		

The message is MIGUEL HAS ARRIVED.

85. Given $f(x)=x^3-1$, we have the following.

$S=19$; $f(19)=19^3-1=6859-1=6858$	$E=5$; $f(5)=5^3=125-1=124$
$N=14$; $f(14)=14^3-1=2744-1=2743$	$D=4$; $f(4)=4^3-1=64-1=63$
$H=8$; $f(8)=8^3-1=512-1=511$	$E=5$; $f(5)=5^3-1=125-1=124$
$L=12$; $f(12)=12^3-1=1728-1=1727$	$P=16$; $f(16)=16^3-1=4096-1=4095$

Given $f(x)=x^3-1$, find $f^{-1}(x)$.

Step 1 Replace $f(x)=x^3-1$ with *y* and interchange *x* and *y*.

$$y=x^3-1$$
$$x=y^3-1$$

Step 2 Solve for *y*.

$$x=y^3-1 \Rightarrow x+1=y^3 \Rightarrow \sqrt[3]{x+1}=y$$

Step 3 Replace *y* with $f^{-1}(x)$.

$$f^{-1}(x)=\sqrt[3]{x+1}$$

87. Answers will vary.
In the encoding/decoding process, you want to ensure that one value to be encoded will yield one encoded value (so the encoding relation itself must be a function). In order to ensure that one encoded value will yield only one decoded value, your decoding relation must also be a function. To ensure this, the original encoding function must be one-to one.

Section 4.2: Exponential Functions

Connections (page 414)

1. $e^1 \approx 1+1+\frac{1^2}{2\cdot1}+\frac{1^3}{3\cdot2\cdot1}+\frac{1^4}{4\cdot3\cdot2\cdot1}+\frac{1^5}{5\cdot4\cdot3\cdot2\cdot1}=1+1+\frac{1}{2}+\frac{1}{6}+\frac{1}{24}+\frac{1}{120}\approx 2.717$

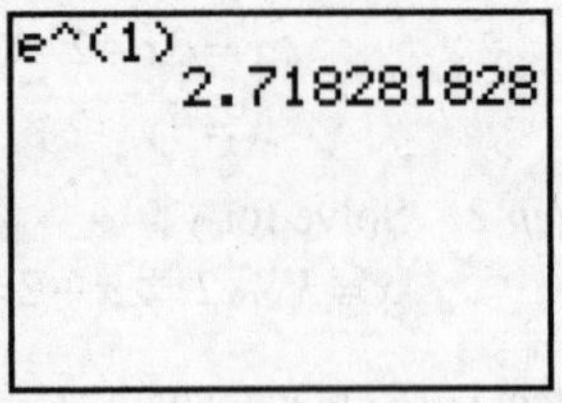

2. $e^{-.05} \approx 1+(-.05)+\frac{(-.05)^2}{2\cdot1}+\frac{(-.05)^3}{3\cdot2\cdot1}+\frac{(-.05)^4}{4\cdot3\cdot2\cdot1}+\frac{(-.05)^5}{5\cdot4\cdot3\cdot2\cdot1}$

$=1-.05+\frac{.0025}{2}-\frac{.000125}{6}+\frac{.00000625}{24}-\frac{.0000003125}{120}\approx .9512$

3. $\frac{x^6}{6\cdot5\cdot4\cdot3\cdot2\cdot1}$

Exercises

1. $f(x)=3^x$

$f(2)=3^2=9$

3. $f(x)=3^x$

$f(-2)=3^{-2}=\frac{1}{3^2}=\frac{1}{9}$

5. $g(x)=\left(\frac{1}{4}\right)^x$

$g(2)=\left(\frac{1}{4}\right)^2=\frac{1}{16}$

7. $g(x)=\left(\frac{1}{4}\right)^x$

$g(-2)=\left(\frac{1}{4}\right)^{-2}=4^2=16$

9. $f(x)=3^x$

$f\left(\frac{3}{2}\right)=3^{3/2}\approx 5.196$

11. $g(x)=\left(\frac{1}{4}\right)^x$

$g(2.34)=\left(\frac{1}{4}\right)^{2.34}\approx .039$

13. The y-intercept of $f(x)=3^x$ is 1, and the x-axis is a horizontal asymptote. Make a table of values.

x	$f(x)$
-2	$\frac{1}{9}\approx .1$
-1	$\frac{1}{3}\approx .3$
$-\frac{1}{2}$	$\approx .6$
0	1
$\frac{1}{2}$	≈ 1.7
1	3
2	9

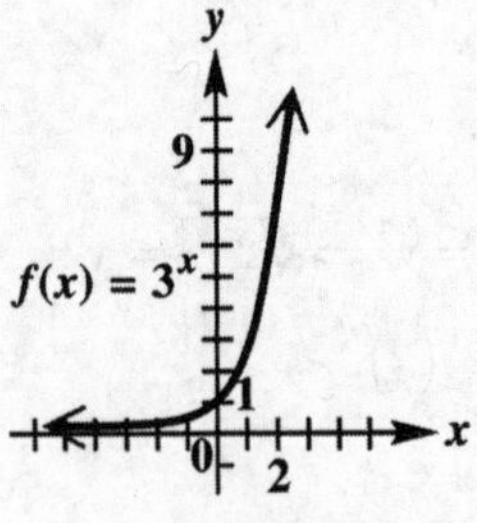

Plot these points and draw a smooth curve through them. This is an increasing function. The domain is $(-\infty,\infty)$ and the range is $(0,\infty)$ and is one-to-one.

15. The y-intercept of $f(x)=\left(\frac{1}{3}\right)^x$ is 1, and the x-axis is a horizontal asymptote. Make a table of values.

x	$f(x)$
-2	9
-1	3
$-\frac{1}{2}$	≈ 1.7
0	1
$\frac{1}{2}$	$\approx .6$
1	$\frac{1}{3}\approx .3$
2	$\frac{1}{9}\approx .1$

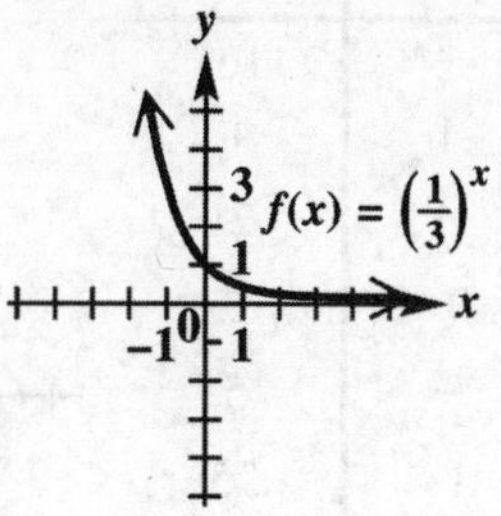

Plot these points and draw a smooth curve through them. This is a decreasing function. The domain is $(-\infty,\infty)$ and the range is $(0,\infty)$ and is one-to-one. Note: Since $f(x)=\left(\frac{1}{3}\right)^x=\left(3^{-1}\right)^x=3^{-x}$, the graph of $f(x)=\left(\frac{1}{3}\right)^x$ is the reflection of the graph of $f(x)=3^x$ (Exercise 13) about the y-axis.

17. The y-intercept of $f(x)=\left(\frac{3}{2}\right)^x$ is 1, and the x-axis is a horizontal asymptote. Make a table of values.

x	$f(x)$
-2	$\approx .4$
-1	$\approx .7$
$-\frac{1}{2}$	$\approx .8$
0	1
$\frac{1}{2}$	≈ 1.2
1	1.5
2	2.25

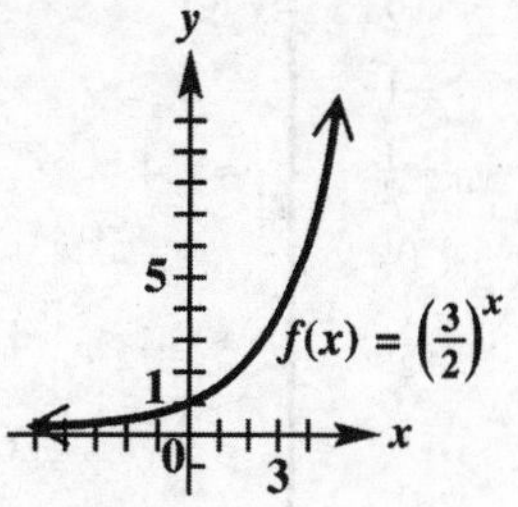

Plot these points and draw a smooth curve through them. This is an increasing function. The domain is $(-\infty,\infty)$ and the range is $(0,\infty)$ and is one-to-one.

19. The y-intercept of $f(x)=10^x$ is 1, and the x-axis is a horizontal asymptote. Make a table of values.

x	$f(x)$
-2	.01
-1	.1
$-\frac{1}{2}$	$\approx .3$
0	1
$\frac{1}{2}$	≈ 3.2
1	10
2	100

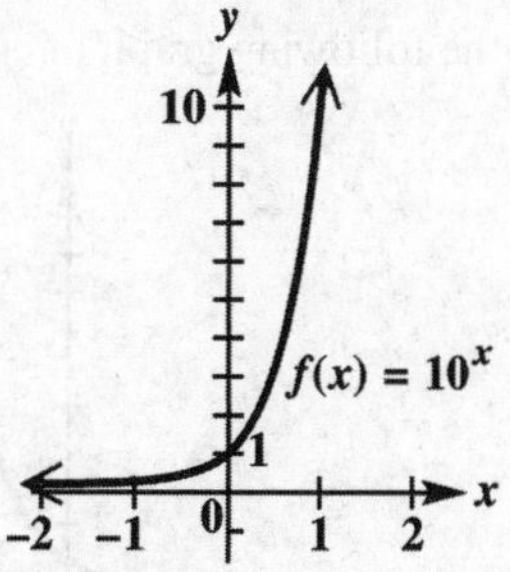

Plot these points and draw a smooth curve through them. This is an increasing function. The domain is $(-\infty,\infty)$ and the range is $(0,\infty)$ and is one-to-one.

21. The y-intercept of $f(x)=4^{-x}$ is 1, and the x-axis is a horizontal asymptote. Make a table of values.

x	$f(x)$
−2	16
−1	4
$-\frac{1}{2}$	2
0	1
$\frac{1}{2}$	.5
1	.25
2	.0625

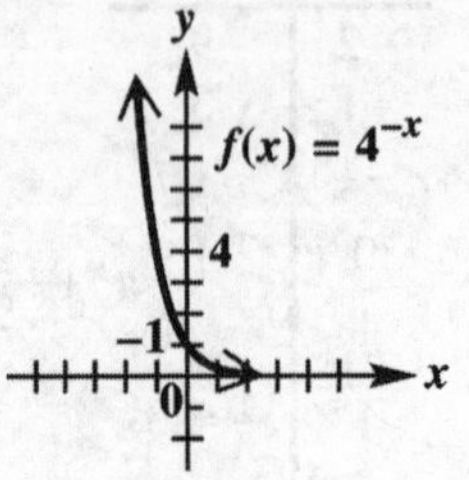

Plot these points and draw a smooth curve through them. This is a decreasing function. The domain is $(-\infty,\infty)$ and the range is $(0,\infty)$ and is one-to-one. Note: The graph of $f(x)=4^{-x}$ is the reflection of the graph of $f(x)=4^{x}$ (Exercise 14) about the y-axis.

23. The y-intercept of $f(x)=2^{|x|}$ is 1, and the x-axis is a horizontal asymptote. Make a table of values.

x	$f(x)$
−2	4
−1	2
$-\frac{1}{2}$	≈1.4
0	1
$\frac{1}{2}$	≈1.4
1	2
2	4

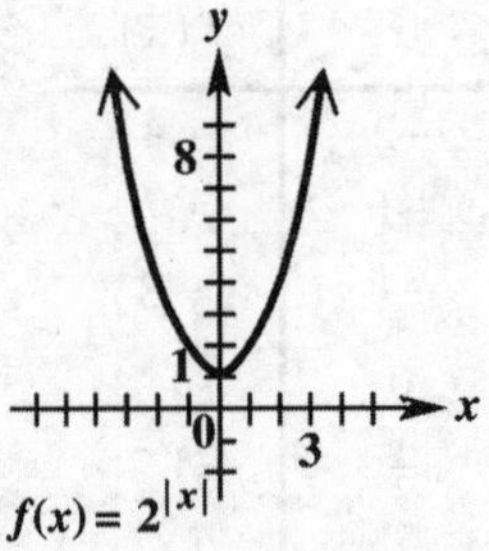

Plot these points and draw a smooth curve through them. The domain is $(-\infty,\infty)$ and the range is $[1,\infty)$ and is not one-to-one. Note: For $x<0$, $|x|=-x$, so the graph is the same as that of $f(x)=2^{-x}$. For $x\geq 0$, we have $|x|=x$, so the graph is the same as that of $f(x)=2^{x}$. Since $|-x|=|x|$, the graph is symmetric with respect to the y-axis.

For Exercises 25 – 27, refer to the following graph of $f(x)=2^{x}$.

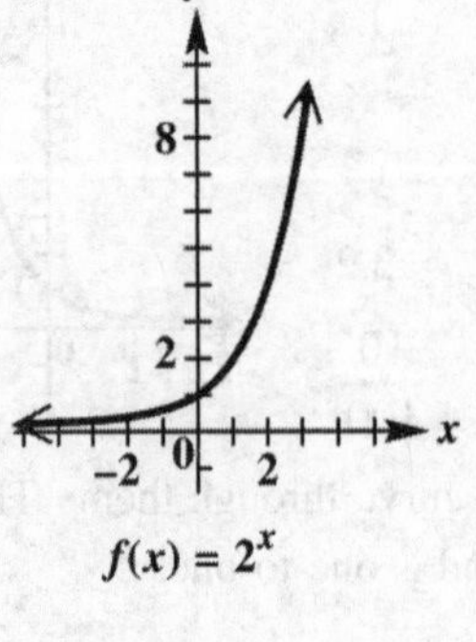

25. The graph of $f(x)=2^x+1$ is obtained by translating the graph of $f(x)=2^x$ up 1 unit.

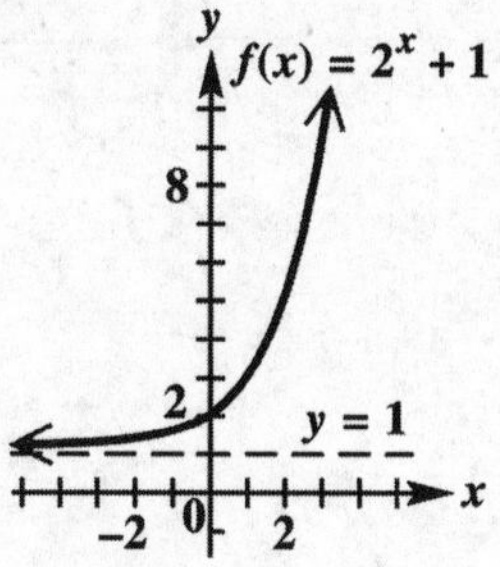

27. Since $f(x)=2^{x+1}=2^{x-(-1)}$, the graph is obtained by translating the graph of $f(x)=2^x$ to the left 1 unit.

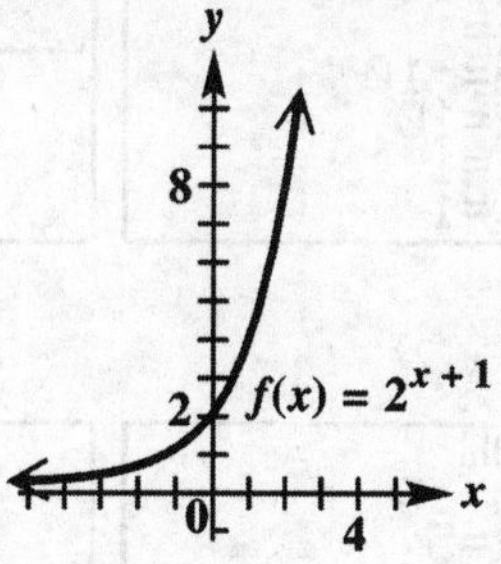

For Exercises 29 –31, refer to the following graph of $f(x)=\left(\frac{1}{3}\right)^x$.

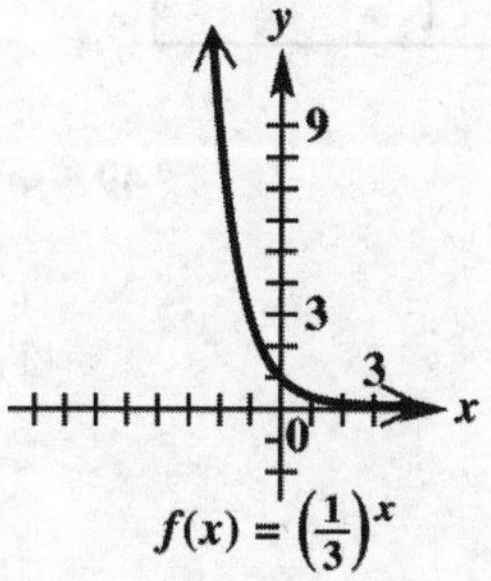

29. The graph of $f(x)=\left(\frac{1}{3}\right)^x-2$ obtained by translating the graph of $f(x)=\left(\frac{1}{3}\right)^x$ down 2 units.

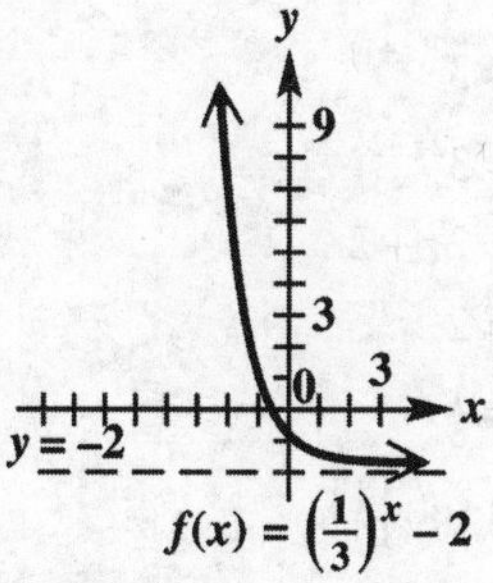

31. Since $f(x)=\left(\frac{1}{3}\right)^{x+2}=\left(\frac{1}{3}\right)^{x-(-2)}$, the graph is obtained by translating the graph of $f(x)=\left(\frac{1}{3}\right)^x$ 2 units to the left.

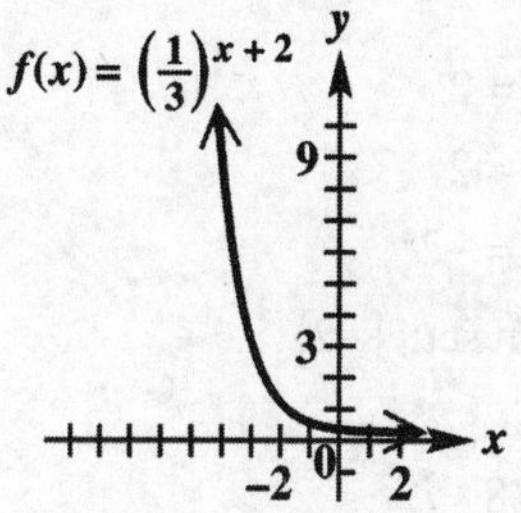

33. $a=2.3$
Since graph A is increasing, $a>1$. Since graph A is the middle of the three increasing graphs, the value of a must be the middle of the three values of a greater than 1.

35. $a=.75$
Since graph C is decreasing, $0<a<1$. Since graph C decreases at the slowest rate of the three decreasing graphs, the value of a must be the closest to 1 of the three values of less than 1.

37. $a=.31$
Since graph E is decreasing, $0<a<1$. Since graph E decreases at the fastest rate of the three decreasing graphs, the value of a must be the closest to 0 of the three values of a less than 1.

39. $f(x)=\frac{e^x-e^{-x}}{2}$

```
WINDOW
 Xmin=-10
 Xmax=10
 Xscl=1
 Ymin=-10
 Ymax=10
 Yscl=1
 Xres=1
```

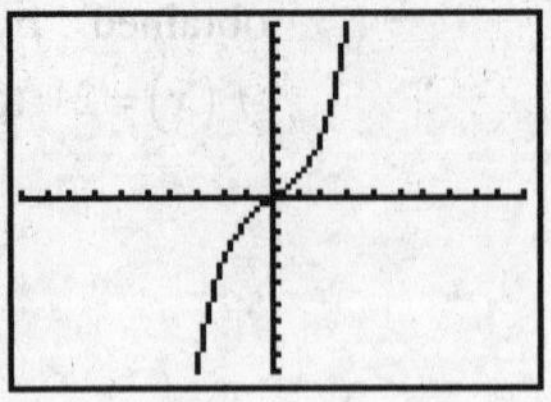

41. $f(x)=x\cdot 2^x$

```
WINDOW
 Xmin=-5
 Xmax=5
 Xscl=1
 Ymin=-2
 Ymax=2
 Yscl=1
 Xres=1
```

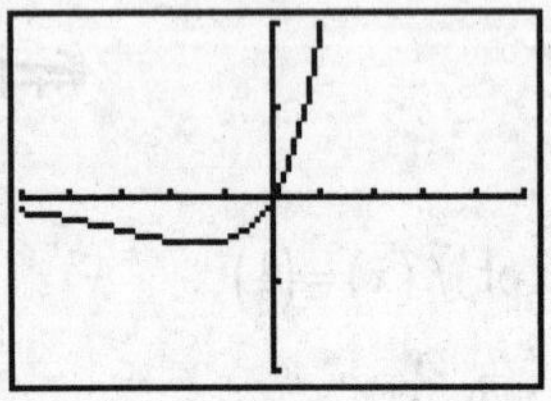

43.
$$4^x=2$$
$$\left(2^2\right)^x=2^1$$
$$2^{2x}=2^1$$
$$2x=1$$
$$x=\tfrac{1}{2}$$

Solution set: $\left\{\tfrac{1}{2}\right\}$

45.
$$\left(\tfrac{1}{2}\right)^k=4$$
$$\left(2^{-1}\right)^k=2^2$$
$$2^{-k}=2$$
$$-k=2$$
$$k=-2$$

Solution set: $\{-2\}$

47.
$$2^{3-y}=8$$
$$2^{3-y}=2^3$$
$$3-y=3$$
$$-y=0$$
$$y=0$$

Solution set: $\{0\}$

49.
$$e^{4x-1}=\left(e^2\right)^x$$
$$e^{4x-1}=e^{2x}$$
$$4x-1=2x$$
$$-1=-2x$$
$$\tfrac{1}{2}=x$$

Solution set: $\left\{\tfrac{1}{2}\right\}$

51.
$$27^{4z}=9^{z+1}$$
$$\left(3^3\right)^{4z}=\left(3^2\right)^{z+1}$$
$$3^{3(4z)}=3^{2(z+1)}$$
$$3^{12z}=3^{2z+2}$$
$$12z=2z+2$$
$$10z=2$$
$$z=\tfrac{1}{5}$$

Solution set: $\left\{\tfrac{1}{5}\right\}$

53.
$$4^{x-2}=2^{3x+3}$$
$$\left(2^2\right)^{x-2}=2^{3x+3}$$
$$2^{2(x-2)}=2^{3x+3}$$
$$2^{2x-4}=2^{3x+3}$$
$$2x-4=3x+3$$
$$-4=x+3$$
$$-7=x$$

Solution set: $\{-7\}$

55. $\left(\frac{1}{e}\right)^{-x} = \left(\frac{1}{e^2}\right)^{x+1}$

$\left(e^{-1}\right)^{-x} = \left(e^{-2}\right)^{x+1}$

$e^x = e^{-2(x+1)}$

$e^x = e^{-2x-2}$

$x = -2x - 2$

$3x = -2$

$x = -\frac{2}{3}$

Solution set: $\left\{-\frac{2}{3}\right\}$

57. $\left(\sqrt{2}\right)^{x+4} = 4^x$

$\left(2^{1/2}\right)^{x+4} = \left(2^2\right)^x$

$2^{(1/2)(x+4)} = 2^{2x}$

$2^{(1/2)x+2} = 2^{2x}$

$\frac{1}{2}x + 2 = 2x$

$2 = \frac{3}{2}x$

$\frac{2}{3} \cdot 2 = x$

$x = \frac{4}{3}$

Solution set: $\left\{\frac{4}{3}\right\}$

59. $\frac{1}{27} = b^{-3} \Rightarrow 3^{-3} = b^{-3} \Rightarrow b = 3$

Alternate solution:

$\frac{1}{27} = b^{-3} \Rightarrow \frac{1}{27} = \frac{1}{b^3} \Rightarrow 27 = b^3 \Rightarrow b = \sqrt[3]{27} = 3$

Solution set: $\{3\}$

61. $4 = r^{2/3} \Rightarrow 4^{3/2} = \left(r^{2/3}\right)^{3/2} \Rightarrow \left(\pm\sqrt{4}\right)^3 = r \Rightarrow (\pm 2)^3 = r \Rightarrow \pm 8 = r$

Recall from Chapter 1 that it is necessary to check all proposed solutions in the original equation when you raise both sides to a power.

Check $r = -8$.

$4 = r^{2/3}$

$4 = (-8)^{2/3}$?

$4 = \left(\sqrt[3]{-8}\right)^2$

$4 = (-2)^2$

$4 = 4$

This is a true statement.
-8 is a solution.

Check $r = 8$.

$4 = r^{2/3}$

$4 = 8^{2/3}$?

$4 = \left(\sqrt[3]{8}\right)^2$

$4 = 2^2$

$4 = 4$

This is a true statement.
8 is a solution.

Solution set: $\{-8, 8\}$

63. (a) Use the compound interest formula to find the future value, $A = P\left(1 + \frac{r}{m}\right)^{tm}$, given $m = 2$, $P = 8906.54$, $r = .05$, and $t = 9$.

$$A = P\left(1 + \frac{r}{m}\right)^{tm} = (8906.54)\left(1 + \frac{.05}{2}\right)^{9(2)} = (8906.54)(1 + .025)^{18} \approx 13{,}891.16276$$

Rounding to the nearest cent, the future value is \$13,891.16.
The amount of interest would be \$13,891.16 − \$8906.54 = \$4984.62.

(b) Use the continuous compounding interest formula to find the future value, $A = Pe^{rt}$, given $P = 8906.54$, $r = .05$, and $t = 9$.

$$A = Pe^{rt} = 8906.54e^{.05(9)} = 8906.54e^{.45} \approx 8906.54(1.568312) \approx 13{,}968.23521$$

Rounding to the nearest cent, the future value is \$13,968.24.
The amount of interest would be \$13,968.24 − \$8906.54 = \$5061.70.

65. Use the compound interest formula to find the present amount, $A = P\left(1+\frac{r}{m}\right)^{tm}$, given $m = 4$, $A = 25{,}000$, $r = .06$, and $t = \frac{11}{4}$.

$$A = P\left(1+\tfrac{r}{m}\right)^{tm}$$

$$25{,}000 = P\left(1+\tfrac{.06}{4}\right)^{(11/4)(4)} \Rightarrow 25{,}000 = P(1.015)^{11} \Rightarrow P = \frac{25{,}000}{(1.015)^{11}} \approx \$21{,}223.33083$$

Rounding to the nearest cent, the present value is \$21,223.33.

67. Use the compound interest formula to find the present value, $A = P\left(1+\frac{r}{m}\right)^{tm}$, given $m = 4$, $A = 5{,}000$, $r = .035$, and $t = 10$.

$$A = P\left(1+\tfrac{r}{m}\right)^{tm}$$

$$5{,}000 = P\left(1+\tfrac{.035}{4}\right)^{10(4)} \Rightarrow 5{,}000 = P(1.00875)^{40} \Rightarrow P = \frac{5{,}000}{(1.00875)^{40}} \approx \$3528.808535$$

Rounding to the nearest cent, the present value is \$3528.81.

69. Use the compound interest formula to find the interest rate, $A = P\left(1+\frac{r}{m}\right)^{tm}$, given $m = 4$, $A = 1500$, $P = 1200$, and $t = 5$.

$$A = P\left(1+\tfrac{r}{m}\right)^{tm}$$

$$1500 = 1200\left(1+\tfrac{r}{4}\right)^{5(4)} \Rightarrow 1500 = 1200\left(1+\tfrac{r}{4}\right)^{20} \Rightarrow 1.25 = \left(1+\tfrac{r}{4}\right)^{20}$$

$$(1.25)^{\frac{1}{20}} = 1+\tfrac{r}{4} \Rightarrow (1.25)^{\frac{1}{20}} - 1 = \tfrac{r}{4} \Rightarrow 4\left[(1.25)^{\frac{1}{20}} - 1\right] = r$$

$$r \approx .044878604$$

The interest rate, to the nearest tenth, is 4.5%.

71. For each bank we need to calculate $\left(1+\frac{r}{m}\right)^{m}$. Since the base, $1+\frac{r}{m}$, is greater than 1, we need only compare the three values calculated to determine which bank will yield the least amount of interest. It is understood that the amount of time, t, and the principal, P, are the same for all three banks.

Bank A: Calculate $\left(1+\frac{r}{m}\right)^{m}$ where $m = 1$ and $r = .064$.

$$\left(1+\tfrac{.064}{1}\right)^{1} = (1+.064)^{1} = (1.064)^{1} = 1.064$$

Bank B: Calculate $\left(1+\frac{r}{m}\right)^{m}$ where $m = 12$ and $r = .063$.

$$\left(1+\tfrac{.063}{12}\right)^{12} = (1+.00525)^{12} = (1.00525)^{12} \approx 1.064851339$$

Bank C: Calculate $\left(1+\frac{r}{m}\right)^{m}$ where $m = 4$ and $r = .0635$.

$$\left(1+\tfrac{.0635}{4}\right)^{4} = (1+.015875)^{4} = (1.015875)^{4} \approx 1.06502816$$

Bank A will charge you the least amount of interest, even though it has the highest stated rate.

73. (a)

```
WINDOW
 Xmin=-1000
 Xmax=11000
 Xscl=1000
 Ymin=0
 Ymax=1200
 Yscl=100
 Xres=1
```

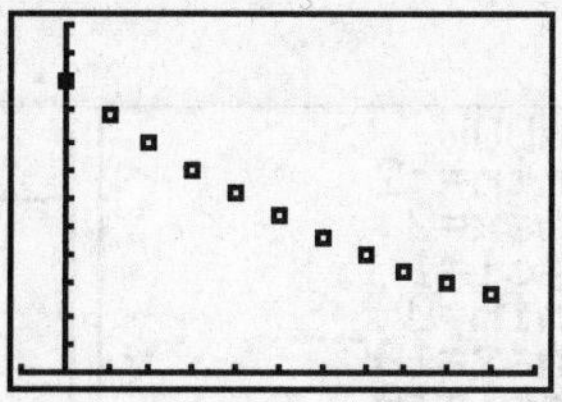

(b) From the graph above, we can see that the data are not linear but exponentially decreasing.

(c)

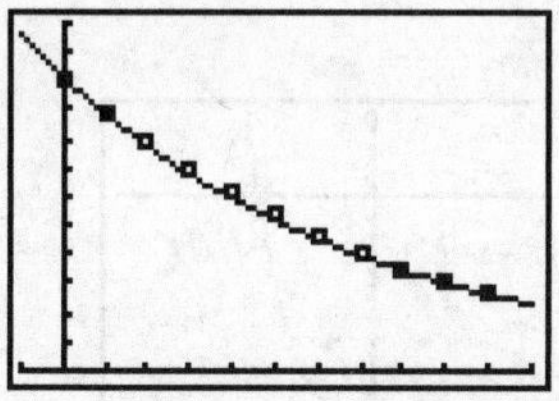

(d) $P(x) = 1013e^{-.0001341x}$

$$P(1500) = 1013e^{-.0001341(1500)} \approx 1013(.817790) \approx 828$$

$$P(11{,}000) = 1013e^{-.0001341(11{,}000)} \approx 1013(.228756) \approx 232$$

When the altitude is 1500 m, the function P gives a pressure of 828 mb, which is less than the actual value of 846 mb. When the altitude is 11,000 m, the function P gives a pressure of 232 mb, which is more than the actual value of 227 mb.

75. (a) Evaluate $T = 50{,}000(1+.06)^n$ where $n = 4$.

$$T = 50{,}000(1+.06)^4 = 50{,}000(1.06)^4 \approx 63{,}123.848$$

Total population after 4 years is about 63,000.

(b) Evaluate $T = 30{,}000(1+.12)^n$ where $n = 3$.

$$T = 30{,}000(1+.12)^3 = 30{,}000(1.12)^3 = 42{,}147.84$$

There would be about 42,000 deer after 3 years.

(c) Evaluate $T = 45{,}000(1+.08)^n$ where $n = 5$.

$$T = 45{,}000(1+.08)^5 = 45{,}000(1.08)^5 \approx 66{,}119.76346$$

There would be about 66,000 deer after 5 years. Thus, we can expect about $66{,}000 - 45{,}000 = 21{,}000$ additional deer after 5 years.

77. $5e^{3x} = 75$

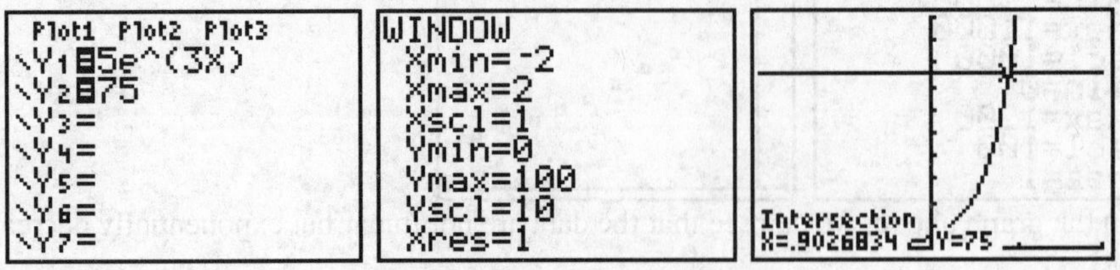

Since $5e^{3x} = 75 \Rightarrow e^{3x} = 15$ we could also do the following.

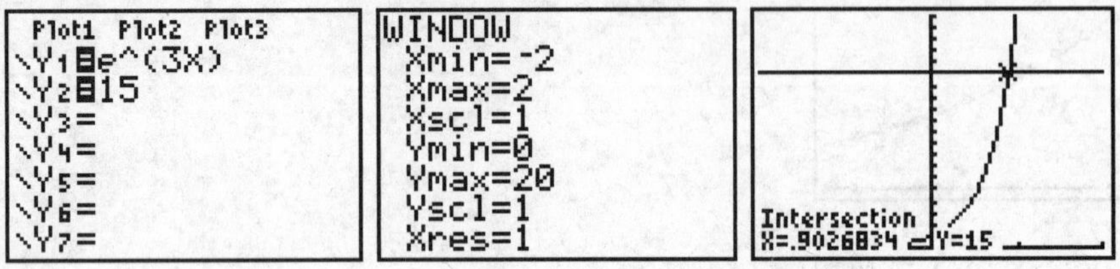

Solution set: {.9}

79. $3x + 2 = 4^x$
We can see from the following screens that there are two solutions.

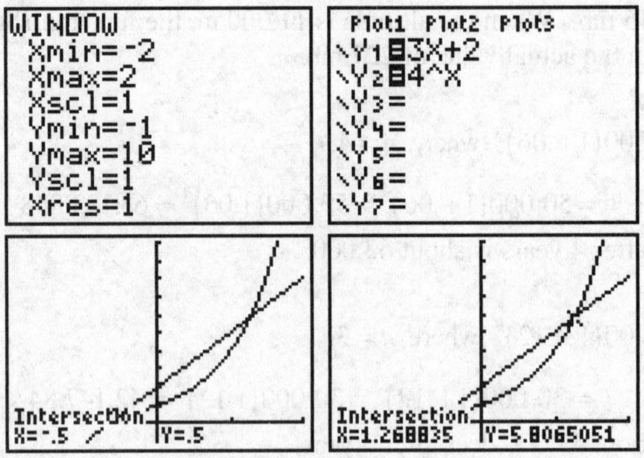

Solution set: {–.5, 1.3}

81. Answers will vary.

83. If the graph of the exponential function $f(x) = a^x$ contains the point (3, 8), we have $a^3 = 8$. This implies $a = \sqrt[3]{8} = 2$. Thus, the equation which satisfies the given condition is $f(x) = 2^x$.

85. $f(t) = 3^{2t+3} = 3^{2t} \cdot 3^3 = 27 \cdot (3^2)^t = 27 \cdot 9^t$

87. Answers will vary.

89. Yes; $f(x) = a^x$ is a one-to-one function. Therefore, an inverse function exists for *f*.

90. Since $f(x) = a^x$ has an inverse, the graph of $f^{-1}(x)$ will be the reflection of f across the line $y = x$.

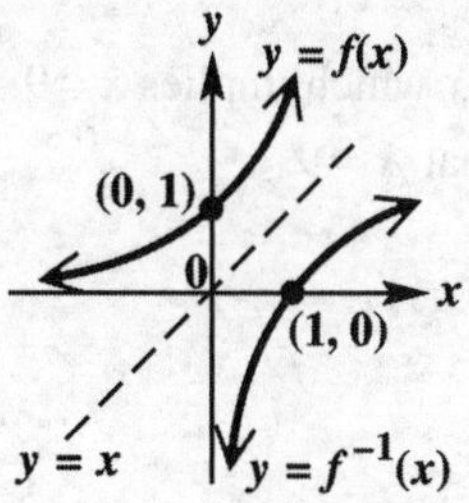

91. Since $f(x) = a^x$ has an inverse, we find it as follows.

$$y = a^x$$
$$x = a^y$$

92. If $a = 10$, the equation for $f^{-1}(x)$ will be given by $x = 10^y$.

93. If $a = e$, the equation for $f^{-1}(x)$ will be given by $x = e^y$.

94. If the point (p, q) is on the graph of f, then the point (q, p) is in the graph of f^{-1}.

Section 4.3: Logarithmic Functions

Connections (page 427)

1.
$$\begin{aligned} \log_{10} 458.3 &\approx 2.661149857 \\ +\log_{10} 294.6 &\approx 2.469232743 \\ \hline &\approx 5.130382600 \\ 10^{5.130382600} &\approx 135{,}015.18 \end{aligned}$$

A calculator gives $(458.3)(294.6) = 135{,}015.18$.

2. Answers will vary.

Exercises

1. **(a)** C; $\log_2 16 = 4$ because $2^4 = 16$.

(b) A; $\log_3 1 = 0$ because $3^0 = 1$.

(c) E; $\log_{10} .1 = -1$ because $10^{-1} = .1$.

(d) B; $\log_2 \sqrt{2} = \frac{1}{2}$ because $2^{1/2} = \sqrt{2}$.

(e) F; $\log_e \left(\frac{1}{e^2}\right) = -2$ because $e^{-2} = \frac{1}{e^2}$.

(f) D; $\log_{1/2} 8 = -3$ because $\left(\frac{1}{2}\right)^{-3} = 8$.

3. $3^4 = 81$ is equivalent to $\log_3 81 = 4$.

5. $\left(\frac{2}{3}\right)^{-3} = \frac{27}{8}$ is equivalent to $\log_{2/3} \frac{27}{8} = -3$.

7. $\log_6 36 = 2$ is equivalent to $6^2 = 36$.

9. $\log_{\sqrt{3}} 81 = 8$ is equivalent to $\left(\sqrt{3}\right)^8 = 81$.

11. Answers will vary.

13.
$$x = \log_5 \frac{1}{625}$$
$$5^x = \frac{1}{625} \Rightarrow 5^x = \frac{1}{5^4}$$
$$5^x = 5^{-4} \Rightarrow x = -4$$

Solution set: $\{-4\}$

15.
$$x = \log_{10} .001$$
$$10^x = .001 \Rightarrow 10^x = 10^{-3}$$
$$x = -3$$

Solution set: $\{-3\}$

17.
$$x = \log_8 \sqrt[4]{8}$$
$$8^x = \sqrt[4]{8} \Rightarrow 8^x = 8^{1/4}$$
$$x = \frac{1}{4}$$

Solution set: $\left\{\frac{1}{4}\right\}$

19. $x = 3^{\log_3 8}$; Writing as a logarithmic equation we have $\log_3 8 = \log_3 x$ which implies $x = 8$.
Using the Theorem of Inverses on page 426, we can directly state that $x = 8$.
Solution set: $\{8\}$

21. $x = 2^{\log_2 9}$ Writing as a logarithmic equation we have $\log_2 9 = \log_2 x$ which implies $x = 9$.
Using the Theorem of Inverses on page 426, we can directly state that $x = 9$.
Solution set: $\{9\}$

23. $\log_x 25 = -2 \Rightarrow x^{-2} = 25 \Rightarrow x^{-2} = 5^2 \Rightarrow \left(x^{-2}\right)^{-1/2} = \left(5^2\right)^{-1/2}$

$x = 5^{-1}$ You do not include a $\pm$ since the base, x, cannot be negative.

$x = \frac{1}{5}$

Solution set: $\left\{\frac{1}{5}\right\}$

25. $\log_4 x = 3 \Rightarrow 4^3 = x \Rightarrow 64 = x$

Solution set: $\{64\}$

27. $x = \log_4 \sqrt[3]{16} \Rightarrow 4^x = \sqrt[3]{16} \Rightarrow 4^x = (16)^{1/3} \Rightarrow 4^x = \left(4^2\right)^{1/3} \Rightarrow 4^x = 4^{2/3} \Rightarrow x = \frac{2}{3}$

Solution set: $\left\{\frac{2}{3}\right\}$

29. $\log_x 3 = -1 \Rightarrow x^{-1} = 3 \Rightarrow \left(x^{-1}\right)^{-1} = 3^{-1} \Rightarrow x = \frac{1}{3}$

Solution set: $\left\{\frac{1}{3}\right\}$

31. Answers will vary.

For Exercises 33 – 35, refer to the following graph of $f(x) = \log_2 x$.

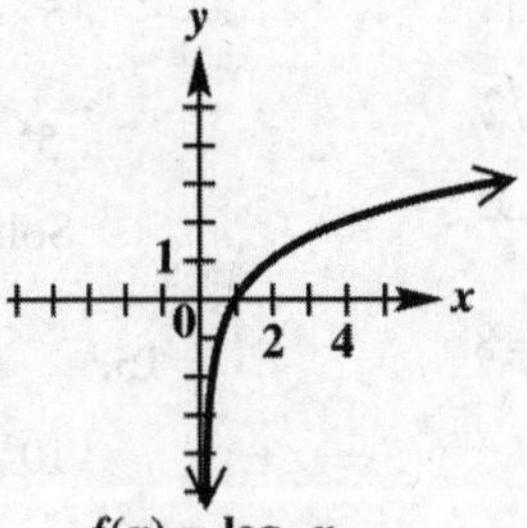

33. The graph of $f(x) = (\log_2 x) + 3$ is obtained by translating the graph of $f(x) = \log_2 x$ up 3 units.

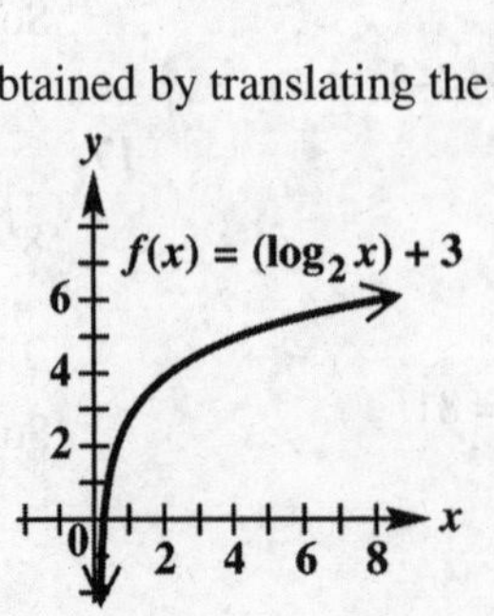

35. To find the graph of $f(x)=\left|\log_2(x+3)\right|$, translate the graph of $f(x)=\log_2 x$ to the left 3 units to obtain the graph of $\log_2(x+3)$. (See Exercise 34.) For the portion of the graph where $f(x)\geq 0$, that is, where $x\geq -2$, use the same graph as in 34. For the portion of the graph in 34 where $f(x)<0$, $-3<x<-2$, reflect the graph about the *x*-axis. In this way, each negative value of $f(x)$ on the graph in 34 is replaced by its opposite, which is positive. The graph has a vertical asymptote at $x=-3$.

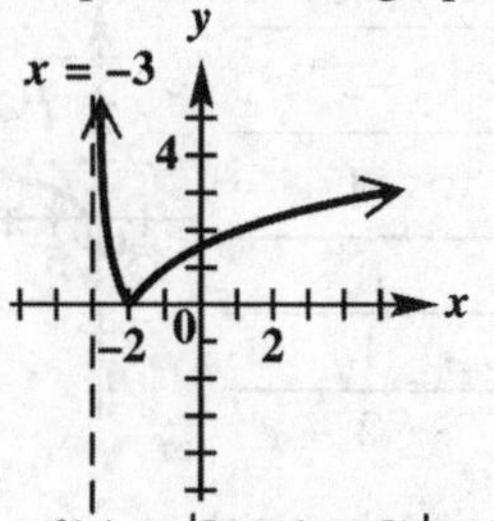

$f(x)=\left|\log_2(x+3)\right|$

For Exercise 37, refer to the following graph of $f(x)=\log_{1/2}x$.

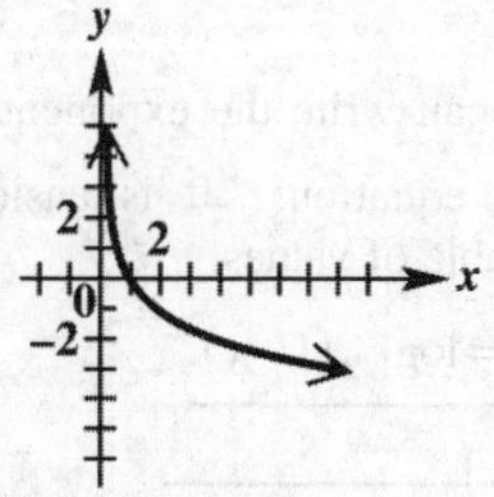

$f(x)=\log_{1/2}x$

37. The graph of $f(x)=\log_{1/2}(x-2)$ is obtained by translating the graph of $f(x)=\log_{1/2}x$ to the right 2 units. The graph has a vertical asymptote at $x=2$.

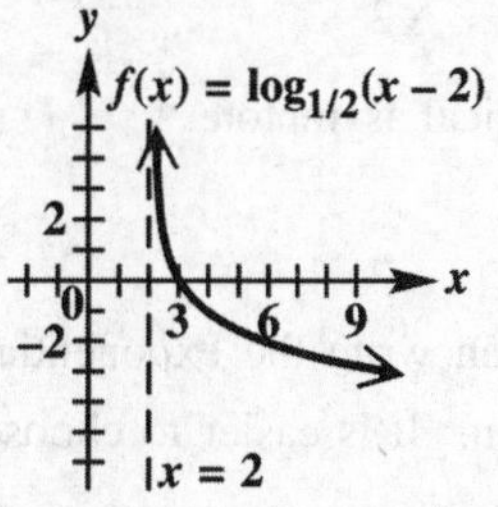

39. Because $f(x)=\log_2 x$ has a vertical asymptote, which is the *y*-axis (the line $x=0$), *x*-intercept of 1, and is increasing, the correct choice is the graph in E.

41. Because $f(x)=\log_2\frac{1}{x}=\log_2 x^{-1}=-\log_2 x$, it has a vertical asymptote, which is the *y*-axis (the line $x=0$), has an *x*-intercept 1, and is the reflection of $f(x)=\log_2 x$ across the *x*-axis, it is decreasing and the correct choice is the graph in B

43. Because $f(x)=\log_2(x-1)$ represents the horizontal shift of $f(x)=\log_2 x$ to the right 1 unit, the function has a vertical asymptote which is the line $x=1$, has an *x*-intercept when $x-1=1\Rightarrow x=2$, and is increasing, the correct choice is the graph in F.

45. $f(x)=\log_5 x$

Since $f(x)=y=\log_5 x$, we can write the exponential form as $x=5^y$ to find ordered pairs that satisfy the equation. It is easier to choose values for y and find the corresponding values of x. Make a table of values.

x	$y=\log_5 x$
$\frac{1}{25}=.04$	-2
$\frac{1}{5}=.2$	-1
1	0
5	1
25	2

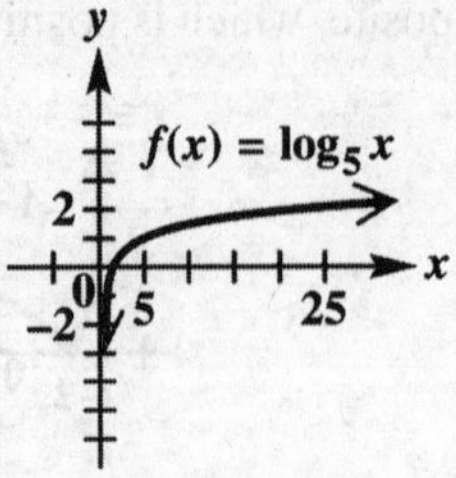

The graph can also be found by reflecting the graph of $f(x)=5^x$ about the line $y=x$. The graph has the y-axis as a vertical asymptote.

47. $f(x)=\log_{1/2}(1-x)$

Since $f(x)=y=\log_{1/2}(1-x)$, we can write the exponential form as $1-x=\left(\frac{1}{2}\right)^y \Rightarrow x=1-\left(\frac{1}{2}\right)^y$ to find ordered pairs that satisfy the equation. It is easier to choose values for y and find the corresponding values of x. Make a table of values.

x	$y=\log_{1/2}(1-x)$
-3	-2
-1	-1
0	0
$\frac{1}{2}=.5$	1
$\frac{3}{4}=.75$	2

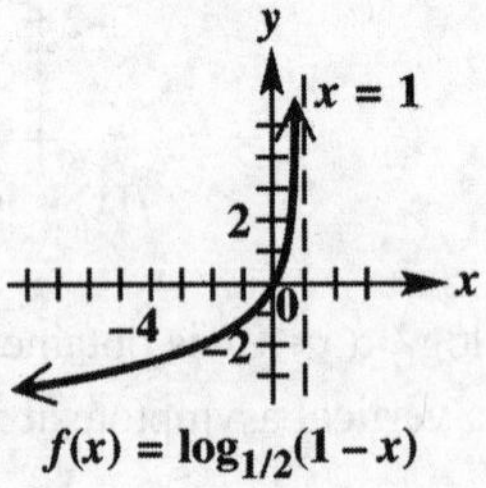

The graph has the line $x=1$ as a vertical asymptote.

49. $f(x)=\log_3(x-1)$

Since $f(x)=y=\log_3(x-1)$, we can write the exponential form as $x-1=3^y \Rightarrow x=3^y+1$ to find ordered pairs that satisfy the equation. It is easier to choose values for y and find the corresponding values of x. Make a table of values.

x	$y=\log_3(x-1)$
$\frac{10}{9}\approx 1.1$	-2
$\frac{4}{3}\approx 1.3$	-1
2	0
4	1
10	2

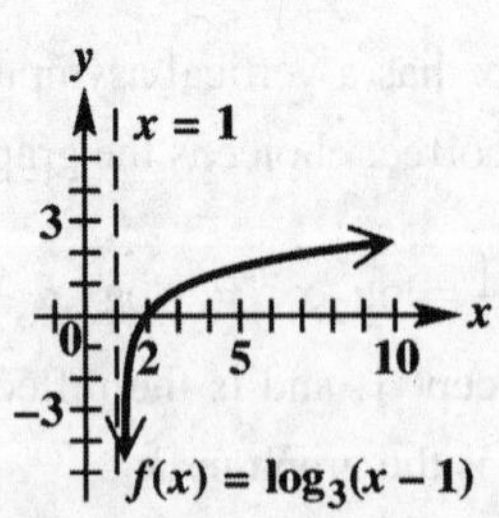

The vertical asymptote will be $x = 1$.

51. $f(x) = x \log_{10} x$

```
WINDOW
 Xmin=-1
 Xmax=5
 Xscl=1
 Ymin=-1
 Ymax=3
 Yscl=1
 Xres=1
```

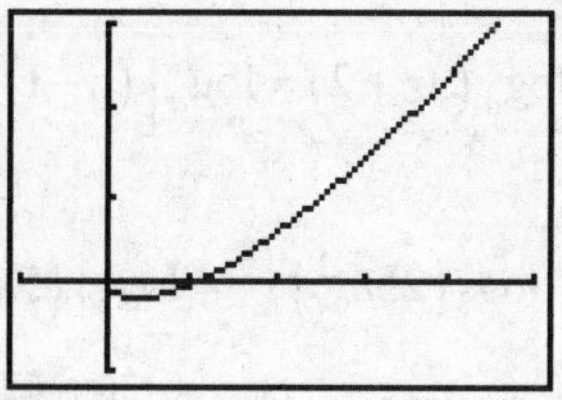

53. If x and y are positive numbers, $\log_a \frac{x}{y} = \underline{\log_a x - \log_a y}$.

54. Since $\log_2 \frac{x}{4} = \log_2 x - \log_2 4$ by the quotient rule, the graph of $y = \log_2 \frac{x}{4}$ can be obtained by shifting the graph of $y = \log_2 x$ down $\log_2 4 = 2$ units.

55. Graph $f(x) = \log_2 \frac{x}{4}$ and $g(x) = \log_2 x$ on the same axes. Since $f(x) = y = \log_2 \frac{x}{4}$, we can write the exponential form as $\frac{x}{4} = 2^y \Rightarrow x = 4 \cdot 2^y$ to find ordered pairs that satisfy the equation. Also, since $g(x) = y = \log_2 x$, we can write the exponential form as $x = 2^y$ to find ordered pairs that satisfy the equation. It is easier to choose values for y and find the corresponding values of x. Make a table of values.

x	$f(x) = \log_2 \frac{x}{4}$	x	$g(x) = \log_2 x$
1	−2	$\frac{1}{4} = .25$	−2
2	−1	$\frac{1}{2} = .5$	−1
4	0	1	0
8	1	2	1
16	2	4	2

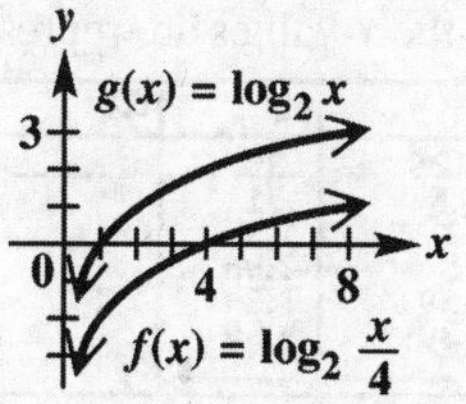

The graph of f is 2 units below the graph of g. This supports the answer in Exercise 54.

56. If $x = 4$, $\log_2 \frac{x}{4} = \underline{0}$; since $\log_2 x = \underline{2}$ and $\log_2 4 = \underline{2}$, $\log_2 x - \log_2 4 = \underline{0}$. By the quotient rule, $\log_2 \frac{x}{4} = \log_2 x - \log_2 4$. Both sides should equal 0. Since 2 – 2 = 0, they do.

57. $\log_2 \frac{6x}{y} = \log_2 6x - \log_2 y = \log_2 6 + \log_2 x - \log_2 y$

59. $\log_5 \frac{5\sqrt{7}}{3} = \log_5 5\sqrt{7} - \log_5 3 = \log_5 5 + \log_5 \sqrt{7} - \log_5 3 = 1 + \log_5 7^{1/2} - \log_5 3 = 1 + \frac{1}{2}\log_5 7 - \log_5 3$

61. $\log_4(2x + 5y)$
Since this is a sum, none of the logarithm properties apply, so this expression cannot be simplified.

63. $\log_m \sqrt{\frac{5r^3}{z^5}} = \log_m \left(\frac{5r^3}{z^5}\right)^{1/2} = \frac{1}{2}\log_m \frac{5r^3}{z^5} = \frac{1}{2}\left(\log_m 5r^3 - \log_m z^5\right)$
$= \frac{1}{2}\left(\log_m 5 + \log_m r^3 - \log_m z^5\right) = \frac{1}{2}\left(\log_m 5 + 3\log_m r - 5\log_m z\right)$

65. $\log_a x + \log_a y - \log_a m = \log_a xy - \log_a m = \log_a \frac{xy}{m}$

67. $2\log_m a - 3\log_m b^2 = \log_m a^2 - \log_m \left(b^2\right)^3 = \log_m a^2 - \log_m b^6 = \log_m \frac{a^2}{b^6}$

69. $2\log_a(z-1)+\log_a(3z+2),\ z>1$

$$2\log_a(z-1)+\log_a(3z+2)=\log_a(z-1)^2+\log_a(3z+2)=\log_a\left[(z-1)^2(3z+2)\right]$$

71. $$-\tfrac{2}{3}\log_5 5m^2+\tfrac{1}{2}\log_5 25m^2=\log_5\left(5m^2\right)^{-2/3}+\log_5\left(25m^2\right)^{1/2}=\log_5\left[\left(5m^2\right)^{-2/3}\cdot\left(25m^2\right)^{1/2}\right]$$
$$=\log_5\left(5^{-2/3}m^{-4/3}\cdot 5m\right)=\log_5\left(5^{-2/3}\cdot 5^1\cdot m^{-4/3}\cdot m^1\right)$$
$$=\log_5\left(5^{1/3}\cdot m^{-1/3}\right)=\log_5\frac{5^{1/3}}{m^{1/3}}\ \text{or}\ \log_5\sqrt[3]{\frac{5}{m}}$$

73. $\log_{10}6=\log_{10}(2\cdot 3)=\log_{10}2+\log_{10}3=.3010+.4771=.7781$

75. $$\log_{10}\tfrac{9}{4}=\log_{10}9-\log_{10}4=\log_{10}3^2-\log_{10}2^2$$
$$=2\log_{10}3-2\log_{10}2=2(.4771)-2(.3010)=.9542-.6020=.3522$$

77. $$\log_{10}\sqrt{30}=\log_{10}30^{1/2}=\tfrac{1}{2}\log_{10}30=\tfrac{1}{2}\log_{10}(10\cdot 3)$$
$$=\tfrac{1}{2}(\log_{10}10+\log_{10}3)=\tfrac{1}{2}(1+.4771)=\tfrac{1}{2}(1.4771)\approx .7386$$

79. **(a)** If the x-values are representing years, 3 months is $\frac{3}{12}=\frac{1}{4}=.25$ yr and 6 months is $\frac{6}{12}=\frac{1}{2}=.5$ yr.

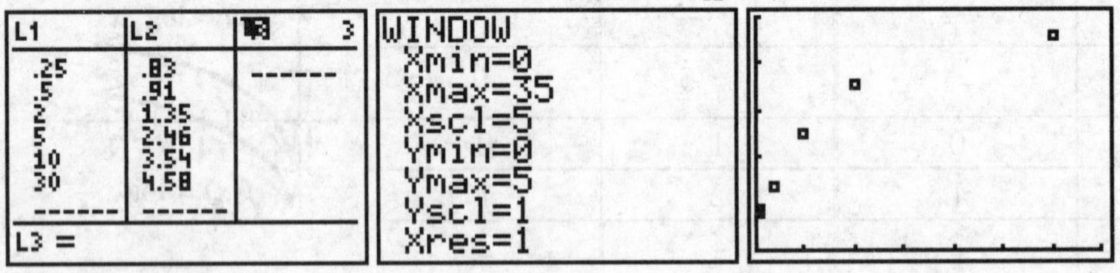

(b) Answers will vary.

81. $f(x)=\log_a x$ and $f(3)=2$

$2=\log_a 3\Rightarrow a^2=3\Rightarrow\left(a^2\right)^{1/2}=3^{1/2}\Rightarrow a=\sqrt{3}$

(There is no $\pm$ because a must be positive and not equal to 1.)

We now have $f(x)=\log_{\sqrt{3}}x$.

(a)
$$f\left(\tfrac{1}{9}\right)=\log_{\sqrt{3}}\tfrac{1}{9}$$
$$y=\log_{\sqrt{3}}\tfrac{1}{9}$$
$$\left(\sqrt{3}\right)^y=\tfrac{1}{9}$$
$$\left(3^{1/2}\right)^y=\tfrac{1}{3^2}$$
$$3^{y/2}=3^{-2}$$
$$\tfrac{y}{2}=-2$$
$$y=-4$$

(b)
$$f(27)=\log_{\sqrt{3}}27$$
$$y=\log_{\sqrt{3}}27$$
$$\left(\sqrt{3}\right)^y=27$$
$$\left(3^{1/2}\right)^y=3^3$$
$$3^{y/2}=3^3$$
$$\tfrac{y}{2}=3$$
$$y=6$$

83. In the formula $A = P\left(1+\frac{r}{m}\right)^{tm}$ we substitute $A = 2P$ since we want the present value to be doubled in the future. Thus, we need to solve for t in the equation $2P = P\left(1+\frac{r}{m}\right)^{tm}$.

$$2P = P\left(1+\frac{r}{m}\right)^{tm} \Rightarrow 2 = \left(1+\frac{r}{m}\right)^{tm}$$

$$2^{\frac{1}{tm}} = \left[\left(1+\frac{r}{m}\right)^{tm}\right]^{\frac{1}{tm}} \Rightarrow 2^{\frac{1}{tm}} = \left(1+\frac{r}{m}\right)$$

$$\log_2\left(1+\frac{r}{m}\right) = \frac{1}{tm} \Rightarrow tm = \frac{1}{\log_2\left(1+\frac{r}{m}\right)}$$

$$t = \frac{1}{m\log_2\left(1+\frac{r}{m}\right)} \Rightarrow t = \frac{1}{\log_2\left(1+\frac{r}{m}\right)^m}$$

85. $\log_{10} x = x - 2$

The x-coordinates of the intersection points will be the solutions to the given equation. There are two points of intersection, hence there are two possible solutions.

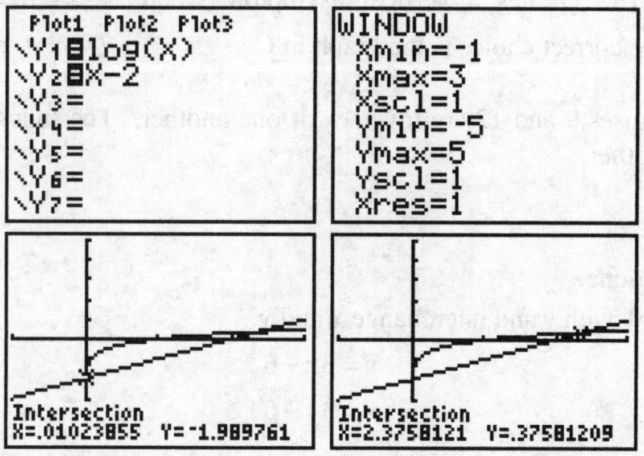

Solution set: {.01, 2.38}

87. Prove that $\log_a \frac{x}{y} = \log_a x - \log_a y$.

Let $m = \log_a x$ and $n = \log_a y$. Changing to exponential form we have $a^m = x$ and $a^n = y$. Since $\frac{x}{y} = \frac{a^m}{a^n}$ we have $\frac{x}{y} = a^{m-n}$. Changing to logarithmic form, we have $\log_a \frac{x}{y} = m - n$. Substituting for m and n we have $\log_a \frac{x}{y} = \log_a x - \log_a y$.

Summary Exercises on Inverse, Exponential, and Logarithmic Functions

1. $f(x) = 3x - 4,\ g(x) = \frac{x+4}{3}$

$(f \circ g)(x) = f\left[g(x)\right] = 3\left(\frac{x+4}{3}\right) - 4 = x + 4 - 4 = x$

$(g \circ f)(x) = g\left[f(x)\right] = \frac{(3x-4)+4}{3} = \frac{3x}{3} = x$

Since $(f \circ g)(x) = x$ and $(g \circ f)(x) = x$, these functions are inverses.

3. $f(x) = 1 + \log_2 x,\ g(x) = 2^{x-1}$

$(f \circ g)(x) = f\left[g(x)\right] = f\left(2^{x-1}\right) = 1 + \log_2 2^{x-1} = 1 + (x-1)\log_2 2 = 1 + x - 1 = x$

$(g \circ f)(x) = g\left[f(x)\right] = g(1 + \log_2 x) = 2^{(1+\log_2 x - 1)} = 2^{\log_2 x} = x$

Since $(f \circ g)(x) = x$ and $(g \circ f)(x) = x$, these functions are inverses.

5. Since any horiztontal line when passed through the graph of this function will touch the graph in at most one place, the function is one-to-one. A sketch of the graph of the inverse function is as follows.

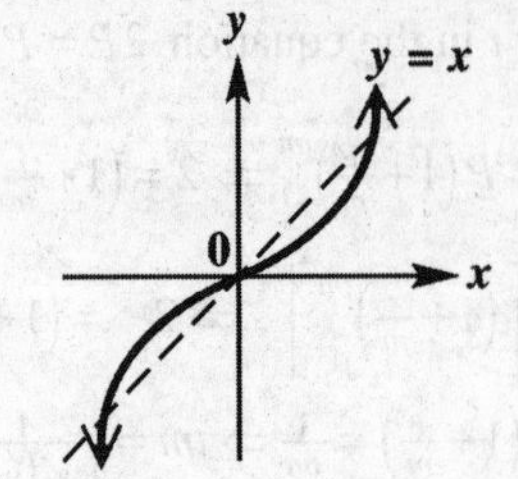

7. Since a horiztontal line when passed through the graph of this function will touch the graph in more than one place, the function is not one-to-one.

9. Because $f(x) = \log_3(x+2)$ has a vertical asymptote when $x+2=0 \Rightarrow x=-2$, x-intercept when $x+2=1 \Rightarrow x=-1$, and is increasing, the correct choice is the graph in B.

11. Because $f(x) = \log_2(5-x)$ has a vertical asymptote when $5-x=0 \Rightarrow x=5$, x-intercept when $5-x=1 \Rightarrow x=4$. The correct choice is the graph in C.

13. The functions in Exercises 9 and 12 are inverses of one another. The functions in Eercises 10 and 11 are inverses of one another.

15. $f(x) = 3x-6$

This function is one-to-one.

Step 1 Replace $f(x)$ with y and interchange x and y.

$$y = 3x-6$$
$$x = 3y-6$$

Step 2 Solve for y.

$$x = 3y-6$$
$$x+6 = 3y$$
$$\tfrac{x+6}{3} = y$$

Step 3 Replace y with $f^{-1}(x)$.

$$f^{-1}(x) = \tfrac{x+6}{3}$$

For both $f(x)$ and $f^{-1}(x)$, the domain is $(-\infty, \infty)$ and the range is $(-\infty, \infty)$.

17. $f(x) = 3x^2$

If $x=1$, $f(1) = 3(1)^2 = 3(1) = 3$. Also if $x=-1$, $f(-1) = 3(-1)^2 = 3(1) = 3$.

Since two different values of x lead to the same value of y, the function is not one-to-one.

19. $f(x) = \sqrt[3]{5-x^4}$

If $x=1$, $f(1) = \sqrt[3]{5-1^4} = \sqrt[3]{5-1} = \sqrt[3]{4}$. Also if $x=-1$, $f(-1) = \sqrt[3]{5-(-1)^4} = \sqrt[3]{5-1} = \sqrt[3]{4}$.

Since two different values of x lead to the same value of y, the function is not one-to-one.

21. $\left(\tfrac{1}{10}\right)^{-3} = 1000$ is equivalent to $\log_{1/10} 1000 = -3$.

23. $\left(\sqrt{3}\right)^4 = 9$ is equivalent to $\log_{\sqrt{3}} 9 = 4.$

25. $2^x = 32$ is equivalent to $\log_2 32 = x.$

27. $3x = 7^{\log_7 6} \Rightarrow 3x = 6 \Rightarrow x = 2$

Solution set: $\{2\}$

29. $\log_{10} .01 = x \Rightarrow 10^x = .01 \Rightarrow 10^x = 10^{-2} \Rightarrow x = -2$

Solution set: $\{-2\}$

31. $\log_x \sqrt[3]{5} = \frac{1}{3} \Rightarrow x^{1/3} = \sqrt[3]{5} \Rightarrow x^{1/3} = 5^{1/3} \Rightarrow \left(x^{1/3}\right)^3 = \left(5^{1/3}\right)^3 \Rightarrow x = 5$

Recall from Chapter 1 that it is necessary to check all proposed solutions in the original equation when you raise both sides to a power.

$$\begin{aligned} &\text{Check } x = 5. \\ \log_x \sqrt[3]{5} &= \tfrac{1}{3} \\ \log_5 \sqrt[3]{5} &= \tfrac{1}{3} \quad ? \\ \log_5 5^{1/3} &= \tfrac{1}{3} \\ \tfrac{1}{3}\log_5 5 &= \tfrac{1}{3} \\ \tfrac{1}{3}\cdot 1 &= \tfrac{1}{3} \\ \tfrac{1}{3} &= \tfrac{1}{3} \end{aligned}$$

This is a true statement.

Solution set: $\{5\}$

33. $2x - 1 = \log_6 6^x \Rightarrow 2x - 1 = x \Rightarrow -1 = -x \Rightarrow 1 = x$

Solution set: $\{1\}$

35. $\log_2 6 + \log_2 x = 5 \Rightarrow \log_2 6x = 5 \Rightarrow 2^5 = 6x \Rightarrow 32 = 6x \Rightarrow x = \frac{32}{6} = \frac{16}{3}$

Solution set: $\left\{\frac{16}{3}\right\}$

Section 4.4: Evaluating Logarithms and the Change-of-Base Theorem

1. For $f(x) = a^x$, where $a > 0$, the function is *increasing* over its entire domain.

3. $f(x) = 5^x$

This function is one-to-one.

Step 1 Replace $f(x)$ with y and interchange x and y.

$$y = 5^x$$
$$x = 5^y$$

Step 2 Solve for y.

$$x = 5^y$$
$$y = \log_5 x$$

Step 3 Replace y with $f^{-1}(x)$.

$$f^{-1}(x) = \log_5 x$$

5. A base e logarithm is called a natural logarithm, while a base 10 logarithm is called a common logarithm.

7. $\log_2 0$ is undefined because there is no power of 2 that yields a result of 0. In other words, the equation $2^x = 0$ has no solution.

9. $\log 8 = .90308999$

11. $\log 36 \approx 1.5563$

13. $\log .042 \approx -1.3768$

15. $\log\left(2\times 10^4\right) \approx 4.3010$

17. $\ln 36 \approx 3.5835$

19. $\ln .042 \approx -3.1701$

21. $\ln\left(2\times e^4\right) \approx 4.6931$

23. Grapefruit, 6.3×10^{-4}

$$\text{pH} = -\log\left[\text{H}_3\text{0}^+\right] = -\log\left(6.3\times 10^{-4}\right) = -\left(\log 6.3 + \log 10^{-4}\right) = -(.7793-4) = -.7993+4 \approx 3.2$$

The answer is rounded to the nearest tenth because it is customary to round pH values to the nearest tenth. The pH of grapefruit is 3.2.

25. Limes, 1.6×10^{-2}

$$\text{pH} = -\log\left[\text{H}_3\text{0}^+\right] = -\log\left(1.6\times 10^{-2}\right) = -\left(\log 1.6 + \log 10^{-2}\right) = -(.2041-2) = -(-1.7959) \approx 1.8$$

The pH of limes is 1.8.

27. Soda pop, 2.7

$$\text{pH} = -\log\left[\text{H}_3\text{0}^+\right] \Rightarrow 2.7 = -\log\left[\text{H}_3\text{0}^+\right] \Rightarrow -2.7 = \log\left[\text{H}_3\text{0}^+\right] \Rightarrow \left[\text{H}_3\text{0}^+\right] = 10^{-2.7}$$

$$\left[\text{H}_3\text{0}^+\right] \approx 2.0\times 10^{-3}$$

29. Beer, 4.8

$$\text{pH} = -\log\left[H_3O^+\right] \Rightarrow 4.8 = -\log\left[H_3O^+\right] \Rightarrow -4.8 = \log\left[H_3O^+\right] \Rightarrow \left[H_3O^+\right] = 10^{-4.8}$$

$$\left[H_3O^+\right] \approx 1.6\times 10^{-5}$$

31. Wetland, 2.49×10^{-5}

$$\text{pH} = -\log\left[H_3O^+\right] = -\log\left(2.49\times 10^{-5}\right) = -\left(\log 2.49 + \log 10^{-5}\right) = -\log 2.49 - (-5) = -\log 2.49 + 5$$

$\text{pH} \approx 4.6$

Since the pH is between 4.0 and 6.0, it is a poor fen.

33. Wetland, 2.49×10^{-7}

$$\text{pH} = -\log\left[H_3O^+\right] = -\log\left(2.49\times 10^{-7}\right) = -\left(\log 2.49 + \log 10^{-7}\right) = -\log 2.49 - (-7) = -\log 2.49 + 7$$

$\text{pH} \approx 6.6$

Since the pH is greater than 6.0, it is a rich fen.

35. $\log_2 5 = \frac{\ln 5}{\ln 2} \approx \frac{1.6094}{.6931} \approx 2.3219$

We could also have used the common logarithm. $\log_2 5 = \frac{\log 5}{\log 2} \approx \frac{.6990}{.3010} \approx 2.3219$

37. $\log_8 .59 = \frac{\log .59}{\log 8} \approx \frac{-.2291}{.9031} \approx -.2537$

We could also have used the natural logarithm. $\log_8 .59 = \frac{\ln .59}{\ln 8} \approx \frac{-.5276}{2.0794} \approx -.2537$

39. Since $\sqrt{13} = 13^{1/2}$, we have $\log_{\sqrt{13}} 12 = \frac{\ln 12}{\ln\sqrt{13}} = \frac{\ln 12}{\frac{1}{2}\ln 13} \approx \frac{2.4849}{1.2825} \approx 1.9376.$

The required logarithm can also be found by entering $\ln\sqrt{13}$ directly into the calculator.
We could also have used the common logarithm. $\log_{\sqrt{13}} 12 = \frac{\log 12}{\log\sqrt{13}} = \frac{\log 12}{\frac{1}{2}\log 13} \approx \frac{1.0792}{.5570} \approx 1.9376.$

41. $\log_{.32} 5 = \frac{\log 5}{\log .32} \approx \frac{.6990}{-.4949} \approx -1.4125$

We could also have used the natural logarithm. $\log_{.32} 5 = \frac{\ln 5}{\ln .32} \approx \frac{1.6094}{-1.1394} \approx -1.4125$

43. $2\ln 3x = \ln(3x)^2 = \ln\left(3^2x^2\right) = \ln 9x^2$; It is the same as D.

45. $\ln\left(b^4\sqrt{a}\right) = \ln\left(b^4a^{1/2}\right) = \ln b^4 + \ln a^{1/2} = 4\ln b + \frac{1}{2}\ln a = 4v + \frac{1}{2}u$

47. $\ln\sqrt{\frac{a^3}{b^5}} = \ln\left(\frac{a^3}{b^5}\right)^{1/2} = \ln\left(\frac{a^{3/2}}{b^{5/2}}\right) = \ln a^{3/2} - \ln b^{5/2} = \frac{3}{2}\ln a - \frac{5}{2}\ln b = \frac{3}{2}u - \frac{5}{2}v$

49. $g(x) = e^x$

(a) $g(\ln 3) = e^{\ln 3} = 3$

(b) $g\left[\ln\left(5^2\right)\right] = e^{\ln 5^2} = 5^2$ or 25

(c) $g\left[\ln\left(\frac{1}{e}\right)\right] = e^{\ln(1/e)} = \frac{1}{e}$

51. $f(x) = \ln x$

(a) $f\left(e^5\right) = \ln e^5 = 5$

(b) $f\left(e^{\ln 3}\right) = \ln e^{\ln 3} = \ln 3$

(c) $f\left(e^{2\ln 3}\right) = \ln e^{2\ln 3} = 2\ln 3$ or $\ln 9$.

53. $f(x) = \ln|x|$

The domain of f is all real numbers except 0: $(-\infty, 0) \cup (0, \infty)$ and the range is $(-\infty, \infty)$.

Since $f(-x) = \ln|-x| = \ln|x| = f(x)$, this is an even function and symmetric with respect to the y-axis.

55. When $X \geq 4$, $4 - X \leq 0$, and we cannot obtain a real value for the logarithm of a non-positive number.

57. $f(x) = \ln e^2 x = \ln e^2 + \ln x = 2 + \ln x$

$f(x) = \ln e^2 x$ is a vertical shift of the graph of $f(x) = \ln x$, 2 units up.

59. $d = 10\log\frac{I}{I_0}$, where d is the decibel rating.

(a) $d = 10\log\frac{100I_0}{I_0}$
$= 10\log_{10} 100 = 10(2) = 20$

(b) $d = 10\log\frac{1000I_0}{I_0}$
$= 10\log_{10} 1000 = 10(3) = 30$

(c) $d = 10\log\frac{100{,}000I_0}{I_0}$
$= 10\log_{10} 100{,}000 = 10(5) = 50$

(d) $d = 10\log\frac{1{,}000{,}000I_0}{I_0}$
$= 10\log_{10} 1{,}000{,}000 = 10(6) = 60$

(e) $I = 2I_0$

$d = 10\log\frac{2I_0}{I_0} = 10\log 2 \approx 3.0103$

The described rating is increased by about 3 decimals.

61. $r = \log_{10}\frac{I}{I_0}$, where r is the Richter scale rating of an earthquake.

(a) $r = \log_{10}\frac{1000I_0}{I_0} = \log_{10} 1000 = 3$

(b) $r = \log_{10}\frac{1{,}000{,}000I_0}{I_0} = \log_{10} 1{,}000{,}000 = 6$

(c) $r = \log_{10}\frac{100{,}000{,}000I_0}{I_0} = \log_{10} 100{,}000{,}000 = 8$

63. $r = \log_{10}\frac{I}{I_0}$

$8.1 = \log_{10}\frac{I}{I_0} \Rightarrow 10^{8.1} = \frac{I}{I_0} \Rightarrow I_0 10^{8.1} = I \Rightarrow I \approx 125{,}892{,}541 I_0$

The reading was about 126,000,000 I_0.

65. $f(x) = -269 + 73\ln x$ and in the year 2004, $x = 104$.

$f(104) = -269 + 73\ln 104 \approx 70$

Thus, the number of visitors in the year 2004 will be about 70 million. We must assume that the rate of increase continues to be logarithmic.

67. If $a = .36$, then $S(n) = a\ln\left(1+\frac{n}{a}\right) = .36\ln\left(1+\frac{n}{.36}\right)$.

(a) $S(100) = .36\ln\left(1+\frac{100}{.36}\right) \approx 2.0269 \approx 2$

(b) $S(200) = .36\ln\left(1+\frac{200}{.36}\right) \approx 2.2758 \approx 2$

(c) $S(150) = .36\ln\left(1+\frac{150}{.36}\right) \approx 2.1725 \approx 2$

(d) $S(10) = .36\ln\left(1+\frac{10}{.36}\right) \approx 1.2095 \approx 1$

69. The index of diversity H for 2 species is given by $H = -[P_1 \log_2 P_1 + P_2 \log_2 P_2]$. When $P_1 = \frac{50}{100} = .5$ and $P_2 = \frac{50}{100} = .5$ we have $H = -[.5\log_2 .5 + .5\log_2 .5]$. Since $\log_2 .5 = \log_2 \frac{1}{2} = \log_2 2^{-1} = -1$, we have $H = -[.5(-1)+.5(-1)] = -(-1) = 1$. Thus, the index of diversity is 1.

71. $T(k) = 1.03k \ln\frac{C}{C_0}$

Since $10 \le k \le 16$ and $\frac{C}{C_0} = 2$, the range for $T = 1.03k\ln\frac{C}{C_0}$ will be between $T(10)$ and $T(16)$. Since $T(10) = 1.03(10)\ln 2 \approx 7.1$ and $T(16) = 1.03(16)\ln 2 \approx 11.4$, the predicted increased global temperature due to the greenhouse effect from a doubling of the carbon dioxide in the atmosphere is between 7°F and 11°F.

73. (a) In L_1 and L_2 enter the natural D and P, respectively.

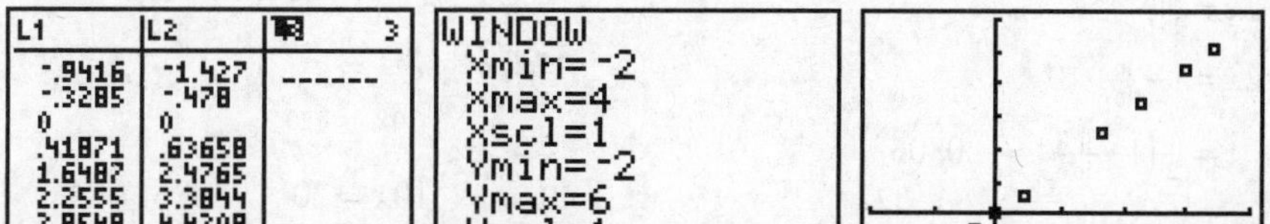

If we let $x = \ln D$ and $y = \ln P$, then the data points appear to be linear. Note: There is one more row not shown in the list on the left, namely (3.4045, 5.1047).

(b) Choose two points from the list and find the equation through them. If we use (0, 0), representing Earth and $(2.9549, 4.4308)$ representing Uranus, we obtain $m = \frac{4.4308-0}{2.9549-0} \approx 1.5$. Since the y-intercept is 0, the equation is $y = 1.5x$ or $\ln P = 1.5\ln D$. Note: Since the points lie approximately but not exactly on a line, a slightly different equation will be found if a different pair of points is used.

(c) For Pluto, $D = 39.5$, so $\ln P = 1.5\ln D = 1.5\ln 39.5$. Solve this equation for P.

$$P = e^{1.5\ln 39.5} = e^{\ln 39.5^{1.5}} = (39.5)^{1.5} \approx 248.3$$

The linear equation predicts that the period of the planet Pluto is 248.3 years, which is very close to the true value of 248.5 years.

Section 4.5: Exponential and Logarithmic Equations

1. Since x is the exponent to which 7 must be raised in order to obtain 19, the solution is $\log_7 19$ or $\frac{\log 19}{\log 7}$ or $\frac{\ln 19}{\ln 7}$.

3. Since x is the exponent to which $\frac{1}{2}$ must be raised in order to obtain 12, the solution is $\log_{1/2} 12$ or $\frac{\log 12}{\log\left(\frac{1}{2}\right)}$ or $\frac{\ln 12}{\ln\left(\frac{1}{2}\right)}$.

5. $3^x = 6$

$\ln 3^x = \ln 6 \Rightarrow x \ln 3 = \ln 6$

$x = \frac{\ln 6}{\ln 3} \approx 1.6309$

Solution set: $\{1.6309\}$

7. $6^{1-2x} = 8$

$$\begin{aligned}
\ln 6^{1-2x} &= \ln 8 \\
(1-2x)\ln 6 &= \ln 8 \\
1-2x &= \tfrac{\ln 8}{\ln 6} \\
2x &= 1 - \tfrac{\ln 8}{\ln 6} \\
x &= \tfrac{1}{2}\left(1 - \tfrac{\ln 8}{\ln 6}\right) \approx -.0803
\end{aligned}$$

or

$$\begin{aligned}
\ln 6^{1-2x} &= \ln 8 \\
(1-2x)\ln 6 &= \ln 8 \\
\ln 6 - 2x\ln 6 &= \ln 8 \\
-2x\ln 6 &= \ln 8 - \ln 6 \\
-x\ln 6^2 &= \ln \tfrac{8}{6} \\
-x\ln 36 &= \ln \tfrac{4}{3} \\
x &= -\frac{\ln\frac{4}{3}}{\ln 36} \approx -.0803
\end{aligned}$$

Solution set: $\{-.0803\}$

9. $2^{x+3} = 5^x$

$$\begin{aligned}
\ln 2^{x+3} &= \ln 5^x \\
(x+3)\ln 2 &= x\ln 5 \\
x\ln 2 + 3\ln 2 &= x\ln 5 \\
x\ln 2 - x\ln 5 &= -3\ln 2 \\
x(\ln 2 - \ln 5) &= -\ln 2^3 \\
x\left(\ln \tfrac{2}{5}\right) &= -\ln 8 \\
x &= \frac{-\ln 8}{\ln \frac{2}{5}} \approx 2.2694
\end{aligned}$$

Solution set: $\{2.2694\}$

11. $e^{x-1} = 4$

$$\begin{aligned}
\ln e^{x-1} &= \ln 4 \\
x - 1 &= \ln 4 \\
x &= \ln 4 + 1 \approx 2.3863
\end{aligned}$$

Solution set: $\{2.3863\}$

13. $2e^{5x+2} = 8$

$$\begin{aligned}
e^{5x+2} &= 4 \\
\ln e^{5x+2} &= \ln 4 \\
5x + 2 &= \ln 4 \\
5x &= \ln 4 - 2 \\
x &= \tfrac{1}{5}(\ln 4 - 2) \approx -.1227
\end{aligned}$$

Solution set: $\{-.1227\}$

15. $2^x = -3$ has no solution since 2 raised to any power is positive.

Solution set: $\varnothing$

17. $e^{8x} \cdot e^{2x} = e^{20}$

$$\begin{aligned}
e^{10x} &= e^{20} \\
10x &= 20 \\
x &= 2
\end{aligned}$$

Solution set: $\{2\}$

19. $100(1.02)^{x/4} = 200$

$$\begin{aligned}
1.02^{x/4} &= 2 \\
\ln\left(1.02^{x/4}\right) &= \ln 2 \\
\tfrac{x}{4}\ln(1.02) &= \ln 2 \\
x\ln(1.02) &= 4\ln 2 \\
x\ln(1.02) &= \ln 2^4 \\
x\ln(1.02) &= \ln 16 \\
x &= \frac{\ln 16}{\ln(1.02)} \approx 140.0112
\end{aligned}$$

Solution set: $\{140.0112\}$

21. $\ln(6x+1) = \ln 3$

$$\begin{aligned}
6x + 1 &= 3 \\
6x &= 2 \\
x &= \tfrac{2}{6} = \tfrac{1}{3}
\end{aligned}$$

Solution set: $\left\{\frac{1}{3}\right\}$

23. $\log 4x - \log(x-3) = \log 2$

$\log \frac{4x}{x-3} = \log 2 \Rightarrow \frac{4x}{x-3} = 2 \Rightarrow 4x = 2(x-3) \Rightarrow 4x = 2x-6 \Rightarrow 2x = -6 \Rightarrow x = -3$

Since x is negative, $4x$ is negative. Therefore, $\log 4x$ is not defined. Thus, the proposed solution must be discarded.

Solution set: $\varnothing$

25. $\log(2x-1) + \log 10x = \log 10 \Rightarrow \log\left[(2x-1)(10x)\right] = \log 10 \Rightarrow (2x-1)(10x) = 10$

$20x^2 - 10x = 10 \Rightarrow 20x^2 - 10x - 10 = 0 \Rightarrow 2x^2 - x - 1 = 0 \Rightarrow (2x+1)(x-1) = 0$

$$2x+1=0 \text{ or } x-1=0$$
$$x = -\tfrac{1}{2} \qquad x = 1$$

Since $x = -\frac{1}{2}$ is negative, $10x$ is negative. Therefore, $\log 10x$ is not defined. This proposed solution must be discarded.

Solution set: $\{1\}$

27. $\log(x+25) = 1 + \log(2x-7) \Rightarrow \log(x+25) - \log(2x-7) = 1 \Rightarrow \log_{10} \frac{x+25}{2x-7} = 1$

$\frac{x+25}{2x-7} = 10^1 \Rightarrow x+25 = 10(2x-7) \Rightarrow x+25 = 20x-70 \Rightarrow 25 = 19x-70 \Rightarrow 95 = 19x \Rightarrow 5 = x$

Solution set: $\{5\}$

29. $\log x + \log(x-21) = 2 \Rightarrow \log_{10}\left[x(x-21)\right] = 2$

$x(x-21) = 10^2 \Rightarrow x^2 - 21x = 100 \Rightarrow x^2 - 21x - 100 = 0 \Rightarrow (x+4)(x-25) = 0$

$$x+4=0 \text{ or } x-25=0$$
$$x = -4 \qquad x = 25$$

Since the negative solution $(x=-4)$ is not in the domain of $\log x$, it must be discarded.

Solution set: $\{25\}$

31. $\ln(5+4x) - \ln(3+x) = \ln 3$

$\ln \frac{5+4x}{3+x} = \ln 3 \Rightarrow \frac{5+4x}{3+x} = 3 \Rightarrow 5+4x = 3(3+x) \Rightarrow 5+4x = 9+3x \Rightarrow x+5 = 9 \Rightarrow x = 4$

Solution set: $\{4\}$

33. $\log_6 4x - \log_6(x-3) = \log_6 12$

$\log_6 \frac{4x}{x-3} = \log_6 12 \Rightarrow \frac{4x}{x-3} = 12 \Rightarrow 4x = 12(x-3) \Rightarrow 4x = 12x-36 \Rightarrow 36 = 8x \Rightarrow \frac{36}{8} = x \Rightarrow x = \frac{9}{2}$

Solution set: $\left\{\frac{9}{2}\right\}$

35. $5^{x+2} = 2^{2x-1} \Rightarrow \ln 5^{x+2} = \ln 2^{2x-1} \Rightarrow (x+2)\ln 5 = (2x-1)\ln 2 \Rightarrow x\ln 5 + 2\ln 5 = 2x\ln 2 - \ln 2$

$x\ln 5 + \ln 5^2 = x\ln 2^2 - \ln 2 \Rightarrow x\ln 5 + \ln 25 = x\ln 4 - \ln 2 \Rightarrow \ln 25 + \ln 2 = x\ln 4 - x\ln 5$

$\ln 25 + \ln 2 = x(\ln 4 - \ln 5) \Rightarrow \frac{\ln 25 + \ln 2}{\ln 4 - \ln 5} = x \Rightarrow x = \frac{\ln 50}{\ln \frac{4}{5}} \Rightarrow x \approx -17.5314$

Solution set: $\{-17.5314\}$

37. $\ln e^x - \ln e^3 = \ln e^5 \Rightarrow x - 3 = 5 \Rightarrow x = 8$

Solution set: $\{8\}$

39. $\log_2(\log_2 x) = 1 \Rightarrow \log_2 x = 2^1 \Rightarrow \log_2 x = 2 \Rightarrow x = 2^2 \Rightarrow x = 4 \Rightarrow$

Solution set: {4}

41. $\log x^2 = (\log x)^2 \Rightarrow 2\log x = (\log x)^2 \Rightarrow (\log x)^2 - 2\log x = 0 \Rightarrow \log x(\log x - 2) = 0$

$$\log_{10} x = 0 \quad \text{or} \quad \log_{10} x - 2 = 0$$
$$x = 10^0 \qquad \log_{10} x = 2$$
$$x = 1 \qquad x = 10^2 = 100$$

Solution set: {1, 100}

43. Answers will vary.
One should not immediately reject a negative answer when solving equations involving logarithms. One must examine what happens to an answer when substituted back into the original equation. An answer (whether negative, positive, or zero) must not allow a nonpositive value in the argument of the logarithm. If it does, regardless of its sign, it must be rejected.

45. $I = \frac{E}{R}\left(1 - e^{-Rt/2}\right)$ for t

$$RI = R\left[\frac{E}{R}\left(1 - e^{-Rt/2}\right)\right]$$
$$RI = E\left(1 - e^{-Rt/2}\right)$$
$$RI = E - Ee^{-Rt/2}$$
$$RI + Ee^{-Rt/2} = E$$
$$Ee^{-Rt/2} = E - RI$$
$$\frac{Ee^{-Rt/2}}{E} = \frac{E - RI}{E}$$
$$e^{-Rt/2} = 1 - \frac{RI}{E}$$
$$\ln e^{-Rt/2} = \ln\left(1 - \frac{RI}{E}\right)$$
$$-\frac{Rt}{2} = \ln\left(1 - \frac{RI}{E}\right)$$
$$-\frac{2}{R}\left(-\frac{Rt}{2}\right) = -\frac{2}{R}\ln\left(1 - \frac{RI}{E}\right)$$
$$t = -\frac{2}{R}\ln\left(1 - \frac{RI}{E}\right)$$

47. $p = a + \frac{k}{\ln x}$ for x

$$p - a = \frac{k}{\ln x}$$
$$(\ln x)(p - a) = k$$
$$\ln x = \frac{k}{p - a}$$
$$x = e^{k/(p-a)}$$

49. The expression e^{2x} is equivalent to $\left(e^x\right)^2$ by the power rule for exponents, $\left(a^m\right)^n = a^{mn}$.

50. $(e^x)^2 - 4e^x + 3 = 0$
$(e^x - 1)(e^x - 3) = 0$

51. $(e^x - 1)(e^x - 3) = 0$

$$e^x - 1 = 0 \quad \text{or} \quad e^x - 3 = 0$$
$$e^x = 1 \qquad e^x = 3$$
$$\ln e^x = \ln 1 \qquad \ln e^x = \ln 3$$
$$x = 0 \quad \text{or} \quad x = \ln 3$$

Solution set: $\{0, \ln 3\}$

52. The graph intersects the *x*-axis at 0 and $1.099 \approx \ln 3$.

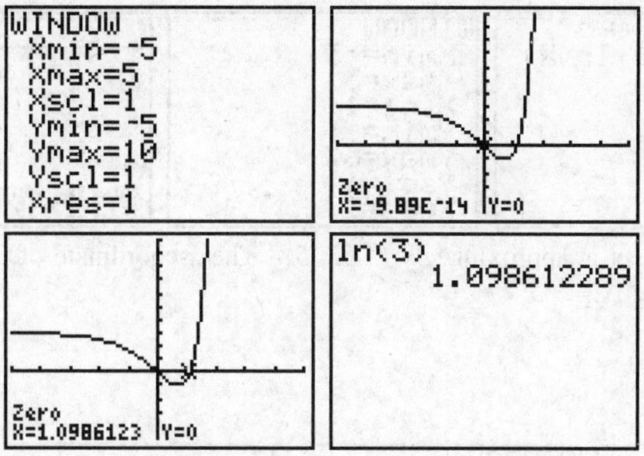

53. From the graph, we see that $y > 0$ on $(-\infty, 0) \cup (\ln 3, \infty)$. The solution set of the inequality $e^{2x} - 4e^{x} + 3 > 0$ is $(-\infty, 0) \cup (\ln 3, \infty)$.

54. From the graph we see that $y < 0$ on $(0, \ln 3)$, so the solution set of the inequality $e^{2x} = 4e^{x} + 3 < 0$ is $(0, \ln 3)$.

55. *Step 1* Replace $f(x) = e^{x+1} - 4$ with *y* and interchange *x* and *y*.

$$y = e^{x+1} - 4$$
$$x = e^{y+1} - 4$$

Step 2 Solve for *y*.

$$x = e^{y+1} - 4 \Rightarrow x + 4 = e^{y+1} \Rightarrow \ln(x+4) = y + 1 \Rightarrow \ln(x+4) - 1 = y$$

Step 3 Replace *y* with $f^{-1}(x)$.

$$f^{-1}(x) = \ln(x+4) - 1$$

Domain: $(-4, \infty)$; Range: $(-\infty, \infty)$

57. $\log_3 x > 3 \Rightarrow \log_3 x - 3 > 0$

Graph $y = \log_3 x - 3$ using change-of-base theorem, graph $y = \frac{\ln x}{\ln 3} - 3$ or $y = \frac{\log x}{\log 3} - 3$.

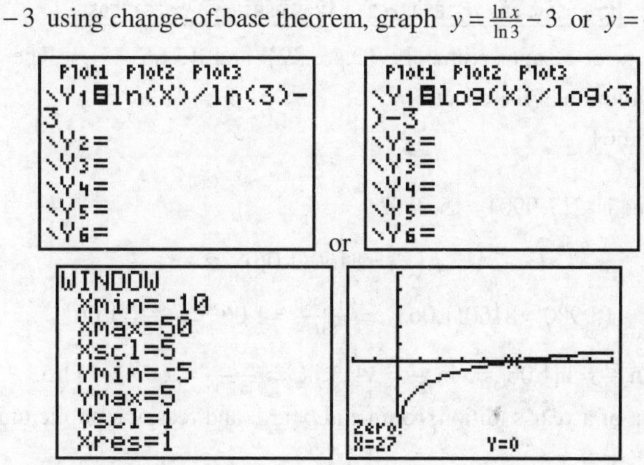

The graph is positive in the interval (27, ∞), so the solution to the original inequality is (27, ∞).

59. $e^x + \ln x = 5$

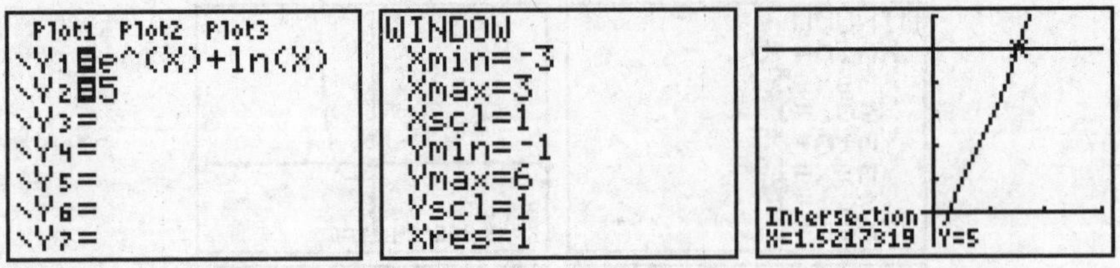

The two graphs intersect at approximately (1.52, 5). The x-coordinate of this point is the solution of the equation.

Solution set: $\{1.52\}$

61. $2e^x + 1 = 3e^{-x}$

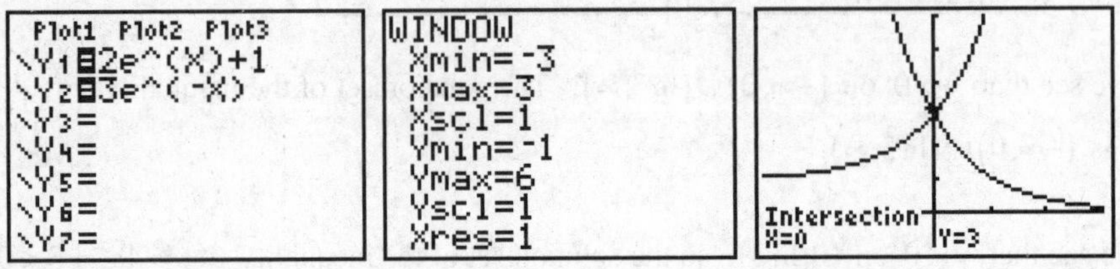

The two curves intersect at the point (0, 3). The x-coordinate of this point is the solution of the equation.

Solution set: $\{0\}$

63. $\log x = x^2 - 8x + 14$

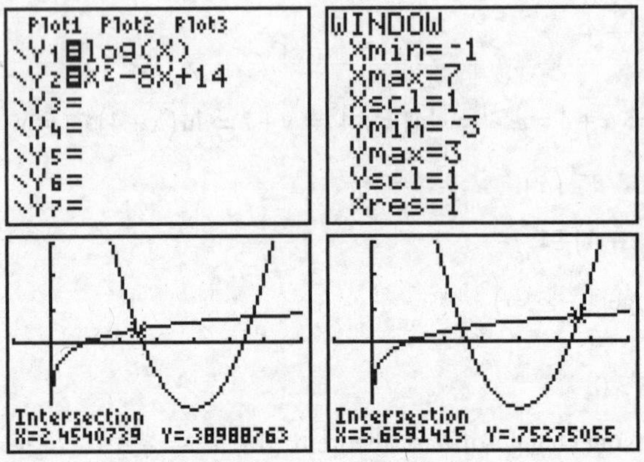

The two graphs intersect at approximately $(2.45, .39)$ and $(5.66, .75)$. The x-coordinate of these points represent the solution of the equation.

Solution set: $\{2.45, 5.66\}$

65. Double the 2000 value is $2(7{,}990) = 15{,}980$.

$$f(x) = 8160(1.06)^x$$

$$15{,}980 = 8160(1.06)^x \Rightarrow \frac{15{,}980}{8160} = 1.06^x \Rightarrow \frac{47}{24} = 1.06^x$$

$$\ln\frac{47}{24} = \ln 1.06^x \Rightarrow \ln\frac{47}{24} = x\ln 1.06 \Rightarrow \frac{\ln\frac{47}{24}}{\ln 1.06} = x \Rightarrow x \approx 11.53$$

During 2011, the cost of a year's tuition, room and board, and fees at a public university will be double the cost in 2000.

67. $f(x)=\dfrac{25}{1+1364.3e^{-x/9.316}}$

(a) In 1997, $x = 97$.

$$f(97)=\frac{25}{1+1364.3e^{-97/9.316}}\approx 24$$

In 1997, about 24% of U.S. children lived in a home without a father.

(b) $10=\dfrac{25}{1+1364.3e^{-x/9.316}}\Rightarrow 10\left(1+1364.3e^{-x/9.316}\right)=25\Rightarrow 10+13{,}643e^{-x/9.316}=25$

$13{,}643e^{-x/9.316}=15\Rightarrow e^{-x/9.316}=\frac{15}{13{,}643}\Rightarrow -\frac{x}{9.316}=\ln\frac{15}{13{,}643}\Rightarrow x=-9.316\ln\frac{15}{13{,}643}\approx 63.47$

During 1963, 10% of U.S. children lived in a home without a father.

69. $\ln(1-P)=-.0034-.0053T$

(a) Change this equation to exponential form, then isolate P.

$$1-P=e^{-.0034-.0053T}\Rightarrow P(T)=1-e^{-.0034-.0053T}$$

(b)

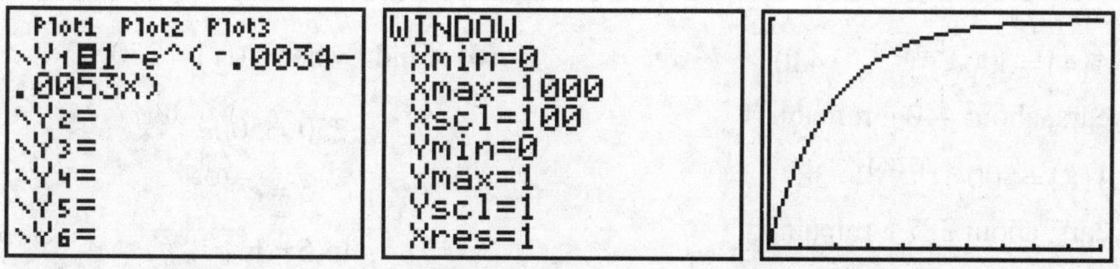

From the graph one can see that initially there is a rapid reduction of carbon dioxide emissions. However, after a while there is little benefit in raising taxes further.

(c) $P(60)=1-e^{-.00340.0053(60)}\approx .275$ or 27.5%

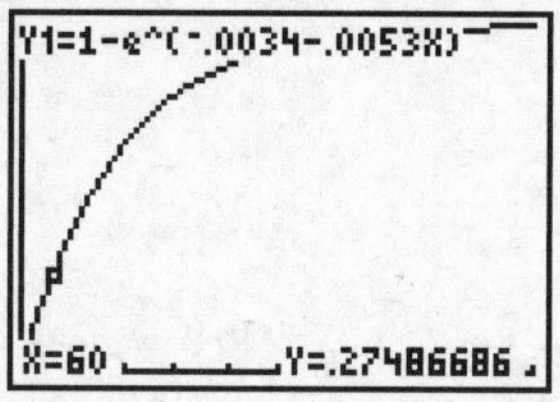

The reduction in carbon emissions from a tax of \$60 per ton of carbon is 27.5%.

(d) We must determine T when $P = .5$.

$.5=1-e^{-.0034-.0053T}\Rightarrow .5-1=-e^{-.0034-.0053T}\Rightarrow -.5=-e^{-.0034-.0053T}$

$.5=e^{-.0034-.0053T}\Rightarrow \ln .5=-.0034-.0053T\Rightarrow \ln .5+.0034=-.0053T\Rightarrow T=\frac{\ln .5+.0034}{-.0053}\approx 130.14$

The value T = \$130.14 will give a 50% reduction in carbon emissions.

71. $A=P\left(1+\frac{r}{m}\right)^{tm}$

To solve for t, substitute A = 30,000, P = 27,000, r = .04, and m = 4.

$$30{,}000=27{,}000\left(1+\tfrac{.04}{4}\right)^{t(4)}\Rightarrow \frac{30{,}000}{27{,}000}=(1+.01)^{4t}\Rightarrow \tfrac{10}{9}=1.01^{4t}$$

$$\ln\tfrac{10}{9}=\ln\left(1.01^{4t}\right)\Rightarrow \ln\tfrac{10}{9}=4t\ln 1.01\Rightarrow t=\frac{\ln\frac{10}{9}}{4\ln 1.01}\approx 2.6$$

To the nearest tenth of a year, Tom will be ready to buy a car in 2.6 yr.

73. $A = P\left(1+\frac{r}{m}\right)^{tm}$

To solve for r, substitute $A = 2500$, $P = 2000$, $t = 3.5$, and $m = 2$.

$$2500 = 2000\left(1+\frac{r}{2}\right)^{(3.5)(2)} \Rightarrow 1.25 = \left(1+\frac{r}{2}\right)^7 \Rightarrow \sqrt[7]{1.25} = 1+\frac{r}{2}$$

$$\sqrt[7]{1.25} - 1 = \frac{r}{2} \Rightarrow r = 2\left(\sqrt[7]{1.25}-1\right) \Rightarrow r \approx .0648$$

The interest rate is about 6.48%.

Section 4.6: Applications and Models of Exponential Growth and Decay

1. The equation $2e^{.02x} = 6$ represents an initial amount of 2 and a final amount 6 (triple that of 2). The correct choice is B.

3. The equation $y = 2e^{.02(3)}$ represents the amount after 3 yr. The correct choice is C.

5. $A(t) = 500e^{-.032t}$

(a) $t = 4 \Rightarrow A(4) = 500e^{-.032(4)} \approx 440$

After 4 years, about 440 g remain.

(b) $t = 8 \Rightarrow A(8) = 500e^{-.032(8)} \approx 387$

After 8 years, about 387 g remain.

(c) $t = 20 \Rightarrow A(20) = 500e^{-.032(20)} \approx 264$

After 20 years, about 264 g remain.

(d) Find t when $A(t) = 250$.

$$250 = 500e^{-.032t}$$
$$.5 = e^{-.032t}$$
$$\ln .5 = \ln e^{-.032t}$$
$$\ln .5 = -.032t$$
$$t = \frac{\ln .5}{-.032} \approx 21.66$$

The half-life is about 21.66 yr.

7. $A(t) = A_0 e^{-.00043t}$

Find t when $A(t) = \frac{1}{2}A_0$.

$$\tfrac{1}{2}A_0 = A_0 e^{-.00043t} \Rightarrow \tfrac{1}{2} = e^{-.00043t} \Rightarrow \ln\tfrac{1}{2} = \ln e^{-.00043t} \Rightarrow \ln\tfrac{1}{2} = -.00043t \Rightarrow t = \frac{\ln\frac{1}{2}}{-.00043} \approx 1611.97$$

The half-life is about 1611.97 yr.

9. $p(h) = 86.3 \ln h - 680$

(a) $h = 3000 \Rightarrow p(3000) = 86.3\ln 3000 - 680 \approx 11$

At 3000 ft, about 11% of moisture falls as snow.

(b) $h = 4000 \Rightarrow p(4000) = 86.3\ln 4000 - 680 \approx 36$

At 4000 ft, about 36% of moisture falls as snow.

(c) $h = 7000 \Rightarrow p(7000) = 86.3\ln 7000 - 680 \approx 84$

At 7000 ft, about 84% of moisture falls as snow.

11. From Example 5, we have the amount of radiocarbon present after t years is given by $y = y_0 e^{-(\ln 2)(1/5700)t}$, where y_0 is the initial amount present. If we let $y = \frac{1}{3}y_0$, we can solve for t.

$$\tfrac{1}{3}y_0 = y_0 e^{-(\ln 2)(1/5700)t} \Rightarrow \tfrac{1}{3} = e^{-(\ln 2)(1/5700)t} \Rightarrow \ln\tfrac{1}{3} = \ln e^{-(\ln 2)(1/5700)t}$$

$$\ln\tfrac{1}{3} = -\frac{\ln 2}{5700}t \Rightarrow -\frac{5700}{\ln 2}\ln\tfrac{1}{3} = t \Rightarrow -\frac{5700}{\ln 2}\left(\ln 1 - \ln 3\right) = t \Rightarrow t = \frac{5700\ln 3}{\ln 2} \approx 9034.29$$

The Egyptian died about 9000 yr ago.

13. Since $y = y_0 e^{-(\ln 2)(1/5700)t}$, where y_0 is the initial amount present. If we let $y = .15y_0$, we can solve for *t*.

$$.15y_0 = y_0 e^{-(\ln 2)(1/5700)t} \Rightarrow .15 = e^{-(\ln 2)(1/5700)t} \Rightarrow \ln .15 = \ln e^{-(\ln 2)(1/5700)t}$$

$$\ln .15 = -\tfrac{\ln 2}{5700}t \Rightarrow -\tfrac{5700}{\ln 2}\ln .15 = t \Rightarrow t = -\tfrac{5700 \ln .15}{\ln 2} \approx 15{,}600.70$$

The paintings are about 15,600 yr old.

15. From Example 6, we have the temperature, $f(t)$, of a body at time t after being introduced into an environment having constant temperature T_0 is $f(t) = T_0 + Ce^{-kt}$, where *C* and *k* are constants. From the given information, when $t = 0$, $T_0 = 0$, and the temperature of the water is $f(0) = 100$.

$$100 = 0 + Ce^{-0k} \Rightarrow 100 = C$$

Thus, we have $f(t) = 0 + 100e^{-kt} = 100e^{-kt}$. Also, when $t = \frac{24}{60} = \frac{2}{5}$ hr, $f\left(\frac{2}{5}\right) = 50$. Using this information, we have the following.

$$50 = 100e^{-(2/5)k} \Rightarrow \tfrac{1}{2} = e^{-(2/5)k} \Rightarrow \ln \tfrac{1}{2} = \ln e^{-(2/5)k} \Rightarrow \ln \tfrac{1}{2} = -\tfrac{2}{5}k$$

$$\ln 1 - \ln 2 = -\tfrac{2}{5}k \Rightarrow \ln 2 = \tfrac{2}{5}k \Rightarrow k = \tfrac{5}{2}\ln 2 \approx 1.733$$

Thus, the model is $f(t) = 100e^{-1.733t}$. To find the temperature after $\frac{96}{60} = \frac{8}{5}$ hrs, we find $f\left(\frac{8}{5}\right)$.

Since $f\left(\frac{8}{5}\right) = 100e^{-1.733(8/5)} \approx 6.25$, the temperature after 96 minutes is about 6.25°C.

Note: We could have used the exact value of *k* to perform the calculations.

$$f\left(\tfrac{8}{5}\right) = 100e^{-\left(\frac{5}{2}\ln 2\right)\left(\frac{8}{5}\right)} = 100e^{-4\ln 2} = 100e^{\ln \frac{1}{16}} = 100 \cdot \tfrac{1}{16} = 6.25$$

17. **(a)** A point on the graph of $f(x) = A_0 a^{x-1950}$ is $(1950, .05)$.

Since $f(1950) = A_0 a^{1950-1950} = .05$, we have $A_0 a^0 = .05 \Rightarrow A_0 = .05$. Thus, we have the function $f(x) = .05a^{x-1950}$. Since the point $(2000, .35)$ is also on the graph of the function, we have $f(2000) = .05a^{2000-1950} = .35 \Rightarrow a^{50} = 7 \Rightarrow a = \sqrt[50]{7} \approx 1.04$. Finally, we have the function $f(x) = .05(1.04)^{x-1950}$.

(b) If you think of $f(x) = .05(1.04)^{x-1950}$ as a function in the form of $A = P\left(1 + \frac{r}{m}\right)^{tm}$ where $m = 1$ (compounded annually), we have $f(x) = .05(1 + .04)^{x-1950} = P(1+r)^t$. Thus, the average annual percent increase would be about 4%.

19. Given *P* = 60,000 and *t* = 5, substitute *r* = .07 and *m* = 4 into the compound interest formula, $A = P\left(1 + \frac{r}{m}\right)^{tm}$. We have $A = 60{,}000\left(1 + \frac{.07}{4}\right)^{5(4)} = 60{,}000(1.0175)^{20} \approx 84{,}886.69$.

The interest from this investment would be \$84,886.69 – \$60,000 = \$24,886.69.

Given *P* = 60,000 and *t* = 5, substitute *r* = .0675 into the continuous compounding formula, $A = Pe^{rt}$.

$$A = 60{,}000e^{.0675(5)} = 60{,}000e^{.3375} \approx 84{,}086.38$$

The interest from this investment would be \$84,086.38 – \$60,000 = \$24,086.38.

(a) The investment that offers 7% compounded quarterly will earn more interest than the investment that offers 6.75% compounded continuously.

(b) Note that \$24,886.69 – \$24,086.38 = \$800.31. The investment that offers 7% compounded quarterly will earn \$800.31 more in interest. Note: Keeping all digits in the calculator rather than rounding the two amounts of interest to the nearest cent before subtracting them will yield a final answer of 800.315242 ≈ \$800.32. This discrepancy is insignificant.

21. $A = Pe^{rt} \Rightarrow 2P = Pe^{.025t}\, 2 = e^{.025t} \Rightarrow \ln 2 = .025t \Rightarrow t \approx 27.73$
The doubling time is about 27.73 yr if interest is compounded continuously.

23. $A = Pe^{rt}$

$3P = Pe^{.05t} \Rightarrow 3 = e^{.05t} \Rightarrow \ln 3 = \ln e^{.05t} \Rightarrow \ln 3 = .05t \Rightarrow t = \frac{\ln 3}{.05} \approx 21.97$
It will take about 21.97 years for the investment to triple.

25. **(a)** A point associated with the graph of $f(x) = P_0 a^{x-2000}$ is $(2000, 1)$. Since $f(2000) = P_0 a^{2000-2000} = 1$, we have $P_0 a^0 = 1 \Rightarrow P_0 = 1$. Thus, we have $f(x) = a^{x-2000}$. Since the point $(2025, 1.4)$ is projected to be on the graph, we have the following.

$$f(2025) = a^{2025-2000} = 1.4 \Rightarrow a^{25} = 1.4 \Rightarrow a = \sqrt[25]{1.4} \approx 1.01355$$

(b) From part a we have $f(x) = (1.01355)^{x-2000}$. To find the population projected for 2010, we must find $f(2010)$. Thus $f(2010) = (1.01355)^{2010-2000} = (1.01355)^{10} \approx 1.14$ billion is the estimated population in 2010.

(c) We must solve $(1.01355)^{x-2000} = 1.5$ for x.

$$(1.01355)^{x-2000} = 1.5 \Rightarrow \ln(1.01355)^{x-2000} = \ln 1.5 \Rightarrow (x-2000)\ln(1.01355) = \ln 1.5$$

$$x - 2000 = \frac{\ln 1.5}{\ln(1.01355)} \Rightarrow x = 2000 + \frac{\ln 1.5}{\ln(1.01355)} \approx 2030.13$$

In 2030, it is projected that the population will reach 1.5 billion.

27. $f(x) = 26.6e^{.131x}$

(a) In 1995, $x = 4$, so $f(4) = 26.6e^{.131(4)} = 26.6e^{.524} \approx 44.9$
The estimated gambling revenues in 1995 is \$44.9 billion.

(b) We must solve $30 = 26.6e^{.131x}$ for x.

$$30 = 26.6e^{.131x} \Rightarrow \frac{30}{26.6} = e^{.131x} \Rightarrow \ln \frac{30}{26.6} = \ln e^{.131x}$$

$$\ln \frac{30}{26.6} = .131x \Rightarrow x = \frac{\ln \frac{30}{26.6}}{.131} \approx 1 \text{ when rounded to the nearest whole number}$$

This corresponds to the revenues reaching \$30 billion in 1992.

29. $L = 9 + 2e^{.15t}$

(a) In 1982, $t = 0$, so $L = 9 + 2e^{.15(0)} \approx 11$.

(b) In 1986, $t = 4$, so $L = 9 + 2e^{.15(4)} \approx 12.6$.

(c) In 1992, $t = 10$, so $L = 9 + 2e^{.15(10)} \approx 18.0$.

(d)

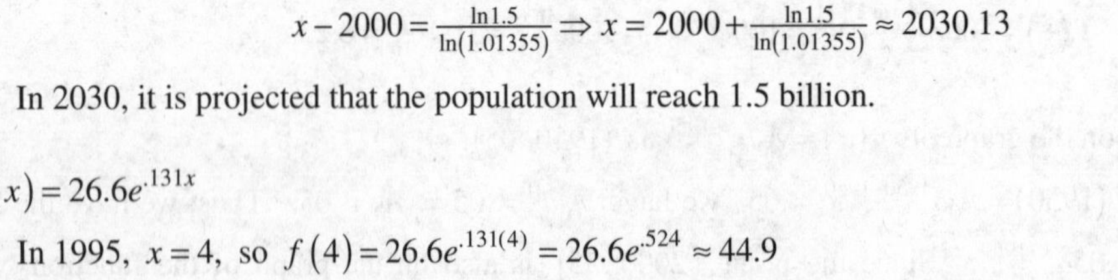

(e) According to this equation, living standards are increasing, but at a slow rate.

31. $f(t) = 200(.90)^{t-1}$

Find t when $f(t) = 50$.

$$50 = 200(.90)^{t-1}$$
$$.25 = (.90)^{t-1}$$
$$\ln .25 = \ln\left[(.90)^{t-1}\right]$$
$$\ln .25 = (t-1)\ln .90$$
$$t - 1 = \frac{\ln .25}{\ln .90} \Rightarrow t = 1 + \frac{\ln .25}{\ln .90} \approx 14.2$$

The dose will reach a level of 50 mg in about 14.2 hr.

33. The year 2002 corresponds to $t = 8$. Since $P(8) = 17.77e^{.0305(8)} = 17.77e^{.244} \approx 22.7$, approximately 22.7% of the freshman class of 2002 had an A or A+ high school grade average.

35. $S(t) = S_0 e^{-at}$

(a) $S(t) = 50{,}000e^{-.10t}$

$$S(1) = 50{,}000e^{-.10(1)} = 50{,}000e^{-.1} \approx 45{,}200$$
$$S(3) = 50{,}000e^{-.10(3)} = 50{,}000e^{-.3} \approx 37{,}000$$

(b) $S(t) = 80{,}000e^{-.05t}$

$$S(2) = 80{,}000e^{-.05(2)} = 80{,}000e^{-.1} \approx 72{,}400$$
$$S(10) = 80{,}000e^{-.05(10)} = 80{,}000e^{-.5} \approx 48{,}500$$

37. Use the formula for continuous compounding with $r = .06$, $P = 2$, and $A = 3(2) = 6$.

$$6 = 2e^{.06t} \Rightarrow 3 = e^{.06t} \Rightarrow \ln 3 = \ln e^{.06t} \Rightarrow \ln 3 = .06t \Rightarrow t = \frac{\ln 3}{.06} \approx 18.3$$

The cost will triple in about 18.3 yr.

39. Use the formula for continuous compounding with $r = .02$.

$$A = Pe^{rt} \Rightarrow 2P = Pe^{.02t} \Rightarrow 2 = e^{.02t} \Rightarrow \ln 2 = \ln e^{.02t} \Rightarrow \ln 2 = .02t \Rightarrow t = \frac{\ln 2}{.02} \approx 34.7$$

It will take about 34.7 yr before twice as much electricity is needed.

41. **(a)**

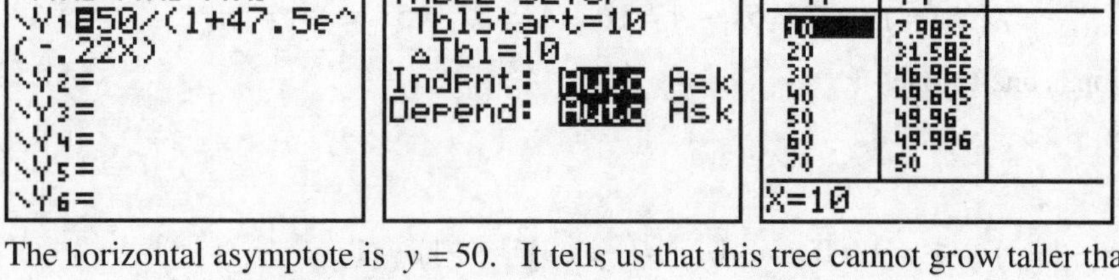

(b) The horizontal asymptote is $y = 50$. It tells us that this tree cannot grow taller than 50 ft.

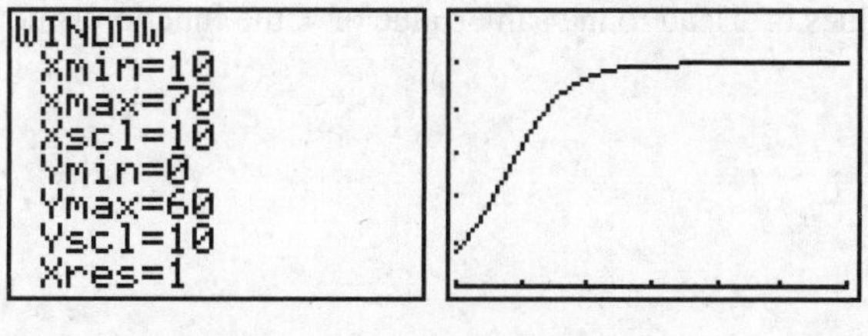

Continued on next page

41. (continued)

(c) We can see from the graphing calculator that after about 19.4 yr, the tree is 30 ft tall.

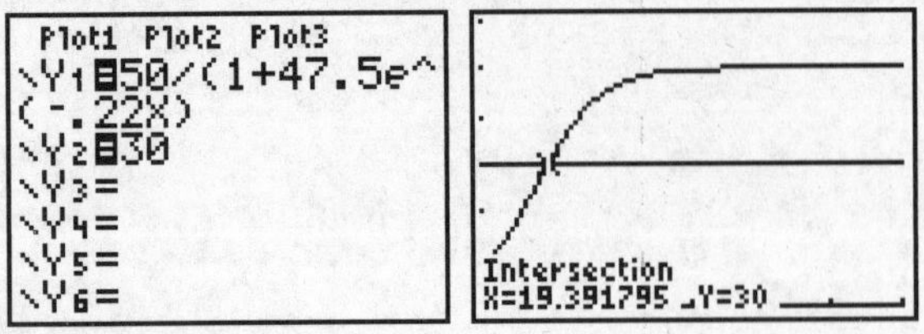

This agrees with the algebraic solution.

$$30 = \frac{50}{1+47.5e^{-.22x}} \Rightarrow 30\left(1+47.5e^{-.22x}\right) = 50 \Rightarrow 30 + 1425e^{-.22x} = 50 \Rightarrow 1425e^{-.22x} = 20$$

$$e^{-.22x} = \frac{20}{1425} \Rightarrow \ln e^{-.22x} = \ln\frac{20}{1425} \Rightarrow -.22x = \ln\frac{20}{1425} \Rightarrow x = \frac{\ln\frac{20}{1425}}{-.22} \approx 19.4$$

Chapter 4: Review Exercises

1. This is not a one-to-one function since a horizontal line can intersect the graph in more than one point.

3. $y = 5x - 4$

Looking at this function graphed on a TI-83, we can see that it appears that any horizontal line passed through the function will intersect the graph in at most one place.

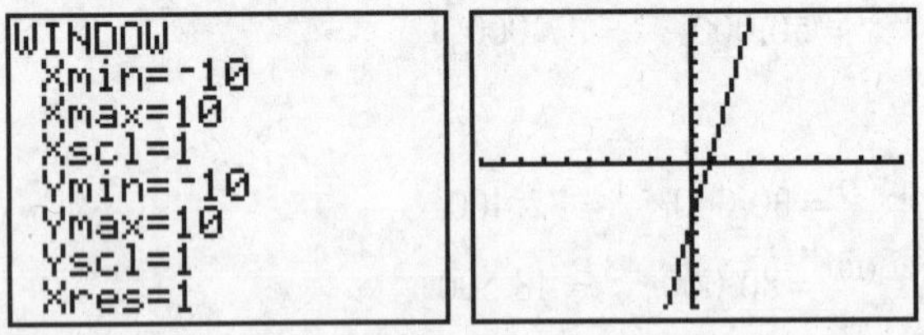

If we attempt to find the inverse function, we see that this function can be found.

Step 1 Interchange x and y.

$x = 5y - 4$

Step 2 Solve for y.

$x = 5y - 4 \Rightarrow x + 4 = 5y \Rightarrow y = \frac{x+4}{5}$

Step 3 Replace y with $f^{-1}(x)$.

$f^{-1}(x) = \frac{x+4}{5}$

Also, an acceptable way of showing that a function is one-to-one is to assume that you have two equal y-values $\left(f(x_1) = f(x_2)\right)$ and show that they must have come from the same x-value $(x_1 = x_2)$.

$$f(x_1) = f(x_2) \Rightarrow 5x_1 - 4 = 5x_2 - 4 \Rightarrow 5x_1 = 5x_2 \Rightarrow x_1 = x_2$$

So, the function is one-to-one.

5. $y = (x+3)^2$

If $x = -2$, $y = (-2+3)^2 = 1^2 = 1$. If $x = -4$, $y = (-4+3)^2 = (-1)^2 = 1$.

Since two different values of x lead to the same value of y, the function is not one-to-one.

7. $f(x) = x^3 - 3$

This function is one-to-one.

(a) *Step 1* Replace $f(x)$ with y and interchange x and y.

$$y = x^3 - 3$$
$$x = y^3 - 3$$

Step 2 Solve for y.

$$x = y^3 - 3 \Rightarrow x + 3 = y^3 \Rightarrow y = \sqrt[3]{x+3}$$

Step 3 Replace y with $f^{-1}(x)$.

$$f^{-1}(x) = \sqrt[3]{x+3}$$

9. $f^{-1}(\$50{,}000)$ represents the number of years after 2004 required for the investment to reach \$50,000.

11. To have an inverse, a function must be a <u>one-to-one</u> function.

13. $y = \log_{.3} x$

The point (1, 0) is on the graph of every function of the form $y = \log_a x$, so the correct choice must be either B or C. Since the base is $a = .3$ and $0 < .3 < 1$, $y = \log_{.3} x$ is a decreasing function, and so the correct choice must be B.

15. $y = \ln x = \log_e x$

The point (1, 0) is on the graph of every function of the form $y = \log_a x$, so the correct choice must be either B or C. Since the base is $a = e$ and $e > 1$, $y = \ln x$ is an increasing function, and so the correct choice must be C.

17. $2^5 = 32$ is written in logarithmic form as $\log_2 32 = 5$.

19. $\left(\frac{3}{4}\right)^{-1} = \frac{4}{3}$ is written in logarithmic form as $\log_{3/4} \frac{4}{3} = -1$.

21. $\log_3 4$ is the logarithm to the base 3 of 4. ($\log_4 3$ would be the logarithm to the base 4 of 3.)

22. The exact value of $\log_3 9$ is 2 since $3^2 = 9$.

23. The exact value of $\log_3 27$ is 3 since $3^3 = 27$.

24. $\log_3 16$ must lie between 2 and 3. Because the function defined by $y = \log_3 x$ is increasing and $9 < 16 < 27$, we have $\log_3 9 < \log_3 16 < \log_3 27$.

25. By the change-of-base theorem, $\log_3 16 = \frac{\log 16}{\log 3} = \frac{\ln 16}{\ln 3} \approx 2.523719014$. This value is between 2 and 3, as predicted in Exercise 24.

26. The exact value of $\log_5 \frac{1}{5}$ is -1 since $5^{-1} = \frac{1}{5}$. The exact value of $\log_5 1$ is 0 since $5^0 = 1$.

27. $\log_5 .68$ must lie between -1 and 0. Since the function defined by $y = \log_5 x$ is increasing and $\frac{1}{5} = .2 < .68 < 1$, we must have $\log_5 .2 < \log_5 .68 < \log_5 1$. By the change-of-base theorem, we have $\log_5 .68 = \frac{\log .68}{\log 5} = \frac{\ln .68}{\ln 5} \approx -.2396255723$. This value is between -1 and 0, as predicted above.

29. $\log 3.45 \approx .5378$ is written in exponential form as $10^{.5378} \approx 3.45$.

31. Let $f(x) = \log_a x$ be the required function.

Then $f(81) = 4 \Rightarrow \log_a 81 = 4 \Rightarrow a^4 = 81 \Rightarrow a^4 = 3^4 \Rightarrow a = 3$. The base is 3.

33. $\log_3 \frac{mn}{5r} = \log_3 mn - \log_3 5r = \log_3 m + \log_3 n - (\log_3 5 + \log_3 r) = \log_3 m + \log_3 n - \log_3 5 - \log_3 r$

35. $\log_7(7k + 5r^2)$

Since this is the logarithm of a sum, this expression cannot be simplified.

37. $\log .0411 \approx -1.3862$

39. $\ln 144{,}000 \approx 11.8776$

41. To find $\log_{2/3} \frac{5}{8}$, use the change-of-base theorem. We have $\log_{2/3} \frac{5}{8} = \frac{\log \frac{5}{8}}{\log \frac{2}{3}} = \frac{\ln \frac{5}{8}}{\ln \frac{2}{3}} \approx 1.1592$.

43. $x^{-3} = \frac{8}{27} \Rightarrow \left(\frac{1}{x}\right)^3 = \left(\frac{2}{3}\right)^3 \Rightarrow \frac{1}{x} = \frac{2}{3} \Rightarrow x = \frac{3}{2}$

Solution set: $\left\{\frac{3}{2}\right\}$

45. $4^{x+3} = 5^{2-x}$

Take the natural logarithms of both sides. Note: You could also solve by taking the common logarithm of both sides.

$$\ln 4^{x+3} = \ln 5^{2-x}$$
$$(x+3)\ln 4 = (2-x)\ln 5$$
$$x\ln 4 + 3\ln 4 = 2\ln 5 - x\ln 5$$
$$x\ln 4 + x\ln 5 = 2\ln 5 - 3\ln 4$$
$$x(\ln 4 + \ln 5) = \ln 5^2 - \ln 4^3$$
$$x(\ln 4 + \ln 5) = \ln 25 - \ln 64$$
$$x = \frac{\ln 25 - \ln 64}{\ln 4 + \ln 5}$$
$$x = \frac{\ln \frac{25}{64}}{\ln 20} \approx -.3138$$

Solution set: $\{-.3138\}$

47. $\log_{64} x = \frac{1}{3}$

$$64^{1/3} = x$$
$$x = \sqrt[3]{64} = 4$$

Solution set: $\{4\}$

49. $\log_{16} \sqrt{x+1} = \frac{1}{4}$

$$\sqrt{x+1} = 16^{1/4}$$
$$\left(\sqrt{x+1}\right)^2 = \left(16^{1/4}\right)^2$$
$$x+1 = 16^{1/2}$$
$$x+1 = \sqrt{16}$$
$$x+1 = 4$$
$$x = 3$$

Since the solution involves squaring both sides, the proposed solution must be checked in the original equation.

Check $x = 3$.

$$\log_{16} \sqrt{x+1} = \frac{1}{4}$$
$$\log_{16} \sqrt{3+1} = \frac{1}{4}\ ?$$
$$\log_{16} \sqrt{4} = \frac{1}{4}$$
$$\log_{16} 4^{1/2} = \frac{1}{4}$$
$$\frac{1}{2}\log_{16} 4 = \frac{1}{4}$$
$$\frac{1}{2}\log_{16} \sqrt{16} = \frac{1}{4}$$
$$\frac{1}{2}\log_{16} 16^{1/2} = \frac{1}{4}$$
$$\frac{1}{2} \cdot \frac{1}{2} = \frac{1}{4}$$
$$\frac{1}{4} = \frac{1}{4}$$

This is a true statement.
3 is a solution.

Solution set: $\{3\}$

51. $\log x + \log(x-3) = 1$

$$\log_{10} x(x-3) = 1$$
$$10^1 = x(x-3)$$
$$10 = x^2 - 3x$$
$$0 = x^2 - 3x - 10$$
$$0 = (x+2)(x-5)$$
$$x+2=0 \quad \text{or} \quad x-5=0$$
$$x=-2 \qquad x=5$$

Since the negative solution $(x=-2)$ is not in the domain of $\log x$, it must be discarded.
Solution set: {5}

53. $S = a\ln\left(1+\frac{n}{a}\right)$ for n

$$\frac{S}{a} = \ln\left(1+\frac{n}{a}\right)$$
$$e^{S/a} = 1+\frac{n}{a}$$
$$e^{S/a} - 1 = \frac{n}{a}$$
$$n = a\left(e^{S/a} - 1\right)$$

55. (a) $8.3 = \log_{10}\frac{I}{I_0}$

$$\frac{I}{I_0} = 10^{8.3}$$
$$I = 10^{8.3} I_0 \approx 199{,}526{,}231.5 I_0$$

The magnitude was about $200{,}000{,}000 I_0$.

(b) $7.1 = \log_{10}\frac{I}{I_0}$

$$\frac{I}{I_0} = 10^{7.1}$$
$$I = 10^{7.1} I_0 \approx 12{,}589{,}254.12 I_0$$

The magnitude was about $13{,}000{,}000 I_0$.

(c) $\frac{200{,}000{,}000 I_0}{13{,}000{,}000 I_0} = \frac{200}{13} \approx 15.38$

The 1906 earthquake had a magnitude more than 15 times greater than the 1989 earthquake. Note: If the more precise values found in parts a and b were used, the 1906 earthquake had a magnitude of almost 16 times greater than the 1989 earthquake.

57. Substitute $A = 5760$, $P = 3500$, $t = 10$, $m = 1$ into the formula $A = P\left(1+\frac{r}{m}\right)^{tm}$.

$$5760 = 3500\left(1+\frac{r}{1}\right)^{10(1)} \Rightarrow \frac{288}{175} = (1+r)^{10} \Rightarrow \left(\frac{288}{175}\right)^{1/10} = 1+r \Rightarrow \left(\frac{288}{175}\right)^{1/10} - 1 = r \Rightarrow r \approx .051$$

The annual interest rate, to the nearest tenth, is 5.1%.

59. First, substitute $P = 10{,}000$, $r = .08$, $t = 12$, and $m = 1$ into the formula $A = P\left(1+\frac{r}{m}\right)^{tm}$.

$$A = 10{,}000\left(1+\frac{.08}{1}\right)^{12(1)} = 10{,}000(1.08)^{12} \approx 25{,}181.70$$

After the first 12 yr, there would be about \$25,181.70 in the account. To finish off the 21-year period, substitute $P = 25{,}181.70$, $r = .10$, $t = 9$, and $m = 2$ into the formula $A = P\left(1+\frac{r}{m}\right)^{tm}$.

$$A = 25{,}181.70\left(1+\frac{.10}{2}\right)^{9(2)} = 25{,}181.70(1+.05)^{18} = 25{,}181.70(1.05)^{18} \approx 60{,}602.76$$

At the end of the 21-year period, about \$60,606.76 would be in the account. Note: If it was possible to transfer the money accrued after the 12 years to the new account without rounding, the amount after the 21-year period would be \$60,606.77. The difference is not significant.

61. To find t, substitute $a = 2$, $P = 1$, and $r = .04$ into $A = Pe^{rt}$ and solve.

$$2 = 1\cdot e^{.04t} \Rightarrow 2 = e^{.04t} \Rightarrow \ln 2 = \ln e^{.04t} \Rightarrow \ln 2 = .04t \Rightarrow t = \frac{\ln 2}{.04} \approx 17.3$$

It would take about 17.3 yr.

63. Double the 2003 total payoff value is $2(152.7)=305.4$. Using the function $f(x)=93.54e^{.16x}$, we solve for x when $f(x)=305.4$.

$$93.54e^{.16x}=305.4 \Rightarrow e^{.16x}=\frac{305.4}{93.54} \Rightarrow \ln e^{.16x}=\ln\frac{305.4}{93.54} \Rightarrow .16x=\ln\frac{305.4}{93.54} \Rightarrow x=\frac{\ln\frac{305.4}{93.54}}{.16}\approx 7.40$$

Since x represents the number of years since 2000, in 2007 the total payoff value will be double of 2003.

65. $f(x)=\log_4\left(2x^2-x\right)$

(a) Use the change-of-base theorem with base e to write the function as $f(x)=\frac{\ln(2x^2-x)}{\ln 4}$.

(b)

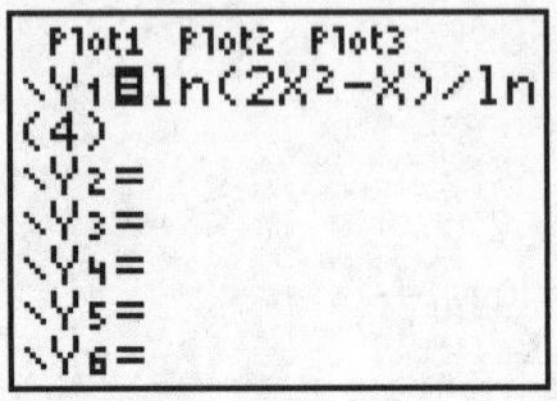

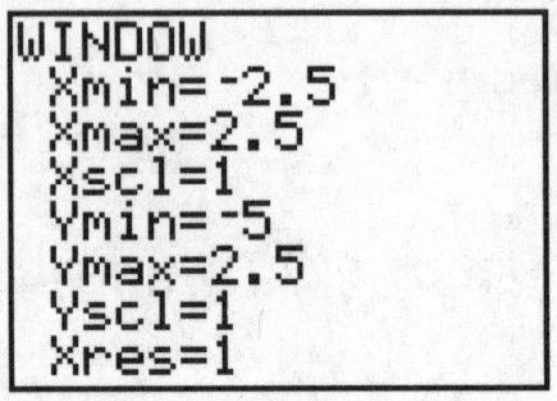

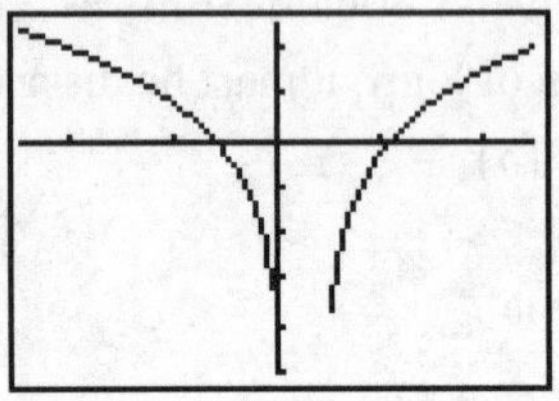

(c) From the graph, the x-intercepts are $-\frac{1}{2}$ and 1.

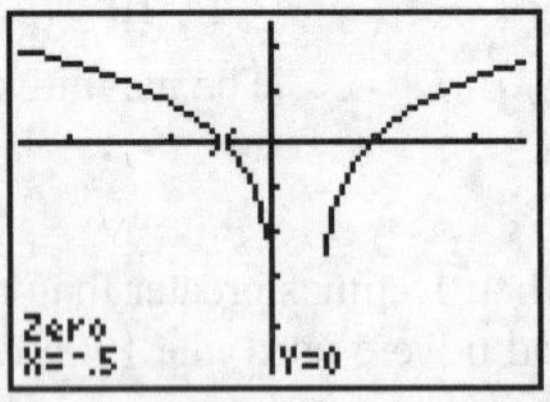

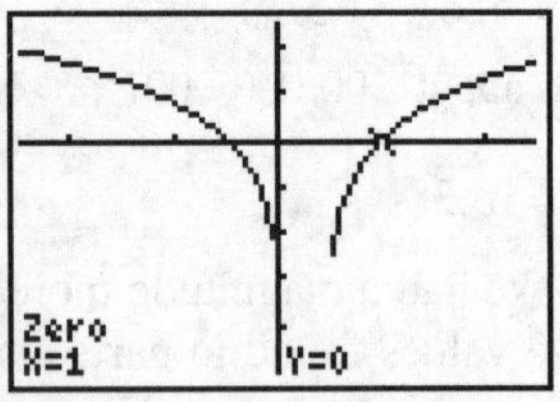

(d) From the graph, the vertical asymptotes are $x=0$ and $x=\frac{1}{2}$. This be can verified algebraically.

The vertical asymptotes will occur when $2x^2-x=0$.

$$2x^2-x=0 \Rightarrow x(2x-1)=0 \Rightarrow x=0 \text{ or } x=\tfrac{1}{2}$$

(e) To make a y-intercept, $x=0$ must be in the domain, which is not the case here.

Chapter 4: Test

1. **(a)** $f(x)=\sqrt[3]{2x-7}$

Since it is a cube root, $2x-7$ may be any real number.
Domain: $(-\infty,\infty)$

Since the cube root of any real number is also any real number.
Range: $(-\infty,\infty)$

(b) $f(x)=\sqrt[3]{2x-7}$

The graph of f passes the horizontal line test, and thus is a one-to-one function.

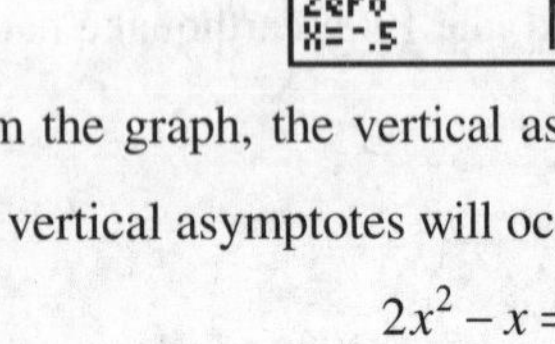

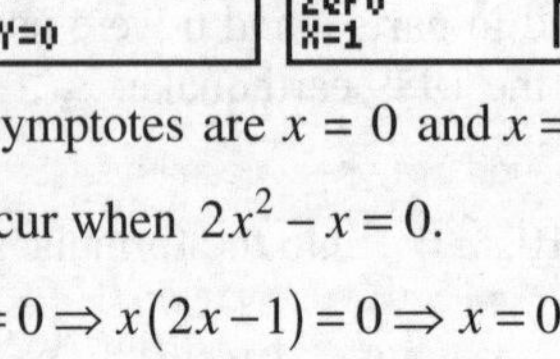

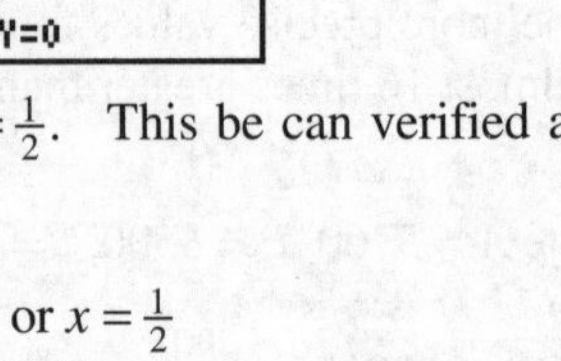

Continued on next page

1. (continued)

(c) *Step 1* Replace $f(x)$ with y and interchange x and y.

$$y = \sqrt[3]{2x-7}$$
$$x = \sqrt[3]{2y-7}$$

Step 2 Solve for y.

$$x = \sqrt[3]{2y-7} \Rightarrow x^3 = \left(\sqrt[3]{2y-7}\right)^3 \Rightarrow x^3 = 2y-7 \Rightarrow x^3+7 = 2y \Rightarrow \tfrac{x^3+7}{2} = y$$

Step 3 Replace y with $f^{-1}(x)$.

$$f^{-1}(x) = \tfrac{x^3+7}{2}$$

(d) Since the domain and range of f is $(-\infty, \infty)$, the domain and range of f^{-1} is also $(-\infty, \infty)$.

(e)

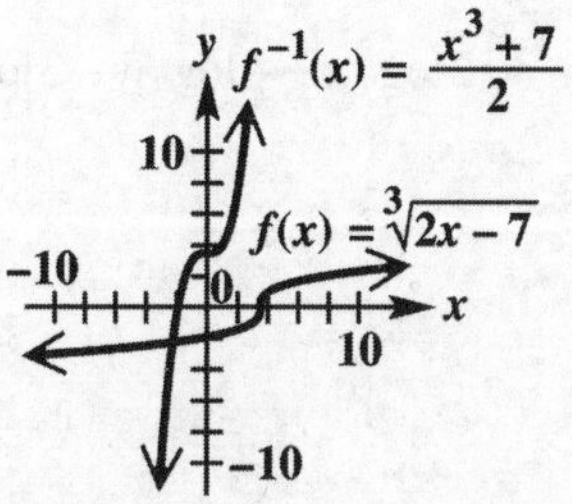

These graphs are reflections of each other across the line $y = x$.

2. **(a)** $y = \log_{1/3} x$

The point (1, 0) is on the graph of every function of the form $y = \log_a x$, so the correct choice must be either B or C. Since the base is $a = \frac{1}{3}$ and $0 < \frac{1}{3} < 1$, $y = \log_{1/3} x$ is a decreasing function, and so the correct choice must be B.

(b) $y = e^x$

The point (0, 1) is on the graph since $e^0 = 1$, so the correct choice must be either A or D. Since the base is e and $e > 1$, $y = e^x$ is an increasing function, and so the correct choice must be A.

(c) $y = \ln x$ or $y = \log_e x$

The point (1, 0) is on the graph of every function of the form $y = \log_a x$, so the correct choice must be B or C. Since the base is $a = e$ and $e > 1$, $y = \ln x$ is an increasing function, and the correct choice must be C.

(d) $y = \left(\frac{1}{3}\right)^x$

The point (0, 1) is on the graph since $\left(\frac{1}{3}\right)^0 = 1$, so the correct choice must be either A or D. Since the base is $\frac{1}{3}$ and $0 < \frac{1}{3} < 1$, $y = \left(\frac{1}{3}\right)^x$ is a decreasing function, and so the correct choice must be D.

3. $\left(\frac{1}{8}\right)^{2x-3} = 16^{x+1} \Rightarrow \left(2^{-3}\right)^{2x-3} = \left(2^4\right)^{x+1} \Rightarrow 2^{-3(2x-3)} = 2^{4(x+1)} \Rightarrow 2^{-6x+9} = 2^{4x+4}$

$$-6x+9 = 4x+4 \Rightarrow -10x+9 = 4 \Rightarrow -10x = -5 \Rightarrow x = \tfrac{1}{2}$$

Solution set: $\left\{\frac{1}{2}\right\}$

4. **(a)** $4^{3/2} = 8$ is written in logarithmic form as $\log_4 8 = \frac{3}{2}$.

(b) $\log_8 4 = \frac{2}{3}$ is written in exponential form as $8^{2/3} = 4$.

5. They are inverses of each other.

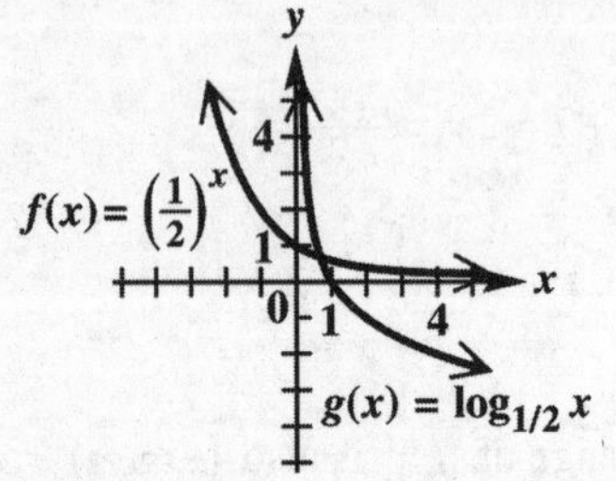

6. $\log_7 \frac{x^2 \sqrt[4]{y}}{z^3} = \log_7 x^2 + \log_7 \sqrt[4]{y} - \log_7 z^3 = \log_7 x^2 + \log_7 y^{1/4} - \log_7 z^3 = 2\log_7 x + \frac{1}{4}\log_7 y - 3\log_7 z$

7. $\log 237.4 \approx 2.3755$

8. $\ln .0467 \approx -3.0640$

9. $\log_9 13 = \frac{\ln 13}{\ln 9} = \frac{\log 13}{\log 9} \approx 1.1674$

10. $\log\left(2.49 \times 10^{-3}\right) \approx -2.6038$

11. $\log_x 25 = 2$

$x^2 = 25$

$x^2 = 5^2$

$x = 5$

Solution set: $\{5\}$

12. $\log_4 32 = x$

$4^x = 32$

$\left(2^2\right)^x = 2^5$

$2^{2x} = 2^5$

$2x = 5$

$x = \frac{5}{2}$

Solution set: $\left\{\frac{5}{2}\right\}$

13. $\log_2 x + \log_2 (x+2) = 3 \Rightarrow \log_2 x(x+2) = 3 \Rightarrow 2^3 = x(x+2)$

$8 = x^2 + 2x \Rightarrow 0 = x^2 + 2x - 8 \Rightarrow 0 = (x+4)(x-2)$

$x + 4 = 0$ or $x - 2 = 0$

$x = -4 \qquad x = 2$

Since the negative solution $(x = -4)$ is not in the domain of $\log_2 x$, it must be discarded.

Solution set: $\{2\}$

14.
$$5^{x+1} = 7^x$$
$$\ln 5^{x+1} = \ln 7^x$$
$$(x+1)\ln 5 = x\ln 7$$
$$x\ln 5 + \ln 5 = x\ln 7$$
$$\ln 5 = x\ln 7 - x\ln 5$$
$$\ln 5 = x(\ln 7 - \ln 5)$$
$$x = \frac{\ln 5}{\ln 7 - \ln 5} = \frac{\ln 5}{\ln \frac{7}{5}} \approx 4.7833$$

Solution set: {4.7833}

15. $\ln x - 4\ln 3 = \ln \frac{5}{x}$
$$\ln x - \ln 3^4 = \ln \frac{5}{x}$$
$$\ln x - \ln 81 = \ln \frac{5}{x}$$
$$\ln \frac{x}{81} = \ln \frac{5}{x}$$
$$\frac{x}{81} = \frac{5}{x}$$
$$x^2 = 405$$
$$x = \pm\sqrt{405} \approx \pm 20.1246$$

Since the negative solution $(x = -20.1246)$ is not in the domain of $\ln x$, it must be discarded.

Solution set: {20.1246}

16. Answers will vary.
$\log_5 27$ is the exponent to which 5 must be raised in order to obtain 27. To approximate $\log_5 27$ on your calculator, use the change-of-base formula; $\log_5 27 = \frac{\log 27}{\log 5} = \frac{\ln 27}{\ln 5} \approx 2.048.$

17. $v(t) = 176(1 - e^{-.18t})$
Find the time t at which $v(t) = 147$.
$$147 = 176(1 - e^{-.18t}) \Rightarrow \frac{147}{176} = 1 - e^{-.18t} \Rightarrow -e^{-.18t} = \frac{147}{176} - 1 \Rightarrow -e^{-.18t} = -\frac{29}{176}$$
$$e^{-.18t} = \frac{29}{176} \Rightarrow \ln e^{-.18t} = \ln \frac{29}{176} \Rightarrow -.18t = \ln \frac{29}{176} \Rightarrow t = \frac{\ln \frac{29}{176}}{-.18} \approx 10.02$$
It will take the skydiver about 10 sec to attain the speed of 147 ft per sec (100 mph).

18. **(a)** Substitute $P = 5000$, $A = 18{,}000$, $r = .068$, and $m = 12$ into the formula $A = P\left(1 + \frac{r}{m}\right)^{tm}$.
$$18{,}000 = 5000\left(1 + \frac{.068}{12}\right)^{t(12)} \Rightarrow 3.6 = \left(1 + \frac{.068}{12}\right)^{12t} \Rightarrow \ln 3.6 = \ln\left(1 + \frac{.068}{12}\right)^{12t}$$
$$\ln 3.6 = 12t\ln\left(1 + \frac{.068}{12}\right) \Rightarrow t = \frac{\ln 3.6}{12\ln\left(1 + \frac{.068}{12}\right)} \approx 18.9$$
It will take about 18.9 years.

(b) Substitute $P = 5000$, $A = 18{,}000$, and $r = .068$, and into the formula $A = Pe^{rt}$.
$$18{,}000 = 5000e^{.068t} \Rightarrow 3.6 = e^{.068t} \Rightarrow \ln 3.6 = \ln e^{.068t} \Rightarrow \ln 3.6 = .068t \Rightarrow t = \frac{\ln 3.6}{.068} \approx 18.8$$
It will take about 18.8 years.

19. $A(t) = 600e^{-.05t}$

(a) $A(12) = 600e^{-.05(12)} = 600e^{-.6} \approx 329.3$
The amount of radioactive material present after 12 days is about 329.3 g.

(b) Since $A(0) = 600e^{-.05(0)} = 600e^0 = 600$ g is the amount initially present, we seek to find t when $A(t) = \frac{1}{2}(600) = 300$ g is present.
$$300 = 600e^{-.05t} \Rightarrow .5 = e^{-.05t} \Rightarrow \ln .5 = \ln e^{-.05t} \Rightarrow \ln .5 = -.05t \Rightarrow t = \frac{\ln .5}{-.05} \approx 13.9$$
The half-life of the material is about 13.9 days.

20. Let $x = 0$ correspond to the year 2000. The population of New York (in millions) can be approximated by $y = 18.15e^{.0021x}$. The population of Florida (in millions) can be approximated by $y = 15.23e^{.0131x}$.

Graphing Calculator Solution:
Graph the two functions on the same screen and use the "intersect" option to find the x-coordinate of the intersection.

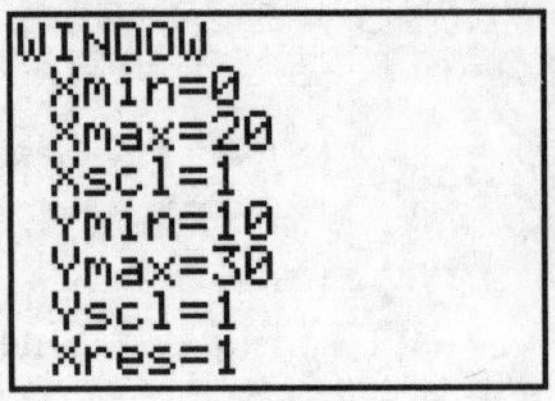

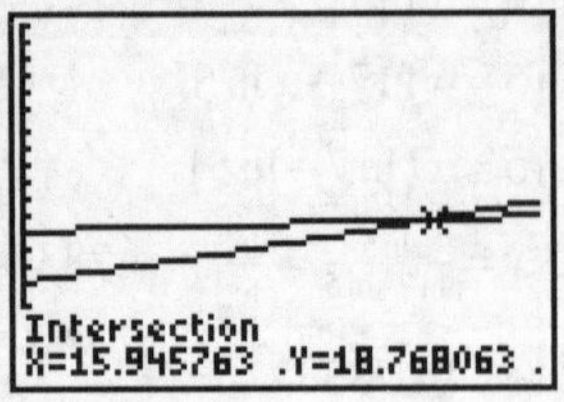

Algebraic Solution:
Set the two y-values equal to each other and solve for x.

$$18.15e^{.0021x} = 15.23e^{.0131x}$$

$$\frac{18.15}{15.23} = \frac{e^{.0131x}}{e^{.0021x}}$$

$$\frac{18.15}{15.23} = e^{.0131x-.0021x}$$

$$\frac{18.15}{15.23} = e^{.011x}$$

$$\ln\frac{18.15}{15.23} = \ln e^{.011x}$$

$$\ln\frac{18.15}{15.23} = .011x$$

$$x = \frac{\ln\frac{18.15}{15.23}}{.011} \approx 15.9$$

$x \approx 15.9$ corresponds to the end of the year 2015. Near the end of 2015 the populations will be equal.

Chapter 5

TRIGONOMETRIC FUNCTIONS

Section 5.1: Angles

1. Answers will vary.

3. Let $x =$ the measure of the angle.
If the angle is its own complement, then we have the following.

$$x + x = 90$$
$$2x = 90$$
$$x = 45$$

A 45° angle is its own complement.

5. 30°

(a) $90° - 30° = 60°$

(b) $180° - 30° = 150°$

7. 45°

(a) $90° - 45° = 45°$

(b) $180° - 45° = 135°$

9. 54°

(a) $90° - 54° = 36°$

(b) $180° - 54° = 126°$

11. $\dfrac{25\,\text{minutes}}{60\,\text{minutes}} = \dfrac{x}{360°} \Rightarrow x = \dfrac{25}{60}(360) = 25(6) = 150°$

13. The two angles form a straight angle.

$$7x + 11x = 180 \Rightarrow 18x = 180 \Rightarrow x = 10$$

The measures of the two angles are $(7x)° = [7(10)]° = 70°$ and $(11x)° = [11(10)]° = 110°$.

15. The two angles form a right angle.

$$(5k+5) + (3k+5) = 90 \Rightarrow 8k + 10 = 90 \Rightarrow 8k = 80 \Rightarrow k = 10$$

The measures of the two angles are $(5k+5)° = [5(10)+5]° = (50+5)° = 55°$ and $(3k+5)° = [3(10)+5]° = (30+5)° = 35°$.

17. The sum of the measures of two supplementary angles is 180°.

$$(6x-4) + (8x-12) = 180 \Rightarrow 14x - 16 = 180 \Rightarrow 14x = 196 \Rightarrow x = 14$$

Since $(6x-4)° = [6(14)-4]° = (84-4)° = 80°$ and $(8x-12)° = [8(14)-12]° = (112-12)° = 100°$, the angle measures are 80° and 100°.

19. If an angle measures x degrees and two angles are complementary if their sum is 90°, then the complement of an angle of $x°$ is $(90 - x)°$.

21. The first negative angle coterminal with x between 0° and 60° is $(x - 360)°$.

23.
$$\begin{array}{r} 62^\circ\ 18' \\ +21^\circ\ 41' \\ \hline 83^\circ\ 59' \end{array}$$

25. $71^\circ 18' - 47^\circ 29' = 70^\circ 78' - 47^\circ 29'$
$$\begin{array}{r} 70^\circ\ 78' \\ -47^\circ\ 29' \\ \hline 23^\circ\ 49' \end{array}$$

27. $90^\circ - 51^\circ 28' = 89^\circ 60' - 51^\circ 28'$
$$\begin{array}{r} 89^\circ\ 60' \\ -51^\circ\ 28' \\ \hline 38^\circ\ 32' \end{array}$$

29. $90^\circ - 72^\circ 58' 11'' = 89^\circ 59' 60'' - 72^\circ 58' 11''$
$$\begin{array}{r} 89^\circ\ 59'\ 60'' \\ -72^\circ\ 58'\ 11'' \\ \hline 17^\circ\ \ 1'\ 49'' \end{array}$$

31. $20^\circ 54' = 20^\circ + \frac{54}{60}^\circ = 20^\circ + .900^\circ = 20.900^\circ$

33. $91^\circ 35' 54'' = 91^\circ + \frac{35}{60}^\circ + \frac{54}{3600}^\circ$
$\approx 91^\circ + .5833^\circ + .0150^\circ \approx 91.598^\circ$

35 $274^\circ 18' 59'' = 274^\circ + \frac{18}{60}^\circ + \frac{59}{3600}^\circ$
$\approx 274^\circ + .3000^\circ + .0164^\circ$
$\approx 274.316^\circ$

37. $31.4296^\circ = 31^\circ + .4296^\circ = 31^\circ + .4296(60')$
$= 31^\circ + 25.776' = 31^\circ + 25' + .776'$
$= 31^\circ + 25' + .776(60'')$
$= 31^\circ 25' 46.56'' \approx 31^\circ 25' 47''$

39. $89.9004^\circ = 89^\circ + .9004^\circ = 89^\circ + .9004(60')$
$= 89^\circ + 54.024' = 89^\circ + 54' + .024'$
$= 89^\circ + 54' + .024(60'')$
$= 89^\circ 54' 1.44'' \approx 89^\circ 54' 1''$

41. $178.5994^\circ = 178^\circ + .5994^\circ = 178^\circ + .5994(60') = 178^\circ + 35.964' = 178^\circ + 35' + .964'$
$= 178^\circ + 35' + .964(60'') = 178^\circ 35' 57.84'' \approx 178^\circ 35' 58''$

43. Answers will vary.

45. -40° is coterminal with $360^\circ + (-40^\circ) = 320^\circ$.

47. -125° is coterminal with $360^\circ + (-125^\circ) = 235^\circ$.

49. 539° is coterminal with $539^\circ - 360^\circ = 179^\circ$.

51. 850° is coterminal with $850^\circ - 2(360^\circ) = 850^\circ - 720^\circ = 130^\circ$.

53. 30°
A coterminal angle can be obtained by adding an integer multiple of 360°.
$30^\circ + n \cdot 360^\circ$

55. 135°
A coterminal angle can be obtained by adding an integer multiple of 360°.
$135^\circ + n \cdot 360^\circ$

57. -90°
A coterminal angle can be obtained by adding an integer multiple of 360°.
$-90^\circ + n \cdot 360^\circ$

59. The answers to Exercises 56 and 57 give the same set of angles since -90° is coterminal with $-90^\circ + 360^\circ = 270^\circ$.

For Exercises 61 – 67, angles other than those given are possible.

61.

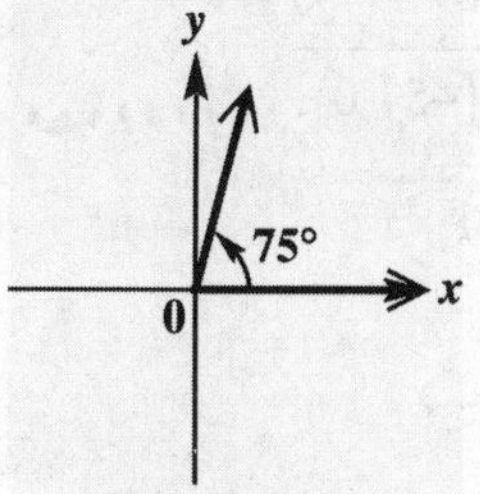

435°; –285°; quadrant I

75° is coterminal with 75° + 360° = 435° and 75° – 360° = –285°. These angles are in quadrant I.

63.

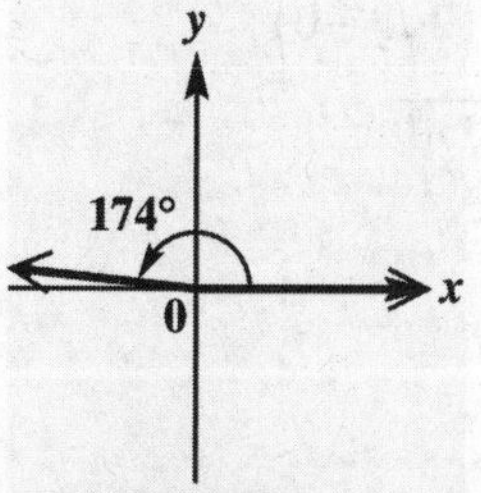

534°; –186°; quadrant II

174° is coterminal with 174° + 360° = 534° and 174° – 360° = –186°. These angles are in quadrant II.

65.

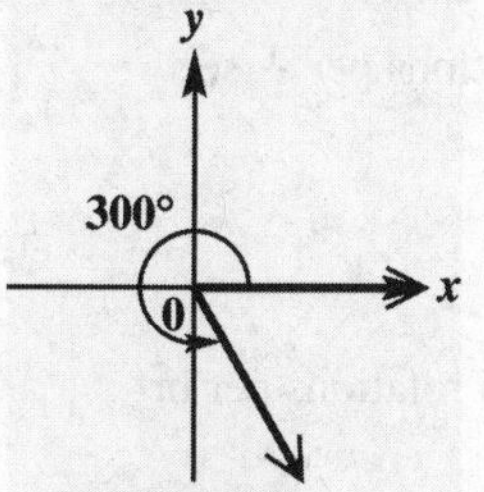

660°; –60°; quadrant IV

300° is coterminal with 300° + 360° = 660° and 300° – 360° = –60°. These angles are in quadrant IV.

67.

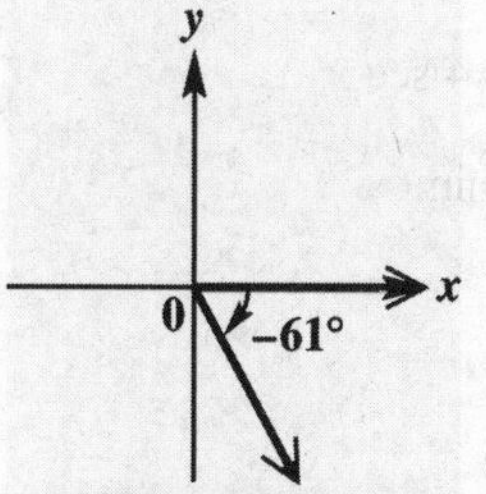

299°; –421°; quadrant IV

–61° is coterminal with –61° + 360° = 299° and –61° – 360° = –421°. These angles are in quadrant IV.

69.

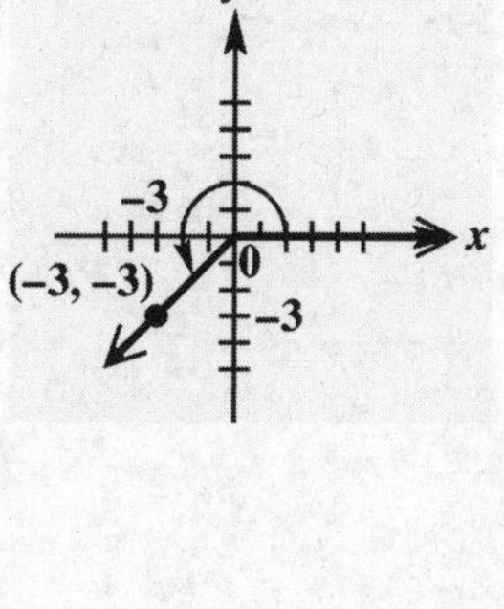

Points: $(0,0)$ and $(-3,-3)$

$$
\begin{aligned}
r &= \sqrt{(-3-0)^2+(-3-0)^2} \\
&= \sqrt{(-3)^2+(-3)^2} \\
&= \sqrt{9+9} \\
&= \sqrt{18} \\
&= \sqrt{9\cdot 2} = 3\sqrt{2}
\end{aligned}
$$

71.

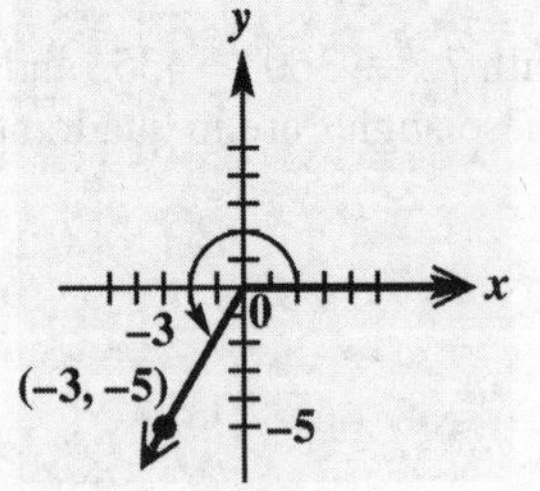

Points: $(0,0)$ and $(-3,-5)$

$$\begin{aligned} r &= \sqrt{(-3-0)^2+(-5-0)^2} \\ &= \sqrt{(-3)^2+(-5)^2} \\ &= \sqrt{9+25} \\ &= \sqrt{34} \end{aligned}$$

73.

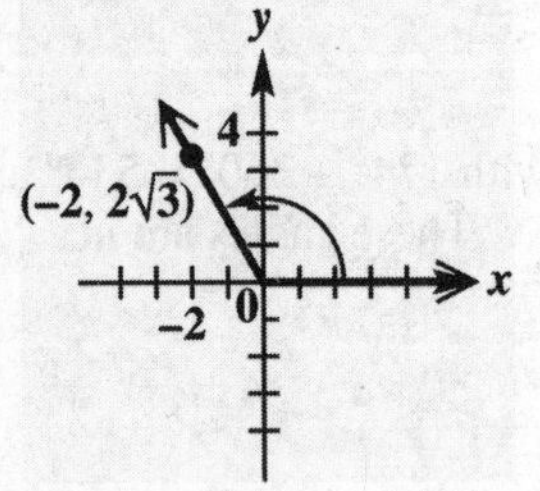

Points: $(0,0)$ and $\left(-2,2\sqrt{3}\right)$

$$\begin{aligned} r &= \sqrt{(-2-0)^2+\left(2\sqrt{3}-0\right)^2} \\ &= \sqrt{(-2)^2+\left(2\sqrt{3}\right)^2} \\ &= \sqrt{4+12} \\ &= \sqrt{16}=4 \end{aligned}$$

75. 45 revolutions per min $= \frac{45}{60}$ revolution per sec $= \frac{3}{4}$ revolution per sec

A turntable will make $\frac{3}{4}$ revolution in 1 sec.

77. 600 rotations per min $= \frac{600}{60}$ rotations per sec $= 10$ rotations per sec $= 5$ rotations per $\frac{1}{2}$ sec

$= 5(360^\circ)$ per $\frac{1}{2}$ sec $= 1800^\circ$ per $\frac{1}{2}$ sec

A point on the edge of the tire will move 1800° in $\frac{1}{2}$ sec.

79. 75° per min $= 75^\circ(60)$ per hr $= 4500^\circ$ per hr $= \frac{4500^\circ}{360^\circ}$ rotations per hr $= 12.5$ rotations per hr

The pulley makes 12.5 rotations in 1 hr.

81. The earth rotates 360° in 24 hr. 360° is equal to $360(60') = 21{,}600'$.

$$\frac{24\text{ hr}}{21{,}600'} = \frac{x}{1'} \Rightarrow x = \frac{24}{21{,}600}\text{ hr} = \frac{24}{21{,}600}(60\text{ min}) = \frac{1}{15}\text{ min} = \frac{1}{15}(60\text{ sec}) = 4\text{ sec}$$

It should take the motor 4 sec to rotate the telescope through an angle of 1 min.

Section 5.2: Trigonometric Functions

1.

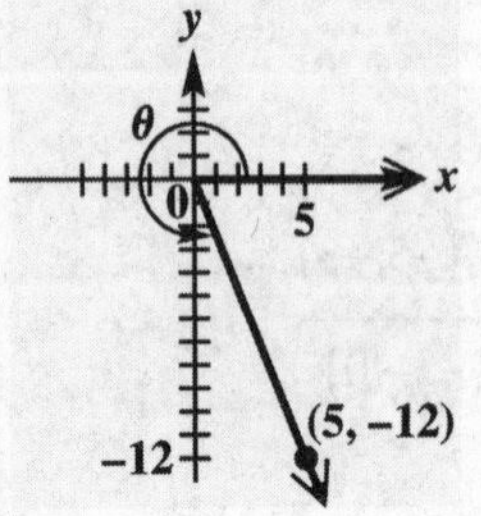

3. $(-3,4)$

$x=-3, y=4$ and $r=\sqrt{x^2+y^2}=\sqrt{(-3)^2+4^2}=\sqrt{9+16}=\sqrt{25}=5$

$\sin\theta=\frac{y}{r}=\frac{4}{5}$ $\qquad$ $\cot\theta=\frac{x}{y}=\frac{-3}{4}=-\frac{3}{4}$

$\cos\theta=\frac{x}{r}=\frac{-3}{5}=-\frac{3}{5}$ $\qquad$ $\sec\theta=\frac{r}{x}=\frac{5}{-3}=-\frac{5}{3}$

$\tan\theta=\frac{y}{x}=\frac{4}{-3}=-\frac{4}{3}$ $\qquad$ $\csc\theta=\frac{r}{y}=\frac{5}{4}$

5. $(0,2)$

$x=0, y=2$, and $r=\sqrt{x^2+y^2}=\sqrt{0^2+2^2}=\sqrt{0+4}=\sqrt{4}=2$

$\sin\theta=\frac{y}{r}=\frac{2}{2}=1$ $\qquad$ $\cot\theta=\frac{x}{y}=\frac{0}{2}=0$

$\cos\theta=\frac{x}{r}=\frac{0}{2}=0$ $\qquad$ $\sec\theta=\frac{r}{x}=\frac{2}{0}$ undefined

$\tan\theta=\frac{y}{x}=\frac{2}{0}$ undefined $\qquad$ $\csc\theta=\frac{r}{y}=\frac{2}{2}=1$

7. $(1,\sqrt{3})$

$x=1,\ y=\sqrt{3}$, and $r=\sqrt{x^2+y^2}=\sqrt{1^2+(\sqrt{3})^2}=\sqrt{1+3}=\sqrt{4}=2$

$\sin\theta=\frac{y}{r}=\frac{\sqrt{3}}{2}$ $\qquad$ $\cot\theta=\frac{x}{y}=\frac{1}{\sqrt{3}}=\frac{1}{\sqrt{3}}\cdot\frac{\sqrt{3}}{\sqrt{3}}=\frac{\sqrt{3}}{3}$

$\cos\theta=\frac{x}{r}=\frac{1}{2}$ $\qquad$ $\sec\theta=\frac{r}{x}=\frac{2}{1}=2$

$\tan\theta=\frac{y}{x}=\frac{\sqrt{3}}{1}=\sqrt{3}$ $\qquad$ $\csc\theta=\frac{r}{y}=\frac{2}{\sqrt{3}}=\frac{2}{\sqrt{3}}\cdot\frac{\sqrt{3}}{\sqrt{3}}=\frac{2\sqrt{3}}{3}$

9. $(-2,0)$

$x=-2,\ y=0$, and $r=\sqrt{x^2+y^2}=\sqrt{(-2)^2+0^2}=\sqrt{4+0}=\sqrt{4}=2$

$\sin\theta=\frac{y}{r}=\frac{0}{2}=0$ $\qquad$ $\cot\theta=\frac{x}{y}=\frac{-2}{0}$ undefined

$\cos\theta=\frac{x}{r}=\frac{-2}{2}=-1$ $\qquad$ $\sec\theta=\frac{r}{x}=\frac{2}{-2}=-1$

$\tan\theta=\frac{y}{x}=\frac{0}{-2}=0$ $\qquad$ $\csc\theta=\frac{r}{y}=\frac{2}{0}$ undefined

11. Answers will vary.
For any nonquadrantal angle θ, a point on the terminal side of θ will be of the form (x,y) where $x,y\neq 0$. Now $\sin\theta=\frac{y}{r}$ and $\csc\theta=\frac{r}{y}$ both exist and are simply reciprocals of each other, and hence will have the same sign.

In Exercises 13 & 15, $r=\sqrt{x^2+y^2}$, which is positive.

13. In quadrant II, x is negative, so $\frac{x}{r}$ is negative.

15. In quadrant IV, x is positive and y is negative, so $\frac{y}{x}$ is negative.

17. Since $x \ge 0$, the graph of the line $2x+y=0$ is shown to the right of the y-axis. A point on this line is (1, −2) since $2(1)+(-2)=0$. The corresponding value of r is $r=\sqrt{1^2+(-2)^2}=\sqrt{1+4}=\sqrt{5}$.

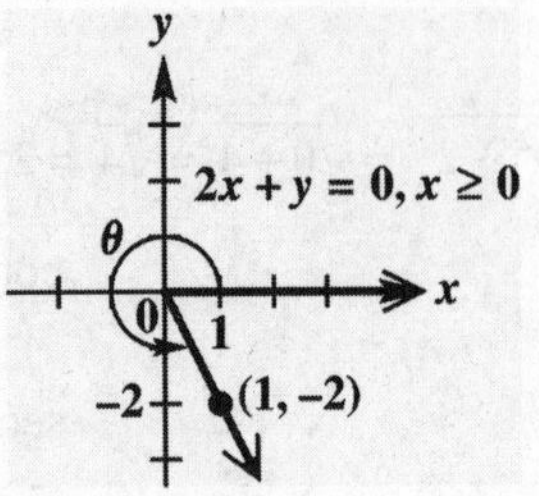

$\sin\theta=\frac{y}{r}=\frac{-2}{\sqrt{5}}=-\frac{2}{\sqrt{5}}\cdot\frac{\sqrt{5}}{\sqrt{5}}=-\frac{2\sqrt{5}}{5}$ $\qquad$ $\cot\theta=\frac{x}{y}=\frac{1}{-2}=-\frac{1}{2}$

$\cos\theta=\frac{x}{r}=\frac{1}{\sqrt{5}}=\frac{1}{\sqrt{5}}\cdot\frac{\sqrt{5}}{\sqrt{5}}=\frac{\sqrt{5}}{5}$ $\qquad$ $\sec\theta=\frac{r}{x}=\frac{\sqrt{5}}{1}=\sqrt{5}$

$\tan\theta=\frac{y}{x}=\frac{-2}{1}=-2$ $\qquad$ $\csc\theta=\frac{r}{y}=\frac{\sqrt{5}}{-2}=-\frac{\sqrt{5}}{2}$

19. Since $x \le 0$, the graph of the line $-6x-y=0$ is shown to the left of the y-axis. A point on this graph is $(-1,6)$ since $-6(-1)-6=0$. The corresponding value of r is $r=\sqrt{(-1)^2+6^2}=\sqrt{1+36}=\sqrt{37}$.

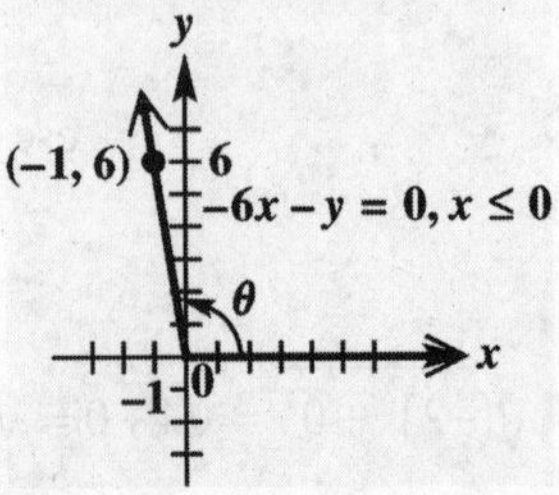

$\sin\theta=\frac{y}{r}=\frac{6}{\sqrt{37}}=\frac{6}{\sqrt{37}}\cdot\frac{\sqrt{37}}{\sqrt{37}}=\frac{6\sqrt{37}}{37}$ $\qquad$ $\cot\theta=\frac{x}{y}=\frac{-1}{6}=-\frac{1}{6}$

$\cos\theta=\frac{x}{r}=\frac{-1}{\sqrt{37}}=-\frac{1}{\sqrt{37}}\cdot\frac{\sqrt{37}}{\sqrt{37}}=-\frac{\sqrt{37}}{37}$ $\qquad$ $\sec\theta=\frac{r}{x}=\frac{\sqrt{37}}{-1}=-\sqrt{37}$

$\tan\theta=\frac{y}{x}=\frac{6}{-1}=-6$ $\qquad$ $\csc\theta=\frac{r}{y}=\frac{\sqrt{37}}{6}$

21. The quadrantal angle $\theta = 450°$ is coterminal with $450° - 360° = 90°$. A point on the terminal side of θ is of the form $(0, y)$, where y is a positive real number. The corresponding value of r is $r = \sqrt{0^2 + y^2} = y$. The six trigonometric function values of θ are as follows.

$\sin\theta = \frac{y}{r} = \frac{y}{y} = 1$ $\qquad$ $\cot\theta = \frac{x}{y} = \frac{0}{y} = 0$

$\cos\theta = \frac{x}{r} = \frac{0}{y} = 0$ $\qquad$ $\sec\theta = \frac{r}{x} = \frac{y}{0}$ undefined

$\tan\theta = \frac{y}{x} = \frac{y}{0}$ undefined $\qquad$ $\csc\theta = \frac{r}{y} = \frac{y}{y} = 1$

For Exercises 23 – 27, all angles are quadrantal angles. For $0°$ we will choose the point $(1,0)$, so $x = 1$, $y = 0$, and $r = 1$. For $90°$ we will choose the point $(0,1)$, so $x = 0$, $y = 1$, and $r = 1$. For $180°$ we will choose the point $(-1,0)$, so $x = -1$, $y = 0$, and $r = 1$. Finally, for $270°$ we will choose the point $(0,-1)$, so $x = 0$, $y = -1$, and $r = 1$.

23. $4\csc 270° + 3\cos 180°$

$\csc 270° = \frac{r}{y} = \frac{1}{-1} = -1$ and $\cos 180° = \frac{x}{r} = \frac{-1}{1} = -1$

$4\csc 270° + 3\cos 180° = 4(-1) + 3(-1) = -4 + (-3) = -7$

25. $2\sec 0° + 4\cot^2 90° + \cos 360°$

$\sec 0° = \frac{r}{x} = \frac{1}{1} = 1$, $\cot 90° = \frac{x}{y} = \frac{0}{1} = 0$, and $\cos 360° = \cos 0° = \frac{x}{r} = \frac{1}{1} = 1$

$2\sec 0° + 4\cot^2 90° + \cos 360° = 2(1) + 4(0)^2 + 1 = 2 + 4(0) + 1 = 2 + 0 + 1 = 3$

27. $\sin^2 360° + \cos^2 360°$

$\sin 360° = \sin 0° = \frac{y}{r} = \frac{0}{1} = 0$ and $\cos 360° = \cos 0° = \frac{x}{r} = \frac{1}{1} = 1$

$\sin^2 360° + \cos^2 360° = 0^2 + 1^2 = 0 + 1 = 1$

29. $\sin[n \cdot 180°]$

This angle is a quadrantal angle whose terminal side lies on either the positive part of the *x*-axis or the negative part of the *x*-axis. Any point on these terminal sides would have the form $(k,0)$, where k is any real number, $k \neq 0$.

$$\sin[n \cdot 180°] = \frac{y}{r} = \frac{0}{\sqrt{0^2 + k^2}} = \frac{0}{\sqrt{k^2}} = \frac{0}{|k|} = 0$$

31. $\tan[(2n+1) \cdot 90°]$

This angle is a quadrantal angle whose terminal side lies on either the positive part of the *y*-axis or the negative part of the *y*-axis. Any point on these terminal sides would have the form $(0,k)$, where k is any real number, $k \neq 0$.

$$\tan[(2n+1) \cdot 90°] = \frac{y}{x} = \frac{k}{0} \text{ undefined}$$

33. Using a calculator, tan 25° = .466307658 and cot 65° = .466307658. We can conjecture that the tangent and cotangent of complementary angles are equal. Trying another pair of complementary angles we obtain $\tan 45° = .\cot 45° = 1$. Therefore, our conjecture appears to be true.

35. Using a calculator, cos 20° = .93969262 and cos (–20°) = .93969262. We can conjecture that the cosines of an angle and its negative are equal. Using a circle, and angle θ having the point (x, y) on its terminal side has a corresponding angle $-\theta$ with point $(x, -y)$ on its terminal side. From the definition of cosine, $\cos(-\theta) = \frac{x}{r}$ and $\cos\theta = \frac{x}{r}$. The cosines are equal.

In Exercises 37 – 41, make sure your calculator is in the modes indicated in the instructions.

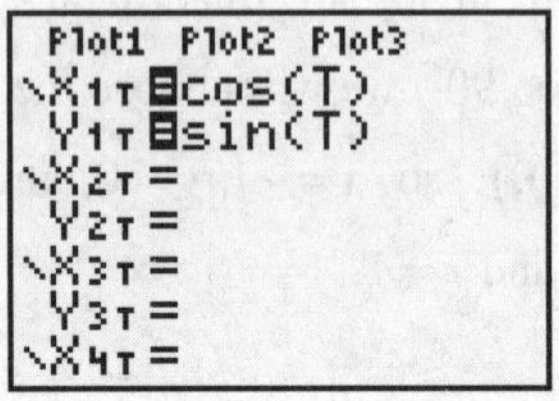

37. Use the TRACE feature to move around the circle in quadrant I. We see that cos 40° ≈ .766 so, $T = 40°$.

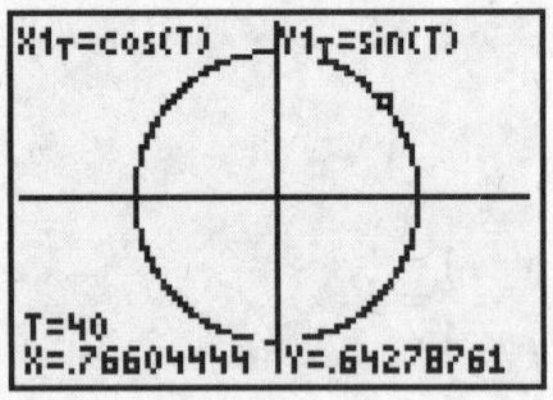

39. Use the TRACE feature to move around the circle in quadrant I. We see that cos 45° = sin 45°, so $T = 45°$.

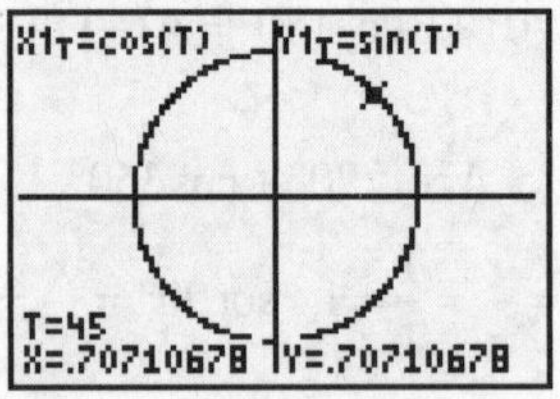

41. As T increases from 90° to 180°, the cosine decreases and the sine decreases.

43. –1 is its own reciprocal.
$\cos\theta = \sec\theta = -1$
$\cos 180° = \sec 180° = -1$
Therefore, $\theta = 180°$.

45. $\cot\theta = \frac{1}{\tan\theta} = \frac{1}{-\frac{1}{5}} = -5$

47. $\tan\theta = \frac{1}{\cot\theta} = \frac{1}{-\frac{\sqrt{5}}{3}} = -\frac{3}{\sqrt{5}}$

$$= -\frac{3}{\sqrt{5}} \cdot \frac{\sqrt{5}}{\sqrt{5}} = -\frac{3\sqrt{5}}{5}$$

49. $\cos\theta = \frac{1}{\sec\theta} = \frac{1}{9.80425133} \approx .10199657$

51. The value of $\cos\theta$ cannot exceed 1.

53. $\tan\theta = \frac{1}{\cot\theta} = \frac{1}{\frac{\sqrt{3}}{3}} = \frac{3}{\sqrt{3}} = \frac{3}{\sqrt{3}} \cdot \frac{\sqrt{3}}{\sqrt{3}} = \sqrt{3}$

55. $\tan(3\theta - 4°) = \frac{1}{\cot(5\theta - 8°)} \Rightarrow \tan(3\theta - 4°) = \tan(5\theta - 8°)$

The second equation is true if $3\theta - 4° = 5\theta - 8°$, so solving this equation will give a value (but not the only value) for which the given equation is true.

$$3\theta - 4° = 5\theta - 8° \Rightarrow 4° = 2\theta \Rightarrow \theta = 2°$$

57. $\sin\theta > 0$ implies θ is in quadrant I or II. $\cos\theta < 0$ implies θ is in quadrant II or III. Thus, θ must be in quadrant II.

59. $\tan\theta > 0$ implies θ is in quadrant I or III. $\cot\theta > 0$ also implies θ is in quadrant I or III. Thus, θ is in quadrant I or III.

61. 129° is in quadrant II.
$\sin 129°: +, \cos 129°: -, \tan 129°: -$

63. 298° is in quadrant IV
$\sin 298°: -, \cos 298°: +, \tan 298°: -$

65. Since $-82° + 360° = 278°$, $-82°$ is in quadrant IV.
$\sin(-82°): -, \cos(-82°): +, \tan(-82°): -$

67. $\tan 30° = \dfrac{\sin 30°}{\cos 30°}$

$\cos 30° < 1$, so $\tan 30° = \dfrac{\sin 30°}{\cos 30°} > \sin 30°$; that is, $\tan 30°$ is greater than $\sin 30°$.

69. $\sec 33° = \dfrac{1}{\cos 33°}$; since $\cos 33° < 1$, $\dfrac{1}{\cos 33°} > \cos 33°$.
$\sin 33° < \cos 33° < \sec 33°$.
Therefore, sec 33° is greater than sin 33°.

71. Since $-1 \le \cos\theta \le 1$ for all θ and -1.001 is not in this range, $\cos\theta = -1.001$ is impossible.

73. $\cot\theta$ can take on all values. Thus, $\cot\theta = -12.1$ is possible.

75. $\tan\theta$ can take on all values. Thus, $\tan\theta = 1$ is possible.

77. $\tan\theta = 2$ is possible, but when $\tan\theta = 2$, $\cot\theta = \dfrac{1}{\tan\theta} = \dfrac{1}{2}$. $\tan\theta = 2$ and $\cot\theta = \dfrac{1}{2}$ is impossible.

79. Find $\sin\theta$, if $\cos\theta = -\dfrac{1}{4}$, with θ in quadrant II.

Start with the identity $\sin^2\theta + \cos^2\theta = 1$. Replace $\cos\theta$ with $-\dfrac{1}{4}$.

$$\sin^2\theta + \left(-\frac{1}{4}\right)^2 = 1 \Rightarrow \sin^2\theta + \frac{1}{16} = 1 \Rightarrow \sin^2\theta = \frac{15}{16} \Rightarrow \sin\theta = \pm\sqrt{\frac{15}{16}} = \pm\frac{\sqrt{15}}{4}$$

Since θ is in quadrant II, $\sin\theta > 0$, so $\sin\theta = \dfrac{\sqrt{15}}{4}$.

81. Find $\sec\theta$, if $\tan\theta = \dfrac{\sqrt{7}}{3}$, and θ is in quadrant III.

Start with the identity $\tan^2\theta + 1 = \sec^2\theta$. Replace $\tan\theta$ with $\dfrac{\sqrt{7}}{3}$.

$$\sec^2\theta = \left(\frac{\sqrt{7}}{3}\right)^2 + 1 \Rightarrow \sec^2\theta = \frac{7}{9} + \frac{9}{9} \Rightarrow \sec^2\theta = \frac{16}{9} \Rightarrow \sec\theta = \pm\sqrt{\frac{16}{9}} = \pm\frac{4}{3}$$

Since θ is in quadrant III, $\sec\theta < 0$, so $\sec\theta = -\dfrac{4}{3}$.

83. Find $\sin\theta$, if $\sec\theta = 2$, with θ in quadrant IV.

Start with the identity $\cos\theta = \frac{1}{\sec\theta}$ We have $\cos\theta = \frac{1}{\sec\theta} = \frac{1}{2}$. Now use the identity $\sin^2\theta + \cos^2\theta = 1$ and replace $\cos\,\theta$ with $\frac{1}{2}$.

$$\sin^2\theta + \left(\frac{1}{2}\right)^2 = 1 \Rightarrow \sin^2\theta + \frac{1}{4} = 1 \Rightarrow \sin^2\theta = \frac{3}{4} \Rightarrow \sin\theta = \pm\sqrt{\frac{3}{4}} = \pm\frac{\sqrt{3}}{2}$$

Since θ is in quadrant IV, $\sin\theta < 0$; therefore, $\sin\theta = -\frac{\sqrt{3}}{2}$.

85. Find $\tan\theta$, if $\sin\theta = .49268329$, with θ in quadrant II.
Start with the identity $\sin^2\theta + \cos^2\theta = 1$. Replace $\sin\theta$ with .49268329.

$$(.49268329)^2 + \cos^2\theta = 1 \Rightarrow .24273682 + \cos^2\theta \approx 1$$
$$\cos^2\theta \approx .75726318 \Rightarrow \cos\theta \approx \pm.87020870$$

Since θ is in quadrant II, $\cos\theta < 0$; therefore, $\cos\theta \approx -.87020870$. Since $\tan\theta = \frac{\sin\theta}{\cos\theta}$, we have $\tan\theta \approx \frac{.49268329}{-.87020870} \approx -.56616682$.

For Exercises 87 – 91, remember that *r* is always positive.

87. $\tan\theta = -\frac{15}{8} = \frac{15}{-8}$, with θ in quadrant II

$\tan\theta = \frac{y}{x}$ and θ is in quadrant II, so let $y = 15$ and $x = -8$.

$$x^2 + y^2 = r^2 \Rightarrow (-8)^2 + 15^2 = r^2 \Rightarrow 64 + 225 = r^2 \Rightarrow 289 = r^2 \Rightarrow r = 17, \text{ since } r \text{ is positive}$$

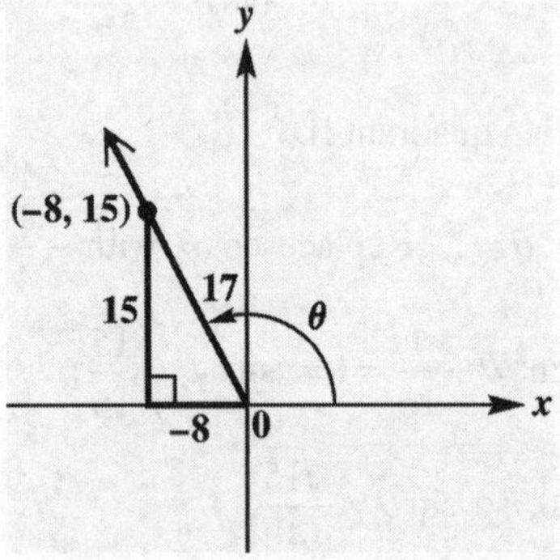

$\sin\theta = \frac{y}{r} = \frac{15}{17}$

$\cos\theta = \frac{x}{r} = \frac{-8}{17} = -\frac{8}{17}$

$\tan\theta = \frac{y}{x} = \frac{15}{-8} = -\frac{15}{8}$

$\cot\theta = \frac{x}{y} = \frac{-8}{15} = -\frac{8}{15}$

$\sec\theta = \frac{r}{x} = \frac{17}{-8} = -\frac{17}{8}$

$\csc\theta = \frac{r}{y} = \frac{17}{15}$

89. $\tan\theta = \sqrt{3} = \dfrac{-\sqrt{3}}{-1}$

$\tan\theta = \dfrac{y}{x}$ and θ is in quadrant III, so let $y = -\sqrt{3}$ and $x = -1$.

$$x^2 + y^2 = r^2 \Rightarrow (-1)^2 + \left(-\sqrt{3}\right)^2 = r^2 \Rightarrow 1 + 3 = r^2 \Rightarrow 4 = r^2 \Rightarrow r = 2, \text{ since } r \text{ is positive}$$

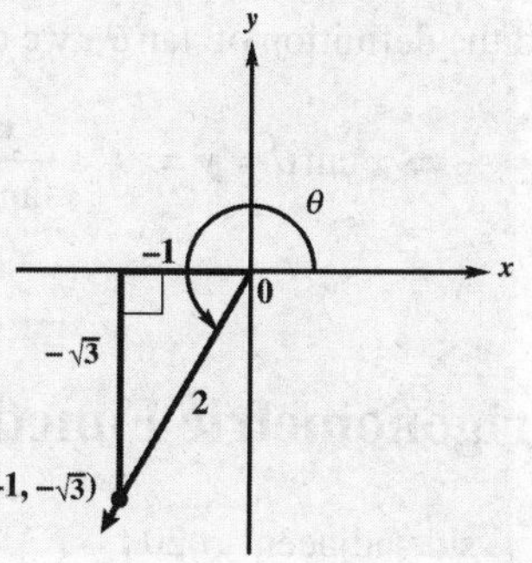

$\sin\theta = \dfrac{y}{r} = \dfrac{-\sqrt{3}}{2} = -\dfrac{\sqrt{3}}{2}$

$\cos\theta = \dfrac{x}{r} = \dfrac{-1}{2} = -\dfrac{1}{2}$

$\tan\theta = \dfrac{y}{x} = \dfrac{-\sqrt{3}}{-1} = \sqrt{3}$

$\cot\theta = \dfrac{x}{y} = \dfrac{-1}{-\sqrt{3}} = \dfrac{1}{\sqrt{3}} = \dfrac{1}{\sqrt{3}} \cdot \dfrac{\sqrt{3}}{\sqrt{3}} = \dfrac{\sqrt{3}}{3}$

$\sec\theta = \dfrac{r}{x} = \dfrac{2}{-1} = -2$

$\csc\theta = \dfrac{r}{y} = \dfrac{2}{-\sqrt{3}} = -\dfrac{2}{\sqrt{3}} \cdot \dfrac{\sqrt{3}}{\sqrt{3}} = -\dfrac{2\sqrt{3}}{3}$

91. $\cot\theta = -1.49586 = \dfrac{1.49586}{-1}$, with θ in quadrant IV

$\cot\theta = \dfrac{x}{y}$ and θ is in quadrant IV, let $x = 1.49586$ and $y = -1$.

$$x^2 + y^2 = r^2 \Rightarrow (1.49586)^2 + (-1)^2 = r^2 \Rightarrow 2.23760 + 1 \approx r^2$$

$$3.23760 \approx r^2 \Rightarrow r \approx 1.79933, \text{ since } r \text{ is positive}$$

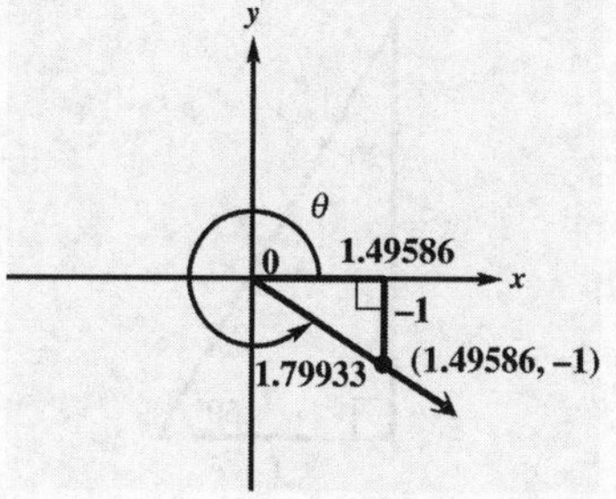

$\sin\theta = \dfrac{y}{r} \approx \dfrac{-1}{1.79933} \approx -.555762$

$\cos\theta = \dfrac{x}{r} \approx \dfrac{1.49586}{1.79933} \approx .831343$

$\tan\theta = \dfrac{y}{x} \approx \dfrac{-1}{1.49586} \approx -.668512$

$\cot\theta = \dfrac{x}{y} \approx \dfrac{1.49586}{-1} \approx -1.49586$

$\sec\theta = \dfrac{r}{x} \approx \dfrac{1.79933}{1.49586} \approx 1.20287$

$\csc\theta = \dfrac{r}{y} \approx \dfrac{1.79933}{-1} \approx -1.79933$

93. $x^2 + y^2 = r^2 \Rightarrow \dfrac{x^2 + y^2}{y^2} = \dfrac{r^2}{y^2} \Rightarrow \dfrac{x^2}{y^2} + \dfrac{y^2}{y^2} = \dfrac{r^2}{y^2} \Rightarrow \left(\dfrac{x}{y}\right)^2 + 1 = \left(\dfrac{r}{y}\right)^2 \Rightarrow 1 + \left(\dfrac{x}{y}\right)^2 = \left(\dfrac{r}{y}\right)^2$

Since $\cot\theta = \dfrac{x}{y}$ and $\csc\theta = \dfrac{r}{y}$, we have $1 + (\cot\theta)^2 = (\csc\theta)^2$ or $1 + \cot^2\theta = \csc^2\theta$.

95. The statement is false. For example, $\sin 30° + \cos 30° \approx .5 + .8660 = 1.3660 \neq 1.$

97. Let h = the height of the tree.

$$\cos 70° = \frac{50 \text{ ft}}{h} \Rightarrow h\cos 70° = 50 \Rightarrow h = \frac{50}{\cos 70°} = \frac{50}{0.3420} \approx 146 \text{ feet}$$

99. (a) From the figure in the text and the definition of $\tan\theta$, we can see that $\tan\theta = \frac{y}{x}$.

(b) Solving for x we have, $\tan\theta = \frac{y}{x} \Rightarrow x\tan\theta = y \Rightarrow x = \frac{y}{\tan\theta}$.

101. Answers will vary.

Section 5.3: Evaluating Trigonometric Functions

1. $\sin A = \frac{\text{side opposite}}{\text{hypotenuse}} = \frac{21}{29}$; $\cos A = \frac{\text{side adjacent}}{\text{hypotenuse}} = \frac{20}{29}$; $\tan A = \frac{\text{side opposite}}{\text{side adjacent}} = \frac{21}{20}$

3. $\sin A = \frac{\text{side opposite}}{\text{hypotenuse}} = \frac{n}{p}$; $\cos A = \frac{\text{side adjacent}}{\text{hypotenuse}} = \frac{m}{p}$; $\tan A = \frac{\text{side opposite}}{\text{side adjacent}} = \frac{n}{m}$

For Exercises 5 – 9, refer to the Function Values of Special Angles chart on page 497 of your text.

5. C; $\sin 30° = \frac{1}{2}$

7. B; $\tan 45° = 1$

9. E; $\csc 60° = \frac{1}{\sin 60°} = \frac{1}{\frac{\sqrt{3}}{2}} = \frac{2}{\sqrt{3}} = \frac{2}{\sqrt{3}} \cdot \frac{\sqrt{3}}{\sqrt{3}} = \frac{2\sqrt{3}}{3}$

For Exercises 11 – 15, refer to the following figure (Figure 26 from page 496 of your text).

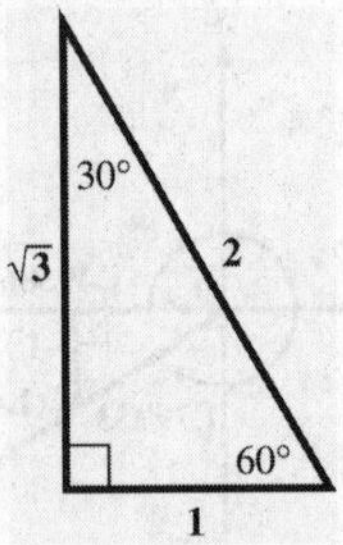

11. $\tan 30° = \frac{\text{side opposite}}{\text{side adjacent}}$

$$= \frac{1}{\sqrt{3}} = \frac{1}{\sqrt{3}} \cdot \frac{\sqrt{3}}{\sqrt{3}} = \frac{\sqrt{3}}{3}$$

13. $\sin 30° = \frac{\text{side opposite}}{\text{hypotenuse}} = \frac{1}{2}$

15. $\sec 30° = \frac{\text{hypotenuse}}{\text{side adjacent}}$

$$= \frac{2}{\sqrt{3}} = \frac{2}{\sqrt{3}} \cdot \frac{\sqrt{3}}{\sqrt{3}} = \frac{2\sqrt{3}}{3}$$

For Exercises 17 & 19, refer to the following figure (Figure 27 from page 496 of your text).

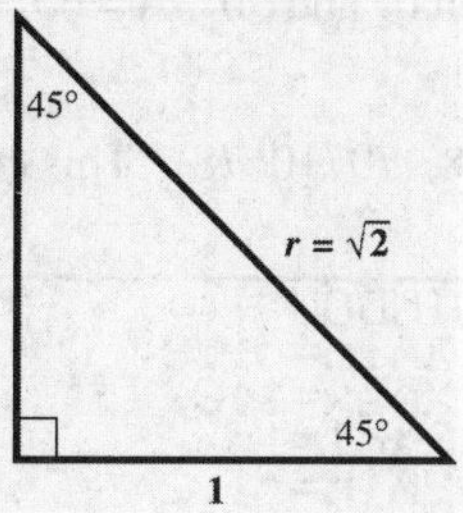

17. $\csc 45° = \dfrac{\text{hypotenuse}}{\text{side opposite}} = \dfrac{\sqrt{2}}{1} = \sqrt{2}$

19. $\cos 45° = \dfrac{\text{side adjacent}}{\text{hypotenuse}} = \dfrac{1}{\sqrt{2}}$

$= \dfrac{1}{\sqrt{2}} \cdot \dfrac{\sqrt{2}}{\sqrt{2}} = \dfrac{\sqrt{2}}{2}$

21.

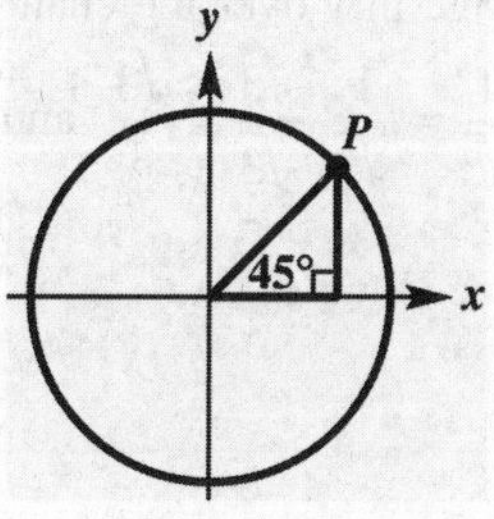

22. $\sin 45° = \dfrac{y}{4} \Rightarrow y = 4\sin 45° = 4 \cdot \dfrac{\sqrt{2}}{2} = 2\sqrt{2}$

$\cos 45° = \dfrac{x}{4} \Rightarrow x = 4\cos 45° = 4 \cdot \dfrac{\sqrt{2}}{2} = 2\sqrt{2}$

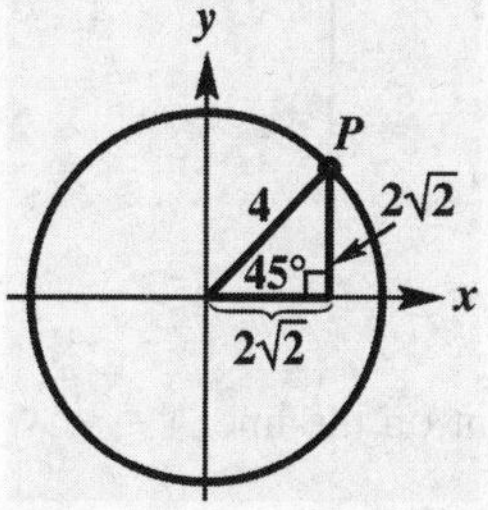

23. The legs of the right triangle provide the coordinates of P. P is $\left(2\sqrt{2}, 2\sqrt{2}\right)$.

24.

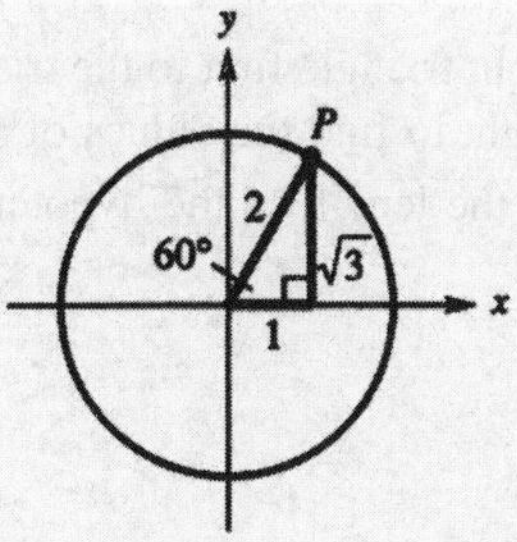

$\sin 60° = \dfrac{y}{2} \Rightarrow y = 2\sin 60° = 2 \cdot \dfrac{\sqrt{3}}{2} = \sqrt{3}$ and $\cos 60° = \dfrac{x}{2} \Rightarrow x = 2\cos 60° = 2 \cdot \dfrac{1}{2} = 1$

The legs of the right triangle provide the coordinates of P. P is $\left(1, \sqrt{3}\right)$.

25. Y_1 is $\sin x$ and Y_2 is $\tan x$.

$\sin 0° = 0$	$\tan 0° = 0$
$\sin 30° = .5$	$\tan 30° \approx .57735$
$\sin 45° \approx .70711$	$\tan 45° = 1$
$\sin 60° \approx .86603$	$\tan 60° = 1.7321$
$\sin 90° = 1$	$\tan 90°$: undefined

27. Since $\sin 60° = \dfrac{\sqrt{3}}{2}$ and 60° is between 0° and 90°, A = 60°.

29. The point of intersection is (.70710678, .70710678). This corresponds to the point $\left(\dfrac{\sqrt{2}}{2}, \dfrac{\sqrt{2}}{2}\right)$.

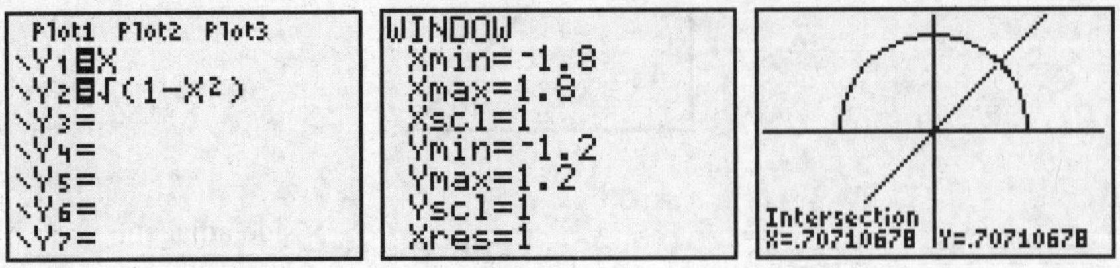

These coordinates are the sine and cosine of 45°.

31.

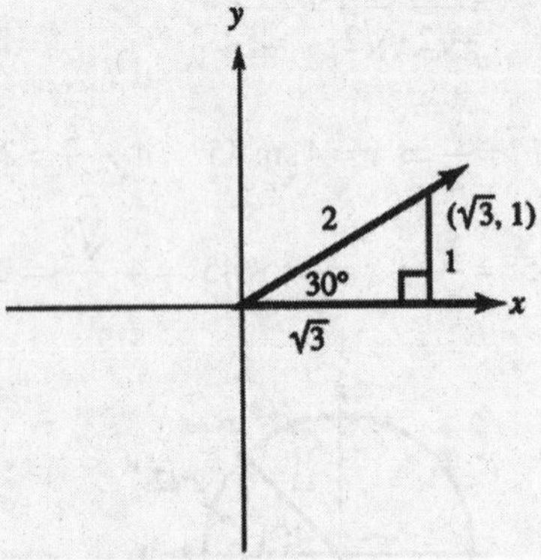

The line passes through (0, 0) and $\left(\sqrt{3}, 1\right)$. The slope is change in y over the change in x. Thus, $m = \dfrac{1}{\sqrt{3}} = \dfrac{1}{\sqrt{3}} \cdot \dfrac{\sqrt{3}}{\sqrt{3}} = \dfrac{\sqrt{3}}{3}$ and the equation of the line is $y = \dfrac{\sqrt{3}}{3}x$.

33. One point on the line $y = \sqrt{3}x$ is the origin $(0,0)$. Let (x, y) be any other point on this line. Then, by the definition of slope, $m = \dfrac{y-0}{x-0} = \dfrac{y}{x} = \sqrt{3}$, but also, by the definition of tangent, $\tan\theta = \sqrt{3}$. Because $\tan 60° = \sqrt{3}$, the line $y = \sqrt{3}x$ makes a 60° angle with the positive x-axis (See Exercise 30).

35. Apply the relationships between the lengths of the sides of a 30° − 60° right triangle first to the triangle on the left to find the values of y and x, and then to the triangle on the right to find the values of z and w. In the 30° − 60° right triangle, the side opposite the 30° angle is $\frac{1}{2}$ the length of the hypotenuse. The longer leg is $\sqrt{3}$ times the shorter leg.

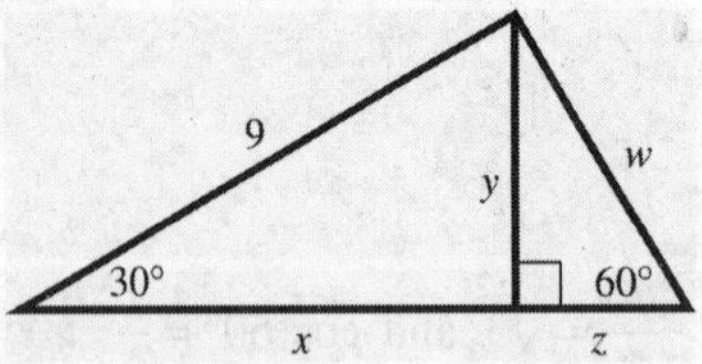

Thus, we have the following.

$$y = \frac{1}{2}(9) = \frac{9}{2} \text{ and } x = y\sqrt{3} = \frac{9\sqrt{3}}{2}$$

$$y = z\sqrt{3}, \text{ so } z = \frac{y}{\sqrt{3}} = \frac{\frac{9}{2}}{\sqrt{3}} = \frac{9\sqrt{3}}{6} = \frac{3\sqrt{3}}{2}, \text{ and } w = 2z, \text{ so } w = 2\left(\frac{3\sqrt{3}}{2}\right) = 3\sqrt{3}$$

37. Apply the relationships between the lengths of the sides of a $45°-45°$ right triangle to the triangle on the left to find the values of p and r. In the $45°-45°$ right triangle, the sides opposite the $45°$ angles measure the same. The hypotenuse is $\sqrt{2}$ times the measure of a leg.

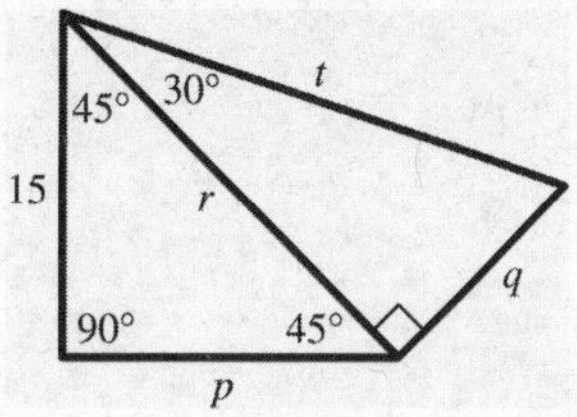

Thus, we have the following.

$$p = 15 \text{ and } r = p\sqrt{2} = 15\sqrt{2}$$

Apply the relationships between the lengths of the sides of a $30°-60°$ right triangle next to the triangle on the right to find the values of q and t. In the $30°-60°$ right triangle, the side opposite the $60°$ angle is $\sqrt{3}$ times as long as the side opposite to the $30°$ angle. The length of the hypotenuse is 2 times as long as the shorter leg (opposite the $30°$ angle).

Thus, we have the following.

$$r = q\sqrt{3} \Rightarrow q = \frac{r}{\sqrt{3}} = \frac{15\sqrt{2}}{\sqrt{3}} = \frac{15\sqrt{2}}{\sqrt{3}} \cdot \frac{\sqrt{3}}{\sqrt{3}} = 5\sqrt{6} \text{ and } t = 2q = 2\left(5\sqrt{6}\right) = 10\sqrt{6}$$

39. Since $A = \frac{1}{2}bh$, we have $A = \frac{1}{2} \cdot s \cdot s = \frac{1}{2}s^2$ or $A = \frac{s^2}{2}$.

41. F; $212° - 180° = 32°$
(212° is in quadrant III)

43. B; $-60° + 360° = 300°$ and
$360° - 300° = 60°$
(300° is in quadrant IV)

45. B; $480° - 360° = 120°$ and
$180° - 120° = 60°$
(120° is in quadrant II)

47. Answers will vary.

49. Yes, the angles must be coterminal. Additional answers will vary.

	θ	$\sin\theta$	$\cos\theta$	$\tan\theta$	$\cot\theta$	$\sec\theta$	$\csc\theta$
51.	45°	$\frac{\sqrt{2}}{2}$	$\frac{\sqrt{2}}{2}$	1	1	$\sqrt{2}$	$\sqrt{2}$
53.	120°	$\frac{\sqrt{3}}{2}$	$\cos 120° = -\cos 60° = -\frac{1}{2}$	$-\sqrt{3}$	$\cot 120° = -\cot 60° = -\frac{\sqrt{3}}{3}$	$\sec 120° = -\sec 60° = -2$	$\frac{2\sqrt{3}}{3}$
55.	150°	$\sin 150° = \sin 30° = \frac{1}{2}$	$-\frac{\sqrt{3}}{2}$	$-\frac{\sqrt{3}}{3}$	$\cot 150° = -\cot 30° = -\sqrt{3}$	$\sec 150° = -\sec 30° = -\frac{2\sqrt{3}}{3}$	2
57.	240°	$-\frac{\sqrt{3}}{2}$	$-\frac{1}{2}$	$\tan 240° = \tan 60° = \sqrt{3}$	$\cot 240° = \cot 60° = \frac{\sqrt{3}}{3}$	-2	$-\frac{2\sqrt{3}}{3}$

59. To find the reference angle for 315°, sketch this angle in standard position.

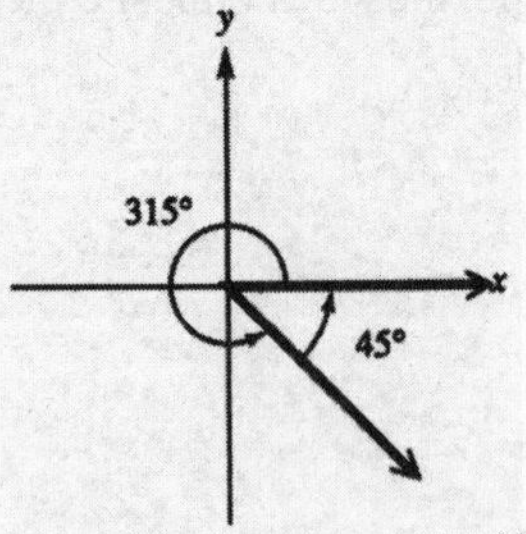

$$\sin 315° = -\sin 45° = -\frac{\sqrt{2}}{2}$$

$$\cos 315° = \cos 45° = \frac{\sqrt{2}}{2}$$

$$\tan 315° = -\tan 45° = -1$$

$$\cot 315° = -\cot 45° = -1$$

$$\sec 315° = \sec 45° = \sqrt{2}$$

$$\csc 315° = -\csc 45° = -\sqrt{2}$$

The reference angle is $360° - 315° = 45°$. Since 315° lies in quadrant IV, the sine, tangent, cotangent, and cosecant are negative.

61. To find the reference angle for −300°, sketch this angle in standard position.

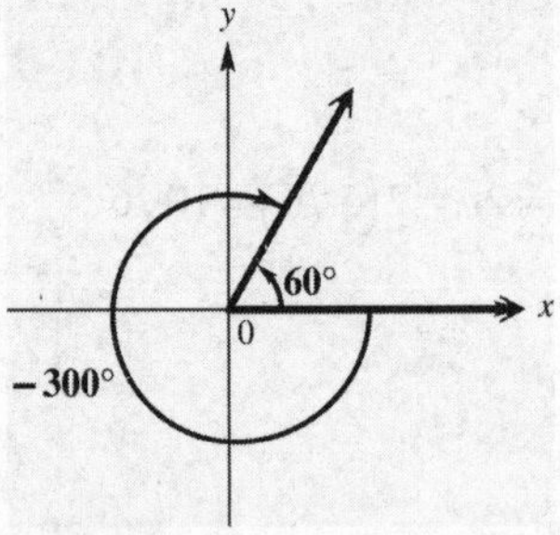

$$\sin(-300°) = \sin 60° = \frac{\sqrt{3}}{2}$$

$$\cos(-300°) = \cos 60° = \frac{1}{2}$$

$$\tan(-300°) = \tan 60° = \sqrt{3}$$

$$\cot(-300°) = \cot 60° = \frac{\sqrt{3}}{3}$$

$$\sec(-300°) = \sec 60° = 2$$

$$\csc(-300°) = \csc 60° = \frac{2\sqrt{3}}{3}$$

The reference angle for −300° is $-300° + 360° = 60°$. Because −300° lies in quadrant I, the values of all of its trigonometric functions will be positive, so these values will be identical to the trigonometric function values for 60°. See the Function Values of Special Angles table on page 497.)

63. To find the reference angle for 750°, sketch this angle in standard position.

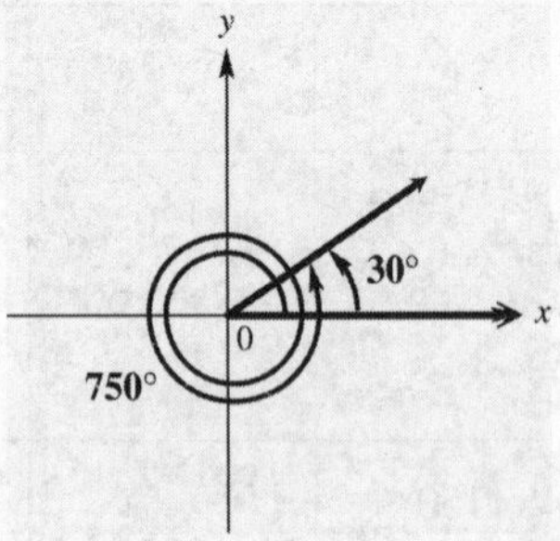

$$\sin 750° = \sin 30° = \frac{1}{2}$$

$$\cos 750° = \cos 30° = \frac{\sqrt{3}}{2}$$

$$\tan 750° = \tan 30° = \frac{\sqrt{3}}{3}$$

$$\cot 750° = \cot 30° = \sqrt{3}$$

$$\sec 750° = \sec 30° = \frac{2\sqrt{3}}{3}$$

$$\csc 750° = \csc 30° = 2$$

750° is coterminal with 30° because $750° - 2 \cdot 360° = 750° - 720° = 30°$. Since 750° lies in quadrant I, the values of all of its trigonometric functions will be positive, so these values will be identical to the trigonometric function values for 30°.

65. Since $-510°$ is coterminal with an angle of $-510° + 2 \cdot 360° = -510° + 720° = 210°$, it lies in quadrant III. Its reference angle is $210° - 180° = 30°$. Since the cosine is negative in quadrant III, we have $\cos(-510°) = -\cos 30° = -\frac{\sqrt{3}}{2}$.

67. Since $1500°$ is coterminal with an angle of $1500° - 4 \cdot 360° = 1500° - 1440° = 60°$, it lies in quadrant I. Because $1500°$ lies in quadrant I, the values of all of its trigonometric functions will be positive, so $\sin 1500° = \sin 60° = \frac{\sqrt{3}}{2}$.

69. $\sin(30° + 60°) \stackrel{?}{=} \sin 30° \cdot \cos 60° + \sin 60° \cdot \cos 30°$

Evaluate each side to determine whether this equation is true or false.

$$\sin(30° + 60°) = \sin 90° = 1 \text{ and } \sin 30° \cdot \cos 60° + \sin 60° \cdot \cos 30° = \frac{1}{2} \cdot \frac{1}{2} + \frac{\sqrt{3}}{2} \cdot \frac{\sqrt{3}}{2} = \frac{1}{4} + \frac{3}{4} = 1$$

Since, 1 = 1, the statement is true.

71. $\cos 60° \stackrel{?}{=} 2\cos 30°$

Evaluate each side to determine whether this statement is true or false.

$$\cos 60° = \frac{1}{2} \text{ and } 2\cos 30° = 2\left(\frac{\sqrt{3}}{2}\right) = \sqrt{3}$$

Since $\frac{1}{2} \neq \sqrt{3}$, the statement is false.

73. $\sin 120° \stackrel{?}{=} \sin 180° \cdot \cos 60° - \sin 60° \cdot \cos 180°$

Evaluate each side to determine whether this statement is true or false.

$$\sin 120° = \frac{\sqrt{3}}{2} \text{ and } \sin 180° \cdot \cos 60° - \sin 60° \cdot \cos 180° = 0\left(\frac{1}{2}\right) - \left(\frac{\sqrt{3}}{2}\right)(-1) = 0 - \left(-\frac{\sqrt{3}}{2}\right) = \frac{\sqrt{3}}{2}$$

Since $\frac{\sqrt{3}}{2} = \frac{\sqrt{3}}{2}$, the statement is true.

75. $\sin 38° 42' \approx .6252427$

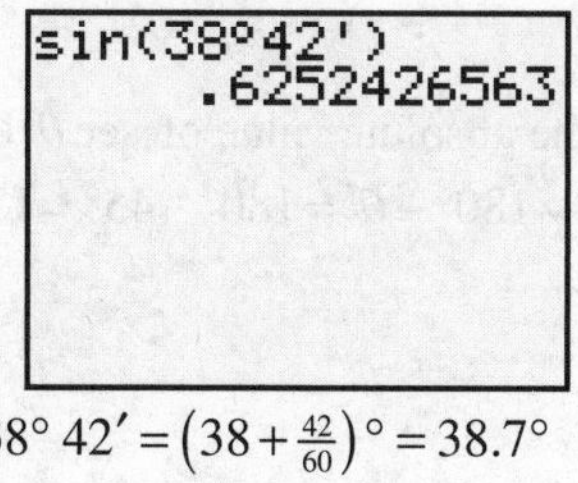

$38° 42' = \left(38 + \frac{42}{60}\right)° = 38.7°$

77. $\sec 13° 15' \approx 1.0273488$

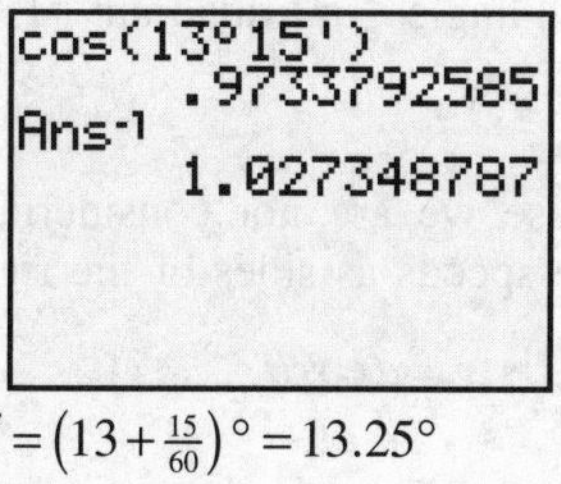

$13°15' = \left(13 + \frac{15}{60}\right)° = 13.25°$

79. $\cot 183° 48' \approx 15.055723$

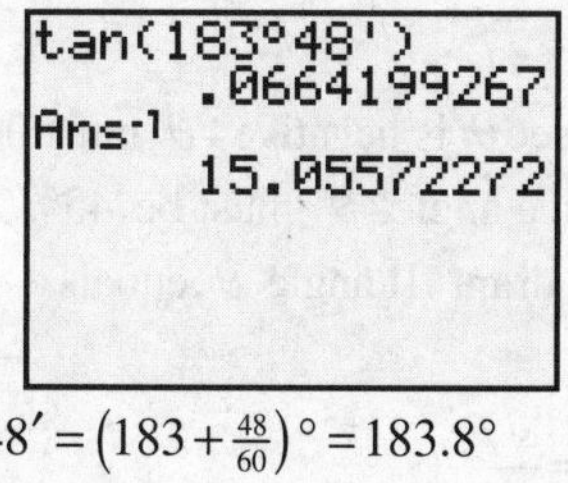

$183°48' = \left(183 + \frac{48}{60}\right)° = 183.8°$

81. $\sec 312° 12' \approx 1.4887142$

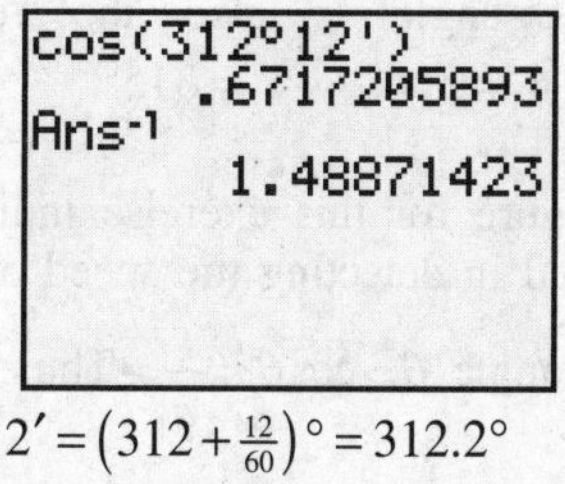

$312°12' = \left(312 + \frac{12}{60}\right)° = 312.2°$

83. $\sin(-317°\,36') \approx .6743024$

```
sin(-317°36')
   .6743023876
```

$-317°36' = -\left(317 + \frac{36}{60}\right)° = -317.6°$

85. $\cos(-15') \approx .9999905$

```
cos(-0°15')
   .9999904807
```

$-15' = -\frac{15}{60}' = -.25°$

87. $\dfrac{1}{\cot 23.4°} = \tan 23.4° \approx .4327386$

```
tan(23.4)
   .4327386422
```

89. $\dfrac{\cos 77°}{\sin 77°} = \cot 77° \approx .2308682$

```
tan(77)
   4.331475874
Ans-1
   .2308681911
```

91. $\tan\theta = 1.4739716$

```
tan-1(1.4739716)
   55.84549629
```

$\theta \approx 55.845496°$

93. $\cot\theta = 1.2575516$

```
1/1.2575516
   .7951959983
tan-1(Ans)
   38.49157974
```

$\theta \approx 38.491580°$

95. $\cos\theta = \dfrac{\sqrt{3}}{2}$

Since $\cos\theta$ is positive, θ must lie in quadrants I or IV. Since one angle, namely $30°$, lies in quadrant I, that angle is also the reference angle, θ'. The angle in quadrant IV will be $360° - \theta' = 360° - 30° = 330°$.

97. $\sec\theta = -\sqrt{2}$

Since $\sec\theta$ is negative, θ must lie in quadrants II or III. Since the absolute value of $\sec\theta$ is $\sqrt{2}$, the reference angle, θ' must be $45°$. The quadrant II angle θ equals $180° - \theta' = 180° - 45° = 135°$, and the quadrant III angle θ equals $180° + \theta' = 180° + 45° = 225°$.

99. $\cos\theta = \dfrac{\sqrt{2}}{2}$

Since $\cos\theta$ is positive, θ must lie in quadrants I or IV. Since one angle, namely $45°$, lies in quadrant I, that angle is also the reference angle, θ'. The angle in quadrant IV will be $360° - \theta' = 360° - 45° = 315°$.

101. The figure for this exercise indicates a right triangle. Because we are not considering the time involved in detecting the speed of the car, we will consider the speeds as sides of the right triangle. Given angle θ, $\cos\theta = \dfrac{r}{a}$. Thus, the speed that the radar detects is $r = a\cos\theta$.

103.(a) $\theta_1 = 40°, c_2 = 1.5\times10^8$ m per sec, and $c_1 = 3\times10^8$ m per sec

$$\frac{c_1}{c_2} = \frac{\sin\theta_1}{\sin\theta_2} \Rightarrow \sin\theta_2 = \frac{c_2\sin\theta_1}{c_1} \Rightarrow \sin\theta_2 = \frac{(1.5\times10^8)(\sin 40°)}{3\times10^8} \Rightarrow \theta_2 = \sin^{-1}\left[\frac{(1.5\times10^8)(\sin 40°)}{3\times10^8}\right] \approx 19°$$

(b) $\theta_1 = 62°,\ c_2 = 2.6\times10^8$ m per sec and $c_1 = 3\times10^8$ m per sec

$$\frac{c_1}{c_2} = \frac{\sin\theta_1}{\sin\theta_2} \Rightarrow \sin\theta_2 = \frac{c_2\sin\theta_1}{c_1} \Rightarrow \sin\theta_2 = \frac{(2.6\times10^8)(\sin 62°)}{3\times10^8} \Rightarrow \theta_2 = \sin^{-1}\left[\frac{(2.6\times10^8)(\sin 62°)}{3\times10^8}\right] \approx 50°$$

105. $\theta_1 = 90° - 29.6° = 60.4°,\ c_1 = 3\times10^8$ m per sec, and $c_2 = 2.254\times10^8\ c_1 = 3\times10^8$ m per sec

$$\frac{c_1}{c_2} = \frac{\sin\theta_1}{\sin\theta_2} \Rightarrow \sin\theta_2 = \frac{c_2\sin\theta_1}{c_1}$$

$$\sin\theta_2 = \frac{(2.254\times10^8)(\sin 60.4°)}{3\times10^8} = \frac{2.254}{3}(\sin 60.4°) \Rightarrow \theta_2 = \sin^{-1}\left(\frac{2.254}{3}(\sin 60.4°)\right) \approx 40.8°$$

Light from the object is refracted at an angle of 40.8° from the vertical. Light from the horizon is refracted at an angle of 48.7° from the vertical. Therefore, the fish thinks the object lies at an angle of 48.7° – 40.8° = 7.9° above the horizon.

107. Using the values for K_1 and K_2 from Exercise 106, determine V_2 when $D = 200,\ \theta = -3.5°$, V_1=90 mph = 30 mph · 1 hr/ 3600 sec · 5280 ft/1 mi = 132 ft per sec.

$$D = \frac{1.05\left(V_1^2 - V_2^2\right)}{64.4(K_1 + K_2 + \sin\theta)} \Rightarrow 200 = \frac{1.05\left(132^2 - V_2^2\right)}{64.4\left[.4 + .02 + \sin(-3.5°)\right]}$$

$$200 = \frac{1.05\left(132^2\right) - 1.05V_2^2}{23.12} \Rightarrow 200(23.12) = 18{,}295.2 - 1.05V_2^2 \Rightarrow 4624 = 18{,}295.2 - 1.05V_2^2$$

$$-13{,}671.2 = -1.05V_2^2 \Rightarrow V_2^2 = \frac{-13{,}671.2}{-1.05} \Rightarrow V_2^2 = 13020.19048 \Rightarrow V_2 \approx 114.106$$

$V_2 \approx 114$ ft/sec · 3600 sec/hr · 1 mi/5280 ft ≈ 78 mph

109. $F = W\sin\theta$

$F = 2100\sin 1.8° \approx 65.96$ lb

111. $F = W\sin\theta$

$$-130 = 2600\sin\theta \Rightarrow \frac{-130}{2600} = \sin\theta \Rightarrow -.05 = \sin\theta \Rightarrow \theta = \sin^{-1}(-.05) \approx -2.87°$$

113. $R = \dfrac{V^2}{g(f + \tan\theta)}$

(a) Since 45 mph = 66 ft/sec, $V = 66$, $\theta = 3°$, $g = 32.2$, and $f = .14$, we have the following.

$$R = \frac{V^2}{g(f + \tan\theta)} = \frac{66^2}{32.2(.14 + \tan 3°)} \approx 703 \text{ ft}$$

(b) Since there are 5280 ft in one mile and 3600 sec in one min, we have the following.

$$70 \text{ mph} = 70 \text{ mph} \cdot 1 \text{ hr}/\ 3600 \text{ sec} \cdot 5280 \text{ ft}/1 \text{ mi} = 102\frac{2}{3} \text{ ft per sec} \approx 102.67 \text{ ft per sec}$$

Since $V = 102.67$, $\theta = 3°$, $g = 32.2$, and $f = .14$, we have the following.

$$R = \frac{V^2}{g(f + \tan\theta)} \approx \frac{102.67^2}{32.2(.14 + \tan 3°)} \approx 1701 \text{ ft}$$

(c) Intuitively, increasing θ would make it easier to negotiate the curve at a higher speed much like is done at a race track. Mathematically, a larger value of θ (acute) will lead to a larger value for $\tan\theta$. If $\tan\theta$ increases, then the ratio determining R will *decrease*. Thus, the radius can be smaller and the curve sharper if θ is increased.

$$R = \frac{V^2}{g(f + \tan\theta)} = \frac{66^2}{32.2(.14 + \tan 4°)} \approx 644 \text{ ft and } R = \frac{V^2}{g(f + \tan\theta)} \approx \frac{102.67^2}{32.2(.14 + \tan 4°)} \approx 1559 \text{ ft}$$

As predicted, both values are less.

Section 5.4: Solving Right Triangles

1. 20,385.5 to 20,386.5

3. 8958.5 to 8959.5

5. Answer will vary.
It would be cumbersome to write 2 as 2.00 or 2.000, for example, if the measurements had 3 or 4 significant digits (depending on the problem). In the formula, it is understood that 2 is an exact value. Since the radius measurement, 54.98 cm, has four significant digits, an appropriate answer would be 345.4 cm.

7. If h is the actual height of a building and the height is measured as 58.6 ft, then $|h - 58.6| \le \underline{.05}$.

9. $A = 36°20'$, $c = 964$ m

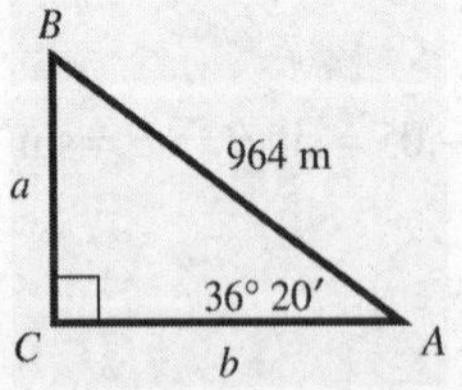

$$A + B = 90° \Rightarrow B = 90° - A \Rightarrow B = 90° - 36°20' = 89°60' - 36°20' = 53°40'$$

$$\sin A = \frac{a}{c} \Rightarrow \sin 36°20' = \frac{a}{964} \Rightarrow a = 964 \sin 36°20' \approx 571 \text{m} \text{ (rounded to three significant digits)}$$

$$\cos A = \frac{b}{c} \Rightarrow \cos 36°20' = \frac{b}{964} \Rightarrow b = 964 \cos 36°20' \approx 777 \text{ m} \text{ (rounded to three significant digits)}$$

11. $N = 51.2°$, $m = 124$ m

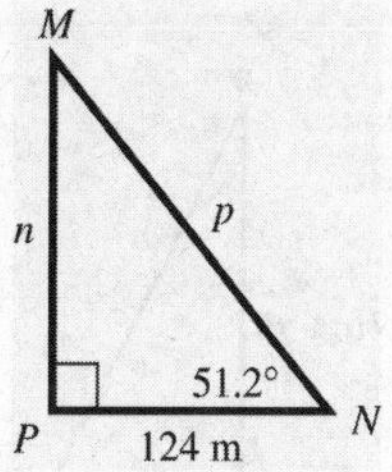

$$M + N = 90° \Rightarrow M = 90° - N \Rightarrow M = 90° - 51.2° = 38.8°$$

$$\tan N = \frac{n}{m} \Rightarrow \tan 51.2° = \frac{n}{124} \Rightarrow n = 124 \tan 51.2° \approx 154 \text{ m (rounded to three significant digits)}$$

$$\cos N = \frac{m}{p} \Rightarrow \cos 51.2° = \frac{124}{p} \Rightarrow p = \frac{124}{\cos 51.2°} \approx 198 \text{ m (rounded to three significant digits)}$$

13. No; You need to have at least one side to solve the triangle.

15. Answers will vary.

If you know one acute angle, the other acute angle may be found by subtracting the given acute angle from 90°. If you know one of the sides, then choose two of the trigonometric ratios involving sine, cosine or tangent that involve the known side in order to find the two unknown sides.

17. $A = 28.00°$, $c = 17.4$ ft

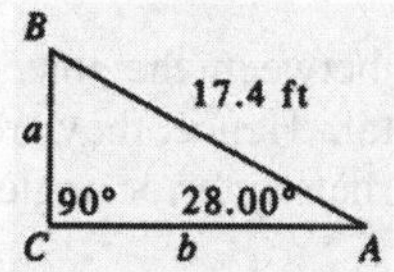

$$A + B = 90°$$
$$B = 90° - A$$
$$B = 90° - 28.00° = 62.00°$$

$$\sin A = \frac{a}{c} \Rightarrow \sin 28.00° = \frac{a}{17.4} \Rightarrow a = 17.4 \sin 28.00° \approx 8.17 \text{ ft (rounded to three significant digits)}$$

$$\cos A = \frac{b}{c} \Rightarrow \cos 28.00° = \frac{b}{17.4} \Rightarrow b = 17.4 \cos 28.00° \approx 15.4 \text{ ft (rounded to three significant digits)}$$

19. Solve the right triangle with $B = 73.00°$, $b = 128$ in. and $C = 90°$

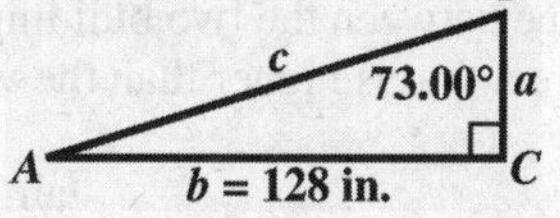

$$A + B = 90° \Rightarrow A = 90° - B \Rightarrow A = 90° - 73.00° = 17.00°$$

$$\tan B° = \frac{b}{a} \Rightarrow \tan 73.00° = \frac{128}{a} \Rightarrow a = \frac{128}{\tan 73.00°} \Rightarrow a = 39.1 \text{ in (rounded to three significant digits)}$$

$$\sin B° = \frac{b}{c} \Rightarrow \sin 73.00° = \frac{128}{c} \Rightarrow c = \frac{128}{\sin 73.00°} \Rightarrow c = 134 \text{ in (rounded to three significant digits)}$$

21. $a = 76.4$ yd, $b = 39.3$ yd

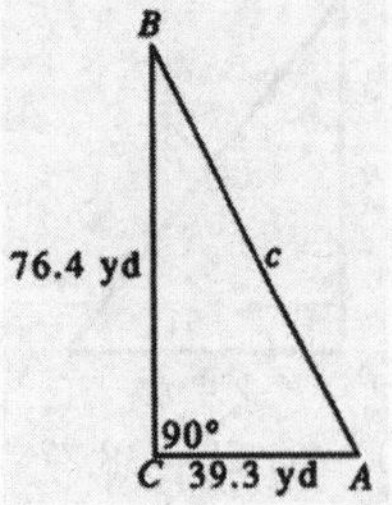

$$c^2 = a^2 + b^2 \Rightarrow c = \sqrt{a^2 + b^2} = \sqrt{(76.4)^2 + (39.3)^2} = \sqrt{5836.96 + 1544.49} = \sqrt{7381.45} \approx 85.9 \text{ yd}$$

(rounded to three significant digits)

We will determine the measurements of both A and B by using the sides of the right triangle. In practice, once you find one of the measurements, subtract it from $90°$ to find the other.

$$\tan A = \frac{a}{b} \Rightarrow \tan A = \frac{76.4}{39.3} \approx 1.944020356 \Rightarrow A \approx \tan^{-1}(1.944020356) \approx 62.8° \approx 62°50'$$

$$\tan B = \frac{b}{a} \Rightarrow \tan B = \frac{39.3}{76.4} \approx .5143979058 \Rightarrow B \approx \tan^{-1}(.5143979058) \approx 27.2° \approx 27°10'$$

23. The angle of elevation from X to Y is 90° whenever Y is directly above X.

25. Answers will vary.
The angle of elevation and the angle of depression are measured between the line of sight and a horizontal line. So, in the diagram, lines AD and CB are both horizontal. Hence, they are parallel. The line formed by AB is a transversal and angles DAB and ABC are alternate interior angle and thus have the same measure.

27. It should be shown as an angle measured clockwise from due north.

29. $\sin 43°50' = \frac{d}{13.5} \Rightarrow d = 13.5 \sin 43°50' \approx 9.3496000$

The ladder goes up the wall 9.35 m. (rounded to three significant digits)

31. Let x represent the horizontal distance between the two buildings and y represent the height of the portion of the building across the street that is higher than the window.

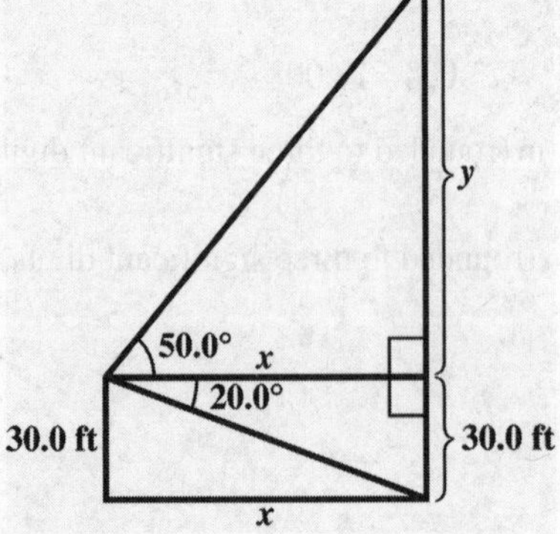

$$\tan 20.0° = \frac{30.0}{x} \Rightarrow x = \frac{30.3}{\tan 20.0°} \approx 82.4$$

$$\tan 50.0° = \frac{y}{x}$$

$$y = x \tan 50.0° = \left(\frac{30.0}{\tan 20.0°}\right) \tan 50.0°$$

$$\text{height} = y + 30.0$$

$$\text{height} = \left(\frac{30.0}{\tan 20.0°}\right) \tan 50.0° + 30.0$$

$$\text{height} \approx 128.2295$$

We have the following.

The height of the building across the street is about 128 ft. (rounded to three significant digits)

33. The altitude of an isosceles triangle bisects the base as well as the angle opposite the base. The two right triangles formed have interior angles, which have the same measure angle. The lengths of the corresponding sides also have the same measure. Since the altitude bisects the base, each leg (base) of the right triangles is $\frac{42.36}{2} = 21.18$ in.

Let x = the length of each of the two equal sides of the isosceles triangle.

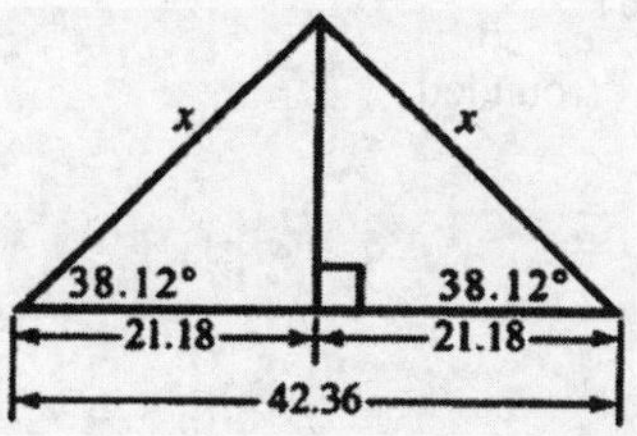

$$\cos 38.12° = \frac{21.18}{x} \Rightarrow x\cos 38.12° = 21.18 \Rightarrow x = \frac{21.18}{\cos 38.12°} \approx 26.921918$$

The length of each of the two equal sides of the triangle is 26.92 in. (rounded to four significant digits)

35. In order to find the angle of elevation, θ, we need to first find the length of the diagonal of the square base. The diagonal forms two isosceles right triangles. Each angle formed by a side of the square and the diagonal measures 45°.

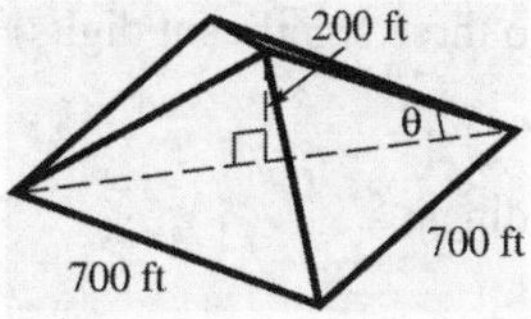

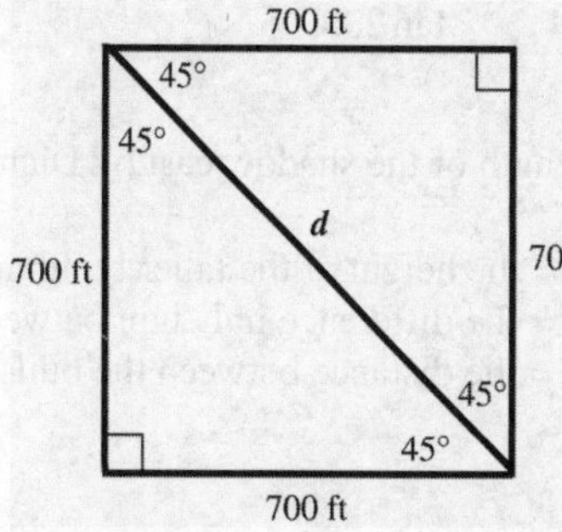

By the Pythagorean theorem, $700^2 + 700^2 = d^2 \Rightarrow 2\cdot 700^2 = d^2 \Rightarrow d = \sqrt{2\cdot 700^2} \Rightarrow d = 700\sqrt{2}$. Thus, length of the diagonal is $700\sqrt{2}$ ft. To to find the angle, θ, we consider the following isosceles triangle.

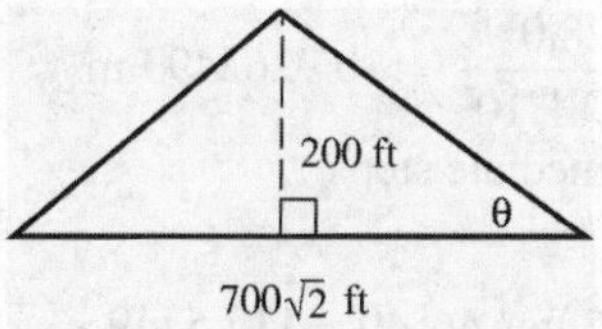

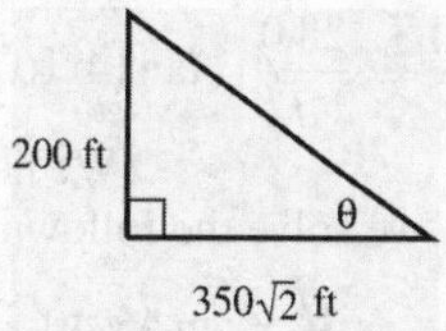

The height of the pyramid bisects the base of this triangle and forms two right triangles. We can use one of these triangles to find the angle of elevation, θ.

$$\tan\theta = \frac{200}{350\sqrt{2}} \approx .4040610178 \Rightarrow \theta \approx \tan^{-1}(.4040610178) \approx 22.0017$$

Rounding this figure to two significant digits, we have $\theta \approx 22°$.

37. Let h represent the height of the tower.

In triangle ABC we have the following.

$$\tan 34.6° = \frac{h}{40.6}$$
$$h = 40.6 \tan 34.6° \approx 28.0081$$

The height of the tower is 28.0 m. (rounded to three significant digits)

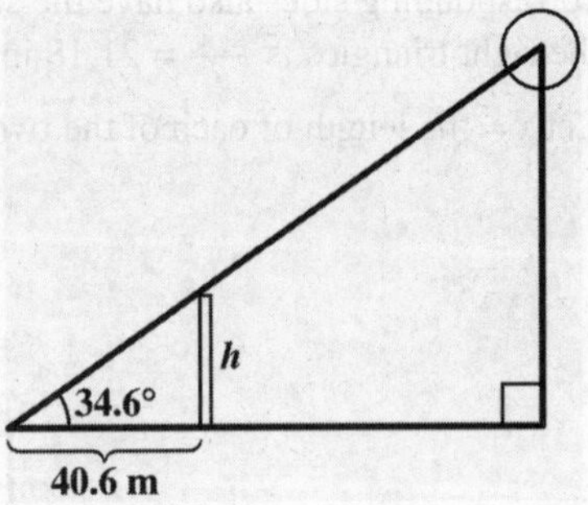

39. Let x = the length of the shadow cast by Diane Carr.

$$\tan 23.4° = \frac{5.75}{x}$$
$$x \tan 23.4° = 5.75$$
$$x = \frac{5.75}{\tan 23.4°} \approx 13.2875$$

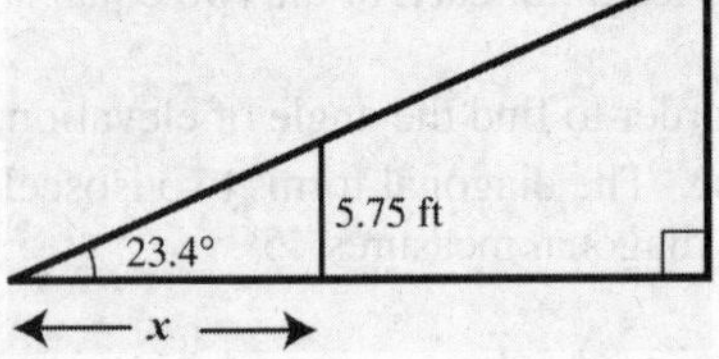

The length of the shadow cast by Diane Carr is 13.3 ft. (rounded to three significant digits)

41. Let x = the height of the taller building;
h = the difference in height between the shorter and taller buildings;
d = the distance between the buildings along the ground.

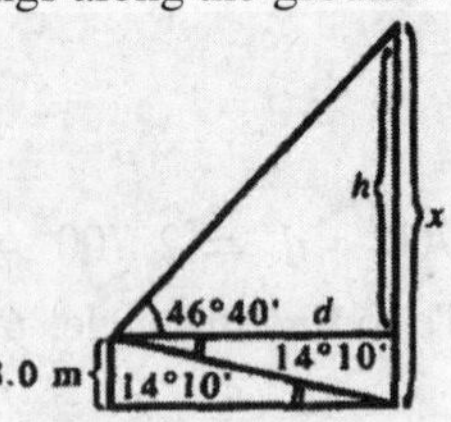

$$\frac{28.0}{d} = \tan 14°10' \Rightarrow 28.0 = d \tan 14°10' \Rightarrow d = \frac{28.0}{\tan 14°10'} \approx 110.9262493 \text{ m}$$

(We hold on to these digits for the intermediate steps.)

To find h, we solve the following.

$$\frac{h}{d} = \tan 46°40' \Rightarrow h = d \tan 46°40' \approx (110.9262493)\tan 46°40' \approx 117.5749$$

Thus, the value of h rounded to three significant digits is 118 m.
Since $x = h + 28.0 = 118 + 28.0 \approx 146\text{m}$, the height of the taller building is 146 m.

43. (a) Let x = the height of the peak above 14,545 ft.

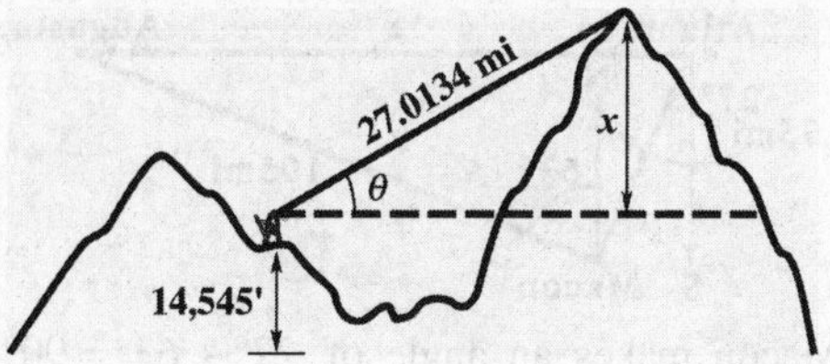

Since the diagonal of the right triangle formed is in miles, we must first convert this measurement to feet. Since there are 5280 ft in one mile, we have the length of the diagonal is $27.0134(5280) = 142,630.752$. To find the value of x, we solve the following.

$$\sin 5.82° = \frac{x}{142,630.752} \Rightarrow x = 142,630.752 \sin 5.82° \approx 14,463.2674$$

Thus, the value of x rounded to five significant digits is 14,463 ft. Thus, the total height is about 14,545 + 14,463 = 29,008 ft.

(b) The curvature of the earth would make the peak appear shorter than it actually is. Initially the surveyors did not think Mt. Everest was the tallest peak in the Himalayas. It did not look like the tallest peak because it was farther away than the other large peaks.

45. Let x = the distance the plane is from its starting point.

In the figure, the measure of angle ACB is $40° + (180° - 130°) = 40° + 50° = 90°$.

Therefore, triangle ACB is a right triangle.

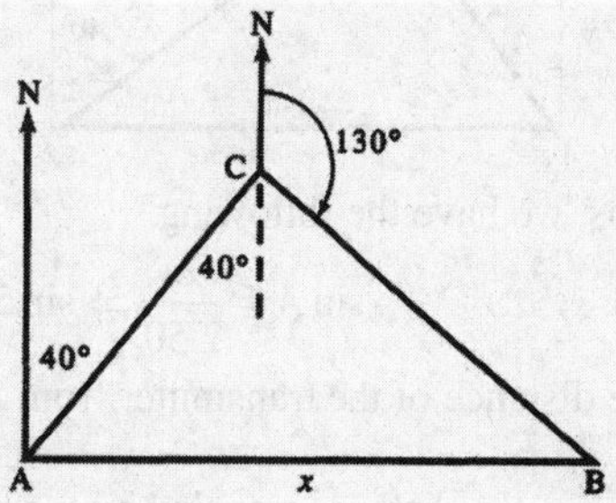

Since $d = rt$, the distance traveled in 1.5 hr is (1.5 hr)(110 mph) = 165 mi. The distance traveled in 1.3 hr is (1.3 hr)(110 mph) = 143 mi.

Using the Pythagorean theorem, we have the following.

$$x^2 = 165^2 + 143^2 \Rightarrow x^2 = 27,225 + 20,449 \Rightarrow x^2 = 47,674 \Rightarrow x \approx 218.3438$$

The plane is 220 mi from its starting point. (rounded to two significant digits)

47. Let x = distance the ships are apart.

In the figure, the measure of angle CAB is $130° - 40° = 90°$. Therefore, triangle CAB is a right triangle.

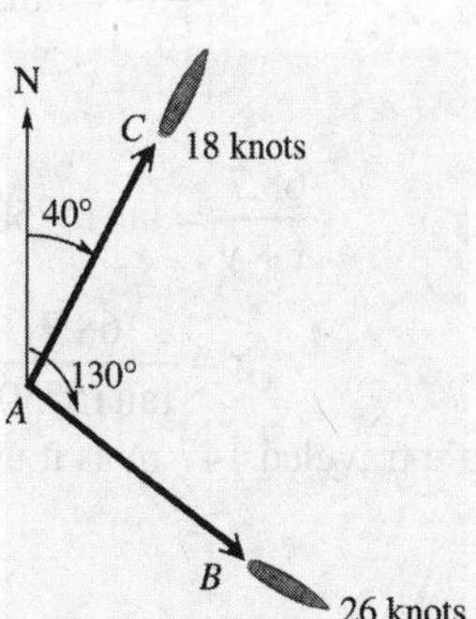

Since $d = rt$, the distance traveled by the first ship in 1.5 hr is (1.5 hr)(18 knots) = 27 nautical mi and the second ship is (1.5hr)(26 knots) = 39 nautical mi.

Applying the Pythagorean theorem, we have the following.

$$x^2 = 27^2 + 39^2 \Rightarrow x^2 = 729 + 1521 \Rightarrow x^2 = 2250 \Rightarrow x = \sqrt{2250} \approx 47.4342$$

The ships are 47 nautical mi apart. (rounded to 2 significant digits)

49. Let x = the distance from Atlanta to Augusta.

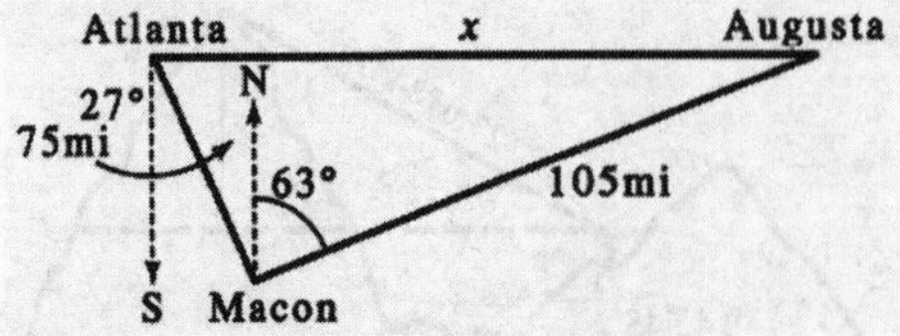

The line from Atlanta to Macon makes an angle of $27° + 63° = 90°$, with the line from Macon to Augusta. Since $d = rt$, the distance from Atlanta to Macon is $60\left(1\frac{1}{4}\right) = 75$ mi. The distance from Macon to Augusta is $60\left(1\frac{3}{4}\right) = 105$ mi.
Use the Pythagorean theorem to find x, we have the following.

$$x^2 = 75^2 + 105^2 \Rightarrow x^2 = 5635 + 11{,}025 \Rightarrow x^2 = 16{,}650 \approx 129.0349$$

The distance from Atlanta to Augusta is 130 mi. (rounded to two significant digits)

51. Let C = the location of the transmitter;
a = the distance of the transmitter from B.

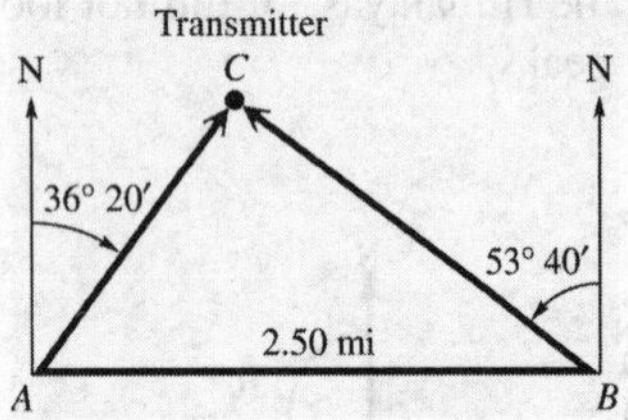

The measure of angle CBA is
$90° - 53°40' = 89°60' - 53°40' = 36°20'$.
The measure of angle CAB
$90° - 36°20' = 89°60' - 36°20' = 53°40'$.
Since $A + B = 90°$, so $C = 90°$.

Thus, we have the following.

$$\sin A = \frac{a}{2.50} \Rightarrow \sin 53°40' = \frac{a}{2.50} \Rightarrow a = 2.50 \sin 53°40' \approx 2.0140$$

The distance of the transmitter from B is 2.01 mi. (rounded to 3 significant digits)

53. Let x = the distance traveled by the whale as it approaches the tower;
y = the distance from the tower to the whale as it turns.

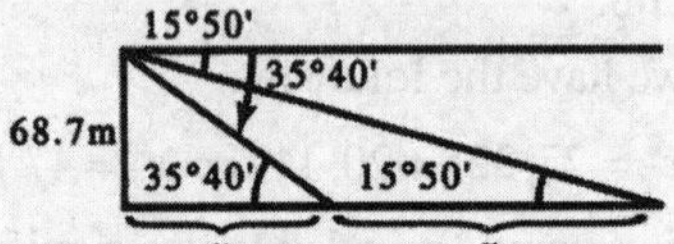

$$\frac{68.7}{y} = \tan 35°40' \Rightarrow 68.7 y \tan 35°40' \Rightarrow y = \frac{68.7}{\tan 35°40'}$$

and

$$\frac{68.7}{x+y} = \tan 15°50' \Rightarrow 68.7 = (x+y)\tan 15°50' \Rightarrow x + y = \frac{68.7}{\tan 15°50'}$$

$$x = \frac{68.7}{\tan 15°50'} - y \Rightarrow x = \frac{68.7}{\tan 15°50'} - \frac{68.7}{\tan 35°40'} \approx 146.5190$$

The whale traveled 147 m as it approached the lighthouse. (rounded to three significant digits)

55. Let x = the height of Mt. Whitney above the level of the road;
y = the distance shown in the figure below.

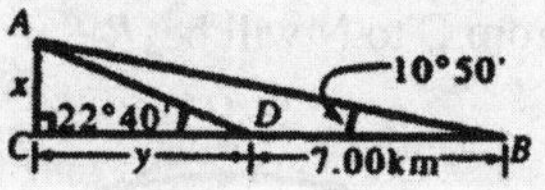

In triangle ADC, $\tan 22°40' = \dfrac{x}{y} \Rightarrow y\tan 22°40' = x \Rightarrow y = \dfrac{x}{\tan 22°40'}$. (1)

In triangle ABC, we have the following.

$$\tan 10°50' = \frac{x}{y+7.00} \Rightarrow (y+7.00)\tan 10°50' = x$$

$$y\tan 10°50' + 7.00\tan 10°50' = x \Rightarrow y = \frac{x - 7.00\tan 10°50'}{\tan 10°50'} \text{ (2)}$$

Setting equations 1 and 2 equal to each other, we have the following.

$$\frac{x}{\tan 22°40'} = \frac{x - 7.00\tan 10°50'}{\tan 10°50'}$$
$$x\tan 10°50' = x\tan 22°40' - 7.00(\tan 10°50')(\tan 22°40')$$
$$7.00(\tan 10°50')(\tan 22°40') = x\tan 22°40' - x\tan 10°50'$$
$$7.00(\tan 10°50')(\tan 22°40') = x(\tan 22°40' - \tan 10°50')$$
$$\frac{7.00(\tan 10°50')(\tan 22°40')}{\tan 22°40' - \tan 10°50'} = x$$
$$x \approx 2.4725.$$

The height of the top of Mt. Whitney above road level is 2.47 km. (rounded to three significant digits)

57. Let x = the minimum distance that a plant needing full sun can be placed from the fence.

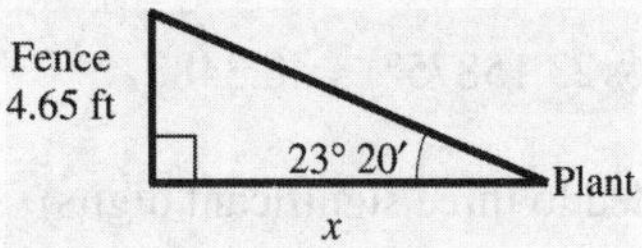

$$\tan 23°20' = \frac{4.65}{x} \Rightarrow x\tan 23°20' = 4.65 \Rightarrow x = \frac{4.65}{\tan 23°20'} \approx 10.7799$$

The minimum distance is 10.8 ft. (rounded to three significant digits)

59. (a) If $\theta = 37°$, then $\dfrac{\theta}{2} = \dfrac{37°}{2} = 18.5°$.

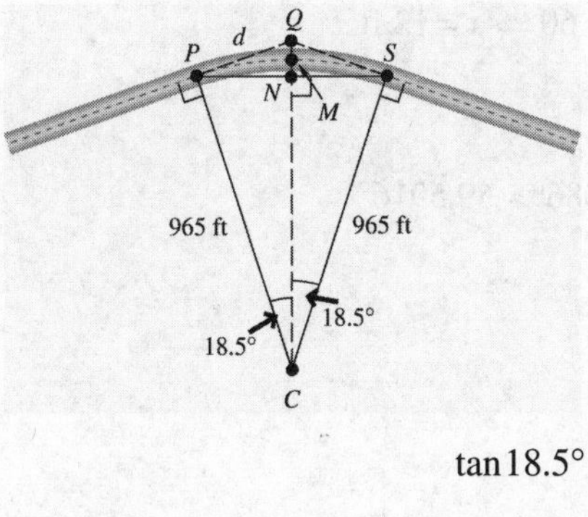

To find the distance between P and Q, d, we first note that angle QPC is a right angle. Hence, triangle QPC is a right triangle and we can solve the following.

$$\tan 18.5° = \frac{d}{965} \Rightarrow d = 965\tan 18.5° \approx 322.8845$$

The distance between P and Q, is 323 ft. (rounded to three significant digits)

Continued on next page

59. (continued)

(b) Since we are dealing with a circle, the distance between M and C is R. If we let x be the distance from N to M, then the distance from C to N will be $R-x$.

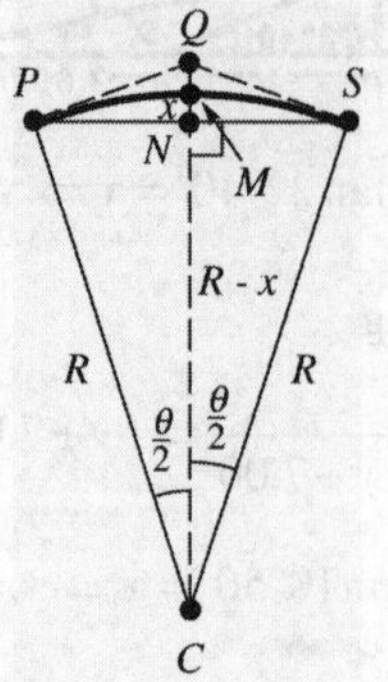

Since triangle CNP is a right triangle, we can set up the following equation.

$$\cos\frac{\theta}{2}=\frac{R-x}{R}\Rightarrow R\cos\frac{\theta}{2}=R-x\Rightarrow x=R-R\cos\frac{\theta}{2}\Rightarrow x=R\left(1-\cos\frac{\theta}{2}\right)$$

61. (a) $$\theta\approx\frac{57.3S}{R}=\frac{57.3(336)}{600}=32.088°$$

$$d=R\left(1-\cos\frac{\theta}{2}\right)=600(1-\cos 16.044°)\approx 23.3702\text{ ft}$$

The distance is 23.4 ft. (rounded to three significant digits)

(b) $$\theta\approx\frac{57.3S}{R}=\frac{57.3(485)}{600}=46.3175°$$

$$d=R\left(1-\cos\frac{\theta}{2}\right)=600(1-\cos 23.15875°)\approx 48.3488$$

The distance is 48.3 ft. (rounded to three significant digits)

(c) The faster the speed, the more land needs to be cleared on the inside of the curve.

Chapter 5: Review Exercises

1. The complement of 35° is $90°-35°=55°$. The supplement of 35° is $180°-35°=145°$.

$$\frac{20}{8}=\frac{30}{x}\Rightarrow\frac{5}{2}=\frac{30}{x}\Rightarrow 5x=60\Rightarrow x=12\text{ ft}$$

3. $$59°35'30"=59°+\left(\frac{35}{60}\right)^{\circ}+\left(\frac{30}{3600}\right)^{\circ}\approx 59°+.583°+.0086°\approx 59.5916°$$

5. $270°+n\cdot 360°$ is coterminal with $270°$ for all n.

7. $x = 1,\ y = -\sqrt{3}$ and $r = \sqrt{x^2 + y^2} = \sqrt{1^2 + \left(-\sqrt{3}\right)^2} = \sqrt{1+3} = \sqrt{4} = 2$

$\sin\theta = \frac{y}{r} = \frac{-\sqrt{3}}{2} = -\frac{\sqrt{3}}{2}$

$\cos\theta = \frac{x}{r} = \frac{1}{2}$

$\tan\theta = \frac{y}{x} = \frac{-\sqrt{3}}{1} = -\sqrt{3}$

$\cot\theta = \frac{x}{y} = \frac{1}{-\sqrt{3}} = -\frac{1}{\sqrt{3}} \cdot \frac{\sqrt{3}}{\sqrt{3}} = -\frac{\sqrt{3}}{3}$

$\sec\theta = \frac{r}{x} = \frac{2}{1} = 2$

$\csc\theta = \frac{r}{y} = \frac{2}{-\sqrt{3}} = -\frac{2}{\sqrt{3}} \cdot \frac{\sqrt{3}}{\sqrt{3}} = -\frac{2\sqrt{3}}{3}$

9. $(3, -4)$

$x = 3, y = -4$ and $r = \sqrt{3^2 + (-4)^2} = \sqrt{9+16} = \sqrt{25} = 5$

$\sin\theta = \frac{y}{r} = \frac{-4}{5} = -\frac{4}{5}$

$\cos\theta = \frac{x}{r} = \frac{3}{5}$

$\tan\theta = \frac{y}{x} = \frac{-4}{3} = -\frac{4}{3}$

$\cot\theta = \frac{x}{y} = \frac{3}{-4} = -\frac{3}{4}$

$\sec\theta = \frac{r}{x} = \frac{5}{3}$

$\csc\theta = \frac{r}{y} = \frac{5}{-4} = -\frac{5}{4}$

11. $\left(-2\sqrt{2},\ 2\sqrt{2}\right)$

$x = -2\sqrt{2},\ y = 2\sqrt{2}$, and $r = \sqrt{\left(-2\sqrt{2}\right)^2 + \left(2\sqrt{2}\right)^2} = \sqrt{8+8} = \sqrt{16} = 4$

$\sin\theta = \frac{y}{r} = \frac{2\sqrt{2}}{4} = \frac{\sqrt{2}}{2}$

$\cos\theta = \frac{x}{r} = \frac{-2\sqrt{2}}{4} = -\frac{\sqrt{2}}{2}$

$\tan\theta = \frac{y}{x} = \frac{2\sqrt{2}}{-2\sqrt{2}} = -1$

$\cot\theta = \frac{x}{y} = \frac{-2\sqrt{2}}{2\sqrt{2}} = -1$

$\sec\theta = \frac{r}{x} = \frac{4}{-2\sqrt{2}} = -\frac{2}{\sqrt{2}} = -\frac{2}{\sqrt{2}} \cdot \frac{\sqrt{2}}{\sqrt{2}} = -\sqrt{2}$

$\csc\theta = \frac{r}{y} = \frac{4}{2\sqrt{2}} = \frac{2}{\sqrt{2}} = \frac{2}{\sqrt{2}} \cdot \frac{\sqrt{2}}{\sqrt{2}} = \sqrt{2}$

13.

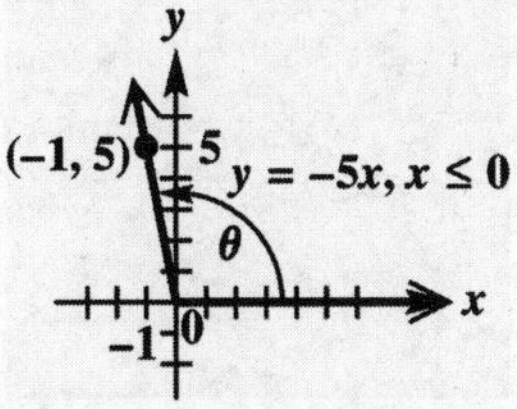

15. **(a)** For any angle θ, $\sec\theta \ge 1$ or $\sec\theta \le -1$. Therefore, $\sec\theta = -\frac{2}{3}$ is impossible.

(b) $\tan\theta$ can take on all values. Therefore, $\tan\theta = 1.4$ is possible.

(c) For any angle θ, $\csc\theta \ge 1$ or $\csc\theta \le -1$. Therefore, $\csc\theta = 5$ is possible.

17. $\cos\theta = -\frac{5}{8} = \frac{-5}{8}$, with θ in quadrant III

$\cos\theta = \frac{x}{r}$ and θ in quadrant III, so let $x = -5$, $r = 8$.

$$x^2 + y^2 = r^2 \Rightarrow (-5)^2 + y^2 = 8^2 \Rightarrow 25 + y^2 = 64 \Rightarrow y^2 = 39 \Rightarrow y = \pm\sqrt{39}$$

θ is in quadrant III, so $y = -\sqrt{39}$.

$\sin\theta = \frac{y}{r} = \frac{-\sqrt{39}}{8} = -\frac{\sqrt{39}}{8}$

$\cos\theta = \frac{x}{r} = -\frac{5}{8}$

$\tan\theta = \frac{y}{x} = \frac{-\sqrt{39}}{-5} = \frac{\sqrt{39}}{5}$

$\cot\theta = \frac{x}{y} = \frac{-5}{-\sqrt{39}} = \frac{5}{\sqrt{39}} \cdot \frac{\sqrt{39}}{\sqrt{39}} = \frac{5\sqrt{39}}{39}$

$\sec\theta = \frac{r}{x} = \frac{8}{-5} = -\frac{8}{5}$

$\csc\theta = \frac{r}{y} = \frac{8}{-\sqrt{39}} = -\frac{8}{\sqrt{39}}$

$= -\frac{8}{\sqrt{39}} \cdot \frac{\sqrt{39}}{\sqrt{39}} = -\frac{8\sqrt{39}}{39}$

19. Since $\cot\theta = \frac{1}{\tan\theta}$, use the calculator to find $\frac{1}{1.6778490}$ or 1.6778490^{-1}. The result would be .5960011.

21. $\sin A = \frac{\text{side opposite}}{\text{hypotenuse}} = \frac{8}{17}$

$\cos A = \frac{\text{side adjacent}}{\text{hypotenuse}} = \frac{15}{17}$

$\tan A = \frac{\text{side opposite}}{\text{side adjacent}} = \frac{8}{15}$

$\cot A = \frac{\text{side adjacent}}{\text{side opposite}} = \frac{15}{8}$

$\sec A = \frac{\text{hypotenuse}}{\text{side adjacent}} = \frac{17}{15}$

$\csc A = \frac{\text{hypotenuse}}{\text{side opposite}} = \frac{17}{8}$

23.

θ	$\sin\theta$	$\cos\theta$	$\tan\theta$	$\cot\theta$	$\sec\theta$	$\csc\theta$
30°	$\frac{1}{2}$	$\frac{\sqrt{3}}{2}$	$\frac{\sqrt{3}}{3}$	$\sqrt{3}$	$\frac{2\sqrt{3}}{3}$	2
45°	$\frac{\sqrt{2}}{2}$	$\frac{\sqrt{2}}{2}$	1	1	$\sqrt{2}$	$\sqrt{2}$
60°	$\frac{\sqrt{3}}{2}$	$\frac{1}{2}$	$\sqrt{3}$	$\frac{\sqrt{3}}{3}$	2	$\frac{2\sqrt{3}}{3}$

25. 300°

This angle lies in quadrant IV, so the reference angle is 360° – 300° = 60°. Since 300° is in quadrant IV, the sine, tangent, cotangent and cosecant are negative.

$\sin 300° = -\sin 60° = -\frac{\sqrt{3}}{2}$

$\cos 300° = \cos 60° = \frac{1}{2}$

$\tan 300° = -\tan 60° = -\sqrt{3}$

$\cot 300° = -\cot 60° = -\frac{\sqrt{3}}{3}$

$\sec 300° = \sec 60° = 2$

$\csc 300° = -\csc 60° = -\frac{2\sqrt{3}}{3}$

27. $-390°$ is coterminal with $-390° + 2 \cdot 360° = -390° + 720° = 330°$. This angle lies in quadrant IV. The reference angle is $360° - 330° = 30°$. Since $-390°$ is in quadrant IV, the sine, tangent, cotangent, and cosecant are negative.

$\sin(-390°) = -\sin 30° = -\frac{1}{2}$

$\cos(-390°) = \cos 30° = \frac{\sqrt{3}}{2}$

$\tan(-390°) = -\tan 30° = -\frac{\sqrt{3}}{3}$

$\cot(-390°) = -\cot 30° = -\sqrt{3}$

$\sec(-390°) = \sec 30° = \frac{2\sqrt{3}}{3}$

$\csc(-390°) = -\csc 30° = -2$

29. $\sec 222° 30' \approx -1.3563417$

$222° 30' = \left(222 + \frac{30}{60}\right)° = 222.5°$

31. $\tan 11.7689° \approx .20834446$

33. If $\theta = 135°$, $\theta' = 180° - 135° = 45°$.
If $\theta = 45°$, $\theta' = 45°$.
If $\theta = 300°$, $\theta' = 360° - 300° = 60°$.
If θ=140°, $\theta' = 180° - 140° = 40°$.

Of these reference angles, 40° is the only one which is not a special angle, so D, tan 140°, is the only one which cannot be determined exactly using the methods of this chapter.

35. $\cot\theta = 1.1249386$

$\theta \approx 41.635092°$

37. No, $\cot 25° = \frac{1}{\tan 25°} \neq \tan^{-1} 25°$.

39. $A = 58°\ 30'$, $c = 748$

$A + B = 90° \Rightarrow B = 90° - A \Rightarrow B = 90° - 58°30' = 89°60' - 58°30' = 31°30'$

$\sin A = \frac{a}{c} \Rightarrow \sin 58°30' = \frac{a}{748} \Rightarrow a = 748 \sin 58°30' \approx 638$ (rounded to three significant digits)

$\cos A = \frac{b}{c} \Rightarrow \cos 58°30' = \frac{b}{748} \Rightarrow b = 748 \cos 58°30' \approx 391$ (rounded to three significant digits)

41. Let x = height of the tower.

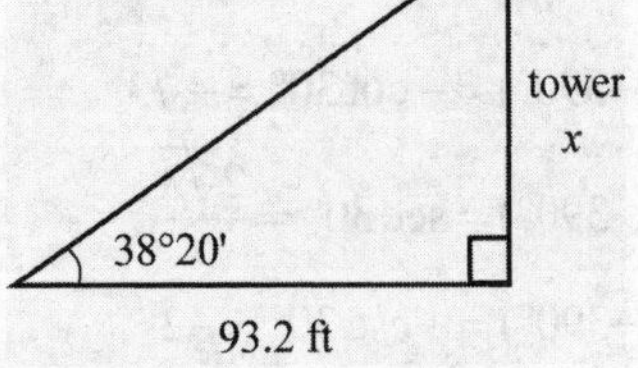

$$\tan 38°20' = \frac{x}{93.2}$$
$$x = 93.2 \tan 38°20'$$
$$x \approx 73.6930$$

The height of the tower is 73.7 ft. (rounded to three significant digits)

43. Let h = height of the tower.

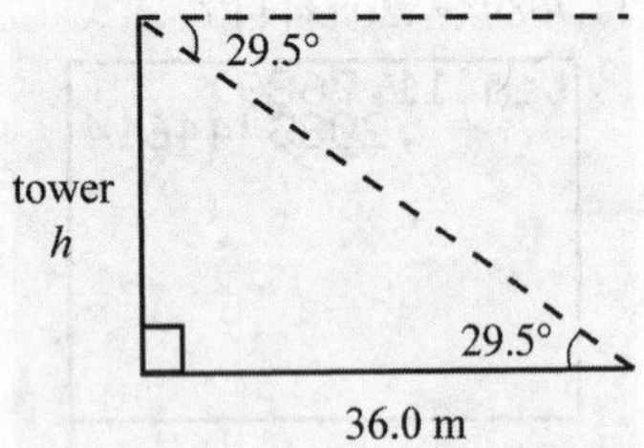

$$\tan 29.5° = \frac{h}{36.0}$$
$$h = 36.0 \tan 29.5°$$
$$h \approx 20.3678$$

The height of the tower is 20.4 m. (rounded to three significant digits)

45. Algebraic Solution:
Let x = the side adjacent to 13.7° in the smaller triangle;
h is the height of Mt. Kilimanjaro.

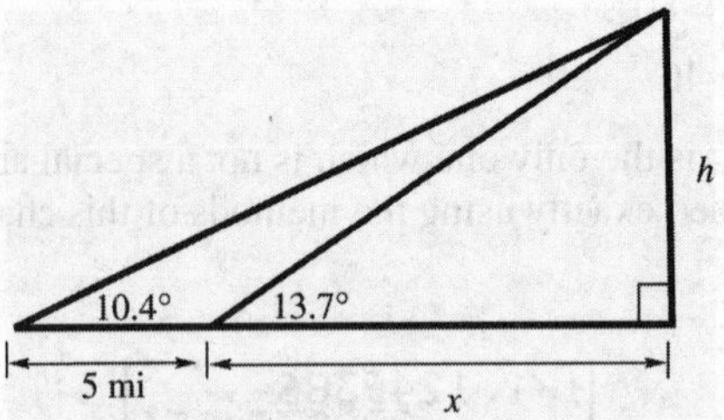

In the larger triangle, we have $\tan 10.4° = \frac{h}{5+x} \Rightarrow h = (5+x)\tan 10.4°$.

In the smaller triangle, we have $\tan 13.7° = \frac{h}{x} \Rightarrow h = x \tan 13.7°$.

Substitute for h in this equation and solve for x.

$$(5+x)\tan 10.4° = x \tan 13.7°$$
$$5\tan 10.4° + x\tan 10.4° = x\tan 13.7°$$
$$5\tan 10.4° = x\tan 13.7° - x\tan 10.4°$$
$$5\tan 10.4° = x(\tan 13.7° - \tan 10.4°)$$
$$\frac{5\tan 10.4°}{\tan 13.7° - \tan 10.4°} = x$$

Substituting for x in the equation for the smaller triangle, we have the following.

$$h = x\tan 13.7° \Rightarrow h = \frac{5\tan 10.4° \tan 13.7°}{\tan 13.7° - \tan 10.4°} \approx 3.7136$$

Continued on next page

45. (continued)

Graphing Calculator Solution:

The first line considered is $y = (\tan 10.4°)x$ and the second is $y = (\tan 13.7°)(x - 5)$.

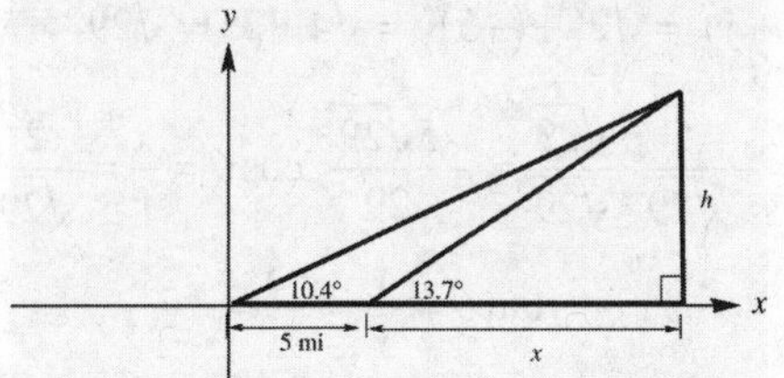

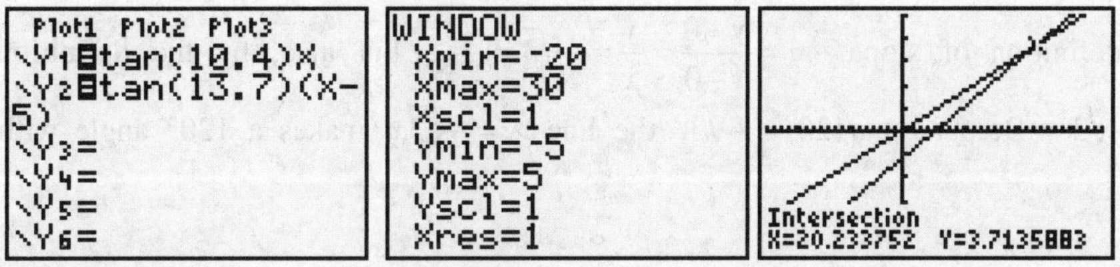

The height of Mt. Kilimanjaro.is approximately 3.7136 mi. This is approximately

$$3.7136 \text{ mi} \cdot \frac{5280 \text{ ft}}{1 \text{ mi}} \approx 19{,}600 \text{ ft.} \quad \text{(rounded to nearest hundred feet)}$$

47. Draw triangle ABC and extend north-south lines from points A and B. Angle ABX is 55° (alternate interior angles of parallel lines cut by a transversal have the same measure) so Angle ABC is $55° + 35° = 90°$.

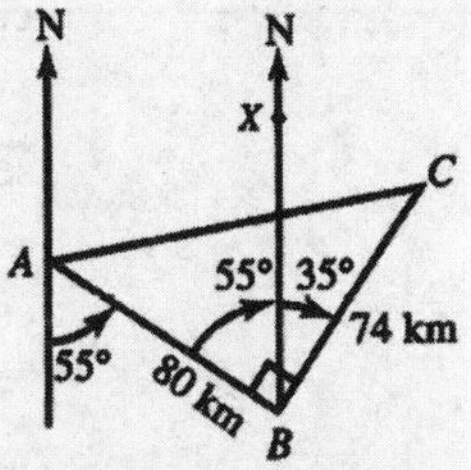

Since angle ABC is a right angle, use the Pythagorean theorem to find the distance from A to C.

$$(AC)^2 = 80^2 + 74^2 \Rightarrow (AC)^2 = 6400 + 5476 \Rightarrow (AC)^2 = 11{,}876 \Rightarrow AC = \sqrt{11{,}876} \approx 108.9771$$

It is 110 km from A to C. (rounded to two significant digits)

Chapter 5: Test

1. $360° + (-157°) = 203°$

2. **(a)** If θ is in the interval $(90°, 180°)$, then $90° < \theta < 180° \Rightarrow 45° < \frac{\theta}{2} < 90°$. Thus, $\frac{\theta}{2}$ lies in quadrant I and $\cos\frac{\theta}{2}$ is positive.

(b) If θ is in the interval $(90°, 180°)$ then $90° < \theta < 180° \Rightarrow 270° < \theta + 180° < 360°$. Thus, $\theta + 180°$ lies in quadrant IV and $\cot(\theta + 180°)$ is negative.

3. If $\cos\theta < 0$, then θ is in quadrant II or III. If $\cot\theta > 0$, then θ is in quadrant I or III. Therefore, θ terminates in quadrant III.

4. $(2,-5)$

$x = 2,\ y = -5,$ and $r = \sqrt{x^2 + y^2} = \sqrt{2^2 + (-5)^2} = \sqrt{4+25} = \sqrt{29}$

$$\sin\theta = \frac{y}{r} = \frac{-5}{\sqrt{29}} = -\frac{5}{\sqrt{29}}\cdot\frac{\sqrt{29}}{\sqrt{29}} = -\frac{5\sqrt{29}}{29};\ \cos\theta = \frac{x}{r} = \frac{2}{\sqrt{29}} = \frac{2}{\sqrt{29}}\cdot\frac{\sqrt{29}}{\sqrt{29}} = \frac{2\sqrt{29}}{29}$$

$$\tan\theta = \frac{y}{x} = \frac{-5}{2} = -\frac{5}{2}$$

5. One point on the line $y = -\sqrt{3}x$, is the origin $(0,0)$. Let (x, y) be any other point on this line. Then, by the definition of slope, $m = \frac{y-0}{x-0} = \frac{y}{x} = -\sqrt{3} = \frac{\sqrt{3}}{-1}$, but also, by the definition of tangent, $\tan\theta = -\sqrt{3}$. Because $\tan 120° = -\sqrt{3}$, the line $y = -\sqrt{3}x$ makes a $120°$ angle with the positive x-axis.

6. $\cos\theta = \frac{4}{5}$, with θ in quadrant IV

$\cos\theta = \frac{x}{r}$ so let $x = 4,\ r = 5.$

$$x^2 + y^2 = r^2 \Rightarrow 4^2 + y^2 = 5^2 \Rightarrow 16 + y^2 = 25 \Rightarrow y^2 = 9 \Rightarrow y = \pm 3$$

θ is in quadrant IV, so $y = -3$.

$\cos\theta = \frac{x}{r} = \frac{4}{5}$ $\qquad$ $\cot\theta = \frac{x}{y} = \frac{4}{-3} = -\frac{4}{3}$

$\sin\theta = \frac{y}{r} = \frac{-3}{5} = -\frac{3}{5}$ $\qquad$ $\sec\theta = \frac{r}{x} = \frac{5}{4}$

$\tan\theta = \frac{y}{x} = \frac{-3}{4} = -\frac{3}{4}$ $\qquad$ $\csc\theta = \frac{r}{y} = \frac{5}{-3} = -\frac{5}{3}$

7. Apply the relationships between the lengths of the sides of a $30°-60°$ right triangle first to the triangle on the right to find the values of y and w. In the $30°-60°$ right triangle, the side opposite the $60°$ angle is $\sqrt{3}$ times as long as the side opposite to the $30°$ angle. The length of the hypotenuse is 2 times as long as the shorter leg (opposite the $30°$ angle).

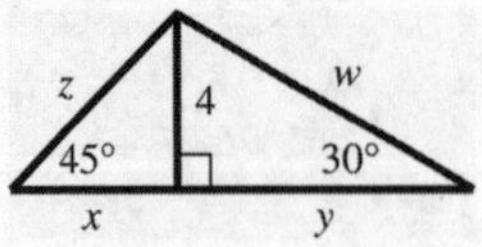

Thus, we have the following.

$$y = 4\sqrt{3} \text{ and } w = 2(4) = 8$$

Apply the relationships between the lengths of the sides of a $45°-45°$ right triangle next to the triangle on the left to find the values of x and z. In the $45°-45°$ right triangle, the sides opposite the $45°$ angles measure the same. The hypotenuse is $\sqrt{2}$ times the measure of a leg.
Thus, we have the following.

$$x = 4 \text{ and } z = 4\sqrt{2}$$

8. $\cot(-750°)$

$-750°$ is coterminal with $-750° + 3 \cdot 360° = -750° + 1080° = 330°$, which is in quadrant IV. The cotangent is negative in quadrant IV and the reference angle is $360° - 330° = 30°$.

$$\cot(-750°) = -\cot 30° = -\sqrt{3}$$

9. **(a)** false

(b) false

10. **(a)** $\sin 78°21' \approx .97939940$

$78°21' = \left(78 + \frac{21}{60}\right)° = 78.35°$

(b) $\tan 117.689° \approx -1.9056082$

(c) $\sec 58.9041° \approx 1.9362132$

11. Since $\sin^{-1}\left(-\frac{2}{3}\right) \approx -41.8$, add $360°$ to obtain one angle in the interval $[0°, 360°)$.

Since $-41.8° + 360° = 318.2°$ is in quadrant IV, the reference angle is $360° - 318.2° = 41.8°$. Thus, the other angle, which lies in quadrant III is $180° + 41.8° = 221.8°$.

12. $A = 58°30'$, $a = 748$

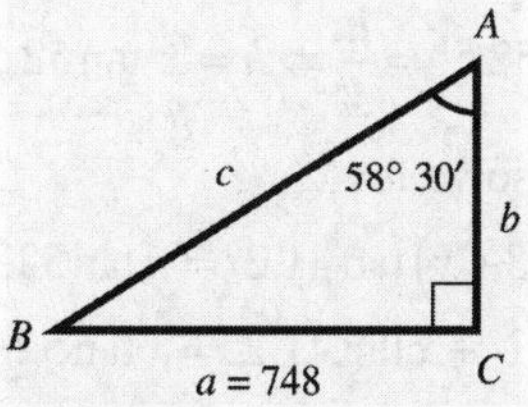

$A + B = 90° \Rightarrow B = 90° - A \Rightarrow B = 90° - 58°30' = 89°60' - 58°30' = 31°30'$

$\tan A = \frac{a}{b} \Rightarrow \tan 58°30' = \frac{748}{b} \Rightarrow b \tan 58°30' = 748 \Rightarrow b = \frac{748}{\tan 58°30'} \approx 458$ (rounded to three significant digits)

$\sin A = \frac{a}{c} \Rightarrow \sin 58°30' = \frac{748}{c} \Rightarrow c \sin 58°30' = 748 \Rightarrow c = \frac{748}{\sin 58°30'} \approx 877$ (rounded to three significant digits)

13. Let x = the height of the flagpole.

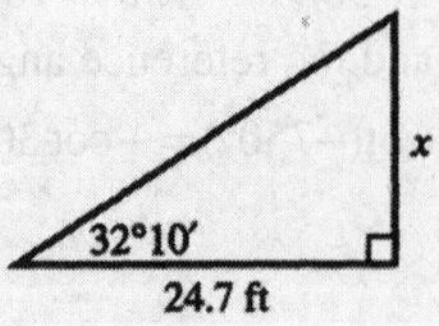

$$\tan 32°10' = \frac{x}{24.7} \Rightarrow x = 24.7 \tan 32°10' \approx 15.5344$$

The flagpole is approximately 15.5 ft high. (rounded to three significant digits)

14. Draw triangle ACB and extend north-south lines from points A and C. Angle ACD is 62° (alternate interior angles of parallel lines cut by a transversal have the same measure), so Angle ACB is 62° + 28° = 90°.

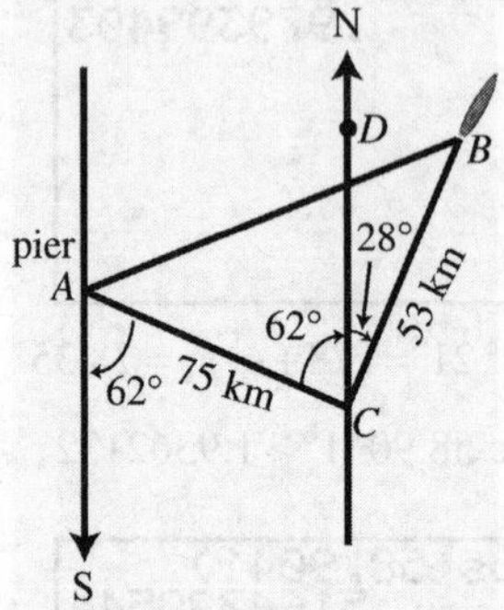

Since angle ACB is a right angle, use the Pythagorean theorem to find the distance from A to B.

$$(AB)^2 = 75^2 + 53^2 \Rightarrow (AB)^2 = 5625 + 2809 \Rightarrow (AB)^2 = 8434 \Rightarrow AB = \sqrt{8434} \approx 91.8368$$

It is 92 km from the pier to the boat. (rounded to two significant digits)

15. Let x = the side adjacent to 52.5° in the smaller triangle.

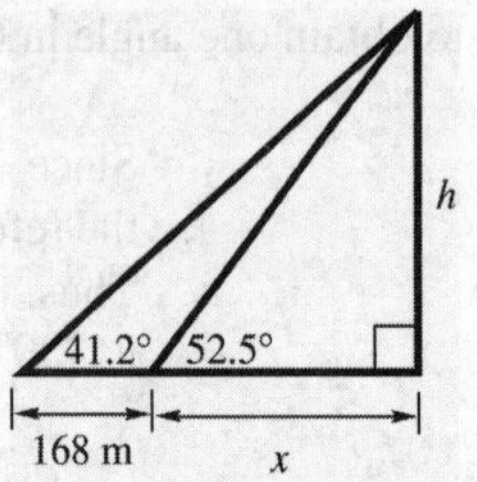

In the larger triangle, we have $\tan 41.2° = \frac{h}{168 + x} \Rightarrow h = (168 + x)\tan 41.2°$.

In the smaller triangle, we have $\tan 52.5° = \frac{h}{x} \Rightarrow h = x \tan 52.5°$.

Substitute for h in this equation and solve for x.

$$(168 + x)\tan 41.2° = x \tan 52.5°$$
$$168 \tan 41.2° + x \tan 41.2° = x \tan 52.5°$$
$$168 \tan 41.2° = x \tan 52.5° - x \tan 41.2°$$
$$168 \tan 41.2° = x(\tan 52.5° - \tan 41.2°)$$
$$\frac{168 \tan 41.2°}{\tan 52.5° - \tan 41.2°} = x$$

Substituting for x in the equation for the smaller triangle, we have the following.

$$h = x \tan 52.5° \Rightarrow h = \frac{168 \tan 41.2° \tan 52.5°}{\tan 52.5° - \tan 41.2°} \approx 448.0432$$

The height of the triangle is approximately 448 m. (rounded to three significant digits)

Chapter 6
CIRCULAR FUNCTIONS AND THEIR GRAPHS

Section 6.1: Radian Measure

1. $60° = 60\left(\frac{\pi}{180}\text{ radian}\right) = \frac{\pi}{3}\text{ radians}$

3. $150° = 150\left(\frac{\pi}{180}\text{ radian}\right) = \frac{5\pi}{6}\text{ radians}$

5. $315° = 315\left(\frac{\pi}{180}\text{ radian}\right) = \frac{7\pi}{4}\text{ radians}$

7. $-45° = -45°\left(\frac{\pi}{180°}\text{ radian}\right) = -\frac{\pi}{4}\text{ radian}$

9. $39° = 39\left(\frac{\pi}{180}\text{ radian}\right) \approx .68\text{ radian}$

11. $139°10' = \left(139 + \frac{10}{60}\right)° \approx 139.1666667\left(\frac{\pi}{180}\text{ radian}\right) \approx 2.43\text{ radians}$

13. $64.29° = 64.29\left(\frac{\pi}{180}\text{ radian}\right) \approx 1.122\text{ radians}$

15. Since θ is in quadrant I, $0 < \theta < \frac{\pi}{2}$. Since $\frac{\pi}{2} \approx 1.57$, 1 is the only integer value in the interval. Thus, the radian measure of θ is 1 radian.

17. Since θ is in quadrant II, $\frac{\pi}{2} < \theta < \pi$. Since $\frac{\pi}{2} \approx 1.57$ and $\pi \approx 3.14$, 2 and 3 are the only integers in the interval. Since θ is closer to π, the radian measure of θ is 3 radians.

19. **(a)** Multiply the degree measure by $\frac{\pi}{180}$ radian and reduce. Your answer will be in radians. Leave the answer as a multiple of π, unless otherwise directed.

(b) Multiply the radian measure by $\frac{180°}{\pi}$ and reduce. Your answer will be in degrees.

21. $\frac{\pi}{3} = \frac{\pi}{3}\left(\frac{180°}{\pi}\right) = 60°$

23. $\frac{7\pi}{4} = \frac{7\pi}{4}\left(\frac{180°}{\pi}\right) = 315°$

25. $\frac{11\pi}{6} = \frac{11\pi}{6}\left(\frac{180°}{\pi}\right) = 330°$

27. $-\frac{\pi}{6} = -\frac{\pi}{6}\left(\frac{180°}{\pi}\right) = -30°$

29. $2\text{ radians} = 2\left(\frac{180°}{\pi}\right) \approx 114.6°$

31. $1.74\text{ radians} = 1.74\left(\frac{180°}{\pi}\right) \approx 99.7°$

33. $-9.84763\text{ radian} = -9.84763\left(\frac{180°}{\pi}\right) \approx -564.2°$

35. $\tan\frac{\pi}{4}=\tan\left(\frac{\pi}{4}\cdot\frac{180°}{\pi}\right)=\tan 45°=1$

36. $\csc\frac{\pi}{4}=\csc\left(\frac{\pi}{4}\cdot\frac{180°}{\pi}\right)=\csc 45°=\sqrt{2}$

37. $\cot\frac{2\pi}{3}=\cot\left(\frac{2\pi}{3}\cdot\frac{180°}{\pi}\right)=\cot 120°=-\cot 60°=-\frac{\sqrt{3}}{3}$

38. $\cos\frac{\pi}{3}=\cos\left(\frac{\pi}{3}\cdot\frac{180°}{\pi}\right)=\cos 60°=\frac{1}{2}$

39. $\sec\pi=\sec\left(\pi\cdot\frac{180°}{\pi}\right)=\sec 180°=-1$

40. $\sin\left(-\frac{7\pi}{6}\right)=\sin\left(-\frac{7\pi}{6}\cdot\frac{180°}{\pi}\right)=\sin(-210°)=\sin(-210°+360°)=\sin 150°=+\sin 30°=\frac{1}{2}$

41. $\cos\left(-\frac{\pi}{6}\right)=\cos\left(-\frac{\pi}{6}\cdot\frac{180°}{\pi}\right)=\cos(-30°)=\cos 30°=\frac{\sqrt{3}}{2}$

42. $\tan\left(-\frac{9\pi}{4}\right)=\tan\left(-\frac{9\pi}{4}\cdot\frac{180°}{\pi}\right)=\tan(-405°)=\tan(-45°)=-\tan 45°=-1$

43. $r=4,\ \theta=\frac{\pi}{2}$

$s=r\theta=4\left(\frac{\pi}{2}\right)=2\pi$

45. $s=6\pi,\ \theta=\frac{3\pi}{4}$

$s=r\theta\Rightarrow r=\frac{s}{\theta}=\frac{6\pi}{\frac{3\pi}{4}}=6\pi\cdot\frac{4}{3\pi}=8$

47. $r=3,\ s=3$

$s=r\theta\Rightarrow\theta=\frac{s}{r}=\frac{3}{3}=1$

49. $r=12.3$ cm, $\theta=\frac{2\pi}{3}$ radians

$s=r\theta=12.3\left(\frac{2\pi}{3}\right)=8.2\pi\approx 25.8$ cm

51. $r=4.82$ m, $\theta=60°$

Converting θ to radians, we have $\theta=60°=60\left(\frac{\pi}{180}\text{ radian}\right)=\frac{\pi}{3}$ radians.

Thus, the arc is $s=r\theta=4.82\left(\frac{\pi}{3}\right)=\frac{4.82\pi}{3}\approx 5.05$ m. (rounded to three significant digits)

53. The formula for arc length is $s=r\theta$. Substituting $2r$ for r we obtain $s=(2r)\theta=2(r\theta)$. The length of the arc is doubled.

For Exercises 55 – 59, note that since 6400 has two significant digits and the angles are given to the nearest degree, we can have only two significant digits in the answers.

55. 9° N, 40° N

$\theta=40°-9°=31°=31\left(\frac{\pi}{180}\text{ radian}\right)=\frac{31\pi}{180}$ radian and $s=r\theta=6400\left(\frac{31\pi}{180}\right)\approx 3500$ km

57. 41° N, 12° S
12° S = –12° N

$$\theta = 41° - (-12°) = 53° = 53\left(\frac{\pi}{180}\text{ radian}\right) = \frac{53\pi}{180}\text{ radian and } s = r\theta = 6400\left(\frac{53\pi}{180}\right) \approx 5900\text{ km}$$

59. $r = 6400$ km, $s = 1200$ km

$$s = r\theta \Rightarrow 1200 = 6400\theta \Rightarrow \theta = \frac{1200}{6400} = \frac{3}{16}$$

Converting $\frac{3}{16}$ radian to degrees we have, $\theta = \frac{3}{16}\left(\frac{180°}{\pi}\right) \approx 11°.$

The north-south distance between the two cities is 11°.
Let x = the latitude of Madison.

$$x - 33° = 11° \Rightarrow x = 44°\text{ N}$$

The latitude of Madison is 44° N.

61. (a) The number of inches lifted is the arc length in a circle with $r = 9.27$ in. and $\theta = 71°50'$.

$$71°50' = \left(71 + \tfrac{50}{60}\right)\left(\frac{\pi}{180°}\right) \text{ and } s = r\theta \Rightarrow s = 9.27\left(71 + \tfrac{50}{60}\right)\left(\frac{\pi}{180°}\right) \approx 11.6221$$

The weight will rise 11.6 in. (rounded to three significant digits)

(b) When the weight is raised 6 in., we have the following.

$$s = r\theta \Rightarrow 6 = 9.27\theta \Rightarrow \theta = \frac{6}{9.27}\text{ radian} = \frac{6}{9.27}\left(\frac{180°}{\pi}\right) \approx 37.0846° = 37° + .0846(60') \approx 37°5'$$

The pulley must be rotated through 37°5′.

63. A rotation of $\theta = 60.0\left(\frac{\pi}{180}\text{ radian}\right) = \frac{\pi}{3}$ radians on the smaller wheel moves through an arc length of

$s = r\theta = 5.23\left(\frac{\pi}{3}\right) \approx 5.4768$ cm. (holding on to more digits for the intermediate steps)

Since both wheels move together, the larger wheel moves 5.48 cm, which rotates it through an angle θ,

where $5.4768 = 8.16\theta \Rightarrow \theta = \frac{5.4768}{8.16} = .671\text{ radian} = .671\left(\frac{180°}{\pi}\right) \approx 38.5°.$

The larger wheel rotates through 38.5°.

65. A rotation of $\theta = 180\left(\frac{\pi}{180}\text{ radian}\right) = \pi$ radians. The chain moves a distance equal to half the arc length of the larger gear. So, for the large gear and pedal, $s = r\theta \Rightarrow 4.72\pi$. Thus, the chain moves 4.72π in. The small gear rotates through an angle as follows.

$$\theta = \frac{s}{r} \Rightarrow \theta = \frac{4.72\pi}{1.38} \approx 3.42\pi$$

θ for the wheel and θ for the small gear are the same, or 3.42π. So, for the wheel, we have the following.

$$s = r\theta \Rightarrow r = 13.6(3.42\pi) \approx 146.12$$

The bicycle will move 146 in. (rounded to three significant digits)

67. Let t = the length of the train.

t is approximately the arc length subtended by 3° 20′. First convert $\theta = 3°20'$ to radians.

$$\theta = 3°20' = \left(3+\tfrac{20}{60}\right)° = 3\tfrac{1}{3}° = \left(3\tfrac{1}{3}\right)\left(\frac{\pi}{180}\text{ radian}\right) = \left(\frac{10}{3}\right)\left(\frac{\pi}{180}\text{ radian}\right) = \frac{\pi}{54}\text{ radian}$$

The length of the train is $t = r\theta \Rightarrow t = 3.5\left(\frac{\pi}{54}\right) \approx .20$ km long. (rounded to two significant digits)

69. $r = 6, \theta = \frac{\pi}{3}$

$$A = \frac{1}{2}r^2\theta \Rightarrow A = \frac{1}{2}(6)^2\left(\frac{\pi}{3}\right) = \frac{1}{2}(36)\left(\frac{\pi}{3}\right) = 6\pi$$

71. $A = 3$ sq units, $r = 2$

$$A = \frac{1}{2}r^2\theta \Rightarrow 3 = \frac{1}{2}(2)^2\theta \Rightarrow 3 = \frac{1}{2}(4)\theta \Rightarrow 3 = 2\theta \Rightarrow \theta = \frac{3}{2} = 1.5\text{ radians}$$

In Exercises 73 – 79, we will be rounding to the nearest tenth.

73. $r = 29.2$ m, $\theta = \frac{5\pi}{6}$ radians

$$A = \frac{1}{2}r^2\theta \Rightarrow A = \frac{1}{2}(29.2)^2\left(\frac{5\pi}{6}\right) = \frac{1}{2}(852.64)\left(\frac{5\pi}{6}\right) \approx 1116.1032$$

The area of the sector is 1116.1 m^2. (1120 m^2 rounded to three significant digits)

75. $r = 30.0$ ft, $\theta = \frac{\pi}{2}$ radians

$$A = \frac{1}{2}r^2\theta \Rightarrow A = \frac{1}{2}(30.0)^2\left(\frac{\pi}{2}\right) = \frac{1}{2}(900)\left(\frac{\pi}{2}\right) = 225\pi \approx 706.8583$$

The area of the sector is 706.9 ft^2. (707 ft^2 rounded to three significant digits)

77. $r = 12.7$ cm, $\theta = 81°$

The formula $A = \frac{1}{2}r^2\theta$ requires that θ be measured in radians. Converting 81° to radians, we have $\theta = 81\left(\frac{\pi}{180}\text{ radian}\right) = \frac{9\pi}{20}$ radians. Since $A = \frac{1}{2}(12.7)^2\left(\frac{9\pi}{20}\right) = \frac{1}{2}(161.29)\left(\frac{9\pi}{20}\right) \approx 114.0092$, the area of the sector is 114.0 cm^2. (114 cm^2 rounded to three significant digits)

79. $r = 40.0$ mi, $\theta = 135°$

The formula $A = \frac{1}{2}r^2\theta$ requires that θ be measured in radians. Converting 135° to radians, we have $\theta = 135\left(\frac{\pi}{180}\text{ radian}\right) = \frac{3\pi}{4}$ radians. Since $A = \frac{1}{2}(40.0)^2\left(\frac{3\pi}{4}\right) = \frac{1}{2}(1600)\left(\frac{3\pi}{4}\right) = 600\pi \approx 1884.9556$, the area of the sector is 1885.0 mi^2. (1880 mi^2 rounded to three significant digits)

81. $A = 16$ in.^{2}, $r = 3.0$ in.

$$A = \frac{1}{2}r^2\theta \Rightarrow 16 = \frac{1}{2}(3)^2\theta \Rightarrow 16 = \frac{9}{2}\theta \Rightarrow \theta = 16\cdot\frac{2}{9} = \frac{32}{9} \approx 3.6\text{ radians}$$ (rounded to two significant digits)

83. (a) The central angle in degrees measures $\frac{360°}{27} = 13\frac{1}{3}°$. Converting to radians, we have the following.

$$13\tfrac{1}{3}° = \left(13\tfrac{1}{3}\right)\left(\frac{\pi}{180}\text{ radian}\right) = \left(\frac{40}{3}\right)\left(\frac{\pi}{180}\text{ radian}\right) = \frac{2\pi}{27}\text{ radian}$$

(b) Since $C = 2\pi r$, and $r = 76$ ft, we have $C = 2\pi(76) = 152\pi \approx 477.5221$. The circumference is 480 ft. (rounded to two significant digits)

(c) Since $r = 76$ ft and $\theta = \frac{2\pi}{27}$, we have $s = r\theta = 76\left(\frac{2\pi}{27}\right) = \frac{152\pi}{27} \approx 17.6860$. Thus, the length of the arc is 17.7 ft. (rounded to three significant digits)

Note: If this measurement is approximated to be $\frac{160}{9}$, then the approximated value would be 17.8 ft, rounded to three significant digits.

(d) Area of sector with $r = 76$ ft and $\theta = \frac{2\pi}{27}$ is as follows.

$$A = \frac{1}{2}r^2\theta \Rightarrow A = \frac{1}{2}(76^2)\frac{2\pi}{27} = \frac{1}{2}(5776)\frac{2\pi}{27} = \frac{5776\pi}{27} \approx 672.0681 \approx 672 \text{ ft}^2$$

85. (a)

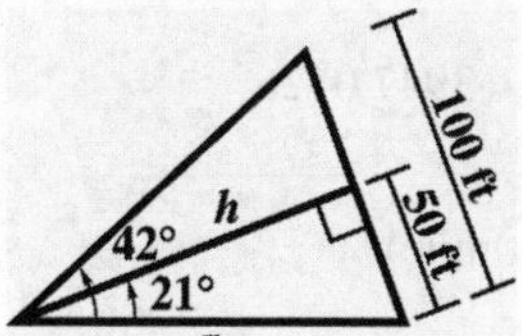

The triangle formed by the central angle and the chord is isosceles. Therefore, the bisector of the central angle is also the perpendicular bisector of the chord.

$$\sin 21° = \frac{50}{r} \Rightarrow r = \frac{50}{\sin 21°} \approx 140 \text{ ft}$$

(b) $r = \frac{50}{\sin 21°}$; $\theta = 42°$

Converting θ to radians, we have $42\left(\frac{\pi}{180}\text{ radian}\right) = \frac{7\pi}{30}$ radian. Solving for the arc length, we have $s = r\theta \Rightarrow s = \frac{50}{\sin 21°}\cdot\frac{7\pi}{30} = \frac{35\pi}{3\sin 21°} \approx 102$ ft.

(c)

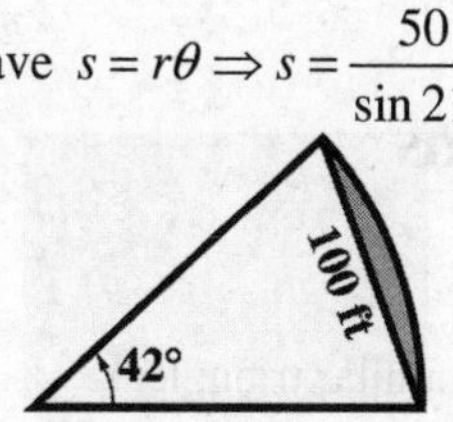

The area of the portion of the circle can be found by subtracting the area of the triangle from the area of the sector. From the figure in part (a), we have $\tan 21° = \frac{50}{h}$ so $h = \frac{50}{\tan 21°}$.

$$A_{\text{sector}} = \frac{1}{2}r^2\theta \Rightarrow A_{\text{sector}} = \frac{1}{2}\left(\frac{50}{\sin 21°}\right)^2\left(\frac{7\pi}{30}\right) \approx 7135 \text{ ft}^2$$

and

$$A_{\text{triangle}} = \frac{1}{2}bh \Rightarrow A_{\text{triangle}} = \frac{1}{2}(100)\left(\frac{50}{\tan 21°}\right) \approx 6513 \text{ ft}^2$$

The area bounded by the arc and the chord is 7135 – 6513 = 622 ft^2.

87. Use the Pythagorean theorem to find the hypotenuse of the triangle, which is also the radius of the sector of the circle.

$$r^2 = 30^2 + 40^2 \Rightarrow r^2 = 900 + 1600 \Rightarrow r^2 = 2500 \Rightarrow r = 50$$

The total area of the lot is the sum of the areas of the triangle and the sector.

Converting $\theta = 60°$ to radians, we have $60\left(\frac{\pi}{180}\text{ radian}\right) = \frac{\pi}{3}$ radians.

$$A_{\text{triangle}} = \frac{1}{2}bh = \frac{1}{2}(30)(40) = 600 \text{ yd}^2$$

and

$$A_{\text{sector}} = \frac{1}{2}r^2\theta = \frac{1}{2}(50)^2\left(\frac{\pi}{3}\right) = \frac{1}{2}(2500)\left(\frac{\pi}{3}\right) = \frac{1250\pi}{3} \text{ yd}^2$$

Total area $A_{\text{triangle}} + A_{\text{sector}} = 600 + \frac{1250\pi}{3} \approx 1908.9969$ or 1900 yd^2, rounded to two significant digits.

89. Converting $\theta = 7°12' = \left(7 + \frac{12}{60}\right)° = 7.2°$ to radians, we have $7.2\left(\frac{\pi}{180}\text{ radian}\right) = \frac{7.2\pi}{180} = \frac{\pi}{25}$ radian.
Solving for the radius with the arc length formula, we have the following.

$$s = r\theta \Rightarrow 496 = r \cdot \frac{\pi}{25} \Rightarrow r = 496 \cdot \frac{25}{\pi} = \frac{12{,}400}{\pi} \approx 3947.0426$$

Thus, the radius is approximately 3947 mi. (rounded to the nearest mile)

Using this approximate radius, we can find the circumference of the Earth. Since $C = 2\pi r$, we have $C \approx 2\pi(3947) \approx 24{,}799.7324$. Thus, the approximate circumference is 24,800 mi. (rounded to three significant digits)

91. If we let $r' = 2r$, then $A_{\text{sector}} = \frac{1}{2}(r')^2\theta = \frac{1}{2}(2r)^2\theta = \frac{1}{2}(4r^2)\theta = 4\left(\frac{1}{2}r^2\theta\right)$. Thus, the area, $\frac{1}{2}r^2\theta$, is quadrupled.

Section 6.2: The Unit Circle and Circular Functions

Connections (page 550)

$PQ = y = \frac{y}{1} = \sin\theta$; $OQ = x = \frac{x}{1} = \cos\theta$; $AB = \frac{AB}{1} = \frac{AB}{AO} = \frac{y}{x} = \tan\theta$ (by similar triangles)

Exercises

1. An angle of $\theta = \frac{\pi}{2}$ radians intersects the unit circle at the point $(0,1)$.

(a) $\sin\theta = y = 1$

(b) $\cos\theta = x = 0$

(c) $\tan\theta = \frac{y}{x} = \frac{1}{0}$; undefined

3. An angle of $\theta = 2\pi$ radians intersects the unit circle at the point $(1,0)$.

(a) $\sin\theta = y = 0$

(b) $\cos\theta = x = 1$

(c) $\tan\theta = \frac{y}{x} = \frac{0}{1} = 0$

5. An angle of $\theta = -\pi$ radians intersects the unit circle at the point $(-1,0)$.

(a) $\sin\theta = y = 0$

(b) $\cos\theta = x = -1$

(c) $\tan\theta = \frac{y}{x} = \frac{0}{-1} = 0$

For Exercises 7 – 21, use the following copy of Figure 11 on page 546 of your text.

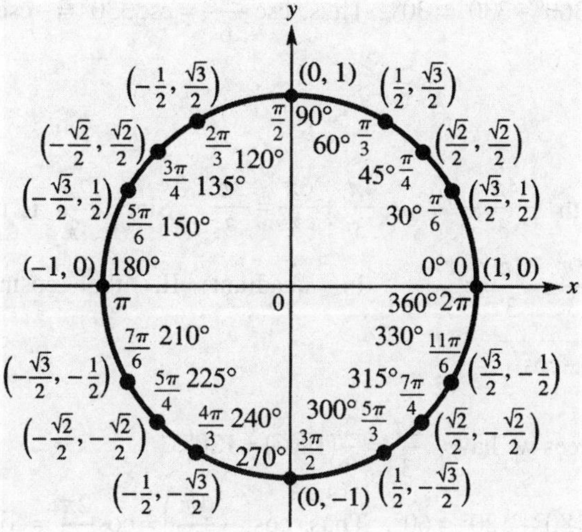

7. Find $\sin\frac{7\pi}{6}$.

Since $\frac{7\pi}{6}$ is in quadrant III, the reference angle is $\frac{7\pi}{6} - \pi = \frac{7\pi}{6} - \frac{6\pi}{6} = \frac{\pi}{6}$. In quadrant III, the sine is negative. Thus, $\sin\frac{7\pi}{6} = -\sin\frac{\pi}{6} = -\frac{1}{2}$.

Converting $\frac{7\pi}{6}$ to degrees we have, $\frac{7\pi}{6} = \frac{7}{6}(180°) = 210°$.

The reference angle is $210° - 180° = 30°$. Thus, $\sin\frac{7\pi}{6} = \sin 210° = -\sin 30° = -\frac{1}{2}$.

9. Find $\tan\frac{3\pi}{4}$.

Since $\frac{3\pi}{4}$ is in quadrant II, the reference angle is $\pi - \frac{3\pi}{4} = \frac{4\pi}{4} - \frac{3\pi}{4} = \frac{\pi}{4}$. In quadrant II, the tangent is negative. Thus, $\tan\frac{3\pi}{4} = -\tan\frac{\pi}{4} = -1$.

Converting $\frac{3\pi}{4}$ to degrees we have, $\frac{3\pi}{4} = \frac{3}{4}(180°) = 135°$.

The reference angle is $180° - 135° = 45°$. Thus, $\tan\frac{3\pi}{4} = \tan 135° = -\tan 45° = -1$.

11. Find $\csc \frac{11\pi}{6}$.

Since $\frac{11\pi}{6}$ is in quadrant IV, the reference angle is $2\pi - \frac{11\pi}{6} = \frac{12\pi}{6} - \frac{11\pi}{6} = \frac{\pi}{6}$. In quadrant IV, the cosecant is negative. Thus, $\csc \frac{11\pi}{6} = -\csc \frac{\pi}{6} = -2$.

Converting $\frac{11\pi}{6}$ to degrees we have, $\frac{11\pi}{6} = \frac{11}{6}(180°) = 330°$.

The reference angle is $360° - 330° = 30°$. Thus, $\csc \frac{11\pi}{6} = \csc 330° = -\csc 30° = -2$.

13. Find $\cos\left(-\frac{4\pi}{3}\right)$.

$-\frac{4\pi}{3}$ is coterminal with $-\frac{4\pi}{3} + 2\pi = -\frac{4\pi}{3} + \frac{6\pi}{3} = \frac{2\pi}{3}$. Since $\frac{2\pi}{3}$ is in quadrant II, the reference angle is $\pi - \frac{2\pi}{3} = \frac{3\pi}{3} - \frac{2\pi}{3} = \frac{\pi}{3}$. In quadrant II, the cosine is negative. Thus, $\cos\left(-\frac{4\pi}{3}\right) = \cos \frac{2\pi}{3} = -\cos \frac{\pi}{3} = -\frac{1}{2}$.

Converting $\frac{2\pi}{3}$ to degrees we have, $\frac{2\pi}{3} = \frac{2}{3}(180°) = 120°$.

The reference angle is $180° - 120° = 60°$. Thus, $\cos\left(-\frac{4\pi}{3}\right) = \cos \frac{2\pi}{3} = \cos 120° = -\cos 60° = -\frac{1}{2}$.

15. Find $\cos \frac{7\pi}{4}$.

Since $\frac{7\pi}{4}$ is in quadrant IV, the reference angle is $2\pi - \frac{7\pi}{4} = \frac{8\pi}{4} - \frac{7\pi}{4} = \frac{\pi}{4}$. In quadrant IV, the cosine is positive. Thus, $\cos \frac{7\pi}{4} = \cos \frac{\pi}{4} = \frac{\sqrt{2}}{2}$.

Converting $\frac{7\pi}{4}$ to degrees we have, $\frac{7\pi}{4} = \frac{7}{4}(180°) = 315°$.

The reference angle is $360° - 315° = 45°$. Thus, $\cos \frac{7\pi}{4} = \cos 315° = \cos 45° = \frac{\sqrt{2}}{2}$.

17. Find $\sin\left(-\frac{4\pi}{3}\right)$

$-\frac{4\pi}{3}$ is coterminal with $-\frac{4\pi}{3} + 2\pi = -\frac{4\pi}{3} + \frac{6\pi}{3} = \frac{2\pi}{3}$. Since $\frac{2\pi}{3}$ is in quadrant II, the reference angle is $\pi - \frac{2\pi}{3} = \frac{3\pi}{3} - \frac{2\pi}{3} = \frac{\pi}{3}$. In quadrant II, the sine is positive. Thus, $\sin\left(-\frac{4\pi}{3}\right) = \sin \frac{2\pi}{3} = \sin \frac{\pi}{3} = \frac{\sqrt{3}}{2}$.

Converting $\frac{2\pi}{3}$ to degrees we have, $\frac{2\pi}{3} = \frac{2}{3}(180°) = 120°$.

The reference angle is $180° - 120° = 60°$. Thus, $\sin\left(-\frac{4\pi}{3}\right) = \sin \frac{2\pi}{3} = \sin 120° = \sin 60° = \frac{\sqrt{3}}{2}$.

19. Find $\sec\frac{23\pi}{6}$.

$\frac{23\pi}{6}$ is coterminal with $\frac{23\pi}{6}-2\pi=\frac{23\pi}{6}-\frac{12\pi}{6}=\frac{11\pi}{6}$. Since $\frac{11\pi}{6}$ is in quadrant IV, the reference angle is $2\pi-\frac{11\pi}{6}=\frac{12\pi}{6}-\frac{11\pi}{6}=\frac{\pi}{6}$. In quadrant IV, the secant is positive.

Thus, $\sec\frac{23\pi}{6}=\sec\frac{11\pi}{6}=\sec\frac{\pi}{6}=\frac{2\sqrt{3}}{3}$.

Converting $\frac{11\pi}{6}$ to degrees we have, $\frac{11\pi}{6}=\frac{11}{6}(180°)=330°$.

The reference angle is $360°-330°=30°$. Thus, $\sec\frac{23\pi}{6}=\sec\frac{11\pi}{6}=\sec 330°=\sec 30°=\frac{2\sqrt{3}}{3}$.

21. Find $\tan\frac{5\pi}{6}$.

Since $\frac{5\pi}{6}$ is in quadrant II, the reference angle is $\pi-\frac{5\pi}{6}=\frac{6\pi}{6}-\frac{5\pi}{6}=\frac{\pi}{6}$.

In quadrant II, the tangent is negative. Thus, $\tan\frac{5\pi}{6}=-\tan\frac{\pi}{6}=-\frac{\sqrt{3}}{3}$.

Converting $\frac{5\pi}{6}$ to degrees we have, $\frac{5\pi}{6}=\frac{5}{6}(180°)=150°$.

The reference angle is $180°-150°=30°$. Thus, $\tan\frac{5\pi}{6}=\tan 150°=-\tan 30°=-\frac{\sqrt{3}}{3}$.

For Exercises 23 – 33, 49 – 53, and 61 – 69, your calculator must be set in radian mode. Keystroke sequences may vary based on the type and/or model of calculator being used. As in Example 3, we will set the calculator to show four decimal digits.

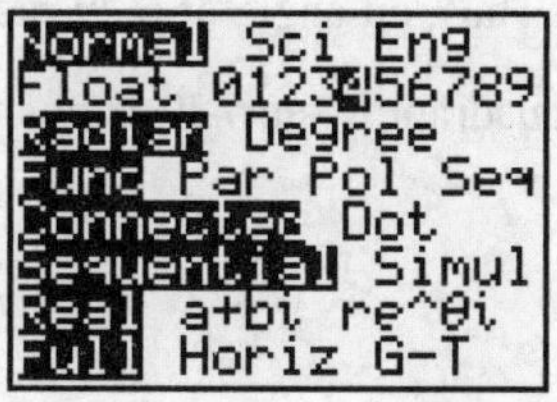

23. $\sin .6109 \approx .5736$

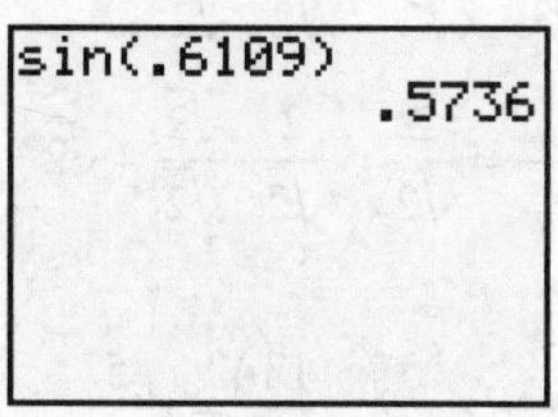

25. $\cos(-1.1519)\approx .4068$

27. $\tan 4.0203 \approx 1.2065$ t

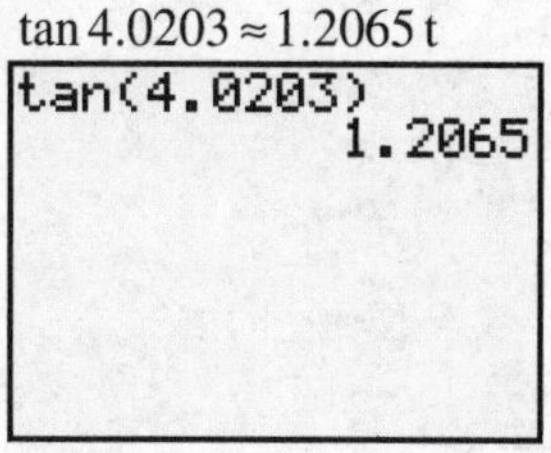

29. $\csc(-9.4946)\approx 14.3338$

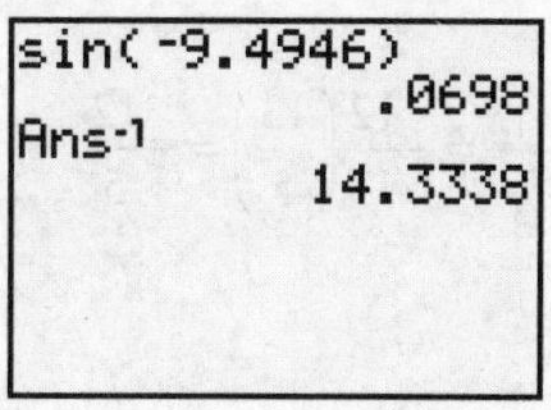

31. $\sec 2.8440 \approx -1.0460$

```
cos(2.8440)
           -.9560
Ans-1
          -1.0460
```

33. $\cot 6.0301 \approx -3.8665$

```
tan(6.0301)
           -.2586
Ans-1
          -3.8665
```

35. $\cos .8 \approx .7$

37. $x = -.65$ when $\theta \approx 4$ radians.

39. $\cos 2$

$\frac{\pi}{2} \approx 1.57$ and $\pi \approx 3.14$, so $\frac{\pi}{2} < 2 < \pi$. Thus, an angle of 2 radians is in quadrant II. (The figure for Exercises 35 – 38 also shows that 2 radians is in quadrant II.) Because values of the cosine function are negative in quadrant II, cos 2 is negative.

41. $\sin 5$

$\frac{3\pi}{2} \approx 4.71$ and $2\pi \approx 6.28$, so $\frac{3\pi}{2} < 5 < 2\pi$. Thus, an angle of 5 radians is in quadrant IV. (The figure for Exercises 35 – 38 also shows that 5 radians is in quadrant IV.) Because values of the sine function are negative in quadrant IV, sin 5 is negative.

43. $\tan 6.29$

$2\pi \approx 6.28$ and $2\pi + \frac{\pi}{2} = \frac{4\pi}{2} + \frac{\pi}{2} = \frac{5\pi}{2} \approx 7.85$, so $2\pi < 6.29 < \frac{5\pi}{2}$. Notice that 2π is coterminal with 0 and $\frac{5\pi}{2}$ is coterminal with $\frac{\pi}{2}$. Thus, an angle of 6.29 radians is in quadrant I. Because values of the tangent function are positive in quadrant I, $\tan 6.29$ is positive.

45. $\sin\theta = y = \frac{\sqrt{2}}{2}$

$\cos\theta = x = \frac{\sqrt{2}}{2}$

$\tan\theta = \frac{y}{x} = \frac{\frac{\sqrt{2}}{2}}{\frac{\sqrt{2}}{2}} = 1$

$\cot\theta = \frac{x}{y} = \frac{\frac{\sqrt{2}}{2}}{\frac{\sqrt{2}}{2}} = 1$

$\sec\theta = \frac{1}{x} = \frac{1}{\frac{\sqrt{2}}{2}} = \frac{2}{\sqrt{2}} = \frac{2}{\sqrt{2}} \cdot \frac{\sqrt{2}}{\sqrt{2}} = \sqrt{2}$

$\csc\theta = \frac{1}{y} = \frac{1}{\frac{\sqrt{2}}{2}} = \frac{2}{\sqrt{2}} = \frac{2}{\sqrt{2}} \cdot \frac{\sqrt{2}}{\sqrt{2}} = \sqrt{2}$

47. $\sin\theta = y = -\frac{12}{13}$

$\cos\theta = x = \frac{5}{13}$

$\tan\theta = \frac{y}{x} = \frac{-\frac{12}{13}}{\frac{5}{13}} = -\frac{12}{13}\left(\frac{13}{5}\right) = -\frac{12}{5}$

$\cot\theta = \frac{x}{y} = \frac{\frac{5}{13}}{-\frac{12}{13}} = \frac{5}{13}\left(-\frac{13}{12}\right) = -\frac{5}{12}$

$\sec\theta = \frac{1}{x} = \frac{1}{\frac{5}{13}} = \frac{13}{5}$

$\csc\theta = \frac{1}{y} = \frac{1}{-\frac{12}{13}} = -\frac{13}{12}$

49. $\tan s = .2126$

```
tan⁻¹(.2126)
          .2095
```

$s \approx .2095$

51. $\sin s = .9918$

```
sin⁻¹(.9918)
         1.4426
```

$s \approx 1.4426$

53. $\sec s = 1.0806$

```
1/1.0806
          .9254
cos⁻¹(Ans)
          .3887
```

$s \approx .3887$

55. $\left[\frac{\pi}{2}, \pi\right]$; $\sin s = \frac{1}{2}$

Recall that $\sin\frac{\pi}{6} = \frac{1}{2}$ and in quadrant II, $\sin s$ is positive. Therefore, $\sin\left(\pi - \frac{\pi}{6}\right) = \sin\frac{5\pi}{6} = \frac{1}{2}$, and thus, $s = \frac{5\pi}{6}$.

57. $\left[\pi, \frac{3\pi}{2}\right]$; $\tan s = \sqrt{3}$

Recall that $\tan\frac{\pi}{3} = \sqrt{3}$ and in quadrant III, $\tan s$ is positive. Therefore, $\tan\left(\pi + \frac{\pi}{3}\right) = \tan\frac{4\pi}{3} = \sqrt{3}$, and thus, $s = \frac{4\pi}{3}$.

59. $\left[\frac{3\pi}{2}, 2\pi\right]$; $\tan s = -1$

Recall that $\tan\frac{\pi}{4} = 1$ and in quadrant IV, $\tan s$ is negative. Therefore, $\tan\left(2\pi - \frac{\pi}{4}\right) = \tan\frac{7\pi}{4} = -1$, and thus, $s = \frac{7\pi}{4}$.

61. s = the length of an arc on the unit circle = 2.5

$x = \cos s \Rightarrow x = \cos 2.5$

$y = \sin s \Rightarrow y = \sin 2.5$

$(-.8011, .5985)$

```
cos(2.5)
         -.8011
sin(2.5)
          .5985
```

63. $s = -7.4$

$x = \cos s \Rightarrow x = \cos(-7.4)$

$y = \sin s \Rightarrow y = \sin(-7.4)$

$(.4385, -.8987)$

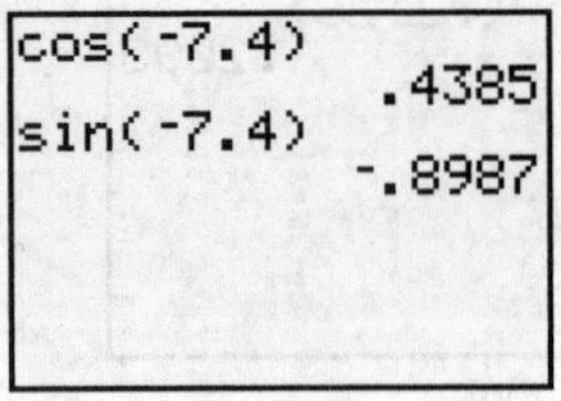

65. $s = 51$

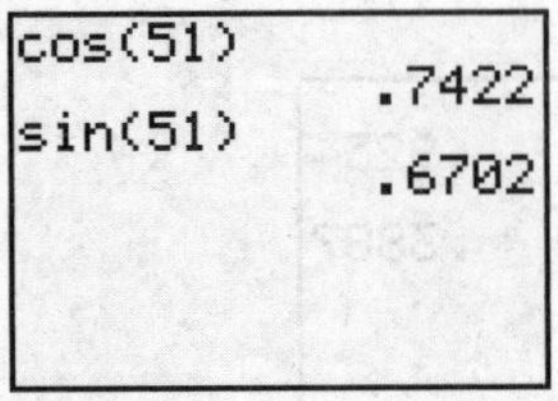

Since cosine and sine are both positive, an angle of 51 radians lies in quadrant I.

67. $s = 65$

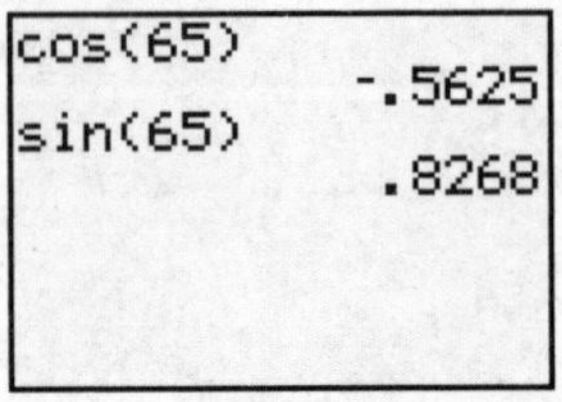

Since cosine is negative and sine is positive, an angle of 65 radians lies in quadrant II.

69. $\theta = \frac{3\pi}{4}$ radians, $t = 8$ sec

$\omega = \frac{\theta}{t} \Rightarrow \theta = \frac{\frac{3\pi}{4}}{8} = \frac{3\pi}{4} \cdot \frac{1}{8} = \frac{3\pi}{32}$ radian per sec

71. $\theta = \frac{2\pi}{9}$ radian, $\omega = \frac{5\pi}{27}$ radian per min

$\omega = \frac{\theta}{t} \Rightarrow \frac{5\pi}{27} = \frac{\frac{2\pi}{9}}{t} \Rightarrow \frac{5\pi}{27} = \frac{2\pi}{9t} \Rightarrow 45\pi t = 54\pi \Rightarrow t = \frac{54\pi}{45\pi} = \frac{6}{5}$ min

73. $\theta = 3.871142$ radians, $t = 21.4693$ sec

$\omega = \frac{\theta}{t} \Rightarrow \omega = \frac{3.871142}{21.4693} \approx .180311$ radian per sec

75. $v = 9$ m per sec, $r = 5$ m

$v = r\omega \Rightarrow 9 = 5\omega \Rightarrow \omega = \frac{9}{5}$ radians per sec

77. $v = 107.692$ m per sec, $r = 58.7413$ m

$v = r\omega \Rightarrow 107.692 = 58.7413\omega \Rightarrow \omega = \frac{107.692}{58.7413} \approx 1.83333$ radians per sec

79. $r = 6$ cm, $\omega = \frac{\pi}{3}$ radians per sec, $t = 9$ sec

$s = r\omega t \Rightarrow s = 6\left(\frac{\pi}{3}\right)(9) = 18\pi \text{ cm}$

81. $s = 6\pi$ cm, $r = 2$ cm, $\omega = \frac{\pi}{4}$ radian per sec

$s = r\omega t \Rightarrow 6\pi = 2\left(\frac{\pi}{4}\right)t \Rightarrow 6\pi = \left(\frac{\pi}{2}\right)t \Rightarrow t = 6\pi\left(\frac{2}{\pi}\right) = 12$ sec \

83. The hour hand of a clock moves through an angle of 2π radians (one complete revolution) in 12 hours, so $\omega = \frac{\theta}{t} = \frac{2\pi}{12} = \frac{\pi}{6}$ radian per hr.

85. The minute hand of a clock moves through an angle of 2π radians in 60 min, and at the tip of the minute hand, $r = 7$ cm, so we have the following.

$$v = \frac{r\theta}{t} \Rightarrow v = \frac{7(2\pi)}{60} = \frac{7\pi}{30} \text{ cm per min}$$

87. At 500 rotations per min, the propeller turns through an angle of $\theta = 500(2\pi) = 1000\pi$ radians in 1 min with $r = \frac{3}{2} = 1.5$ m, we have $v = \frac{r\theta}{t} \Rightarrow v = \frac{1.5(1000\pi)}{1} = 1500\pi$ m per min.

89. The circumference of the unit circle is 2π.
$v = 1$ unit per sec, $s = 2\pi$ units
$v = \frac{s}{t} \Rightarrow 1 = \frac{2\pi}{t} \Rightarrow t = 2\pi$ sec

91. At 200 revolutions per minute, the bicycle tire is moving 200 $(2\pi) = 400\pi$ radians per min. This is the angular velocity ω. The linear velocity of the bicycle is $v = r\omega = 13(400\pi) = 5200\pi$ in. per min. To convert this to miles per hour, we find the following.

$$v = \frac{5200\pi \text{ in.}}{\text{min}} \cdot \frac{60 \text{ min}}{\text{hr}} \cdot \frac{1 \text{ ft}}{12 \text{ in.}} \cdot \frac{1 \text{ mi}}{5280 \text{ ft}} \approx 15.5 \text{ mph}$$

93. **(a)** $\theta = \frac{1}{365}(2\pi) = \frac{2\pi}{365}$ radian

(b) $\omega = \frac{2\pi}{365}$ radian per day $= \frac{2\pi}{365} \cdot \frac{1}{24}$ radian per hr $= \frac{\pi}{4380}$ radian per hr

(c) $v = r\omega \Rightarrow v = (93{,}000{,}000)\left(\frac{\pi}{4380}\right) \approx 66{,}700$ mph

95. **(a)** Since the 56 cm belt goes around in 18 sec, we have the following.

$$v = r\omega \Rightarrow \frac{56}{18} = (12.96)\omega \Rightarrow \frac{28}{9} = (12.96)\omega \Rightarrow \omega = \frac{\frac{28}{9}}{12.96} \approx .24 \text{ radian per sec}$$

(b) Since $s = 56$ cm of belt go around in $t = 18$ sec, the linear velocity is as follows.

$$v = \frac{s}{t} \Rightarrow v = \frac{56}{18} = \frac{28}{9} \approx 3.11 \text{ cm per sec}$$

97. $\omega = (152)(2\pi) = 304\pi$ radians per min $= \frac{304\pi}{60}$ radians per sec $= \frac{76\pi}{15}$ radians per sec

$$v = r\omega \Rightarrow 59.4 = r\left(\frac{76\pi}{15}\right) \Rightarrow r = 59.4\left(\frac{15}{76\pi}\right) \approx 3.73 \text{ cm}$$

99. In one minute, the propeller makes 5000 revolutions. Each revolution is 2π radians, so we have $5000(2\pi) = 10{,}000\pi$ radians per min. Since there are 60 sec in a minute, we have the following.

$$\omega = \frac{10{,}000\pi}{60} = \frac{500\pi}{3} \approx 523.6 \text{ radians per sec}$$

Section 6.3: Graphs of the Sine and Cosine Functions

1. D

3. A

5. $y = 2\cos x$

Amplitude: $|2| = 2$

x	0	$\frac{\pi}{2}$	π	$\frac{3\pi}{2}$	2π
$\cos x$	1	0	-1	0	1
$2\cos x$	2	0	-2	0	2

This table gives five values for graphing one period of the function. Repeat this cycle for the interval $[-2\pi, 0]$.

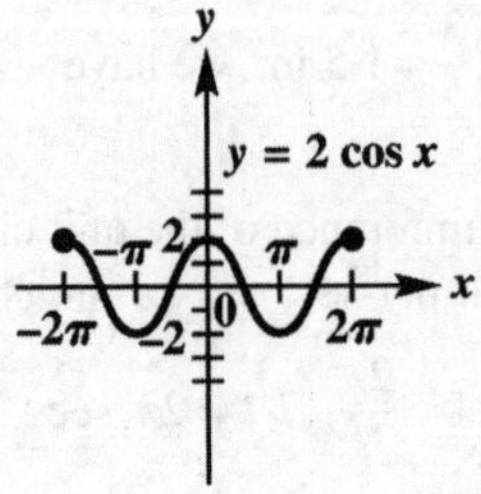

7. $y = \frac{2}{3}\sin x$

Amplitude: $\left|\frac{2}{3}\right| = \frac{2}{3}$

x	0	$\frac{\pi}{2}$	π	$\frac{3\pi}{2}$	2π
$\sin x$	0	1	0	-1	0
$\frac{2}{3}\sin x$	0	$\frac{2}{3} \approx .7$	0	$-\frac{2}{3} \approx -.7$	0

This table gives five values for graphing one period of $y = \frac{2}{3}\sin x$. Repeat this cycle for the interval $[-2\pi, 0]$.

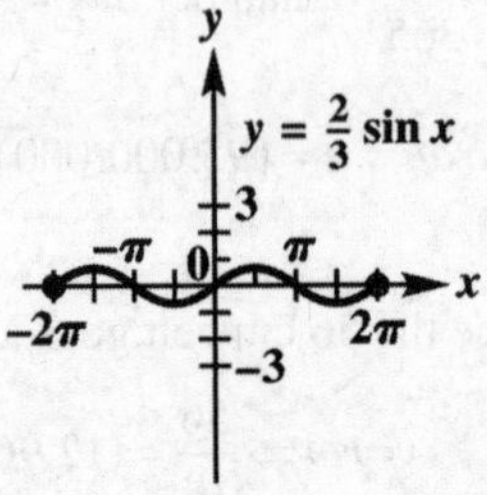

9. $y = -\cos x$

Amplitude: $|-1| = 1$

x	0	$\frac{\pi}{2}$	π	$\frac{3\pi}{2}$	2π
$\cos x$	1	0	-1	0	1
$-\cos x$	-1	0	1	0	-1

This table gives five values for graphing one period of $y = -\cos x$. Repeat this cycle for the interval $[-2\pi, 0]$.

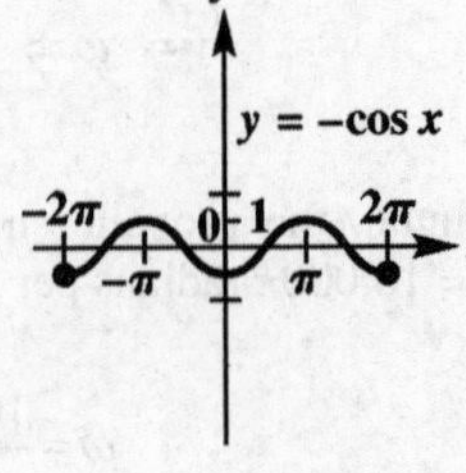

11. $y = -2 \sin x$

Amplitude: $|-2| = 2$

x	0	$\frac{\pi}{2}$	π	$\frac{3\pi}{2}$	2π
$\sin x$	0	1	0	−1	0
$-2 \sin x$	0	−2	0	2	0

This table gives five values for graphing one period of $y = -2\sin x$. Repeat this cycle for the interval $[-2\pi, 0]$.

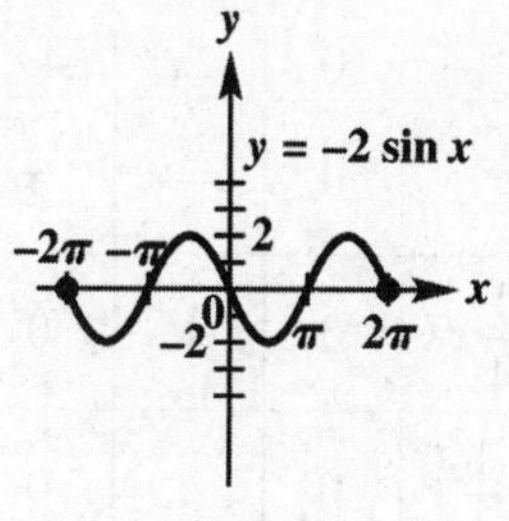

13. $y = \sin \frac{1}{2} x$

Period: $\frac{2\pi}{\frac{1}{2}} = 4\pi$ and Amplitude: $|1| = 1$

Divide the interval $[0, 4\pi]$ into four equal parts to get x-values that will yield minimum and maximum points and x-intercepts. Then make a table. Repeat this cycle for the interval $[-4\pi, 0]$.

x	0	π	2π	3π	4π
$\frac{1}{2}x$	0	$\frac{\pi}{2}$	π	$\frac{3\pi}{2}$	2π
$\sin \frac{1}{2}x$	0	1	0	−1	0

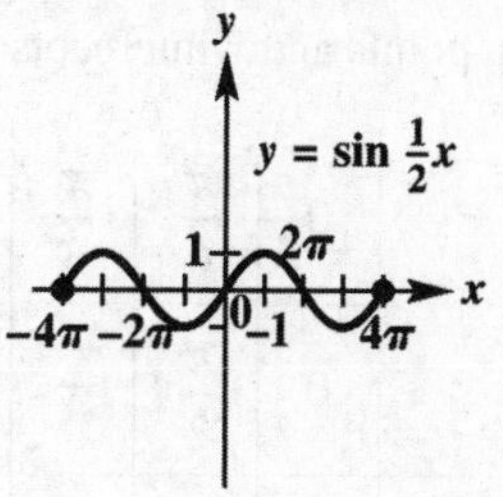

15. $y = \cos 2x$

Period: $\frac{2\pi}{2} = \pi$ and Amplitude: $|1| = 1$

Divide the interval $[0, \pi]$ into four equal parts to get the x-values that will yield minimum and maximum points and x-intercepts. Then make a table. Repeat this cycle for the interval $[-\pi, 0]$.

x	0	$\frac{\pi}{4}$	$\frac{\pi}{2}$	$\frac{3\pi}{4}$	π
$2x$	0	$\frac{\pi}{2}$	π	$\frac{3\pi}{2}$	2π
$\cos 2x$	1	0	−1	0	1

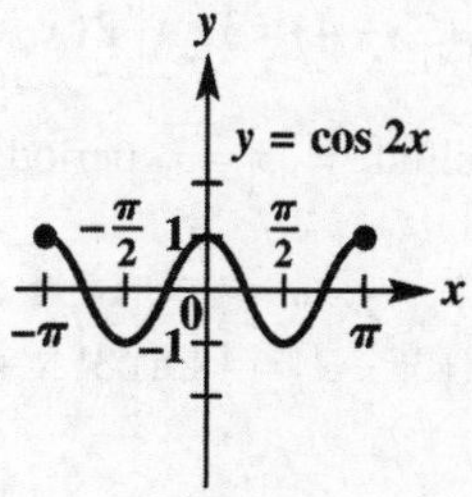

17. $y = 2\sin\frac{1}{4}x$

Period: $\frac{2\pi}{\frac{1}{4}} = 2\pi \cdot \frac{4}{1} = 8\pi$ and Amplitude: $|2| = 2$

Divide the interval $[0, 8\pi]$ into four equal parts to get the x-values that will yield minimum and maximum points and x-intercepts. Then make a table. Repeat this cycle for the interval $[-8\pi, 0]$.

x	0	2π	4π	6π	8π
$\frac{1}{4}x$	0	$\frac{\pi}{2}$	π	$\frac{3\pi}{2}$	2π
$\sin\frac{1}{4}x$	0	1	0	-1	0
$2\sin\frac{1}{4}x$	0	2	0	-2	0

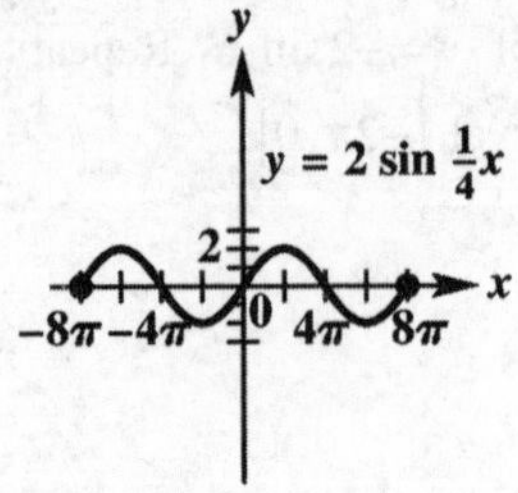

19. $y = -2\cos 3x$

Period: $\frac{2\pi}{3}$ and Amplitude: $|-2| = 2$

Divide the interval $\left[0, \frac{2\pi}{3}\right]$ into four equal parts to get the x-values that will yield minimum and maximum points and x-intercepts. Then make a table. Repeat this cycle for the interval $\left[-\frac{2\pi}{3}, 0\right]$.

x	0	$\frac{\pi}{6}$	$\frac{\pi}{3}$	$\frac{\pi}{2}$	$\frac{2\pi}{3}$
$3x$	0	$\frac{\pi}{2}$	π	$\frac{3\pi}{2}$	2π
$\cos 3x$	-1	0	1	0	-1
$-2\cos 3x$	-2	0	2	0	-2

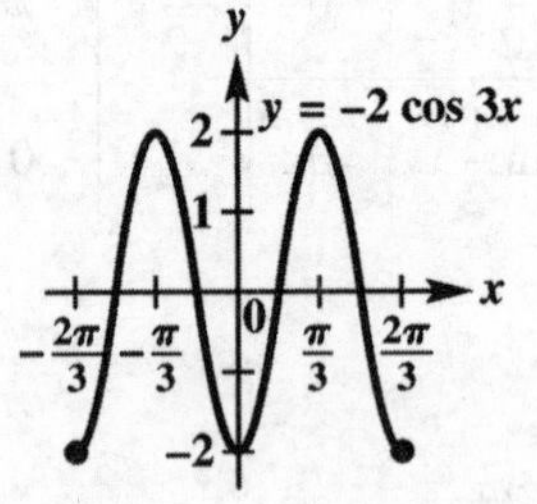

There are other correct answers in Exercise 21

21. $y = 4\sin\frac{1}{2}x$

23. $y = 3\sin(2x - 4) = 3\sin[2(x - 2)]$

The amplitude = $|3| = 3$, period = $\frac{2\pi}{2} = \pi$, and phase shift = 2. This matches choice B.

25. $y = 4\sin(3x - 2) = 4\sin\left[3\left(x - \frac{2}{3}\right)\right]$

The amplitude = $|4| = 4$, period = $\frac{2\pi}{3}$, and phase shift = $\frac{2}{3}$. This matches choice C.

27. $y = \sin\left(x - \frac{\pi}{4}\right)$ represents the graph of $y = \sin x$, shifted to the right $\frac{\pi}{4}$ unit. This matches choice D

29. $y = 1 + \sin x$ represents the graph of $y = \sin x$, shifted up 1 unit. This matches choice B

31. $y = 2\sin(x - \pi)$

amplitude: $|2| = 2$; period: $\frac{2\pi}{1} = 2\pi$; There is no vertical translation.

The phase shift is π units to the right.

33. $y = 4\cos\left(\frac{x}{2} + \frac{\pi}{2}\right) = 4\cos\frac{1}{2}\left[x - (-\pi)\right]$

amplitude: $|4| = 4$; period: $\frac{2\pi}{\frac{1}{2}} = 2\pi \cdot \frac{2}{1} = 4\pi$; There is no vertical translation.

The phase shift is π units to the left.

35. $y = 2 - \sin\left(3x - \frac{\pi}{5}\right) = -\sin 3\left(x - \frac{\pi}{15}\right) + 2$

amplitude: $|-1| = 1$; period: $\frac{2\pi}{3}$; The vertical translation is 2 units up.

The phase shift is $\frac{\pi}{15}$ unit to the right

37. $y = \sin\left(x - \frac{\pi}{4}\right)$

Step 1 Find the interval whose length is $\frac{2\pi}{b}$.

$$0 \le x - \frac{\pi}{4} \le 2\pi \Rightarrow 0 + \frac{\pi}{4} \le x \le 2\pi + \frac{\pi}{4} \Rightarrow \frac{\pi}{4} \le x \le \frac{9\pi}{4}$$

Step 2 Divide the period into four equal parts to get the following x-values.

$$\frac{\pi}{4}, \frac{3\pi}{4}, \frac{5\pi}{4}, \frac{7\pi}{4}, \frac{9\pi}{4}$$

Step 3 Evaluate the function for each of the five x-values

x	$\frac{\pi}{4}$	$\frac{3\pi}{4}$	$\frac{5\pi}{4}$	$\frac{7\pi}{4}$	$\frac{9\pi}{4}$
$x - \frac{\pi}{4}$	0	$\frac{\pi}{2}$	π	$\frac{3\pi}{2}$	2π
$\sin\left(x - \frac{\pi}{4}\right)$	0	1	0	−1	0

Steps 4 and 5 Plot the points found in the table and join them with a sinusoidal curve. By graphing an additional period to the right, we obtain the following graph.

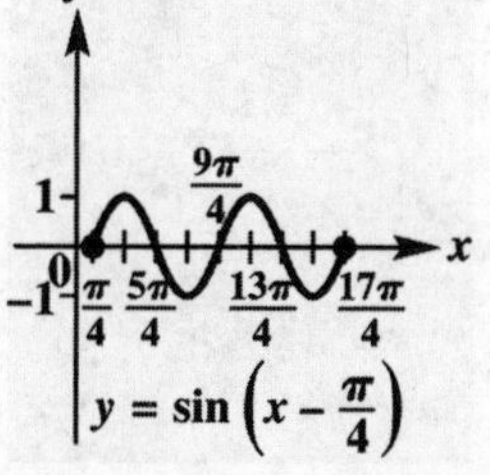

The amplitude is 1.

The period is 2π.

There is no vertical translation.

The phase shift is $\frac{\pi}{4}$ unit to the right.

39. $y = 2\cos\left(x - \frac{\pi}{3}\right)$

Step 1 Find the interval whose length is $\frac{2\pi}{b}$.

$$0 \le x - \frac{\pi}{3} \le 2\pi \Rightarrow 0 + \frac{\pi}{3} \le x \le 2\pi + \frac{\pi}{3} \Rightarrow \frac{\pi}{3} \le x \le \frac{7\pi}{3}$$

Step 2 Divide the period into four equal parts to get the following x-values.

$$\frac{\pi}{3}, \frac{5\pi}{6}, \frac{4\pi}{3}, \frac{11\pi}{6}, \frac{7\pi}{3}$$

Step 3 Evaluate the function for each of the five x-values.

x	$\frac{\pi}{3}$	$\frac{5\pi}{6}$	$\frac{4\pi}{3}$	$\frac{11\pi}{6}$	$\frac{7\pi}{3}$
$x - \frac{\pi}{3}$	0	$\frac{\pi}{2}$	π	$\frac{3\pi}{2}$	2π
$\cos\left(x - \frac{\pi}{3}\right)$	1	0	−1	0	1
$2\cos\left(x - \frac{\pi}{3}\right)$	2	0	−2	0	2

Steps 4 and 5 Plot the points found in the table and join them with a sinusoidal curve. By graphing an additional period to the right, we obtain the following graph.

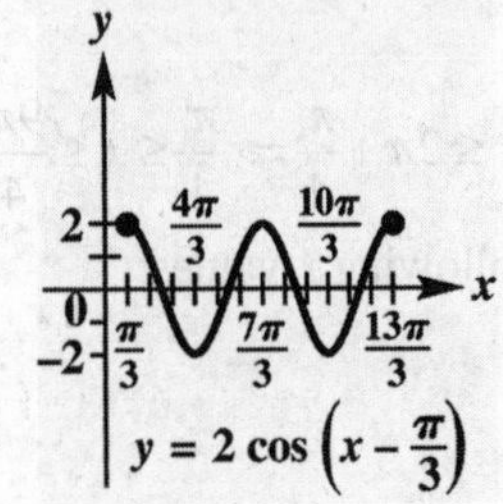

The amplitude is 2.

The period is 2π.

There is no vertical translation.

The phase shift is $\frac{\pi}{3}$ units to the right.

41. $y = -4\sin(2x - \pi) = -4\sin 2\left(x - \frac{\pi}{2}\right)$

Step 1 Find the interval whose length is $\frac{2\pi}{b}$.

$$0 \le 2\left(x - \frac{\pi}{2}\right) \le 2\pi \Rightarrow 0 \le x - \frac{\pi}{2} \le \frac{2\pi}{2} \Rightarrow 0 \le x - \frac{\pi}{2} \le \pi \Rightarrow \frac{\pi}{2} \le x \le \frac{3\pi}{2}$$

Step 2 Divide the period into four equal parts to get the following x-values.

$$\frac{\pi}{2}, \frac{3\pi}{4}, \pi, \frac{5\pi}{4}, \frac{3\pi}{2}$$

Continued on next page

41. (continued)

Step 3 Evaluate the function for each of the five *x*-values

x	$\frac{\pi}{2}$	$\frac{3\pi}{4}$	π	$\frac{5\pi}{4}$	$\frac{3\pi}{2}$
$2\left(x-\frac{\pi}{2}\right)$	0	$\frac{\pi}{2}$	π	$\frac{3\pi}{2}$	2π
$\sin 2\left(x-\frac{\pi}{2}\right)$	0	1	0	−1	0
$-4\sin 2\left(x-\frac{\pi}{2}\right)$	0	−4	0	4	0

Steps 4 and 5 Plot the points found in the table and join them with a sinusoidal curve.

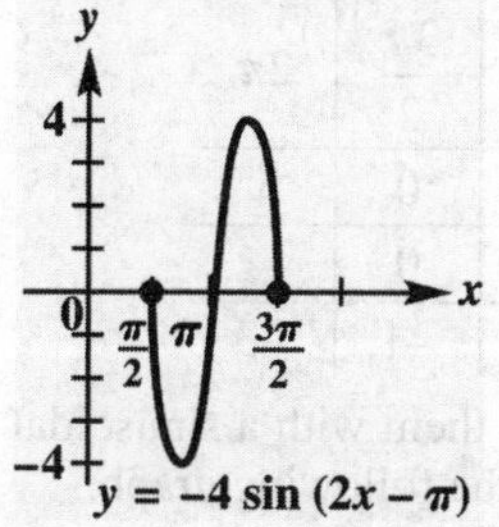

The amplitude is $|-4|$, which is 4.

The period is $\frac{2\pi}{2}$, which is π.

There is no vertical translation.

The phase shift is $\frac{\pi}{2}$ units to the right

43. $y=\frac{1}{2}\cos\left(\frac{1}{2}x-\frac{\pi}{4}\right)=\frac{1}{2}\cos\frac{1}{2}\left(x-\frac{\pi}{2}\right)$

Step 1 Find the interval whose length is $\frac{2\pi}{b}$.

$$0\le\frac{1}{2}\left(x-\frac{\pi}{2}\right)\le 2\pi \Rightarrow 0\le x-\frac{\pi}{2}\le 4\pi \Rightarrow \frac{\pi}{2}\le x\le\frac{8\pi}{2}+\frac{\pi}{2}\Rightarrow\frac{\pi}{2}\le x\le\frac{9\pi}{2}$$

Step 2 Divide the period into four equal parts to get the following *x*-values.

$$\frac{\pi}{2}, \frac{11\pi}{4}, 5\pi, \frac{19\pi}{4}, \frac{9\pi}{2}$$

Step 3 Evaluate the function for each of the five *x*-values.

x	$\frac{\pi}{2}$	$\frac{11\pi}{4}$	5π	$\frac{19\pi}{4}$	$\frac{9\pi}{2}$
$\frac{1}{2}\left(x-\frac{\pi}{2}\right)$	0	$\frac{\pi}{2}$	π	$\frac{3\pi}{2}$	2π
$\cos\frac{1}{2}\left(x-\frac{\pi}{2}\right)$	1	0	−1	0	1
$\frac{1}{2}\cos\frac{1}{2}\left(x-\frac{\pi}{2}\right)$	$\frac{1}{2}$	0	$-\frac{1}{2}$	0	$\frac{1}{2}$

Steps 4 and 5 Plot the points found in the table and join them with a sinusoidal curve.

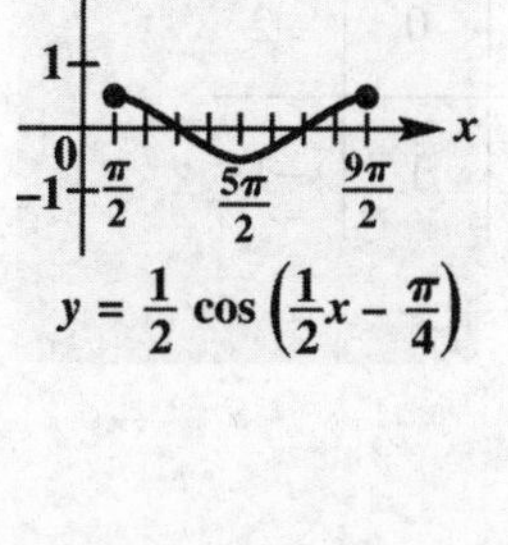

The amplitude is $\frac{1}{2}$.

The period is $\frac{2\pi}{\frac{1}{2}}$, which is 4π.

This is no vertical translation.

The phase shift is $\frac{\pi}{2}$ units to the right.

45. $y = -1 - 2\cos 5x$

Step 1 Find the interval whose length is $\frac{2\pi}{b}$.

$$0 \le 5x \le 2\pi \Rightarrow 0 \le x \le \frac{2\pi}{5}$$

Step 2 Divide the period into four equal parts to get the following x-values.

$$0, \frac{\pi}{10}, \frac{\pi}{5}, \frac{3\pi}{10}, \frac{2\pi}{5}$$

Step 3 Evaluate the function for each of the five x-values.

x	0	$\frac{\pi}{10}$	$\frac{\pi}{5}$	$\frac{3\pi}{10}$	$\frac{2\pi}{5}$
$5x$	0	$\frac{\pi}{2}$	π	$\frac{3\pi}{2}$	2π
$\cos 5x$	1	0	-1	0	1
$-2\cos 5x$	-2	0	2	0	-2
$-1-2\cos 5x$	-3	-1	1	-1	-3

Steps 4 and 5 Plot the points found in the table and join them with a sinusoidal curve. By graphing an additional period to the left, we obtain the following graph.

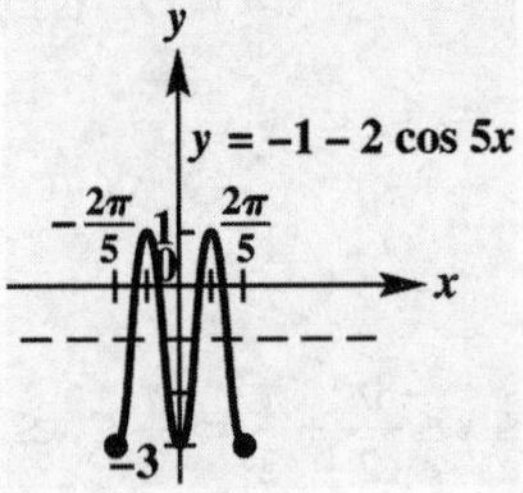

The period is $\frac{2\pi}{5}$.

The amplitude is $|-2|$, which is 2.

The vertical translation is 1 unit down.

There is no phase shift.

47. $y = 1 - 2\cos\frac{1}{2}x$

Step 1 Find the interval whose length is $\frac{2\pi}{b}$.

$$0 \le \frac{1}{2}x \le 2\pi \Rightarrow 0 \le x \le 4\pi$$

Step 2 Divide the period into four equal parts to get the following x-values.

$$0, \pi, 2\pi, 3\pi, 4\pi$$

Step 3 Evaluate the function for each of the five x-values.

x	0	π	2π	3π	4π
$\frac{1}{2}x$	0	$\frac{\pi}{2}$	π	$\frac{3\pi}{2}$	2π
$\cos\frac{1}{2}x$	1	0	-1	0	1
$-2\cos\frac{1}{2}x$	-2	0	2	0	-2
$1-2\cos\frac{1}{2}x$	-1	1	3	1	-1

Continued on next page

47. (continued)

Steps 4 and 5 Plot the points found in the table and join them with a sinusoidal curve. By graphing an additional period to the left, we obtain the following graph.

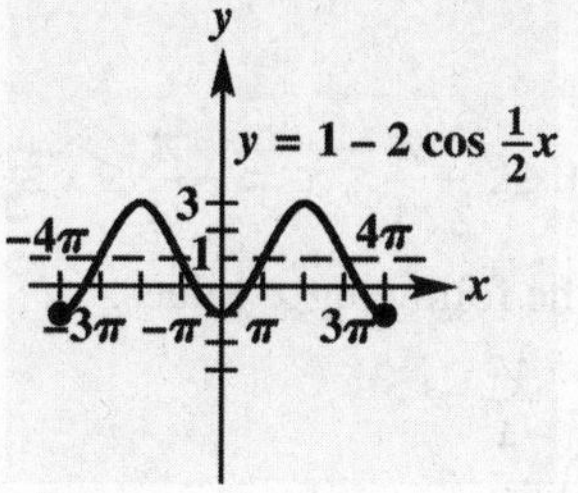

The amplitude is $|-2|$, which is 2.

The period is $\frac{2\pi}{\frac{1}{2}}$, which is 4π.

The vertical translation is 1 unit up.

There is no phase shift.

49. $y=-3+2\sin\left(x+\frac{\pi}{2}\right)$

Step 1 Find the interval whose length is $\frac{2\pi}{b}$.

$$0\le x+\frac{\pi}{2}\le 2\pi \Rightarrow\Rightarrow 0-\frac{\pi}{2}\le x\le 2\pi-\frac{\pi}{2}\Rightarrow -\frac{\pi}{2}\le x\le \frac{3\pi}{2}$$

Step 2 Divide the period into four equal parts to get the following x-values.

$$-\frac{\pi}{2},\ 0,\ \frac{\pi}{2},\ \pi,\ \frac{3\pi}{2}$$

Step 3 Evaluate the function for each of the five x-values

x	$-\frac{\pi}{2}$	0	$\frac{\pi}{2}$	π	$\frac{3\pi}{2}$
$x+\frac{\pi}{2}$	0	$\frac{\pi}{2}$	π	$\frac{3\pi}{2}$	2π
$\sin\left(x+\frac{\pi}{2}\right)$	0	1	0	−1	0
$2\sin\left(x+\frac{\pi}{2}\right)$	0	2	0	−2	0
$-3+2\sin\left(x+\frac{\pi}{2}\right)$	−3	−1	−3	−5	−3

Steps 4 and 5 Plot the points found in the table and join them with a sinusoidal curve.

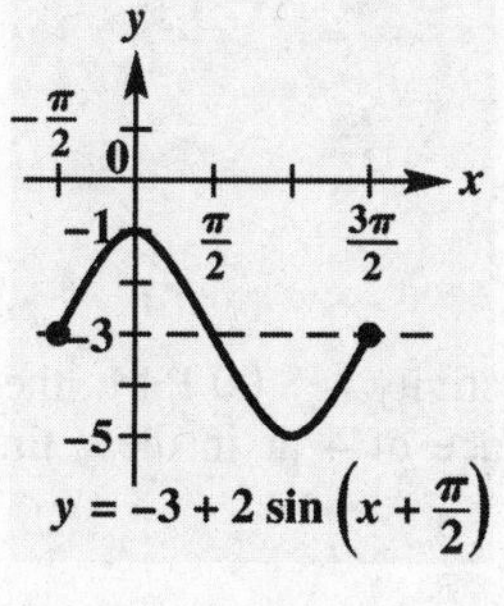

The amplitude is $|2|$, which is 2.

The period is 2π.

The vertical translation is 3 units down.

The phase shift is $\frac{\pi}{2}$ units to the left.

51. $y=\frac{1}{2}+\sin 2\left(x+\frac{\pi}{4}\right)$

Step 1 Find the interval whose length is $\frac{2\pi}{b}$.

$$0\le 2\left(x+\frac{\pi}{4}\right)\le 2\pi \Rightarrow 0\le x+\frac{\pi}{4}\le\frac{2\pi}{2}\Rightarrow 0\le x+\frac{\pi}{4}\le\pi\Rightarrow -\frac{\pi}{4}\le x\le\frac{3\pi}{4}$$

Step 2 Divide the period into four equal parts to get the following *x*-values.

$$-\frac{\pi}{4},\ 0,\ \frac{\pi}{4},\ \frac{\pi}{2},\ \frac{3\pi}{4}$$

Step 3 Evaluate the function for each of the five *x*-values.

x	$-\frac{\pi}{4}$	0	$\frac{\pi}{4}$	$\frac{\pi}{2}$	$\frac{3\pi}{4}$
$2\left(x+\frac{\pi}{4}\right)$	0	$\frac{\pi}{2}$	π	$\frac{3\pi}{2}$	2π
$\sin 2\left(x+\frac{\pi}{4}\right)$	0	1	0	-1	0
$\frac{1}{2}+\sin 2\left(x+\frac{\pi}{4}\right)$	$\frac{1}{2}$	$\frac{3}{2}$	$\frac{1}{2}$	$\frac{1}{2}$	$\frac{1}{2}$

Steps 4 and 5 Plot the points found in the table and join them with a sinusoidal curve.

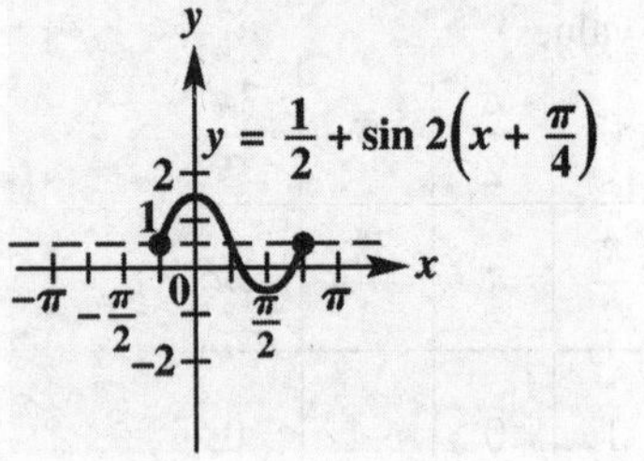

The amplitude is $|1|$, which is 1.

The period is $\frac{2\pi}{2}$, which is π.

The vertical translation is $\frac{1}{2}$ unit up.

The phase shift is $\frac{\pi}{4}$ units to the left.

There are other correct answers in Exercise 53.

53. $y=3\sin 2\left(x-\frac{\pi}{4}\right)$

55. **(a)** The highest temperature is 80°; the lowest is 50°.

(b) The amplitude is $\frac{1}{2}(80°-50°)=\frac{1}{2}(30°)=15°$.

(c) The period is about 35,000 yr.

(d) The trend of the temperature now is downward.

57. **(a)** The latest time that the animals begin their evening activity is 8:00 P.M., the earliest time is 4:00 P.M. So, $4{:}00 \le y \le 8{:}00$. Since there is a difference of 4 hr in these times, the amplitude is $\frac{1}{2}(4)=2$ hr.

(b) The length of this period is 1 yr.

59. The graph repeats each day, so the period is 24 hours.

61. Approximately 6 P.M., approximately 0.2 feet.

63. Approximately 2 A.M.; approximately 2.6 feet.

65. $-1 \le y \le 1$
Amplitude: 1

Period: 8 squares $= 8(30°) = 240°$ or $\frac{4\pi}{3}$

67. $E = 5 \cos 120\pi r$

(a) Amplitude: $|5| = 5$ and Period: $\frac{2\pi}{120\pi} = \frac{1}{60}$ sec

(b) Since the period is $\frac{1}{60}$, one cycle is completed in $\frac{1}{60}$ sec. Therefore, in 1 sec, 60 cycles are completed.

(c) $t = 0,\ E = 5\cos 120\pi(0) = 5\cos 0 = 5(1) = 5$

$t = .03,\ E = 5\cos 120\pi(.03) = 5\cos 3.6\pi \approx 1.545$

$t = .06,\ E = 5\cos 120\pi(.06) = 5\cos 7.2\pi \approx -4.045$

$t = .09,\ E = 5\cos 120\pi(.09) = 5\cos 10.8\pi 0 \approx -4.045$

$t = .12,\ E = 5\cos 120\pi(.12) = 5\cos 14.4\pi \approx 1.545$

(d)

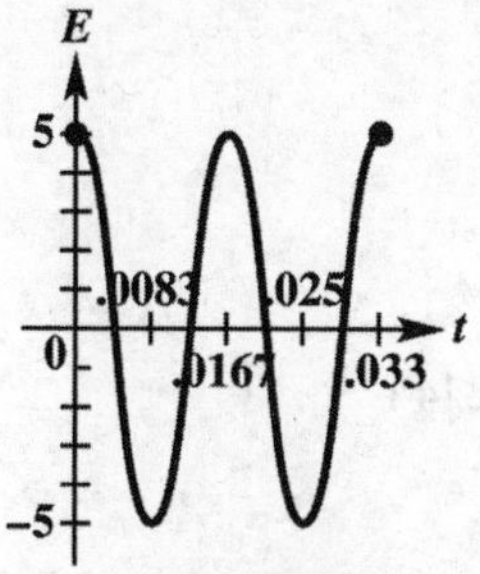

$E = 5 \cos 120\pi t$

69. (a) The graph has a general upward trend along with small annual oscillations.

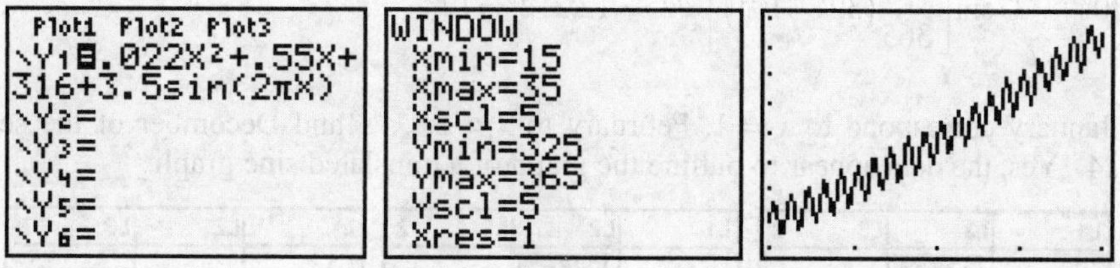

(b) The seasonal variations are caused by the term $3.5\sin 2\pi x$. The maximums will occur when $2\pi x = \frac{\pi}{2} + 2n\pi$, where n is an integer. Since x cannot be negative, n cannot be negative. This is equivalent to the following.

$$2\pi x = \frac{\pi}{2} + 2n\pi,\ n = 0, 1, 2, \ldots \Rightarrow 2x = \frac{1}{2} + 2n,\ n = 0, 1, 2, \ldots \Rightarrow x = \frac{1}{4} + n,\ n = 0, 1, 2, \ldots$$

$$x = \frac{4n+1}{4},\ n = 0, 1, 2, \ldots \Rightarrow x = \frac{1}{4}, \frac{5}{4}, \frac{9}{4}, \ldots$$

Since x is in years, $x = \frac{1}{4}$ corresponds to April when the seasonal carbon dioxide levels are maximum.

Continued on next page

69. (b) (continued)

The minimums will occur when $2\pi x = \frac{3\pi}{2} + 2n\pi$, where n is an integer. Since x cannot be negative, n cannot be negative. This is equivalent to the following.

$$2\pi x = \frac{3\pi}{2} + 2n\pi,\ n = 0, 1, 2, \ldots \Rightarrow 2x = \frac{3}{2} + 2n,\ n = 0, 1, 2, \ldots \Rightarrow x = \frac{3}{4} + n,\ n = 0, 1, 2, \ldots$$

$$x = \frac{4n+3}{4},\ n = 0, 1, 2, \ldots \Rightarrow x = \frac{3}{4}, \frac{7}{4}, \frac{11}{4}, \ldots$$

This is $\frac{1}{2}$ yr later, which corresponds to October.

71. $T(x) = 37\sin\left[\frac{2\pi}{365}(x-101)\right] + 25$

(a) March 1 (day 60): $T(60) = 37\sin\left[\frac{2\pi}{365}(60-101)\right] + 25 \approx 1.001° \approx 1°$

(b) April 1 (day 91): $T(91) = 37\sin\left[\frac{2\pi}{365}(91-101)\right] + 25 \approx 18.662° \approx 19°$

(c) Day 150: $T(150) = 37\sin\left[\frac{2\pi}{365}(150-101)\right] + 25 \approx 52.638° \approx 53°$

(d) June 15 is day 166. $(31+28+31+30+31+15=166)$

$$T(166) = 37\sin\left[\frac{2\pi}{365}(166-101)\right] + 25 \approx 58.286° \approx 58°$$

(e) September 1 is day 244. $(31+28+31+30+31+30+31+31+1=244)$

$$T(244) = 37\sin\left[\frac{2\pi}{365}(244-101)\right] + 25 \approx 48.264° \approx 48°$$

(f) October 31 is day 304. $(31+28+31+30+31+30+31+31+30+31=304)$

$$T(304) = 37\sin\left[\frac{2\pi}{365}(304-101)\right] + 25 \approx 12.212° \approx 12°$$

73. (a) Let January correspond to x = 1, February to x = 2, … , and December of the second year to $x = 24$. Yes, the data appear to outline the graph of a translated sine graph.

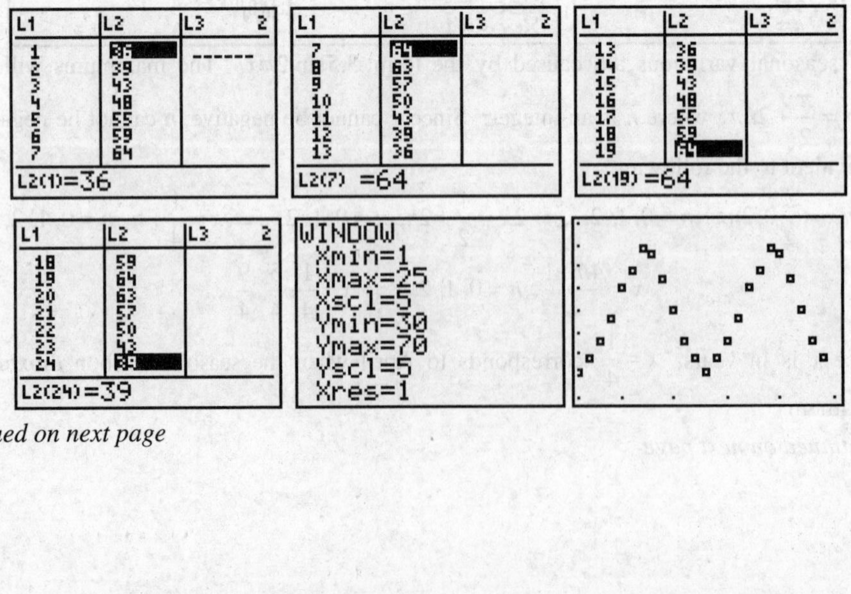

Continued on next page

73. (continued)

(b) The sine graph is vertically centered around the line $y = 50$. This line represents the average yearly temperature in Vancouver of 50°F. (This is also the actual average yearly temperature.)

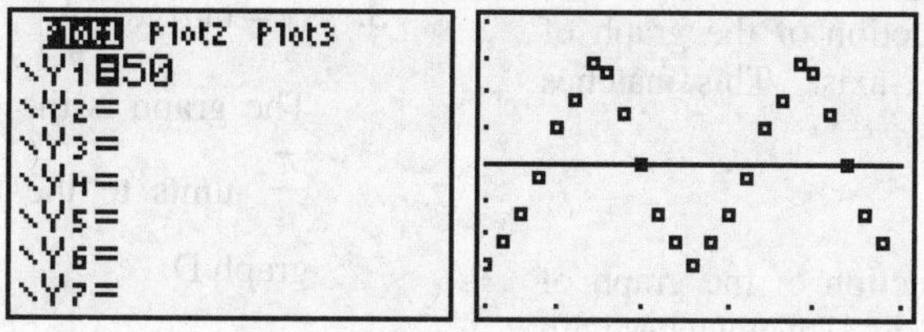

(c) The amplitude of the sine graph is approximately 14 since the average monthly high is 64, the average monthly low is 36, and $\frac{1}{2}(64-36)=\frac{1}{2}(28)=14$. The period is 12 since the temperature cycles every twelve months. Let $b=\frac{2\pi}{12}=\frac{\pi}{6}$. One way to determine the phase shift is to use the following technique. The minimum temperature occurs in January. Thus, when $x = 1$, $b(x - d)$ must equal $\left(-\frac{\pi}{2}\right)+2\pi n$, where n is an integer, since the sine function is minimum at these values. Solving for d, we have the following.

$$\frac{\pi}{6}(1-d)=-\frac{\pi}{2}\Rightarrow 1-d=\frac{6}{\pi}\left(-\frac{\pi}{2}\right)\Rightarrow 1-d=-3\Rightarrow -d=-4\Rightarrow d=4$$

This can be used as a first approximation.

(d) Let $f(x) = a \sin b(x - d) + c$. Since the amplitude is 14, let $a = 14$. The period is equal to 1 yr or 12 mo, so $b=\frac{\pi}{6}$. The average of the maximum and minimum temperatures is as follows.

$$\frac{1}{2}(64+36)=\frac{1}{2}(100)=50$$

Let the vertical translation be $c = 50$.
Since the phase shift is approximately 4, it can be adjusted slightly to give a better visual fit. Try 4.2. Since the phase shift is 4.2, let $d = 4.2$. Thus, $f(x)=14\sin\left[\frac{\pi}{6}(x-4.2)\right]+50$.

(e) Plotting the data with $f(x)=14\sin\left[\frac{\pi}{6}(x-4.2)\right]+50$ on the same coordinate axes gives a good fit.

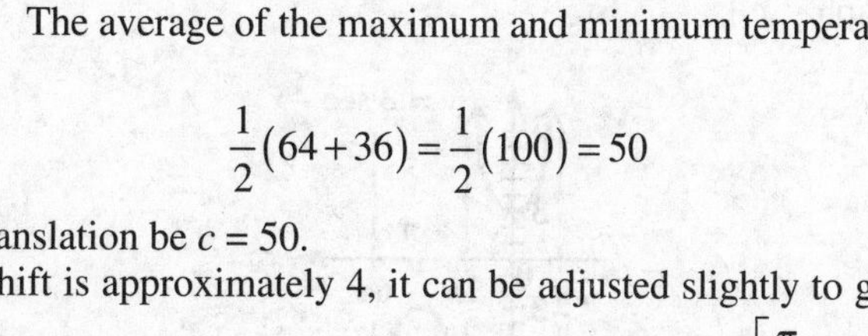

(f)

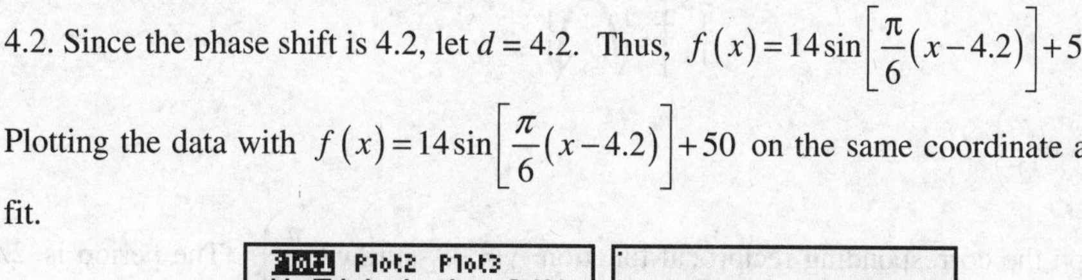

From the sine regression we get the following.

$$y=13.21\sin(.52x-2.18)+49.68=13.21\sin\left[.52(x-4.19)\right]+49.68$$

Section 6.4: Graphs of the Other Circular Functions

1. $y = -\csc x$
The graph is the reflection of the graph of $y = \csc x$ about the x-axis. This matches with graph B.

3. $y = -\tan x$
The graph is the reflection of the graph of $y = \tan x$ about the x-axis. This matches with graph E.

5. $y = \tan\left(x - \dfrac{\pi}{4}\right)$
The graph is the graph of $y = \tan x$ shifted $\dfrac{\pi}{4}$ units to the right. This matches with graph D.

7. $y = 3\sec\dfrac{1}{4}x$

Step 1 Graph the corresponding reciprocal function $y = 3\cos\dfrac{1}{4}x$. The period is $\dfrac{2\pi}{\frac{1}{4}} = 2\pi \cdot \dfrac{4}{1} = 8\pi$ and its amplitude is $|3| = 3$. One period is in the interval $0 \le x \le 8\pi$. Dividing the interval into four equal parts gives us the following key points.

$$(0,1),\ (2\pi,0),\ (4\pi,-1),\ (6\pi,0),\ (8\pi,1)$$

Step 2 The vertical asymptotes of $y = \sec\dfrac{1}{4}x$ are at the x-intercepts of $y = \cos\dfrac{1}{4}x$, which are $x = 2\pi$ and $x = 6\pi$. Continuing this pattern to the left, we also have a vertical asymptote of $x = -2\pi$.

Step 3 Sketch the graph.

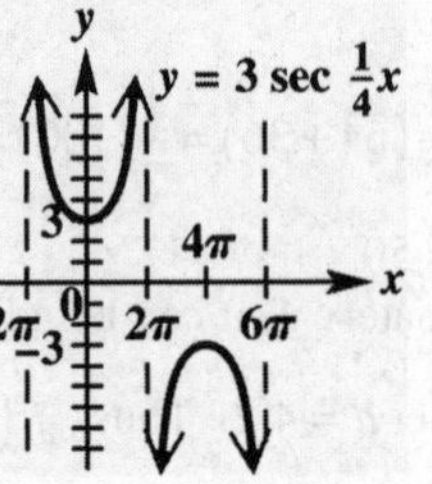

9. $y = -\dfrac{1}{2}\csc\left(x + \dfrac{\pi}{2}\right)$

Step 1 Graph the corresponding reciprocal function $y = -\dfrac{1}{2}\sin\left(x + \dfrac{\pi}{2}\right)$. The period is 2π and its amplitude is $\left|-\dfrac{1}{2}\right| = \dfrac{1}{2}$. One period is in the interval $-\dfrac{\pi}{2} \le x \le \dfrac{3\pi}{2}$. Dividing the interval into four equal parts gives us the following key points.

$$\left(-\frac{\pi}{2},0\right),\ \left(0,-\frac{1}{2}\right),\ \left(\frac{\pi}{2},0\right),\ \left(\pi,\frac{1}{2}\right),\ \left(\frac{3\pi}{2},0\right)$$

Step 2 The vertical asymptotes of $y = -\dfrac{1}{2}\csc\left(x + \dfrac{\pi}{2}\right)$ are at the x-intercepts of $y = -\dfrac{1}{2}\sin\left(x + \dfrac{\pi}{2}\right)$, which are $x = -\dfrac{\pi}{2}$, $x = \dfrac{\pi}{2}$, and $x = \dfrac{3\pi}{2}$.

Continued on next page

9. (continued)

Step 3 Sketch the graph.

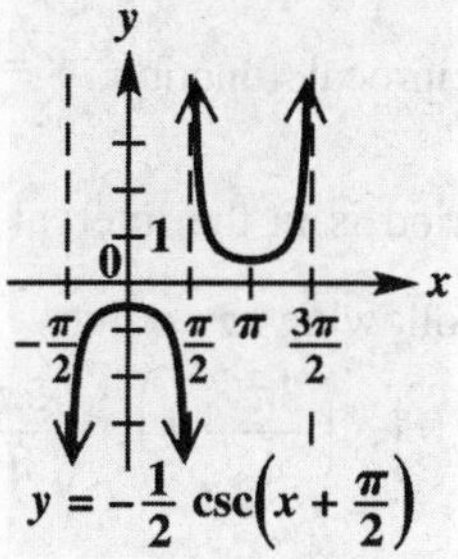

11. $y = \csc\left(x - \frac{\pi}{4}\right)$

Step 1 Graph the corresponding reciprocal function $y = \sin\left(x - \frac{\pi}{4}\right)$ The period is 2π and its amplitude is $|1| = 1$. One period is in the interval $\frac{\pi}{4} \le x \le \frac{9\pi}{4}$. Dividing the interval into four equal parts gives us the following key points.

$$\left(\frac{\pi}{4},0\right), \left(\frac{3\pi}{4},1\right), \left(\frac{5\pi}{4},0\right), \left(\frac{7\pi}{4},-1\right), \left(\frac{9\pi}{4},0\right)$$

Step 2 The vertical asymptotes of $y = \csc\left(x - \frac{\pi}{4}\right)$ are at the x-intercepts of $y = \sin\left(x - \frac{\pi}{4}\right)$, which are $x = \frac{\pi}{4}$, $x = \frac{5\pi}{4}$, and $x = \frac{9\pi}{4}$

Step 3 Sketch the graph.

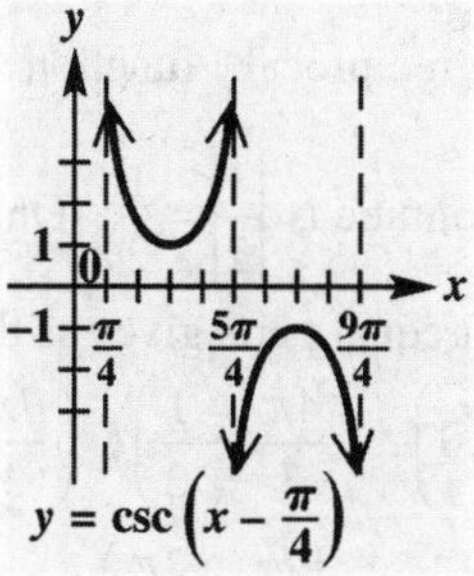

13. $y = \sec\left(x + \frac{\pi}{4}\right)$

Step 1 Graph the corresponding reciprocal function $y = \cos\left(x + \frac{\pi}{4}\right)$. The period is 2π and its amplitude is $|1| = 1$. One period is in the interval $-\frac{\pi}{4} \le x \le \frac{7\pi}{4}$. Dividing the interval into four equal parts gives us the following key points.

$$\left(-\frac{\pi}{4}, 1\right), \left(\frac{\pi}{4}, 0\right), \left(\frac{3\pi}{4}, -1\right), \left(\frac{5\pi}{4}, 0\right), \left(\frac{7\pi}{4}, 1\right)$$

Step 2 The vertical asymptotes of $y = \sec\left(x + \frac{\pi}{4}\right)$ are at the x-intercepts of $y = \cos\left(x + \frac{\pi}{4}\right)$, which are $x = \frac{\pi}{4}$ and $x = \frac{5\pi}{4}$. Continuing this pattern to the right, we also have a vertical asymptote of $x = \frac{9\pi}{4}$.

Step 3 Sketch the graph.

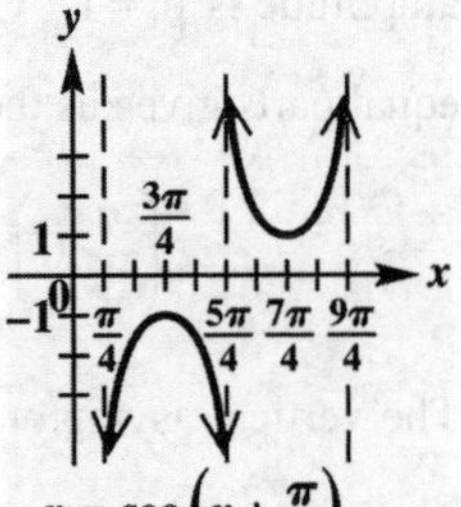

$y = \sec\left(x + \frac{\pi}{4}\right)$

15. $y = \sec\left(\frac{1}{2}x + \frac{\pi}{3}\right) = \sec\frac{1}{2}\left(x + \frac{2\pi}{3}\right)$

Step 1 Graph the corresponding reciprocal function $y = \cos\frac{1}{2}\left(x + \frac{2\pi}{3}\right)$. The period is $\frac{2\pi}{\frac{1}{2}} = 2\pi \cdot \frac{2}{1} = 4\pi$ and its amplitude is $\left|\frac{1}{2}\right| = \frac{1}{2}$. One period is in the interval $-\frac{2\pi}{3} \le x \le \frac{10\pi}{3}$. Dividing the interval into four equal parts gives us the following key points.

$$\left(-\frac{2\pi}{3}, \frac{1}{2}\right), \left(\frac{\pi}{3}, 0\right), \left(\frac{4\pi}{3}, -\frac{1}{2}\right), \left(\frac{7\pi}{3}, 0\right), \left(\frac{10\pi}{3}, \frac{1}{2}\right)$$

Step 2 The vertical asymptotes of $y = \sec\frac{1}{2}\left(x + \frac{2\pi}{3}\right)$ are at the x-intercepts of $y = \cos\frac{1}{2}\left(x + \frac{2\pi}{3}\right)$, which are $x = \frac{\pi}{3}$ and $x = \frac{7\pi}{3}$. Continuing this pattern to the right, we also have a vertical asymptote of $x = \frac{13\pi}{3}$.

Step 3 Sketch the graph.

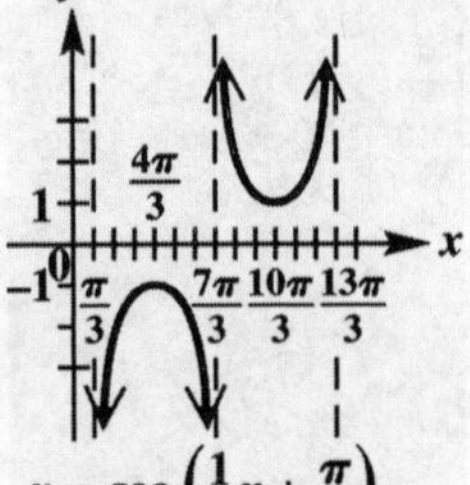

$y = \sec\left(\frac{1}{2}x + \frac{\pi}{3}\right)$

17. $y = 2 + 3\sec(2x - \pi) = 2 + 3\sec 2\left(x - \frac{\pi}{2}\right)$

Step 1 Graph the corresponding reciprocal function $y = 2 + 3\cos 2\left(x - \frac{\pi}{2}\right)$. The period is π and its amplitude is $|3| = 3$. One period is in the interval $\frac{\pi}{2} \le x \le \frac{3\pi}{2}$. Dividing the interval into four equal parts gives us the following key points.

$$\left(\frac{\pi}{2}, 5\right), \left(\frac{3\pi}{4}, 2\right), (\pi, -1), \left(\frac{5\pi}{4}, 2\right), \left(\frac{3\pi}{2}, 5\right)$$

Step 2 The vertical asymptotes of $y = 2 + 3\sec 2\left(x - \frac{\pi}{2}\right)$ are at the x-intercepts of $y = 3\cos 2\left(x - \frac{\pi}{2}\right)$, which are $x = \frac{3\pi}{4}$ and $x = \frac{5\pi}{4}$. Continuing this pattern to the left, we also have a vertical asymptote of $x = \frac{\pi}{4}$.

Step 3 Sketch the graph.

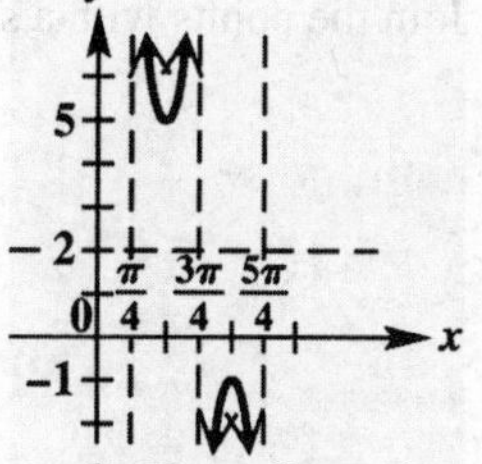

$y = 2 + 3\sec(2x - \pi)$

19. $y = 1 - \frac{1}{2}\csc\left(x - \frac{3\pi}{4}\right)$

Step 1 Graph the corresponding reciprocal function $y = 1 - \frac{1}{2}\sin\left(x - \frac{3\pi}{4}\right)$. The period is 2π and its amplitude is $\frac{1}{2}$. One period is in the interval $\frac{3\pi}{4} \le x \le \frac{11\pi}{4}$. Dividing the interval into four equal parts gives us the following key points.

$$\left(\frac{3\pi}{4}, 1\right), \left(\frac{5\pi}{4}, \frac{1}{2}\right), \left(\frac{7\pi}{4}, 1\right), \left(\frac{9\pi}{4}, \frac{3}{2}\right), \left(\frac{11\pi}{4}, 1\right)$$

Step 2 The vertical asymptotes of $y = 1 - \frac{1}{2}\csc\left(x - \frac{3\pi}{4}\right)$ are at the x-intercepts of $y = -\frac{1}{2}\sin\left(x - \frac{3\pi}{4}\right)$, which are $x = \frac{3\pi}{4}$, $x = \frac{7\pi}{4}$, and $x = \frac{11\pi}{4}$.

Step 3 Sketch the graph.

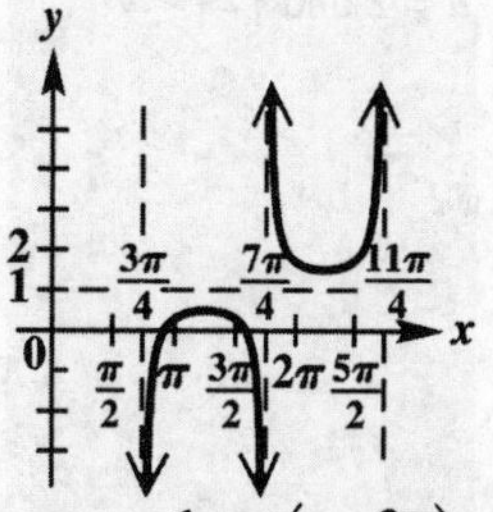

$y = 1 - \frac{1}{2}\csc\left(x - \frac{3\pi}{4}\right)$

21. $y = \tan 4x$

Step 1 Find the period and locate the vertical asymptotes. The period of tangent is $\frac{\pi}{b}$, so the period for this function is $\frac{\pi}{4}$. Tangent has asymptotes of the form $bx = -\frac{\pi}{2}$ and $bx = \frac{\pi}{2}$. Therefore, the asymptotes for $y = \tan 4x$ are as follows.

$$4x = -\frac{\pi}{2} \Rightarrow x = -\frac{\pi}{8} \text{ and } 4x = \frac{\pi}{2} \Rightarrow x = \frac{\pi}{8}.$$

Step 2 Sketch the two vertical asymptotes found in Step 1.

Step 3 Divide the interval into four equal parts.

$$-\frac{\pi}{8}, -\frac{\pi}{16}, 0, \frac{\pi}{16}, \frac{\pi}{8}$$

Step 4 Finding the first-quarter point, midpoint, and third-quarter point, we have the following.

$$\left(-\frac{\pi}{16}, -1\right), (0,0), \left(\frac{\pi}{16}, 1\right)$$

Step 5 Join the points with a smooth curve.

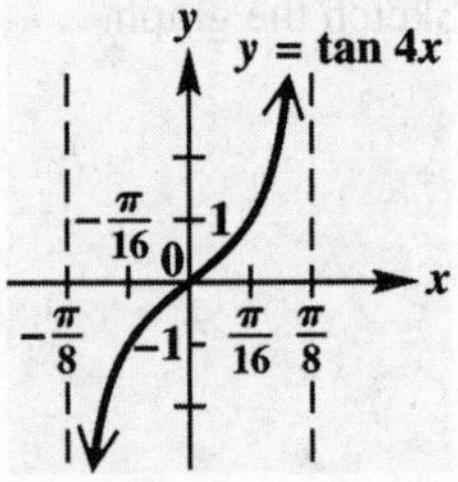

23. $y = 2\tan x$

Step 1 Find the period and locate the vertical asymptotes. The period of tangent is $\frac{\pi}{b}$, so the period for this function is π. Tangent has asymptotes of the form $bx = -\frac{\pi}{2}$ and $bx = \frac{\pi}{2}$. Therefore, the asymptotes for $y = 2\tan x$ are $x = -\frac{\pi}{2}$ and $x = \frac{\pi}{2}$.

Step 2 Sketch the two vertical asymptotes found in Step 1.

Step 3 Divide the interval into four equal parts.

$$-\frac{\pi}{2}, -\frac{\pi}{4}, 0, \frac{\pi}{4}, \frac{\pi}{2}$$

Step 4 Finding the first-quarter point, midpoint, and third-quarter point, we have the following.

$$\left(-\frac{\pi}{4}, -2\right), (0,0), \left(\frac{\pi}{4}, 2\right)$$

Step 5 Join the points with a smooth curve. The graph is "stretched" because $a = 2$ and $|2| > 1$.

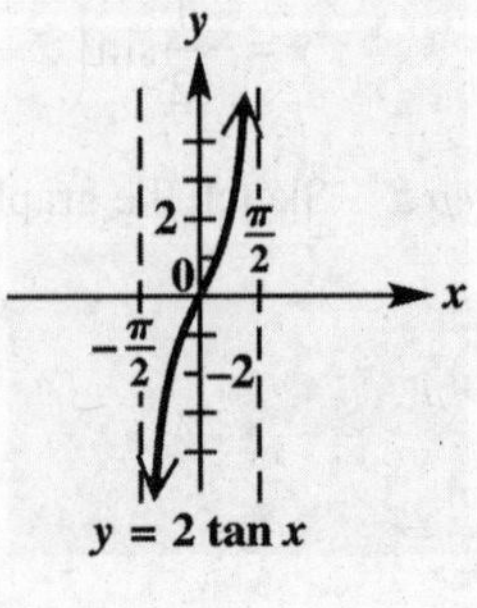

25. $y = 2\tan\frac{1}{4}x$

Step 1 Find the period and locate the vertical asymptotes. The period of tangent is $\frac{\pi}{b}$, so the period for this function is 4π. Tangent has asymptotes of the form $bx = -\frac{\pi}{2}$ and $bx = \frac{\pi}{2}$.

Therefore, the asymptotes for $y = 2\tan\frac{1}{4}x$ are as follows.

$$\frac{1}{4}x = -\frac{\pi}{2} \Rightarrow x = -2\pi \text{ and } \frac{1}{4}x = \frac{\pi}{2} \Rightarrow x = 2\pi$$

Step 2 Sketch the two vertical asymptotes found in Step 1.

Step 3 Divide the interval into four equal parts.

$$-2\pi, -\pi, 0, \pi, 2\pi$$

Step 4 Finding the first-quarter point, midpoint, and third-quarter point, we have the following.

$$(-\pi,-2),\ (0,0),\ (\pi,2)$$

Step 5 Join the points with a smooth curve.

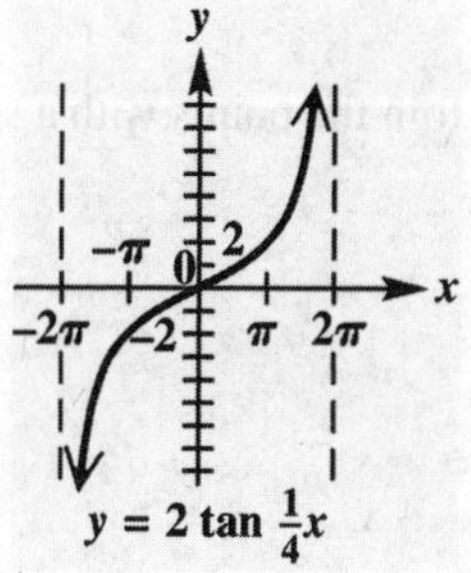

27. $y = \cot 3x$

Step 1 Find the period and locate the vertical asymptotes. The period of cotangent is $\frac{\pi}{b}$, so the period for this function is $\frac{\pi}{3}$. Cotangent has asymptotes of the form $bx = 0$ and $bx = \pi$.

The asymptotes for $y = \cot 3x$ are as follows.

$$3x = 0 \Rightarrow x = 0 \text{ and } 3x = \pi \Rightarrow x = \frac{\pi}{3}$$

Step 2 Sketch the two vertical asymptotes found in Step 1.

Step 3 Divide the interval into four equal parts.

$$0, \frac{\pi}{12}, \frac{\pi}{6}, \frac{\pi}{4}, \frac{\pi}{3}$$

Step 4 Finding the first-quarter point, midpoint, and third-quarter point, we have the following.

$$\left(\frac{\pi}{12},1\right), \left(\frac{\pi}{6},0\right), \left(\frac{\pi}{4},-1\right)$$

Step 5 Join the points with a smooth curve.

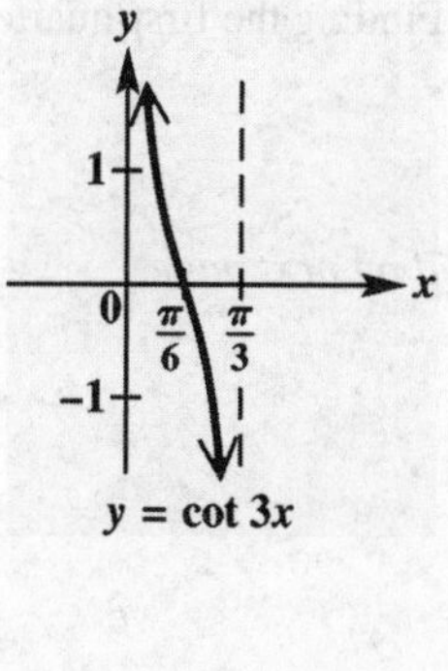

29. $y = -2\tan\frac{1}{4}x$

Step 1 Find the period and locate the vertical asymptotes. The period of tangent is $\frac{\pi}{b}$, so the period for this function is 4π. Tangent has asymptotes of the form $bx = -\frac{\pi}{2}$ and $bx = \frac{\pi}{2}$.

Therefore, the asymptotes for $y = -2\tan\frac{1}{4}x$ are as follows.

$$\frac{1}{4}x = -\frac{\pi}{2} \Rightarrow x = -2\pi \text{ and } \frac{1}{4}x = \frac{\pi}{2} \Rightarrow x = 2\pi.$$

Step 2 Sketch the two vertical asymptotes found in Step 1.

Step 3 Divide the interval into four equal parts.

$$-2\pi, -\pi, 0, \pi, 2\pi$$

Step 4 Finding the first-quarter point, midpoint, and third-quarter point, we have the following.

$$(-\pi, 2),\ (0,0),\ (\pi, -2)$$

Step 5 Join the points with a smooth curve.

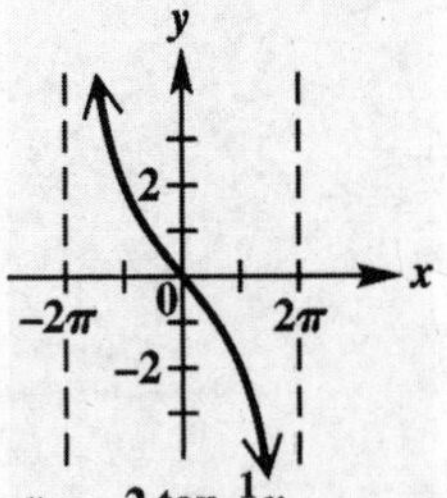

31. $y = \frac{1}{2}\cot 4x$

Step 1 Find the period and locate the vertical asymptotes. The period of cotangent is $\frac{\pi}{b}$, so the period for this function is $\frac{\pi}{4}$. Cotangent has asymptotes of the form $bx = 0$ and $bx = \pi$.

The asymptotes for $y = \frac{1}{2}\cot 4x$ are as follows.

$$4x = 0 \Rightarrow x = 0 \text{ and } 4x = \pi \Rightarrow x = \frac{\pi}{4}$$

Step 2 Sketch the two vertical asymptotes found in Step 1.

Step 3 Divide the interval into four equal parts.

$$0, \frac{\pi}{16}, \frac{\pi}{8}, \frac{3\pi}{16}, \frac{\pi}{4}$$

Step 4 Finding the first-quarter point, midpoint, and third-quarter point, we have the following.

$$\left(\frac{\pi}{16}, \frac{1}{2}\right), \left(\frac{\pi}{8}, 0\right), \left(\frac{3\pi}{16}, -\frac{1}{2}\right)$$

Continued on next page

31. (continued)

Step 5 Join the points with a smooth curve.

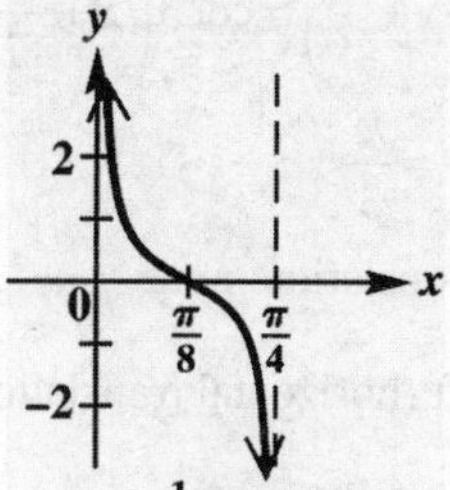

$y = \frac{1}{2}\cot 4x$

33. $y = \tan(2x - \pi) = \tan 2\left(x - \frac{\pi}{2}\right)$

Period: $\frac{\pi}{b} = \frac{\pi}{2}$

Vertical translation: none

Phase shift (horizontal translation): $\frac{\pi}{2}$ units to the right

Because the function is to be graphed over a two-period interval, locate three adjacent vertical asymptotes. Because asymptotes of the graph $y = \tan x$ occur at $-\frac{\pi}{2}$, $\frac{\pi}{2}$, and $\frac{3\pi}{2}$, the following equations can be solved to locate asymptotes.

$$2\left(x - \frac{\pi}{2}\right) = -\frac{\pi}{2},\ 2\left(x - \frac{\pi}{2}\right) = \frac{\pi}{2}, \text{ and } 2\left(x - \frac{\pi}{2}\right) = \frac{3\pi}{2}$$

Solve each of these equations.

$$2\left(x - \frac{\pi}{2}\right) = -\frac{\pi}{2} \Rightarrow x - \frac{\pi}{2} = -\frac{\pi}{4} \Rightarrow x = \frac{\pi}{4}$$

$$2\left(x - \frac{\pi}{2}\right) = \frac{\pi}{2} \Rightarrow x - \frac{\pi}{2} = \frac{\pi}{4} \Rightarrow x = \frac{3\pi}{4}$$

$$2\left(x - \frac{\pi}{2}\right) = \frac{3\pi}{2} \Rightarrow x - \frac{\pi}{2} = \frac{3\pi}{4} \Rightarrow x = \frac{5\pi}{4}$$

Divide the interval $\left(\frac{\pi}{4}, \frac{3\pi}{4}\right)$ into four equal parts to obtain the following key x-values.

first-quarter value: $\frac{3\pi}{8}$ middle value: $\frac{\pi}{2}$; third-quarter value: $\frac{5\pi}{8}$

Evaluating the given function at these three key x-values gives the following points.

$$\left(\frac{3\pi}{8}, -1\right), \left(\frac{\pi}{2}, 0\right), \left(\frac{5\pi}{8}, 1\right)$$

Connect these points with a smooth curve and continue to graph to approach the asymptote $x = \frac{\pi}{4}$ and $x = \frac{3\pi}{4}$ to complete one period of the graph. Sketch the identical curve between the asymptotes $x = \frac{3\pi}{4}$ and $x = \frac{5\pi}{4}$ to complete a second period of the graph.

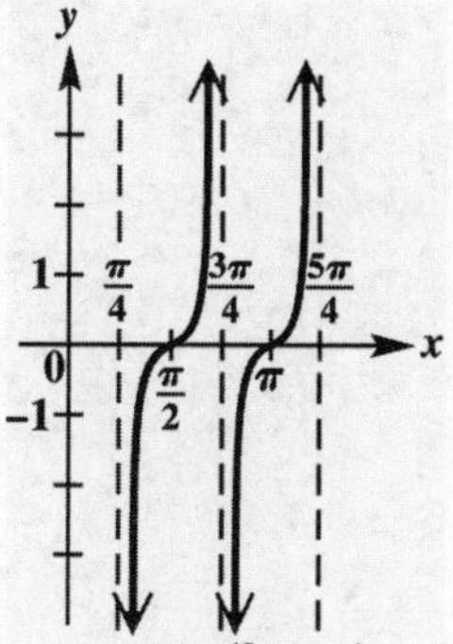

$y = \tan(2x - \pi)$

35. $y = \cot\left(3x + \frac{\pi}{4}\right) = \cot 3\left(x + \frac{\pi}{12}\right)$

Period: $\frac{\pi}{b} = \frac{\pi}{3}$

Vertical translation: none

Phase shift (horizontal translation): $\frac{\pi}{12}$ unit to the left

Because the function is to be graphed over a two-period interval, locate three adjacent vertical asymptotes. Because asymptotes of the graph $y = \cot x$ occur at multiples of π, the following equations can be solved to locate asymptotes.

$$3\left(x + \frac{\pi}{12}\right) = 0,\ 3\left(x + \frac{\pi}{12}\right) = \pi, \text{ and } 3\left(x + \frac{\pi}{12}\right) = 2\pi$$

Solve each of these equations.

$$3\left(x + \frac{\pi}{12}\right) = 0 \Rightarrow x + \frac{\pi}{12} = 0 \Rightarrow x = -\frac{\pi}{12}$$

$$3\left(x + \frac{\pi}{12}\right) = \pi \Rightarrow x + \frac{\pi}{12} = \frac{\pi}{3} \Rightarrow x = \frac{\pi}{3} - \frac{\pi}{12} = \frac{\pi}{4}$$

$$3\left(x + \frac{\pi}{12}\right) = 2\pi \Rightarrow x + \frac{\pi}{12} = \frac{2\pi}{3} \Rightarrow x = \frac{2\pi}{3} - \frac{\pi}{12} \Rightarrow x = \frac{7\pi}{12}$$

Divide the interval $\left(\frac{\pi}{4}, \frac{7\pi}{12}\right)$ into four equal parts to obtain the following key x-values.

first-quarter value: $\frac{\pi}{3}$ middle value: $\frac{5\pi}{12}$; third-quarter value: $\frac{\pi}{2}$

Evaluating the given function at these three key x-values gives the following points.

$$\left(\frac{\pi}{3}, 1\right), \left(\frac{5\pi}{12}, 0\right), \left(\frac{\pi}{2}, -1\right)$$

Connect these points with a smooth curve and continue to graph to approach the asymptote $x = \frac{\pi}{4}$ and $x = \frac{7\pi}{12}$ to complete one period of the graph. Sketch the identical curve between the asymptotes $x = -\frac{\pi}{12}$ and $x = \frac{\pi}{4}$ to complete a second period of the graph.

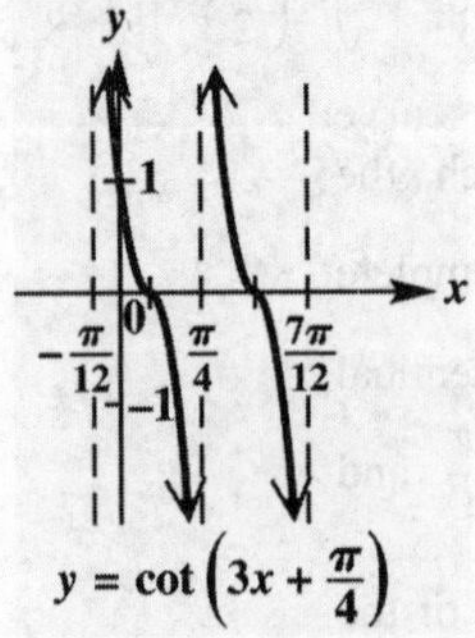

37. $y = 1 + \tan x$

This is the graph of $y = \tan x$ translated vertically 1 unit up.

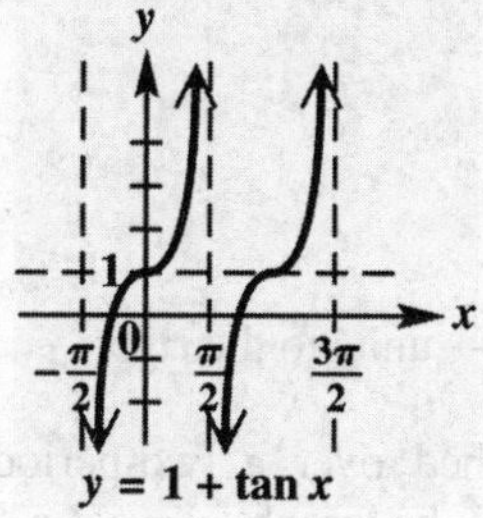

39. $y = 1 - \cot x$

This is the graph of $y = \cot x$ reflected about the x-axis and then translated vertically 1 unit up.

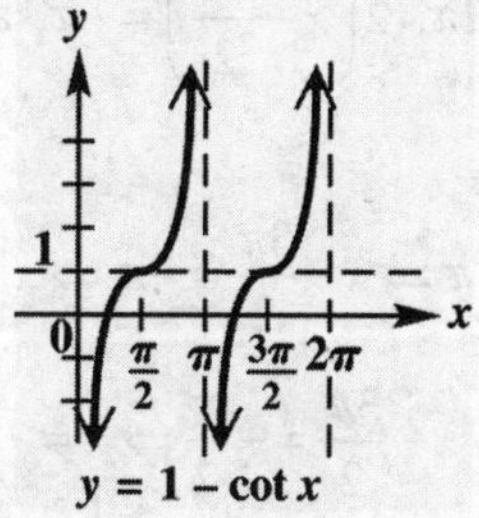

41. $y = -1 + 2\tan x$

This is the graph of $y = 2\tan x$ translated vertically 1 unit down.

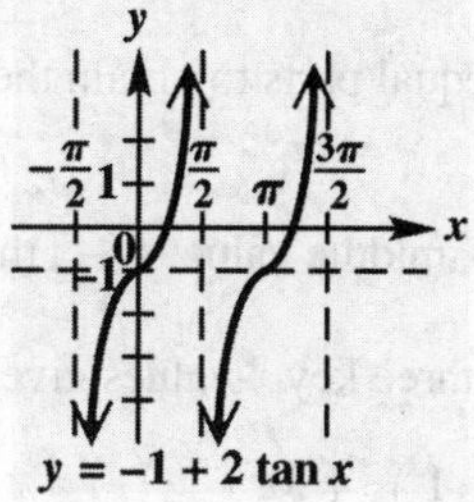

43. $y=-1+\frac{1}{2}\cot(2x-3\pi)=-1+\frac{1}{2}\cot 2\left(x-\frac{3\pi}{2}\right)$

Period: $\frac{\pi}{b}=\frac{\pi}{2}$.

Vertical translation: 1 unit down

Phase shift (horizontal translation): $\frac{3\pi}{2}$ units to the right

Because the function is to be graphed over a two-period interval, locate three adjacent vertical asymptotes. Because asymptotes of the graph $y=\cot x$ occur at multiples of π, the following equations can be solved to locate asymptotes.

$$2\left(x-\frac{3\pi}{2}\right)=-2\pi,\ 2\left(x-\frac{3\pi}{2}\right)=-\pi, \text{ and } 2\left(x-\frac{3\pi}{2}\right)=0$$

Solve each of these equations.

$$2\left(x-\frac{3\pi}{2}\right)=-2\pi\Rightarrow x-\frac{3\pi}{2}=-\pi\Rightarrow x=-\pi+\frac{3\pi}{2}=\frac{\pi}{2}$$

$$2\left(x-\frac{3\pi}{2}\right)=-\pi\Rightarrow x-\frac{3\pi}{2}=-\frac{\pi}{2}\Rightarrow x=-\frac{\pi}{2}+\frac{3\pi}{2}\Rightarrow x=\frac{2\pi}{2}=\pi$$

$$2\left(x-\frac{3\pi}{2}\right)=0\Rightarrow x-\frac{3\pi}{2}=0\Rightarrow x=\frac{3\pi}{2}$$

Divide the interval $\left(\frac{\pi}{2},\pi\right)$ into four equal parts to obtain the following key x-values.

first-quarter value: $\frac{5\pi}{8}$ middle value: $\frac{3\pi}{4}$; third-quarter value: $\frac{7\pi}{8}$

Evaluating the given function at these three key x-values gives the following points.

$$\left(\frac{5\pi}{8},-\frac{1}{2}\right),\ \left(\frac{3\pi}{4},-1\right),\ \left(\frac{7\pi}{8},-\frac{3}{2}\right)$$

Connect these points with a smooth curve and continue to graph to approach the asymptote $x=\frac{\pi}{2}$ and $x=\pi$ to complete one period of the graph. Sketch the identical curve between the asymptotes $x=\pi$ and $x=\frac{3\pi}{2}$ to complete a second period of the graph.

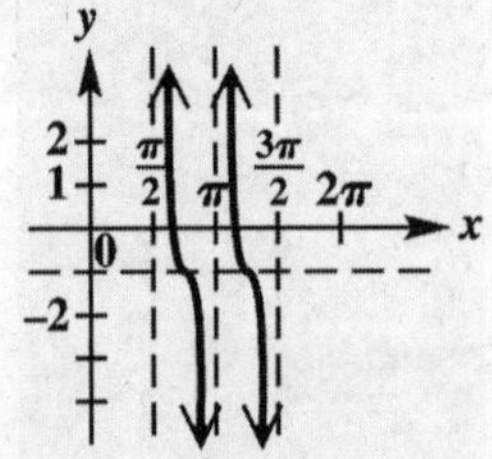

$y=-1+\frac{1}{2}\cot(2x-3\pi)$

45. $y = 1 - 2\cot 2\left(x + \frac{\pi}{2}\right)$

Period: $\frac{\pi}{b} = \frac{\pi}{2}$

Vertical translation: 1 unit up

Phase shift (horizontal translation): $\frac{\pi}{2}$ unit to the left

Because the function is to be graphed over a two-period interval, locate three adjacent vertical asymptotes. Because asymptotes of the graph $y = \cot x$ occur at multiples of π, the following equations can be solved to locate asymptotes.

$$2\left(x + \frac{\pi}{2}\right) = 0,\ 2\left(x + \frac{\pi}{2}\right) = \pi, \text{ and } 2\left(x + \frac{\pi}{2}\right) = 2\pi$$

Solve each of these equations.

$$2\left(x + \frac{\pi}{2}\right) = 0 \Rightarrow x + \frac{\pi}{2} = 0 \Rightarrow x = 0 - \frac{\pi}{2} = -\frac{\pi}{2}$$

$$2\left(x + \frac{\pi}{2}\right) = \pi \Rightarrow x + \frac{\pi}{2} = \frac{\pi}{2} \Rightarrow x = \frac{\pi}{2} - \frac{\pi}{2} \Rightarrow x = 0$$

$$2\left(x + \frac{\pi}{2}\right) = 2\pi \Rightarrow x + \frac{\pi}{2} = \pi \Rightarrow x = \pi - \frac{\pi}{2} = \frac{\pi}{2}$$

Divide the interval $\left(0, \frac{\pi}{2}\right)$ into four equal parts to obtain the following key x-values.

first-quarter value: $\frac{\pi}{8}$ middle value: $\frac{\pi}{4}$; third-quarter value: $\frac{3\pi}{8}$

Evaluating the given function at these three key x-values gives the following points.

$$\left(\frac{\pi}{8}, -1\right), \left(\frac{\pi}{4}, 1\right), \left(\frac{3\pi}{8}, 3\right)$$

Connect these points with a smooth curve and continue to graph to approach the asymptote $x = 0$ and $x = \frac{\pi}{2}$ to complete one period of the graph. Sketch the identical curve between the asymptotes $x = -\frac{\pi}{2}$ and $x = 0$ to complete a second period of the graph.

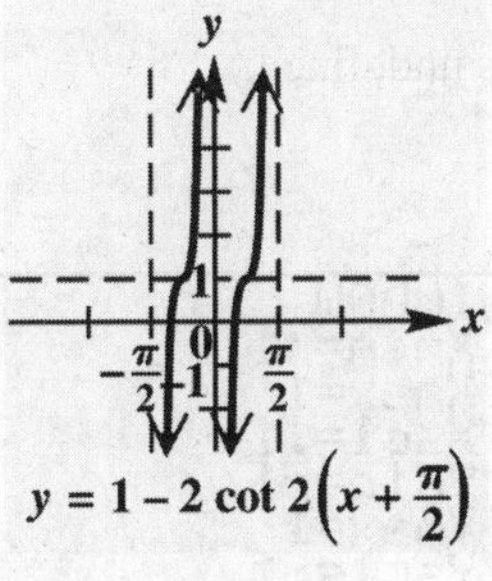

47. True; $\frac{\pi}{2}$ is the smallest positive value where $\cos\frac{\pi}{2} = 0$. Since $\tan\frac{\pi}{2} = \frac{\sin\frac{\pi}{2}}{\cos\frac{\pi}{2}}$, $\frac{\pi}{2}$ is the smallest positive value where the tangent function is undefined. Thus, $k = \frac{\pi}{2}$ is the smallest positive value for which $x = k$ is an asymptote for the tangent function.

49. True; since $\tan x = \dfrac{\sin x}{\cos x}$ and $\sec x = \dfrac{1}{\cos x}$, the tangent and secant functions will be undefined at the same values.

51. False; $\tan(-x) = \dfrac{\sin(-x)}{\cos(-x)} = \dfrac{-\sin x}{\cos x} = -\tan x$ (since sin x is odd and cos x is even) for all x in the domain. Moreover, if $\tan(-x) = \tan x$, then the graph would be symmetric about the y-axis, which it is not.

53. The function tan x has a period of π, so it repeats four times over the interval $(-2\pi, 2\pi]$. Since its range is $(-\infty, \infty)$, $\tan x = c$ has four solutions for every value of c.

54. None; $\cos x \le 1$ for all x, so $\dfrac{1}{\cos x} \ge 1$ and $\sec x \ge 1$. Since $\sec x \ge 1$, sec x has no values in the interval $(-1, 1)$.

55. The domain of the tangent function, $y = \tan x$, is $\left\{x \,\middle|\, x \ne \dfrac{\pi}{2} + n\pi, \text{ where } n \text{ is any integer}\right\}$, and the range is $(-\infty, \infty)$. For the function $f(x) = -4\tan(2x + \pi) = -4\tan 2\left(x + \dfrac{\pi}{2}\right)$, the period is $\dfrac{\pi}{2}$. Therefore, the domain is $\left\{x \,\middle|\, x \ne \dfrac{\pi}{4} + \dfrac{\pi}{2}n, \text{ where } n \text{ is any integer}\right\}$. This can also be written as $\left\{x \,\middle|\, x \ne (2n+1)\dfrac{\pi}{4}, \text{ where } n \text{ is any integer}\right\}$. The range remains $(-\infty, \infty)$.

57. $d = 4\tan 2\pi t$

(a) $d = 4\tan 2\pi(1) = 4\tan 2\pi \approx 4(0) = 0$ m

(b) $d = 4\tan 2\pi(.4) = 4\tan .8\pi \approx 4(-.7265) \approx -2.9$ m

(c) $d = 4\tan 2\pi(.8) = 4\tan 1.6\pi \approx 4(-3.0777) \approx -12.3$ m

(d) $d = 4\tan 2\pi(1.2) = 4\tan 2.4\pi \approx 4(3.0777) \approx 12.3$ m

(e) $t = .25$ leads to $\tan \dfrac{\pi}{2}$, which is undefined.

59. Answers will vary.

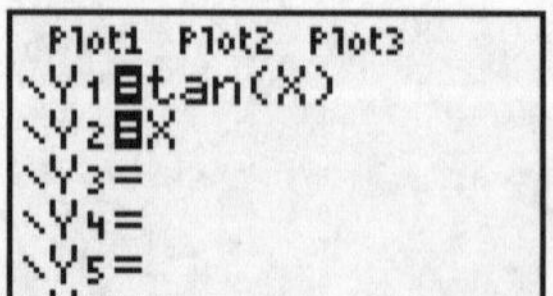

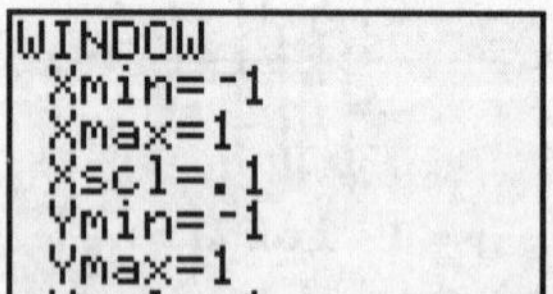

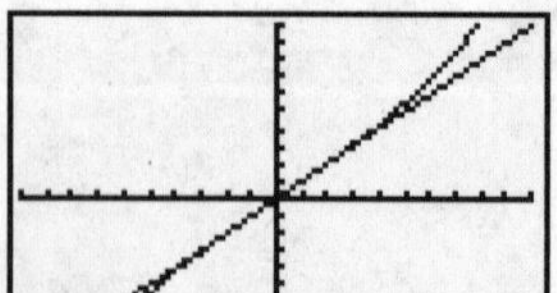

61. Graph the functions.

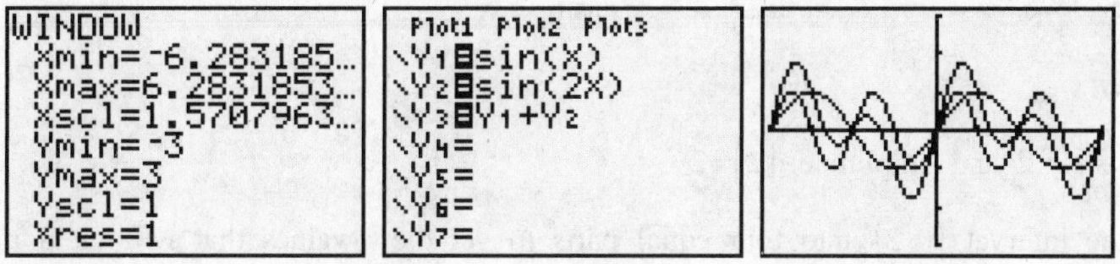

Notice that $Y_1\left(\frac{\pi}{6}\right)+Y_2\left(\frac{\pi}{6}\right)\approx .5+.8660254=1.3660254=Y_3\left(\frac{\pi}{6}\right)=\left(Y_1+Y_2\right)\left(\frac{\pi}{6}\right)$.

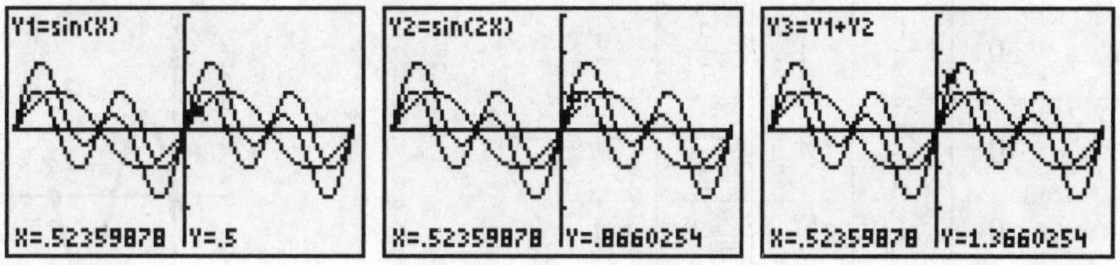

63. π

64. $\pi = x-\frac{\pi}{4} \Rightarrow x=\pi+\frac{\pi}{4}=\frac{5\pi}{4}$

65. The vertical asymptotes in general occur at $x=\frac{5\pi}{4}+n\pi,$ where *n* is an integer.

66. The function $y=-2-\cot\left(x-\frac{\pi}{4}\right)$ is graphed in the window $[-\pi, 2\pi]$ with scale $\frac{\pi}{2}$ (with respect to *x*).

Using the zero feature of the graphing calculator, we see that the smallest positive *x*-intercept is approximately .3217505544.

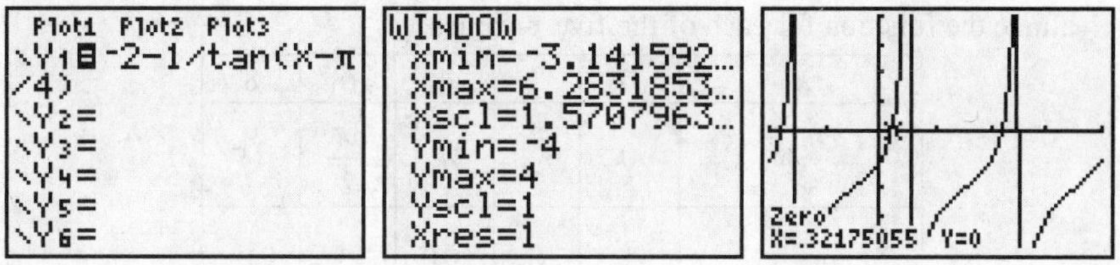

67. $.3217505544+\pi \approx 3.463343208$

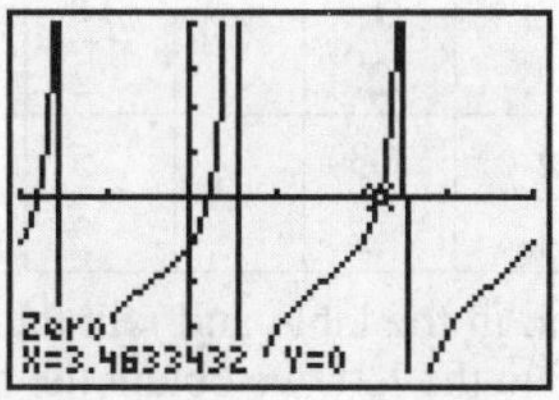

68. $\{x \mid x=.3217505544+n\pi,$ where *n* is an integer$\}$

Summary Exercises on Graphing Circular Functions

1. $y = 2\sin \pi x$

Period: $\dfrac{2\pi}{\pi} = 2$ and Amplitude: $|2| = 2$

Divide the interval $[0, 2]$ into four equal parts to get the x-values that will yield minimum and maximum points and x-intercepts. Then make a table.

x	0	$\frac{1}{2}$	1	$\frac{3}{2}$	2
πx	0	$\frac{\pi}{2}$	π	$\frac{3\pi}{2}$	2π
$\sin \pi x$	0	1	0	-1	0
$2\sin \pi x$	0	2	0	-2	0

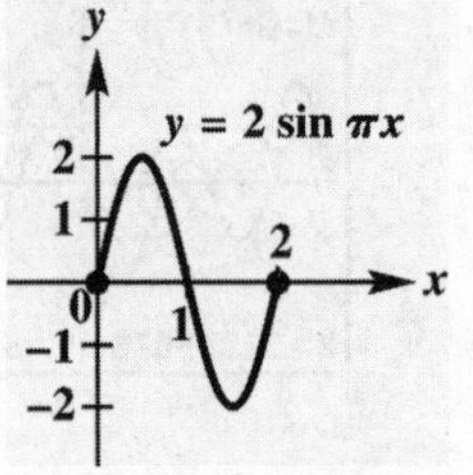

3. $y = -2 + .5\cos \dfrac{\pi}{4} x$

Step 1 To find the interval whose length is $\dfrac{2\pi}{b}$.

$$0 \le \frac{\pi}{4} x \le 2\pi \Rightarrow 0 \le x \le 8$$

Step 2 Divide the period into four equal parts to get the following x-values.

$$0, 2, 4, 6, 8$$

Step 3 Evaluate the function for each of the five x-values.

x	0	2	4	6	8
$\frac{\pi}{4} x$	0	$\frac{\pi}{2}$	π	$\frac{3\pi}{2}$	2π
$\cos \frac{\pi}{4} x$	1	0	-1	0	1
$\frac{1}{2}\cos \frac{\pi}{4} x$	$\frac{1}{2}$	0	$-\frac{1}{2}$	0	$\frac{1}{2}$
$-2 + \frac{1}{2}\cos \frac{\pi}{4} x$	$-\frac{3}{2}$	-2	$-\frac{5}{2}$	-2	$-\frac{3}{2}$

Steps 4 and 5 Plot the points found in the table and join them with a sinusoidal curve. By graphing an additional period to the left, we obtain the following graph.

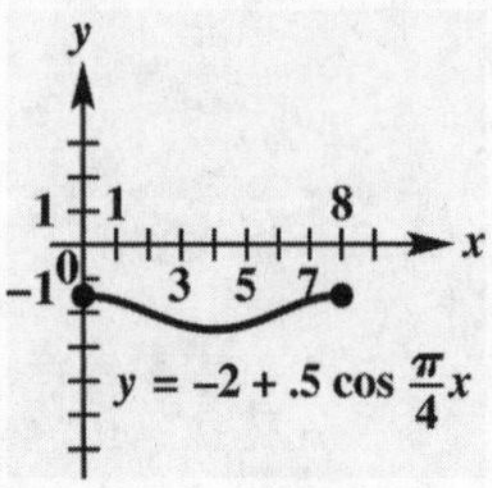

The amplitude is $|.5| = \left|\frac{1}{2}\right|$, which is $\frac{1}{2}$.

The period is 8.

The vertical translation is 2 units down.

There is no phase shift.

5. $y = -4\csc .5x = -4\csc \frac{1}{2}x$

Step 1 Graph the corresponding reciprocal function $y = -4\sin \frac{1}{2}x$ The period is $\frac{2\pi}{\frac{1}{2}} = 2\pi \cdot \frac{2}{1} = 4\pi$ and its amplitude is $|-4| = 4$. One period is in the interval $0 \le x \le 4\pi$. Dividing the interval into four equal parts gives us the following key points.

$$(0,0),\ (\pi,-4),\ (2\pi,0),\ (3\pi,4),\ (4\pi,0)$$

Step 2 The vertical asymptotes of $y = -4\csc \frac{1}{2}x$ are at the x-intercepts of $y = -4\sin \frac{1}{2}x$, which are $x = 0,\ x = 2\pi,$ and $x = 4\pi$.

Step 3 Sketch the graph.

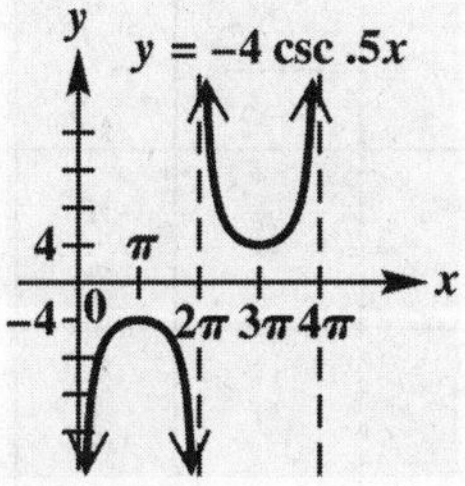

7. $y = -5\sin \frac{x}{3}$

Period: $\frac{2\pi}{\frac{1}{3}} = 2\pi \cdot \frac{3}{1} = 6\pi$ and Amplitude: $|-5| = 5$

Divide the interval $[0, 6\pi]$ into four equal parts to get the x-values that will yield minimum and maximum points and x-intercepts. Then make a table. Repeat this cycle for the interval $[-6\pi, 0]$.

x	0	$\frac{3\pi}{2}$	3π	$\frac{9\pi}{2}$	6π
$\frac{x}{3}$	0	$\frac{\pi}{2}$	π	$\frac{3\pi}{2}$	2π
$\sin \frac{x}{3}$	0	1	0	-1	0
$-5\sin \frac{x}{3}$	0	-5	0	5	0

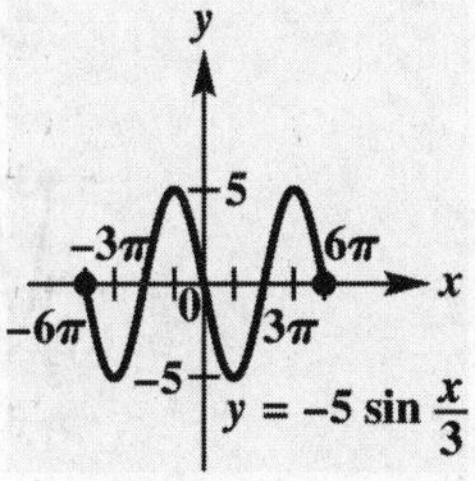

9. $y = 3 - 4\sin(2.5x + \pi) = 3 - 4\sin\left(\frac{5}{2}x + \pi\right) = 3 - 4\sin\frac{5}{2}\left(x + \frac{2\pi}{5}\right)$

Step 1 Find the interval whose length is $\frac{2\pi}{b}$.

$$0 \le \frac{5}{2}\left(x + \frac{2\pi}{5}\right) \le 2\pi \Rightarrow 0 \le x + \frac{2\pi}{5} \le \frac{4\pi}{5} \Rightarrow -\frac{2\pi}{5} \le x \le \frac{2\pi}{5}$$

Step 2 Divide the period into four equal parts to get the following x-values.

$$-\frac{2\pi}{5}, -\frac{\pi}{5}, 0, \frac{\pi}{2}, \frac{2\pi}{5}$$

Step 3 Evaluate the function for each of the five x-values

x	$-\frac{2\pi}{5}$	$-\frac{\pi}{5}$	0	$\frac{\pi}{5}$	$\frac{2\pi}{5}$
$\frac{5}{2}\left(x+\frac{2\pi}{5}\right)$	0	$\frac{\pi}{2}$	π	$\frac{3\pi}{2}$	2π
$\sin\frac{5}{2}\left(x+\frac{2\pi}{5}\right)$	0	1	0	−1	0
$-4\sin\frac{5}{2}\left(x+\frac{2\pi}{5}\right)$	0	−4	0	4	0
$3-4\sin\frac{5}{2}\left(x+\frac{2\pi}{5}\right)$	3	−1	3	7	3

Steps 4 and 5 Plot the points found in the table and join them with a sinusoidal curve. By graphing an additional period to the right, we obtain the following graph.

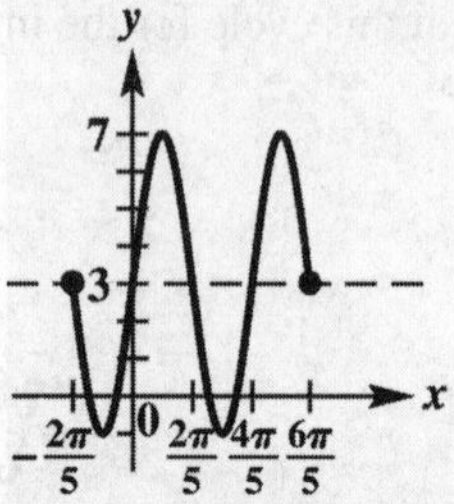

$y = 3 - 4\sin(2.5x + \pi)$

The amplitude is $|-4|$, which is 4.

The period is $\frac{2\pi}{\frac{5}{2}}$, which is $\frac{4\pi}{5}$.

The vertical translation is 3 units up.

The phase shift is $\frac{2\pi}{5}$ units to the left.

Section 6.5: Harmonic Motion

1. $s(0) = 2$ in.; $P = .5$ sec

(a) Given $s(t) = a\cos\omega t$, the period is $\frac{2\pi}{\omega}$ and the amplitude is $|a|$.

$$P = .5 \text{ sec} \Rightarrow .5 = \frac{2\pi}{\omega} \Rightarrow \frac{1}{2} = \frac{2\pi}{\omega} \Rightarrow \omega = 4\pi$$

$$s(0) = 2 = a\cos[\omega(0)] \Rightarrow 2 = a\cos 0 \Rightarrow 2 = a(1) \Rightarrow a = 2$$

Thus, $s(t) = 2\cos 4\pi t$.

(b) Since $s(1) = 2\cos[4\pi(1)] = 2\cos 4\pi = 2(1) = 2$, the weight is neither moving upward nor downward. At $t = 1$, the motion of the weight is changing from up to down.

3. $s(0) = -3$ in.; $P = .8$ sec

(a) Given $s(t) = a\cos\omega t$, the period is $\dfrac{2\pi}{\omega}$ and the amplitude is $|a|$.

$$P = .8 \text{ sec} \Rightarrow .8 = \frac{2\pi}{\omega} \Rightarrow \frac{4}{5} = \frac{2\pi}{\omega} \Rightarrow 4\omega = 10\pi \Rightarrow \omega = \frac{10\pi}{4} = 2.5\pi$$

$$s(0) = -3 = a\cos[\omega(0)] \Rightarrow -3 = a\cos 0 \Rightarrow -3 = a(1) \Rightarrow a = -3$$

Thus, $s(t) = -3\cos 2.5\pi t$.

(b) Since $s(1) = -3\cos[2.5\pi(1)] = -3\cos\dfrac{5\pi}{2} = -3(0) = 0$, the weight is moving upward.

5. Since frequency is $\dfrac{\omega}{2\pi}$, we have $27.5 = \dfrac{\omega}{2\pi} \Rightarrow \omega = 55\pi$. Since $s(0) = .21$, $.21 = a\cos[\omega(0)] \Rightarrow$ $.21 = a\cos 0 \Rightarrow .21 = a(1) \Rightarrow a = .21$. Thus, $s(t) = .21\cos 55\pi t$.

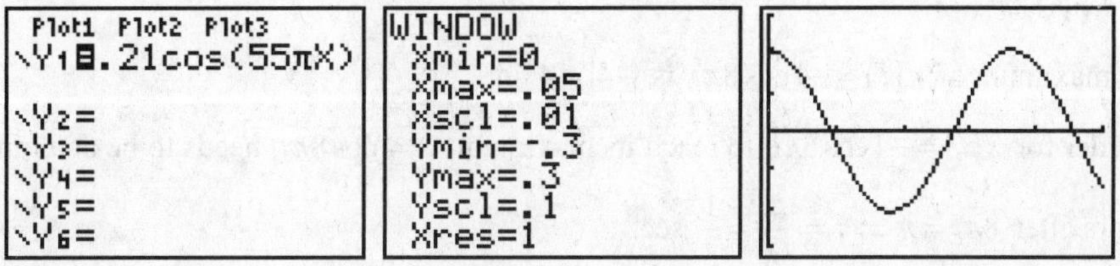

7. Since frequency is $\dfrac{\omega}{2\pi}$, we have $55 = \dfrac{\omega}{2\pi} \Rightarrow \omega = 110\pi$. Since $s(0) = .14$, $.14 = a\cos[\omega(0)] \Rightarrow$ $.14 = a\cos 0 \Rightarrow .14 = a(1) \Rightarrow a = .14$. Thus, $s(t) = .14\cos 110\pi t$.

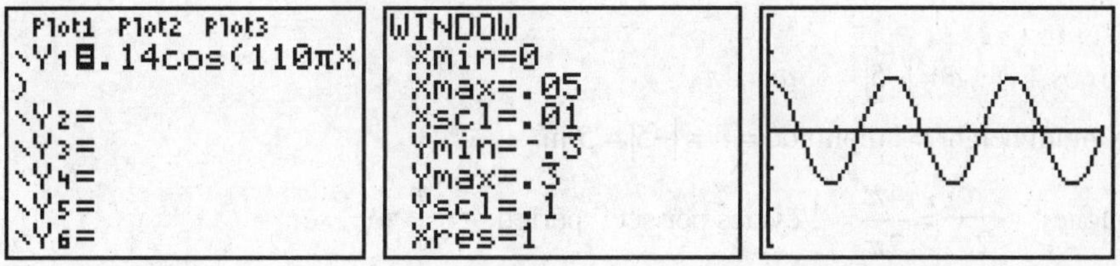

9. **(a)** Since the object is pulled down 4 units, $s(0) = -4$. Thus, we have the following.

$$s(0) = -4 = a\cos[\omega(0)] \Rightarrow -4 = a\cos 0 \Rightarrow -4 = a(1) \Rightarrow a = -4$$

Since the time it takes to complete one oscillation is 3 sec, $P = 3$ sec.

$$P = 3 \text{ sec} \Rightarrow 3 = \frac{2\pi}{\omega} \Rightarrow 3 = \frac{2\pi}{\omega} \Rightarrow 3\omega = 2\pi \Rightarrow \omega = \frac{2\pi}{3}$$

Therefore, $s(t) = -4\cos\dfrac{2\pi}{3}t$.

(b) $s(1) = -4\cos\left[\dfrac{2\pi}{3}(1.25)\right] = -4\cos\left[\dfrac{2\pi}{3}\left(\dfrac{5}{4}\right)\right] = -4\cos\dfrac{5\pi}{6} = -4\left(-\dfrac{\sqrt{3}}{2}\right) = 2\sqrt{3} \approx 3.46$ units

(rounded to three significant digits)

(c) The frequency is the reciprocal of the period, or $\dfrac{1}{3}$.

11. **(a)** $a = 2, \omega = 2$

$s(t) = a \sin \omega t \Rightarrow s(t) = 2 \sin 2t$

amplitude $= |a| = |2| = 2$; period $= \dfrac{2\pi}{\omega} = \dfrac{2\pi}{2} = \pi$; frequency $= \dfrac{\omega}{2\pi} = \dfrac{1}{\pi}$

(b) $a = 2,\ \omega = 4$

$s(t) = a \sin \omega t \Rightarrow s(t) = 2 \sin 4t$

amplitude $= |a| = |2| = 2$; period $= \dfrac{2\pi}{\omega} = \dfrac{2\pi}{4} = \dfrac{\pi}{2}$; frequency $= \dfrac{\omega}{2\pi} = \dfrac{4}{2\pi} = \dfrac{2}{\pi}$

13. Since $P = 2\pi\sqrt{\dfrac{L}{32}}$, $1 = 2\pi\sqrt{\dfrac{L}{32}} \Rightarrow \dfrac{1}{2\pi} = \sqrt{\dfrac{L}{32}} \Rightarrow \dfrac{1}{(2\pi)^2} = \dfrac{L}{32} \Rightarrow \dfrac{1}{4\pi^2} = \dfrac{L}{32} \Rightarrow \dfrac{32}{4\pi^2} = L \Rightarrow L = \dfrac{8}{\pi^2}$ ft.

15. $s(t) = -4 \cos 8\pi t$

(a) The maximum of $s(t) = -4 \cos 8\pi t$ is $|-4| = 4$ in.

(b) In order for $s(t) = -4 \cos 8\pi t$ to reach its maximum, $y = \cos 8\pi t$ needs to be at a minimum. This occurs after $8\pi t = \pi \Rightarrow t = \dfrac{\pi}{8\pi} = \dfrac{1}{8}$ sec.

(c) Since $s(t) = -4 \cos 8\pi t$ and $s(t) = a \cos \omega t$, $\omega = 8\pi$. Therefore, frequency $= \dfrac{\omega}{2\pi} = \dfrac{8\pi}{2\pi} = 4$ cycles per sec. The period is the reciprocal of the frequency, or $\dfrac{1}{4}$ sec.

17. $s(t) = -5 \cos 4\pi t$, $a = |-5| = 5$, $\omega = 4\pi$

(a) maximum height = amplitude = $a = |-5| = 5$ in.

(b) frequency $= \dfrac{\omega}{2\pi} = \dfrac{4\pi}{2\pi} = 2$ cycles per sec; period $= \dfrac{2\pi}{\omega} = \dfrac{1}{2}$ sec

(c) $s(t) = -5 \cos 4\pi t = 5 \Rightarrow \cos 4\pi t = -1 \Rightarrow 4\pi t = \pi \Rightarrow t = \dfrac{1}{4}$

The weight first reaches its maximum height after $\dfrac{1}{4}$ sec.

(d) Since $s(1.3) = -5 \cos\left[4\pi(1.3)\right] = -5 \cos 5.2\pi \approx 4$, after 1.3 sec, the weight is about 4 in. above the equilibrium position.

19. $a = -3$

(a) We will use a model of the form $s(t) = a \cos \omega t$ with $a = -3$.

Since $s(0) = -3 \cos\left[\omega(0)\right] = -3 \cos 0 = -3(1) = -3$,

Using a cosine function rather than a sine function will avoid the need for a phase shift.

Since the frequency $= \dfrac{6}{\pi}$ cycles per sec, by definition, $\dfrac{\omega}{2\pi} = \dfrac{6}{\pi} \Rightarrow \omega\pi = 12\pi \Rightarrow \omega = 12$.

Therefore, a model for the position of the weight at time t seconds is $s(t) = -3 \cos 12t$.

(b) The period is the reciprocal of the frequency, or $\dfrac{\pi}{6}$ sec.

For Exercise 21, we have the following.

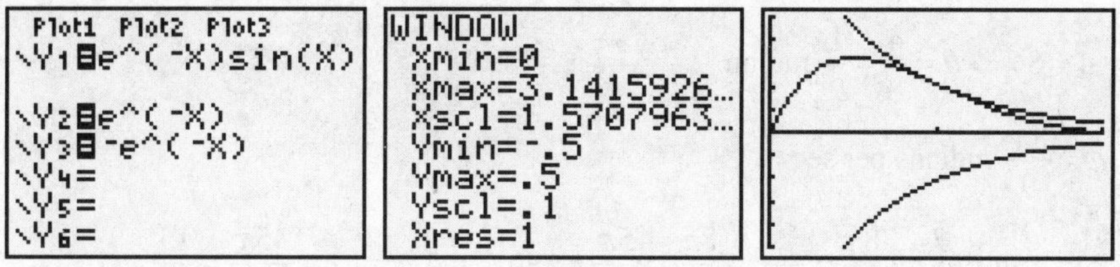

21. Since $e^{-t} \neq 0$, we have $e^{-t}\sin t = 0 \Rightarrow \sin t = 0 \Rightarrow t = 0, \pi$. The x-intercepts of Y_1 are the same as these of $\sin x$.

Chapter 6: Review Exercises

1. **(a)** Since $\frac{\pi}{2} \approx 1.57$ and $\pi \approx 3.14$, we have $\frac{\pi}{2} < 3 < \pi$. Thus, the terminal side is in quadrant II.

(b) Since $\pi \approx 3.14$ and $\frac{3\pi}{2} \approx 4.71$, we have $\pi < 4 < \frac{3\pi}{2}$. Thus, the terminal side is in quadrant III.

(c) Since $-\frac{\pi}{2} \approx -1.57$ and $-\pi \approx -3.14$, we have $-\frac{\pi}{2} > -2 > -\pi$. Thus, the terminal side is in quadrant III.

(d) Since $2\pi \approx 6.28$ and $\frac{5\pi}{2} \approx 7.85$. we have $2\pi < 7 < \frac{5\pi}{2}$. Thus, the terminal side is in quadrant I.

3. $120° = 120\left(\frac{\pi}{180}\text{radian}\right) = \frac{2\pi}{3}\text{radians}$

5. $\frac{5\pi}{4} = \frac{5\pi}{4}\left(\frac{180°}{\pi}\right) = 225°$

7. **(a)** $\frac{9}{10}\cdot\frac{\pi}{180} = \frac{\pi}{200}$

(b) For degrees we have, $3.5 \times .9° = 3.15°$. For radians we have, $3.5 \times \frac{\pi}{200} \approx .055$ radian.

9. $r = 15.2$ cm, $\theta = \frac{3\pi}{4}$

$$s = r\theta \Rightarrow s = 15.2\left(\frac{3\pi}{4}\right) = 11.4\pi \approx 35.8 \text{ cm}$$

11. Because the central angle is very small, the arc length is approximately equal to the length of the inscribed chord. (See directions for Exercises 67 – 68 in Section 6.1)
Let h = height of tree, r = 2000, and $\theta = 1°10'$.

First, convert $\theta = 1°10'$ to radians.

$$\theta = 1°10' = \left(1 + \tfrac{10}{60}\right)° = \left(1\tfrac{1}{6}\right)° = \frac{7}{6}\left(\frac{\pi}{180}\text{radian}\right) = \frac{7\pi}{1080}\text{radian}$$

Thus, we have the following.

$$h \approx r\theta \Rightarrow h \approx 2000\left(\frac{7\pi}{1080}\right) \approx 41 \text{ yd}$$

13. $s=4,\ r=8$

$$s=r\theta \Rightarrow 4=8\theta \Rightarrow \theta=\frac{4}{8}=\frac{1}{2} \text{ radian}$$

15. $\theta=\frac{5\pi}{12},\ \omega=\frac{8\pi}{9}$ radians per sec

$$\omega=\frac{\theta}{t} \Rightarrow \frac{8\pi}{9}=\frac{\frac{5\pi}{12}}{t} \Rightarrow \frac{8\pi}{9}=\frac{5\pi}{12t} \Rightarrow 96\pi t=45\pi \Rightarrow t=\frac{45\pi}{96\pi}=\frac{15}{32} \text{ sec}$$

17. The flywheel is rotating 90 times per sec or $90(2\pi)=180\pi$ radians per sec. Since $r=7$ m, we have the following.

$$v=r\omega \Rightarrow v=7(180\pi)=1260\pi \text{ m per sec}$$

19. If $\theta=2\pi$, then $A=\frac{1}{2}r^2\theta \Rightarrow A=\frac{1}{2}r^2(2\pi)=\pi r^2$. This is the formula for the area of a circle.

21. Find $\tan\left(-\frac{7\pi}{3}\right)$.

$-\frac{7\pi}{3}$ is coterminal with $-\frac{7\pi}{3}+2(2\pi)=-\frac{7\pi}{3}+4\pi=-\frac{7\pi}{3}+\frac{12\pi}{3}=\frac{5\pi}{3}$. Since $\frac{5\pi}{3}$ is in quadrant IV, the reference angle is $2\pi-\frac{5\pi}{3}=\frac{6\pi}{3}-\frac{5\pi}{3}=\frac{\pi}{3}$. In quadrant IV, the tangent is negative. Thus,

$\tan\left(-\frac{7\pi}{3}\right)=\tan\frac{5\pi}{3}=-\tan\frac{\pi}{3}=-\sqrt{3}.$

Converting $\frac{5\pi}{3}$ to degrees, we have $\frac{5\pi}{3}=\frac{5}{3}(180°)=300°$. The reference angle is $360°-300°=60°$.

Thus, $\tan\left(-\frac{7\pi}{3}\right)=\tan\frac{5\pi}{3}=\tan 300°=-\tan 60°=-\sqrt{3}.$

23. $\cos(-.2443)\approx .9703$

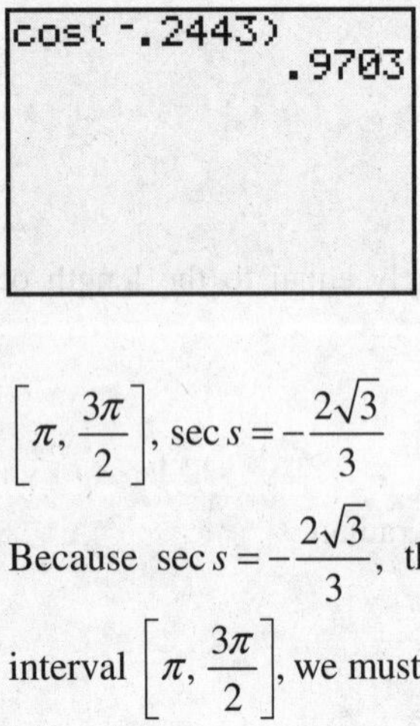

25. $s=\sin^{-1}.4924\approx .5148$

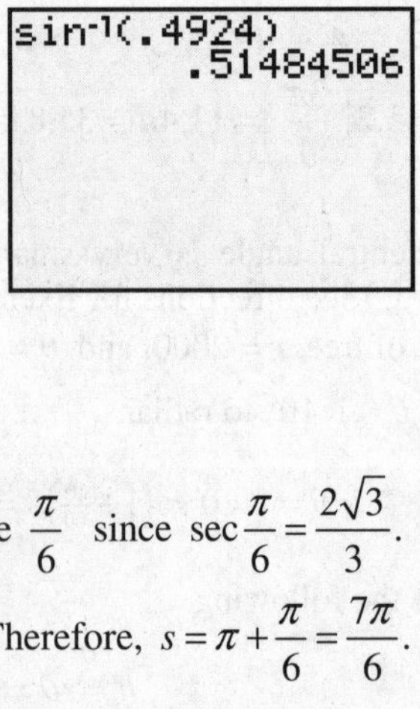

27. $\left[\pi, \frac{3\pi}{2}\right],\ \sec s=-\frac{2\sqrt{3}}{3}$

Because $\sec s=-\frac{2\sqrt{3}}{3}$, the reference angle for s must be $\frac{\pi}{6}$ since $\sec\frac{\pi}{6}=\frac{2\sqrt{3}}{3}$. For s to be in the interval $\left[\pi, \frac{3\pi}{2}\right]$, we must add the reference angle to π. Therefore, $s=\pi+\frac{\pi}{6}=\frac{7\pi}{6}$.

29. **(a)** Because alternate interior angles of parallel lines with transversal have the same measure, the measure of angle ABC is equal to the measure of angle BCD (the angle of elevation). Moreover, triangle BAC is a right triangle and we can write the relation $\sin\theta = \frac{h}{d}$.

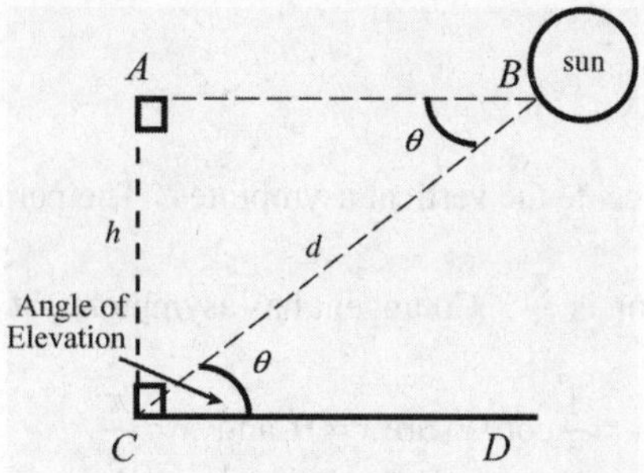

Solving for d we have, $\sin\theta = \frac{h}{d} \Rightarrow d\sin\theta = h \Rightarrow d = h\cdot\frac{1}{\sin\theta} \Rightarrow d = h\csc\theta.$

(b) Since $d = h\csc\theta,$ we substitute $2h$ for d and solve.

$$2h = h\csc\theta \Rightarrow 2 = \csc\theta \Rightarrow \sin\theta = \frac{1}{2} \Rightarrow \theta = \frac{\pi}{6}$$

d is double h when the sun is $\frac{\pi}{6}$ radians (30°) above the horizon.

(c) $\csc\frac{\pi}{2} = 1$ and $\csc\frac{\pi}{3} = \frac{2\sqrt{3}}{3} \approx 1.15$

When the sun is lower in the sky $\left(\theta = \frac{\pi}{3}\right)$, sunlight is filtered by more atmosphere. There is less ultraviolet light reaching the earth's surface, and therefore, there is less likelihood of becoming sunburned. In this case, sunlight passes through 15% more atmosphere.

31. D; The amplitude is $|-3| = 3,$ but the period is $\frac{2\pi}{\frac{1}{2}} = 4\pi.$ All other statements are true.

33. $y = \tan 3x$
Amplitude: not applicable
Period: $\frac{\pi}{3}$
Vertical translation: none
Phase shift: none

35. $y = 2\sin 5x$
Amplitude: $|2| = 2$
Period: $\frac{2\pi}{5}$
Vertical translation: none
Phase shift: none

37. $y = 3 - \frac{1}{4}\cos\frac{2}{3}x$
Amplitude: $\left|-\frac{1}{4}\right| = \frac{1}{4}$
Period: $\frac{2\pi}{\frac{2}{3}} = 3\pi$
Vertical translation: up 3 units
Phase shift: none

39. $y = -\sin\left(x - \frac{3\pi}{4}\right)$
Amplitude: $|-1| = 1$
Period: 2π
Vertical translation: none
Phase shift: $\frac{3\pi}{4}$ units to the right

41. The tangent function has a period of π and x-intercepts at integral multiples of π.

43. The cosine function has a period of 2π and has the value 0 when $x = \dfrac{\pi}{2}$.

45. $y = \dfrac{1}{2}\cot 3x$

Step 1 Find the period and locate the vertical asymptotes. The period of cotangent is $\dfrac{\pi}{b}$, so the period for this function is $\dfrac{\pi}{3}$. Cotangent has asymptotes of the form $bx = 0$ and $bx = \pi$. The asymptotes for $y = \dfrac{1}{2}\cot 3x$ are $x = 0$ and $x = \dfrac{\pi}{3}$.

Step 2 Sketch the two vertical asymptotes found in Step 1.

Step 3 Divide the interval into four equal parts.

$$0, \frac{\pi}{12}, \frac{\pi}{6}, \frac{\pi}{4}, \frac{\pi}{3}$$

Step 4 Finding the first-quarter point, midpoint, and third-quarter point, we have the following.

$$\left(\frac{\pi}{12}, \frac{1}{2}\right), \left(\frac{\pi}{6}, 0\right), \left(\frac{\pi}{4}, -\frac{1}{2}\right)$$

Step 5 Join the points with a smooth curve. The graph is "shrunk" because $a = \dfrac{1}{2}$ and $\left|\dfrac{1}{2}\right| < 1$.

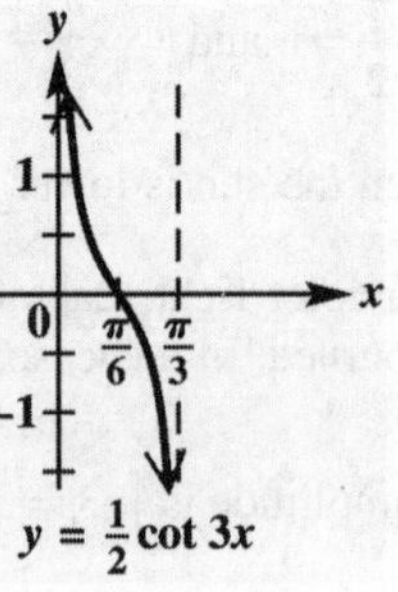

47. $y = \tan\left(x - \dfrac{\pi}{2}\right)$

Period: π

Vertical translation: none

Phase shift (horizontal translation): $\dfrac{\pi}{2}$ units to the right

Because the function is to be graphed over a two-period interval, locate three adjacent vertical asymptotes. Because asymptotes of the graph $y = \tan x$ occur at $-\dfrac{\pi}{2}$, and $\dfrac{\pi}{2}$, the following equations can be solved to locate asymptotes.

$$x - \frac{\pi}{2} = -\frac{\pi}{2} \Rightarrow x = 0 \text{ and } x - \frac{\pi}{2} = \frac{\pi}{2} \Rightarrow x = \pi$$

Divide the interval $(0, \pi)$ into four equal parts to obtain the following key x-values.

$$\text{first-quarter value: } \frac{\pi}{4} \text{ middle value: } \frac{\pi}{2}\text{; third-quarter value: } \frac{3\pi}{4}$$

Continued on next page

47. (continued)

Evaluating the given function at these three key x-values gives the following points.

$$\left(\frac{\pi}{4},-1\right),\ \left(\frac{\pi}{2},0\right),\ \left(\frac{3\pi}{4},1\right)$$

Connect these points with a smooth curve and continue to graph to approach the asymptote $x=0$ and $x=\pi$ to complete one period of the graph.

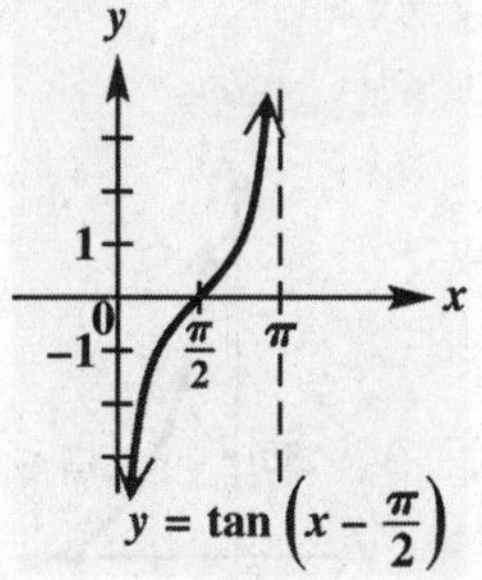

49. $y=-1-3\sin 2x$

Step 1 Find the interval whose length is $\frac{2\pi}{b}$.

$$0\le 2x\le 2\pi \Rightarrow 0\le x\le \pi$$

Step 2 Divide the period into four equal parts to get the following x-values.

$$0,\ \frac{\pi}{4},\ \frac{\pi}{2},\ \frac{3\pi}{4},\ \pi$$

Step 3 Evaluate the function for each of the five x-values.

x	0	$\frac{\pi}{4}$	$\frac{\pi}{2}$	$\frac{3\pi}{4}$	π
$2x$	0	$\frac{\pi}{2}$	π	$\frac{3\pi}{2}$	2π
$\sin 2x$	0	1	0	−1	0
$-3\sin 2x$	0	−3	0	3	0
$-1-3\sin 2x$	−1	−4	−1	2	−1

Steps 4 and 5 Plot the points found in the table and join them with a sinusoidal curve. By graphing an additional period to the left, we obtain the following graph.

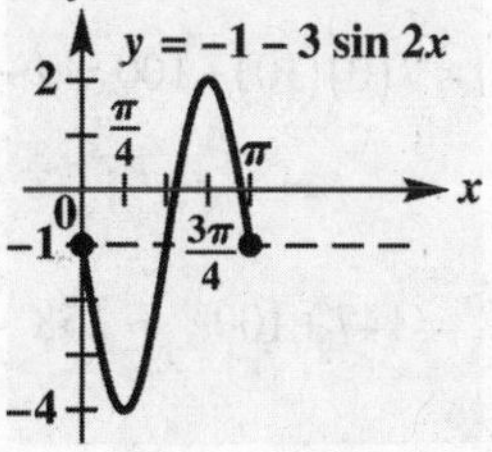

The amplitude is $|-3|$, which is 3.

The period is $\frac{2\pi}{2}=\pi$.

The vertical translation is 1 unit down.

There is no phase shift.

51. (a) The shorter leg of the right triangle has length $h_2 - h_1$. Thus, we have the following.

$$\cot\theta = \frac{d}{h_2 - h_1} \Rightarrow d = (h_2 - h_1)\cot\theta$$

(b) When $h_2 = 55$ and $h_1 = 5$, $d = (55-5)\cot\theta = 50\cot\theta$.

The period is π, but the graph wanted is d for $0 < \theta < \frac{\pi}{2}$. The asymptote is the line $\theta = 0$. Also,

when $\theta = \frac{\pi}{4}, d = 50\cot\frac{\pi}{4} = 50(1) = 50.$

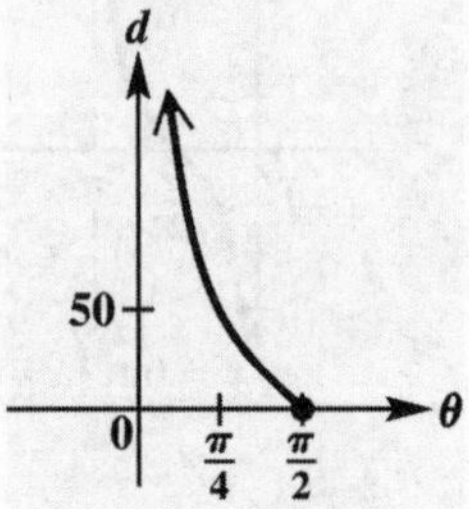

$d = 50 \cot \theta$

53. $t = 60 - 30\cos\frac{x\pi}{6}$

(a) For January, $x = 0$. Thus, $t = 60 - 30\cos\frac{0 \cdot \pi}{6} = 60 - 30\cos 0 = 60 - 30(1) = 60 - 30 = 30°$.

(b) For April, $x = 3$. Thus, $t = 60 - 30\cos\frac{3\pi}{6} = 60 - 30\cos\frac{\pi}{2} = 60 - 30(0) = 60 - 0 = 60°$.

(c) For May, $x = 4$. Thus, $t = 60 - 30\cos\frac{4\pi}{6} = 60 - 30\cos\frac{2\pi}{3} = 60 - 30\left(-\frac{1}{2}\right) = 60 + 15 = 75°$.

(d) For June, $x = 5$. Thus, $t = 60 - 30\cos\frac{5\pi}{6} = 60 - 30\left(-\frac{\sqrt{3}}{2}\right) = 60 + 15\sqrt{3} \approx 86°$.

(e) For August, $x = 7$. Thus, $t = 60 - 30\cos\frac{7\pi}{6} = 60 - 30\left(-\frac{\sqrt{3}}{2}\right) = 60 + 15\sqrt{3} \approx 86°$.

(f) For October, $x = 9$. Thus, $t = 60 - 30\cos\frac{9\pi}{6} = 60 - 30\cos\frac{3\pi}{2} = 60 - 30(0) = 60 - 0 = 60°$.

55. $P(t) = 7(1 - \cos 2\pi t)(t + 10) + 100e^{.2t}$

(a) January 1, base year $t = 0$

$$P(0) = 7(1 - \cos 0)(10) + 100e^{0} = 7(1-1)(10) + 100(1) = 7(0)(10) + 100 = 0 + 100 = 100$$

(b) July 1, base year $t = .5$

$$P(.5) = 7(1 - \cos\pi)(.5 + 10) + 100e^{.2(.5)}$$
$$= 7[1 - (-1)](10.5) + 100e^{.1} = 7(2)(10.5) + 100e^{.1} = 147 + 100e^{.1} \approx 258$$

(c) January 1, following year $t = 1$

$$P(1) = 7(1 - \cos 2\pi)(1 + 10) + 100e^{.2}$$
$$= 7(1-1)(1+10) + 100e^{.2} = 7(0)(11) + 100e^{.2} = 0 + 100e^{.2} = 100e^{.2} \approx 122$$

(d) July 1, following year $t = 1.5$

$$P(1.5) = 7(1 - \cos 3\pi)(1.5 + 10) + 100e^{.2(1.5)}$$
$$= 7[1 - (-1)](11.5) + 100e^{.3} = 7(2)(11.5) + 100e^{.3} = 161 + +100e^{.3} \approx 296$$

57. $s(t) = 4\sin \pi t$

$a = 4,\ \omega = \pi$

amplitude $= |a| = 4$

period $= \dfrac{2\pi}{\omega} = \dfrac{2\pi}{\pi} = 2$

frequency $= \dfrac{\omega}{2\pi} = \dfrac{\pi}{2\pi} = \dfrac{1}{2}$

59. The frequency is the number of cycles in one unit of time.

$$s(1.5) = 4\sin 1.5\pi = 4\sin\frac{3\pi}{2} = 4(-1) = -4;\ s(2) = 4\sin 2\pi = 4(0) = 0$$

$$s(3.25) = 4\sin 3.25\pi = 4\sin\frac{13\pi}{4} = 4\sin\frac{5\pi}{4} = 4\left(-\frac{\sqrt{2}}{2}\right) = -2\sqrt{2}$$

Chapter 6: Test

1. $120° = 120\left(\dfrac{\pi}{180}\text{ radian}\right) = \dfrac{2\pi}{3}\text{ radians}$

2. $-45° = -45\left(\dfrac{\pi}{180}\text{ radian}\right) = -\dfrac{\pi}{4}\text{ radian}$

3. $5° = 5\left(\dfrac{\pi}{180}\text{ radian}\right) = \dfrac{\pi}{36} \approx .09\text{ radian}$

4. $\dfrac{3\pi}{4} = \dfrac{3\pi}{4}\left(\dfrac{180°}{\pi}\right) = 135°$

5. $-\dfrac{7\pi}{6} = -\dfrac{7\pi}{6}\left(\dfrac{180°}{\pi}\right) = -210°$

6. $4 = 4\left(\dfrac{180°}{\pi}\right) \approx 229.18°$

7. $r = 150\text{ cm},\ s = 200\text{ cm}$

(a) $s = r\theta \Rightarrow 200 = 150\theta \Rightarrow \theta = \dfrac{200}{150} = \dfrac{4}{3}$

(b) $A = \dfrac{1}{2}r^2\theta \Rightarrow A = \dfrac{1}{2}(150)^2\left(\dfrac{4}{3}\right) = \dfrac{1}{2}(22{,}500)\left(\dfrac{4}{3}\right) = 15{,}000\text{ cm}^2$

8. $r = \dfrac{1}{2}\text{ in.},\ s = 1\text{ in.}$

$s = r\theta \Rightarrow 1 = \dfrac{1}{2}\theta \Rightarrow \theta = 2\text{ radians}$

9. **(a)** The speed of ray OP is $\omega = \dfrac{\pi}{18}$ radian per sec. Since $\omega = \dfrac{\theta}{t}$, then in 6 sec we have the following.

$$\omega = \frac{\theta}{t} \Rightarrow \frac{\pi}{18} = \frac{\theta}{6} \Rightarrow \theta = \frac{6\pi}{18} = \frac{\pi}{3} \text{ radians}$$

(b) From part (a), P generates an angle of $\dfrac{\pi}{3}$ radians in 6 sec. The distance traveled by P along the circle is $s = r\theta \Rightarrow s = 10\left(\dfrac{\pi}{3}\right) = \dfrac{10\pi}{3}$ cm.

(c) $v = \dfrac{s}{t} \Rightarrow \dfrac{\frac{10\pi}{3}}{6} = \dfrac{10\pi}{3\cdot 6} = \dfrac{5\pi}{9}$ cm per sec.

For Exercises 10 – 13, use the following copy of the figure on pages 546 and 594 of your text.

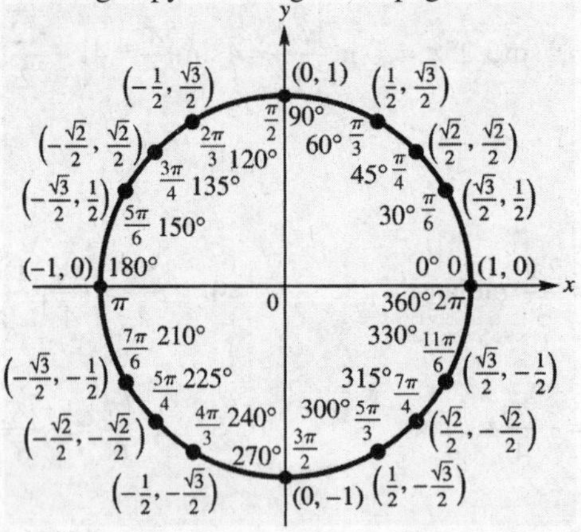

10. Find $\sin\dfrac{3\pi}{4}$.

Since $\dfrac{3\pi}{4}$ is in quadrant II, the reference angle is $\pi - \dfrac{3\pi}{4} = \dfrac{4\pi}{4} - \dfrac{3\pi}{4} = \dfrac{\pi}{4}$. In quadrant II, the sine is positive. Thus, $\sin\dfrac{3\pi}{4} = \sin\dfrac{\pi}{4} = \dfrac{\sqrt{2}}{2}$.

Converting $\dfrac{3\pi}{4}$ to degrees, we have $\dfrac{3\pi}{4} = \dfrac{3}{4}(180°) = 135°$. The reference angle is $180° - 135° = 45°$.

Thus, $\sin\dfrac{3\pi}{4} = \sin 135° = \sin 45° = \dfrac{\sqrt{2}}{2}$.

11. Find $\cos\left(-\dfrac{7\pi}{6}\right)$.

$-\dfrac{7\pi}{6}$ is coterminal with $-\dfrac{7\pi}{6} + 2\pi = -\dfrac{7\pi}{6} + \dfrac{12\pi}{6} = \dfrac{5\pi}{6}$. Since $\dfrac{5\pi}{6}$ is in quadrant II, the reference angle is $\pi - \dfrac{5\pi}{6} = \dfrac{6\pi}{6} - \dfrac{5\pi}{6} = \dfrac{\pi}{6}$. In quadrant II, the cosine is negative. Thus, $\cos\left(-\dfrac{7\pi}{6}\right) = \cos\dfrac{5\pi}{6} = -\cos\dfrac{\pi}{6} = -\dfrac{\sqrt{3}}{2}$.

Converting $\dfrac{5\pi}{6}$ to degrees, we have $\dfrac{5\pi}{6} = \dfrac{5}{6}(180°) = 150°$. The reference angle is $180° - 150° = 30°$.

Thus, $\cos\left(-\dfrac{7\pi}{6}\right) = \cos\dfrac{5\pi}{6} = \cos 150° = -\cos 30° = -\dfrac{\sqrt{3}}{2}$.

12. $\tan\dfrac{3\pi}{2} = \tan 270°$ is undefined.

13. $\sec\dfrac{2\pi}{3} = \sec\left(\dfrac{2\pi}{3}\cdot\dfrac{180°}{\pi}\right) = \sec 120° = -\sec 60° = -2$

14. **(a)** $\sin s = .8258$

$s \approx .9716$

(b) Since $\cos\dfrac{\pi}{3} = \dfrac{1}{2}$ and $0 \le \dfrac{\pi}{3} \le \dfrac{\pi}{2}$, $s = \dfrac{\pi}{3}$.

15. $y = 3 - 6\sin\left(2x + \dfrac{\pi}{2}\right) = 3 - 6\sin 2\left(x + \dfrac{\pi}{4}\right) = 3 - 6\sin 2\left[x - \left(-\dfrac{\pi}{4}\right)\right]$

(a) $\dfrac{2\pi}{2} = \pi$

(b) 6

(c) $[-3, 9]$

(d) The y-intercept occurs when $x = 0$.

$$-6\sin\left(2\cdot 0 + \frac{\pi}{2}\right) + 3 = -6\sin\left(0 + \frac{\pi}{2}\right) + 3 = -6\sin\left(\frac{\pi}{2}\right) + 3 = -6(1) + 3 = -6 + 3 = -3$$

(e) $\dfrac{\pi}{4}$ unit to the left $\left(\text{that is, } -\dfrac{\pi}{4}\right)$

16. $y = -\cos 2x$

Period: $\dfrac{2\pi}{2} = \pi$ and Amplitude: $|-1| = 1$

Divide the interval $[0, \pi]$ into four equal parts to get the x-values that will yield minimum and maximum points and x-intercepts. Then make a table. Repeat this cycle for the interval $[-\pi, 0]$.

x	0	$\frac{\pi}{4}$	$\frac{\pi}{2}$	$\frac{3\pi}{4}$	π
$2x$	0	$\frac{\pi}{2}$	π	$\frac{3\pi}{2}$	2π
$\cos 2x$	1	0	−1	0	1
$-\cos 2x$	−1	0	1	0	−1

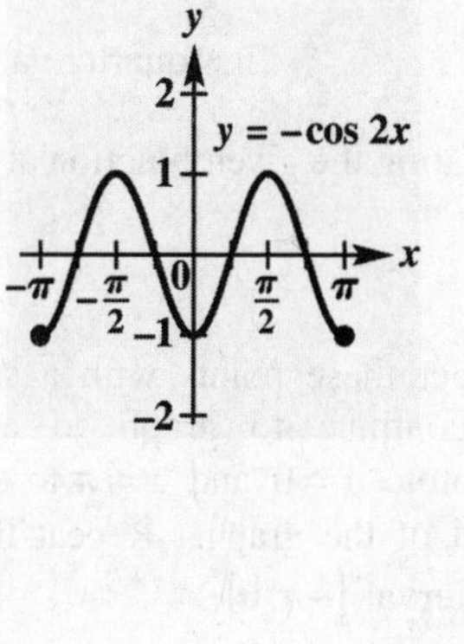

17. $y=-\csc 2x$

Step 1 Graph the corresponding reciprocal function $y=-\sin 2x$ The period is $\frac{2\pi}{2}=\pi$ and its amplitude is $|-1|=1$. One period is in the interval $0\le x\le\pi$. Dividing the interval into four equal parts gives us the following key points.

$$(0,0),\ \left(\frac{\pi}{2},-1\right),\ \left(\frac{\pi}{2},0\right),\ \left(\frac{3\pi}{4},1\right),\ (\pi,0)$$

Step 2 The vertical asymptotes of $y=-\csc 2x$ are at the x-intercepts of $y=-\sin 2x$, which are $x=0, x=\frac{\pi}{2}$, and $x=\pi$. Continuing this pattern to the right, we also have a vertical asymptotes of $x=\frac{3\pi}{2}$ and $x=2\pi$.

Step 3 Sketch the graph.

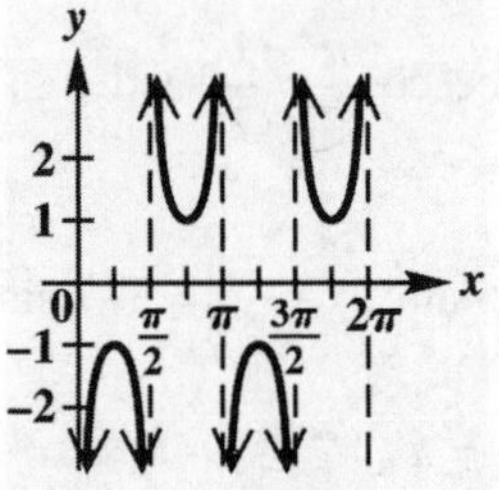

18. $y=\tan\left(x-\frac{\pi}{2}\right)$

Period: π

Vertical translation: none

Phase shift (horizontal translation): $\frac{\pi}{2}$ units to the right

Because the function is to be graphed over a two-period interval, locate three adjacent vertical asymptotes. Because asymptotes of the graph $y=\tan x$ occur at $-\frac{\pi}{2}$, and $\frac{\pi}{2}$, the following equations can be solved to locate asymptotes.

$$x-\frac{\pi}{2}=-\frac{\pi}{2}\Rightarrow x=0 \text{ and } x-\frac{\pi}{2}=\frac{\pi}{2}\Rightarrow x=\pi$$

Divide the interval $(0,\pi)$ into four equal parts to obtain the following key x-values.

first-quarter value: $\frac{\pi}{4}$ middle value: $\frac{\pi}{2}$; third-quarter value: $\frac{3\pi}{4}$

Evaluating the given function at these three key x-values gives the following points.

$$\left(\frac{\pi}{4},-1\right),\ \left(\frac{\pi}{2},0\right),\ \left(\frac{3\pi}{4},1\right)$$

Connect these points with a smooth curve and continue to graph to approach the asymptote $x=0$ and $x=\pi$ to complete one period of the graph. Repeat this cycle for the interval $[-\pi,0]$.

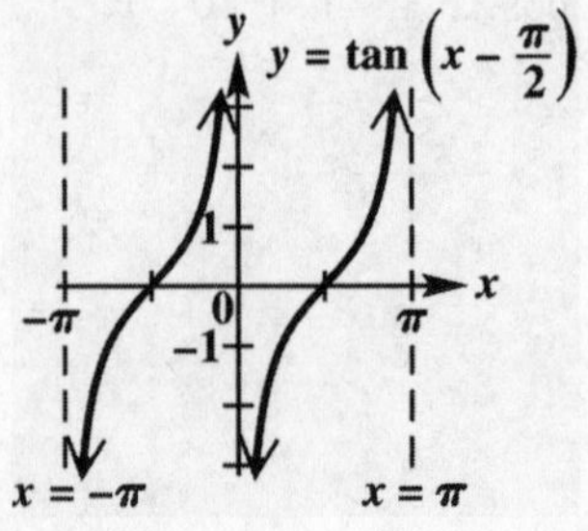

19. $y = -1 + 2\sin(x + \pi)$

Step 1 Find the interval whose length is $\frac{2\pi}{b}$.

$$0 \le x + \pi \le 2\pi \Rightarrow \Rightarrow -\pi \le x \le \pi$$

Step 2 Divide the period into four equal parts to get the following x-values.

$$-\pi,\ -\frac{\pi}{2},\ 0,\ \frac{\pi}{2},\ \pi$$

Step 3 Evaluate the function for each of the five x-values

x	$-\frac{\pi}{2}$	$-\frac{\pi}{2}$	0	$\frac{\pi}{2}$	π
$x+\pi$	0	$\frac{\pi}{2}$	π	$\frac{3\pi}{2}$	2π
$\sin(x+\pi)$	0	1	0	-1	0
$2\sin(x+\pi)$	0	2	0	-2	0
$-1+2\sin(x+\pi)$	-1	1	-1	-3	-1

Steps 4 and 5 Plot the points found in the table and join them with a sinusoidal curve. Repeat this cycle for the interval $[-\pi, 0]$.

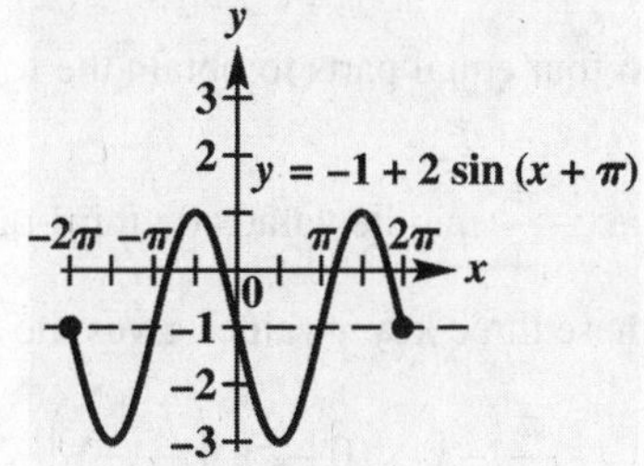

The amplitude is $|2|$, which is 2.

The period is 2π.

The vertical translation is 1 unit down.

The phase shift is π units to the left.

20. $y=-2-\cot\left(x-\frac{\pi}{2}\right)$

Period: $\frac{\pi}{b}=\frac{\pi}{1}=\pi$

Vertical translation: 2 units down

Phase shift (horizontal translation): $\frac{\pi}{2}$ units to the right

Because the function is to be graphed over a two-period interval, locate three adjacent vertical asymptotes. Because asymptotes of the graph $y=\cot x$ occur at multiples of π, the following equations can be solved to locate asymptotes.

$$x-\frac{\pi}{2}=-\pi,\ x-\frac{\pi}{2}=0, \text{ and } x-\frac{\pi}{2}=\pi$$

Solve each of these equations.

$$x-\frac{\pi}{2}=-\pi \Rightarrow x=-\frac{\pi}{2}$$

$$x-\frac{\pi}{2}=0 \Rightarrow x=\frac{\pi}{2}$$

$$x-\frac{\pi}{2}=\pi \Rightarrow x=\frac{3\pi}{2}$$

Divide the interval $\left(-\frac{\pi}{2},\frac{\pi}{2}\right)$ into four equal parts to obtain the following key x-values.

first-quarter value: $-\frac{\pi}{4}$ middle value: 0; third-quarter value: $\frac{\pi}{4}$

Evaluating the given function at these three key x-values gives the following points.

$$\left(-\frac{\pi}{4},-3\right),\ (0,-2),\ \left(\frac{\pi}{4},-1\right)$$

Connect these points with a smooth curve and continue to graph to approach the asymptote $x=-\frac{\pi}{2}$ and $x=\frac{\pi}{2}$ to complete one period of the graph. Sketch the identical curve between the asymptotes $x=\frac{\pi}{2}$ and $x=\frac{3\pi}{2}$ to complete a second period of the graph.

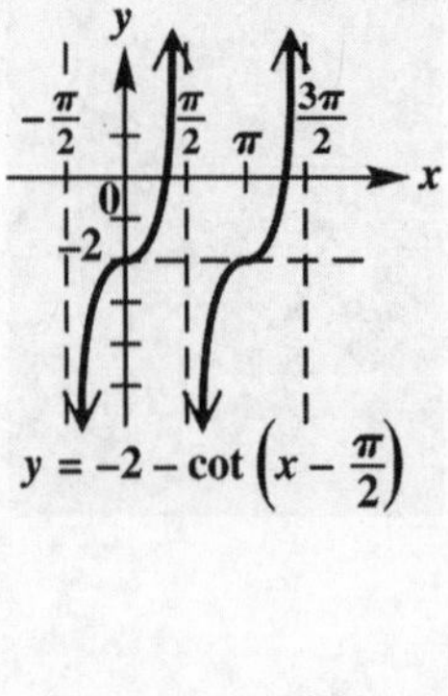

21. **(a)** $f(x) = 17.5\sin\left[\frac{\pi}{6}(x-4)\right] + 67.5$

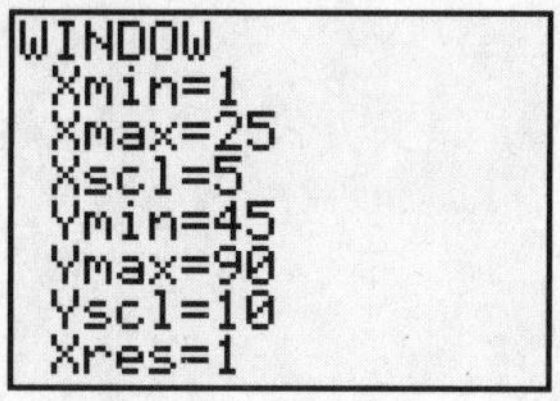

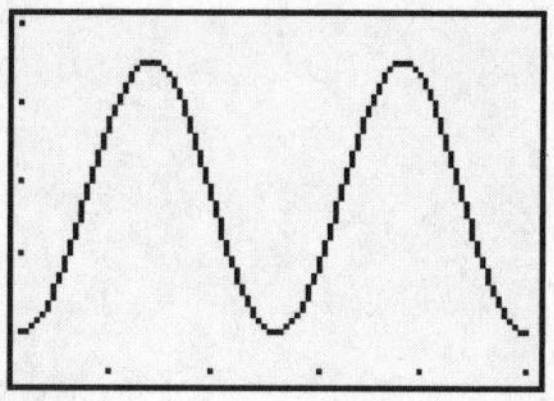

(b) Amplitude: 17.5; Period: $\frac{2\pi}{\frac{\pi}{6}} = 2\pi \cdot \frac{6}{\pi} = 12$;

Phase shift: 4 units to the right; Vertical translation: 67.5 units up

(c) For the month of December, $x = 12$.

$$f(12) = 17.5\sin\left[\frac{\pi}{6}(12-4)\right] + 67.5 = 17.5\sin\left(\frac{4\pi}{3}\right) + 67.5 = 17.5\left(-\frac{\sqrt{3}}{2}\right) + 67.5 \approx 52°$$

(d) A minimum of 50 occurring at $x = 13 = 12 + 1$ implies 50°F in January.

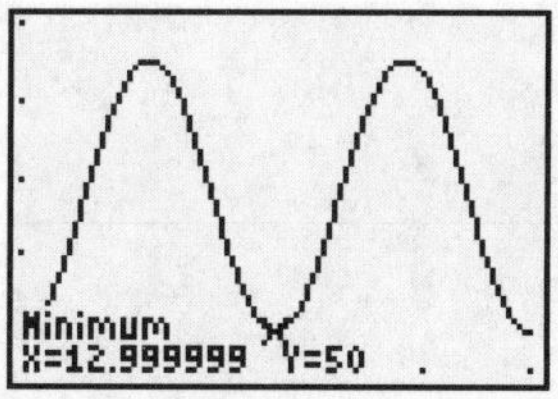

A maximum of 85 occurring at $x = 7$ and $x = 19 = 12 + 7$ implies 85°F in July.

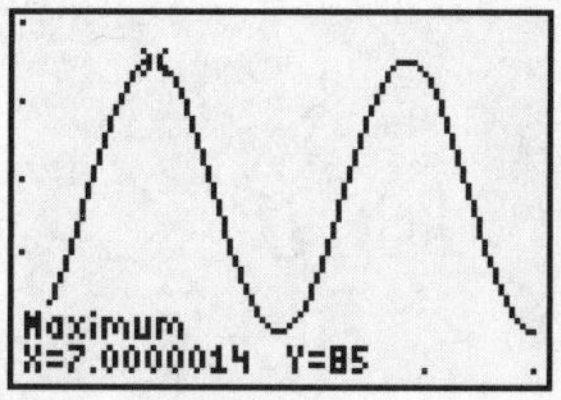

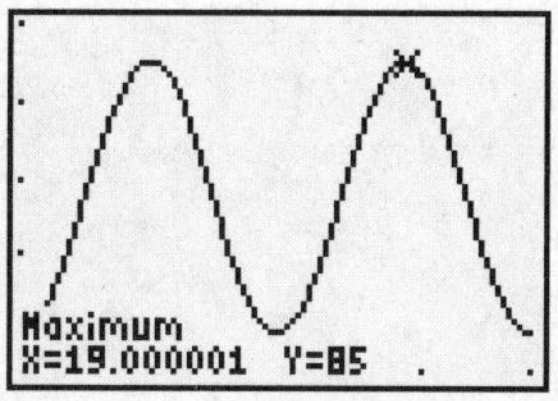

(e) Approximately 67.5° would be an average yearly temperature. This is the vertical translation.

22. $s(t) = -4\cos 8\pi t$, $a = |-4| = 4$, $\omega = 8\pi$

(a) maximum height = amplitude = $a = |-4| = 4$ in.

(b) $s(t) = -4\cos 8\pi t = 4 \Rightarrow \cos 8\pi t = -1 \Rightarrow 8\pi t = \pi \Rightarrow t = \frac{1}{8}$

The weight first reaches its maximum height after $\frac{1}{8}$ sec.

(c) frequency $= \frac{\omega}{2\pi} = \frac{8\pi}{2\pi} = 4$ cycles per sec; period $= \frac{2\pi}{\omega} = \frac{2\pi}{8\pi} = \frac{1}{4}$ sec

Chapter 7

TRIGONOMETRIC IDENTITIES AND EQUATIONS

Section 7.1: Fundamental Identities

1. By a negative-angle identity, $\tan(-x) = -\tan x$. Since $\tan x = 2.6$, $\tan(-x) = -\tan x = -2.6$. Thus, we have the following: If $\tan x = 2.6$, then $\tan(-x) = \underline{-2.6}$.

3. By a reciprocal identity, $\cot x = \frac{1}{\tan x}$. Since $\tan x = 1.6$, $\cot x = \frac{1}{1.6} = .625$. Thus, we have the following: If $\tan x = 1.6$, then $\cot x = \underline{.625}$.

5. $\cos s = \frac{3}{4}$, s is in quadrant I.

An identity that relates sine and cosine is $\sin^2 s + \cos^2 s = 1$.

$$\sin^2 s + \cos^2 s = 1 \Rightarrow \sin^2 s + \left(\frac{3}{4}\right)^2 = 1 \Rightarrow \sin^2 s + \frac{9}{16} = 1 \Rightarrow \sin^2 s = 1 - \frac{9}{16} = \frac{7}{16} \Rightarrow \sin s = \pm\frac{\sqrt{7}}{4}$$

Since s is in quadrant I, $\sin s = \frac{\sqrt{7}}{4}$.

7. $\cos(-s) = \frac{\sqrt{5}}{5}$, $\tan s < 0$

Since $\cos(-s) = \frac{\sqrt{5}}{5}$, we have $\cos s = \frac{\sqrt{5}}{5}$ by a negative angle identity.

An identity that relates sine and cosine is $\sin^2 s + \cos^2 s = 1$.

$$\sin^2 s + \cos^2 s = 1 \Rightarrow \sin^2 s + \left(\frac{\sqrt{5}}{5}\right)^2 = 1 \Rightarrow \sin^2 s + \frac{5}{25} = 1 \Rightarrow \sin^2 s + \frac{1}{5} = 1$$

$$\sin^2 s = 1 - \frac{1}{5} = \frac{4}{5} \Rightarrow \sin s = \pm\frac{2}{\sqrt{5}} = \pm\frac{2}{\sqrt{5}} \cdot \frac{\sqrt{5}}{\sqrt{5}} = \pm\frac{2\sqrt{5}}{5}$$

Since $\tan s < 0$ and $\cos s > 0$, s is in quadrant IV, so $\sin s < 0$. Thus, $\sin s = -\frac{2\sqrt{5}}{5}$.

9. $\sec s = \frac{11}{4}$, $\tan s < 0$

Since $\cos s = \frac{1}{\sec s}$, $\cos s = \frac{1}{\frac{11}{4}} = \frac{4}{11}$. Using the identity $\sin^2 s + \cos^2 s = 1$, we have the following.

$$\sin^2 s + \cos^2 s = 1 \Rightarrow \sin^2 s + \left(\frac{4}{11}\right)^2 = 1 \Rightarrow \sin^2 s + \frac{16}{121} = 1$$

$$\sin^2 s = 1 - \frac{16}{121} \Rightarrow \sin^2 s = \frac{105}{121} \Rightarrow \sin s = \pm\frac{\sqrt{105}}{11}$$

Since $\tan s < 0$ and $\sec s > 0$, s is in quadrant IV, so $\sin s < 0$. Thus, $\sin s = -\frac{\sqrt{105}}{11}$.

11. The quadrants are given so that one can determine which sign $(+ \text{ or } -)$ $\sin s$ will take. Since $\sin s = \dfrac{1}{\csc s}$, the sign of $\sin s$ will be the same as $\csc s$.

12. $\sin(-x) = \underline{-\sin x}$

13. Since $f(-x) = \sin(-x) = -\sin x = -f(x)$, $f(x) = \sin x$ is odd.

14. $\cos(-x) = \underline{\cos x}$

15. Since $f(-x) = \cos(-x) = \cos x = f(x)$, $f(x) = \cos x$ is even

16. $\tan(-x) = \underline{-\tan x}$

17. Since $f(-x) = \tan(-x) = -\tan x = -f(x)$, $f(x) = \tan x$ is odd.

19. This is the graph of $f(x) = \csc x$. It is symmetric about the origin. Moreover, since $f(-x) = \csc(-x) = \dfrac{1}{\sin(-x)} = \dfrac{1}{-\sin x} = -\csc x = -f(x)$, $f(-x) = -f(x)$.

21. $\sin\theta = \dfrac{2}{3}, \theta$ in quadrant II

Since θ is in quadrant II, the sine and cosecant function values are positive. The cosine, tangent, cotangent, and secant function values are negative.

$$\sin^2\theta + \cos^2\theta = 1 \Rightarrow \cos^2\theta = 1 - \sin^2\theta = 1 - \left(\frac{2}{3}\right)^2 = 1 - \frac{4}{9} = \frac{5}{9} \Rightarrow \cos\theta = -\frac{\sqrt{5}}{3}, \text{ since } \cos\theta < 0$$

$$\tan\theta = \frac{\sin\theta}{\cos\theta} = \frac{\frac{2}{3}}{-\frac{\sqrt{5}}{3}} = -\frac{2}{\sqrt{5}} = -\frac{2}{\sqrt{5}} \cdot \frac{\sqrt{5}}{\sqrt{5}} = -\frac{2\sqrt{5}}{5}; \cot\theta = \frac{1}{\tan\theta} = \frac{1}{-\frac{2}{\sqrt{5}}} = -\frac{\sqrt{5}}{2}$$

$$\sec\theta = \frac{1}{\cos\theta} = \frac{1}{-\frac{\sqrt{5}}{3}} = -\frac{3}{\sqrt{5}} = -\frac{3}{\sqrt{5}} \cdot \frac{\sqrt{5}}{\sqrt{5}} = -\frac{3\sqrt{5}}{5}; \csc\theta = \frac{1}{\sin\theta} = \frac{1}{\frac{2}{3}} = \frac{3}{2}$$

23. $\tan\theta = -\dfrac{1}{4}, \theta$ in quadrant IV

Since θ is in quadrant IV, the cosine and secant function values are positive. The sine, tangent, cotangent, and cosecant function values are negative.

$$\sec^2\theta = 1 + \tan^2\theta = 1 + \left(-\frac{1}{4}\right)^2 = 1 + \frac{1}{16} = \frac{17}{16} \Rightarrow \sec\theta = \frac{\sqrt{17}}{4}, \text{ since } \sec\theta > 0$$

$$\cos\theta = \frac{1}{\sec\theta} = \frac{1}{\frac{\sqrt{17}}{4}} = \frac{4}{\sqrt{17}} = \frac{4}{\sqrt{17}} \cdot \frac{\sqrt{17}}{\sqrt{17}} = \frac{4\sqrt{17}}{17}$$

$$\sin^2\theta + \cos^2\theta = 1 \Rightarrow \sin^2\theta = 1 - \cos^2\theta = 1 - \left(\frac{4}{\sqrt{17}}\right)^2$$

$$\sin^2\theta = 1 - \frac{16}{17} = \frac{1}{17} \Rightarrow \sin\theta = -\frac{1}{\sqrt{17}} = -\frac{1}{\sqrt{17}} \cdot \frac{\sqrt{17}}{\sqrt{17}} = -\frac{\sqrt{17}}{17}, \text{ since } \sin\theta < 0$$

$$\csc\theta = \frac{1}{\sin\theta} = \frac{1}{-\frac{1}{\sqrt{17}}} = -\sqrt{17}$$

25. $\cot\theta = \frac{4}{3}, \sin\theta > 0$

Since $\cot\theta > 0$ and $\sin\theta > 0, \theta$ is in quadrant I, so all the function values are positive.

$$\tan = \frac{1}{\cot\theta} = \frac{1}{\frac{4}{3}} = \frac{3}{4}$$

$$\sec^2\theta = 1 + \tan^2\theta = 1 + \left(\frac{3}{4}\right)^2 = 1 + \frac{9}{16} = \frac{25}{16} \Rightarrow \sec\theta = \frac{5}{4}, \text{ since } \sec\theta > 0$$

$$\cos\theta = \frac{1}{\sec\theta} = \frac{1}{\frac{5}{4}} = \frac{4}{5}$$

$$\sin^2\theta = 1 - \cos^2\theta = 1 - \left(\frac{4}{5}\right)^2 = 1 - \frac{16}{25} = \frac{9}{25} \Rightarrow \sin\theta = \frac{3}{5}, \text{ since } \sin\theta > 0$$

$$\csc\theta = \frac{1}{\sin\theta} = \frac{1}{\frac{3}{5}} = \frac{5}{3}$$

27. $\sec\theta = \frac{4}{3}, \sin\theta < 0$

Since $\sec\theta > 0$ and $\sin\theta < 0, \theta$ is in quadrant IV. Since θ is in quadrant IV, the cosine function value is positive. The tangent, cotangent, and cosecant function values are negative.

$$\cos\theta = \frac{1}{\sec\theta} = \frac{1}{\frac{4}{3}} = \frac{3}{4}$$

$$\sin^2\theta = 1 - \cos^2\theta = 1 - \left(\frac{3}{4}\right)^2 = 1 - \frac{9}{16} = \frac{7}{16} \Rightarrow \sin\theta = -\frac{\sqrt{7}}{4}, \text{ since } \sin\theta < 0$$

$$\tan\theta = \frac{\sin\theta}{\cos\theta} = \frac{-\frac{\sqrt{7}}{4}}{\frac{3}{4}} = -\frac{\sqrt{7}}{3};\ \cot\theta = \frac{1}{\tan\theta} = -\frac{1}{-\frac{\sqrt{7}}{3}} = -\frac{3}{\sqrt{7}}\cdot\frac{\sqrt{7}}{\sqrt{7}} = -\frac{3\sqrt{7}}{7}$$

$$\csc\theta = \frac{1}{\sin\theta} = -\frac{1}{-\frac{\sqrt{7}}{4}} = -\frac{4}{\sqrt{7}}\cdot\frac{\sqrt{7}}{\sqrt{7}} = -\frac{4\sqrt{7}}{7}$$

29. Since $\frac{\cos x}{\sin x} = \cot x$, choose expression B.

31. Since $\cos(-x) = \cos x$, choose expression E.

33. Since $1 = \sin^2 x + \cos^2 x$, choose expression A.

35. Since $\sec^2 x - 1 = \tan^2 x = \frac{\sin^2 x}{\cos^2 x}$, choose expression A.

37. Since $1 + \sin^2 x = \left(\csc^2 x - \cot^2 x\right) + \sin^2 x$, choose expression D.

39. It is incorrect to state $1+\cot^2=\csc^2$. Cotangent and cosecant are functions of some variable such as $\theta, x,$ or t. An acceptable statement would be $1+\cot^2\theta=\csc^2\theta$.

41. Find $\sin\theta$ if $\cos\theta=\dfrac{x}{x+1}$.

Since $\sin^2\theta+\cos^2\theta=1$ and $\cos\theta=\dfrac{x}{x+1}$, we have the following.

$$\sin^2\theta=1-\cos^2\theta=1-\left(\frac{x}{x+1}\right)^2=1-\frac{x^2}{(x+1)^2}=\frac{(x+1)^2-x^2}{(x+1)^2}=\frac{x^2+2x+1-x^2}{(x+1)^2}=\frac{2x+1}{(x+1)^2}$$

Thus, $\sin\theta=\dfrac{\pm\sqrt{2x+1}}{x+1}$.

43. $\sin^2x+\cos^2x=1\Rightarrow\sin^2x=1-\cos^2x\Rightarrow\sin x=\pm\sqrt{1-\cos^2x}$

45. $\tan^2x+1=\sec^2x\Rightarrow\tan^2x=\sec^2x-1\Rightarrow\tan x=\pm\sqrt{\sec^2-1}$

47. $\csc x=\dfrac{1}{\sin x}\Rightarrow\csc x=\dfrac{1}{\pm\sqrt{1-\cos^2x}}=\dfrac{\pm1}{\sqrt{1-\cos^2x}}\cdot\dfrac{\sqrt{1-\cos^2x}}{\sqrt{1-\cos^2x}}=\dfrac{\pm\sqrt{1-\cos^2x}}{1-\cos^2x}$

49. $\cot\theta\sin\theta=\dfrac{\cos\theta}{\sin\theta}\cdot\sin\theta=\cos\theta$

51. $\cos\theta\csc\theta=\cos\theta\cdot\dfrac{1}{\sin\theta}=\dfrac{\cos\theta}{\sin\theta}=\cot\theta$

53. $\sin^2\theta\left(\csc^2\theta-1\right)=\sin^2\theta\left(\dfrac{1}{\sin^2\theta}-1\right)=\dfrac{\sin^2\theta}{\sin^2\theta}-\sin^2\theta=1-\sin^2\theta=\cos^2\theta$

55. $(1-\cos\theta)(1+\sec\theta)=1+\sec\theta-\cos\theta-\cos\theta\sec\theta=1+\sec\theta-\cos\theta-\cos\theta\left(\dfrac{1}{\cos\theta}\right)$

$=1+\sec\theta-\cos\theta-1=\sec\theta-\cos\theta$

57. $\dfrac{\cos^2\theta-\sin^2\theta}{\sin\theta\cos\theta}=\dfrac{\cos^2\theta}{\sin\theta\cos\theta}-\dfrac{\sin^2\theta}{\sin\theta\cos\theta}=\dfrac{\cos\theta}{\sin\theta}-\dfrac{\sin\theta}{\cos\theta}=\cot\theta-\tan\theta$

59. $\sec\theta-\cos\theta=\dfrac{1}{\cos\theta}-\cos\theta=\dfrac{1}{\cos\theta}-\dfrac{\cos^2\theta}{\cos\theta}=\dfrac{1-\cos^2\theta}{\cos\theta}=\dfrac{\sin^2\theta}{\cos\theta}=\dfrac{\sin\theta}{\cos\theta}\cdot\sin\theta=\tan\theta\sin\theta$

61. $\sin\theta(\csc\theta-\sin\theta)=\sin\theta\csc\theta-\sin^2\theta=\sin\theta\cdot\dfrac{1}{\sin\theta}-\sin^2\theta=1-\sin^2\theta=\cos^2\theta$

63. $\sin^2\theta+\tan^2\theta+\cos^2\theta=\left(\sin^2\theta+\cos^2\theta\right)+\tan^2\theta=1+\tan^2\theta=\sec^2\theta$

65. Since $\cos x = \frac{1}{5}$, which is positive, x is in quadrant I or quadrant IV.

$$\sin x = \pm\sqrt{1-\cos^2 x} = \pm\sqrt{1-\left(\frac{1}{5}\right)^2} = \pm\sqrt{\frac{24}{25}} = \pm\frac{\sqrt{24}}{5} = \pm\frac{2\sqrt{6}}{5}$$

$$\tan x = \frac{\sin x}{\cos x} = \frac{\pm\frac{2\sqrt{6}}{5}}{\frac{1}{5}} = \pm 2\sqrt{6};\ \sec x = \frac{1}{\cos x} = \frac{1}{\frac{1}{5}} = 5$$

Quadrant I:

$$\frac{\sec x - \tan x}{\sin x} = \frac{5-2\sqrt{6}}{\frac{2\sqrt{6}}{5}} = \frac{25-10\sqrt{6}}{2\sqrt{6}} = \frac{25-10\sqrt{6}}{2\sqrt{6}}\cdot\frac{\sqrt{6}}{\sqrt{6}} = \frac{25\sqrt{6}-60}{12}$$

Quadrant IV:

$$\frac{\sec x - \tan x}{\sin x} = \frac{5-\left(-2\sqrt{6}\right)}{-\frac{2\sqrt{6}}{5}} = \frac{25+10\sqrt{6}}{-2\sqrt{6}} = \frac{25+10\sqrt{6}}{-2\sqrt{6}}\cdot\frac{-\sqrt{6}}{-\sqrt{6}} = \frac{-25\sqrt{6}-60}{12}$$

67. $y = \sin(-2x) \Rightarrow y = -\sin(2x)$

68. It is the negative of $\sin(2x)$.

69. $y = \cos(-4x) \Rightarrow y = \cos(4x)$

70. It is the same function.

71. **(a)** $y = \sin(-4x) \Rightarrow y = -\sin(4x)$

(b) $y = \cos(-2x) \Rightarrow y = \cos(2x)$

(c) $y = -5\sin(-3x) \Rightarrow y = -5[-\sin(3x)] \Rightarrow y = 5\sin(3x)$

In Exercises 73 & 75, the functions are graphed in the following window.

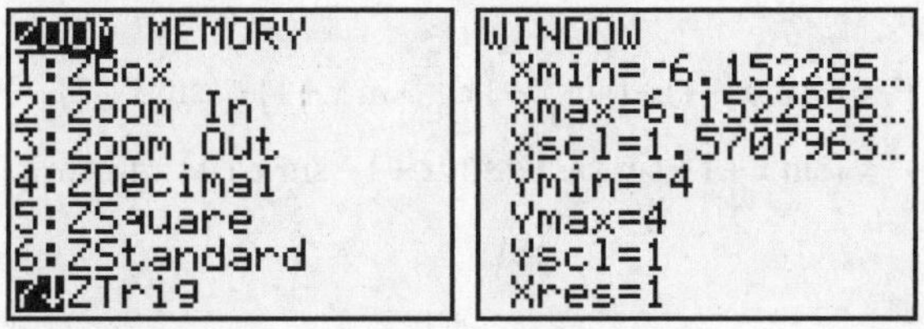

73. The equation $2\sin s = \sin 2s$ is not an identity.

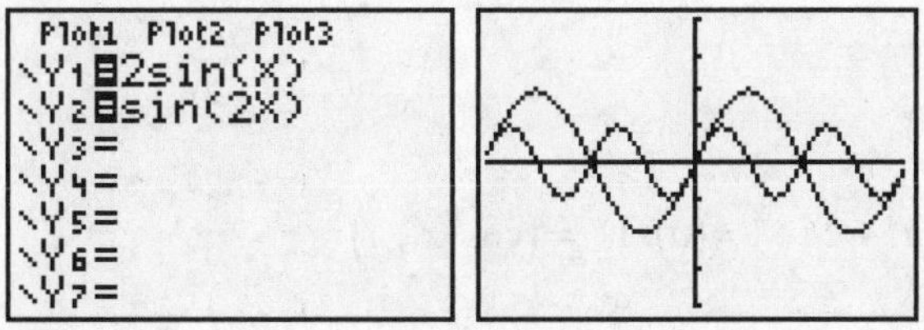

75. The equation $\cos 2x = \cos^2 x - \sin^2 x$ is an identity.

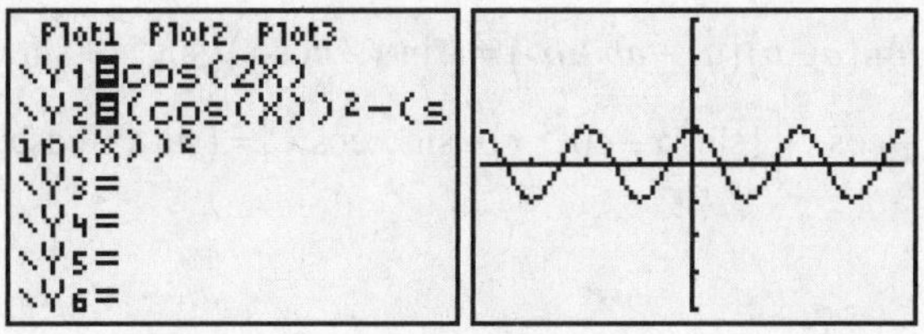

Section 7.2: Verifying Trigonometric Identities

1. $$\cot\theta+\frac{1}{\cot\theta}=\cot\theta+\tan\theta=\frac{\cos\theta}{\sin\theta}+\frac{\sin\theta}{\cos\theta}=\frac{\cos^2\theta+\sin^2\theta}{\sin\theta\cos\theta}=\frac{1}{\sin\theta\cos\theta}\text{ or }\csc\theta\sec\theta$$

3. $$\tan s\,(\cot s+\csc s)=\frac{\sin s}{\cos s}\left(\frac{\cos s}{\sin s}+\frac{1}{\sin s}\right)=1+\frac{1}{\cos s}=1+\sec s$$

5. $$\frac{1}{\csc^2\theta}+\frac{1}{\sec^2\theta}=\sin^2\theta+\cos^2\theta=1$$

7. $$\frac{\cos x}{\sec x}+\frac{\sin x}{\csc x}=\frac{\cos x}{\frac{1}{\cos x}}+\frac{\sin x}{\frac{1}{\sin x}}=\cos x\left(\frac{\cos x}{1}\right)+\sin x\left(\frac{\sin x}{1}\right)=\cos^2 x+\sin^2 x=1$$

9. $$(1+\sin t)^2+\cos^2 t=1+2\sin t+\sin^2 t+\cos^2 t$$
$$=1+2\sin t+\left(\sin^2 t+\cos^2 t\right)=1+2\sin t+1=2+2\sin t$$

11. $$\frac{1}{1+\cos x}-\frac{1}{1-\cos x}=\frac{1-\cos x}{(1+\cos x)(1-\cos x)}-\frac{1+\cos x}{(1+\cos x)(1-\cos x)}=\frac{(1-\cos x)-(1+\cos x)}{(1+\cos x)(1-\cos x)}$$
$$=\frac{1-\cos x-1-\cos x}{1-\cos^2 x}=-\frac{2\cos x}{\sin^2 x}$$
or $$-\frac{2\cos x}{\sin^2 x}=-\frac{2\cos x}{\sin x\sin x}=-2\left(\frac{\cos x}{\sin x}\right)\left(\frac{1}{\sin x}\right)=-2\cot x\csc x$$

13. $\sin^2\theta-1=(\sin\theta+1)(\sin\theta-1)$

15. $$(\sin x+1)^2-(\sin x-1)^2=\left[(\sin x+1)+(\sin x-1)\right]\left[(\sin x+1)-(\sin x-1)\right]$$
$$=(\sin x+1+\sin x-1)(\sin x+1-\sin x+1)=(2\sin x)(2)=4\sin x$$

17. $2\sin^2 x+3\sin x+1$

Let $a=\sin x$.

$$2\sin^2 x+3\sin x+1=2a^2+3a+1=(2a+1)(a+1)=(2\sin x+1)(\sin x+1)$$

19. $\cos^4 x+2\cos^2 x+1$

Let $\cos^2 x=a$.

$$\cos^4 x+2\cos^2 x+1=a^2+2a+1=(a+1)^2=\left(\cos^2 x+1\right)^2$$

21. $\sin^3 x-\cos^3 x$

Let $\sin x=a$ and $\cos x=b$.

$$\sin^3 x-\cos^3 x=a^3-b^3=(a-b)\left(a^2+ab+b^2\right)=(\sin x-\cos x)\left(\sin^2 x+\sin x\cos x+\cos^2 x\right)$$
$$=(\sin x-\cos x)\left[\left(\sin^2 x+\cos^2 x\right)+\sin x\cos x\right]=(\sin x-\cos x)(1+\sin x\cos x)$$

23. $\tan\theta\cos\theta = \dfrac{\sin\theta}{\cos\theta}\cos\theta = \sin\theta$

25. $\sec r\cos r = \dfrac{1}{\cos r}\cdot\cos r = 1$

27. $\dfrac{\sin\beta\tan\beta}{\cos\beta} = \tan\beta\tan\beta = \tan^2\beta$

29. $\sec^2 x - 1 = \dfrac{1}{\cos^2 x} - 1 = \dfrac{1}{\cos^2 x} - \dfrac{\cos^2 x}{\cos^2 x} = \dfrac{1-\cos^2 x}{\cos^2 x} = \dfrac{\sin^2 x}{\cos^2 x} = \tan^2 x$

31. $\dfrac{\sin^2 x}{\cos^2 x} + \sin x\csc x = \tan^2 x + \sin x\cdot\dfrac{1}{\sin x} = \tan^2 x + 1 = \sec^2 x$

33. Verify $\dfrac{\cot\theta}{\csc\theta} = \cos\theta.$

$$\frac{\cot\theta}{\csc\theta} = \frac{\frac{\cos\theta}{\sin\theta}}{\frac{1}{\sin\theta}} = \frac{\cos\theta}{\sin\theta}\cdot\frac{\sin\theta}{1} = \cos\theta$$

35. Verify $\dfrac{1-\sin^2\beta}{\cos\beta} = \cos\beta.$

$$\frac{1-\sin^2\beta}{\cos\beta} = \frac{\cos^2\beta}{\cos\beta} = \cos\beta$$

37. Verify

$$\cos^2\theta(\tan^2\theta+1) = \cos^2\theta\left(\frac{\sin^2\theta}{\cos^2\theta}+1\right)$$
$$= \cos^2\theta\left(\frac{\sin^2\theta}{\cos^2\theta}+\frac{\cos^2\theta}{\cos^2\theta}\right) = \cos^2\theta\left(\frac{\sin^2\theta+\cos^2\theta}{\cos^2\theta}\right) = \cos^2\theta\left(\frac{1}{\cos^2\theta}\right) = 1$$

39. Verify $\cot s + \tan s = \sec s\csc s.$

$$\cot s + \tan s = \frac{\cos s}{\sin s} + \frac{\sin s}{\cos s}$$
$$= \frac{\cos^2 s}{\sin s\cos s} + \frac{\sin^2 s}{\sin s\cos s} = \frac{\cos^2 s + \sin^2 s}{\cos s\sin s} = \frac{1}{\cos s\sin s} = \frac{1}{\cos s}\cdot\frac{1}{\sin s} = \sec s\csc s$$

41. Verify $\dfrac{\cos\alpha}{\sec\alpha} + \dfrac{\sin\alpha}{\csc\alpha} = \sec^2\alpha - \tan^2\alpha.$

Working with the left side, we have $\dfrac{\cos\alpha}{\sec\alpha} + \dfrac{\sin\alpha}{\csc\alpha} = \dfrac{\cos\alpha}{\frac{1}{\cos\alpha}} + \dfrac{\sin\alpha}{\frac{1}{\sin\alpha}} = \cos^2\alpha + \sin^2\alpha = 1.$

Working with the right side, we have $\sec^2\alpha - \tan^2\alpha = 1.$

Since $\dfrac{\cos\alpha}{\sec\alpha} + \dfrac{\sin\alpha}{\csc\alpha} = 1 = \sec^2\alpha - \tan^2\alpha,$ the statement has been verified.

43. Verify $\sin^4\theta - \cos^4\theta = 2\sin^2\theta - 1.$

$$\sin^4\theta - \cos^4\theta = \left(\sin^2\theta+\cos^2\theta\right)\left(\sin^2\theta-\cos^2\theta\right) = 1\cdot\left(\sin^2\theta-\cos^2\theta\right) = \sin^2\theta - \cos^2\theta$$
$$= \sin^2\theta - \left(1-\sin^2\theta\right) = \sin^2\theta - 1 + \sin^2\theta = 2\sin^2\theta - 1$$

45. Verify $\left(1-\cos^2\alpha\right)\left(1+\cos^2\alpha\right) = 2\sin^2\alpha - \sin^4\alpha.$

$$\left(1-\cos^2\alpha\right)\left(1+\cos^2\alpha\right) = \sin^2\alpha\left(1+\cos^2\alpha\right) = \sin^2\alpha\left(2-\sin^2\alpha\right) = 2\sin^2\alpha - \sin^4\alpha$$

47. Verify $\dfrac{\cos\theta+1}{\tan^2\theta}=\dfrac{\cos\theta}{\sec\theta-1}$.

Work with the left side.

$$\frac{\cos\theta+1}{\tan^2\theta}=\frac{\cos\theta+1}{\sec^2\theta-1}=\frac{\cos\theta+1}{\frac{1}{\cos^2\theta}-1}$$

$$=\frac{(\cos\theta+1)\cos^2\theta}{\left(\frac{1}{\cos^2\theta}-1\right)\cos^2\theta}=\frac{\cos^2\theta(\cos\theta+1)}{1-\cos^2\theta}=\frac{\cos^2\theta(\cos\theta+1)}{(1+\cos\theta)(1-\cos\theta)}=\frac{\cos^2\theta}{1-\cos\theta}$$

Now work with the right side.

$$\frac{\cos\theta}{\sec\theta-1}=\frac{\cos\theta}{\frac{1}{\cos\theta}-1}=\frac{\cos\theta}{\frac{1}{\cos\theta}}\cdot\frac{\cos\theta}{\cos\theta}=\frac{\cos^2\theta}{1-\cos\theta}$$

Since $\dfrac{\cos\theta+1}{\tan^2\theta}=\dfrac{\cos^2\theta}{1-\cos\theta}=\dfrac{\cos\theta}{\sec\theta-1}$, the statement has been verified.

49. Verify $\dfrac{1}{1-\sin\theta}+\dfrac{1}{1+\sin\theta}=2\sec^2\theta$.

$$\frac{1}{1-\sin\theta}+\frac{1}{1+\sin\theta}=\frac{1+\sin\theta}{(1+\sin\theta)(1-\sin\theta)}+\frac{1-\sin\theta}{(1+\sin\theta)(1-\sin\theta)}$$

$$=\frac{(1+\sin\theta)+(1-\sin\theta)}{(1+\sin\theta)(1-\sin\theta)}=\frac{1+\sin\theta+1-\sin\theta}{(1+\sin\theta)(1-\sin\theta)}=\frac{2}{1-\sin^2\theta}=\frac{2}{\cos^2\theta}=2\sec^2\theta$$

51. Verify $\dfrac{\tan s}{1+\cos s}+\dfrac{\sin s}{1-\cos s}=\cot s+\sec s\csc s$.

$$\frac{\tan s}{1+\cos s}+\frac{\sin s}{1-\cos s}=\frac{\tan s(1-\cos s)}{(1+\cos s)(1-\cos s)}+\frac{\sin s(1+\cos s)}{(1+\cos s)(1-\cos s)}$$

$$=\frac{\tan s(1-\cos s)+\sin s(1+\cos s)}{(1+\cos s)(1-\cos s)}=\frac{\tan s-\sin s+\sin s+\sin s\cos s}{1-\cos^2 s}$$

$$=\frac{\tan s+\sin s\cos s}{\sin^2 s}=\frac{\tan s}{\sin^2 s}+\frac{\sin s\cos s}{\sin^2 s}=\tan s\cdot\frac{1}{\sin^2 s}+\frac{\cos s}{\sin s}$$

$$=\frac{\sin s}{\cos s}\cdot\frac{1}{\sin^2 s}+\cot s=\frac{1}{\cos s}\cdot\frac{1}{\sin s}+\cot s=\sec s\csc s+\cot s$$

53. Verify $\dfrac{\cot\alpha+1}{\cot\alpha-1}=\dfrac{1+\tan\alpha}{1-\tan\alpha}$.

$$\frac{\cot\alpha+1}{\cot\alpha-1}=\frac{\frac{\cos\alpha}{\sin\alpha}+1}{\frac{\cos\alpha}{\sin\alpha}-1}=\frac{\frac{\cos\alpha}{\sin\alpha}+1}{\frac{\cos\alpha}{\sin\alpha}-1}\cdot\frac{\sin\alpha}{\sin\alpha}$$

$$=\frac{\cos\alpha+\sin\alpha}{\cos\alpha-\sin\alpha}=\frac{\cos\alpha+\sin\alpha}{\cos\alpha-\sin\alpha}\cdot\frac{\frac{1}{\cos\alpha}}{\frac{1}{\cos\alpha}}=\frac{\frac{\cos\alpha}{\cos\alpha}+\frac{\sin\alpha}{\cos\alpha}}{\frac{\cos\alpha}{\cos\alpha}-\frac{\sin\alpha}{\cos\alpha}}=\frac{1+\tan\alpha}{1-\tan\alpha}$$

55. Verify $\sin^2\alpha\sec^2\alpha+\sin^2\alpha\csc^2\alpha=\sec^2\alpha$.

$$\sin^2\alpha\sec^2\alpha+\sin^2\alpha\csc^2\alpha=\sin^2\alpha\cdot\frac{1}{\cos^2\alpha}+\sin^2\alpha\cdot\frac{1}{\sin^2\alpha}=\frac{\sin^2\alpha}{\cos^2\alpha}+1=\tan^2\alpha+1=\sec^2\alpha$$

57. Verify $\sec^4 x-\sec^2 x=\tan^4 x+\tan^2 x$.
Simplify left side.

$$\sec^4 x-\sec^2 x=\sec^2 x\left(\sec^2 x-1\right)=\sec^2 x\tan^2 x=\tan^2 x\sec^2 x$$

Simplify right side.

$$\tan^4 x+\tan^2 x=\tan^2 x\left(\tan^2 x+1\right)=\tan^2 x\sec^2 x$$

Since $\sec^4 x-\sec^2 x=\tan^2 x\sec^2 x=\tan^4 x+\tan^2 x$, the statement has been verified.

59. Verify $\sin\theta+\cos\theta=\dfrac{\sin\theta}{1-\frac{\cos\theta}{\sin\theta}}+\dfrac{\cos\theta}{1-\frac{\sin\theta}{\cos\theta}}$.

Working with the right side, we have the following.

$$\frac{\sin\theta}{1-\frac{\cos\theta}{\sin\theta}}+\frac{\cos\theta}{1-\frac{\sin\theta}{\cos\theta}}=\frac{\sin\theta}{1-\frac{\cos\theta}{\sin\theta}}\cdot\frac{\sin\theta}{\sin\theta}+\frac{\cos\theta}{1-\frac{\sin\theta}{\cos\theta}}\cdot\frac{\cos\theta}{\cos\theta}=\frac{\sin^2\theta}{\sin\theta-\cos\theta}+\frac{\cos^2\theta}{\cos\theta-\sin\theta}$$

$$=\frac{\sin^2\theta}{\sin\theta-\cos\theta}+\frac{\cos^2\theta}{-(\sin\theta-\cos\theta)}=\frac{\sin^2\theta}{\sin\theta-\cos\theta}-\frac{\cos^2\theta}{\sin\theta-\cos\theta}$$

$$=\frac{\sin^2\theta-\cos^2\theta}{\sin\theta-\cos\theta}=\frac{(\sin\theta+\cos\theta)(\sin\theta-\cos\theta)}{\sin\theta-\cos\theta}=\sin\theta+\cos\theta$$

61. Verify $\dfrac{\sec^4 s-\tan^4 s}{\sec^2 s+\tan^2 s}=\sec^2 s-\tan^2 s$.

$$\frac{\sec^4 s-\tan^4 s}{\sec^2 s+\tan^2 s}=\frac{\left(\sec^2 s+\tan^2 s\right)\left(\sec^2 s-\tan^2 s\right)}{\sec^2 s+\tan^2 s}=\sec^2 s-\tan^2 s$$

63. Verify $\dfrac{\tan^2 t-1}{\sec^2 t}=\dfrac{\tan t-\cot t}{\tan t+\cot t}$.

Working with the right side, we have the following.

$$\frac{\tan t-\cot t}{\tan t+\cot t}=\frac{\tan t-\frac{1}{\tan t}}{\tan t+\frac{1}{\tan t}}=\frac{\tan t-\frac{1}{\tan t}}{\tan t+\frac{1}{\tan t}}\cdot\frac{\tan t}{\tan t}=\frac{\tan^2 t-1}{\tan^2 t+1}=\frac{\tan^2 t-1}{\sec^2 t}$$

65. Verify $\dfrac{1+\cos x}{1-\cos x}-\dfrac{1-\cos x}{1+\cos x}=4\cot x\csc x$.

$$\frac{1+\cos x}{1-\cos x}-\frac{1-\cos x}{1+\cos x}=\frac{(1+\cos x)^2}{(1+\cos x)(1-\cos x)}-\frac{(1-\cos x)^2}{(1+\cos x)(1-\cos x)}$$

$$=\frac{1+2\cos x+\cos^2 x}{(1+\cos x)(1-\cos x)}-\frac{1-2\cos x+\cos^2 x}{(1+\cos x)(1-\cos x)}$$

$$=\frac{1+2\cos x+\cos^2 x-1+2\cos x-\cos^2 x}{(1+\cos x)(1-\cos x)}$$

$$=\frac{4\cos x}{1-\cos^2 x}=\frac{4\cos x}{\sin^2 x}=4\cdot\frac{\cos x}{\sin x}\cdot\frac{1}{\sin x}=4\cot x\csc x$$

67. Verify $(\sec\alpha+\csc\alpha)(\cos\alpha-\sin\alpha)=\cot\alpha-\tan\alpha$.

$$(\sec\alpha+\csc\alpha)(\cos\alpha-\sin\alpha)=\left(\frac{1}{\cos\alpha}+\frac{1}{\sin\alpha}\right)(\cos\alpha-\sin\alpha)$$

$$=\frac{\cos\alpha}{\cos\alpha}-\frac{\sin\alpha}{\cos\alpha}+\frac{\cos\alpha}{\sin\alpha}-\frac{\sin\alpha}{\sin\alpha}=1-\tan\alpha+\cot\alpha-1=\cot\alpha-\tan\alpha$$

69. One example does not verify a statement to be true. However, if you find one example where it shows the statement is false, then that one example is enough to state that the statement is false. For example, if the student let $\theta=45°$ (or $\frac{\pi}{4}$ radians), then the student would have observed $\cos 45°+\sin 45°=\frac{\sqrt{2}}{2}+\frac{\sqrt{2}}{2}=\frac{2\sqrt{2}}{2}=\sqrt{2}\neq 1$. This would show that $\cos\theta+\sin\theta=1$ is not an identity.

In Exercises 71 – 77, the functions are graphed in the following window.

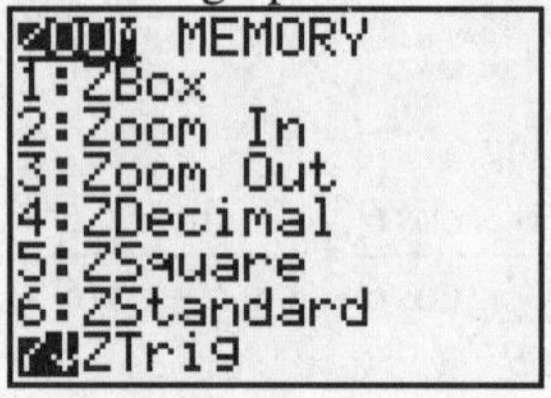

71. $(\sec\theta+\tan\theta)(1-\sin\theta)$ appears to be equivalent to $\cos\theta$.

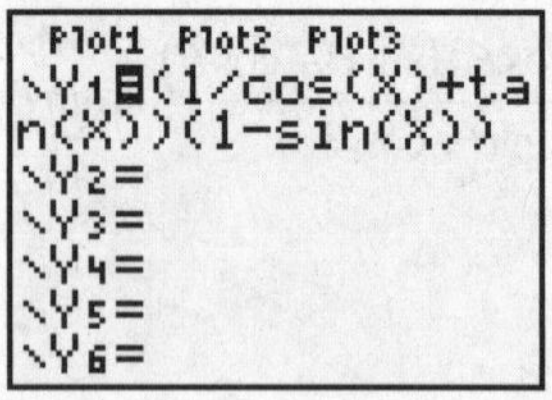

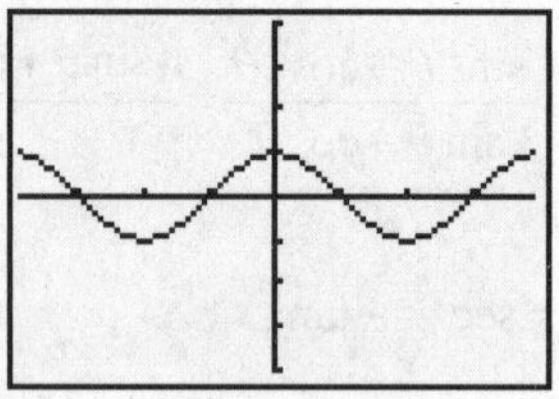

$$(\sec\theta+\tan\theta)(1-\sin\theta)=\left(\frac{1}{\cos\theta}+\frac{\sin\theta}{\cos\theta}\right)(1-\sin\theta)=\left(\frac{1+\sin\theta}{\cos\theta}\right)(1-\sin\theta)$$

$$=\frac{(1+\sin\theta)(1-\sin\theta)}{\cos\theta}=\frac{1-\sin^2\theta}{\cos\theta}=\frac{\cos^2\theta}{\cos\theta}=\cos\theta$$

73. $\dfrac{\cos\theta+1}{\sin\theta+\tan\theta}$ appears to be equivalent to $\cot\theta$.

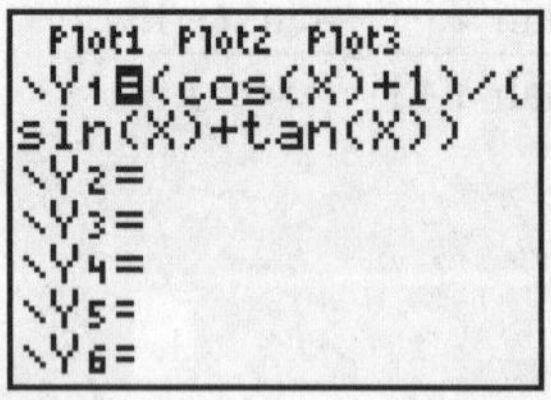

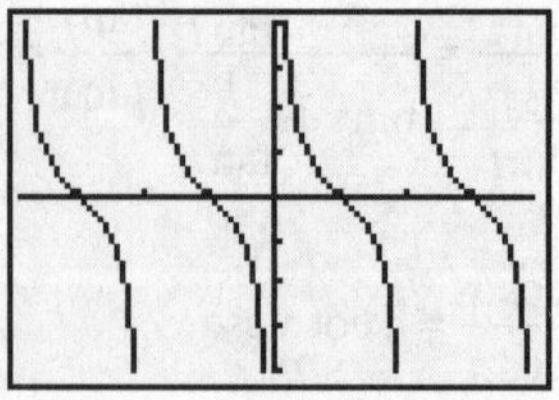

$$\frac{\cos\theta+1}{\sin\theta+\tan\theta}=\frac{1+\cos\theta}{\sin\theta+\frac{\sin\theta}{\cos\theta}}=\frac{1+\cos\theta}{\sin\theta\left(1+\frac{1}{\cos\theta}\right)}$$

$$=\frac{1+\cos\theta}{\sin\theta\left(1+\frac{1}{\cos\theta}\right)}\cdot\frac{\cos\theta}{\cos\theta}=\frac{(1+\cos\theta)\cos\theta}{\sin\theta(\cos\theta+1)}=\frac{\cos\theta}{\sin\theta}=\cot\theta$$

75. Is $\dfrac{2+5\cos s}{\sin s}=2\csc s+5\cot s$ an identity?

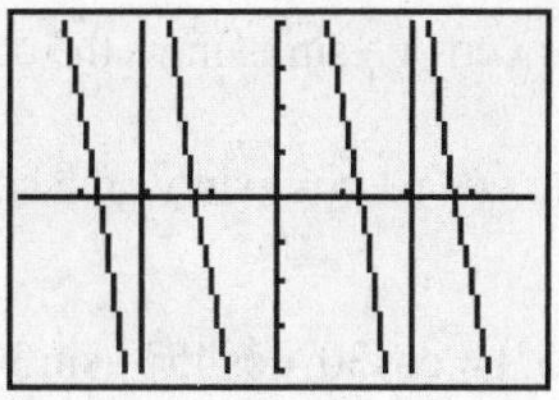

The graphs of $y=\dfrac{2+5\cos x}{\sin x}$ and $y=2\csc x+5\cot x$ appear to be the same. The given equation may be an identity. Since $\dfrac{2+5\cos s}{\sin s}=\dfrac{2}{\sin s}+\dfrac{5\cos s}{\sin s}=2\csc s+5\cot s,$ the given statement is an identity.

77. Is $\dfrac{\tan s-\cot s}{\tan s+\cot s}=2\sin^2 s$ an identity?

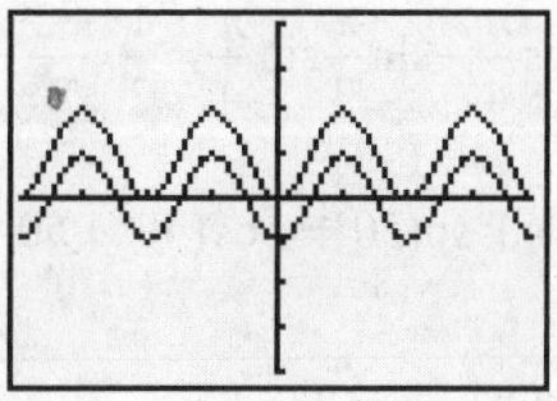

The graphs of $y=\dfrac{\tan x-\cot x}{\tan x+\cot x}$ and $y=2\sin^2 x$ are not the same. The given statement is not an identity.

79. Show that $\sin(\csc s)=1$ is not an identity.

We need to find only one value for which the statement is false. Let $s = 2$. Use a calculator to find that sin (csc 2) $\approx .891094$, which is not equal to 1.

$\sin(\csc s)=1$ does not hold true for *all* real numbers s. Thus, it is not an identity.

81. Show that $\csc t=\sqrt{1+\cot^2 t}$ is not an identity.

Let $t=\dfrac{\pi}{4}$. We have $\csc\dfrac{\pi}{4}=\sqrt{2}$ and $\sqrt{1+\cot^2\dfrac{\pi}{4}}=\sqrt{1+1^2}=\sqrt{1+1}=\sqrt{2}$. But let $t=-\dfrac{\pi}{4}$. We have,

$\csc-\dfrac{\pi}{4}=-\sqrt{2}$ and $\sqrt{1+\cot^2\left(-\dfrac{\pi}{4}\right)}=\sqrt{1+(-1)^2}=\sqrt{1+1}=\sqrt{2}.$

$\csc t=\sqrt{1+\cot^2 t}$ does not hold true for *all* real numbers s. Thus, it is not an identity.

83. $\sin x=\sqrt{1-\cos^2 x}$ is a true statement when $\sin x\ge 0$.

85. **(a)** $P=ky^2$ and $y=4\cos(2\pi t)$

$$P=ky^2=k\left[4\cos(2\pi t)\right]^2=k\left[16\cos^2(2\pi t)\right]=16k\cos^2(2\pi t)$$

(b) $P=16k\cos^2(2\pi t)=16k\left[1-\sin^2(2\pi t)\right]$

Section 7.3: Sum and Difference Identities

1. Since $\cos(x+y)=\cos x\cos y-\sin x\sin y,$ the correct choice is F.

3. Since $\sin(x+y)=\sin x\cos y+\cos x\sin y,$ the correct choice is C.

5. $\cos 75^\circ=\cos(30^\circ+45^\circ)=\cos 30^\circ\cos 45^\circ-\sin 30^\circ\sin 45^\circ=\frac{\sqrt{3}}{2}\cdot\frac{\sqrt{2}}{2}-\frac{1}{2}\cdot\frac{\sqrt{2}}{2}=\frac{\sqrt{6}}{4}-\frac{\sqrt{2}}{4}=\frac{\sqrt{6}-\sqrt{2}}{4}$

7. $\cos 105^\circ=\cos(60^\circ+45^\circ)=\cos 60^\circ\cos 45^\circ-\sin 60^\circ\sin 45^\circ=\frac{1}{2}\cdot\frac{\sqrt{2}}{2}-\frac{\sqrt{3}}{2}\cdot\frac{\sqrt{2}}{2}=\frac{\sqrt{2}}{4}-\frac{\sqrt{6}}{4}=\frac{\sqrt{2}-\sqrt{6}}{4}$

9. $\cos\left(\frac{7\pi}{12}\right)=\cos\left(\frac{4\pi}{12}+\frac{3\pi}{12}\right)=\cos\left(\frac{\pi}{3}+\frac{\pi}{4}\right)$

$$=\cos\frac{\pi}{3}\cos\frac{\pi}{4}-\sin\frac{\pi}{3}\sin\frac{\pi}{4}=\frac{1}{2}\cdot\frac{\sqrt{2}}{2}-\frac{\sqrt{3}}{2}\cdot\frac{\sqrt{2}}{2}=\frac{\sqrt{2}}{4}-\frac{\sqrt{6}}{4}=\frac{\sqrt{2}-\sqrt{6}}{4}$$

11. $\cos 40^\circ\cos 50^\circ-\sin 40^\circ\sin 50^\circ=\cos(40^\circ+50^\circ)=\cos 90^\circ=0$

13. $\tan 87^\circ=\cot(90^\circ-87^\circ)=\cot 3^\circ$

15. $\cos\frac{\pi}{12}=\sin\left(\frac{\pi}{2}-\frac{\pi}{12}\right)=\sin\frac{5\pi}{12}$

17. $\sin\frac{5\pi}{8}=\cos\left(\frac{\pi}{2}-\frac{5\pi}{8}\right)=\cos\left(\frac{4\pi}{8}-\frac{5\pi}{8}\right)=\cos\left(-\frac{\pi}{8}\right)$

19. $\sec 146^\circ 42'=\csc(90^\circ-146^\circ 42')=\csc\left[-(146^\circ 42'-90^\circ)\right]=\csc(-56^\circ 42')$

21. Since $\frac{\pi}{6}=\frac{\pi}{2}-\frac{\pi}{3}$, $\cot\frac{\pi}{3}=\tan\frac{\pi}{6}$.

$\cot\frac{\pi}{3}=\underline{\tan}\frac{\pi}{6}$

23. Since $90^\circ-57^\circ=33^\circ$, $\sin 57^\circ=\cos 33^\circ$.

$\sin 57^\circ=\underline{\cos}33^\circ$

25. $\tan\theta=\cot(45^\circ+2\theta)$

Since $\tan\theta=\cot(90^\circ-\theta)$, $90^\circ-\theta=45^\circ+2\theta\Rightarrow 90^\circ=45^\circ+3\theta\Rightarrow 3\theta=45^\circ\Rightarrow\theta=15^\circ$.

27. $\sin(3\theta-15^\circ)=\cos(\theta+25^\circ)$

Since $\sin\theta=\cos(90^\circ-\theta)$, we have the following.

$$\sin(3\theta-15^\circ)=\cos\left[90^\circ-(3\theta-15^\circ)\right]=\cos(90^\circ-3\theta+15^\circ)=\cos(105^\circ-3\theta)$$

We can next solve the equation $\cos(105^\circ-3\theta)=\cos(\theta+25^\circ)$.

$$\cos(105^\circ-3\theta)=\cos(\theta+25^\circ)\Rightarrow 105^\circ-3\theta=\theta+25^\circ\Rightarrow 105^\circ=4\theta+25^\circ\Rightarrow 4\theta=80^\circ\Rightarrow\theta=20^\circ$$

29. $\sin\frac{5\pi}{12}=\sin\left(\frac{\pi}{4}+\frac{\pi}{6}\right)=\sin\frac{\pi}{4}\cos\frac{\pi}{6}+\cos\frac{\pi}{4}\sin\frac{\pi}{6}=\frac{\sqrt{2}}{2}\cdot\frac{\sqrt{3}}{2}+\frac{\sqrt{2}}{2}\cdot\frac{1}{2}=\frac{\sqrt{6}}{4}+\frac{\sqrt{2}}{4}=\frac{\sqrt{6}+\sqrt{2}}{4}$

31. $\tan\frac{\pi}{12}=\tan\left(\frac{\pi}{4}-\frac{\pi}{6}\right)=\frac{\tan\frac{\pi}{4}-\tan\frac{\pi}{6}}{1+\tan\frac{\pi}{4}\tan\frac{\pi}{6}}=\frac{1-\frac{\sqrt{3}}{3}}{1+\frac{\sqrt{3}}{3}}=\frac{1-\frac{\sqrt{3}}{3}}{1+\frac{\sqrt{3}}{3}}\cdot\frac{3}{3}=\frac{3-\sqrt{3}}{3+\sqrt{3}}$

$$=\frac{3-\sqrt{3}}{3+\sqrt{3}}\cdot\frac{3-\sqrt{3}}{3-\sqrt{3}}=\frac{\left(3-\sqrt{3}\right)^2}{3^2-\left(\sqrt{3}\right)^2}=\frac{9-6\sqrt{3}+3}{9-3}=\frac{12-6\sqrt{3}}{6}=2-\sqrt{3}$$

33. $\sin\left(-\frac{7\pi}{12}\right)=\sin\left(-\frac{\pi}{3}-\frac{\pi}{4}\right)=\sin\left(-\frac{\pi}{3}\right)\cos\frac{\pi}{4}-\cos\left(-\frac{\pi}{3}\right)\sin\frac{\pi}{4}=-\sin\frac{\pi}{3}\cos\frac{\pi}{4}-\cos\frac{\pi}{3}\sin\frac{\pi}{4}$

$$=-\frac{\sqrt{3}}{2}\frac{\sqrt{2}}{2}\cdot-\frac{1}{2}\cdot\frac{\sqrt{2}}{2}=-\frac{\sqrt{6}}{4}-\frac{\sqrt{2}}{4}=\frac{-\sqrt{6}-\sqrt{2}}{4}$$

35. $\sin 76°\cos 31°-\cos 76°\sin 31°=\sin(76°-31°)=\sin 45°=\frac{\sqrt{2}}{2}$

37. $\frac{\tan 80°+\tan 55°}{1-\tan 80°\tan 55°}=\tan\left(80°+55°\right)=\tan 135°=-1$

39. $\cos\left(90°-\theta\right)=\cos 90°\cos\theta+\sin 90°\sin\theta=(0)\cos\theta+(1)\sin\theta=0+\sin\theta=\sin\theta$

41. $\cos\left(x-\frac{3\pi}{2}\right)=\cos x\cos\frac{3\pi}{2}+\sin x\sin\frac{3\pi}{2}=\cos x(0)+\sin x(-1)=0-\sin x=-\sin x$

43. $\sin\left(45°+\theta\right)=\sin 45°\cos\theta+\sin\theta\cos 45°=\frac{\sqrt{2}}{2}\sin\theta+\frac{\sqrt{2}}{2}\cos\theta=\frac{\sqrt{2}}{2}\left(\sin\theta+\cos\theta\right)$

45. $\sin\left(\frac{5\pi}{6}-x\right)=\sin\frac{5\pi}{6}\cos x-\cos\frac{5\pi}{6}\sin x=\frac{1}{2}\cos x-\frac{\sqrt{3}}{2}\sin x=\frac{1}{2}\left(\cos x-\sqrt{3}\sin x\right)$

47. $\tan\left(60°+\theta\right)=\frac{\tan 60°+\tan\theta}{1-\tan 60°\tan\theta}=\frac{\sqrt{3}+\tan\theta}{1-\sqrt{3}\tan\theta}$

49. $\tan\left(x+\frac{\pi}{6}\right)=\frac{\tan x+\tan\frac{\pi}{6}}{1-\tan x\tan\frac{\pi}{6}}=\frac{\tan x+\frac{1}{\sqrt{3}}}{1-\tan x\left(\frac{1}{\sqrt{3}}\right)}=\frac{\sqrt{3}\tan x+1}{\sqrt{3}-\tan x}$

51. $\cos s = \frac{3}{5}$, $\sin t = \frac{5}{13}$, and s and t are in quadrant I.

In order to substitute into sum and difference identities, we need to find the values of sin s and cos t, and also the values of tan s and tan t. Because s and t are both in quadrant I, the values of sin s and cos t, tan s, and tan t will be positive.

$$\sin s = \sqrt{1-\left(\frac{3}{5}\right)^2} = \sqrt{1-\frac{9}{25}} = \sqrt{\frac{16}{25}} = \frac{4}{5};\ \cos t = \sqrt{1-\left(\frac{5}{13}\right)^2} = \sqrt{1-\frac{25}{169}} = \sqrt{\frac{144}{169}} = \frac{12}{13}$$

$$\tan s = \frac{\sin s}{\cos s} = \frac{\frac{4}{5}}{\frac{3}{5}} = \frac{4}{3};\ \tan t = \frac{\sin t}{\cos t} = \frac{\frac{5}{13}}{\frac{12}{13}} = \frac{5}{12}$$

(a) $\cos(s+t) = \cos s\cos t - \sin s\sin t = \left(\frac{3}{5}\right)\left(\frac{12}{13}\right) - \left(\frac{4}{5}\right)\left(\frac{5}{13}\right) = \frac{36}{65} - \frac{20}{65} = \frac{16}{65}$

(b) $\sin(s-t) = \sin s\cos t - \cos s\sin t = \left(\frac{4}{5}\right)\left(\frac{12}{13}\right) - \left(\frac{3}{5}\right)\left(\frac{5}{13}\right) = \frac{48}{65} - \frac{15}{65} = \frac{33}{65}$

(c) $\tan(s+t) = \frac{\tan s + \tan t}{1-\tan s\tan t} = \frac{\frac{4}{3}+\frac{5}{12}}{1-\left(\frac{4}{3}\right)\left(\frac{5}{12}\right)} = \frac{48+15}{36-20} = \frac{63}{16}$

(d) From parts (a) and (c), cos $(s+t) > 0$ and tan $(s+t) > 0$. The only quadrant in which the values of both the cosine and the tangent are positive is quadrant I, so $s+t$ is in quadrant I.

53. $\sin s = \frac{2}{3}$ and $\sin t = -\frac{1}{3}$, s is in quadrant II and t is in quadrant IV.

In order to substitute into sum and difference identities, we need to find the values of cos s and cos t, and also the values of tan s and tan t. Because s is in quadrant II and t is in quadrant IV, the values of cos s, tan s, and tan t will be negative, while cos t will be positive.

$$\cos s = -\sqrt{1-\left(\frac{2}{3}\right)^2} = -\sqrt{1-\frac{4}{9}} = -\sqrt{\frac{5}{9}} = -\frac{\sqrt{5}}{3};\ \cos t = \sqrt{1-\left(-\frac{1}{3}\right)^2} = \sqrt{1-\frac{1}{9}} = \sqrt{\frac{8}{9}} = \frac{\sqrt{8}}{3} = \frac{2\sqrt{2}}{3}$$

$$\tan s = \frac{\sin s}{\cos s} = \frac{\frac{2}{3}}{-\frac{\sqrt{5}}{3}} = -\frac{2}{\sqrt{5}} = -\frac{2\sqrt{5}}{5};\ \tan t = \frac{\sin t}{\cos t} = \frac{-\frac{1}{3}}{\frac{2\sqrt{2}}{3}} = -\frac{1}{2\sqrt{2}} = -\frac{\sqrt{2}}{4}$$

(a) $\cos(s+t) = \cos s\cos t - \sin s\sin t = \left(-\frac{\sqrt{5}}{3}\right)\left(\frac{2\sqrt{2}}{3}\right) - \left(\frac{2}{3}\right)\left(-\frac{1}{3}\right) = \frac{-2\sqrt{10}}{9} + \frac{2}{9} = \frac{-2\sqrt{10}+2}{9}$

(b) $\sin(s-t) = \sin s\cos t - \cos s\sin t = \left(\frac{2}{3}\right)\left(\frac{2\sqrt{2}}{3}\right) - \left(-\frac{\sqrt{5}}{3}\right)\left(-\frac{1}{3}\right) = \frac{4\sqrt{2}}{9} - \frac{\sqrt{5}}{9} = \frac{4\sqrt{2}-\sqrt{5}}{9}$

(c) Different forms of tan $(s+t)$ will be obtained depending on whether tan s and tan t are written with rationalized denominators.

$$\tan(s+t) = \frac{-\frac{2\sqrt{5}}{5}+\left(-\frac{\sqrt{2}}{4}\right)}{1-\left(-\frac{2\sqrt{5}}{5}\right)\left(-\frac{\sqrt{2}}{4}\right)} = \frac{-8\sqrt{5}-5\sqrt{2}}{20-2\sqrt{10}} \quad \text{or}$$

$$\tan(s+t) = \frac{-\frac{2}{\sqrt{5}}+\left(-\frac{1}{2\sqrt{2}}\right)}{1-\left(-\frac{2}{\sqrt{5}}\right)\left(-\frac{1}{2\sqrt{2}}\right)} = \frac{-4\sqrt{2}-\sqrt{5}}{2\sqrt{10}-2} = \frac{4\sqrt{2}+\sqrt{5}}{2-2\sqrt{10}}$$

(d) To find the quadrant of $s+t$, notice from the preceding that $\cos(s+t) = \frac{-2\sqrt{10}+2}{9} \approx -.5 < 0$ and $\tan(s+t) = \frac{-8\sqrt{5}-5\sqrt{2}}{20-2\sqrt{10}} \approx -1.8 < 0$. The only quadrant in which the values of cosine and tangent are negative is quadrant II. Therefore, $s+t$ is in quadrant II.

55. $\cos s = -\frac{8}{17}$ and $\cos t = -\frac{3}{5}$, *s* and *t* are in quadrant III

In order to substitute into sum and difference identities, we need to find the values of sin *s* and sin *t*, and also the values of tan *s* and tan *t*. Because *s* and *t* are both in quadrant III, the values of sin *s* and sin *t* will be negative, while tan *s* and tan *t* will be positive.

$$\sin s = -\sqrt{1-\cos^2 s} = -\sqrt{1-\left(-\frac{8}{17}\right)^2} = -\sqrt{1-\frac{64}{289}} = -\sqrt{\frac{225}{289}} = -\frac{15}{17}$$

$$\sin t = -\sqrt{1-\cos^2 t} = -\sqrt{1-\left(-\frac{3}{5}\right)^2} = -\sqrt{1-\frac{9}{25}} = -\sqrt{\frac{16}{25}} = -\frac{4}{5}$$

$$\tan s = \frac{\sin s}{\cos s} = \frac{-\frac{15}{17}}{-\frac{8}{17}} = \frac{15}{8};\ \tan t = \frac{\sin t}{\cos t} = \frac{-\frac{4}{5}}{-\frac{3}{5}} = \frac{4}{3}$$

(a) $\cos(s+t) = \cos s\cos t - \sin s\sin t = \left(-\frac{8}{17}\right)\left(-\frac{3}{5}\right) - \left(-\frac{15}{17}\right)\left(-\frac{4}{5}\right) = \frac{24}{85} - \frac{60}{85} = -\frac{36}{85}$

(b) $\sin(s-t) = \sin s\cos t - \cos s\sin t = \left(-\frac{15}{17}\right)\left(-\frac{3}{5}\right) - \left(-\frac{8}{17}\right)\left(-\frac{4}{5}\right) = \frac{45}{85} - \frac{32}{85} = \frac{13}{85}$

(c) $\tan(s+t) = \frac{\frac{15}{8}+\frac{4}{3}}{1-\left(\frac{15}{8}\right)\left(\frac{4}{3}\right)} = \frac{45+32}{24-60} = \frac{77}{-36} = -\frac{77}{36}$

(d) From parts (a) and (c), cos $(s + t) < 0$ and tan $(s + t) < 0$. The only quadrant in which the values of both the cosine and the tangent are negative is quadrant II, so $s + t$ is in quadrant II.

57. $\cos 195° = \cos(180° + 15°)$

$$= \cos 180° \cos 15° - \sin 180° \sin 15° = (-1)\cos 15° - (0)\sin 15° = -\cos 15° - 0 = -\cos 15°$$

58. $-\cos 15° = -\cos(45° - 30°)$

$$= -(\cos 45° \cos 30° + \sin 45° \sin 30°) = -\left(\frac{\sqrt{2}}{2}\cdot\frac{\sqrt{3}}{2} + \frac{\sqrt{2}}{2}\cdot\frac{1}{2}\right) = -\left(\frac{\sqrt{6}}{4} + \frac{\sqrt{2}}{4}\right) = \frac{-\sqrt{6}-\sqrt{2}}{4}$$

59. $\cos 195° = -\cos 15° = \frac{-\sqrt{6}-\sqrt{2}}{4}$

60. (a) $\cos 255° = \cos(180° + 75°) = \cos 180° \cos 75° - \sin 180° \sin 75° = (-1)\cos 75° - (0)\sin 75°$

$$= -\cos 75° = -\cos(45° + 30°) = -(\cos 45° \cos 30° - \sin 45° \sin 30°)$$

$$= -\left(\frac{\sqrt{2}}{2}\cdot\frac{\sqrt{3}}{2} - \frac{\sqrt{2}}{2}\cdot\frac{1}{2}\right) = -\left(\frac{\sqrt{6}}{4} - \frac{\sqrt{2}}{4}\right) = -\left(\frac{\sqrt{6}-\sqrt{2}}{4}\right) = \frac{\sqrt{2}-\sqrt{6}}{4}$$

(b) $\cos\frac{11\pi}{12} = \cos\left(\frac{12\pi}{12} - \frac{\pi}{12}\right) = \cos\left(\pi - \frac{\pi}{12}\right) = \cos\pi\cos\frac{\pi}{12} + \sin\pi\sin\frac{\pi}{12} = (-1)\cos\frac{\pi}{12} + (0)\sin\frac{\pi}{12}$

$$= -\cos\frac{\pi}{12} = -\cos\left(\frac{3\pi}{12} - \frac{2\pi}{12}\right) = -\cos\left(\frac{\pi}{4} - \frac{\pi}{6}\right) = -\left(\cos\frac{\pi}{4}\cos\frac{\pi}{6} + \sin\frac{\pi}{4}\sin\frac{\pi}{6}\right)$$

$$= -\left(\frac{\sqrt{2}}{2}\cdot\frac{\sqrt{3}}{2} + \frac{\sqrt{2}}{2}\cdot\frac{1}{2}\right) = -\left(\frac{\sqrt{6}}{4} + \frac{\sqrt{2}}{4}\right) = -\left(\frac{\sqrt{6}+\sqrt{2}}{4}\right) = \frac{-\sqrt{6}-\sqrt{2}}{4}$$

61. $\sin 165° = \sin(180° - 15°) = \sin 180° \cos 15° - \cos 180° \sin 15°$

$$= (0)\cos 15° - (-1)\sin 15° = 0 + \sin 15° = \sin 15° = \sin(45° - 30°)$$

$$= \sin 45° \cos 30° - \cos 45° \sin 30° = \frac{\sqrt{2}}{2}\cdot\frac{\sqrt{3}}{2} - \frac{\sqrt{2}}{2}\cdot\frac{1}{2} = \frac{\sqrt{6}}{4} - \frac{\sqrt{2}}{4} = \frac{\sqrt{6}-\sqrt{2}}{4}$$

63. $\sin 255° = \sin(270° - 15°) = \sin 270° \cos 15° - \cos 270° \sin 15°$

$$= (-1)\cos 15° - (0)\sin 15° = -\cos 15° - 0 = -\cos 15°$$

Now use a difference identity to find $\cos 15°$.

$\cos 15° = \cos(45° - 30°) = (\cos 45° \cos 30° + \sin 45° \sin 30°)$

$$= \frac{\sqrt{2}}{2}\cdot\frac{\sqrt{3}}{2} + \frac{\sqrt{2}}{2}\cdot\frac{1}{2} = \frac{\sqrt{6}}{4} + \frac{\sqrt{2}}{4} = \frac{\sqrt{6}+\sqrt{2}}{4}$$

Thus, $\sin 255° = -\cos 15° = -\left(\frac{\sqrt{6}+\sqrt{2}}{4}\right) = \frac{-\sqrt{6}-\sqrt{2}}{4}.$

65. $\tan\frac{11\pi}{12} = \tan\left(\pi - \frac{\pi}{12}\right) = \frac{\tan\pi - \tan\frac{\pi}{12}}{1 + \tan\pi\tan\frac{\pi}{12}} = -\tan\frac{\pi}{12}$

Now use a difference identity to find $\tan\frac{\pi}{12}$.

$$\tan\frac{\pi}{12} = \tan\left(\frac{\pi}{4} - \frac{\pi}{6}\right) = \frac{\tan\frac{\pi}{4} - \tan\frac{\pi}{6}}{1 + \tan\frac{\pi}{4}\tan\frac{\pi}{6}} = \frac{1 - \frac{\sqrt{3}}{3}}{1 + 1\cdot\frac{\sqrt{3}}{3}} = \frac{1 - \frac{\sqrt{3}}{3}}{1 + \frac{\sqrt{3}}{3}} = \frac{\frac{3-\sqrt{3}}{3}}{\frac{3+\sqrt{3}}{3}}$$

$$= \frac{3-\sqrt{3}}{3+\sqrt{3}} = \frac{3-\sqrt{3}}{3+\sqrt{3}}\cdot\frac{3-\sqrt{3}}{3-\sqrt{3}} = \frac{9-6\sqrt{3}+3}{9-3} = \frac{12-6\sqrt{3}}{6} = \frac{6(2-\sqrt{3})}{6} = 2-\sqrt{3}$$

Thus, $\tan\frac{11\pi}{12} = -\tan\frac{\pi}{12} = -(2-\sqrt{3}) = -2+\sqrt{3}.$

67. $\cos(90° - \theta) = \sin\theta;\ \theta = 90° - A$

$$\cos(90° - \theta) = \sin\theta \Rightarrow \cos[90° - (90° - A)] = \sin(90° - A)$$

$$\cos(90° - 90° + A) = \sin(90° - A) \Rightarrow \cos A = \sin(90° - A)$$

69. To follow Example 5 (c) to find $\tan(270° - \theta)$, we would need to use the tangent of a difference formula, $\tan(A - B) = \frac{\tan A - \tan B}{1 + \tan A \tan B}$. In this formula, $A = 270°$ and $\tan 270°$ is undefined.

71. $\sin\left(\frac{\pi}{2} + x\right)$ appears to be equivalent to $\cos x$.

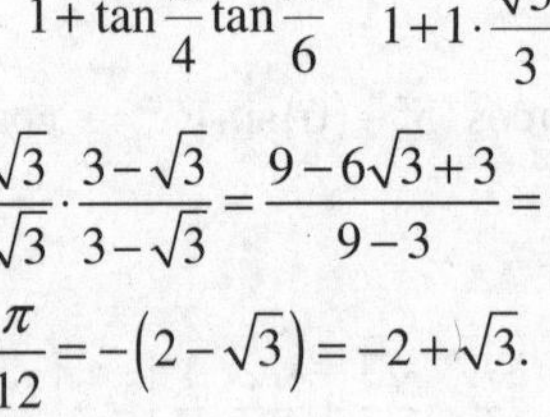

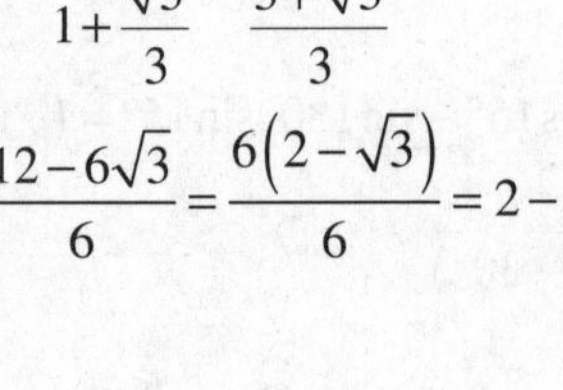

$$\sin\left(\frac{\pi}{2} + x\right) = \sin\frac{\pi}{2}\cos x + \sin x \cos\frac{\pi}{2} = 1\cdot\cos x + \sin x\cdot 0 = \cos x + 0 = \cos x$$

73. Verify $\sin(x+y)+\sin(x-y)=2\sin x\cos y$ is an identity.

$$\begin{aligned}\sin(x+y)+\sin(x-y)&=(\sin x\cos y+\cos x\sin y)+(\sin x\cos y-\cos x\sin y)\\&=2\sin x\cos y\end{aligned}$$

75. Verify $\dfrac{\cos(\alpha-\beta)}{\cos\alpha\sin\beta}=\tan\alpha+\cot\beta$ is an identity.

$$\frac{\cos(\alpha-\beta)}{\cos\alpha\sin\beta}=\frac{\cos\alpha\cos\beta+\sin\alpha\sin\beta}{\cos\alpha\sin\beta}=\frac{\cos\alpha\cos\beta}{\cos\alpha\sin\beta}+\frac{\sin\alpha\sin\beta}{\cos\alpha\sin\beta}=\frac{\cos\beta}{\sin\beta}+\frac{\sin\alpha}{\cos\alpha}=\cot\beta+\tan\alpha$$

77. Verify that $\dfrac{\sin(x-y)}{\sin(x+y)}=\dfrac{\tan x-\tan y}{\tan x+\tan y}$ is an identity.

$$\frac{\sin(x-y)}{\sin(x+y)}=\frac{\sin x\cos y-\cos x\sin y}{\sin x\cos y+\cos x\sin y}=\frac{\frac{\sin x\cos y}{\cos x\cos y}-\frac{\cos x\sin y}{\cos x\cos y}}{\frac{\sin x\cos y}{\cos x\cos y}+\frac{\cos x\sin y}{\cos x\cos y}}$$

$$=\frac{\frac{\sin x}{\cos x}\cdot\frac{\cos y}{\cos y}-\frac{\cos x}{\cos x}\cdot\frac{\sin y}{\cos y}}{\frac{\sin x}{\cos x}\cdot\frac{\cos y}{\cos y}+\frac{\cos x}{\cos x}\cdot\frac{\sin y}{\cos y}}=\frac{\frac{\sin x}{\cos x}\cdot1-1\cdot\frac{\sin y}{\cos y}}{\frac{\sin x}{\cos x}\cdot1+1\cdot\frac{\sin y}{\cos y}}=\frac{\frac{\sin x}{\cos x}-\frac{\sin y}{\cos y}}{\frac{\sin x}{\cos x}+\frac{\sin y}{\cos y}}=\frac{\tan x-\tan y}{\tan x+\tan y}$$

79. Since there are 60 cycles per sec, the number of cycles in .05 sec is given by the following.

(.05 sec)(60 cycles per sec) = 3 cycles

81. (a) $F=\dfrac{.6W\sin(\theta+90°)}{\sin 12°}=\dfrac{.6(170)\sin(30+90)°}{\sin 12°}=\dfrac{102\sin 120°}{\sin 12°}\approx 425\text{ lb}$

(This is a good reason why people frequently have back problems.)

(b) $F=\dfrac{.6W\sin(\theta+90°)}{\sin 12°}=\dfrac{.6W(\sin\theta\cos 90°+\sin 90°\cos\theta)}{\sin 12°}=\dfrac{.6W(\sin\theta\cdot 0+1\cdot\cos\theta)}{\sin 12°}$

$=\dfrac{.6W(0+\cos\theta)}{\sin 12°}=\dfrac{.6}{\sin 12°}W\cos\theta\approx 2.9W\cos\theta$

(c) F will be maximum when $\cos\theta=1$ or $\theta=0°$. ($\theta=0°$ corresponds to the back being horizontal which gives a maximum force on the back muscles. This agrees with intuition since stress on the back increases as one bends farther until the back is parallel with the ground.)

83. (a) Graph $P=\dfrac{a}{r}\cos\left[\dfrac{2\pi r}{\lambda}-ct\right]=\dfrac{.4}{10}\cos\left[\dfrac{2\pi(10)}{4.9}-1026t\right]=.04\cos\left(\dfrac{20\pi}{4.9}-1026t\right)$.

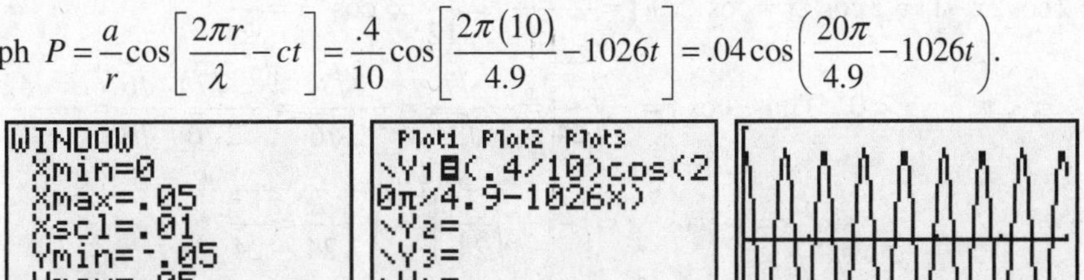

The pressure P is oscillating.

Continued on next page

83. (continued)

(b) Graph $P=\frac{a}{r}\cos\left[\frac{2\pi r}{\lambda}-ct\right]=\frac{3}{r}\cos\left[\frac{2\pi(r)}{4.9}-1026(10)\right]=\frac{3}{r}\cos\left(\frac{2\pi r}{4.9}-10,260\right)$.

The pressure oscillates, and amplitude decreases as r increases.

(c) $P=\frac{a}{r}\cos\left[\frac{2\pi r}{\lambda}-ct\right]$

Let $r=n\lambda$.

$$P=\frac{a}{r}\cos\left[\frac{2\pi r}{\lambda}-ct\right]=\frac{a}{n\lambda}\cos\left[\frac{2\pi n\lambda}{\lambda}-ct\right]=\frac{a}{n\lambda}\cos[2\pi n-ct]$$

$$=\frac{a}{n\lambda}\left[\cos(2\pi n)\cos(ct)+\sin(2\pi n)\sin(ct)\right]=\frac{a}{n\lambda}\left[(1)\cos(ct)+(0)\sin(ct)\right]$$

$$=\frac{a}{n\lambda}\left[\cos(ct)+0\right]=\frac{a}{n\lambda}\cos(ct)$$

Section 7.4: Double-Angle Identities and Half-Angle Identities

1. $\cos 2\theta=\frac{3}{5}$, θ is in quadrant I.

$$\cos 2\theta=2\cos^2\theta-1\Rightarrow\frac{3}{5}=2\cos^2\theta-1\Rightarrow 2\cos^2\theta=\frac{3}{5}+1=\frac{8}{5}\Rightarrow\cos^2\theta=\frac{8}{10}=\frac{4}{5}$$

Since θ is in quadrant I, $\cos\theta>0$. Thus, $\cos\theta=\sqrt{\frac{4}{5}}=\frac{2}{\sqrt{5}}=\frac{2\sqrt{5}}{5}$.

Since θ is in quadrant I, $\sin\theta>0$.

$$\sin\theta=\sqrt{1-\cos^2\theta}=\sqrt{1-\left(\frac{2\sqrt{5}}{5}\right)^2}=\sqrt{1-\frac{20}{25}}=\sqrt{\frac{5}{25}}=\sqrt{\frac{1}{5}}=\frac{1}{\sqrt{5}}=\frac{1}{\sqrt{5}}\cdot\frac{\sqrt{5}}{\sqrt{5}}=\frac{\sqrt{5}}{5}$$

3. $\cos 2x=-\frac{5}{12}, \frac{\pi}{2}<x<\pi$

$$\cos 2x=2\cos^2 x-1\Rightarrow 2\cos^2 x=\cos 2x+1=-\frac{5}{12}+1=\frac{7}{12}\Rightarrow\cos^2 x=\frac{7}{24}$$

Since $\frac{\pi}{2}<x<\pi, \cos x<0$. Thus, $\cos x=-\sqrt{\frac{7}{24}}=-\frac{\sqrt{7}}{\sqrt{24}}=-\frac{\sqrt{7}}{2\sqrt{6}}=-\frac{\sqrt{7}}{2\sqrt{6}}\cdot\frac{\sqrt{6}}{\sqrt{6}}=-\frac{\sqrt{42}}{12}$.

$$\sin^2 x=1-\cos^2 x=1-\left(-\sqrt{\frac{7}{24}}\right)^2=1-\frac{7}{24}=\frac{17}{24}$$

Since $\frac{\pi}{2}<x<\pi, \sin x>0$. Thus, $\sin x=\sqrt{\frac{17}{24}}=\frac{\sqrt{17}}{\sqrt{24}}=\frac{\sqrt{17}}{2\sqrt{6}}=\frac{\sqrt{17}}{2\sqrt{6}}\cdot\frac{\sqrt{6}}{\sqrt{6}}=\frac{\sqrt{102}}{12}$.

5. $\sin\theta = \frac{2}{5}, \cos\theta < 0$

$$\cos 2\theta = 1 - 2\sin^2\theta \Rightarrow \cos 2\theta = 1 - 2\left(\frac{2}{5}\right)^2 1 - 2\cdot\frac{4}{25} = 1 - \frac{8}{25} = \frac{17}{25}$$

$$\cos^2 2\theta + \sin^2 2\theta = 1 \Rightarrow \sin^2 2\theta = 1 - \cos^2 2\theta \Rightarrow \sin^2 2\theta = 1 - \left(\frac{17}{25}\right)^2 = 1 - \frac{289}{625} = \frac{336}{625}$$

Since $\cos\theta < 0, \sin 2\theta < 0$ because $\sin 2\theta = 2\sin\theta\cos\theta < 0$ and $\sin\theta > 0.$

$$\sin 2\theta = -\sqrt{\frac{336}{625}} = -\frac{\sqrt{336}}{25} = -\frac{4\sqrt{21}}{25}$$

7. $\tan x = 2, \cos x > 0$

$$\tan 2x = \frac{2\tan x}{1 - \tan^2 x} = \frac{2(2)}{1 - 2^2} = \frac{4}{1 - 4^2} = -\frac{4}{3}$$

Since both $\tan x$ and $\cos x$ are positive, x must be in quadrant I. Since $0° < x < 90°$, then $0° < 2x < 180°$. Thus, $2x$ must be in either quadrant I or quadrant II. Hence, $\sec 2x$ could be positive or negative.

$$\sec^2 2x = 1 + \tan^2 2x = 1 + \left(-\frac{4}{3}\right) = 1 + \frac{16}{9} = \frac{25}{9}$$

$$\sec 2x = \pm\frac{5}{3} \Rightarrow \cos 2x = \frac{1}{\sec 2x} = \pm\frac{3}{5}$$

$$\cos^2 2x + \sin^2 2x = 1 \Rightarrow \sin^2 2x = 1 - \cos^2 2x \Rightarrow \sin^2 2x = 1 - \left(\pm\frac{3}{5}\right)^2 \Rightarrow \sin^2 2x = 1 - \frac{9}{25} = \frac{16}{25}$$

In quadrants I and II, $\sin 2x > 0$. Thus, we have $\sin 2x = \sqrt{\frac{16}{25}} = \frac{4}{5}$.

9. $\sin\theta = -\frac{\sqrt{5}}{7}, \cos\theta > 0$

$$\cos^2\theta = 1 - \sin^2\theta = 1 - \left(-\frac{\sqrt{5}}{7}\right)^2 = 1 - \frac{5}{49} = \frac{44}{49}$$

Since $\cos\theta > 0$, $\cos\theta = \sqrt{\frac{44}{49}} = \frac{\sqrt{44}}{7} = \frac{2\sqrt{11}}{7}$.

$$\cos 2\theta = 1 - 2\sin^2\theta = 1 - 2\left(-\frac{\sqrt{5}}{7}\right)^2 = 1 - 2\cdot\frac{5}{49} = 1 - \frac{10}{49} = \frac{39}{49}$$

$$\sin 2\theta = 2\sin\theta\cos\theta = 2\left(-\frac{\sqrt{5}}{7}\right)\left(\frac{2\sqrt{11}}{7}\right) = -\frac{4\sqrt{55}}{49}$$

11. $\cos^2 15° - \sin^2 15° = \cos\left[2(15°)\right] = \cos 30° = \frac{\sqrt{3}}{2}$

13. $1 - 2\sin^2 15° = \cos\left[2(15°)\right] = \cos 30° = \frac{\sqrt{3}}{2}$

15. $2\cos^2 67\frac{1}{2}^\circ - 1 = \cos^2 67\frac{1}{2}^\circ - \sin^2 67\frac{1}{2}^\circ = \cos 2\left(67\frac{1}{2}^\circ\right) = \cos 135^\circ = -\frac{\sqrt{2}}{2}$

17. $\dfrac{\tan 51^\circ}{1-\tan^2 51^\circ}$

Since $\dfrac{2\tan A}{1-\tan^2 A} = \tan 2A$, we have the following.

$$\frac{1}{2}\left(\frac{2\tan A}{1-\tan^2 A}\right) = \frac{1}{2}\tan 2A \Rightarrow \frac{\tan A}{1-\tan^2 A} = \frac{1}{2}\tan 2A \Rightarrow \frac{\tan 51^\circ}{1-\tan^2 51^\circ} = \frac{1}{2}\tan\left[2(51^\circ)\right] = \frac{1}{2}\tan(102^\circ)$$

19. $\frac{1}{4} - \frac{1}{2}\sin^2 47.1^\circ = \frac{1}{4}\left(1 - 2\sin^2 47.1^\circ\right) = \frac{1}{4}\cos\left[2(47.1^\circ)\right] = \frac{1}{4}\cos 94.2^\circ$

21. $\cos 3x = \cos(2x+x) = \cos 2x\cos x - \sin 2x \sin x = \left(1-2\sin^2 x\right)\cos x - (2\sin x\cos x)\sin x$

$$= \cos x - 2\sin^2 x\cos x - 2\sin^2 x\cos x = \cos x - 4\sin^2 x\cos x = \cos x\left(1-4\sin^2 x\right)$$
$$= \cos x\left[1-4\left(1-\cos^2 x\right)\right] = \cos x\left(-3+4\cos^2 x\right) = -3\cos x + 4\cos^3 x$$

23. $\tan 3x = \tan(2x+x) = \dfrac{\tan 2x + \tan x}{1-\tan 2x\tan x} = \dfrac{\frac{2\tan x}{1-\tan^2 x} + \tan x}{1 - \frac{2\tan x}{1-\tan^2 x}\cdot\tan x} = \dfrac{\frac{2\tan x}{1-\tan^2 x} + \frac{\left(1-\tan^2 x\right)\tan x}{1-\tan^2 x}}{\frac{1-\tan^2 x}{1-\tan^2 x} - \frac{2\tan^2 x}{1-\tan^2 x}}$

$$= \frac{\frac{2\tan x}{1-\tan^2 x} + \frac{\tan x - \tan^3 x}{1-\tan^2 x}}{\frac{1-\tan^2 x}{1-\tan^2 x} - \frac{2\tan^2 x}{1-\tan^2 x}}\cdot\frac{1-\tan^2 x}{1-\tan^2 x} = \frac{2\tan x + \tan x - \tan^3 x}{1-\tan^2 x - 2\tan^2 x} = \frac{3\tan x - \tan^3 x}{1-3\tan^2 x}$$

Exercise 25 is graphed in the following window.

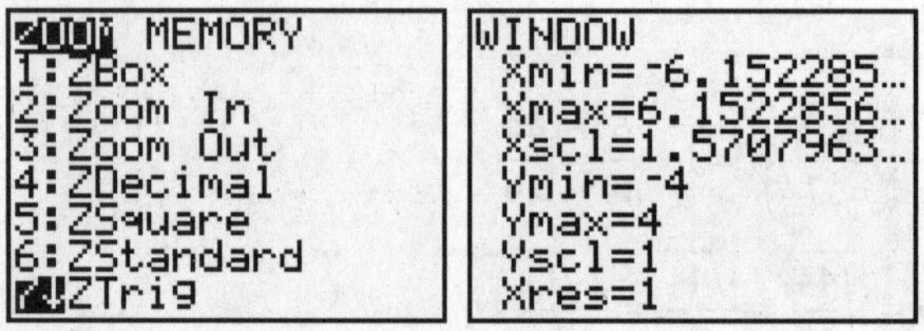

25. $\cos^4 x - \sin^4 x$ appears to be equivalent to $\cos 2x$.

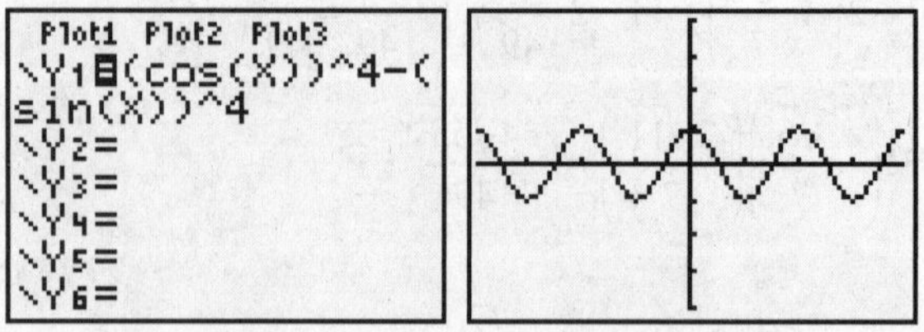

$$\cos^4 x - \sin^4 x = \left(\cos^2 x + \sin^2 x\right)\left(\cos^2 x - \sin^2 x\right) = 1\cdot\cos 2x = \cos 2x$$

27. Verify $(\sin x + \cos x)^2 = \sin 2x + 1$ is an identity.

$$(\sin x + \cos x)^2 = \sin^2 x + 2\sin x\cos x + \cos^2 x = \left(\sin^2 x + \cos^2 x\right) + 2\sin x\cos x = 1 + \sin 2x$$

29. Verify that $\sin 4x = 4\sin x\cos x\cos 2x$ is an identity.

$\sin 4x = \sin 2(2x) = 2\sin 2x\cos 2x = 2(2\sin x\cos x)\cos 2x = 4\sin x\cos x\cos 2x$

31. Verify $\dfrac{2\cos 2\theta}{\sin 2\theta} = \cot\theta - \tan\theta$ is an identity.

Work with the right side.

$$\cot\theta - \tan\theta = \frac{\cos\theta}{\sin\theta} - \frac{\sin\theta}{\cos\theta}$$

$$= \frac{\cos\theta}{\sin\theta}\cdot\frac{\cos\theta}{\cos\theta} - \frac{\sin\theta}{\cos\theta}\cdot\frac{\sin\theta}{\sin\theta} = \frac{\cos^2\theta - \sin^2\theta}{\sin\theta\cos\theta} = \frac{2(\cos^2\theta - \sin^2\theta)}{2\sin\theta\cos\theta} = \frac{2\cos 2\theta}{\sin 2\theta}$$

33. Verify $\sin 2x\cos 2x = \sin 2x - 4\sin^3 x\cos x$ is an identity.

$\sin 2x\cos 2x = (2\sin x\cos x)(1 - 2\sin^2 x) = 2\sin x\cos x - 4\sin^3 x\cos x = \sin 2x - 4\sin^3 x\cos x$

35. Verify $\tan x + \cot x = 2\csc 2x$ is an identity.

$$\tan x + \cot x = \frac{\sin x}{\cos x}\cdot\frac{\sin x}{\sin x} + \frac{\cos x}{\sin x}\cdot\frac{\cos x}{\cos x} = \frac{\sin^2 x + \cos^2 x}{\cos x\sin x} = \frac{1}{\cos x\sin x} = \frac{2}{2\cos x\sin x} = \frac{2}{\sin 2x} = 2\csc 2x$$

37. Verify $\sec^2\dfrac{x}{2} = \dfrac{2}{1+\cos x}$ is an identity.

$$\sec^2\frac{x}{2} = \frac{1}{\cos^2\frac{x}{2}} = \frac{1}{\left(\pm\sqrt{\frac{1+\cos x}{2}}\right)^2} = \frac{1}{\frac{1+\cos x}{2}} = \frac{2}{1+\cos x}$$

39. Verify $\sin^2\dfrac{x}{2} = \dfrac{\tan x - \sin x}{2\tan x}$ is an identity.

Work with the left side.

$$\sin^2\frac{x}{2} = \left(\pm\sqrt{\frac{1-\cos x}{2}}\right)^2 = \frac{1-\cos x}{2}$$

Work with the right side.

$$\frac{\tan x - \sin x}{2\tan x} = \frac{\frac{\sin x}{\cos x} - \sin x}{2\cdot\frac{\sin x}{\cos x}} = \frac{\frac{\sin x}{\cos x} - \sin x}{2\cdot\frac{\sin x}{\cos x}}\cdot\frac{\cos x}{\cos x} = \frac{\sin x - \cos x\sin x}{2\sin x} = \frac{\sin x(1-\cos x)}{2\sin x} = \frac{1-\cos x}{2}$$

Since $\sin^2\dfrac{x}{2} = \dfrac{1-\cos x}{2} = \dfrac{\tan x - \sin x}{2\tan x}$, the statement has been verified.

41. $2\sin 58°\cos 102° = 2\left(\frac{1}{2}\left[\sin(58°+102°) + \sin(58°-102°)\right]\right) = \sin 160° + \sin(-44°) = \sin 160° - \sin 44°$

43. $5\cos 3x\cos 2x = 5\left(\frac{1}{2}\left[\cos(3x+2x) + \cos(3x-2x)\right]\right) = \frac{5}{2}(\cos 5x + \cos x) = \frac{5}{2}\cos 5x + \frac{5}{2}\cos x$

45. $\cos 4x - \cos 2x = -2\sin\left(\frac{4x+2x}{2}\right)\sin\left(\frac{4x-2x}{2}\right) = -2\sin\frac{6x}{2}\sin\frac{2x}{2} = -2\sin 3x\sin x$

47. $\sin 25° + \sin(-48°) = 2\sin\left(\frac{25° + (-48°)}{2}\right)\cos\left(\frac{25° - (-48°)}{2}\right)$

$$= 2\sin\frac{-23°}{2}\cos\frac{73°}{2} = 2\sin(-11.5°)\cos 36.5° = -2\sin 11.5°\cos 36.5°$$

49. $\cos 4x + \cos 8x = 2\cos\left(\frac{4x + 8x}{2}\right)\cos\left(\frac{4x - 8x}{2}\right)$

$$= 2\cos\frac{12x}{2}\cos\frac{-4x}{2} = 2\cos 6x\cos(-2x) = 2\cos 6x\cos 2x$$

51. $\sin 67.5° = \sin\left(\frac{135°}{2}\right)$

Since 67.5° is in quadrant I, $\sin 67.5° > 0$.

$$\sin 67.5° = \sqrt{\frac{1-\cos 135°}{2}} = \sqrt{\frac{1-(-\cos 45°)}{2}} = \sqrt{\frac{1+\frac{\sqrt{2}}{2}}{2}} = \sqrt{\frac{1+\frac{\sqrt{2}}{2}}{2}\cdot\frac{2}{2}} = \frac{\sqrt{2+\sqrt{2}}}{\sqrt{4}} = \frac{\sqrt{2+\sqrt{2}}}{2}$$

53. $\cos 195° = \cos\left(\frac{390°}{2}\right)$

Since 195° is in quadrant III, $\cos 195° < 0$.

$$\cos 195° = -\sqrt{\frac{1+\cos 390°}{2}} = -\sqrt{\frac{1+\cos 30°}{2}} = -\sqrt{\frac{1+\frac{\sqrt{3}}{2}}{2}} = -\sqrt{\frac{2+\sqrt{3}}{4}} = \frac{-\sqrt{2+\sqrt{3}}}{2}$$

55. $\cos 165° = \cos\left(\frac{330°}{2}\right)$

Since 165° is in quadrant II, $\cos 165° < 0$.

$$\cos 165° = -\sqrt{\frac{1+\cos 330°}{2}} = -\sqrt{\frac{1+\cos 30°}{2}} = -\sqrt{\frac{1+\frac{\sqrt{3}}{2}}{2}} = -\sqrt{\frac{2+\sqrt{3}}{4}} = \frac{-\sqrt{2+\sqrt{3}}}{2}$$

57. To find $\sin 7.5°$, you could use the half-angle formulas for sine and cosine as follows.

$$\sin 7.5° = \sqrt{\frac{1-\cos 15°}{2}} \text{ and } \cos 15° = -\sqrt{\frac{1+\cos 30°}{2}} = \sqrt{\frac{1+\frac{\sqrt{3}}{2}}{2}} = \sqrt{\frac{2+\sqrt{3}}{4}} = \frac{\sqrt{2+\sqrt{3}}}{2}$$

$$\text{Thus, } \sin 7.5° = \sqrt{\frac{1-\cos 15°}{2}} = \sqrt{\frac{1-\frac{\sqrt{2+\sqrt{3}}}{2}}{2}} = \sqrt{\frac{2-\sqrt{2+\sqrt{3}}}{4}} = \frac{\sqrt{2-\sqrt{2+\sqrt{3}}}}{2}.$$

59. Find $\cos\frac{x}{2}$, given $\cos x = \frac{1}{4}$, with $0 < x < \frac{\pi}{2}$.

Since $0 < x < \frac{\pi}{2} \Rightarrow 0 < \frac{x}{2} < \frac{\pi}{4}$, $\cos\frac{x}{2} > 0$.

$$\cos\frac{x}{2} = \sqrt{\frac{1+\cos x}{2}} = \sqrt{\frac{1+\frac{1}{4}}{2}} = \sqrt{\frac{4+1}{8}} = \sqrt{\frac{5}{8}} = \frac{\sqrt{5}}{\sqrt{8}} = \frac{\sqrt{5}}{2\sqrt{2}} = \frac{\sqrt{5}}{2\sqrt{2}} \cdot \frac{\sqrt{2}}{\sqrt{2}} = \frac{\sqrt{10}}{4}$$

61. Find $\tan\frac{\theta}{2}$, given $\sin\theta = \frac{3}{5}$, with $90° < \theta < 180°$.

To find $\tan\frac{\theta}{2}$, we need the values of $\sin\theta$ and $\cos\theta$. We know $\sin\theta = \frac{3}{5}$.

$$\cos\theta = \pm\sqrt{1-\left(\frac{3}{5}\right)^2} = \pm\sqrt{1-\frac{9}{25}} = \pm\sqrt{\frac{16}{25}} = \pm\frac{4}{5}$$

Since $90° < \theta < 180°$ (θ is in quadrant II), $\cos\theta < 0$. Thus, $\cos\theta = -\frac{4}{5}$.

$$\tan\frac{\theta}{2} = \frac{\sin\theta}{1+\cos\theta} = \frac{\frac{3}{5}}{1+\left(-\frac{4}{5}\right)} = \frac{\frac{3}{5}}{1+\left(-\frac{4}{5}\right)} \cdot \frac{5}{5} = \frac{3}{5-4} = \frac{3}{1} = 3$$

63. Find $\sin\frac{x}{2}$, given $\tan x = 2$, with $0 < x < \frac{\pi}{2}$.

Since x is in quadrant I, $\sec x > 0$.

$\sec^2 x = \tan^2 x + 1 \Rightarrow \sec^2 x = 2^2 + 1 = 4 + 1 = 5 \Rightarrow \sec x = \sqrt{5}$

$$\cos x = \frac{1}{\sec x} = \frac{1}{\sqrt{5}} = \frac{1}{\sqrt{5}} \cdot \frac{\sqrt{5}}{\sqrt{5}} = \frac{\sqrt{5}}{5}$$

Since $0 < x < \frac{\pi}{2} \Rightarrow 0 < \frac{x}{2} < \frac{\pi}{4}$, $\frac{x}{2}$ is in quadrant I, Thus, $\sin\frac{x}{2} > 0$.

$$\sin\frac{x}{2} = \sqrt{\frac{1-\cos x}{2}} = \sqrt{\frac{1-\frac{\sqrt{5}}{5}}{2}} = \frac{\sqrt{50-10\sqrt{5}}}{10}$$

65. Find $\tan\frac{\theta}{2}$, given $\tan\theta=\frac{\sqrt{7}}{3}$, with $180°<\theta<270°$.

$$\sec^2\theta=\tan^2\theta+1\Rightarrow\sec^2\theta=\left(\frac{\sqrt{7}}{3}\right)^2+1=\frac{7}{9}+1=\frac{16}{9}$$

Since θ is in quadrant III, $\sec\theta<0$ and $\sin\theta<0$.

$$\sec\theta=-\sqrt{\frac{16}{9}}=-\frac{4}{3}\text{ and }\cos\theta=\frac{1}{\sec\theta}=\frac{1}{-\frac{4}{3}}=-\frac{3}{4}$$

$$\sin\theta=-\sqrt{1-\cos^2\theta}=-\sqrt{1-\left(-\frac{3}{4}\right)^2}=-\sqrt{1-\frac{9}{16}}=-\frac{\sqrt{7}}{4}$$

$$\tan\frac{\theta}{2}=\frac{\sin\theta}{1+\cos\theta}=\frac{-\frac{\sqrt{7}}{4}}{1+\left(-\frac{3}{4}\right)}=\frac{-\sqrt{7}}{4-3}=-\sqrt{7}$$

67. $\sqrt{\frac{1-\cos 40°}{2}}=\sin\frac{40°}{2}=\sin 20°$

69. $\sqrt{\frac{1-\cos 147°}{1+\cos 147°}}=\tan\frac{147°}{2}=\tan 73.5°$

71. $\frac{1-\cos 59.74°}{\sin 59.74°}=\tan\frac{59.74°}{2}=\tan 29.87°$

73. $\tan\frac{A}{2}=\frac{\sin A}{1+\cos A}=\frac{\sin A}{1+\cos A}\cdot\frac{1-\cos A}{1-\cos A}=\frac{\sin A(1-\cos A)}{1-\cos^2 A}=\frac{\sin A(1-\cos A)}{\sin^2 A}=\frac{1-\cos A}{\sin A}$

75. $\sin\frac{\theta}{2}=\frac{1}{m}, m=\frac{3}{2}$

Since $\sin\frac{\theta}{2}=\frac{1}{\frac{3}{2}}=\frac{2}{3}$ and $\sin^2\frac{\theta}{2}=\frac{1-\cos\theta}{2}$, we have the following.

$$\left(\frac{2}{3}\right)^2=\frac{1-\cos\theta}{2}\Rightarrow\frac{4}{9}=\frac{1-\cos\theta}{2}\Rightarrow\frac{8}{9}=1-\cos\theta\Rightarrow-\frac{1}{9}=-\cos\theta\Rightarrow\cos\theta=\frac{1}{9}$$

Thus, we have $\theta=\cos^{-1}\frac{1}{9}\approx 84°$.

77. $\sin\frac{\theta}{2}=\frac{1}{m}, \theta=30°$

$\sin\frac{30°}{2}=\frac{1}{m}\Rightarrow\sin 15°=\frac{1}{m}$

$m=\frac{1}{\sin 15°}\approx 3.9$

79. **(a)** $\cos\frac{\theta}{2} = \frac{R-b}{R}$

(b) $\tan\frac{\theta}{4} = \frac{1-\cos\frac{\theta}{2}}{\sin\frac{\theta}{2}} = \frac{1-\frac{R-b}{R}}{\frac{50}{R}} = \frac{R-(R-b)}{50} = \frac{R-R+b}{50} = \frac{b}{50}$

(c) If $\tan\frac{\theta}{4} = \frac{12}{50}$, then $\frac{\theta}{4} = \tan^{-1}\frac{12}{50} \approx 13.4957 \Rightarrow \theta \approx 53.9828 \approx 54°$.

81. From Example 5, $W = \frac{(163\sin 120\pi t)^2}{15} \Rightarrow W \approx 1771.3(\sin 120\pi t)^2$.

Thus, we have the following.

$$\begin{aligned}1771.3(\sin 120\pi t)^2 &= 1771.3\sin 120\pi t \cdot \sin 120\pi t\\ &= (1771.3)\left(\frac{1}{2}\right)\left[\cos(120\pi t - 120\pi t) - \cos(120\pi t + 120\pi t)\right]\\ &= 885.6(\cos 0 - \cos 240\pi t) = 885.6(1-\cos 240\pi t)\\ &= -885.6\cos 240\pi t + 885.6\end{aligned}$$

If we compare this to $W = a\cos(\omega t) + c$, then $a = -885.6$, $c = 885.6$, and $\omega = 240\pi$.

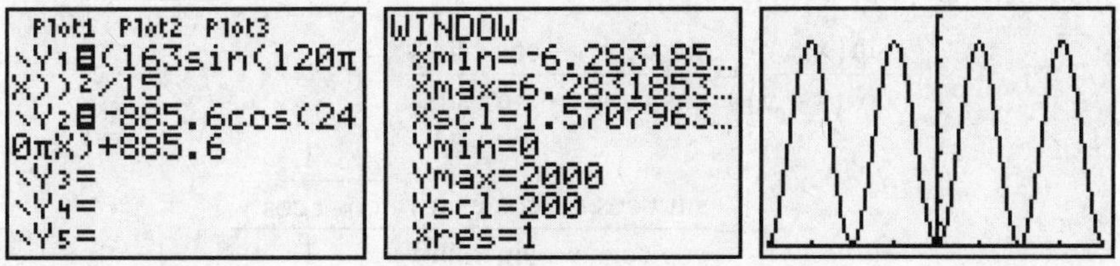

Summary Exercises on Verifying Trigonometric Identities

For the following exercises, other solutions are possible.

1. Verify $\tan\theta + \cot\theta = \sec\theta\csc\theta$ is an identity.

Starting on the left side, we have the following.

$$\begin{aligned}\tan\theta + \cot\theta &= \frac{\sin\theta}{\cos\theta} + \frac{\cos\theta}{\sin\theta} = \frac{\sin^2\theta}{\cos\theta\sin\theta} + \frac{\cos^2\theta}{\cos\theta\sin\theta}\\ &= \frac{\sin^2\theta + \cos^2\theta}{\cos\theta\sin\theta} = \frac{1}{\cos\theta\sin\theta} = \frac{1}{\cos\theta}\cdot\frac{1}{\sin\theta} = \sec\theta\csc\theta\end{aligned}$$

3. Verify $\tan\frac{x}{2} = \csc x - \cot x$ is an identity.

Starting on the right side, we have the following.

$$\csc x - \cot x = \frac{1}{\sin x} - \frac{\cos x}{\sin x} = \frac{1-\cos x}{\sin x} = \tan\frac{x}{2}$$

5. Verify $\frac{\sin t}{1+\cos t} = \frac{1-\cos t}{\sin t}$ is an identity.

Starting on the left side, we have the following.

$$\frac{\sin t}{1+\cos t} = \frac{\sin t}{1+\cos t}\cdot\frac{1-\cos t}{1-\cos t} = \frac{\sin t(1-\cos t)}{1-\cos^2 t} = \frac{\sin t(1-\cos t)}{\sin^2 t} = \frac{1-\cos t}{\sin t}$$

7. Verify $\sin 2\theta = \dfrac{2\tan\theta}{1+\tan^2\theta}$ is an identity.

Starting on the right side, we have the following.

$$\frac{2\tan\theta}{1+\tan^2\theta} = \frac{2\tan\theta}{\sec^2\theta} = \frac{2\cdot\dfrac{\sin\theta}{\cos\theta}}{\dfrac{1}{\cos^2\theta}} = 2\cdot\frac{\sin\theta}{\cos\theta}\cdot\frac{\cos^2\theta}{1} = 2\sin\theta\cos\theta = \sin 2\theta$$

9. Verify $\cot\theta - \tan\theta = \dfrac{2\cos^2\theta - 1}{\sin\theta\cos\theta}$ is an identity.

Starting on the left side, we have the following.

$$\cot\theta - \tan\theta = \frac{\cos\theta}{\sin\theta} - \frac{\sin\theta}{\cos\theta} = \frac{\cos^2\theta}{\sin\theta\cos\theta} - \frac{\sin^2\theta}{\sin\theta\cos\theta}$$
$$= \frac{\cos^2\theta - \sin^2\theta}{\sin\theta\cos\theta} = \frac{\cos^2\theta - (1-\cos^2\theta)}{\sin\theta\cos\theta} = \frac{\cos^2\theta - 1 + \cos^2\theta}{\sin\theta\cos\theta} = \frac{2\cos^2\theta - 1}{\sin\theta\cos\theta}$$

11. Verify $\dfrac{\sin(x+y)}{\cos(x-y)} = \dfrac{\cot x + \cot y}{1+\cot x\cot y}$ is an identity.

Starting on the left side, we have the following.

$$\frac{\sin(x+y)}{\cos(x-y)} = \frac{\sin x\cos y + \cos x\sin y}{\cos x\cos y + \sin x\sin y}$$
$$= \frac{\sin x\cos y + \cos x\sin y}{\cos x\cos y + \sin x\sin y}\cdot\frac{\dfrac{1}{\cos x\cos y}}{\dfrac{1}{\cos x\cos y}}$$
$$= \frac{\dfrac{\sin x\cos y}{\cos x\cos y} + \dfrac{\cos x\sin y}{\cos x\cos y}}{\dfrac{\cos x\cos y}{\cos x\cos y} + \dfrac{\sin x\sin y}{\cos x\cos y}}$$
$$= \frac{\dfrac{\sin x}{\cos x} + \dfrac{\sin y}{\cos y}}{1 + \dfrac{\sin x}{\cos x}\cdot\dfrac{\sin y}{\cos y}}$$
$$= \frac{\cot x + \cot y}{1+\cot x\cot y}$$

13. Verify $\dfrac{\sin\theta + \tan\theta}{1+\cos\theta} = \tan\theta$ is an identity.

Starting on the left side, we have the following.

$$\frac{\sin\theta+\tan\theta}{1+\cos\theta} = \frac{\sin\theta + \dfrac{\sin\theta}{\cos\theta}}{1+\cos\theta} = \frac{\sin\theta + \dfrac{\sin\theta}{\cos\theta}}{1+\cos\theta}\cdot\frac{\cos\theta}{\cos\theta} = \frac{\sin\theta\cos\theta + \sin\theta}{\cos\theta(1+\cos\theta)} = \frac{\sin\theta(\cos\theta+1)}{\cos\theta(1+\cos\theta)} = \frac{\sin\theta}{\cos\theta} = \tan\theta$$

15. Verify $\cos x = \dfrac{1-\tan^2 \frac{x}{2}}{1+\tan^2 \frac{x}{2}}$ is an identity.

Starting on the right side, we have the following.

$$\frac{1-\tan^2 \frac{x}{2}}{1+\tan^2 \frac{x}{2}} = \frac{1-\left(\frac{1-\cos x}{\sin x}\right)^2}{1+\left(\frac{1-\cos x}{\sin x}\right)^2} = \frac{1-\frac{(1-\cos x)^2}{\sin^2 x}}{1+\frac{(1-\cos x)^2}{\sin^2 x}} = \frac{1-\frac{(1-\cos x)^2}{\sin^2 x}}{1+\frac{(1-\cos x)^2}{\sin^2 x}} \cdot \frac{\sin^2 x}{\sin^2 x} = \frac{\sin^2 x-(1-\cos x)^2}{\sin^2 x+(1-\cos x)^2}$$

$$= \frac{\sin^2 x-\left(1-2\cos x+\cos^2 x\right)}{\sin^2 x+\left(1-2\cos x+\cos^2 x\right)} = \frac{\sin^2 x-1+2\cos x-\cos^2 x}{\sin^2 x+1-2\cos x+\cos^2 x}$$

$$= \frac{\left(1-\cos^2 x\right)-1+2\cos x-\cos^2 x}{\left(\sin^2 x+\cos^2 x\right)+1-2\cos x} = \frac{1-\cos^2 x-1+2\cos x-\cos^2 x}{1+1-2\cos x}$$

$$= \frac{2\cos x-2\cos^2 x}{2-2\cos x} = \frac{2\cos x(1-\cos x)}{2(1-\cos x)} = \cos x$$

17. Verify $\dfrac{\tan^2 t+1}{\tan t \csc^2 t} = \tan t$ is an identity.

Starting on the left side, we have the following.

$$\frac{\tan^2 t+1}{\tan t\csc^2 t} = \frac{\frac{\sin^2 t}{\cos^2 t}+1}{\frac{\sin t}{\cos t}\cdot\frac{1}{\sin^2 t}} = \frac{\frac{\sin^2 t}{\cos^2 t}+1}{\frac{1}{\cos t\sin t}} = \frac{\frac{\sin^2 t}{\cos^2 t}+1}{\frac{1}{\cos t\sin t}}\cdot\frac{\cos^2 t\sin t}{\cos^2 t\sin t}$$

$$= \frac{\sin^3 t+\cos^2 t\sin t}{\cos t} = \frac{\sin t\left(\sin^2 t+\cos^2 t\right)}{\cos t} = \frac{\sin t(1)}{\cos t} = \frac{\sin t}{\cos t} = \tan t$$

19. Verify $\tan 4\theta = \dfrac{2\tan 2\theta}{2-\sec^2 2\theta}$ is an identity.

Starting on the right side, we have the following.

$$\frac{2\tan 2\theta}{2-\sec^2 2\theta} = \frac{2\cdot\frac{\sin 2\theta}{\cos 2\theta}}{2-\frac{1}{\cos^2 2\theta}} = \frac{2\cdot\frac{\sin 2\theta}{\cos 2\theta}}{2-\frac{1}{\cos^2 2\theta}}\cdot\frac{\cos^2 2\theta}{\cos^2 2\theta} = \frac{2\sin 2\theta\cos 2\theta}{2\cos^2 2\theta-1} = \frac{\sin\left[2(2\theta)\right]}{\cos\left[2(2\theta)\right]} = \frac{\sin 4\theta}{\cos 4\theta} = \tan 4\theta$$

21. Verify $\dfrac{\cot s-\tan s}{\cos s+\sin s} = \dfrac{\cos s-\sin s}{\sin s\cos s}$ is an identity.

Starting on the left side, we have the following.

$$\frac{\cot s-\tan s}{\cos s+\sin s} = \frac{\frac{\cos s}{\sin s}-\frac{\sin s}{\cos s}}{\cos s+\sin s} = \frac{\frac{\cos s}{\sin s}-\frac{\sin s}{\cos s}}{\cos s+\sin s}\cdot\frac{\sin s\cos s}{\sin s\cos s}$$

$$= \frac{\cos^2 s-\sin^2 s}{(\cos s+\sin s)\sin s\cos s} = \frac{(\cos s+\sin s)(\cos s-\sin s)}{(\cos s+\sin s)\sin s\cos s} = \frac{\cos s-\sin s}{\sin s\cos s}$$

23. Verify $\dfrac{\tan(x+y)-\tan y}{1+\tan(x+y)\tan y}=\tan x$ is an identity.

Starting on the left side, we have the following.

$$\begin{aligned}\frac{\tan(x+y)-\tan y}{1+\tan(x+y)\tan y}&=\frac{\dfrac{\tan x+\tan y}{1-\tan x\tan y}-\tan y}{1+\dfrac{\tan x+\tan y}{1-\tan x\tan y}\cdot\tan y}\\&=\frac{\dfrac{\tan x+\tan y}{1-\tan x\tan y}-\tan y}{1+\dfrac{\tan x+\tan y}{1-\tan x\tan y}\cdot\tan y}\cdot\frac{1-\tan x\tan y}{1-\tan x\tan y}\\&=\frac{\tan x+\tan y-\tan y(1-\tan x\tan y)}{1-\tan x\tan y+(\tan x+\tan y)\tan y}\\&=\frac{\tan x+\tan x\tan^2 y}{1-\tan x\tan y+\tan x\tan y+\tan^2 y}\\&=\frac{\tan x(1+\tan^2 y)}{1+\tan^2 y}\\&=\tan x\end{aligned}$$

25. Verify $\dfrac{\cos^4 x-\sin^4 x}{\cos^2 x}=1-\tan^2 x$ is an identity.

Starting on the left side, we have the following.

$$\begin{aligned}\frac{\cos^4 x-\sin^4 x}{\cos^2 x}&=\frac{(\cos^2 x+\sin^2 x)(\cos^2 x-\sin^2 x)}{\cos^2 x}\\&=\frac{(1)(\cos^2 x-\sin^2 x)}{\cos^2 x}\\&=\frac{\cos^2 x-\sin^2 x}{\cos^2 x}\\&=\frac{\cos^2 x}{\cos^2 x}-\frac{\sin^2 x}{\cos^2 x}\\&=1-\tan^2 x\end{aligned}$$

27. Verify $\dfrac{2(\sin x-\sin^3 x)}{\cos x}=\sin 2x$ is an identity.

Starting on the left side, we have the following.

$$\begin{aligned}\frac{2(\sin x-\sin^3 x)}{\cos x}&=\frac{2\sin x(1-\sin^2 x)}{\cos x}\\&=\frac{2\sin x\cos^2 x}{\cos x}\\&=2\sin x\cos x\\&=\sin 2x\end{aligned}$$

Section 7.5: Inverse Circular Functions

1. For a function to have an inverse, it must be one-to-one.

3. The range of $y = \cos^{-1} x$ equals the domain of $y = \cos x$.

5. If a function f has an inverse and $f(\pi) = -1$, then $f^{1}(-1) = \pi$.

7. **(a)** [−1, 1]

(b) $\left[-\frac{\pi}{2}, \frac{\pi}{2}\right]$

(c) increasing

(d) −2 is not in the domain.

9. **(a)** $(-\infty, \infty)$

(b) $\left(-\frac{\pi}{2}, \frac{\pi}{2}\right)$

(c) increasing

(d) no

11. $\cos^{-1}\frac{1}{a}$

13. $y = \sin^{-1} 0$

$\sin y = 0, \ -\frac{\pi}{2} \le y \le \frac{\pi}{2}$

Since $\sin 0 = 0, \ y = 0.$

15. $y = \cos^{-1}(-1)$

$\cos y = -1, \ 0 \le y \le \pi$

Since $\cos \pi = -1, \ y = \pi.$

17. $y = \sin^{-1}(-1)$

$\sin y = -1, \ -\frac{\pi}{2} \le y \le \frac{\pi}{2}$

Since $\sin\frac{\pi}{2} = 1, \ y = -\frac{\pi}{2}.$

19. $y = \arctan 0$

$\tan y = 0, \ -\frac{\pi}{2} < y < \frac{\pi}{2}$

Since $\tan 0 = 0, y = 0.$

21. $y = \arccos 0$

$\cos y = 0, \ 0 \le y \le \pi$

Since $\cos\frac{\pi}{2} = 0, \ y = \frac{\pi}{2}.$

23. $y = \sin^{-1}\frac{\sqrt{2}}{2}$

$\sin y = \frac{\sqrt{2}}{2}, \ -\frac{\pi}{2} \le y \le \frac{\pi}{2}$

Since $\sin\frac{\pi}{4} = \frac{\sqrt{2}}{2}, \ y = \frac{\pi}{4}.$

25. $y = \arccos\left(-\frac{\sqrt{3}}{2}\right)$

$\cos y = -\frac{\sqrt{3}}{2}, \ 0 \le y \le \pi$

Since $\cos\frac{5\pi}{6} = -\frac{\sqrt{3}}{2}, \ y = \frac{5\pi}{6}.$

27. $y = \cot^{-1}(-1)$

$\cot y = -1, \ 0 < y < \pi$

y is in quadrant II.

The reference angle is $\frac{\pi}{4}$.

Since $\cot\frac{3\pi}{4} = 1, \ y = \frac{3\pi}{4}.$

29. $y = \csc^{-1}(-2)$

$\csc y = -2, \ -\frac{\pi}{2} \le y \le \frac{\pi}{2}, \ y \ne 0$

y is in quadrant IV.

The reference angle is $\frac{\pi}{6}$.

Since $\csc\left(-\frac{\pi}{6}\right) = -2, \ y = -\frac{\pi}{6}.$

31. $y = \text{arc}\sec\left(\frac{2\sqrt{3}}{3}\right)$

$\sec y = \frac{2\sqrt{3}}{3},\ 0 \le y \le \pi,\ y \ne \frac{\pi}{2}$

Since $\sec\frac{\pi}{6} = \frac{2\sqrt{3}}{3},\ y = \frac{\pi}{6}.$

33. $\theta = \arctan(-1)$

$\tan\ \theta = -1,\ -90° < \theta < 90°$

is in quadrant IV.
The reference angle is 45°.
Thus, $\theta = -45°$.

35. $\theta = \arcsin\left(-\frac{\sqrt{3}}{2}\right)$

$\sin\theta = -\frac{\sqrt{3}}{2},\ -90° \le \theta \le 90°$

θ is in quadrant IV.
The reference angle is 60°.
$\theta = -60°$.

37. $\theta = \cot^{-1}\left(-\frac{\sqrt{3}}{3}\right)$

$\cot\ \theta = -\frac{\sqrt{3}}{3},\ 0° < \theta < 180°$

θ is in quadrant II.
The reference angle is 60°.
$\theta = 180° - 60° = 120°$

39. $\theta = \sec^{-1}(-2)$

$\sec\ \theta = -2,\ 0° \le \theta \le 180°, \theta \ne 90°$

θ is in quadrant II.
The reference angle is 60°.
$\theta = 180° - 60° = 120°$.

For Exercises 41 – 45, be sure that your calculator is in degree mode. Keystroke sequences may vary based on the type and/or model of calculator being used.

41. $\theta = \sin^{-1}(-.13349122)$

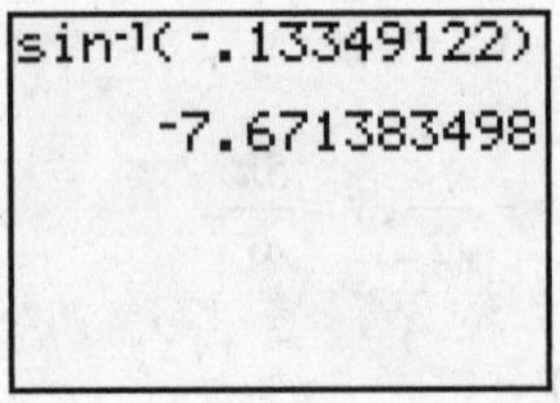

$\sin^{-1}(-.13349122) = -7.6713835°$

43. $\theta = \arccos(-.39876459)$

$\arccos(-.39876459) \approx 113.500970°$

45. $\theta = \csc^{-1} 1.9422833$

$\csc^{-1} 1.9422833 \approx 30.987961°$

For Exercises 47 – 51, be sure that your calculator is in radian mode. Keystroke sequences may vary based on the type and/or model of calculator being used.

47. $y = \arctan 1.1111111$

$\arctan 1.1111111 \approx .83798122$

49. $y = \cot^{-1}(-.92170128)$

$\cot^{-1}(-.91270128) \approx 2.3154725$

51. $y = \arcsin .92837781$

$\arcsin .92837781 \approx 1.1900238$

53.

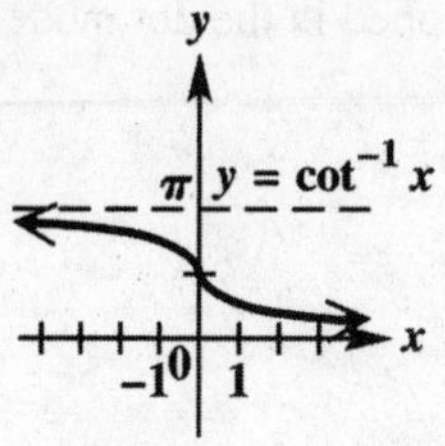

Domain: $(-\infty, \infty)$; Range: $(0, \pi)$

54.

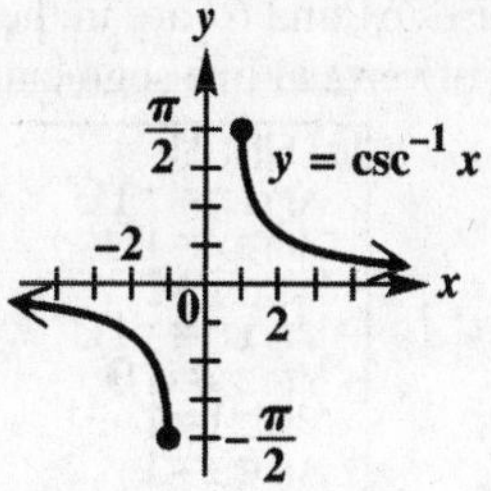

Domain: $(-\infty, -1] \cup [1, \infty)$;

Range: $\left[-\frac{\pi}{2}, 0\right) \cup \left(0, \frac{\pi}{2}\right]$

55.

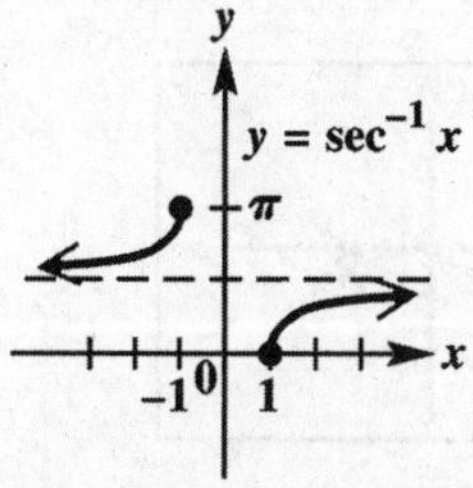

Domain: $(-\infty, -1] \cup [1, \infty)$;

Range: $\left[0, \frac{\pi}{2}\right) \cup \left(\frac{\pi}{2}, \pi\right]$

56.

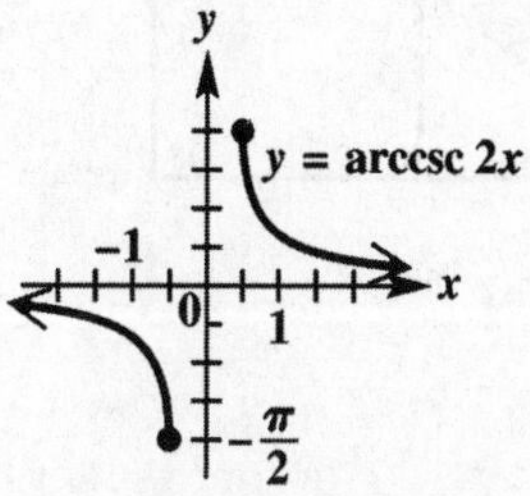

Domain: $\left(-\infty, -\frac{1}{2}\right] \cup \left[\frac{1}{2}, \infty\right)$;

Range: $\left[-\frac{\pi}{2}, 0\right) \cup \left(0, \frac{\pi}{2}\right]$

57.

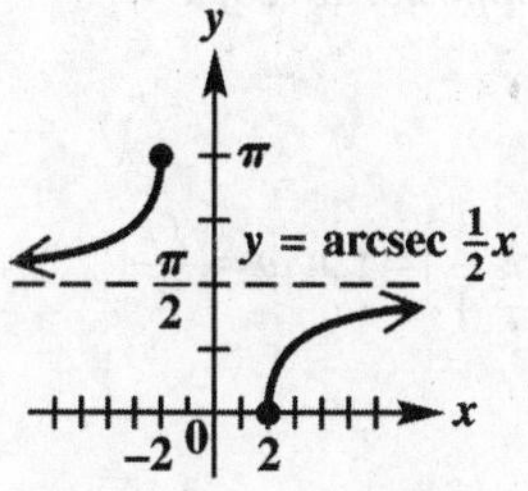

Domain: $(-\infty, -2] \cup [2, \infty)$; Range: $\left[0, \frac{\pi}{2}\right) \cup \left(\frac{\pi}{2}, \pi\right]$

58. 1.003 is not in the domain of $y = \sin^{-1} x$. (Alternatively, you could state that 1.003 is not in the range of $y = \sin x$.)

59. The domain of $y = \tan^{-1} x$ is $(-\infty, \infty)$. (Alternatively, you could state that the range of $y = \tan x$ is $(-\infty, \infty)$.)

60. $f\left[f^{-1}(x)\right] = f\left[\frac{x+2}{3}\right] = 3\left(\frac{x+2}{3}\right) - 2 = x + 2 - 2 = x$

$f^{-1}\left[f(x)\right] = f^{-1}[3x-2] = \frac{(3x-2)+2}{3} = \frac{3x}{3} = x$

In each case the result is x. The graph is a straight line bisecting the first and third quadrants I and III (i.e., $y = x$).

The graphs for Exercises 61 and 62 are in the standard window. Exercise 62 is graphed in the dot mode to avoid the appearance of vertical line segments.

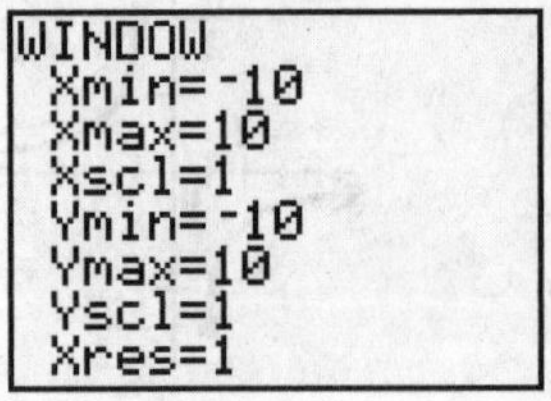

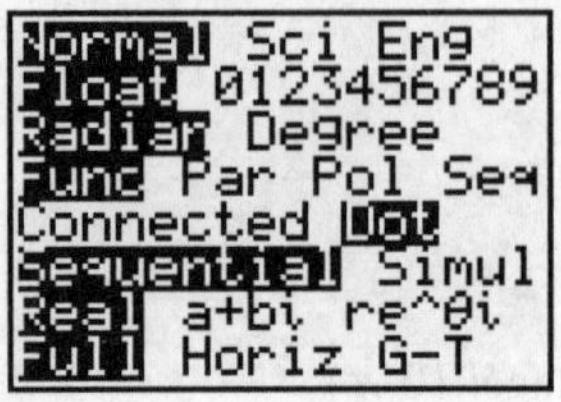

61. It is the graph of $y = x$.

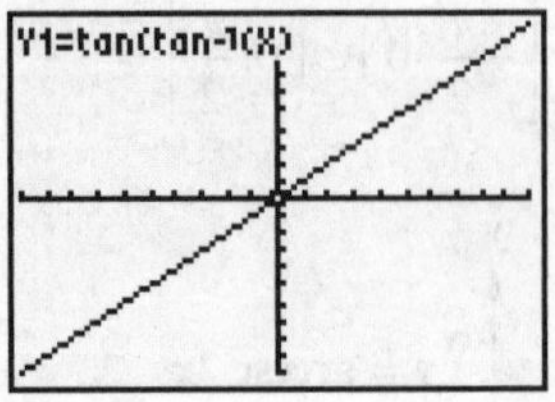

62. It does not agree because the range of the inverse tangent function is $\left(-\dfrac{\pi}{2}, \dfrac{\pi}{2}\right)$, not $(-\infty, \infty)$, as was the case in Exercise 61.

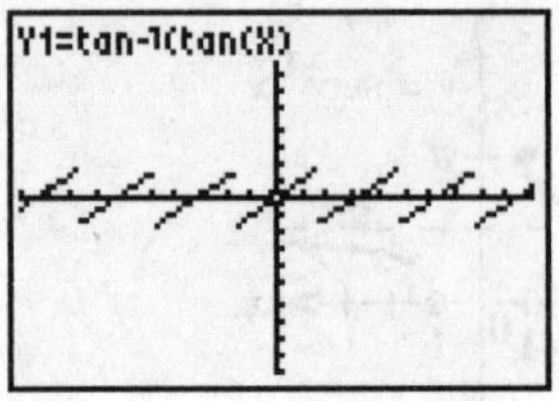

63. $\tan\left(\arccos\dfrac{3}{4}\right)$

Let $\omega = \arccos\dfrac{3}{4}$, so that $\cos\omega = \dfrac{3}{4}$. Since arccos is defined only in quadrants I and II, and $\dfrac{3}{4}$ is positive, ω is in quadrant I. Sketch ω and label a triangle with the side opposite ω equal to $\sqrt{4^2 - 3^2} = \sqrt{16-9} = \sqrt{7}$.

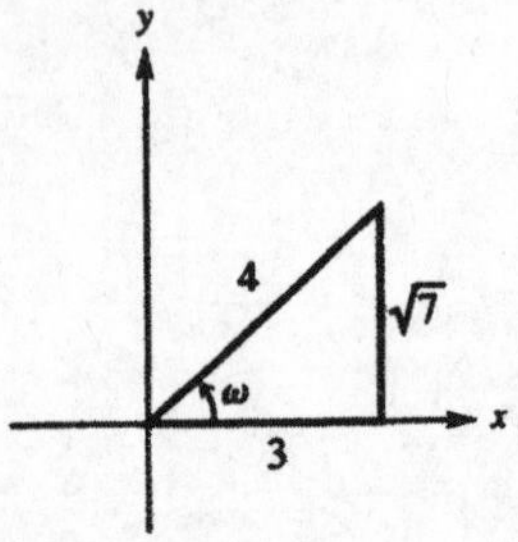

$$\tan\left(\arccos\frac{3}{4}\right) = \tan\omega = \frac{\sqrt{7}}{3}$$

64. $\sin\left(\arccos\dfrac{1}{4}\right)$

Let $\theta = \arccos\dfrac{1}{4}$, so that $\cos\theta = \dfrac{1}{4}$. Since arccos is defined only in quadrants I and II, and $\dfrac{1}{4}$ is positive, θ is in quadrant I. Sketch θ and label a triangle with the side opposite θ equal to $\sqrt{4^2-1^2} = \sqrt{16-1} = \sqrt{15}$.

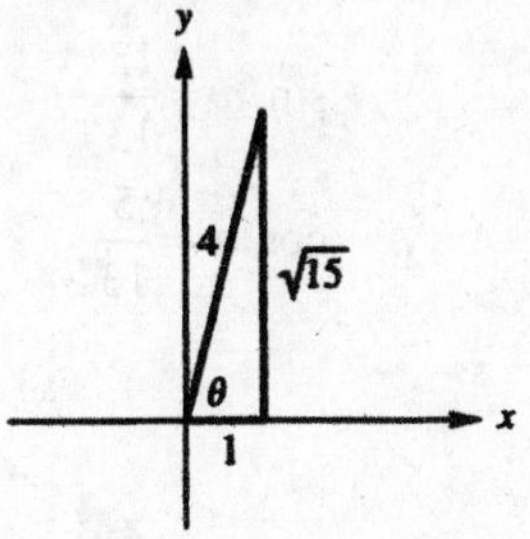

$$\sin\left(\arccos\frac{1}{4}\right) = \sin\theta = \frac{\sqrt{15}}{4}$$

65. $\cos(\tan^{-1}(-2))$

Let $\omega = \tan^{-1}(-2)$, so that $\tan\omega = -2$. Since $\tan^{-1}$ is defined only in quadrants I and IV, and -2 is negative, ω is in quadrant IV. Sketch ω and label a triangle with the hypotenuse equal to $\sqrt{(-2)^2+1} = \sqrt{4+1} = \sqrt{5}$.

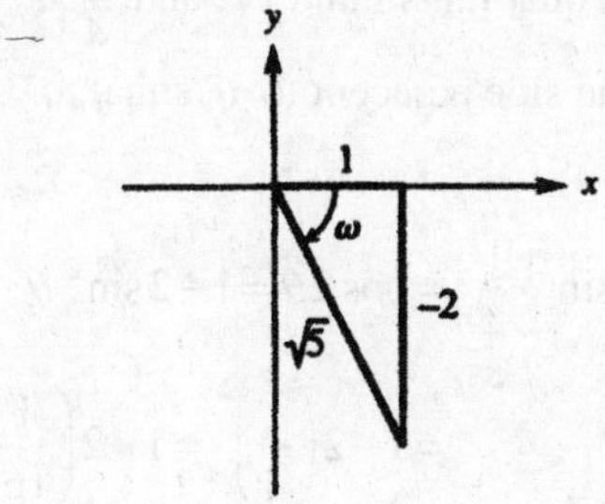

$$\cos(\tan^{-1}(-2)) = \cos\omega = \frac{\sqrt{5}}{5}$$

66. $\sec\left(\sin^{-1}\left(-\dfrac{1}{5}\right)\right)$

Let $\theta = \sin^{-1}\left(-\dfrac{1}{5}\right)$, so that $\sin\theta = -\dfrac{1}{5}$. Since arcsin is defined only in quadrants I and IV, and $-\dfrac{1}{5}$ is negative, θ is in quadrant IV. Sketch θ and label a triangle with the side adjacent to θ equal to $\sqrt{5^2-(-1)^2} = \sqrt{25-1} = \sqrt{24} = 2\sqrt{6}$.

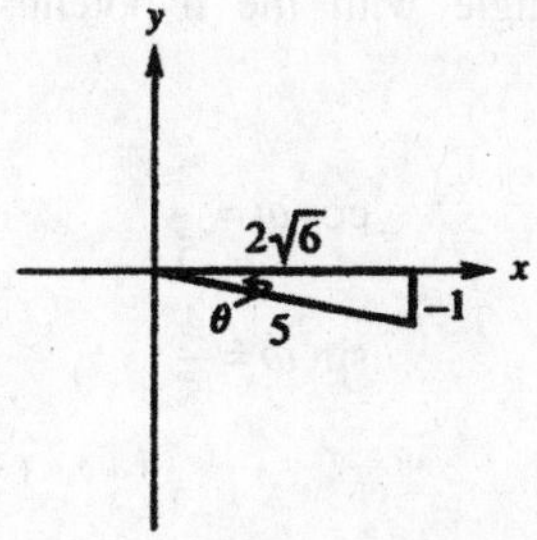

$$\sec\left(\sin^{-1}\left(-\frac{1}{5}\right)\right) = \sec\theta = \frac{5}{2\sqrt{6}} = \frac{5\sqrt{6}}{12}$$

67. $\sin\left(2\tan^{-1}\frac{12}{5}\right)$

Let $\omega = \tan^{-1}\frac{12}{5}$, so that $\tan\omega = \frac{12}{5}$. Since $\tan^{-1}$ is defined only in quadrants I and IV, and $\frac{12}{5}$ is positive, ω is in quadrant I. Sketch ω and label a right triangle with the hypotenuse equal to $\sqrt{12^2+5^2} = \sqrt{144+25} = \sqrt{169} = 13.$

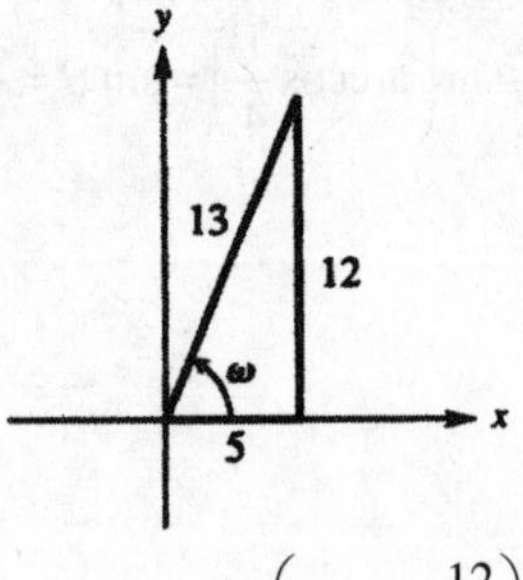

$$\sin\omega = \frac{12}{13}$$
$$\cos\omega = \frac{5}{13}$$

$$\sin\left(2\tan^{-1}\frac{12}{5}\right) = \sin(2\omega) = 2\sin\omega\cos\omega = 2\left(\frac{12}{13}\right)\left(\frac{5}{13}\right) = \frac{120}{169}$$

68. $\cos\left(2\sin^{-1}\frac{1}{4}\right)$

Let $\theta = \sin^{-1}\frac{1}{4}$, so that $\sin\theta = \frac{1}{4}$. Since $\sin^{-1}$ is defined only in quadrants I and IV, and $\frac{1}{4}$ is positive, θ is in quadrant I. Sketch θ and label a triangle with the side adjacent to θ equal to $\sqrt{4^2-1^2} = \sqrt{16-1} = \sqrt{15}.$

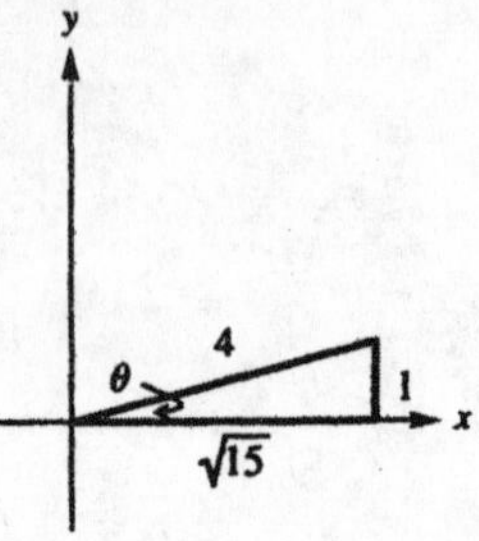

$$\begin{aligned}\cos\left(2\sin^{-1}\frac{1}{4}\right) &= \cos 2\theta = 1-2\sin^2\theta\\ &= 1-2\left(\frac{1}{4}\right)^2 = 1-2\left(\frac{1}{16}\right)\\ &= 1-\frac{1}{8} = \frac{7}{8}\end{aligned}$$

69. $\cos\left(2\arctan\frac{4}{3}\right)$

Let $\omega = \arctan\frac{4}{3}$, so that $\tan\omega = \frac{4}{3}$. Since arctan is defined only in quadrants I and IV, and $\frac{4}{3}$ is positive, ω is in quadrant I. Sketch ω and label a triangle with the hypotenuse equal to $\sqrt{4^2+3^2} = \sqrt{16+9} = \sqrt{25} = 5.$

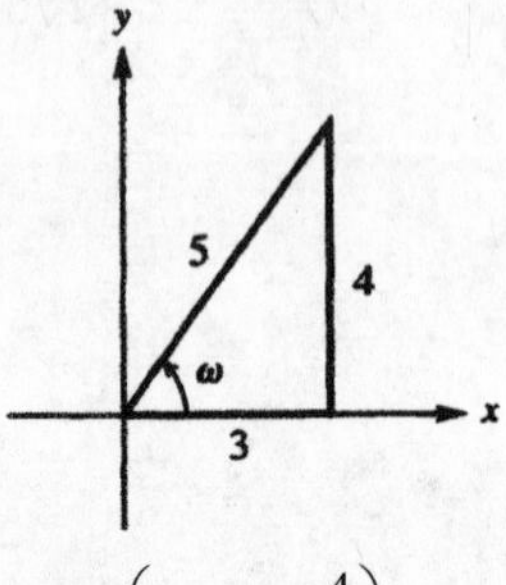

$$\cos\omega = \frac{3}{5}$$
$$\sin\omega = \frac{4}{5}$$

$$\cos\left(2\arctan\frac{4}{3}\right) = \cos(2\omega) = \cos^2\omega - \sin^2\omega = \left(\frac{3}{5}\right)^2 - \left(\frac{4}{5}\right)^2 = \frac{9}{25} - \frac{16}{25} = -\frac{7}{25}$$

70. $\tan\left(2\cos^{-1}\frac{1}{4}\right)$

Let $\theta=\cos^{-1}\frac{1}{4}$, so that $\cos\theta=\frac{1}{4}$. Since $\cos^{-1}$ is defined only in quadrants I and II, and $\frac{1}{4}$ is positive, θ is in quadrant I. Sketch θ and label a triangle with the side opposite θ equal to $\sqrt{4^2-1^2}=\sqrt{16-1}=\sqrt{15}.$

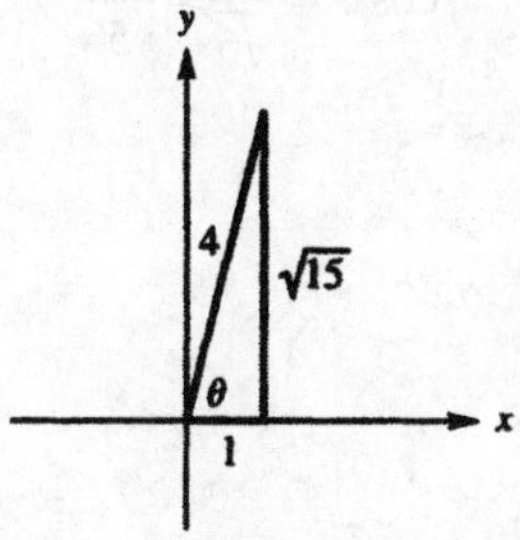

$$\tan\theta=\frac{\sqrt{15}}{1}=\sqrt{15}$$

$$\tan\left(2\cos^{-1}\frac{1}{4}\right)=\tan 2\theta=\frac{2\tan\theta}{1-\tan^2\theta}=\frac{2\sqrt{15}}{1-\left(\sqrt{15}\right)^2}=\frac{2\sqrt{15}}{-14}=-\frac{\sqrt{15}}{7}$$

71. $\sin\left(2\cos^{-1}\frac{1}{5}\right)$

Let $\theta=\cos^{-1}\frac{1}{5}$, so that $\cos\theta=\frac{1}{5}$. The inverse cosine function yields values only in quadrants I and II, and since $\frac{1}{5}$ is positive, θ is in quadrant I. Sketch θ and label the sides of the right triangle. By the Pythagorean theorem, the length opposite to θ will be $\sqrt{5^2-1^2}=\sqrt{24}=2\sqrt{6}.$

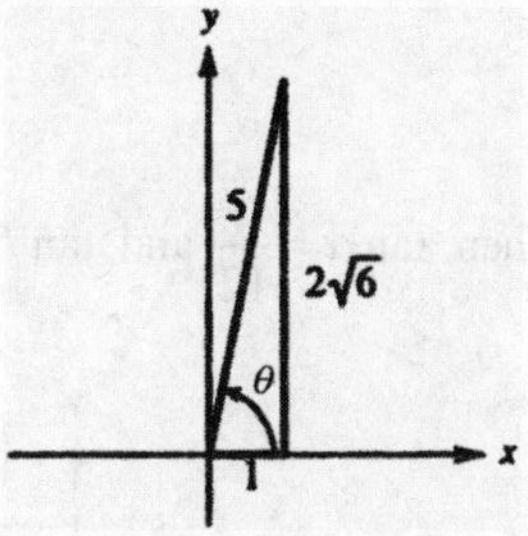

From the figure, $\sin\theta=\frac{2\sqrt{6}}{5}$. Then, $\sin\left(2\cos^{-1}\frac{1}{5}\right)=\sin 2\theta=2\sin\theta\cos\theta=2\left(\frac{2\sqrt{6}}{5}\right)\left(\frac{1}{5}\right)=\frac{4\sqrt{6}}{25}.$

72. $\cos\left(2\tan^{-1}(-2)\right)$

Let $\theta = \arctan(-2)$, so that $\tan\theta = -2$. Since arctan is defined only in quadrants I and IV, and –2 is negative, θ is in quadrant IV. Sketch θ and label a triangle with the hypotenuse equal to $\sqrt{(-2)^2+1^2} = \sqrt{4+1} = \sqrt{5}$.

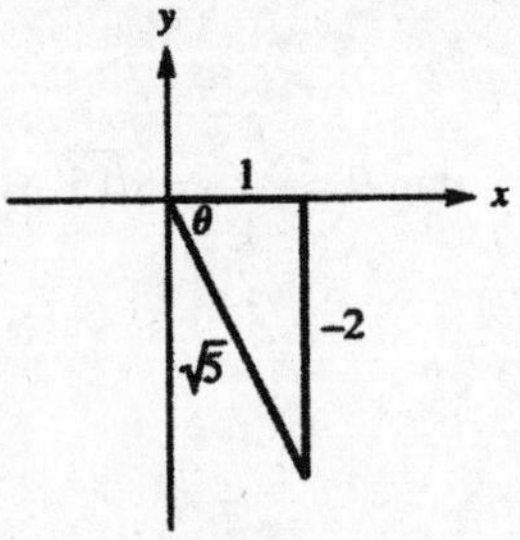

$$\cos\theta = \frac{1}{\sqrt{5}} = \frac{\sqrt{5}}{5}$$

$$\cos\left(2\tan^{-1}(-2)\right) = \cos 2\theta = 2\cos^2\theta - 1 = 2\left(\frac{1}{\sqrt{5}}\right)^2 - 1 = \frac{2}{5} - 1 = -\frac{3}{5}$$

73. $\sec(\sec^{-1} 2)$

Since secant and inverse secant are inverse functions, $\sec\left(\sec^{-1} 2\right) = 2$.

74. $\csc\left(\csc^{-1}\sqrt{2}\right) = \csc\frac{\pi}{4} = \sqrt{2}$

Also, since cosecant and inverse cosecant are inverse functions, $\csc\left(\csc^{-1}\sqrt{2}\right) = \sqrt{2}$.

75. $\cos\left(\tan^{-1}\frac{5}{12} - \cot^{-1}\frac{3}{4}\right)$

Let $\alpha = \tan^{-1}\frac{5}{12}$ and $\beta = \tan^{-1}\frac{4}{3}$. Then $\tan\alpha = \frac{5}{12}$ and $\tan\beta = \frac{3}{4}$. Sketch angles α and β, both in quadrant I.

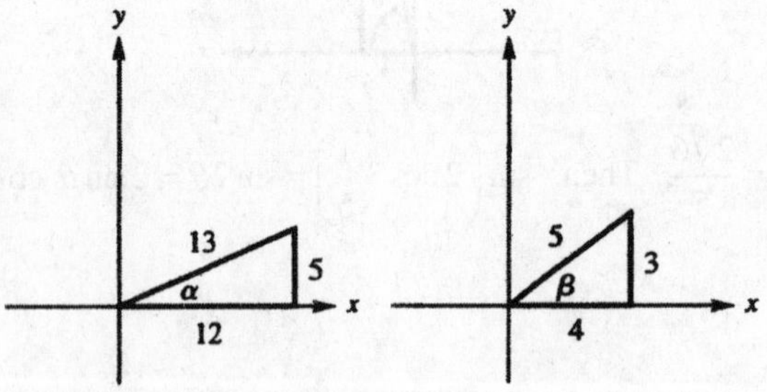

We have $\sin\alpha = \frac{5}{13}$, $\cos\alpha = \frac{12}{13}$, $\sin\beta = \frac{3}{5}$, and $\cos\beta = \frac{4}{5}$.

$$\cos\left(\tan^{-1}\frac{5}{12} - \tan^{-1}\frac{3}{4}\right) = \cos(\alpha-\beta) = \cos\alpha\cos\beta + \sin\alpha\sin\beta$$

$$= \left(\frac{12}{13}\right)\left(\frac{4}{5}\right) + \left(\frac{5}{13}\right)\left(\frac{3}{5}\right) = \frac{48}{65} + \frac{15}{65} = \frac{63}{65}$$

76. $\cos\left(\sin^{-1}\frac{3}{5}+\cos^{-1}\frac{5}{13}\right)$

Let $\omega_1=\sin^{-1}\frac{3}{5}$ and $\omega_2=\cos^{-1}\frac{5}{13}$. Then $\sin\omega_1=\frac{3}{5}$ and $\cos\omega_2=\frac{5}{13}$. Sketch ω_1 and ω_2 in quadrant I.

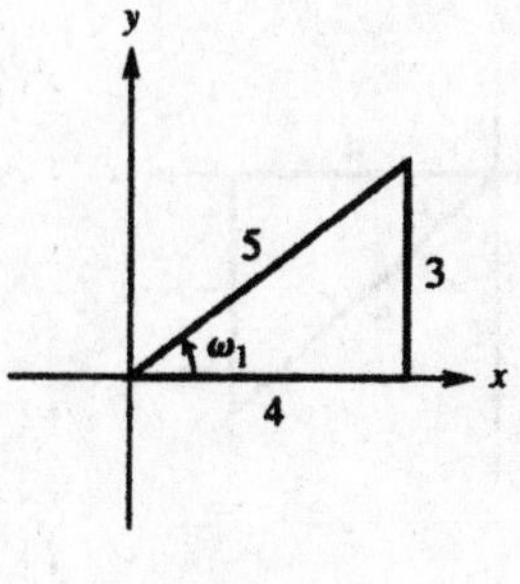

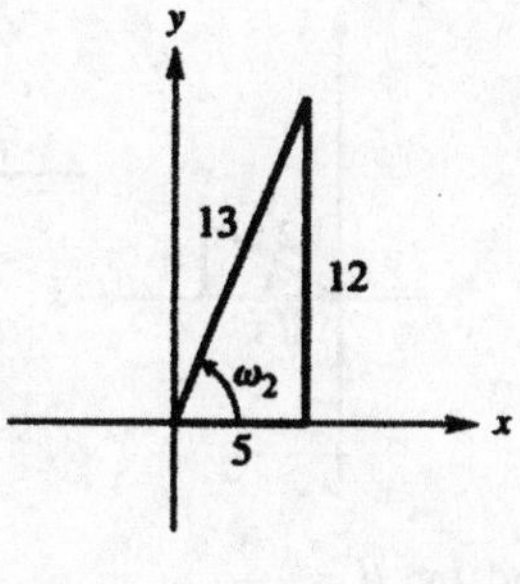

We have $\sin\omega_1=\frac{3}{5}$, $\cos\omega_1=\frac{4}{5}$, $\cos\omega_2=\frac{5}{13}$, and $\sin\omega_2=\frac{12}{13}$.

$$\cos\left(\arcsin\frac{3}{5}+\arccos\frac{5}{13}\right)=\cos(\omega_1+\omega_2)=\cos\omega_1\cos\omega_2-\sin\omega_1\sin\omega_2$$

$$=\left(\frac{4}{5}\right)\left(\frac{5}{13}\right)-\left(\frac{3}{5}\right)\left(\frac{12}{13}\right)=\frac{20}{65}-\frac{36}{65}=-\frac{16}{65}$$

77. $\sin\left(\sin^{-1}\frac{1}{2}+\tan^{-1}(-3)\right)$

Let $\sin^{-1}\frac{1}{2}=A$ and $\tan^{-1}(-3)=B$. Then $\sin A=\frac{1}{2}$ and $\tan B=-3$. Sketch angle A in quadrant I and angle B in quadrant IV.

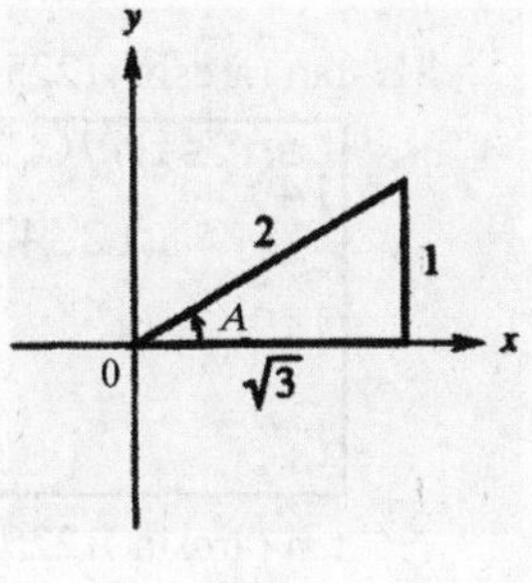

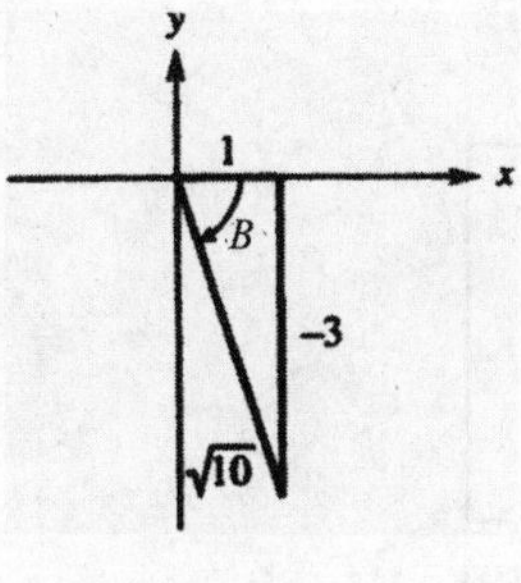

We have $\cos A=\frac{\sqrt{3}}{2}$, $\sin A=\frac{1}{2}$, $\cos B=\frac{1}{\sqrt{10}}=\frac{\sqrt{10}}{10}$, and $\sin B=\frac{-3}{\sqrt{10}}=-\frac{3\sqrt{10}}{10}$.

$$\sin\left(\sin^{-1}\frac{1}{2}+\tan^{-1}(-3)\right)=\sin(A+B)=\sin A\cos B+\cos A\sin B$$

$$=\frac{1}{2}\cdot\frac{1}{\sqrt{10}}+\frac{\sqrt{3}}{2}\cdot\frac{-3}{\sqrt{10}}=\frac{1-3\sqrt{3}}{2\sqrt{10}}=\frac{\sqrt{10}-3\sqrt{30}}{20}$$

78. $\tan\left(\cos^{-1}\frac{\sqrt{3}}{2}-\sin^{-1}\left(-\frac{3}{5}\right)\right)$

Let $\alpha=\cos^{-1}\frac{\sqrt{3}}{2}$, $\beta=\sin^{-1}\left(-\frac{3}{5}\right)$. Sketch angle α in quadrant I and angle β in quadrant IV.

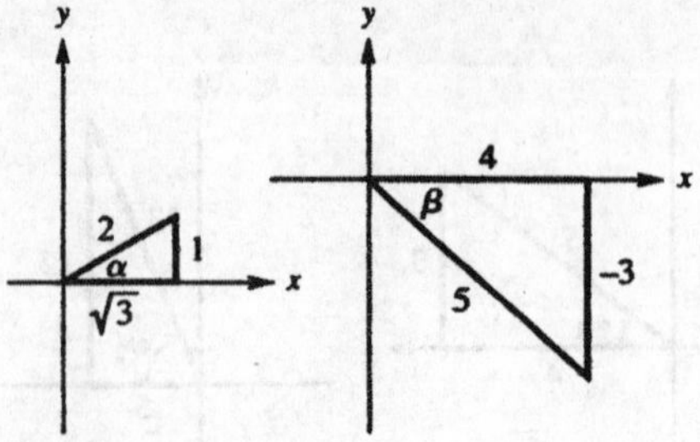

We have $\tan\alpha=\frac{1}{\sqrt{3}}$ and $\tan\beta=-\frac{3}{4}$.

$$\tan\left(\cos^{-1}\frac{\sqrt{3}}{2}-\sin^{-1}\left(-\frac{3}{5}\right)\right)=\tan(\alpha-\beta)=\frac{\tan\alpha-\tan\beta}{1+\tan\alpha\,\tan\beta}=\frac{\frac{1}{\sqrt{3}}-\left(-\frac{3}{4}\right)}{1+\left(\frac{1}{\sqrt{3}}\right)\left(-\frac{3}{4}\right)}=\frac{\frac{4+3\sqrt{3}}{4\sqrt{3}}}{\frac{4\sqrt{3}-3}{4\sqrt{3}}}$$

$$=\frac{4+3\sqrt{3}}{4\sqrt{3}-3}=\frac{4+3\sqrt{3}}{-3+4\sqrt{3}}\cdot\frac{-3-4\sqrt{3}}{-3-4\sqrt{3}}$$

$$=\frac{-12-25\sqrt{3}-36}{9-48}=\frac{-48-25\sqrt{3}}{-39}=\frac{48+25\sqrt{3}}{39}$$

For Exercises 79–82, your calculator could be in either degree or radian mode. Keystroke sequences may vary based on the type and/or model of calculator being used.

79. $\cos\left(\tan^{-1}.5\right)$

$\cos(\tan^{-1}.5)\approx .894427191$

80. $\sin\left(\cos^{-1}.25\right)$

$\sin\left(\cos^{-1}.25\right)\approx .9682458366$

81. tan (arcsin .12251014)

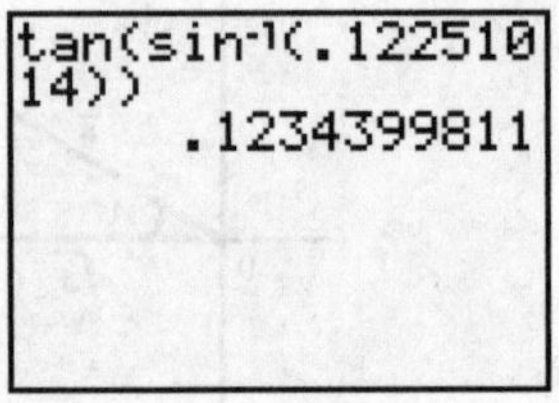

tan (arcsin .12251014) ≈ .1234399811

82. cot (arccos .58236841)

cot (arccos .58236841) ≈ .716386406

83. $\sin(\arccos u)$

Let $\theta = \arccos u$, so $\cos\theta = u = \frac{u}{1}$. Since $u > 0$, $0 < \theta < \frac{\pi}{2}$.

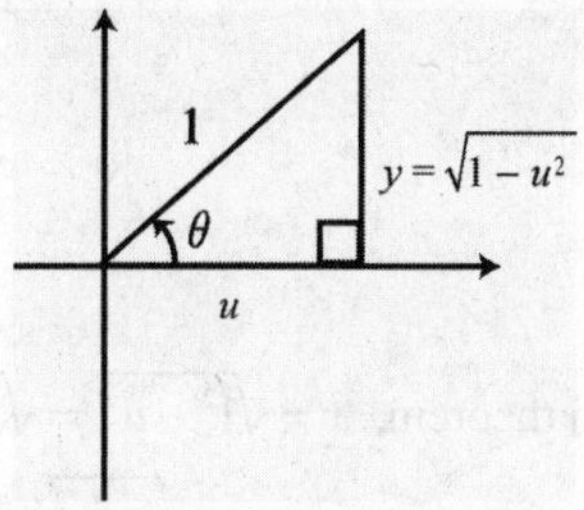

Since $y > 0$, from the Pythagorean theorem, $y = \sqrt{1^2 - u^2} = \sqrt{1-u^2}$.

Therefore, $\sin\theta = \frac{\sqrt{1-u^2}}{1} = \sqrt{1-u^2}$. Thus, $\sin(\arccos u) = \sqrt{1-u^2}$.

84. $\tan(\arccos u)$

Let $\theta = \arccos u$, so $\cos\theta = u = \frac{u}{1}$. Since $u > 0$, $0 < \theta < \frac{\pi}{2}$.

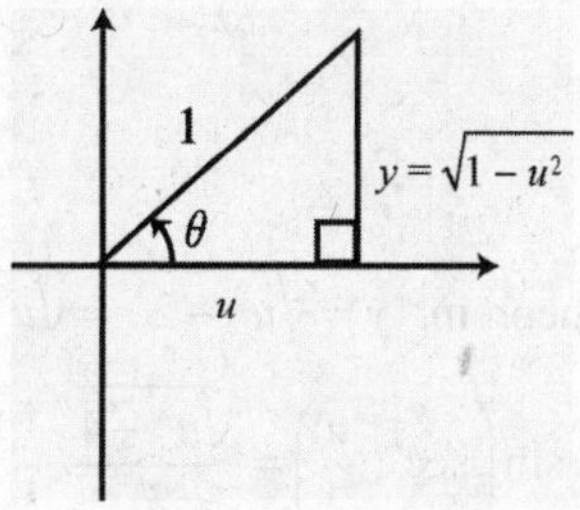

Since $y > 0$, from the Pythagorean theorem, $y = \sqrt{1^2 - u^2} = \sqrt{1-u^2}$.

Therefore, $\tan\theta = \frac{\sqrt{1-u^2}}{u}$. Thus, $\tan(\arccos u) = \frac{\sqrt{1-u^2}}{u}$.

85. $\cos(\arcsin u)$

Let $\theta = \arcsin u$, so $\sin\theta = u = \frac{u}{1}$. Since $u > 0$, $0 < \theta < \frac{\pi}{2}$.

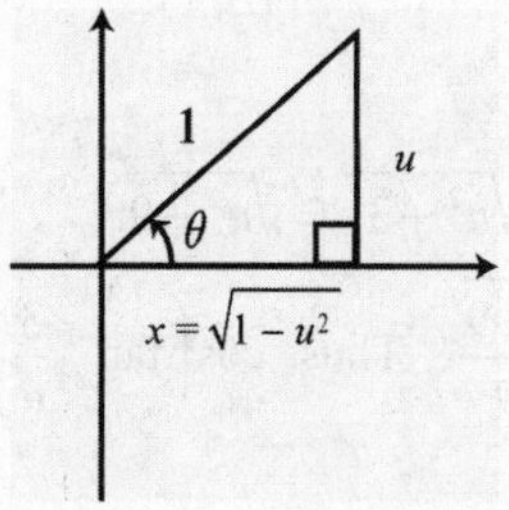

Since $x > 0$, from the Pythagorean theorem, $x = \sqrt{1^2 - u^2} = \sqrt{1-u^2}$.

Therefore, $\cos\theta = \frac{\sqrt{1-u^2}}{1} = \sqrt{1-u^2}$. Thus, $\cos(\arcsin u) = \sqrt{1-u^2}$

86. $\cot(\arcsin u)$

Let $\theta = \arcsin u$, so $\sin\theta = u = \dfrac{u}{1}$. Since $u > 0$, $0 < \theta < \dfrac{\pi}{2}$.

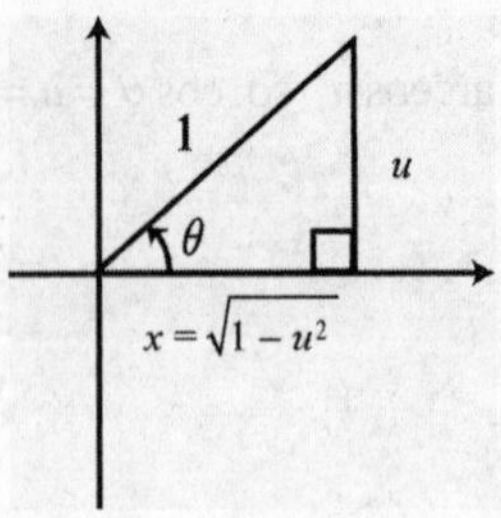

Since $x > 0$, from the Pythagorean theorem, $x = \sqrt{1^2 - u^2} = \sqrt{1-u^2}$.

Therefore, $\cot\theta = \dfrac{\sqrt{1-u^2}}{u}$. Thus, $\cot(\arcsin u) = \dfrac{\sqrt{1-u^2}}{u}$.

87. $\sin\left(\sec^{-1}\dfrac{u}{2}\right)$

Let $\theta = \sec^{-1}\dfrac{u}{2}$, so $\sec\theta = \dfrac{u}{2}$. Since $u > 0$, $0 < \theta < \dfrac{\pi}{2}$.

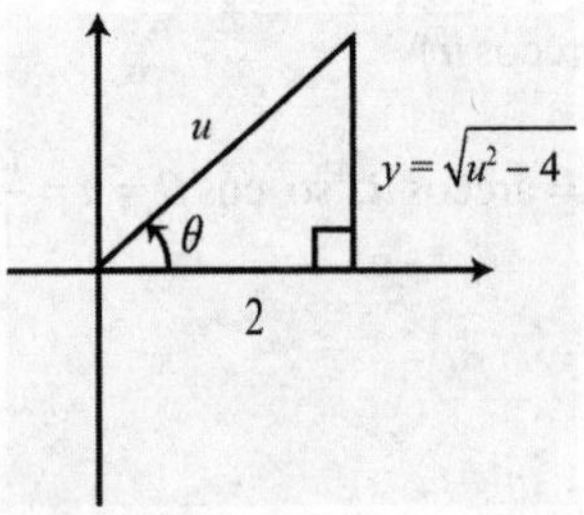

Since $y > 0$, from the Pythagorean theorem, $y = \sqrt{u^2 - 2^2} = \sqrt{u^2 - 4}$.

Therefore, $\sin\theta = \dfrac{\sqrt{u^2-4}}{u}$. Thus, $\sin\left(\sec^{-1}\dfrac{u}{2}\right) = \dfrac{\sqrt{u^2-4}}{u}$.

88. $\cos\left(\tan^{-1}\dfrac{3}{u}\right)$

Let $\theta = \tan^{-1}\dfrac{3}{u}$, so $\tan\theta = \dfrac{3}{u}$. Since $u > 0$, $0 < \theta < \dfrac{\pi}{2}$.

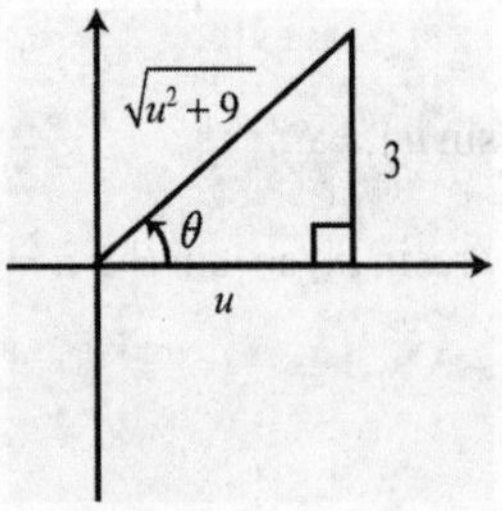

From the Pythagorean theorem, $r = \sqrt{u^2 + 3^2} = \sqrt{u^2 + 9}$.

Therefore, $\cos\theta = \dfrac{u}{\sqrt{u^2+9}} = \dfrac{u\sqrt{u^2+9}}{u^2+9}$. Thus, $\cos\left(\tan^{-1}\dfrac{3}{u}\right) = \dfrac{u\sqrt{u^2+9}}{u^2+9}$.

89. $\tan\left(\sin^{-1}\dfrac{u}{\sqrt{u^2+2}}\right)$

Let $\theta = \sin^{-1}\dfrac{u}{\sqrt{u^2+2}}$, so $\sin\theta = \dfrac{u}{\sqrt{u^2+2}}$. Since $u > 0$, $0 < \theta < \dfrac{\pi}{2}$.

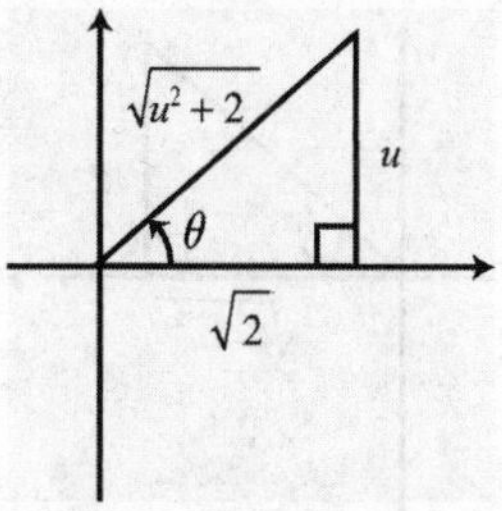

Since $x > 0$, from the Pythagorean theorem, $x = \sqrt{\left(\sqrt{u^2+2}\right)^2 - u^2} = \sqrt{u^2+2-u^2} = \sqrt{2}$.

Therefore, $\tan\theta = \dfrac{u}{\sqrt{2}} = \dfrac{u\sqrt{2}}{2}$. Thus, $\tan\left(\sin^{-1}\dfrac{u}{\sqrt{u^2+2}}\right) = \dfrac{u\sqrt{2}}{2}$.

90. $\sec\left(\cos^{-1}\dfrac{u}{\sqrt{u^2+5}}\right)$

Let $\theta = \cos^{-1}\dfrac{u}{\sqrt{u^2+5}}$, so $\cos\theta = \dfrac{u}{\sqrt{u^2+5}}$. Since $u > 0$, $0 < \theta < \dfrac{\pi}{2}$.

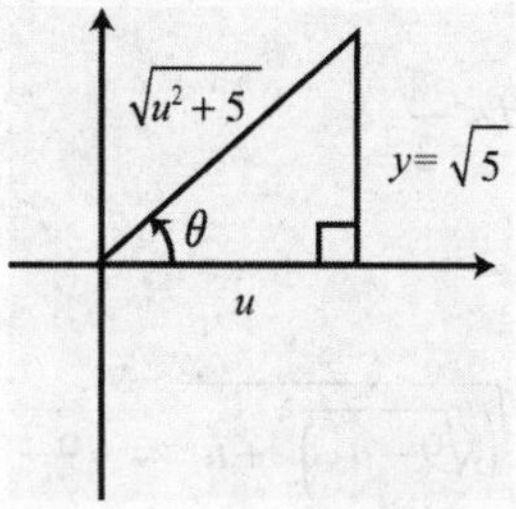

Since $y > 0$, from the Pythagorean theorem, $x = \sqrt{\left(\sqrt{u^2+5}\right)^2 - u^2} = \sqrt{u^2+5-u^2} = \sqrt{5}$. Therefore,

$\sec\theta = \dfrac{\sqrt{u^2+5}}{u}$. Thus, $\sec\left(\cos^{-1}\dfrac{u}{\sqrt{u^2+5}}\right) = \dfrac{\sqrt{u^2+5}}{u}$.

Also note, $\sec\left(\cos^{-1}\dfrac{u}{\sqrt{u^2+5}}\right) = \dfrac{1}{\cos\left(\cos^{-1}\dfrac{u}{\sqrt{u^2+5}}\right)} = \dfrac{1}{\dfrac{u}{\sqrt{u^2+5}}} = \dfrac{\sqrt{u^2+5}}{u}$.

91. $\sec\left(\text{arc cot}\frac{\sqrt{4-u^2}}{u}\right)$

Let $\theta = \text{arc cot}\frac{\sqrt{4-u^2}}{u}$, so $\cot\theta = \frac{\sqrt{4-u^2}}{u}$. Since $u > 0$, $0 < \theta < \frac{\pi}{2}$.

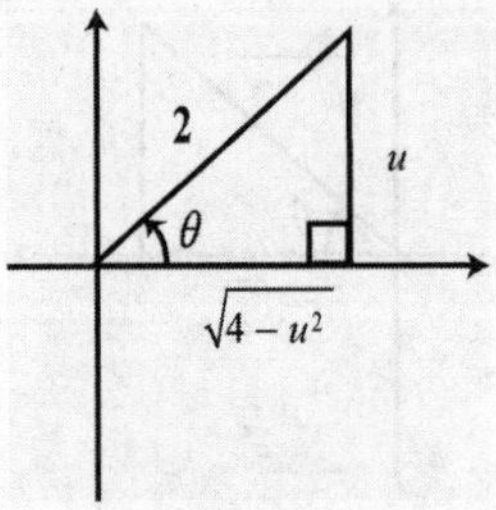

From the Pythagorean theorem, $r = \sqrt{\left(\sqrt{4-u^2}\right)^2 + u^2} = \sqrt{4-u^2+u^2} = \sqrt{4} = 2$.

Therefore, $\sec\theta = \frac{2}{\sqrt{4-u^2}} = \frac{2\sqrt{4-u^2}}{4-u^2}$. Thus, $\sec\left(\text{arc cot}\frac{\sqrt{4-u^2}}{u}\right) = \frac{2\sqrt{4-u^2}}{4-u^2}$.

92. $\csc\left(\arctan\frac{\sqrt{9-u^2}}{u}\right)$

Let $\theta = \arctan\frac{\sqrt{9-u^2}}{u}$, so

$\tan\theta = \frac{\sqrt{9-u^2}}{u}$. Since $u > 0$, $0 < \theta < \frac{\pi}{2}$.

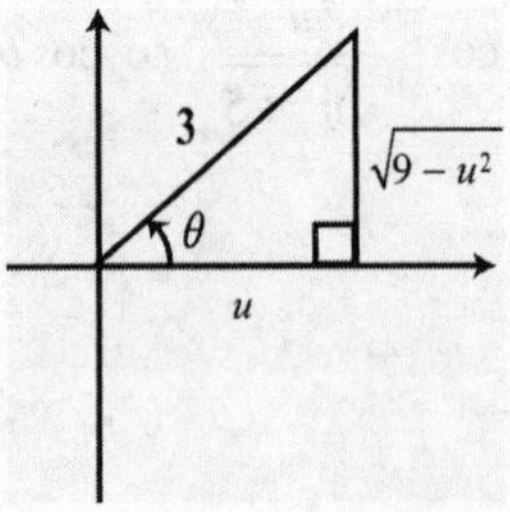

From the Pythagorean theorem, $r = \sqrt{\left(\sqrt{9-u^2}\right)^2 + u^2} = \sqrt{9-u^2+u^2} = \sqrt{9} = 3$. Therefore,

$\csc\theta = \frac{3}{\sqrt{9-u^2}} = \frac{3\sqrt{9-u^2}}{9-u^2}$. Thus, $\csc\left(\arctan\frac{\sqrt{9-u^2}}{u}\right) = \frac{3\sqrt{9-u^2}}{9-u^2}$.

93. (a) $\theta = \arcsin\sqrt{\frac{42^2}{2(42^2)+64(0)}}$

$= \arcsin\sqrt{\frac{42^2}{2(42^2)+0}} = \arcsin\sqrt{\frac{42^2}{2(42^2)}} = \arcsin\sqrt{\frac{1}{2}} = \arcsin\frac{1}{\sqrt{2}} = \arcsin\frac{\sqrt{2}}{2} = 45°$

(b) $\theta = \arcsin\sqrt{\frac{v^2}{2v^2+64(6)}} = \arcsin\sqrt{\frac{v^2}{2v^2+384}}$

As v gets larger and larger, $\sqrt{\frac{v^2}{2v^2+384}} \approx \sqrt{\frac{1}{2}} = \frac{\sqrt{2}}{2}$. Thus, $\theta \approx \arcsin\frac{\sqrt{2}}{2} = 45°$.

The equation of the asymptote is $\theta = 45°$.

94. $\theta = 2\arcsin\dfrac{1}{m}$

(a) $m = 1.2 \Rightarrow \theta = 2\arcsin\dfrac{1}{1.2} = 2\arcsin\dfrac{1}{\frac{6}{5}} = 2\arcsin\dfrac{5}{6} \approx 113°$

(b) $m = 1.5 \Rightarrow \theta = 2\arcsin\dfrac{1}{1.5} = 2\arcsin\dfrac{1}{\frac{3}{2}} = 2\arcsin\dfrac{2}{3} \approx 84°$

(c) $m = 2 \Rightarrow \theta = 2\arcsin\dfrac{1}{2} = 2(30°) = 60°$

(d) $m = 2.5 \Rightarrow \theta = 2\arcsin\dfrac{1}{2.5} = 2\arcsin\dfrac{1}{\frac{5}{2}} = 2\arcsin\dfrac{2}{5} \approx 47°$

95. $\theta = \tan^{-1}\left(\dfrac{x}{x^2+2}\right)$

(a) $x = 1,\ \theta = \tan^{-1}\left(\dfrac{1}{1^2+2}\right) = \tan^{-1}\left(\dfrac{1}{3}\right) \approx 18°$

(b) $x = 2,\ \theta = \tan^{-1}\left(\dfrac{2}{2^2+2}\right) = \tan^{-1}\dfrac{2}{6} = \tan^{-1}\dfrac{1}{3} \approx 18°$

(c) $x = 3,\ \theta = \tan^{-1}\left(\dfrac{3}{3^2+2}\right) = \tan^{-1}\dfrac{3}{11} \approx 15°$

(d) $\tan(\theta+\alpha) = \dfrac{1+1}{x} = \dfrac{2}{x}$ and $\tan\alpha = \dfrac{1}{x}$

$$\tan(\theta+\alpha) = \frac{\tan\theta + \tan\alpha}{1-\tan\theta\tan\alpha} \Rightarrow \frac{2}{x} = \frac{\tan\theta + \frac{1}{x}}{1-\tan\theta\left(\frac{1}{x}\right)} \Rightarrow \frac{2}{x} = \frac{x\tan\theta + 1}{x - \tan\theta}$$

$$2(x-\tan\theta) = x(x\tan\theta+1) \Rightarrow 2x - 2\tan\theta = x^2\tan\theta + x \Rightarrow 2x - x = x^2\tan\theta + 2\tan\theta$$

$$x = \tan\theta\left(x^2+2\right) \Rightarrow \tan\theta = \frac{x}{x^2+2} \Rightarrow \theta = \tan^{-1}\left(\frac{x}{x^2+2}\right)$$

(e) If we graph $y_1 = \tan^{-1}\left(\dfrac{x}{x^2+2}\right)$ using a graphing calculator, the maximum value of the function occurs when x is 1.4142151 m. (Note: Due to the computational routine, there may be a discrepancy in the last few decimal places.)

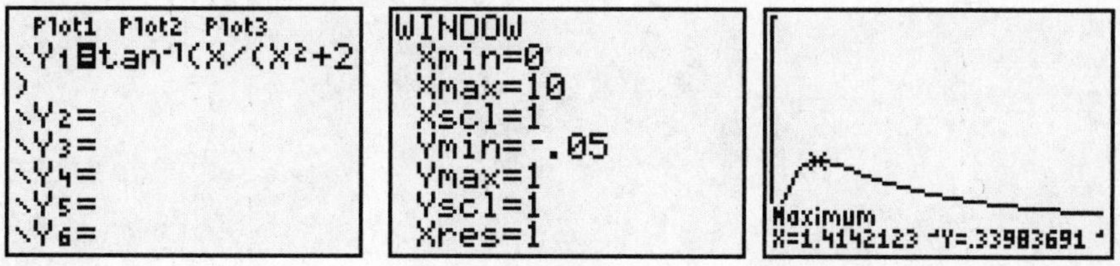

(f) $x = \sqrt{(1)(2)} = \sqrt{2}$

96. Let A be the triangle to the "right" of θ and let B be the angle to the "left" of θ. Then $A+\theta+B=\pi$ (since the angles sum to π radians) and $\theta=\pi-A-B$.

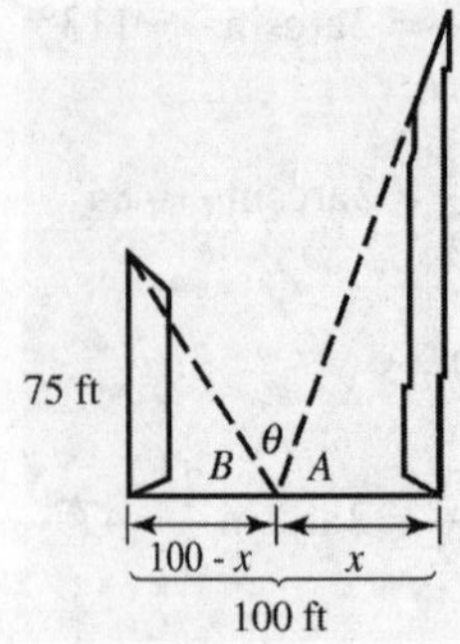

$\tan A=\dfrac{150}{x}$, so $A=\arctan\left(\dfrac{150}{x}\right)$ and $\tan B=\dfrac{75}{100-x}$, so $B=\arctan\left(\dfrac{75}{100-x}\right)$.

As a result, $\theta=\pi-B-A\Rightarrow\theta=\pi-\arctan\left(\dfrac{75}{100-x}\right)-\arctan\left(\dfrac{150}{x}\right)$.

97. Since the diameter of the earth is 7927 miles at the equator, the radius of the earth is 3963.5 miles. Then $\cos\theta=\dfrac{3963.5}{20,000+3963.5}=\dfrac{3963.5}{23,963.5}$ and $\theta=\arccos\left(\dfrac{3963.5}{23,963.5}\right)\approx 80.48°$.

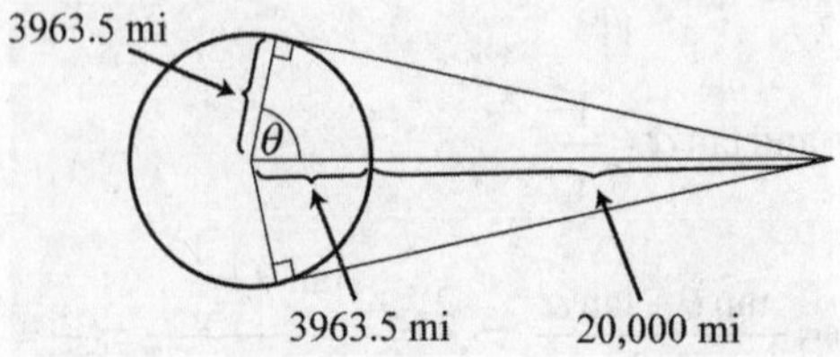

The percent of the equator that can be seen by the satellite is $\dfrac{2\theta}{360}\cdot 100=\dfrac{2(80.48)}{360}\approx 44.7\%$.

Section 7.6: Trigonometric Equations

1. Solve the linear equation for $\cot x$.

3. Solve the quadratic equation for $\sec x$ by factoring.

5. Solve the quadratic equation for $\sin x$ using the quadratic formula.

7. Use the identity to rewrite as an equation with one trigonometric function.

9. Since $2x = \frac{2\pi}{3}, 2\pi, \frac{8\pi}{3} \Rightarrow x = \frac{2\pi}{6}, \frac{2\pi}{2}, \frac{8\pi}{6} \Rightarrow x = \frac{\pi}{3}, \pi, \frac{4\pi}{3}$, the solution set is $\left\{\frac{\pi}{3}, \pi, \frac{4\pi}{3}\right\}$.

11. $2\cot x + 1 = -1 \Rightarrow 2\cot x = -2 \Rightarrow \cot x = -1$

Over the interval $[0, 2\pi)$, the equation $\cot x = -1$ has two solutions, the angles in quadrants II and IV that have a reference angle of $\frac{\pi}{4}$. These are $\frac{3\pi}{4}$ and $\frac{7\pi}{4}$.

Solution set: $\left\{\frac{3\pi}{4}, \frac{7\pi}{4}\right\}$

13. $2\sin x + 3 = 4 \Rightarrow 2\sin x = 1 \Rightarrow \sin x = \frac{1}{2}$

Over the interval $[0, 2\pi)$, the equation $\sin x = \frac{1}{2}$ has two solutions, the angles in quadrants I and II that have a reference angle of $\frac{\pi}{6}$. These are $\frac{\pi}{6}$ and $\frac{5\pi}{6}$.

Solution set: $\left\{\frac{\pi}{6}, \frac{5\pi}{6}\right\}$

15. $\tan^2 x + 3 = 0 \Rightarrow \tan^2 x = -3$

The square of a real number cannot be negative, so this equation has no solution.
Solution set: $\varnothing$

17. $(\cot x - 1)\left(\sqrt{3}\cot x + 1\right) = 0$

$$\cot x - 1 = 0 \Rightarrow \cot x = 1 \text{ or } \sqrt{3}\cot x + 1 = 0 \Rightarrow \sqrt{3}\cot x = -1 \Rightarrow \cot x = -\frac{1}{\sqrt{3}} \Rightarrow \cot x = -\frac{\sqrt{3}}{3}$$

Over the interval $[0, 2\pi)$, the equation $\cot x = 1$ has two solutions, the angles in quadrants I and III that have a reference angle of $\frac{\pi}{4}$. These are $\frac{\pi}{4}$ and $\frac{5\pi}{4}$. In the same interval, $\cot x = -\frac{\sqrt{3}}{3}$ also has two solutions. The angles in quadrants II and IV that have a reference angle of $\frac{\pi}{3}$ are $\frac{2\pi}{3}$ and $\frac{5\pi}{3}$.

Solution set: $\left\{\frac{\pi}{4}, \frac{2\pi}{3}, \frac{5\pi}{4}, \frac{5\pi}{3}\right\}$

19. $\cos^2 x + 2\cos x + 1 = 0$

$$\cos^2 x + 2\cos x + 1 = 0 \Rightarrow (\cos x + 1)^2 = 0 \Rightarrow \cos x + 1 = 0 \Rightarrow \cos x = -1$$

Over the interval $[0, 2\pi)$, the equation $\cos x = -1$ has one solution. This solution is π.

Solution set: $\{\pi\}$

21. $-2\sin^2 x = 3\sin x + 1$

$$-2\sin^2 x = 3\sin x + 1 \Rightarrow 2\sin^2 x + 3\sin x + 1 = 0 \Rightarrow (2\sin x + 1)(\sin x + 1) = 0$$

$$2\sin x + 1 = 0 \Rightarrow \sin x = -\frac{1}{2} \text{ or } \sin x + 1 = 0 \Rightarrow \sin x = -1$$

Over the interval $[0, 2\pi)$, the equation $\sin x = -\frac{1}{2}$ has two solutions. The angles in quadrants III and IV that have a reference angle of $\frac{\pi}{6}$ are $\frac{7\pi}{6}$ and $\frac{11\pi}{6}$. In the same interval, $\sin x = -1$ when the angle is $\frac{3\pi}{2}$.

Solution set: $\left\{\frac{7\pi}{6}, \frac{3\pi}{2}, \frac{11\pi}{6}\right\}$

23. $\left(\cot\theta - \sqrt{3}\right)\left(2\sin\theta + \sqrt{3}\right) = 0$

$$\cot\theta - \sqrt{3} = 0 \Rightarrow \cot\theta = \sqrt{3} \text{ or } 2\sin\theta + \sqrt{3} = 0 \Rightarrow 2\sin\theta = -\sqrt{3} \Rightarrow \sin\theta = -\frac{\sqrt{3}}{2}$$

Over the interval $[0°, 360°)$, the equation $\cot\theta = \sqrt{3}$ has two solutions, the angles in quadrants I and III that have a reference angle of 30°. These are 210° and 330°. In the same interval, the equation $\sin\theta = -\frac{\sqrt{3}}{2}$ has two solutions, the angles in quadrants III and IV that have a reference angle of 60°. These are 240° and 300°.

Solution set: $\{30°, 210°, 240°, 300°\}$

25. $2\sin\theta - 1 = \csc\theta$

$$2\sin\theta - 1 = \csc\theta \Rightarrow 2\sin\theta - 1 = \frac{1}{\sin\theta} \Rightarrow 2\sin^2\theta - \sin\theta = 1$$

$$\sin^2\theta - \sin\theta - 1 = 0 \Rightarrow (2\sin\theta + 1)(\sin\theta - 1) = 0$$

$$2\sin\theta + 1 = 0 \Rightarrow \sin\theta = -\frac{1}{2} \text{ or } \sin\theta - 1 = 0 \Rightarrow \sin\theta = 1$$

Over the interval $[0°, 360°)$, the equation $\sin\theta = -\frac{1}{2}$ has two solutions, the angles in quadrants III and IV that have a reference angle of 30°. These are 210° and 330°. In the same interval, the only angle θ for which $\sin\theta = 1$ is 90°.

Solution set: $\{90°, 210°, 330°\}$

27. $\tan\theta - \cot\theta = 0$

$$\tan\theta - \cot\theta = 0 \Rightarrow \tan\theta - \frac{1}{\tan\theta} = 0 \Rightarrow \tan^2\theta - 1 = 0 \Rightarrow \tan^2\theta = 1 \Rightarrow \tan\theta = \pm 1$$

Over the interval $[0°, 360°)$, the equation $\tan\theta = 1$ has two solutions, the angles in quadrants I and III that have a reference angle of 45°. These are 45° and 225°. In the same interval, the equation $\tan\theta = -1$ has two solutions, the angles in quadrants II and IV that have a reference angle of 45°. These are 135° and 315°.

Solution set: $\{45°, 135°, 225°, 315°\}$

29. $\csc^2\theta - 2\cot\theta = 0$

$$\csc^2\theta - 2\cot\theta = 0 \Rightarrow \left(1 + \cot^2\theta\right) - 2\cot\theta = 0 \Rightarrow \cot^2\theta - 2\cot\theta + 1 = 0$$

$$(\cot\theta - 1)^2 = 0 \Rightarrow \cot\theta - 1 = 0 \Rightarrow \cot\theta = 1$$

Over the interval $[0°, 360°)$, the equation $\cot\theta = 1$ has two solutions, the angles in quadrants I and III that have a reference angle of 45°. These are 45° and 225°.

Solution set: $\{45°, 225°\}$

31. $2\tan^2\theta\sin\theta - \tan^2\theta = 0$

$$2\tan^2\theta\sin\theta - \tan^2\theta = 0 \Rightarrow \tan^2\theta\left(2\sin\theta - 1\right) = 0$$

$$\tan^2\theta = 0 \Rightarrow \tan\theta = 0 \text{ or } 2\sin\theta - 1 = 0 \Rightarrow 2\sin\theta = 1 \Rightarrow \sin\theta = \frac{1}{2}$$

Over the interval $[0°, 360°)$, the equation $\tan\theta = 0$ has two solutions. These are 0° and 180°. In the same interval, the equation $\sin\theta = \frac{1}{2}$ has two solutions, the angles in quadrants I and II that have a reference angle of 30°. These are 30° and 150°.

Solution set: $\{0°, 30°, 150°, 180°\}$

33. $\sec^2\theta\tan\theta = 2\tan\theta$

$$\sec^2\theta\tan\theta = 2\tan\theta \Rightarrow \sec^2\theta\tan\theta - 2\tan\theta = 0 \Rightarrow \tan\theta\left(\sec^2\theta - 2\right) = 0$$

$$\tan\theta = 0 \text{ or } \sec^2\theta - 2 = 0 \Rightarrow \sec^2\theta = 2 \Rightarrow \sec\theta = \pm\sqrt{2}$$

Over the interval $[0°, 360°)$, the equation $\tan\theta = 0$ has two solutions. These are 0° and 180°. In the same interval, the equation $\sec\theta = \sqrt{2}$ has two solutions, the angles in quadrants I and IV that have a reference angle of 45°. These are 45° and 315°. Finally, the equation $\sec\theta = -\sqrt{2}$ has two solutions, the angles in quadrants II and III that have a reference angle of 45°. These are 135° and 225°.

Solution set: $\{0°, 45°, 135°, 180°, 225°, 315°\}$

For Exercises 35 - 41, make sure your calculator is in degree mode.

35. $9\sin^2\theta - 6\sin\theta = 1$

$$9\sin^2\theta - 6\sin\theta = 1 \Rightarrow 9\sin^2\theta - 6\sin\theta - 1 = 0$$

We use the quadratic formula with $a = 9$, $b = -6$, and $c = -1$.

$$\sin\theta = \frac{6 \pm \sqrt{36-4(9)(-1)}}{2(9)} = \frac{6 \pm \sqrt{36+36}}{18} = \frac{6 \pm \sqrt{72}}{18} = \frac{6 \pm 6\sqrt{2}}{18} = \frac{1 \pm \sqrt{2}}{3}$$

Since $\sin\theta = \frac{1+\sqrt{2}}{3} > 0$ (and less than 1), we will obtain two angles. One angle will be in quadrant I and the other will be in quadrant II. Using a calculator, if $\sin\theta = \frac{1+\sqrt{2}}{3} \approx .80473787$, the quadrant I angle will be approximately 53.6°. The quadrant II angle will be approximately $180° - 53.6° = 126.4°$.

Since $\sin\theta = \frac{1-\sqrt{2}}{3} < 0$ (and greater than – 1), we will obtain two angles. One angle will be in quadrant III and the other will be in quadrant IV. Using a calculator, if $\sin\theta = \frac{1-\sqrt{2}}{3} \approx -.13807119$, then $\theta \approx -7.9°$. Since this solution is not in the interval [0°, 360°), we must use it as a reference angle to find angles in the interval. Our reference angle will be 7.9°. The angle in quadrant III will be approximately $180° + 7.9° = 187.9°$. The angle in quadrant IV will be approximately $360° - 7.9° = 352.1°$.

Solution set: $\{53.6°, 126.4°, 187.9°, 352.1°\}$

37. $\tan^2\theta + 4\tan\theta + 2 = 0$

We use the quadratic formula with $a = 1$, $b = 4$, and $c = 2$.

$$\tan\theta = \frac{-4 \pm \sqrt{16-4(1)(2)}}{2(1)} = \frac{-4 \pm \sqrt{16-8}}{2} = \frac{-4 \pm \sqrt{8}}{2} = \frac{-4 \pm 2\sqrt{2}}{2} = -2 \pm \sqrt{2}$$

Since $\tan\theta = -2 + \sqrt{2} < 0$, we will obtain two angles. One angle will be in quadrant II and the other will be in quadrant IV. Using a calculator, if $\tan\theta = -2 + \sqrt{2} = -.5857864$, then $\theta \approx -30.4°$. Since this solution is not in the interval [0°, 360°), we must use it as a reference angle to find angles in the interval. Our reference angle will be 30.4°. The angle in quadrant II will be approximately $180° - 30.4° = 149.6°$. The angle in quadrant IV will be approximately $360° - 30.4° = 329.6°$.

Since $\tan\theta = -2 - \sqrt{2} < 0$, we will obtain two angles. One angle will be in quadrant II and the other will be in quadrant IV. Using a calculator, if $\tan\theta = -2 - \sqrt{2} = -3.4142136$, then $\theta \approx -73.7°$. Since this solution is not in the interval [0°, 360°), we must use it as a reference angle to find angles in the interval. Our reference angle will be 73.7°. The angle in quadrant II will be approximately $180° - 73.7° = 106.3°$. The angle in quadrant IV will be approximately $360° - 73.7° = 286.3°$.

Solution set: $\{106.3°, 149.6°, 286.3°, 329.6°\}$

39. $\sin^2\theta - 2\sin\theta + 3 = 0$

We use the quadratic formula with $a = 1$, $b = -2$, and $c = 3$.

$$\sin\theta = \frac{2 \pm \sqrt{4-(4)(1)(3)}}{2(1)} = \frac{2 \pm \sqrt{4-12}}{2} = \frac{2 \pm \sqrt{-8}}{2} = \frac{2 \pm 2i\sqrt{2}}{2} = 1 \pm i\sqrt{2}$$

Since $1 \pm i\sqrt{2}$ is not a real number, the equation has no real solutions.

Solution set: $\varnothing$

41. $\cot\theta + 2\csc\theta = 3$

$$\cot\theta + 2\csc\theta = 3 \Rightarrow \frac{\cos\theta}{\sin\theta} + \frac{2}{\sin\theta} = 3 \Rightarrow \cos\theta + 2 = 3\sin\theta \Rightarrow (\cos\theta + 2)^2 = (3\sin\theta)^2$$

$$\cos^2\theta + 4\cos\theta + 4 = 9\sin^2\theta \Rightarrow \cos^2\theta + 4\cos\theta + 4 = 9\left(1 - \cos^2\theta\right)$$

$$\cos^2\theta + 4\cos\theta + 4 = 9 - 9\cos^2\theta \Rightarrow 10\cos^2\theta + 4\cos\theta - 5 = 0$$

We use the quadratic formula with $a = 10$, $b = 4$, and $c = -5$.

$$\cos\theta = \frac{-4 \pm \sqrt{4^2 - 4(10)(-5)}}{2(10)} = \frac{-4 \pm \sqrt{16 + 200}}{20} = \frac{-4 \pm \sqrt{216}}{20} = \frac{-4 \pm 6\sqrt{6}}{20} = \frac{-2 \pm 3\sqrt{6}}{10}$$

Since $\cos\theta = \frac{-2+3\sqrt{6}}{10} > 0$ (and less than 1), we will obtain two angles. One angle will be in quadrant I and the other will be in quadrant IV. Using a calculator, if $\cos\theta = \frac{-2+3\sqrt{6}}{10} \approx .53484692$, the quadrant I angle will be approximately 57.7°. The quadrant IV angle will be approximately $360° - 57.7° = 302.3°$.

Since $\cos\theta = \frac{-2-3\sqrt{6}}{10} < 0$ (and greater than – 1), we will obtain two angles. One angle will be in quadrant II and the other will be in quadrant III. Using a calculator, if $\cos\theta = \frac{-2-3\sqrt{6}}{10} \approx -.93484692$, the quadrant II angle will be approximately 159.2°. The reference angle is $180° - 159.2° = 20.8°$. Thus, the quadrant III angle will be approximately $180° + 20.8° = 200.8°$.

Since the solution was found by squaring both sides of an equation, we must check that each proposed solution is a solution of the original equation. 302.3° and 200.8° do not satisfy our original equation. Thus, they are not elements of the solution set.

Solution set: $\{57.7°, 159.2°\}$

In Exercises 43 & 45, if you are using a calculator, make sure it is in radian mode.

43. $3\sin^2 x - \sin x - 1 = 0$

We use the quadratic formula with $a = 3$, $b = -1$, and $c = -1$.

$$\sin x = \frac{-(-1) \pm \sqrt{(-1)^2 - 4(3)(-1)}}{2(3)} = \frac{1 \pm \sqrt{1+12}}{6} = \frac{1 \pm \sqrt{13}}{6}$$

Since $\sin x = \frac{1+\sqrt{13}}{6} > 0$ (and less than 1), we will obtain two angles. One angle will be in quadrant I and the other will be in quadrant II. Using a calculator, if $\sin x = \frac{1+\sqrt{13}}{6} \approx .76759188$, the quadrant I angle will be approximately .88. The quadrant II angle will be approximately $\pi - .88 \approx 2.26$.

Since $\sin x = \frac{1-\sqrt{13}}{6} < 0$ (and greater than – 1), we will obtain two angles. One angle will be in quadrant III and the other will be in quadrant IV. Using a calculator, if $\sin x = \frac{1-\sqrt{13}}{6} \approx -.43425855$, then $x \approx -.45$. Since this solution is not in the interval $[0, 2\pi)$, we must use it as a reference angle to find angles in the interval. Our reference angle will be .45. The angle in quadrant III will be approximately $\pi + .45 \approx 3.59$. The angle in quadrant IV will be approximately $2\pi - .45 \approx 5.83$.

Thus, the solutions are approximately $.9 + 2n\pi$, $2.3 + 2n\pi$, $3.6 + 2n\pi$, and $5.8 + 2n\pi$, where n is any integer.

45. $4\cos^2 x-1=0$

$$4\cos^2 x-1=0\Rightarrow \cos^2 x=\frac{1}{4}\Rightarrow \cos x=\pm\frac{1}{2}$$

Over the interval $[0,2\pi)$, the equation $\cos x=\frac{1}{2}$ has two solutions. The angles in quadrants I and IV that have a reference angle of $\frac{\pi}{3}$ are $\frac{\pi}{3}$ and $\frac{5\pi}{3}$. In the same interval, $\cos x=-\frac{1}{2}$ has two solutions. The angles in quadrants II and III that have a reference angle of $\frac{\pi}{3}$ are $\frac{2\pi}{3}$ and $\frac{4\pi}{3}$.

Thus, the solutions are $\frac{\pi}{3}+2n\pi, \frac{2\pi}{3}+2n\pi, \frac{4\pi}{3}+2n\pi$, and $\frac{5\pi}{3}+2n\pi$, where n is any integer. This can also be written as $\frac{\pi}{3}+n\pi$ and $\frac{2\pi}{3}+n\pi$, where n is any integer.

In Exercises 47 – 49, if you are using a calculator, make sure it is in degree mode.

47. $5\sec^2\theta=6\sec\theta$

$$5\sec^2\theta=6\sec\theta\Rightarrow 5\sec^2\theta-6\sec\theta=0\Rightarrow \sec\theta(5\sec\theta-6)=0$$

$$\sec\theta=0 \text{ or } 5\sec\theta-6=0\Rightarrow \sec\theta=\frac{6}{5}$$

$\sec\theta=0$ is an impossible values since the secant function must be either ≥ 1 or ≤ -1.

Since $\sec\theta=\frac{6}{5}>1$, we will obtain two angles. One angle will be in quadrant I and the other will be in quadrant IV. Using a calculator, if $\sec\theta=\frac{6}{5}=1.2$, the quadrant I angle will be approximately $33.6°$.

The quadrant IV angle will be approximately $360°-33.6°=326.4°$.

Thus, the solutions are approximately $33.6°+360°n$ and $326.4°+360°n$, where n is any integer.

49. $\frac{2\tan\theta}{3-\tan^2\theta}=1$

$$\frac{2\tan\theta}{3-\tan^2\theta}=1\Rightarrow 2\tan\theta=3-\tan^2\theta\Rightarrow \tan^2\theta+2\tan\theta-3=0\Rightarrow (\tan\theta-1)(\tan\theta+3)=0$$

$$\tan\theta-1=0\Rightarrow \tan\theta=1 \text{ or } \tan\theta+3=0\Rightarrow \tan\theta=-3$$

Over the interval $[0°,360°)$, the equation $\tan\theta=1$ has two solutions $45°$ and $225°$. Over the same interval, the equation $\tan\theta=-3$ has two solutions that are approximately $-71.6°+180°=108.4°$ and $-71.6°+360°=288.4°$.

Thus, the solutions are $45°+360°n, 108.4°+360°n, 225°+360°n$ and $288.4°+360°n$, where n is any integer. Since the period of the tangent function is $180°$, the solutions can also be written as $45°+n\cdot 180°$ and $108°+n\cdot 180°$, where n is any integer.

51. The x-intercept method is shown in the following windows.

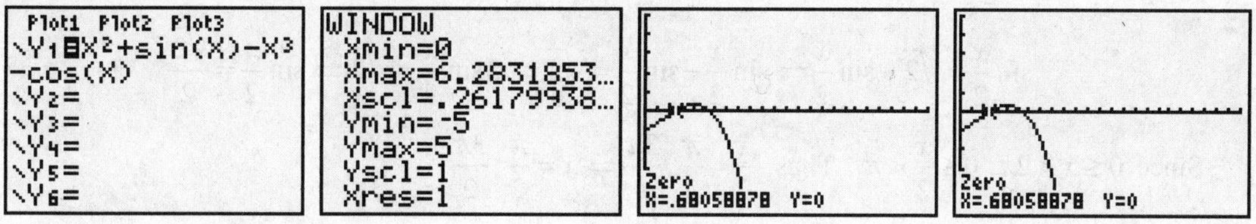

Solution set: $\{.6806, 1.4159\}$

53. $\dfrac{\tan 2\theta}{2} \neq \tan\theta$ for all values of θ.

55. $\cos 2x = \dfrac{\sqrt{3}}{2}$

Since $0 \le x < 2\pi$, $0 \le 2x < 4\pi$. Thus, $2x = \dfrac{\pi}{6}, \dfrac{11\pi}{6}, \dfrac{13\pi}{6}, \dfrac{23\pi}{6} \Rightarrow x = \dfrac{\pi}{12}, \dfrac{11\pi}{12}, \dfrac{13\pi}{12}, \dfrac{23\pi}{12}$.

Solution set: $\dfrac{\pi}{12}, \dfrac{11\pi}{12}, \dfrac{13\pi}{12}, \dfrac{23\pi}{12}$

57. $\sin 3x = -1$

Since $0 \le x < 2\pi$, $0 \le 3x < 6\pi$. Thus, $3x = \dfrac{3\pi}{2}, \dfrac{7\pi}{2}, \dfrac{11\pi}{2} \Rightarrow x = \dfrac{\pi}{2}, \dfrac{7\pi}{6}, \dfrac{11\pi}{6}$.

Solution set: $\left\{\dfrac{\pi}{2}, \dfrac{7\pi}{6}, \dfrac{11\pi}{6}\right\}$

59. $3\tan 3x = \sqrt{3} \Rightarrow \tan 3x = \dfrac{\sqrt{3}}{3}$

Since $0 \le x < 2\pi$, $0 \le 3x < 6\pi$.

Thus, $3x = \dfrac{\pi}{6}, \dfrac{7\pi}{6}, \dfrac{13\pi}{6}, \dfrac{19\pi}{6}, \dfrac{25\pi}{6}, \dfrac{31\pi}{6}$ implies $x = \dfrac{\pi}{18}, \dfrac{7\pi}{18}, \dfrac{13\pi}{18}, \dfrac{19\pi}{18}, \dfrac{25\pi}{18}, \dfrac{31\pi}{18}$.

Solution set: $\left\{\dfrac{\pi}{18}, \dfrac{7\pi}{18}, \dfrac{13\pi}{18}, \dfrac{19\pi}{18}, \dfrac{25\pi}{18}, \dfrac{31\pi}{18}\right\}$

61. $\sqrt{2}\cos 2x = -1 \Rightarrow \cos 2x = \dfrac{-1}{\sqrt{2}} = -\dfrac{\sqrt{2}}{2}$

Since $0 \le x < 2\pi$, $0 \le 2x < 4\pi$. Thus, $2x = \dfrac{3\pi}{4}, \dfrac{5\pi}{4}, \dfrac{11\pi}{4}, \dfrac{13\pi}{4} \Rightarrow x = \dfrac{3\pi}{8}, \dfrac{5\pi}{8}, \dfrac{11\pi}{8}, \dfrac{13\pi}{8}$.

Solution set: $\left\{\dfrac{3\pi}{8}, \dfrac{5\pi}{8}, \dfrac{11\pi}{8}, \dfrac{13\pi}{8}\right\}$

63. $\sin\frac{x}{2}=\sqrt{2}-\sin\frac{x}{2}$

$$\sin\frac{x}{2}=\sqrt{2}-\sin\frac{x}{2}\Rightarrow\sin\frac{x}{2}+\sin\frac{x}{2}=\sqrt{2}\Rightarrow 2\sin\frac{x}{2}=\sqrt{2}\Rightarrow\sin\frac{x}{2}=\frac{\sqrt{2}}{2}$$

Since $0\le x<2\pi$, $0\le\frac{x}{2}<\pi$. Thus, $\frac{x}{2}=\frac{\pi}{4},\frac{3\pi}{4}\Rightarrow x=\frac{\pi}{2},\frac{3\pi}{2}$.

Solution set: $\left\{\frac{\pi}{2},\frac{3\pi}{2}\right\}$

65. $\sin x=\sin 2x$

$$\sin x=\sin 2x\Rightarrow\sin x=2\sin x\cos x\Rightarrow\sin x-2\sin x\cos x=0\Rightarrow\sin x(1-2\cos x)=0$$

Over the interval $[0,2\pi)$, we have the following.

$$1-2\cos x=0\Rightarrow-2\cos x=-1\Rightarrow\cos x=\frac{1}{2}\Rightarrow x=\frac{\pi}{3}\text{ or }\frac{5\pi}{3}$$

$$\sin x=0\Rightarrow x=0\text{ or }\pi$$

Solution set: $\left\{0,\frac{\pi}{3},\pi,\frac{5\pi}{3}\right\}$

67. $8\sec^2\frac{x}{2}=4\Rightarrow\sec^2\frac{x}{2}=\frac{1}{2}\Rightarrow\sec\frac{x}{2}=\pm\frac{\sqrt{2}}{2}$

Since $-\frac{\sqrt{2}}{2}$ is not in the interval $(-\infty,-1]$ and $\frac{\sqrt{2}}{2}$ is not in the interval $[1,\infty)$, this equation has no solution.

Solution set: $\varnothing$

69. $\sin\frac{x}{2}=\cos\frac{x}{2}$

$$\sin\frac{x}{2}=\cos\frac{x}{2}\Rightarrow\sin^2\frac{x}{2}=\cos^2\frac{x}{2}\Rightarrow\sin^2\frac{x}{2}=1-\sin^2\frac{x}{2}\Rightarrow 2\sin^2\frac{x}{2}=1$$

$$\sin^2\frac{x}{2}=\frac{1}{2}\Rightarrow\sin\frac{x}{2}=\pm\sqrt{\frac{1}{2}}\Rightarrow\sin\frac{x}{2}=\pm\frac{\sqrt{2}}{2}$$

Since $0\le x<2\pi$, $0\le\frac{x}{2}<\pi$. If $\sin\frac{x}{2}=\frac{\sqrt{2}}{2}$, $\frac{x}{2}=\frac{\pi}{4},\frac{3\pi}{4}\Rightarrow x=\frac{\pi}{2},\frac{3\pi}{2}$. If $\sin\frac{x}{2}=-\frac{\sqrt{2}}{2}$, there are no solutions in the interval $[0,\pi)$.

Since the solution was found by squaring an equation, the proposed solutions must be checked.

Check $x=\frac{\pi}{2}$	Check $x=\frac{3\pi}{2}$
$\sin\frac{x}{2}=\cos\frac{x}{2}$	$\sin\frac{x}{2}=\cos\frac{x}{2}$
$\sin\frac{\frac{\pi}{2}}{2}=\cos\frac{\frac{\pi}{2}}{2}$?	$\sin\frac{\frac{3\pi}{2}}{2}=\cos\frac{\frac{3\pi}{2}}{2}$?
$\sin\frac{\pi}{4}=\cos\frac{\pi}{4}$?	$\sin\frac{3\pi}{4}=\cos\frac{3\pi}{4}$?
$\frac{\sqrt{2}}{2}=\frac{\sqrt{2}}{2}$ True	$\frac{\sqrt{2}}{2}=-\frac{\sqrt{2}}{2}$ False
$\frac{\pi}{2}$ is a solution.	$\frac{3\pi}{2}$ is not a solution.

Solution set: $\left\{\frac{\pi}{2}\right\}$

71. $\sqrt{2}\sin 3\theta-1=0$

$$\sqrt{2}\sin 3\theta-1=0\Rightarrow\sqrt{2}\sin 3\theta=1\Rightarrow\sin 3\theta=\frac{1}{\sqrt{2}}\Rightarrow\sin 3\theta=\frac{\sqrt{2}}{2}$$

Since $0\le\theta<360°$, $0°\le 3\theta<1080°$. In quadrant I and II, sine is positive. Thus, $3\theta=45°,135°,405°,495°,765°,855°\Rightarrow\theta=15°,45°,135°,165°,255°,285°$.

Solution set: $\{15°,45°,135°,165°,255°,285°\}$

73. $\cos\frac{\theta}{2}=1$

Since $0\le\theta<360°$, $0°\le\frac{\theta}{2}<180°$. Thus, $\frac{\theta}{2}=0°\Rightarrow\theta=0°$.

Solution set: $\{0°\}$

75. $2\sqrt{3}\sin\frac{\theta}{2}=3$

$$2\sqrt{3}\sin\frac{\theta}{2}=3\Rightarrow\sin\frac{\theta}{2}=\frac{3}{2\sqrt{3}}\Rightarrow\sin\frac{\theta}{2}=\frac{3\sqrt{3}}{6}\Rightarrow\sin\frac{\theta}{2}=\frac{\sqrt{3}}{2}$$

Since $0\le\theta<360°$, $0°\le\frac{\theta}{2}<180°$. Thus, $\frac{\theta}{2}=60°,120°\Rightarrow\theta=120°,240°$.

Solution set: $\{120°,240°\}$

77. $2\sin\theta = 2\cos 2\theta$

$$2\sin\theta = 2\cos 2\theta \Rightarrow \sin\theta = \cos 2\theta \Rightarrow \sin\theta = 1-2\sin^2\theta$$
$$2\sin^2\theta + \sin\theta - 1 = 0 \Rightarrow (2\sin\theta - 1)(\sin\theta + 1) = 0$$
$$2\sin\theta - 1 = 0 \text{ or } \sin\theta + 1 = 0$$

Over the interval $[0°, 360°)$, we have the following.

$$2\sin\theta - 1 = 0 \Rightarrow 2\sin\theta = 1 \Rightarrow \sin\theta = \frac{1}{2} \Rightarrow \theta = 30° \text{ or } 150°$$
$$\sin\theta + 1 = 0 \Rightarrow \sin\theta = -1 \Rightarrow \theta = 270°$$

Solution set: $\{30°, 150°, 270°\}$

In Exercises 79 – 85, we are to find all solutions.

79. $1-\sin\theta = \cos 2\theta$

$$1-\sin\theta = \cos 2\theta \Rightarrow 1-\sin\theta = 1-2\sin^2\theta \Rightarrow 2\sin^2\theta - \sin\theta = 0 \Rightarrow \sin\theta(2\sin\theta - 1) = 0$$

Over the interval $[0°, 360°)$, we have the following.

$$\sin\theta = 0 \Rightarrow \theta = 0° \text{ or } 180°$$
$$2\sin\theta - 1 = 0 \Rightarrow \sin\theta = \frac{1}{2} \Rightarrow \theta = 30° \text{ or } 150°$$

Solution set: $\{0° + 360°n,\ 30° + 360°n,\ 150° + 360°n,\ 180° + 360°n$, where n is any integer$\}$ or

$\{180°n,\ 30° + 360°n,\ 150° + 360°n$, where n is any integer$\}$

81. $\csc^2\frac{\theta}{2} = 2\sec\theta$

$$\csc^2\frac{\theta}{2} = 2\sec\theta \Rightarrow \frac{1}{\sin^2\frac{\theta}{2}} = \frac{2}{\cos\theta} \Rightarrow 2\sin^2\frac{\theta}{2} = \cos\theta$$
$$2\left(\frac{1-\cos\theta}{2}\right) = \cos\theta \Rightarrow 1-\cos\theta = \cos\theta \Rightarrow 1 = 2\cos\theta \Rightarrow \cos\theta = \frac{1}{2}$$

Over the interval $[0°, 360°)$, we have the following.

$$\cos\theta = \frac{1}{2} \Rightarrow \theta = 60° \text{ or } 300°$$

Solution set: $\{60° + 360°n,\ 300° + 360°n$, where n is any integer$\}$

83. $2-\sin 2\theta = 4\sin 2\theta$

$$2-\sin 2\theta = 4\sin 2\theta \Rightarrow 2 = 5\sin 2\theta \Rightarrow \sin 2\theta = \frac{2}{5} \Rightarrow \sin 2\theta = .4$$

Since $0 \le \theta < 360°$, $0° \le 2\theta < 720°$. In quadrant I and II, sine is positive.

$$\sin 2\theta = .4 \Rightarrow 2\theta = 23.6°, 156.4°, 383.6°, 516.4°$$

Thus, $\theta = 11.8°, 78.2°, 191.8°, 258.2°$.

Solution set: $\{11.8° + 360°n,\ 78.2° + 360°n,\ 191.8° + 360°n,\ 258.2° + 360°n$, where n is any integer$\}$

or $\{11.8° + 180°n,\ 78.2° + 180°n$, where n is any integer$\}$

85. $2\cos^2 2\theta = 1 - \cos 2\theta$

$$2\cos^2 2\theta = 1 - \cos 2\theta \Rightarrow 2\cos^2 2\theta + \cos 2\theta - 1 = 0 \Rightarrow (2\cos 2\theta - 1)(\cos 2\theta + 1) = 0$$

Since $0 \le \theta < 360° \Rightarrow 0° \le 2\theta < 720°$, we have the following.

$$2\cos 2\theta - 1 = 0 \Rightarrow 2\cos 2\theta = 1 \Rightarrow \cos 2\theta = \frac{1}{2}$$

$$2\theta = 60°,\ 300°,\ 420°,\ 660° \Rightarrow \theta = 30°,\ 150°,\ 210°,\ 330°$$

or

$$\cos 2\theta + 1 = 0 \Rightarrow \cos 2\theta = -1$$

$$2\theta = 180°,\ 540° \Rightarrow \theta = 90°,\ 270°$$

Solution set: $\{30° + 360°n,\ 90° + 360°n,\ 150° + 360°n,\ 210° + 360°n,\ 270° + 360°n,$ $330° + 360°n$, where n is any integer$\}$ or

$\{30° + 180°n,\ 90° + 180°n,\ 150° + 180°n$, where n is any integer$\}$

87. $P = A\sin(2\pi ft + \phi)$

(a) $0 = .004\sin\left[2\pi(261.63)t + \frac{\pi}{7}\right] \Rightarrow 0 = \sin(1643.87t + .45)$

Since $1643.87t + .45 = n\pi$, we have $t = \frac{n\pi - .45}{1643.87}$, where n is any integer.

If $n = 0$, then $t \approx .000274$. If $n = 1$, then $t \approx .00164$. If $n = 2$, then $t \approx .00355$. If $n = 3$, then $t \approx .00546$. The only solutions for t in the interval $[0, .005]$ are .00164 and .00355.

(b) We must solve the trigonometric equation $P = 0$ to determine when $P \le 0$. From the graph we can estimate that $P \le 0$ on the interval $[.00164, .00355]$.

(c) $P < 0$ implies that there is a decrease in pressure so an eardrum would be vibrating outward.

89. (a)

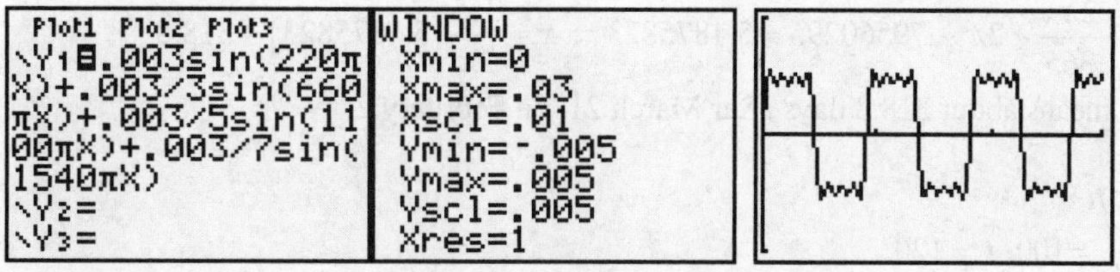

(b) The graph is periodic, and the wave has "jagged square" tops and bottoms.

(c) The eardrum is moving outward when $P < 0$.

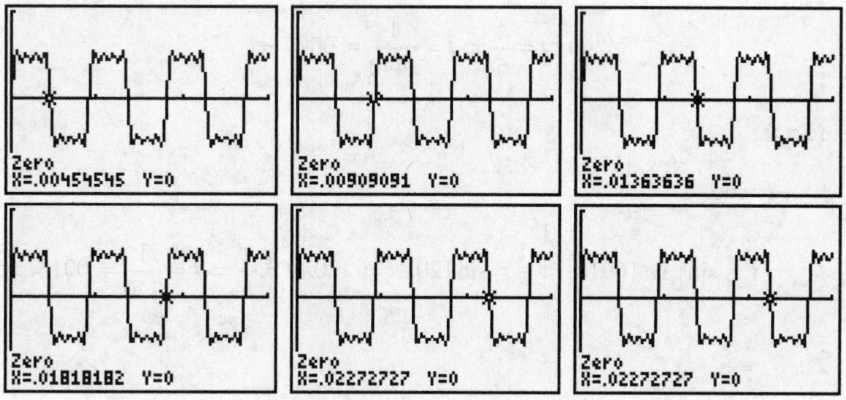

This occurs for the time intervals $(.0045, .0091), (.0136, .0182), (.0227, .0273)$.

91. $h = \frac{35}{3} + \frac{7}{3}\sin\frac{2\pi x}{365}$

(a) Find x such that $h = 14$.

$$14 = \frac{35}{3} + \frac{7}{3}\sin\frac{2\pi x}{365} \Rightarrow 14 - \frac{35}{3} = \frac{7}{3}\sin\frac{2\pi x}{365} \Rightarrow \frac{7}{3} = \frac{7}{3}\sin\frac{2\pi x}{365} \Rightarrow \sin\frac{2\pi x}{365} = 1$$

$$\frac{2\pi x}{365} = \frac{\pi}{2} \pm 2\pi n \Rightarrow x = \left(\frac{\pi}{2} \pm 2\pi n\right)\left(\frac{365}{2\pi}\right) = \frac{365}{4} \pm 365n = 91.25 \pm 365n,\ n \text{ is any integer.}$$

$x = 91.25$ means about 91.3 days after March 21, on June 20.

(b) h assumes its least value when $\sin\frac{2\pi x}{365}$ takes on its least value, which is -1.

$$\sin\frac{2\pi x}{365} = -1 \Rightarrow \frac{2\pi x}{365} = \frac{3\pi}{2} \pm 2\pi n$$

$$x = \left(\frac{3\pi}{2} \pm 2\pi n\right)\left(\frac{365}{2\pi}\right) = \frac{3(365)}{4} \pm 365n = 273.75 \pm 365n,\ n \text{ is any integer.}$$

$x = 273.75$ means about 273.8 days after March 21, on December 19.

(c) Let $h = 10$.

$$10 = \frac{35}{3} + \frac{7}{3}\sin\frac{2\pi x}{365} \Rightarrow 30 = 35 + 7\sin\frac{2\pi x}{365} \Rightarrow -5 = 7\sin\frac{2\pi x}{365}$$

$$-\frac{5}{7} = \sin\frac{2\pi x}{365} \Rightarrow -.71428571 = \sin\left(\frac{2\pi x}{365}\right)$$

In quadrant III and IV, sine is negative. In quadrant III, we have the following.

$$\frac{2\pi x}{365} = \pi + .79560295 \approx 3.9371956 \Rightarrow x \approx \frac{365}{2\pi}(3.9371956) \approx 228.7$$

$x = 228.7$ means 228.7 days after March 21, on November 4.
In quadrant IV, we have the following.

$$\frac{2\pi x}{365} \approx 2\pi - .79560295 \approx 5.4875823 \Rightarrow x \approx \frac{365}{2\pi}(5.4875823) \approx 318.8$$

$x = 318.8$ means about 318.8 days after March 21, on February 2.

93. $i = I_{\max} \sin 2\pi ft$

Let $i = 50$, $I_{\max} = 100$, $f = 120$.

$$50 = 100\sin\left[2\pi(120)t\right] \Rightarrow 50 = 100\sin 240\pi t \Rightarrow \sin 240\pi t = \frac{1}{2}$$

$$240\pi t = \frac{\pi}{6} \Rightarrow t = \frac{1}{1440} \approx .0007 \text{ sec}$$

95. $i = I_{\max} \sin 2\pi ft$

Let $i = \frac{1}{2} I_{\max}$, $f = 60$.

$$\frac{1}{2} I_{\max} = I_{\max} \sin\left[2\pi(60)t\right] \Rightarrow \frac{1}{2} = \sin 120\pi t \Rightarrow 120\pi t = \frac{\pi}{6} \Rightarrow t = \frac{1}{720} \approx .0014 \text{ sec}$$

97. $V = \cos 2\pi t, 0 \le t \le \frac{1}{2}$

(a) $V = 0, \cos 2\pi t = 0 \Rightarrow 2\pi t = \cos^{-1} 0 \Rightarrow 2\pi t = \frac{\pi}{2} \Rightarrow t = \frac{\frac{\pi}{2}}{2\pi} = \frac{1}{4}$ sec

(b) $V = .5, \cos 2\pi t = .5 \Rightarrow 2\pi t = \cos^{-1}(.5) \Rightarrow 2\pi t = \frac{\pi}{3} \Rightarrow t = \frac{\frac{\pi}{3}}{2\pi} = \frac{1}{6}$ sec

(c) $V = .25, \cos 2\pi t = .25 \Rightarrow 2\pi t = \cos^{-1}(.25) \Rightarrow 2\pi t \approx 1.3181161 \Rightarrow t \approx \frac{1.3181161}{2\pi} \approx .21$ sec

99. $s(t) = \sin t + 2\cos t$

(a) $s(t) = \frac{2+\sqrt{3}}{2} \Rightarrow s(t) = \frac{2}{2} + \frac{\sqrt{3}}{2} = 2\left(\frac{1}{2}\right) + \frac{\sqrt{3}}{2} = 2\cos\left(\frac{\pi}{3}\right) + \sin\left(\frac{\pi}{3}\right)$

One such value is $\frac{\pi}{3}$.

(b) $s(t) = \frac{3\sqrt{2}}{2} \Rightarrow s(t) = \frac{2\sqrt{2}}{2} + \frac{\sqrt{2}}{2} = 2\left(\frac{\sqrt{2}}{2}\right) + \frac{\sqrt{2}}{2} = 2\cos\left(\frac{\pi}{4}\right) + \sin\left(\frac{\pi}{4}\right)$

One such value is $\frac{\pi}{4}$.

Section 7.7: Equations Involving Inverse Trigonometric Functions

1. Since arcsin 0 = 0, the correct choice is C.

3. Since $\arccos\left(-\frac{\sqrt{2}}{2}\right) = \frac{3\pi}{4}$, the correct choice is C.

5. $y = 5\cos x \Rightarrow \frac{y}{5} = \cos x \Rightarrow x = \arccos\frac{y}{5}$

7. $2y = \cot 3x \Rightarrow 3x = \text{arccot}\, 2y \Rightarrow x = \frac{1}{3}\text{arccot}\, 2y$

9. $y = 3\tan 2x \Rightarrow \frac{y}{3} = \tan 2x \Rightarrow 2x = \arctan\frac{y}{3} \Rightarrow x = \frac{1}{2}\arctan\frac{y}{3}$

11. $y = 6\cos\frac{x}{4} \Rightarrow \frac{y}{6} = \cos\frac{x}{4} \Rightarrow \frac{x}{4} = \arccos\frac{y}{6} \Rightarrow x = 4\arccos\frac{y}{6}$

13. $y = -2\cos 5x \Rightarrow -\frac{y}{2} = \cos 5x \Rightarrow 5x = \arccos\left(-\frac{y}{2}\right) \Rightarrow x = \frac{1}{5}\arccos\left(-\frac{y}{2}\right)$

15. $y = \cos(x+3) \Rightarrow x+3 = \arccos y \Rightarrow x = -3 + \arccos y$

17. $y = \sin x - 2 \Rightarrow y+2 = \sin x \Rightarrow x = \arcsin(y+2)$

19. $y = 2\sin x - 4 \Rightarrow y + 4 = 2\sin x \Rightarrow \frac{y+4}{2} = \sin x \Rightarrow x = \arcsin\left(\frac{y+4}{2}\right)$

21. Firstly, $\sin x - 2 \neq \sin(x-2)$. If you think of the graph of $y = \sin x - 2$, this represents the graph of $f(x) = \sin x$, shifted 2 units down. If you think of the graph of $y = \sin(x-2)$, this represents the graph of $f(x) = \sin x$, shifted 2 units right.

23. $\frac{4}{3}\cos^{-1}\frac{y}{4} = \pi \Rightarrow \cos^{-1}\frac{y}{4} = \frac{3\pi}{4} \Rightarrow \frac{y}{4} = \cos\frac{3\pi}{4} \Rightarrow \frac{y}{4} = -\frac{\sqrt{2}}{2} \Rightarrow y = -2\sqrt{2}$

Solution set: $\{-2\sqrt{2}\}$

25. $2\arccos\left(\frac{y-\pi}{3}\right) = 2\pi$

$$2\arccos\left(\frac{y-\pi}{3}\right) = 2\pi \Rightarrow \arccos\left(\frac{y-\pi}{3}\right) = \pi \Rightarrow \frac{y-\pi}{3} = \cos\pi$$
$$\frac{y-\pi}{3} = -1 \Rightarrow y - \pi = -3 \Rightarrow y = \pi - 3$$

Solution set: $\{\pi - 3\}$

27. $\arcsin x = \arctan\frac{3}{4}$

Let $\arctan\frac{3}{4} = u$, so $\tan u = \frac{3}{4}$, u is in quadrant I. Sketch a triangle and label it. The hypotenuse is $\sqrt{3^2 + 4^2} = \sqrt{9+16} = \sqrt{25} = 5$.

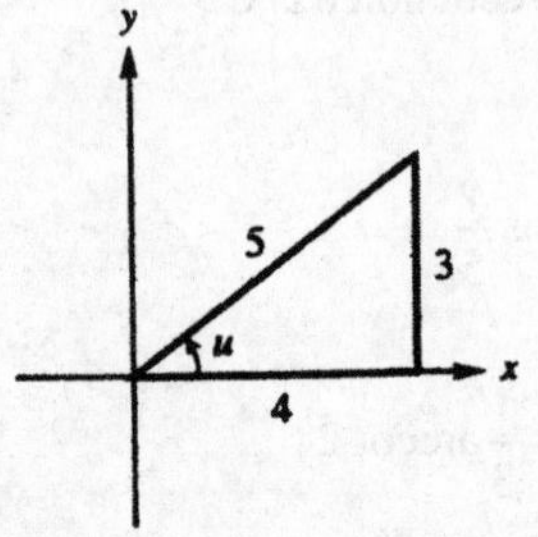

Therefore, $\sin u = \frac{3}{r} = \frac{3}{5}$. This equation becomes $\arcsin x = u$, or $x = \sin u$. Thus, $x = \frac{3}{5}$.

Solution set: $\left\{\frac{3}{5}\right\}$

29. $\cos^{-1} x = \sin^{-1} \frac{3}{5}$

Let $\sin^{-1} \frac{3}{5} = u$, so $\sin u = \frac{3}{5}$. Sketch a triangle and label it. The hypotenuse is $\sqrt{3^2 + 4^2} = \sqrt{9+16} = \sqrt{25} = 5.$

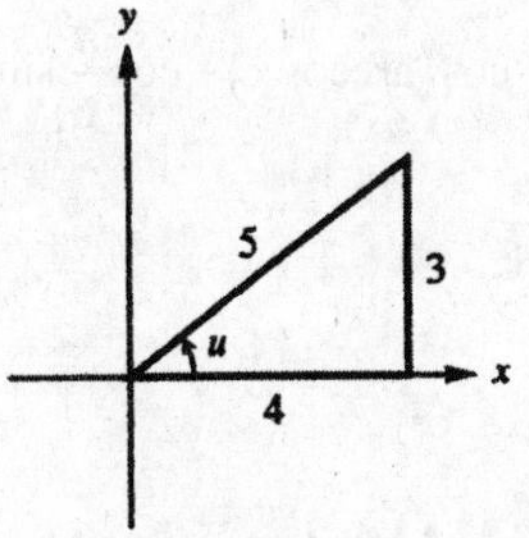

Therefore, $\cos u = \frac{4}{5}$. The equation becomes $\cos^{-1} x = u$, or $x = \cos u$. Thus, $x = \frac{4}{5}$.

Solution set: $\left\{\frac{4}{5}\right\}$

31. $\sin^{-1} x - \tan^{-1} 1 = -\frac{\pi}{4}$

$\sin^{-1} x - \tan^{-1} 1 = -\frac{\pi}{4} \Rightarrow \sin^{-1} x = \tan^{-1} 1 - \frac{\pi}{4} \Rightarrow \sin^{-1} x = \frac{\pi}{4} - \frac{\pi}{4} \Rightarrow \sin^{-1} x = 0 \Rightarrow \sin 0 = x \Rightarrow x = 0$

Solution set: $\{0\}$

33. $\arccos x + 2 \arcsin \frac{\sqrt{3}}{2} = \pi$

$$\arccos x + 2 \arcsin \frac{\sqrt{3}}{2} = \pi \Rightarrow \arccos x = \pi - 2 \arcsin \frac{\sqrt{3}}{2} \Rightarrow \arccos x = \pi - 2\left(\frac{\pi}{3}\right)$$

$$\arccos x = \pi - \frac{2\pi}{3} \Rightarrow \arccos x = \frac{\pi}{3} \Rightarrow x = \cos \frac{\pi}{3} \Rightarrow x = \frac{1}{2}$$

Solution set: $\left\{\frac{1}{2}\right\}$

35. $\arcsin 2x + \arccos x = \frac{\pi}{6}$

$$\arcsin 2x + \arccos x = \frac{\pi}{6} \Rightarrow \arcsin 2x = \frac{\pi}{6} - \arccos x \Rightarrow 2x = \sin\left(\frac{\pi}{6} - \arccos x\right)$$

Use the identity $\sin(A-B) = \sin A\cos B - \cos A\sin B$.

$$2x = \sin\frac{\pi}{6}\cos(\arccos x) - \cos\frac{\pi}{6}\sin(\arccos x)$$

Let $u = \arccos x$. Thus, $\cos u = x = \frac{x}{1}$.

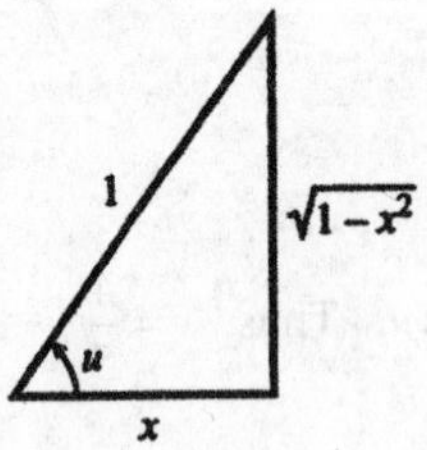

$\sin u = \sqrt{1-x^2}$

$$2x = \sin\frac{\pi}{6}\cdot\cos u - \cos\frac{\pi}{6}\sin u \Rightarrow 2x = \frac{1}{2}x - \frac{\sqrt{3}}{2}\left(\sqrt{1-x^2}\right) \Rightarrow 4x = x - \sqrt{3}\cdot\sqrt{1-x^2}$$

$$3x = -\sqrt{3}\cdot\sqrt{1-x^2} \Rightarrow (3x)^2 = \left(-\sqrt{3}\cdot\sqrt{1-x^2}\right)^2 \Rightarrow 9x^2 = 3\left(1-x^2\right)$$

$$9x^2 = 3 - 3x^2 \Rightarrow 12x^2 = 3 \Rightarrow x^2 = \frac{3}{12} = \frac{1}{4} \Rightarrow x = \pm\frac{1}{2}$$

Check these proposed solutions since they were found by squaring both side of an equation.

Check $x = \frac{1}{2}$.

$$\arcsin 2x + \arccos x = \frac{\pi}{6}$$

$$\arcsin\left(2\cdot\frac{1}{2}\right) + \arccos\left(\frac{1}{2}\right) = \frac{\pi}{6}\ ?$$

$$\frac{\pi}{2} + \frac{\pi}{3} = \frac{\pi}{6}\ ?$$

$$\frac{5\pi}{6} = \frac{\pi}{6} \text{ False}$$

$\frac{1}{2}$ is not a solution.

Check $x = -\frac{1}{2}$.

$$\arcsin 2x + \arccos x = \frac{\pi}{6}$$

$$\arcsin\left(2\cdot -\frac{1}{2}\right) + \arccos\left(-\frac{1}{2}\right) = \frac{\pi}{6}\ ?$$

$$-\frac{\pi}{2} + \frac{2\pi}{3} = \frac{\pi}{6}\ ?$$

$$\frac{\pi}{6} = \frac{\pi}{6} \text{ True}$$

$-\frac{1}{2}$ is a solution.

Solution set: $\left\{-\frac{1}{2}\right\}$

37. $\cos^{-1} x + \tan^{-1} x = \frac{\pi}{2}$

$$\cos^{-1} x + \tan^{-1} x = \frac{\pi}{2} \Rightarrow \cos^{-1} x = \frac{\pi}{2} - \tan^{-1} x \Rightarrow x = \cos\left(\frac{\pi}{2} - \tan^{-1} x\right)$$

Use the identity $\cos(A - B) = \cos A \cos B + \sin A \sin B$.

$$x = \cos\frac{\pi}{2}\cos\left(\tan^{-1} x\right) + \sin\frac{\pi}{2}\sin\left(\tan^{-1} x\right) \Rightarrow x = 0\cdot\cos\left(\tan^{-1} x\right) + 1\cdot\sin\left(\tan^{-1} x\right) \Rightarrow x = \sin\left(\tan^{-1} x\right)$$

Let $u = \tan^{-1} x$. So, $\tan u = x$.

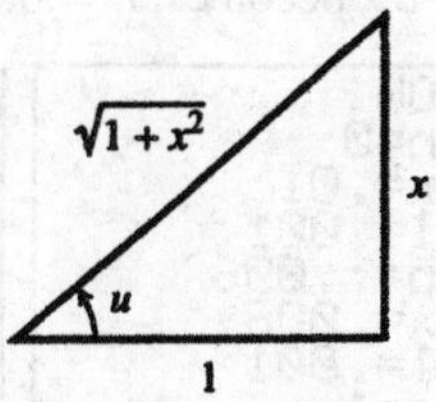

From the triangle, we find $\sin u = \frac{x}{\sqrt{1+x^2}}$, so the equation $x = \sin\left(\tan^{-1} x\right)$ becomes $x = \frac{x}{\sqrt{1+x^2}}$.

Solve this equation.

$$x = \frac{x}{\sqrt{1+x^2}} \Rightarrow x\sqrt{1+x^2} = x \Rightarrow x\sqrt{1+x^2} - x = 0 \Rightarrow x\left(\sqrt{1+x^2} - 1\right) = 0$$

$$x = 0 \text{ or } \sqrt{1+x^2} - 1 = 0 \Rightarrow \sqrt{1+x^2} = 1 \Rightarrow 1 + x^2 = 1 \Rightarrow x^2 = 0 \Rightarrow x = 0$$

Solution set: $\{0\}$

39.

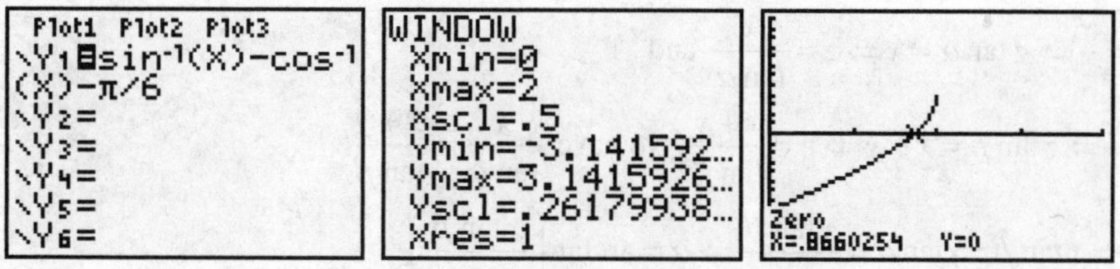

41. The x-intercept method is shown in the following windows.

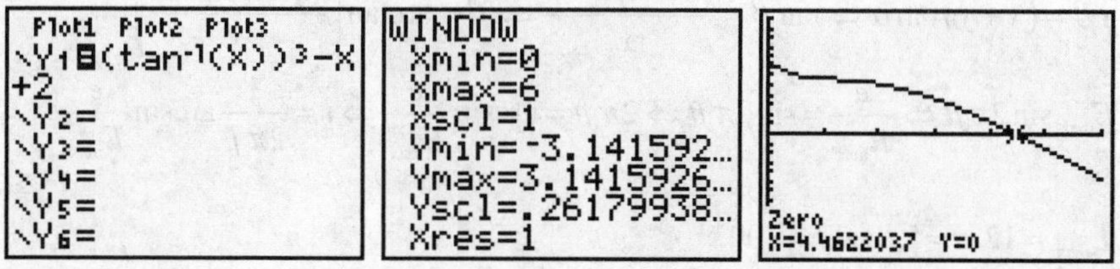

Solution set: $\{4.4622\}$

43. $A=\sqrt{(A_1\cos\phi_1+A_2\cos\phi_2)^2+(A_1\sin\phi_1+A_2\sin\phi_2)^2}$ and $\phi=\arctan\left(\dfrac{A_1\sin\phi_1+A_2\sin\phi_2}{A_1\cos\phi+A_2\cos\phi_2}\right)$

Make sure your calculator is in radian mode.

(a) Let $A_1=.0012$, $\phi_1=.052$, $A_2=.004$, and $\phi_2=.61$.

$$A=\sqrt{(.0012\cos .052+.004\cos .61)^2+(.0012\sin .052+.004\sin .61)^2}\approx .00506$$

$$\phi=\arctan\left(\frac{.0012\sin .052+.004\sin .61}{.0012\cos .052+.004\cos .61}\right)\approx .484$$

If $f=220$, then $P=A\sin(2\pi ft+\phi)$ becomes $P=.00506\sin(440\pi t+.484)$.

(b)

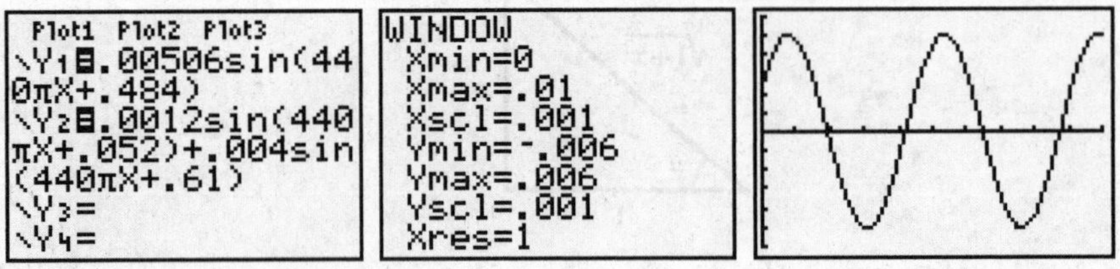

The two graphs are the same.

45. (a) $\tan\alpha=\dfrac{x}{z}$ and $\tan\beta=\dfrac{x+y}{z}$

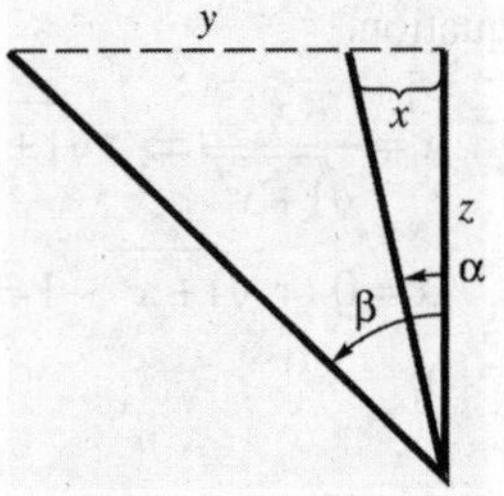

(b) Since $\tan\alpha=\dfrac{x}{z}\Rightarrow z\tan\alpha=x\Rightarrow z=\dfrac{x}{\tan\alpha}$ and

$\tan\beta=\dfrac{x+y}{z}\Rightarrow z\tan\beta=x+y\Rightarrow z=\dfrac{x+y}{\tan\beta}$, we have $\dfrac{x}{\tan\alpha}=\dfrac{x+y}{\tan\beta}$

(c) $(x+y)\tan\alpha=x\tan\beta\Rightarrow\tan\alpha=\dfrac{x\tan\beta}{x+y}\Rightarrow\alpha=\arctan\left(\dfrac{x\tan\beta}{x+y}\right)$

(d) $x\tan\beta=(x+y)\tan\alpha\Rightarrow\tan\beta=\dfrac{(x+y)\tan\alpha}{x}\Rightarrow\beta=\arctan\left(\dfrac{(x+y)\tan\alpha}{x}\right)$

47. (a) $e=E_{max}\sin 2\pi ft\Rightarrow\dfrac{e}{E_{max}}=\sin 2\pi ft\Rightarrow 2\pi ft=\arcsin\dfrac{e}{E_{max}}\Rightarrow t=\dfrac{1}{2\pi f}\arcsin\dfrac{e}{E_{max}}$

(b) Let $E_{max}=12, e=5,$ and $f=100$.

$$t=\frac{1}{2\pi(100)}\arcsin\frac{5}{12}=\frac{1}{200\pi}\arcsin\frac{5}{12}\approx .00068\text{ sec}$$

49. $y=\dfrac{1}{3}\sin\dfrac{4\pi t}{3}$

(a) $3y=\sin\dfrac{4\pi t}{3}\Rightarrow\dfrac{4\pi t}{3}=\arcsin 3y\Rightarrow 4\pi t=3\arcsin 3y\Rightarrow t=\dfrac{3}{4\pi}\arcsin 3y$

(b) If $y=.3$ radian, $t=\dfrac{3}{4\pi}\arcsin .9\Rightarrow t\approx .27\text{ sec}$.

Chapter 7: Review Exercises

1. Since $\sec x = \frac{1}{\cos x}$, the correct choice is B.

3. Since $\tan x = \frac{\sin x}{\cos x}$, the correct choice is C.

5. Since $\tan^2 x = \frac{1}{\cot^2 x}$, the correct choice is D.

7. $\sec^2\theta - \tan^2\theta = \frac{1}{\cos^2\theta} - \frac{\sin^2\theta}{\cos^2\theta} = \frac{1-\sin^2\theta}{\cos^2\theta} = \frac{\cos^2\theta}{\cos^2\theta} = 1$

9. $\tan^2\theta\left(1+\cot^2\theta\right) = \frac{\sin^2\theta}{\cos^2\theta}\left(1+\frac{\cos^2\theta}{\sin^2\theta}\right) = \frac{\sin^2\theta}{\cos^2\theta}\left(\frac{\sin^2\theta+\cos^2\theta}{\sin^2\theta}\right) = \frac{\sin^2\theta}{\cos^2\theta}\left(\frac{1}{\sin^2\theta}\right) = \frac{1}{\cos^2\theta}$

11. $\cos x = \frac{3}{5}$, x is in quadrant IV.

$\sin^2 x = 1-\cos^2 x = 1-\left(\frac{3}{5}\right)^2 = 1-\frac{9}{25} = \frac{16}{25}$

Since x is in quadrant IV, $\sin x < 0$.

$\sin x = -\sqrt{\frac{16}{25}} = -\frac{4}{5}$; $\tan x = \frac{\sin x}{\cos x} = \frac{-\frac{4}{5}}{\frac{3}{5}} = -\frac{4}{3}$; $\cot(-x) = -\cot x = \frac{1}{-\tan x} = \frac{1}{-\left(-\frac{4}{3}\right)} = \frac{3}{4}$

13. Since $\cos 210° = \cos(150°+60°) = \cos 150° \cos 60° - \sin 150° \sin 60°$, the correct choice is E.

15. Since $\tan(-35°) = \cot\left[90°-(-35°)\right] = \cot 125°$, the correct choice is J.

17. Since $\cos 35° = \cos(-35°)$, the correct choice is I.

19. Since $\sin 75° = \sin(15°+60°) = \sin 15° \cos 60° + \cos 15° \sin 60°$, the correct choice is H.

21. Since $\cos 300° = \cos 2(150°) = \cos^2 150° - \sin^2 150°$, the correct choice is G.

23. Find $\sin(x+y)$, $\cos(x-y)$, and $\tan(x+y)$, given $\sin x = -\frac{1}{4}$, $\cos y = -\frac{4}{5}$, x and y are in quadrant III.

Since x and y are in quadrant III, $\cos x$ and $\sin y$ are negative.

$\cos x = -\sqrt{1-\sin^2 x} = -\sqrt{1-\left(-\frac{1}{4}\right)^2} = -\sqrt{1-\frac{1}{16}} = -\sqrt{\frac{15}{16}} = -\frac{\sqrt{15}}{4}$

$\sin y = -\sqrt{1-\cos^2 y} = -\sqrt{1-\left(-\frac{4}{5}\right)^2} = -\sqrt{1-\frac{16}{25}} = -\sqrt{\frac{9}{25}} = -\frac{3}{5}$

Continued on next page

23. (continued)

$$\sin(x+y)=\sin x\cos y+\cos x\sin y=\left(-\frac{1}{4}\right)\left(-\frac{4}{5}\right)+\left(-\frac{\sqrt{15}}{4}\right)\left(-\frac{3}{5}\right)=\frac{4}{20}+\frac{3\sqrt{15}}{20}=\frac{4+3\sqrt{15}}{20}$$

$$\cos(x-y)=\cos x\cos y+\sin x\sin y$$

$$=\left(-\frac{\sqrt{15}}{4}\right)\left(-\frac{4}{5}\right)+\left(-\frac{1}{4}\right)\left(-\frac{3}{5}\right)=\frac{\sqrt{15}}{5}+\frac{3}{20}=\frac{4\sqrt{15}}{20}+\frac{3}{20}=\frac{4\sqrt{15}+3}{20}$$

$$\cos(x+y)=\cos x\cos y-\sin x\sin y$$

$$=\left(-\frac{\sqrt{15}}{4}\right)\left(-\frac{4}{5}\right)-\left(-\frac{1}{4}\right)\left(-\frac{3}{5}\right)=\frac{\sqrt{15}}{5}-\frac{3}{20}=\frac{4\sqrt{15}}{20}-\frac{3}{20}=\frac{4\sqrt{15}-3}{20}$$

$$\tan(x+y)=\frac{\sin(x+y)}{\cos(x+y)}=\frac{\frac{4+3\sqrt{15}}{20}}{\frac{4\sqrt{15}-3}{20}}=\frac{4+3\sqrt{15}}{4\sqrt{15}-3}$$

To find the quadrant of $x + y$, notice that $\sin(x + y) > 0$, which implies $x + y$ is in quadrant I or II. Also $\tan(x + y) > 0$, which implies that $x + y$ is in quadrant I or III. Therefore, $x + y$ is in quadrant I.

25. Find $\cos\frac{\theta}{2}$, given $\cos\theta=-\frac{1}{2}$, $90°<\theta<180°$.

Since $90°<\theta<180° \Rightarrow 45°<\frac{\theta}{2}<90°$, $\frac{\theta}{2}$ is in quadrant I and $\cos\frac{\theta}{2}>0$.

$$\cos\frac{\theta}{2}=\sqrt{\frac{1+\left(-\frac{1}{2}\right)}{2}}=\sqrt{\frac{2-1}{4}}=\sqrt{\frac{1}{4}}=\frac{1}{2}$$

Exercise 27 is graphed in the following window.

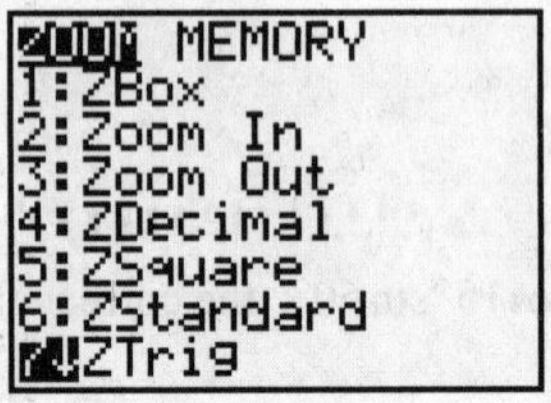

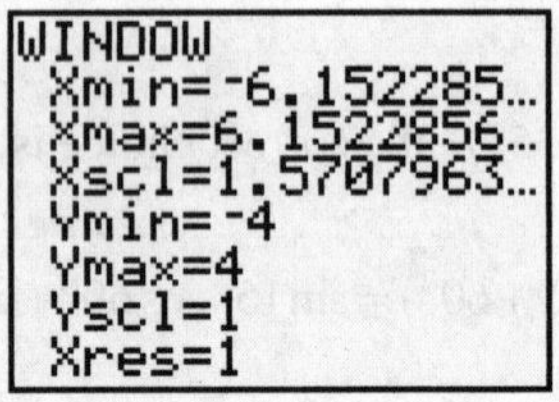

27. $-\frac{\sin 2x+\sin x}{\cos 2x-\cos x}$ appears to be equivalent to $\cot\frac{x}{2}$.

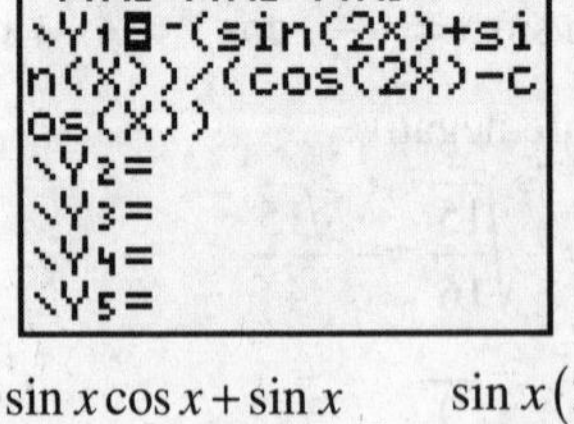

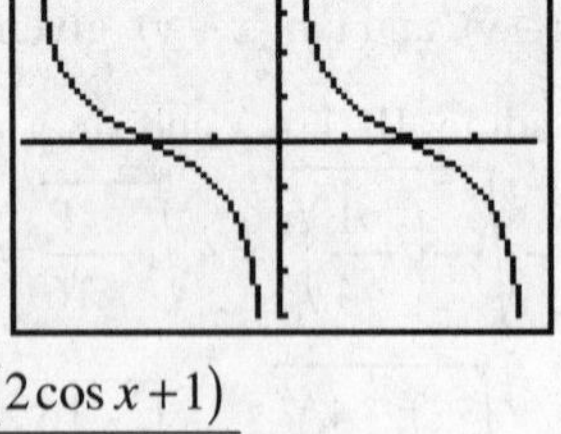

$$-\frac{\sin 2x+\sin x}{\cos 2x-\cos x}=-\frac{2\sin x\cos x+\sin x}{2\cos^2 x-1-\cos x}=-\frac{\sin x(2\cos x+1)}{2\cos^2 x-\cos x-1}$$

$$=-\frac{\sin x(2\cos x+1)}{(2\cos x+1)(\cos x-1)}=-\frac{\sin x}{\cos x-1}=\frac{\sin x}{1-\cos x}=\frac{1}{\frac{1-\cos x}{\sin x}}=\frac{1}{\tan\frac{x}{2}}=\cot\frac{x}{2}$$

29. Verify $\sin^2 x - \sin^2 y = \cos^2 y - \cos^2 x$ is an identity.

$$\sin^2 x - \sin^2 y = (1-\cos^2 x) - (1-\cos^2 y) = 1-\cos^2 x - 1 + \cos^2 y = \cos^2 y - \cos^2 x$$

31. Verify $\dfrac{\sin^2 x}{2-2\cos x} = \cos^2 \dfrac{x}{2}$ is an identity.

$$\frac{\sin^2 x}{2-2\cos x} = \frac{1-\cos^2 x}{2(1-\cos x)} = \frac{(1-\cos x)(1+\cos x)}{2(1-\cos x)} = \frac{1+\cos x}{2} = \cos^2 \frac{x}{2}$$

33. Verify $2\cos A - \sec A = \cos A - \dfrac{\tan A}{\csc A}$ is an identity.

Work with the right side.

$$\cos A - \frac{\tan A}{\csc A} = \cos A - \frac{\frac{\sin A}{\cos A}}{\frac{1}{\sin A}} = \cos A - \frac{\sin^2 A}{\cos A} = \frac{\cos^2 A}{\cos A} - \frac{\sin^2 A}{\cos A} = \frac{\cos^2 A - \sin^2 A}{\cos A}$$

$$= \frac{\cos^2 A - (1-\cos^2 A)}{\cos A} = \frac{2\cos^2 A - 1}{\cos A} = 2\cos A - \frac{1}{\cos A} = 2\cos A - \sec A$$

35. Verify $1+\tan^2 \alpha = 2\tan\alpha \csc 2\alpha$ is an identity.

Work with the right side.

$$2\tan\alpha\csc 2\alpha = \frac{2\tan\alpha}{\sin 2\alpha} = \frac{2\cdot\frac{\sin\alpha}{\cos\alpha}}{2\sin\alpha\cos\alpha} = \frac{2\sin\alpha}{2\sin\alpha\cos^2\alpha} = \frac{1}{\cos^2\alpha} = \sec^2\alpha = 1+\tan^2\alpha$$

37. Verify $\tan\theta\sin 2\theta = 2-2\cos^2\theta$ is an identity.

$$\tan\theta\sin 2\theta = \tan\theta(2\sin\theta\cos\theta) = \frac{\sin\theta}{\cos\theta}(2\sin\theta\cos\theta) = 2\sin^2\theta = 2(1-\cos^2\theta) = 2-2\cos^2\theta$$

39. Verify $2\tan x\csc 2x - \tan^2 x = 1$ is an identity.

$$2\tan x\csc 2x - \tan^2 x = 2\tan x\frac{1}{\sin 2x} - \tan^2 x$$

$$= 2\cdot\frac{\sin x}{\cos x}\cdot\frac{1}{2\sin x\cos x} - \frac{\sin^2 x}{\cos^2 x} = \frac{1}{\cos^2 x} - \frac{\sin^2 x}{\cos^2 x} = \frac{1-\sin^2 x}{\cos^2 x} = \frac{\cos^2 x}{\cos^2 x} = 1$$

41. Verify $\tan\theta\cos^2\theta = \dfrac{2\tan\theta\cos^2\theta - \tan\theta}{1-\tan^2\theta}$ is an identity.

Work with the right side.

$$\frac{2\tan\theta\cos^2\theta - \tan\theta}{1-\tan^2\theta} = \frac{\tan\theta(2\cos^2\theta - 1)}{1-\tan^2\theta} = \frac{\tan\theta(2\cos^2\theta-1)}{1-\frac{\sin^2\theta}{\cos^2\theta}}\cdot\frac{\cos^2\theta}{\cos^2\theta}$$

$$= \frac{\tan\theta\cos^2\theta(2\cos^2\theta-1)}{\cos^2\theta - \sin^2\theta} = \frac{\tan\theta\cos^2\theta(2\cos^2\theta-1)}{2\cos^2\theta-1} = \tan\theta\cos^2\theta$$

43. Verify $2\cos^3 x - \cos x = \dfrac{\cos^2 x - \sin^2 x}{\sec x}$ is an identity.

Work with the right side.

$$\frac{\cos^2 x - \sin^2 x}{\sec x} = \frac{2\cos^2 x - 1}{\frac{1}{\cos x}} \cdot \frac{\cos x}{\cos x} = \left(2\cos^2 x - 1\right)\cos x = 2\cos^3 x - \cos x$$

45. $y = \sin^{-1}\dfrac{\sqrt{2}}{2} \Rightarrow \sin y = \dfrac{\sqrt{2}}{2}$

Since $-\dfrac{\pi}{2} \le y \le \dfrac{\pi}{2}$, $y = \dfrac{\pi}{4}$.

47. $y = \tan^{-1}\left(-\sqrt{3}\right) \Rightarrow \tan y = -\sqrt{3}$

Since $-\dfrac{\pi}{2} < y < \dfrac{\pi}{2}$, $y = -\dfrac{\pi}{3}$.

49. $y = \cos^{-1}\left(-\dfrac{\sqrt{2}}{2}\right) \Rightarrow \cos y = -\dfrac{\sqrt{2}}{2}$

Since $0 \le y \le \pi$, $y = \dfrac{3\pi}{4}$.

51. $y = \sec^{-1}(-2) \Rightarrow \sec y = -2$

Since $0 \le y \le \pi$, $y \ne \dfrac{\pi}{2} \Rightarrow y = \dfrac{2\pi}{3}$.

53. $y = \text{arccot}\,(-1) \Rightarrow \cot y = -1$

Since $0 < y < \pi$, $y = \dfrac{3\pi}{4}$.

55. $\theta = \arcsin\left(-\dfrac{\sqrt{3}}{2}\right) \Rightarrow \sin\theta = -\dfrac{\sqrt{3}}{2}$

Since $-90° \le \theta \le 90°$, $\theta = -60°$.

For Exercises 57 – 61, be sure that your calculator is in degree mode. Keystroke sequences may vary based on the type and/or model of calculator being used.

57. $\theta = \arctan 1.7804675$

$\theta = 60.67924514°$

59. $\theta = \cos^{-1} .80396577$

$\theta \approx 36.4895081°$

61. $\theta = \text{arc}\sec 3.4723155$

$\theta \approx 73.26220613°$

63. $\cos\left(\arccos(-1)\right) = \cos\pi = -1$ or $\cos\left(\arccos(-1)\right) = \cos 180° = -1$

65. $\arccos\left(\cos\dfrac{3\pi}{4}\right) = \arccos\left(-\dfrac{\sqrt{2}}{2}\right) = \dfrac{3\pi}{4}$

67. $\tan^{-1}\left(\tan\frac{\pi}{4}\right)=\tan^{-1}\frac{\sqrt{2}}{2}=\frac{\pi}{4}$

69. $\sin\left(\arccos\frac{3}{4}\right)$

Let $\omega=\arccos\frac{3}{4}$, so that $\cos\omega=\frac{3}{4}$. Since arccos is defined only in quadrants I and II, and $\frac{3}{4}$ is positive, ω is in quadrant I. Sketch ω and label a triangle with the side opposite ω equal to $\sqrt{4^2-3^2}=\sqrt{16-9}=\sqrt{7}$.

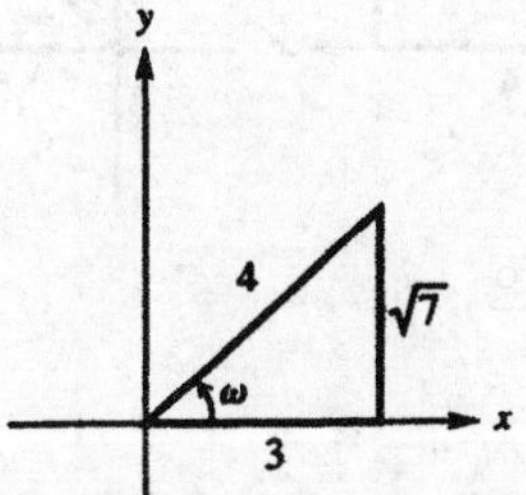

$$\sin\left(\arccos\frac{3}{4}\right)=\sin\omega=\frac{\sqrt{7}}{4}$$

71. $\cos\left(\csc^{-1}(-2)\right)$

Let $\omega=\csc^{-1}(-2)$, so that $\csc\omega=-2$. Since $-\frac{\pi}{2}\le\omega\le\frac{\pi}{2}$ and $\omega\neq 0$, and $\csc\omega=-2$ (negative), ω is in quadrant IV. Sketch ω and label a triangle with side adjacent to ω equal to $\sqrt{2^2-(-1)^2}=\sqrt{4-1}=\sqrt{3}$.

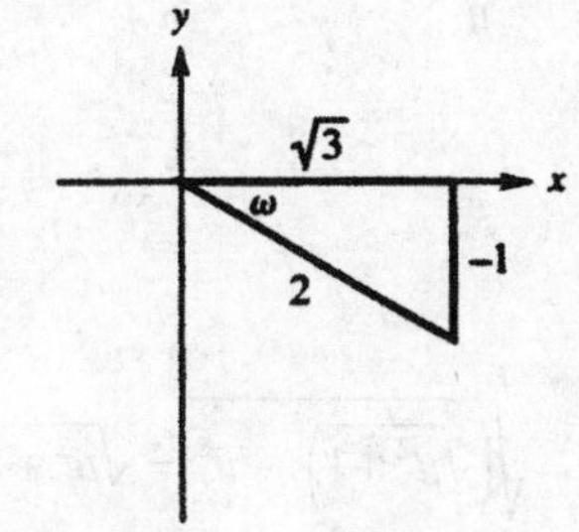

$$\cos\left(\csc^{-1}(-2)\right)=\cos\omega=\frac{\sqrt{3}}{2}$$

73. $\tan\left(\arcsin\frac{3}{5}+\arccos\frac{5}{7}\right)$

Let $\omega_1=\arcsin\frac{3}{5}$, $\omega_2=\arccos\frac{5}{7}$. Sketch angles ω_1 and ω_2 in quadrant I. The side adjacent to ω_1 is $\sqrt{5^2-3^2}=\sqrt{25-9}=\sqrt{16}=4$. The side opposite ω_2 is $\sqrt{7^2-5^2}=\sqrt{49-25}=\sqrt{24}=2\sqrt{6}$.

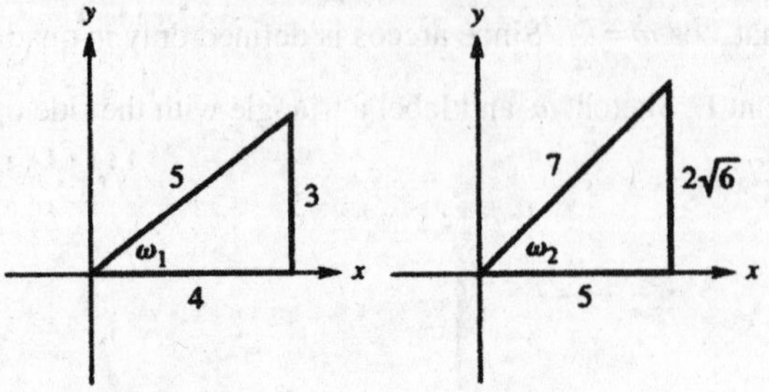

We have $\tan\omega_1=\frac{3}{4}$ and $\tan\omega_2=\frac{2\sqrt{6}}{5}$.

$$\tan\left(\arcsin\frac{3}{5}+\arccos\frac{5}{7}\right)=\tan(\omega_1+\omega_2)=\frac{\tan\omega_1+\tan\omega_2}{1-\tan\omega_1\tan\omega_2}=\frac{\frac{3}{4}+\frac{2\sqrt{6}}{5}}{1-\left(\frac{3}{4}\right)\left(\frac{2\sqrt{6}}{5}\right)}=\frac{\frac{15+8\sqrt{6}}{20}}{\frac{20-6\sqrt{6}}{20}}$$

$$=\frac{15+8\sqrt{6}}{20-6\sqrt{6}}=\frac{15+8\sqrt{6}}{20-6\sqrt{6}}\cdot\frac{20+6\sqrt{6}}{20+6\sqrt{6}}=\frac{588+250\sqrt{6}}{184}=\frac{294+125\sqrt{6}}{92}$$

75. $\tan\left(\operatorname{arcsec}\frac{\sqrt{u^2+1}}{u}\right)$

Let $\theta=\operatorname{arcsec}\frac{\sqrt{u^2+1}}{u}$, so $\sec\theta=\frac{\sqrt{u^2+1}}{u}$.

If $u>0$, $0<\theta<\frac{\pi}{2}$.

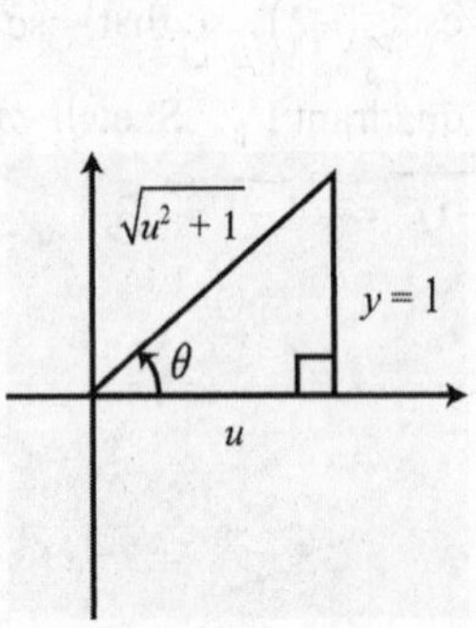

From the Pythagorean theorem, $y=\sqrt{\left(\sqrt{u^2+1}\right)^2-u^2}=\sqrt{u^2+1-u^2}=\sqrt{1}=1$. Therefore $\tan\theta=\frac{1}{u}$.

Thus, $\tan\left(\operatorname{arcsec}\frac{\sqrt{u^2+1}}{u}\right)=\frac{1}{u}$.

77. $2\tan x-1=0$

$$2\tan x-1=0\Rightarrow 2\tan x=1\Rightarrow \tan x=\frac{1}{2}$$

Over the interval $[0,2\pi)$, the equation $\tan x=\frac{1}{2}$ has two solutions. One solution is in quadrant I and the other is in quadrant III. Using a calculator, the quadrant I solution is approximately .463647609. The quadrant III solution would be approximately $.463647609+\pi\approx 3.605240263$.

Solution set: $\{.463647609, 3.605240263\}$

79. $\tan x = \cot x$

Use the identity $\cot x = \dfrac{1}{\tan x}$, $\tan x \neq 0$.

$$\tan x = \cot x \Rightarrow \tan x = \frac{1}{\tan x} \Rightarrow \tan^2 x = 1 \Rightarrow \tan x = \pm 1$$

Over the interval $[0, 2\pi)$, the equation $\tan x = 1$ has two solutions. One solution is in quadrant I and the other is in quadrant III. These solutions are $\dfrac{\pi}{4}$ and $\dfrac{5\pi}{4}$. In the same interval, the equation $\tan x = -1$ has two solutions. One solution is in quadrant II and the other is in quadrant IV. These solutions are $\dfrac{3\pi}{4}$ and $\dfrac{7\pi}{4}$.

Solution set: $\left\{\dfrac{\pi}{4}, \dfrac{3\pi}{4}, \dfrac{5\pi}{4}, \dfrac{7\pi}{4}\right\}$

81. $\tan^2 2x - 1 = 0$

$$\tan^2 2x - 1 = 0 \Rightarrow \tan^2 2x = 1 \Rightarrow \tan 2x = \pm 1$$

Since $0 \le x < 2\pi, 0 \le 2x < 4\pi$. Thus, $2x = \dfrac{\pi}{4}, \dfrac{3\pi}{4}, \dfrac{5\pi}{4}, \dfrac{7\pi}{4}, \dfrac{9\pi}{4}, \dfrac{11\pi}{4}, \dfrac{13\pi}{4}, \dfrac{15\pi}{4}$ implies $x = \dfrac{\pi}{8}, \dfrac{3\pi}{8}, \dfrac{5\pi}{8}, \dfrac{7\pi}{8}, \dfrac{9\pi}{8}, \dfrac{11\pi}{8}, \dfrac{13\pi}{8}, \dfrac{15\pi}{8}$.

Solution set: $\left\{\dfrac{\pi}{8}, \dfrac{3\pi}{8}, \dfrac{5\pi}{8}, \dfrac{7\pi}{8}, \dfrac{9\pi}{8}, \dfrac{11\pi}{8}, \dfrac{13\pi}{8}, \dfrac{15\pi}{8}\right\}$

83. $\cos 2x + \cos x = 0$

$$\cos 2x + \cos x = 0 \Rightarrow 2\cos^2 x - 1 + \cos x = 0 \Rightarrow 2\cos^2 x + \cos x - 1 = 0 \Rightarrow (2\cos x - 1)(\cos x + 1) = 0$$

$$2\cos x - 1 = 0 \Rightarrow 2\cos x = 1 \Rightarrow \cos x = \frac{1}{2} \quad \text{or} \quad \cos x + 1 = 0 \Rightarrow \cos x = -1$$

Over the interval $[0, 2\pi)$, the equation $\cos x = \dfrac{1}{2}$ has two solutions. The angles in quadrants I and IV that have a reference angle of $\dfrac{\pi}{3}$ are $\dfrac{\pi}{3}$ and $\dfrac{5\pi}{3}$. In the same interval, $\cos x = -1$ when the angle is π.

Solution set: $\left\{\dfrac{\pi}{3} + 2n\pi, \pi + 2n\pi, \dfrac{5\pi}{3} + 2n\pi, \text{ where } n \text{ is any integer}\right\}$

85. $\sin^2 \theta + 3\sin\theta + 2 = 0$

$$\sin^2 \theta + 3\sin\theta + 2 = 0 \Rightarrow (\sin\theta + 2)(\sin\theta + 1) = 0$$

In the interval $[0°, 360°)$, we have the following.

$$\sin\theta + 1 = 0 \Rightarrow \sin\theta = -1 \Rightarrow \theta = 270° \text{ and } \sin\theta + 2 = 0 \Rightarrow \sin\theta = -2 < -1 \Rightarrow \text{no solution}$$

Solution set: $\{270°\}$

87. $\sin 2\theta = \cos 2\theta + 1$

$$\sin 2\theta = \cos 2\theta + 1 \Rightarrow (\sin 2\theta)^2 = (\cos 2\theta + 1)^2 \Rightarrow \sin^2 2\theta = \cos^2 2\theta + 2\cos 2\theta + 1$$
$$1 - \cos^2 2\theta = \cos^2 2\theta + 2\cos 2\theta + 1 \Rightarrow 2\cos^2 2\theta + 2\cos 2\theta = 0$$
$$\cos^2 2\theta + \cos 2\theta = 0 \Rightarrow \cos 2\theta(\cos 2\theta + 1) = 0$$

Since $0° \le \theta < 360°$, $0° \le 2\theta < 720°$.

$$\cos 2\theta = 0 \Rightarrow 2\theta = 90°,\ 270°,\ 450°,\ 630° \Rightarrow \theta = 45°,\ 135°,\ 225°,\ 315°$$
$$\cos 2\theta + 1 = 0 \Rightarrow \cos 2\theta = -1 \Rightarrow 2\theta = 180°,\ 540° \Rightarrow \theta = 90°,\ 270°$$

Possible values for θ are $\theta = 45°, 90°, 135°, 225°, 270°, 315°$.

All proposed solutions must be checked since the solutions were found by squaring an equation.

A value for θ will be a solution if $\sin 2\theta - \cos 2\theta = 1$.

$$\theta = 45°, 2\theta = 90° \Rightarrow \sin 90° - \cos 90° = 1 - 0 = 1$$
$$\theta = 90°, 2\theta = 180° \Rightarrow \sin 180° - \cos 180° = 0 - (-1) = 1$$
$$\theta = 135°, 2\theta = 270° \Rightarrow \sin 270° - \cos 270° = -1 - 0 \neq 1$$
$$\theta = 225°, 2\theta = 450° \Rightarrow \sin 450° - \cos 450° = 1 - 0 = 1$$
$$\theta = 270°, 2\theta = 540° \Rightarrow \sin 540° - \cos 540° = 0 - (-1) = 1$$
$$\theta = 315°, 2\theta = 630° \Rightarrow \sin 630° - \cos 630° = -1 - 0 \neq 1$$

Thus, $\theta = 45°, 90°, 225°, 270°$.

Solution set: $\{45°, 90°, 225°, 270°\}$

89. $3\cos^2\theta + 2\cos\theta - 1 = 0$

$$3\cos^2\theta + 2\cos\theta - 1 = 0 \Rightarrow (3\cos\theta - 1)(\cos\theta + 1) = 0$$

In the interval $[0°, 360°)$, we have the following.

$$3\cos\theta - 1 = 0 \Rightarrow \cos\theta = \frac{1}{3} \Rightarrow \theta \approx 70.5° \text{ and } 289.5° \text{ (using a calculator)}$$
$$\cos\theta + 1 = 0 \Rightarrow \cos\theta = -1 \Rightarrow \theta = 180°$$

Solution set: $\{70.5°, 180°, 289.5°\}$

91. $4y = 2\sin x \Rightarrow 2y = \sin x \Rightarrow x = \arcsin 2y$

93. $2y = \tan(3x+2) \Rightarrow 3x + 2 = \arctan 2y \Rightarrow 3x = \arctan 2y - 2 \Rightarrow x = \left(\frac{1}{3}\arctan 2y\right) - \frac{2}{3}$

95. $\frac{4}{3}\arctan\frac{x}{2} = \pi \Rightarrow \arctan\frac{x}{2} = \frac{3\pi}{4}$

But, by definition, the range of arctan is $\left(-\frac{\pi}{2}, \frac{\pi}{2}\right)$. So, this equation has no solution.

Solution set: $\varnothing$

97. $\arccos x + \arctan 1 = \dfrac{11\pi}{12}$

$$\arccos x + \arctan 1 = \frac{11\pi}{12} \Rightarrow \arccos x = \frac{11\pi}{12} - \arctan 1 \Rightarrow \arccos x = \frac{11\pi}{12} - \frac{\pi}{4}$$

$$\arccos x = \frac{11\pi}{12} - \frac{3\pi}{12} = \frac{8\pi}{12} \Rightarrow \arccos x = \frac{2\pi}{3} \Rightarrow \cos\frac{2\pi}{3} = x \Rightarrow x = -\frac{1}{2}$$

Solution set: $\left\{-\frac{1}{2}\right\}$

99. **(a)** Let α be the angle to the left of θ.

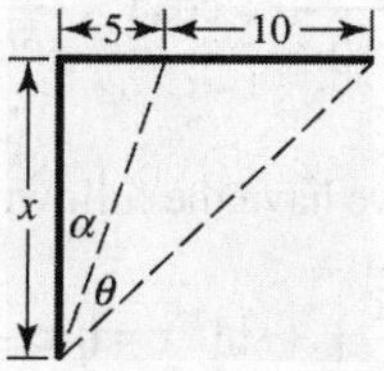

Thus, we have the following.

$$\tan(\alpha+\theta) = \frac{5+10}{x} \Rightarrow \alpha+\theta = \arctan\left(\frac{15}{x}\right) \Rightarrow \theta = \arctan\left(\frac{15}{x}\right) - \alpha \Rightarrow \theta = \arctan\left(\frac{15}{x}\right) - \arctan\left(\frac{5}{x}\right)$$

(b) The maximum occurs at approximately =8.66026 ft. There may be a discrepancy in the final digits.

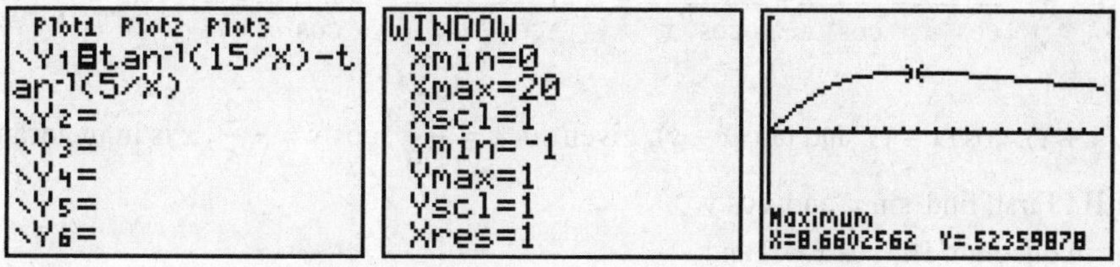

101. If $\theta_1 > 48.8°$, then $\theta_2 > 90°$ and the light beam is completely underwater.

103.

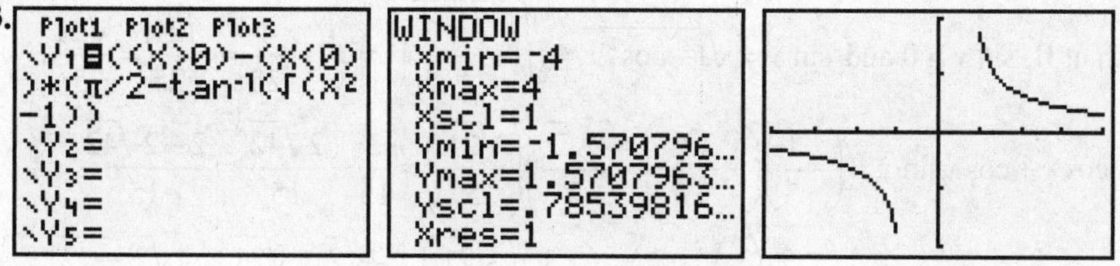

Chapter 7: Test

1. Given $\tan x = -\frac{5}{6}, \frac{3\pi}{2} < x < 2\pi,$ use trigonometric identities to find $\sin x$ and $\cos x$.

$$\sec^2 x = \tan^2 x + 1 \Rightarrow \sec^2 x = \left(-\frac{5}{6}\right)^2 + 1 = \frac{25}{36} + 1 = \frac{61}{36}$$

Since $\frac{3\pi}{2} < x < 2\pi,$ x is in quadrant IV. Thus, $\sec x > 0.$

Therefore, $\sec x = \sqrt{\frac{61}{36}} = \frac{\sqrt{61}}{6} \Rightarrow \cos x = \frac{1}{\sec x} = \frac{1}{\frac{\sqrt{61}}{6}} = \frac{6}{\sqrt{61}} \cdot \frac{\sqrt{61}}{\sqrt{61}} = \frac{6\sqrt{61}}{61}.$

Since $\cos^2 x + \sin^2 x = 1,$ we have the following.

$$\left(\frac{6\sqrt{61}}{61}\right)^2 + \sin^2 x = 1 \Rightarrow \frac{2196}{3721} + \sin^2 x = 1 \Rightarrow \sin^2 x = \frac{1525}{3721}$$

Since x is in quadrant IV, $\sin x < 0$ and $\sin x = -\sqrt{\frac{1525}{3721}} = -\frac{5\sqrt{61}}{61}.$

2. $\tan^2 x - \sec^2 x = \frac{\sin^2 x}{\cos^2 x} - \frac{1}{\cos^2 x} = \frac{\sin^2 x - 1}{\cos^2 x} = \frac{(1-\cos^2 x) - 1}{\cos^2 x} = -\frac{\cos^2 x}{\cos^2 x} = -1$

3. Find $\sin(x + y)$, $\cos(x - y)$, and $\tan(x + y)$, given $\sin x = -\frac{1}{3}$, $\cos y = -\frac{2}{5}$, x is in quadrant III, y is in quadrant II. First, find $\sin x$ and $\cos y$.
Since x is in quadrant III, $\cos x < 0$ and

$$\cos x = -\sqrt{1-\sin^2 x} = -\sqrt{1-\left(-\frac{1}{3}\right)^2} = -\sqrt{1-\frac{1}{9}} = -\sqrt{\frac{8}{9}} = -\frac{2\sqrt{2}}{3}.$$

Since y is in quadrant II, $\sin y > 0$ and $\sin y = \sqrt{1-\cos^2 x} = \sqrt{1-\left(-\frac{2}{5}\right)^2} = \sqrt{1-\frac{4}{25}} = \sqrt{\frac{21}{25}} = \frac{\sqrt{21}}{5}.$

$$\sin(x+y) = \sin x \cos y + \cos x \sin y = \left(-\frac{1}{3}\right)\left(-\frac{2}{5}\right) + \left(-\frac{2\sqrt{2}}{3}\right)\left(\frac{\sqrt{21}}{5}\right) = \frac{2}{15} - \frac{2\sqrt{42}}{15} = \frac{2-2\sqrt{42}}{15}$$

$$\cos(x-y) = \cos x \cos y + \sin x \sin y = \left(-\frac{2\sqrt{2}}{3}\right)\left(-\frac{2}{5}\right) + \left(-\frac{1}{3}\right)\left(\frac{\sqrt{21}}{5}\right) = \frac{4\sqrt{2}}{15} - \frac{\sqrt{21}}{15} = \frac{4\sqrt{2}-\sqrt{21}}{15}$$

In order to find $\tan(x+y)$ using the formula $\tan(x+y) = \frac{\tan x + \tan y}{1 - \tan x \tan y}$, we need to find $\tan x$ and $\tan y$.

$$\tan x = \frac{\sin x}{\cos x} = \frac{-\frac{1}{3}}{-\frac{2\sqrt{2}}{3}} = \frac{1}{2\sqrt{2}} \cdot \frac{\sqrt{2}}{\sqrt{2}} = \frac{\sqrt{2}}{4} \text{ and } \tan y = \frac{\sin y}{\cos y} = \frac{\frac{\sqrt{21}}{5}}{-\frac{2}{5}} = -\frac{\sqrt{21}}{2}$$

$$\tan(x+y) = \frac{\tan x + \tan y}{1 - \tan x \tan y} = \frac{\frac{\sqrt{2}}{4} + \left(-\frac{\sqrt{21}}{2}\right)}{1 - \left(\frac{\sqrt{2}}{4}\right)\left(-\frac{\sqrt{21}}{2}\right)} \cdot \frac{8}{8} = \frac{2\sqrt{2} - 4\sqrt{21}}{8 + \sqrt{42}}$$

4. $\sin(-22.5°) = \pm\sqrt{\dfrac{1-\cos(-45°)}{2}} = \pm\sqrt{\dfrac{1-\frac{\sqrt{2}}{2}}{2}} = \pm\sqrt{\dfrac{2-\sqrt{2}}{4}} = \pm\dfrac{\sqrt{2-\sqrt{2}}}{2}$

Since $-22.5°$ is in quadrant IV, $\sin(-22.5°)$ is negative. Thus, $\sin(-22.5°) = \dfrac{-\sqrt{2-\sqrt{2}}}{2}$.

Exercises 5 –6 are graphed in the following window.

5. $\sec x - \sin x \tan x$ appears to be equivalent to $\cos x$.

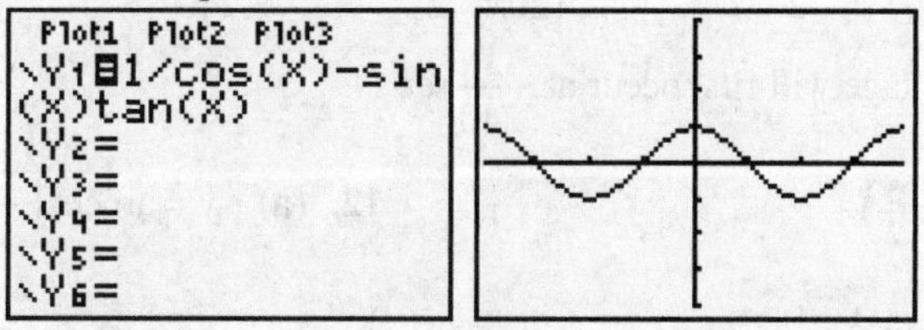

$$\sec x - \sin x \tan x = \frac{1}{\cos x} - \sin x \cdot \frac{\sin x}{\cos x} = \frac{1}{\cos x} - \frac{\sin^2 x}{\cos x} = \frac{1-\sin^2 x}{\cos x} = \frac{\cos^2 x}{\cos x} = \cos x$$

6. $\cot\dfrac{x}{2} - \cot x$ appears to be equivalent to $\csc x$.

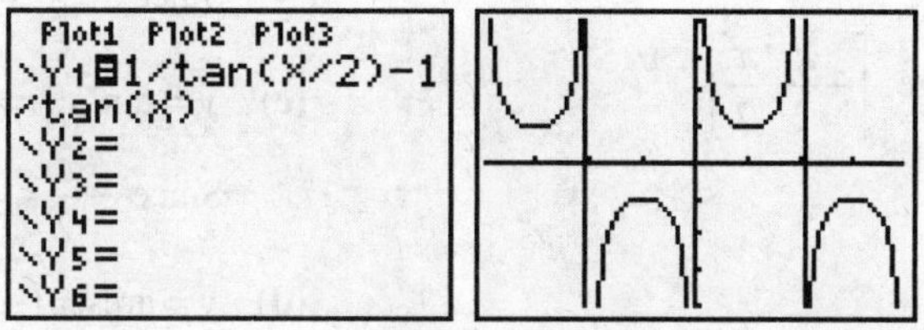

$$\cot\frac{x}{2} - \cot x = \frac{1}{\tan\frac{x}{2}} - \frac{\cos x}{\sin x} = \frac{1}{\frac{\sin x}{1+\cos x}} - \frac{\cos x}{\sin x} = \frac{1+\cos x}{\sin x} - \frac{\cos x}{\sin x} = \frac{1+\cos x - \cos x}{\sin x} = \frac{1}{\sin x} = \csc x$$

7. Verify $\sec^2 B = \dfrac{1}{1-\sin^2 B}$ is an identity.

Work with the right side.

$$\frac{1}{1-\sin^2 B} = \frac{1}{\cos^2 B} = \sec^2 B$$

8. Verify $\cos 2A = \dfrac{\cot A - \tan A}{\csc A \sec A}$ is an identity.

Work with the right side.

$$\frac{\cot A - \tan A}{\csc A \sec A} = \frac{\frac{\cos A}{\sin A} - \frac{\sin A}{\cos A}}{\left(\frac{1}{\sin A}\right)\left(\frac{1}{\cos A}\right)} \cdot \frac{\sin A \cos A}{\sin A \cos A} = \cos^2 A - \sin^2 A = \cos^2 2A$$

9. **(a)** $\cos(270° - \theta) = \cos 270° \cos\theta + \sin 270° \sin\theta = 0 \cdot \cos\theta + (-1)\sin\theta = 0 - \sin\theta = -\sin\theta$

(b) $\sin(\pi + \theta) = \sin\pi\cos\theta + \cos\pi\sin\theta = 0 \cdot \cos\theta + (-1)\sin\theta = 0 - \sin\theta = -\sin\theta$

10. **(a)** $V = 163\sin\omega t$. Since $\sin x = \cos\left(\frac{\pi}{2} - x\right)$, $V = 163\cos\left(\frac{\pi}{2} - \omega t\right)$.

(b) If $V = 163\sin\omega t = 163\sin 120\pi t = 163\cos\left(\frac{\pi}{2} - 120\pi t\right)$, the maximum voltage occurs when $\cos\left(\frac{\pi}{2} - 120\pi t\right) = 1$. Thus, the maximum voltage is $V = 163$ volts.

$\cos\left(\frac{\pi}{2} - 120\pi t\right) = 1$ when $\frac{\pi}{2} - 120\pi t = 2k\pi$, where k is any integer. The first maximum occurs when $\frac{\pi}{2} - 120\pi t = 0 \Rightarrow \frac{\pi}{2} = 120\pi t \Rightarrow \frac{1}{120\pi} \cdot \frac{\pi}{2} = t \Rightarrow t = \frac{1}{240}$.

The maximum voltage will first occur at $\frac{1}{240}$ sec.

11.

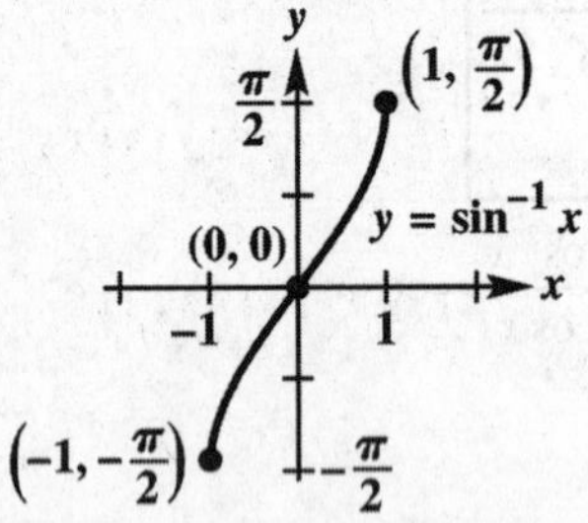

Domain: $[-1, 1]$; Range: $\left[-\frac{\pi}{2}, \frac{\pi}{2}\right]$

12. **(a)** $y = \arccos\left(-\frac{1}{2}\right) \Rightarrow \cos y = -\frac{1}{2}$

Since $0 \le y \le \pi$, $y = \frac{2\pi}{3}$.

(b) $y = \sin^{-1}\left(-\frac{\sqrt{3}}{2}\right) \Rightarrow \sin y = -\frac{\sqrt{3}}{2}$

Since $-\frac{\pi}{2} \le y \le \frac{\pi}{2}$, $y = -\frac{\pi}{3}$.

(c) $y = \tan^{-1} 0 \Rightarrow \tan y = 0$

Since $-\frac{\pi}{2} < y < \frac{\pi}{2}$, $y = 0$.

(d) $y = \text{arcsec}(-2) \Rightarrow \sec y = -2$

Since $0 \le y \le \pi$ and $y \ne \frac{\pi}{2}$, $y = \frac{2\pi}{3}$.

13. **(a)** $\cos\left(\arcsin\frac{2}{3}\right)$

Let $\arcsin\frac{2}{3} = u$, so that $\sin u = \frac{2}{3}$. Since arcsine is defined only in quadrants I and IV, and $\frac{2}{3}$ is positive, u is in quadrant I. Sketch u and label a triangle with the side adjacent u equal to $\sqrt{3^2 - 2^2} = \sqrt{9-4} = \sqrt{5}$.

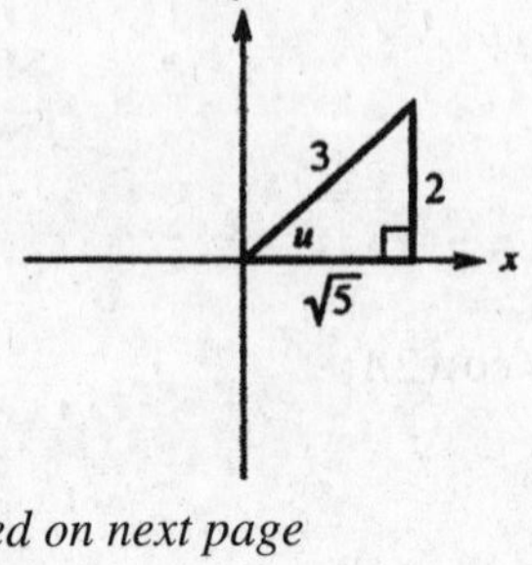

$$\cos\left(\arcsin\frac{2}{3}\right) = \cos u = \frac{\sqrt{5}}{3}$$

Continued on next page

13. (continued)

(b) $\sin\left(2\cos^{-1}\frac{1}{3}\right)$

Let $\theta = \cos^{-1}\frac{1}{3}$, so that $\cos\theta = \frac{1}{3}$. Since arccosine is defined only in quadrants I and II, and $\frac{1}{3}$ is positive, θ is in quadrant I. Sketch θ and label a triangle with the side opposite to θ equal to $\theta = \sqrt{3^2 - (-1)^2} = \sqrt{9-1} = \sqrt{8} = 2\sqrt{2}$.

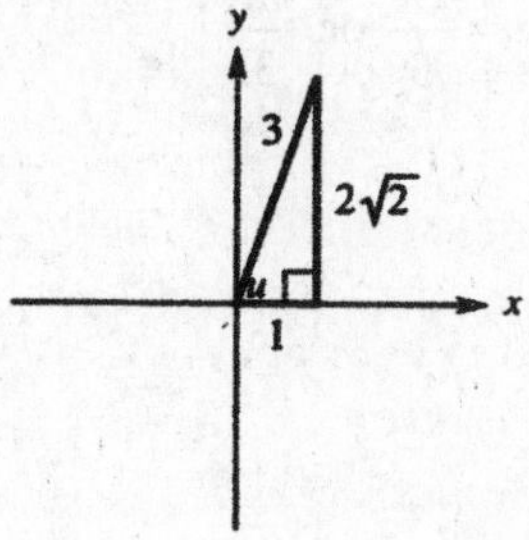

$$\sin\theta = \frac{2\sqrt{2}}{3}$$

$$\sin\left(2\cos^{-1}\frac{1}{3}\right) = \sin 2\theta$$

$$\sin\left(2\cos^{-1}\frac{1}{3}\right) = \sin 2\theta = 2\sin\theta\cos\theta = 2\left(\frac{2\sqrt{2}}{3}\right)\left(\frac{1}{3}\right) = \frac{4\sqrt{2}}{9}$$

14. $\tan(\arcsin u)$

Let $\theta = \arcsin u$, so $\sin\theta = u = \frac{u}{1}$. If $u > 0$, $0 < \theta < \frac{\pi}{2}$.

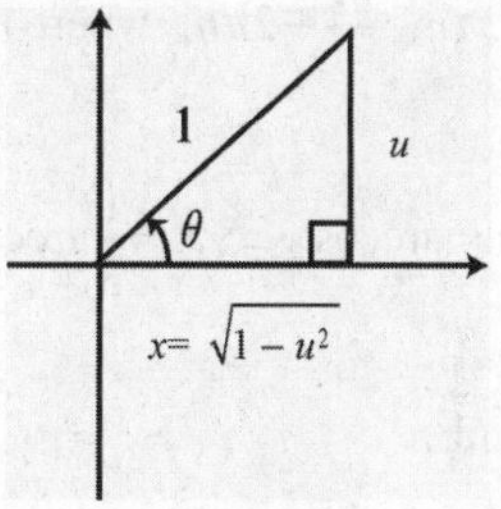

15. $\sin^2\theta = \cos^2\theta + 1$

$$\sin^2\theta = \cos^2\theta + 1 \Rightarrow \cos^2\theta - \sin^2\theta = -1 \Rightarrow \cos 2\theta = -1$$

Since $0° \le \theta < 360°$, then $0° \le 2\theta < 720°$. Thus, $2\theta = 180°, 540° \Rightarrow \theta = 90°, 270°$.

Solution set: $\{90°, 270°\}$

16. $\csc^2\theta - 2\cot\theta = 4$

$$\csc^2\theta - 2\cot\theta = 4 \Rightarrow 1 + \cot^2\theta - 2\cot\theta = 4 \Rightarrow \cot^2\theta - 2\cot - 3 = 0 \Rightarrow (\cot\theta - 3)(\cot\theta + 1) = 0$$

$$\cot\theta + 1 = 0 \Rightarrow \cot\theta = -1 \Rightarrow \theta = 135° \text{ or } 315°$$

$$\cot\theta - 3 = 0 \Rightarrow \cot\theta = 3 \Rightarrow \theta = \cot^{-1} 3$$

Since $\cot\theta = 3 > 0$, we will obtain two angles. One angle will be in quadrant I and the other will be in quadrant III. Using a calculator, if $\cot\theta = 3$, the quadrant I angle will be approximately 18.4°. (Note: You need to calculate $\tan^{-1}\frac{1}{3}$ to obtain this angle.) The quadrant III angle will be approximately $180° + 18.4° = 198.4°$.

Solution set: $\{18.4°, 135°, 198.4°, 315°\}$

17. $\cos x = \cos 2x$

$$\cos x = \cos 2x \Rightarrow \cos 2x - \cos x = 0 \Rightarrow \left(2\cos^2 x - 1\right) - \cos x = 0$$

$$2\cos^2 x - \cos x - 1 = 0 \Rightarrow (2\cos x + 1)(\cos x - 1) = 0$$

$$2\cos x + 1 = 0 \text{ or } \cos x - 1 = 0$$

Over the interval $[0, 2\pi)$, we have the following.

$$2\cos x + 1 = 0 \Rightarrow 2\cos x = -1 \Rightarrow \cos x = -\frac{1}{2} \Rightarrow x = \frac{2\pi}{3} \text{ or } \frac{4\pi}{3}$$

$$\cos x - 1 = 0 \Rightarrow \cos x = 1 \Rightarrow x = 0$$

Solution set: $\left\{0, \frac{2\pi}{3}, \frac{4\pi}{3}\right\}$

18. $2\sqrt{3}\sin\frac{x}{2} = 3 \Rightarrow \sin\frac{x}{2} = \frac{3}{2\sqrt{3}} \Rightarrow \frac{x}{2} = \sin^{-1}\frac{3}{2\sqrt{3}} \Rightarrow \frac{x}{2} = \sin^{-1}\frac{\sqrt{3}}{2}$

Since $0 \le x < 2\pi \Rightarrow 0° \le \frac{x}{2} < \pi$, we have the following.

$$\frac{x}{2} = \frac{\pi}{3}, \frac{2\pi}{3} \Rightarrow x = \frac{2\pi}{3}, \frac{4\pi}{3}$$

Solution set: $\left\{\frac{2\pi}{3} + 2\pi n, \frac{4\pi}{3} + 2\pi n, \text{ where } n \text{ is any integer}\right\}$

19. (a) $y = \cos 3x \Rightarrow 3x = \arccos y \Rightarrow x = \frac{1}{3}\arccos y$

(b) $\arcsin x = \arctan\frac{4}{3}$

Let $\omega = \arctan\frac{4}{3}$. Then $\tan\omega = \frac{4}{3}$. Sketch ω in quadrant I and label a triangle with the hypotenuse equal to $\sqrt{4^2 + 3^2} = \sqrt{16+9} = \sqrt{25} = 5$.

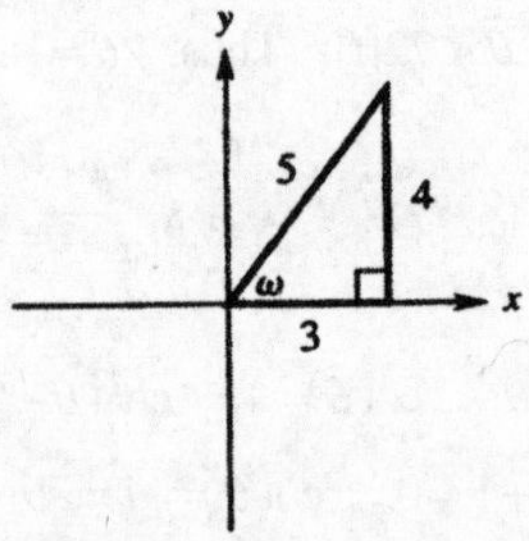

Thus, we have $\arcsin x = \arctan\frac{4}{3} \Rightarrow \arcsin x = \omega \Rightarrow x = \sin\omega = \frac{4}{5}$.

20. $y=\frac{\pi}{8}\cos\left[\pi\left(t-\frac{1}{3}\right)\right]$

Solve $0=\frac{\pi}{8}\cos\left[\pi\left(t-\frac{1}{3}\right)\right]$.

$$0=\frac{\pi}{8}\cos\left[\pi\left(t-\frac{1}{3}\right)\right]\Rightarrow 0=\cos\left[\pi\left(t-\frac{1}{3}\right)\right]$$

$$\pi\left(t-\frac{1}{3}\right)=\arccos 0\Rightarrow \pi\left(t-\frac{1}{3}\right)=\frac{\pi}{2}+n\pi$$

$$t-\frac{1}{3}=\frac{1}{2}+n\Rightarrow t=\frac{1}{2}+\frac{1}{3}+n\Rightarrow t=\frac{5}{6}+n,\text{ where } n \text{ is any integer}$$

In the interval $[0, \pi)$, $n = 0$, 1, and 2 provide valid values for t. Thus, we have the following.

$$t=\frac{5}{6},\ \frac{5}{6}+1,\ \frac{5}{6}+2\Rightarrow t=\frac{5}{6}\text{sec},\ \frac{11}{6}\text{sec},\ \frac{17}{6}\text{sec}$$

Chapter 8
APPLICATIONS OF TRIGONOMETRY

Section 8.1: The Law of Sines

1. A: $\frac{a}{b}=\frac{\sin A}{\sin B}$ can be rewritten as $\frac{a}{\sin A}=\frac{b}{\sin B}$. This is a valid proportion.

B: $\frac{a}{\sin A}=\frac{b}{\sin B}$ is a valid proportion.

C: $\frac{\sin A}{a}=\frac{b}{\sin B}$ cannot be rewritten as $\frac{a}{\sin A}=\frac{b}{\sin B}$. $\frac{\sin A}{a}=\frac{b}{\sin B}$ is not a valid proportion.

D: $\frac{\sin A}{a}=\frac{\sin B}{b}$ is a valid proportion.

3. The measure of angle C is $180°-(60°+75°)=180°-135°=45°$.

$$\frac{a}{\sin A}=\frac{c}{\sin C}\Rightarrow\frac{a}{\sin 60°}=\frac{\sqrt{2}}{\sin 45°}\Rightarrow a=\frac{\sqrt{2}\sin 60°}{\sin 45°}=\frac{\sqrt{2}\cdot\frac{\sqrt{3}}{2}}{\frac{\sqrt{2}}{2}}=\sqrt{2}\cdot\frac{\sqrt{3}}{2}\cdot\frac{2}{\sqrt{2}}=\sqrt{3}$$

5. $A=37°,\ B=48°,\ c=18$ m

$C=180°-A-B\Rightarrow C=180°-37°-48°=95°$

$$\frac{b}{\sin B}=\frac{c}{\sin C}\Rightarrow\frac{b}{\sin 48°}=\frac{18}{\sin 95°}\Rightarrow b=\frac{18\sin 48°}{\sin 95°}\approx 13\text{ m}$$
$$\frac{a}{\sin A}=\frac{c}{\sin C}\Rightarrow\frac{a}{\sin 37°}=\frac{18}{\sin 95°}\Rightarrow a=\frac{18\sin 37°}{\sin 95°}\approx 11\text{ m}$$

7. $A=27.2°,\ C=115.5°,\ c=76.0$ ft

$B=180°-A-C\Rightarrow B=180°-27.2°-115.5°=37.3°$

$$\frac{a}{\sin A}=\frac{c}{\sin C}\Rightarrow\frac{a}{\sin 27.2°}=\frac{76.0}{\sin 115.5°}\Rightarrow a=\frac{76.0\sin 27.2°}{\sin 115.5°}\approx 38.5\text{ ft}$$
$$\frac{b}{\sin B}=\frac{c}{\sin C}\Rightarrow\frac{b}{\sin 37.3°}=\frac{76.0}{\sin 115.5°}\Rightarrow b=\frac{76.0\sin 37.3°}{\sin 115.5°}\approx 51.0\text{ ft}$$

9. $A=68.41°,\ B=54.23°,\ a=12.75$ ft

$C=180°-A-B-C=180°-68.41°-54.23°=57.36°$

$$\frac{a}{\sin A}=\frac{b}{\sin B}\Rightarrow\frac{12.75}{\sin 68.41°}=\frac{b}{\sin 54.23°}\Rightarrow b=\frac{12.75\sin 54.23°}{\sin 68.41°}\approx 11.13\text{ ft}$$
$$\frac{a}{\sin A}=\frac{c}{\sin C}\Rightarrow\frac{12.75}{\sin 68.41°}=\frac{c}{\sin 57.36°}\Rightarrow c=\frac{12.75\sin 57.36°}{\sin 68.41°}\approx 11.55\text{ ft}$$

11. $B = 20°50', AC = 132 \text{ ft}, C = 103°10'$

$A = 180° - B - C \Rightarrow A = 180° - 20°50' - 103°10' \Rightarrow A = 56°00'$

$$\frac{AC}{\sin B} = \frac{AB}{\sin C} \Rightarrow \frac{132}{\sin 20°50'} = \frac{AB}{\sin 103°10'} \Rightarrow AB = \frac{132 \sin 103°10'}{\sin 20°50'} \approx 361 \text{ ft}$$

$$\frac{BC}{\sin A} = \frac{AC}{\sin B} \Rightarrow \frac{BC}{\sin 56°00'} = \frac{132}{\sin 20°50'} \Rightarrow BC = \frac{132 \sin 56°00'}{\sin 20°50'} \approx 308 \text{ ft}$$

13. $A = 39.70°, C = 30.35°, b = 39.74 \text{ m}$

$B = 180° - A - C \Rightarrow B = 180° - 39.70° - 30.35° \Rightarrow B = 109.95° \approx 110.0°$ (rounded)

$$\frac{a}{\sin A} = \frac{b}{\sin B} \Rightarrow \frac{a}{\sin 39.70°} = \frac{39.74}{\sin 109.95°} \Rightarrow a = \frac{39.74 \sin 39.70°}{\sin 110.0°} \approx 27.01 \text{ m}$$

$$\frac{b}{\sin B} = \frac{c}{\sin C} \Rightarrow \frac{39.74}{\sin 109.95°} = \frac{c}{\sin 30.35°} \Rightarrow c = \frac{39.74 \sin 30.35°}{\sin 110.0°} \approx 21.37 \text{ m}$$

15. $B = 42.88°, C = 102.40°, b = 3974 \text{ ft}$

$A = 180° - B - C \Rightarrow A = 180° - 42.88° - 102.40° = 34.72°$

$$\frac{a}{\sin A} = \frac{b}{\sin B} \Rightarrow \frac{a}{\sin 34.72°} = \frac{3974}{\sin 42.88°} \Rightarrow a = \frac{3974 \sin 34.72°}{\sin 42.88°} \approx 3326 \text{ ft}$$

$$\frac{b}{\sin B} = \frac{c}{\sin C} \Rightarrow \frac{3974}{\sin 42.88°} = \frac{c}{\sin 102.40°} \Rightarrow c = \frac{3974 \sin 102.40°}{\sin 42.88°} \approx 5704 \text{ ft}$$

17. Having three angles will not yield a unique triangle. The correct choice is A.

19. The vertical distance from the point (3, 4) to the x-axis is 4.

(a) If h is more than 4, two triangles can be drawn. But h must be less than 5 for both triangles to be on the positive x-axis. So, $4 < h < 5$.

(b) If $h = 4$, then exactly one triangle is possible. If $h > 5$, then only one triangle is possible on the positive x-axis.

(c) If $h < 4$, then no triangle is possible, since the side of length h would not reach the x-axis.

21. $a = 31, b = 26, B = 48°$

$$\frac{\sin A}{a} = \frac{\sin B}{b} \Rightarrow \frac{\sin A}{31} = \frac{\sin 48°}{26} \Rightarrow \sin A = \frac{31 \sin 48°}{26} \approx .88605729 \Rightarrow A \approx 62.4°$$

Another possible value for A is $180° - 62.4° = 117.6°$. Therefore, two triangles are possible.

22. $a = 35, b = 30, A = 40°$

$$\frac{\sin A}{a} = \frac{\sin B}{b} \Rightarrow \frac{\sin 40°}{35} = \frac{\sin B}{30} \Rightarrow \sin B = \frac{30 \sin 40°}{35} \approx .55096081 \Rightarrow B \approx 33.4°$$

Another possible value for B is $180° - 33.4° = 146.6°$, but this is too large to be in a triangle that also has a 40° angle. Therefore, only one triangle is possible.

23. $a = 50, b = 61, A = 58°$

$$\frac{\sin A}{a} = \frac{\sin B}{b} \Rightarrow \frac{\sin 58°}{50} = \frac{\sin B}{61} \Rightarrow \sin B = \frac{61 \sin 58°}{50} \approx 1.03461868$$

Since $\sin B > 1$ is impossible, no triangle is possible for the given parts.

25. $a = \sqrt{6}, b = 2, A = 60°$

$$\frac{\sin B}{b} = \frac{\sin A}{a} \Rightarrow \frac{\sin B}{2} = \frac{\sin 60°}{\sqrt{6}} \Rightarrow \sin B = \frac{2\sin 60°}{\sqrt{6}} = \frac{2\cdot\frac{\sqrt{3}}{2}}{\sqrt{6}} = \frac{\sqrt{3}}{\sqrt{6}} = \sqrt{\frac{3}{6}} = \sqrt{\frac{1}{2}} = \frac{1}{\sqrt{2}}\cdot\frac{\sqrt{2}}{2}$$

$$\sin B = \frac{\sqrt{2}}{2} \Rightarrow B = 45°$$

There is another angle between $0°$ and $180°$ whose sine is $\frac{\sqrt{2}}{2}$: $180° - 45° = 135°$. However, this is too large because $A = 60°$ and $60° + 135° = 195° > 180°$, so there is only one solution, $B = 45°$.

27. $A = 29.7°$, $b = 41.5$ ft, $a = 27.2$ ft

$$\frac{\sin B}{b} = \frac{\sin A}{a} \Rightarrow \frac{\sin B}{41.5} = \frac{\sin 29.7°}{27.2} \Rightarrow \sin B = \frac{41.5\sin 29.7°}{27.2} \approx .75593878$$

There are two angles B between $0°$ and $180°$ that satisfy the condition. Since $\sin B \approx .75593878$, to the nearest tenth value of B is $B_1 = 49.1°$. Supplementary angles have the same sine value, so another possible value of B is $B_2 = 180° - 49.1° = 130.9°$. This is a valid angle measure for this triangle since $A + B_2 = 29.7° + 130.9° = 160.6° < 180°$.

Solving separately for angles C_1 and C_2 we have the following.

$$C_1 = 180° - A - B_1 = 180° - 29.7° - 49.1° = 101.2°$$

$$C_2 = 180° - A - B_2 = 180° - 29.7° - 130.9° = 19.4°$$

29. $B = 74.3°$, $a = 859$ m, $b = 783$ m

$$\frac{\sin A}{a} = \frac{\sin B}{b} \Rightarrow \frac{\sin A}{859} = \frac{\sin 74.3°}{783} \Rightarrow \sin A = \frac{859\sin 74.3°}{783} \approx 1.0561331$$

Since $\sin A > 1$ is impossible, no such triangle exists.

31. $A = 142.13°$, $b = 5.432$ ft, $a = 7.297$ ft

$$\frac{\sin B}{b} = \frac{\sin A}{a} \Rightarrow \sin B = \frac{b\sin A}{a} \Rightarrow \sin B = \frac{5.432\sin 142.13°}{7.297} \approx .45697580 \Rightarrow B \approx 27.19°$$

Because angle A is obtuse, angle B must be acute, so this is the only possible value for B and there is one triangle with the given measurements.

$$C = 180° - A - B \Rightarrow C = 180° - 142.13° - 27.19° \Rightarrow C = 10.68°$$

Thus, $B \approx 27.19°$ and $C \approx 10.68°$.

33. $A = 42.5°$, $a = 15.6$ ft, $b = 8.14$ ft

$$\frac{\sin B}{b} = \frac{\sin A}{a} \Rightarrow \frac{\sin B}{8.14} = \frac{\sin 42.5°}{15.6} \Rightarrow \sin B = \frac{8.14\sin 42.5°}{15.6} \approx .35251951$$

There are two angles B between $0°$ and $180°$ that satisfy the condition. Since $\sin B \approx .35251951$, to the nearest tenth value of B is $B_1 = 20.6°'$. Supplementary angles have the same sine value, so another possible value of B is $B_2 = 180° - 20.6° = 159.4°$. This is not a valid angle measure for this triangle since $A + B_2 = 42.5° + 159.4° = 201.9° > 180°$.

Thus, $C = 180° - 42.5° - 20.6° = 116.9°$. Solving for c, we have the following.

$$\frac{c}{\sin C} = \frac{a}{\sin A} \Rightarrow \frac{c}{\sin 116.9°} = \frac{15.6}{\sin 42.5°} \Rightarrow c = \frac{15.6\sin 116.9°}{\sin 42.5°} \approx 20.6 \text{ ft}$$

35. $B = 72.2°$, $b = 78.3$ m, $c = 145$ m

$$\frac{\sin C}{c} = \frac{\sin B}{b} \Rightarrow \frac{\sin C}{145} = \frac{\sin 72.2°}{78.3} \Rightarrow \sin C = \frac{145 \sin 72.2°}{78.3} \approx 1.7632026$$

Since $\sin C > 1$ is impossible, no such triangle exists.

37. $A = 38°40'$, $a = 9.72$ km, $b = 11.8$ km

$$\frac{\sin B}{b} = \frac{\sin A}{a} \Rightarrow \frac{\sin B}{11.8} = \frac{\sin 38°40'}{9.72} \Rightarrow \sin B = \frac{11.8 \sin 38°40'}{9.72} \approx .75848811$$

There are two angles B between $0°$ and $180°$ that satisfy the condition. Since $\sin B \approx .75848811$, to the nearest tenth value of B is $B_1 = 49.3° \approx 49°20'$. Supplementary angles have the same sine value, so another possible value of B is $B_2 = 180° - 49°20' = 179°60' - 49°20' = 130°40'$. This is a valid angle measure for this triangle since $A + B_2 = 38°40' + 130°40' = 169°20' < 180°$.

Solving separately for triangles AB_1C_1 and AB_2C_2 we have the following.

AB_1C_1:

$$C_1 = 180° - A - B_1 = 180° - 38°40' - 49°20' = 180° - 88°00' = 92°00'$$

$$\frac{c_1}{\sin C_1} = \frac{a}{\sin A} \Rightarrow \frac{c_1}{\sin 92°00'} = \frac{9.72}{\sin 38°40'} \Rightarrow c_1 = \frac{9.72 \sin 92°00'}{\sin 38°40'} \approx 15.5 \text{ km}$$

AB_2C_2:

$$C_2 = 180° - A - B_2 = 180° - 38°40' - 130°40' = 10°40'$$

$$\frac{c_2}{\sin C_2} = \frac{a}{\sin A} \Rightarrow \frac{c_2}{\sin 10°40'} = \frac{9.72}{\sin 38°40'} \Rightarrow c_2 = \frac{9.72 \sin 10°40'}{\sin 38°40'} \approx 2.88 \text{ km}$$

39. $B = 39.68°$, $a = 29.81$ m, $b = 23.76$ m

$$\frac{\sin A}{a} = \frac{\sin B}{b} \Rightarrow \frac{\sin A}{29.81} = \frac{\sin 39.68°}{23.76} \Rightarrow \sin A = \frac{29.81 \sin 39.68°}{23.76} \approx .80108002$$

There are two angles A between $0°$ and $180°$ that satisfy the condition. Since $\sin A \approx .80108002$, to the nearest hundredth value of A is $A_1 = 53.23°$. Supplementary angles have the same sine value, so another possible value of A is $A_2 = 180° - 53.23° = 126.77°$. This is a valid angle measure for this triangle since $B + A_2 = 39.68° + 126.77° = 166.45° < 180°$.

Solving separately for triangles A_1BC_1 and A_2BC_2 we have the following.

A_1BC_1:

$$C_1 = 180° - A_1 - B = 180° - 53.23° - 39.68° = 87.09°$$

$$\frac{c_1}{\sin C_1} = \frac{b}{\sin B} \Rightarrow \frac{c_1}{\sin 87.09°} = \frac{23.76}{\sin 39.68°} \Rightarrow c_1 = \frac{23.76 \sin 87.09°}{\sin 39.68°} \approx 37.16 \text{ m}$$

A_2BC_2:

$$C_2 = 180° - A_2 - B = 180° - 126.77° - 39.68° = 13.55°$$

$$\frac{c_2}{\sin C_2} = \frac{b}{\sin B} \Rightarrow \frac{c_2}{\sin 13.55°} = \frac{23.76}{\sin 39.68°} \Rightarrow c_1 = \frac{23.76 \sin 13.55°}{\sin 39.68°} \approx 8.719 \text{ m}$$

41. $a=\sqrt{5}, c=2\sqrt{5},\ A=30°$

$$\frac{\sin C}{c}=\frac{\sin A}{a}\Rightarrow\frac{\sin C}{2\sqrt{5}}=\frac{\sin 30°}{\sqrt{5}}\Rightarrow\sin C=\frac{2\sqrt{5}\sin 30°}{\sqrt{5}}=\frac{2\sqrt{5}\cdot\frac{1}{2}}{\sqrt{5}}=\frac{\sqrt{5}}{\sqrt{5}}=1\Rightarrow C=90°$$

This is a right triangle.

43. Answers will vary.

45. Let $A=38°\,50'$, $a=21.9$, $b=78.3$.

$$\frac{\sin B}{b}=\frac{\sin A}{a}\Rightarrow\frac{\sin B}{78.3}=\frac{\sin 38°\,50'}{21.9}\Rightarrow\sin B=\frac{78.3\sin 38°\,50'}{21.9}\approx 2.2419439$$

Since $\sin B>1$ is impossible, no such piece of property exists.

47. $B=112°10';\ C=15°20';\ BC=354$ m

$$A=180°-B-C$$
$$A=180°-112°10'-15°20'$$
$$=179°60'-127°30'=52°30'$$

$$\frac{BC}{\sin A}=\frac{AB}{\sin C}$$
$$\frac{354}{\sin 52°30'}=\frac{AB}{\sin 15°20'}$$
$$AB=\frac{354\sin 15°20'}{\sin 52°30'}$$
$$AB\approx 118\text{ m}$$

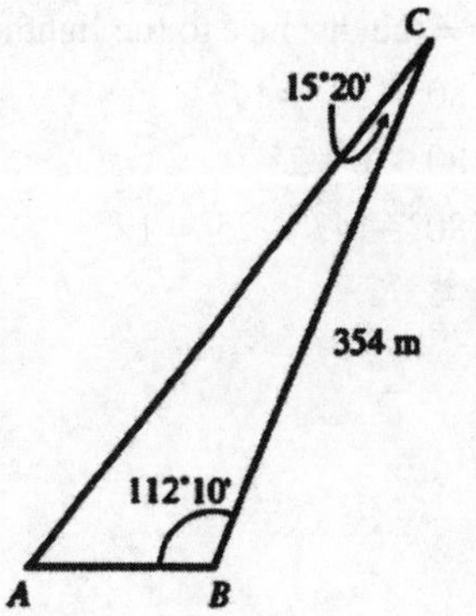

49. Let d = the distance the ship traveled between the two observations;
L = the location of the lighthouse.

$$L=180°-38.8°-44.2$$
$$=97.0°$$

$$\frac{d}{\sin 97°}=\frac{12.5}{\sin 44.2°}$$
$$d=\frac{12.5\sin 97°}{\sin 44.2°}$$
$$d\approx 17.8\text{ km}$$

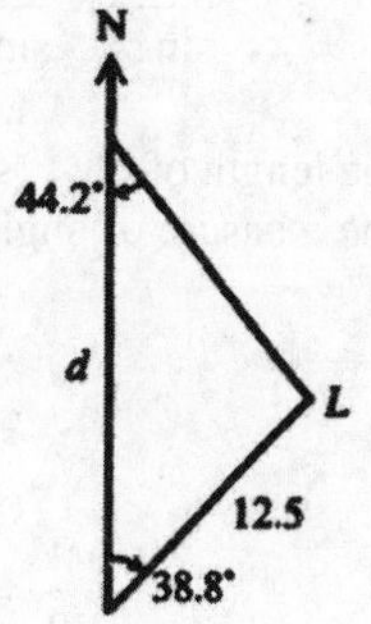

51. $$\frac{x}{\sin 54.8°}=\frac{12.0}{\sin 70.4°}\Rightarrow x=\frac{12.0\sin 54.8°}{\sin 70.4°}\approx 10.4\text{ in.}$$

53. We cannot find θ directly because the length of the side opposite angle θ is not given. Redraw the triangle shown in the figure and label the third angle as α.

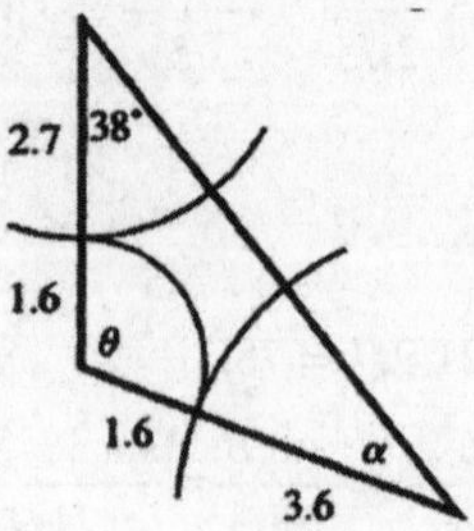

$$\frac{\sin\alpha}{1.6+2.7}=\frac{\sin 38°}{1.6+3.6}$$
$$\frac{\sin\alpha}{4.3}=\frac{\sin 38°}{5.2}$$
$$\sin\alpha=\frac{4.3\sin 38°}{5.2}\approx .50910468$$
$$\alpha\approx\sin^{-1}(.50910468)\approx 31°$$

Thus, $\theta=180°-38°-\alpha\approx 180°-38°-31°=111°$.

55. Let x = the distance to the lighthouse at bearing N 37° E;
y = the distance to the lighthouse at bearing N 25° E.

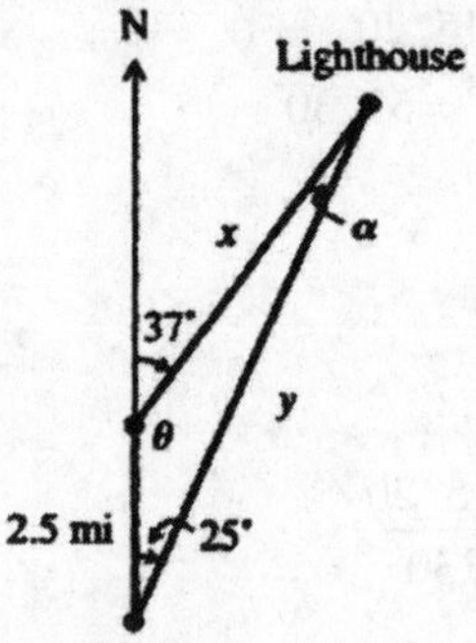

$$\theta=180°-37°=143°$$
$$\alpha=180°-\theta-25°$$
$$=180°-143°-25°=12°$$

$$\frac{2.5}{\sin\alpha}=\frac{x}{\sin 25°}\Rightarrow x=\frac{2.5\sin 25°}{\sin 12°}\approx 5.1\text{ mi}$$
$$\frac{2.5}{\sin\alpha}=\frac{y}{\sin\theta}\Rightarrow\frac{2.5}{\sin 12°}=\frac{y}{\sin 143°}\Rightarrow y=\frac{2.5\sin 143°}{\sin 12°}\approx 7.2\text{ mi}$$

57. Let p be the length of CW. (side opposite to angle P);
W is the measure of angle PWC.

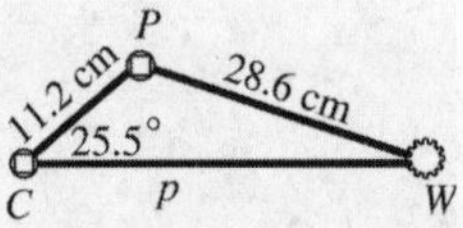

$$\frac{\sin W}{11.2}=\frac{\sin 25.5°}{28.6}\Rightarrow\sin W=\frac{11.2\sin 25.5°}{28.6}\approx .16859176$$
$$W=\sin^{-1}(.16859176)\approx 9.7°\text{ and }B\approx 180°-25.5°-9.7°=144.8°$$
$$\frac{p}{\sin 144.8°}=\frac{28.6}{\sin 25.5°}\Rightarrow p=\frac{28.6\sin 144.8°}{\sin 25.5°}\approx 38.3$$

The distance between the wrist pin (W) and the connecting rod (C) is 38.3 cm.

59. Let x be the distance between the rocket and T_1.
Refer to the diagram for the labeling of the angles.

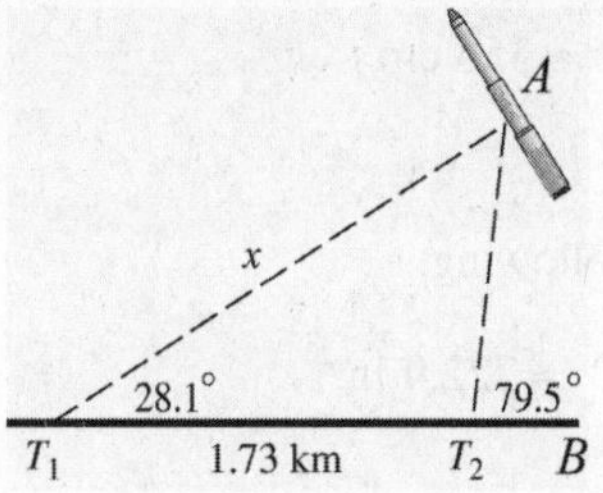

Since angle AT_2B and AT_2T_1 form a line, angle AT_2T_1 is the supplement of angle AT_2B. Thus, the measure of angle AT_2T_1 is the following.

$$180° - 79.5° = 100.5°$$

Since the angles of a triangle must add up to 180°, the measure of angle T_1AT_2 is the following.

$$180° - 100.5° - 28.1° = 51.4°$$

$$\frac{x}{\sin 100.5°} = \frac{1.73}{\sin 51.4°} \Rightarrow x = \frac{1.73 \sin 100.5°}{\sin 51.4°} \approx 2.18 \text{ km}$$

The distance from T_1 to the rocket is 2.18 km.

61. Refer to the diagram for the labeling of sides and other angles.

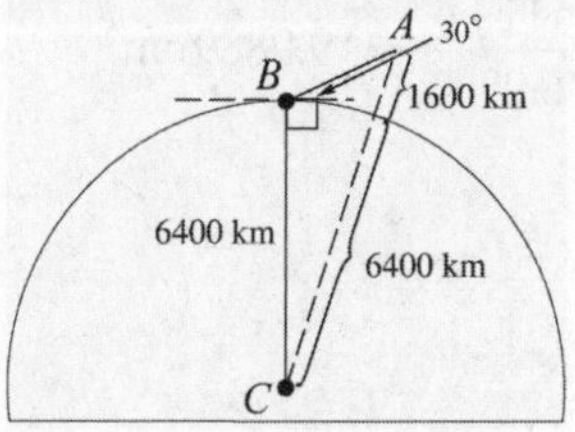

The measure of angle ABC is $90° + 30° = 120°$. The length of BC is 6400 km and the length of AC is 6400 km + 1600 km = 8000 km.

We need to first find the measure of angle BAC.

$$\frac{\sin BAC}{6400} = \frac{\sin 120°}{8000} \Rightarrow \sin BAC = \frac{6400 \sin 120°}{8000} = \frac{4}{5} \cdot \frac{\sqrt{3}}{2} = \frac{2\sqrt{3}}{5} \Rightarrow BAC = \sin^{-1} \frac{2\sqrt{3}}{5} \approx 43.85°$$

Since the angles of a triangle must add up to 180°, the measure of angle BCA is $180° - 120° - 43.85° = 16.15°$.

Since it takes 2 hr (120 min) to make a complete cycle, we can find out how many minutes before noon the satellite is located by solving the following proportion.

$$\frac{x}{120 \text{ min}} = \frac{16.15°}{360°} \Rightarrow x = \frac{120 \cdot 16.15}{360} \approx 5.38 \text{ min}$$

Thus, the satellite will pass through the beam of the antenna at approximately 11:55 A.M.

63. To find the area of the triangle, use $\mathcal{A} = \frac{1}{2}bh$, with $b = 2$ and $h = \sqrt{3}$.

$$\mathcal{A} = \frac{1}{2}(2)(\sqrt{3}) = \sqrt{3}.$$

Now use $\mathcal{A} = \frac{1}{2}ab \sin C$, with $a = 2$, $b = 2$, and $C = 60°$.

$$\mathcal{A} = \frac{1}{2}(2)(2)\sin 60° = \frac{1}{2}(2)(2)\left(\frac{\sqrt{3}}{2}\right) = \sqrt{3}.$$

65. $A = 42.5°$, $b = 13.6$ m, $c = 10.1$ m
Angle A is included between sides b and c. Thus, we have the following.

$$\mathcal{A} = \frac{1}{2}bc \sin A = \frac{1}{2}(13.6)(10.1)\sin 42.5° \approx 46.4 \text{ m}^2$$

67. $B = 124.5°$, $a = 30.4$ cm, $c = 28.4$ cm
Angle B is included between sides a and c. Thus, we have the following.

$$\mathcal{A} = \frac{1}{2}ac\sin B = \frac{1}{2}(30.4)(28.4)\sin 124.5° \approx 356 \text{ cm}^2$$

69. $A = 56.80°$, $b = 32.67$ in., $c = 52.89$ in.
Angle A is included between sides b and c. Thus, we have the following.

$$\mathcal{A} = \frac{1}{2}bc\sin A = \frac{1}{2}(32.67)(52.89)\sin 56.80° \approx 722.9 \text{ in.}^2$$

71. $A = 30.50°$, $b = 13.00$ cm, $C = 112.60°$
In order to use the area formula, we need to find either a or c.
$B = 180° - A - C \Rightarrow B = 180° - 30.50° - 112.60° = 36.90°$

Finding a: $\frac{a}{\sin A} = \frac{b}{\sin B} \Rightarrow \frac{a}{\sin 30.5°} = \frac{13.00}{\sin 36.90°} \Rightarrow a = \frac{13.00\sin 30.5°}{\sin 36.90°} \approx 10.9890\text{cm}$

$\mathcal{A} = \frac{1}{2}ab\sin C = \frac{1}{2}(10.9890)(13.00)\sin 112.60° \approx 65.94 \text{ cm}^2$

Finding c: $\frac{b}{\sin B} = \frac{c}{\sin C} \Rightarrow \frac{13.00}{\sin 36.9°} = \frac{c}{\sin 112.6°} \Rightarrow c = \frac{13.00\sin 112.6°}{\sin 36.9°} \approx 19.9889\text{cm}$

$\mathcal{A} = \frac{1}{2}bc\sin A = \frac{1}{2}(19.9889)(13.00)\sin 30.5° \approx 65.94 \text{ cm}^2$

73. $\mathcal{A} = \frac{1}{2}ab\sin C = \frac{1}{2}(16.1)(15.2)\sin 125° \approx 100 \text{ m}^2$

75. Since $\frac{a}{\sin A} = \frac{b}{\sin B} = \frac{c}{\sin C} = 2r$ and $r = \frac{1}{2}$ (since the diameter is 1), we have the following.

$$\frac{a}{\sin A} = \frac{b}{\sin B} = \frac{c}{\sin C} = 2\left(\frac{1}{2}\right) = 1$$

Then, $a = \sin A$, $b = \sin B$, and $c = \sin C$.

Section 8.2: The Law of Cosines

Connections (page 707)

$P(2,5), Q(-1,3)$, and $R(4,0)$

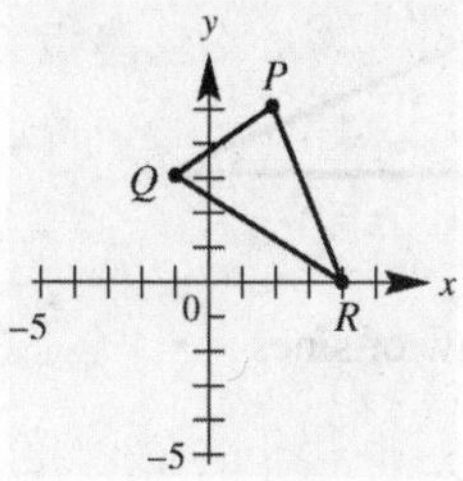

1. $A = \frac{1}{2}\left|(x_1y_2 - y_1x_2 + x_2y_3 - y_2x_3 + x_3y_1 - y_3x_1)\right|$

$= \frac{1}{2}\left|(2\cdot 3 - 5(-1) + (-1)\cdot 0 - 3\cdot 4 + 4\cdot 5 - 0\cdot 2)\right|$

$= \frac{1}{2}\left|(6+5-12+20)\right| = \frac{1}{2}\left|19\right| = \frac{1}{2}\cdot 19 = 9.5$ sq units

2. distance between $P(2,5)$ and $Q(-1,3)$:

$$a = \sqrt{[2-(-1)]^2 + (5-3)^2} = \sqrt{3^2 + 2^2} = \sqrt{9+4} = \sqrt{13} \approx 3.60555$$

distance between $P(2,5)$ and $R(4,0)$:

$$b = \sqrt{(2-4)^2 + (5-0)^2} = \sqrt{(-2)^2 + 5^2} = \sqrt{4+25} = \sqrt{29} \approx 5.38516$$

distance between $Q(-1,3)$ and $R(4,0)$:

$$c = \sqrt{(-1-4)^2 + (3-0)^2} = \sqrt{(-5)^2 + 3^2} = \sqrt{25+9} = \sqrt{34} \approx 5.83095$$

$$s = \frac{1}{2}(a+b+c) = \frac{1}{2}\left(\sqrt{13}+\sqrt{29}+\sqrt{34}\right) = \frac{\sqrt{13}+\sqrt{29}+\sqrt{34}}{2} \approx 7.41083$$

$$A = \sqrt{s(s-a)(s-b)(s-c)} \approx \sqrt{(7.41083)(3.80528)(2.02567)(1.57988)} \approx 9.5 \text{ sq units}$$

or more precisely,

$$A = \sqrt{s(s-a)(s-b)(s-c)}$$

$$= \sqrt{\frac{\sqrt{13}+\sqrt{29}+\sqrt{34}}{2}\left(\frac{\sqrt{13}+\sqrt{29}+\sqrt{34}}{2} - \sqrt{13}\right)\left(\frac{\sqrt{13}+\sqrt{29}+\sqrt{34}}{2} - \sqrt{29}\right)\left(\frac{\sqrt{13}+\sqrt{29}+\sqrt{34}}{2} - \sqrt{34}\right)}$$

$$= \frac{1}{4}\sqrt{\left(\sqrt{13}+\sqrt{29}+\sqrt{34}\right)\left(\sqrt{13}+\sqrt{29}+\sqrt{34}-2\sqrt{13}\right)\left(\sqrt{13}+\sqrt{29}+\sqrt{34}-2\sqrt{29}\right)\left(\sqrt{13}+\sqrt{29}+\sqrt{34}-2\sqrt{34}\right)}$$

$$= \frac{1}{4}\sqrt{\left(\sqrt{13}+\sqrt{29}+\sqrt{34}\right)\left(\sqrt{29}+\sqrt{34}-\sqrt{13}\right)\left(\sqrt{13}+\sqrt{34}-\sqrt{29}\right)\left(\sqrt{13}+\sqrt{29}-\sqrt{34}\right)}$$

$$= \frac{1}{4}\sqrt{\left[\left(\sqrt{13}+\sqrt{29}+\sqrt{34}\right)\left(\sqrt{29}+\sqrt{34}-\sqrt{13}\right)\right]\left[\left(\sqrt{13}+\sqrt{34}-\sqrt{29}\right)\left(\sqrt{13}+\sqrt{29}-\sqrt{34}\right)\right]}$$

$$= \frac{1}{4}\sqrt{\left(2\sqrt{986}+50\right)\left(2\sqrt{986}-50\right)} = \frac{1}{4}\sqrt{\left(2\sqrt{986}\right)^2 - 50^2} = \frac{1}{4}\sqrt{3944-2500} = \frac{1}{4}\sqrt{1444} = \frac{1}{4}\cdot 38 = 9.5 \text{ sq units}$$

3. By the law of cosines, $c^2 = a^2 + b^2 - 2ab\cos C \Rightarrow 2ab\cos C = a^2 + b^2 - c^2 \Rightarrow \cos C = \frac{a^2+b^2-c^2}{2ab}$.

Using the lengths from part 2, we have the following.

$$\cos C = \frac{13+29-34}{2\sqrt{13}\cdot\sqrt{29}} \approx 0.20601 \Rightarrow C \approx 78.1°$$

$$A = \frac{1}{2}ab\sin C = \frac{1}{2}\sqrt{13}\cdot\sqrt{29}\sin 78.1° \approx 9.5 \text{ sq units}$$

Exercises

1. a, b, and C

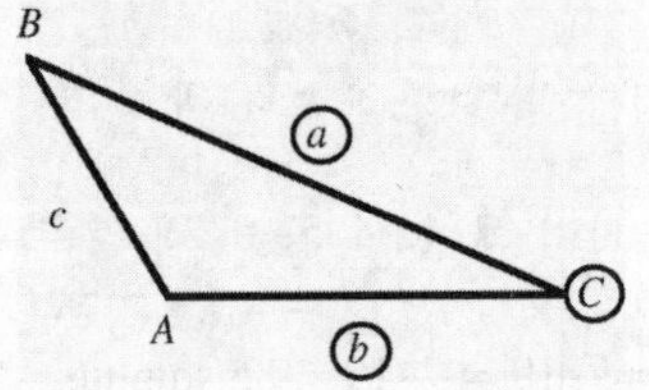

(a) SAS **(b)** law of cosines

3. a, b, and A

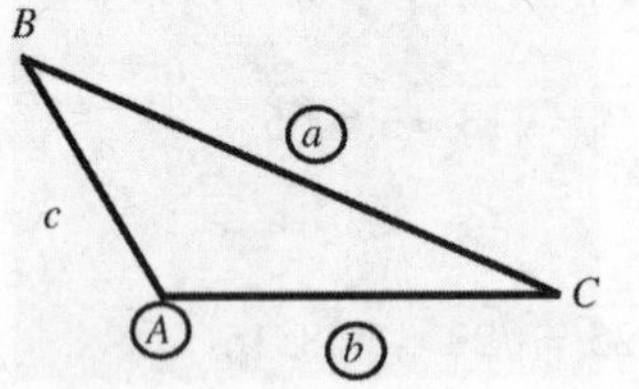

(a) SSA **(b)** law of sines

5. A, B, and c

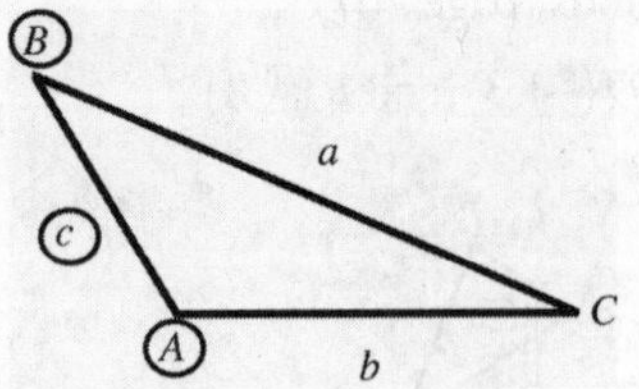

(a) ASA **(b)** law of sines

7. a, B, and C

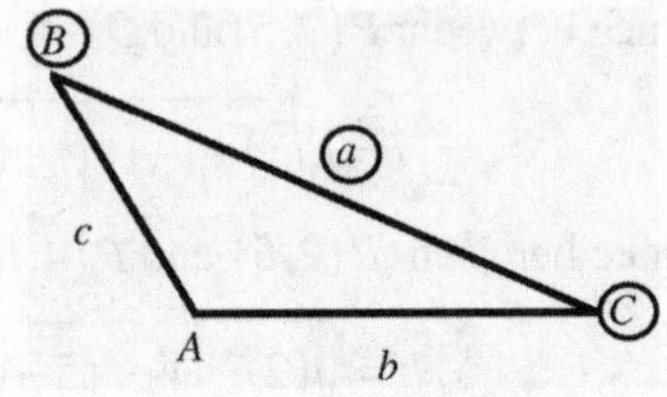

(a) ASA **(b)** law of sines

9. $a^2 = 3^2 + 8^2 - 2(3)(8)\cos 60° = 9 + 64 - 48\left(\frac{1}{2}\right) = 73 - 24 = 49 \Rightarrow a = \sqrt{49} = 7$

11. $\cos\theta = \frac{b^2 + c^2 - a^2}{2bc} = \frac{1^2 + \left(\sqrt{3}\right)^2 - 1^2}{2(1)\left(\sqrt{3}\right)} = \frac{1+3-1}{2\sqrt{3}} = \frac{3}{2\sqrt{3}} \cdot \frac{\sqrt{3}}{\sqrt{3}} = \frac{\sqrt{3}}{2} \Rightarrow \theta = 30°$

13. $A = 61°,\ b = 4,\ c = 6$

Start by finding a with the law of cosines.

$a^2 = b^2 + c^2 - 2bc\cos A \Rightarrow a^2 = 4^2 + 6^2 - 2(4)(6)\cos 61° \approx 28.729 \Rightarrow a \approx 5.36$ (will be rounded as 5.4)

Of the remaining angles B and C, B must be smaller since it is opposite the shorter of the two sides b and c. Therefore, B cannot be obtuse.

$$\frac{\sin A}{a} = \frac{\sin B}{b} \Rightarrow \frac{\sin 61°}{5.36} = \frac{\sin B}{4} \Rightarrow \sin B = \frac{4\sin 61°}{5.36} \approx .65270127 \Rightarrow B \approx 40.7°$$

Thus, $C = 180° - 61° - 40.7° = 78.3°$.

15. $a = 4,\ b = 10,\ c = 8$

We can use the law of cosines to solve for any angle of the triangle. We solve for B, the largest angle. We will know that B is obtuse if $\cos B < 0$.

$$b^2 = a^2 + c^2 - 2ac\cos B \Rightarrow \cos B = \frac{a^2 + c^2 - b^2}{2ac} \Rightarrow \cos B = \frac{4^2 + 8^2 - 10^2}{2(4)(8)} = \frac{-20}{64} = -\frac{5}{16} \Rightarrow B \approx 108.2°$$

We can now use the law of sines or the law of cosines to solve for either A or C. Using the law of cosines to solve for A, we have the following.

$$a^2 = b^2 + c^2 - 2bc\cos A \Rightarrow \cos A = \frac{b^2 + c^2 - a^2}{2bc} \Rightarrow \cos A = \frac{10^2 + 8^2 - 4^2}{2(10)(8)} = \frac{148}{160} = \frac{37}{40} \Rightarrow A \approx 22.3°$$

Thus, $C = 180° - 108.2° - 22.3° = 49.5°$.

17. $a=5, b=7, c=9$

We can use the law of cosines to solve for any angle of the triangle. We solve for C, the largest angle. We will know that C is obtuse if $\cos C<0$.

$$c^2=a^2+b^2-2ab\cos C \Rightarrow \cos C=\frac{a^2+b^2-c^2}{2ab} \Rightarrow \cos C=\frac{5^2+7^2-9^2}{2(5)(7)}=\frac{-7}{70}=-\frac{1}{10} \Rightarrow C\approx 95.7°$$

We can now use the law of sines or the law of cosines to solve for either A or B. Using the law of sines to solve for A, we have the following.

$$\frac{\sin A}{a}=\frac{\sin C}{C} \Rightarrow \frac{\sin A}{5}=\frac{\sin 95.7°}{9} \Rightarrow \sin A=\frac{5\sin 95.7°}{9} \approx .55280865 \Rightarrow A\approx 33.6°$$

Thus, $B=180°-95.7°-33.6°=50.7°$.

19. $A=41.4°$, $b=2.78$ yd, $c=3.92$ yd

First find a.

$$a^2=b^2+c^2-2bc\cos A \Rightarrow a^2=2.78^2+3.92^2-2(2.78)(3.92)\cos 41.4° \approx 6.7460 \Rightarrow a\approx 2.597 \text{ yd}$$

(will be rounded as 2.60)

Find B next, since angle B is smaller than angle C (because $b<c$), and thus angle B must be acute.

$$\frac{\sin B}{b}=\frac{\sin A}{a} \Rightarrow \frac{\sin B}{2.78}=\frac{\sin 41.4°}{2.597} \Rightarrow \sin B=\frac{2.78\sin 41.4°}{2.597} \approx .707091182 \Rightarrow B\approx 45.1°$$

Finally, $C=180°-41.4°-45.1°=93.5°$.

21. $C=45.6°$, $b=8.94$ m, $a=7.23$ m

First find c.

$$c^2=a^2+b^2-2ab\cos C \Rightarrow c^2=7.23^2+8.94^2-2(7.23)(8.94)\cos 45.6° \approx 41.7493 \Rightarrow c\approx 6.461 \text{ m}$$

(will be rounded as 6.46)

Find A next, since angle A is smaller than angle B (because $a<b$), and thus angle A must be acute.

$$\frac{\sin A}{a}=\frac{\sin C}{c} \Rightarrow \frac{\sin A}{7.23}=\frac{\sin 45.6°}{6.461} \Rightarrow \sin A=\frac{7.23\sin 45.6°}{6.461} \approx .79951052 \Rightarrow A\approx 53.1°$$

Finally, $B=180°-53.1°-45.6°=81.3°$.

23. $a=9.3$ cm, $b=5.7$ cm, $c=8.2$ cm

We can use the law of cosines to solve for any of angle of the triangle. We solve for A, the largest angle. We will know that A is obtuse if $\cos A<0$.

$$a^2=b^2+c^2-2bc\cos A \Rightarrow \cos A=\frac{5.7^2+8.2^2-9.3^2}{2(5.7)(8.2)} \approx .14163457 \Rightarrow A\approx 82°$$

Find B next, since angle B is smaller than angle C (because $b<c$), and thus angle B must be acute.

$$\frac{\sin B}{b}=\frac{\sin A}{a} \Rightarrow \frac{\sin B}{5.7}=\frac{\sin 82°}{9.3} \Rightarrow \sin B=\frac{5.7\sin 82°}{9.3} \approx .60693849 \Rightarrow B\approx 37°$$

Thus, $C=180°-82°-37°=61°$.

25. $a = 42.9$ m, $b = 37.6$ m, $c = 62.7$ m
Angle C is the largest, so find it first.

$$c^2 = a^2 + b^2 - 2ab\cos C \Rightarrow \cos C = \frac{42.9^2 + 37.6^2 - 62.7^2}{2(42.9)(37.6)} \approx -.20988940 \Rightarrow C \approx 102.1° \approx 102°10'$$

Find B next, since angle B is smaller than angle A (because $b < a$), and thus angle B must be acute.

$$\frac{\sin B}{b} = \frac{\sin C}{c} \Rightarrow \frac{\sin B}{37.6} = \frac{\sin 102.1°}{62.7} \Rightarrow \sin B = \frac{37.6 \sin 102.1°}{62.7} \approx .58635805 \Rightarrow B \approx 35.9° \approx 35°50'$$

Thus, $A = 180° - 35°50' - 102°10' = 180° - 138° = 42°00'$.

27. $AB = 1240$ ft, $AC = 876$ ft, $BC = 965$ ft
Let $AB = c$, $AC = b$, $BC = a$
Angle C is the largest, so find it first.

$$c^2 = a^2 + b^2 - 2ab\cos C \Rightarrow \cos C = \frac{965^2 + 876^2 - 1240^2}{2(965)(876)} \approx .09522855 \Rightarrow C \approx 84.5° \text{ or } 84°30'$$

Find B next, since angle B is smaller than angle A (because $b < a$), and thus angle B must be acute.

$$\frac{\sin B}{b} = \frac{\sin C}{c} \Rightarrow \frac{\sin B}{876} = \frac{\sin 84°30'}{1240} \Rightarrow \sin B = \frac{876 \sin 84°30'}{1240} \approx .70319925 \Rightarrow B \approx 44.7° \text{ or } 44°10'$$

Thus, $A = 180° - 44°40' - 84°30' = 179°60' - 129°10' = 50°50'$.

29. $A = 80°40'$ $b = 143$ cm, $c = 89.6$ cm

First find a.

$$a^2 = b^2 + c^2 - 2bc\cos A \Rightarrow a^2 = 143^2 + 89.6^2 - 2(143)(89.6)\cos 80°40' \approx 24{,}321.25 \Rightarrow a \approx 156.0 \text{ cm}$$

(will be rounded as 156)

Find C next, since angle C is smaller than angle B (because $c < b$), and thus angle C must be acute.

$$\frac{\sin C}{c} = \frac{\sin A}{a} \Rightarrow \frac{\sin C}{89.6} = \frac{\sin 80°40'}{156.0} \Rightarrow \sin C = \frac{89.6 \sin 80°40'}{156.0} \approx .56675534 \Rightarrow C \approx 34.5° = 34°30'$$

Finally, $B = 180° - 80°40' - 34°30' = 179°60' - 115°10' = 64°50'$

31. $B = 74.80°$, $a = 8.919$ in., $c = 6.427$ in.

First find b.

$$b^2 = a^2 + c^2 - 2ac\cos B \Rightarrow b^2 = 8.919^2 + 6.427^2 - 2(8.919)(6.427)\cos 74.80° \approx 90.7963 \Rightarrow b \approx 9.5287 \text{ in.}$$

(will be rounded as 9.529)

Find C next, since angle C is smaller than angle A (because $c < a$), and thus angle C must be acute.

$$\frac{\sin C}{c} = \frac{\sin B}{b} \Rightarrow \frac{\sin C}{6.427} = \frac{\sin 74.80°}{9.5287} \Rightarrow \sin C = \frac{6.427 \sin 74.80°}{9.5287} \approx .65089267 \Rightarrow C \approx 40.61°$$

Thus, $A = 180° - 74.80° - 40.61° = 64.59°$.

33. $A = 112.8°$, $b = 6.28$ m, $c = 12.2$ m
First find a.

$a^2 = b^2 + c^2 - 2bc\cos A \Rightarrow a^2 = 6.28^2 + 12.2^2 - 2(6.28)(12.2)\cos 112.8° \approx 247.658 \Rightarrow a \approx 15.74$ m (will be rounded as 15.7)

Find B next, since angle B is smaller than angle C (because $b < c$), and thus angle B must be acute.

$$\frac{\sin B}{b} = \frac{\sin A}{a} \Rightarrow \frac{\sin B}{6.28} = \frac{\sin 112.8°}{15.74} \Rightarrow \sin B = \frac{6.28 \sin 112.8°}{15.74} \approx .36780817 \Rightarrow B \approx 21.6°$$

Finally, $C = 180° - 112.8° - 21.6° = 45.6°$.

35. $a = 3.0$ ft, $b = 5.0$ ft, $c = 6.0$ ft
Angle C is the largest, so find it first.

$$c^2 = a^2 + b^2 - 2ab\cos C \Rightarrow \cos C = \frac{3.0^2 + 5.0^2 - 6.0^2}{2(3.0)(5.0)} = -\frac{2}{30} = -\frac{1}{15} \approx -.06666667 \Rightarrow C \approx 94°$$

Find A next, since angle A is smaller than angle B (because $a < b$), and thus angle A must be acute.

$$\frac{\sin A}{a} = \frac{\sin C}{c} \Rightarrow \frac{\sin A}{3} = \frac{\sin 94°}{6} \Rightarrow \sin A = \frac{3\sin 94°}{6} \approx .49878203 \Rightarrow A \approx 30°$$

Thus, $B = 180° - 30° - 94° = 56°$.

37. There are three ways to apply the law of cosines when $a = 3, b = 4$, and $c = 10$.

Solving for A: $a^2 = b^2 + c^2 - 2bc\cos A \Rightarrow \cos A = \dfrac{4^2 + 10^2 - 3^2}{2(4)(10)} = \dfrac{107}{80} = 1.3375$

Solving for B: $b^2 = a^2 + c^2 - 2ac\cos B \Rightarrow \cos B = \dfrac{3^2 + 10^2 - 4^2}{2(3)(10)} = \dfrac{93}{60} = \dfrac{31}{20} = 1.55$

Solving for C: $c^2 = a^2 + b^2 - 2ab\cos C \Rightarrow \cos C = \dfrac{3^2 + 4^2 - 10^2}{2(3)(4)} = \dfrac{-75}{24} = -\dfrac{25}{8} = -3.125$

Since the cosine of any angle of a triangle must be between –1 and 1, a triangle cannot have sides 3, 4, and 10.

39. Find AB, or c, in the following triangle.

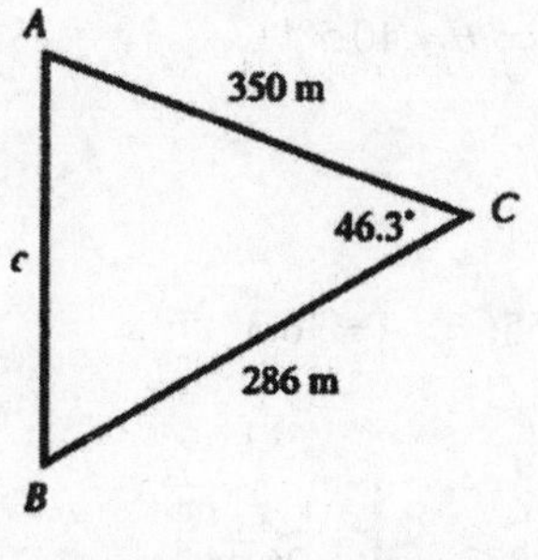

$$c^2 = a^2 + b^2 - 2ab\cos C$$
$$c^2 = 286^2 + 350^2 - 2(286)(350)\cos 46.3°$$
$$c^2 \approx 65{,}981.3$$
$$c \approx 257$$

The length of AB is 257 m.

41. Find *AC*, or *b*, in the following triangle.

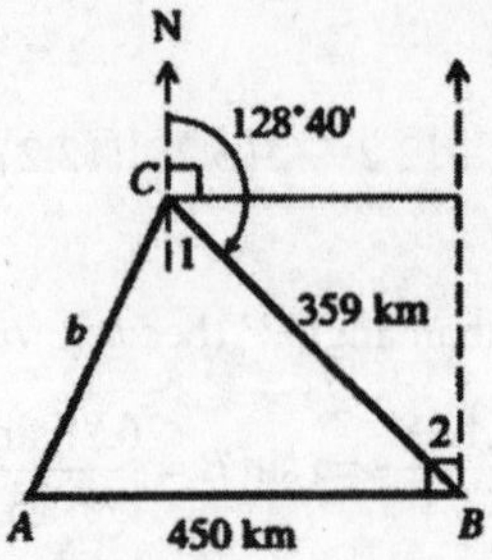

Angle 1 $= 180° - 128°\,40' = 179°60' - 128°\,40' = 51°\,20'$

Angles 1 and 2 are alternate interior angles formed when parallel lines (the north lines) are cut by a transversal, line *BC*, so angle 2 = angle 1 = $51°\,20'$.

Angle ABC = $90° -$ angle 2 $= 89°60' - 51°\,20' = 38°\,40'$.

$b^2 = a^2 + c^2 - 2ac\cos B \Rightarrow b^2 = 359^2 + 450^2 - 2(359)(450)\cos 38°\,40' \approx 79{,}106 \Rightarrow b \approx 281$ km

C is about 281 km from *A*.

43. Sketch a triangle showing the situation as follows.

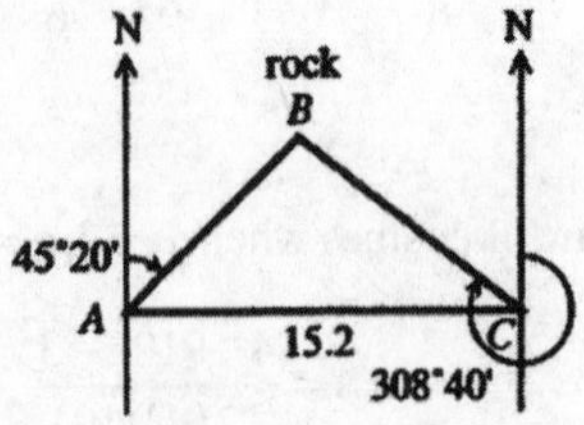

Angle $A = 90° - 45°20' = 89°60' - 45°20' = 44°40'$

Angle $C = 308°40' - 270° = 38°40'$

Angle $B = 180° - A - C = 180° - 44°40' - 38°40' = 179°60' - 83°20' = 96°\,40'$

Since we have only one side of a triangle, use the law of sines to find $BC = a$.

$$\frac{a}{\sin A} = \frac{b}{\sin B} \Rightarrow \frac{a}{\sin 44°\,40'} = \frac{15.2}{\sin 96°\,40'} \Rightarrow a = \frac{15.2\sin 44°\,40'}{\sin 96°\,40'} \approx 10.8$$

The distance between the ship and the rock is 10.8 miles.

45. Use the law of cosines to find the angle, θ.

$$\cos\theta = \frac{20^2 + 16^2 - 13^2}{2(20)(16)} = \frac{487}{640} \approx .76093750 \Rightarrow \theta \approx 40.5°$$

47. Let *A* = the angle between the beam and the 45-ft cable.

$$\cos A = \frac{45^2 + 90^2 - 60^2}{2(45)(90)} = \frac{6525}{8100} = \frac{29}{36} \approx .80555556 \Rightarrow A \approx 36.3°$$

Let *B* = the angle between the beam and the 60-ft cable.

$$\cos B = \frac{90^2 + 60^2 - 45^2}{2(90)(60)} = \frac{9675}{10{,}800} = \frac{43}{48} \approx .89583333 \Rightarrow B \approx 26.4°$$

49. Let A = home plate; B = first base; C = second base; D = third base; P = pitcher's rubber.
Draw AC through P, draw PB and PD.

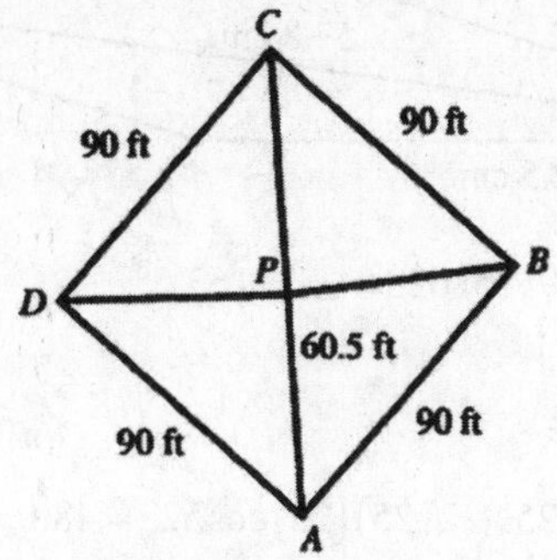

In triangle ABC, angle $B = 90°$, angle A = angle $C = 45°$

$$AC = \sqrt{90^2 + 90^2} = \sqrt{2 \cdot 90^2} = 90\sqrt{2} \text{ and } PC = 90\sqrt{2} - 60.5 \approx 66.8 \text{ ft}$$

In triangle APB, angle $A = 45°$.

$$PB^2 = AP^2 + AB^2 - 2(AP)(AB)\cos A$$
$$PB^2 = 60.5^2 + 90^2 - 2(60.5)(90)\cos 45°$$
$$PB^2 \approx 4059.86$$
$$PB \approx 63.7 \text{ ft}$$

Since triangles APB and APD are congruent, $PB = PD = 63.7$ ft.
The distance to second base is 66.8 ft and the distance to both first and third base is 63.7 ft.

51. Find the distance of the ship from point A.

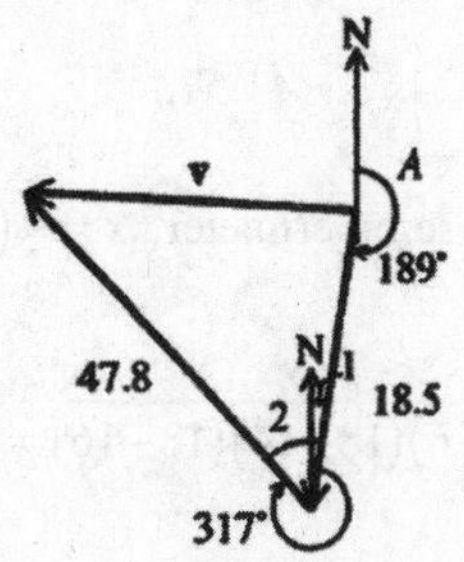

Angle 1 = 189° – 180° = 9°
Angle 2 = 360° – 317° = 43°
Angle 1 + Angle 2 = 9° + 43° = 52°
Use the law of cosines to find v.

$$v^2 = 47.8^2 + 18.5^2 - 2(47.8)(18.5)\cos 52° \approx 1538.23 \Rightarrow v \approx 39.2 \text{ km}$$

53. $\cos A = \dfrac{17^2 + 21^2 - 9^2}{2(17)(21)} = \dfrac{649}{714} \approx .90896359 \Rightarrow A \approx 25°$

Thus, the bearing of B from is $325° + 25° = 350°$.

55. Let c = the length of the property line that cannot be directly measured.
Using the law of cosines, we have the following.

$c^2 = 14.0^2 + 13.0^2 - 2(14.0)(13.0)\cos 70° \approx 240.5 \Rightarrow c \approx 15.5$ ft (rounded to three significant digits)

The length of the property line is approximately 18.0 + 15.5 + 14.0 = 47.5 feet

57. Using the law of cosines we can solve for the measure of angle *A*.

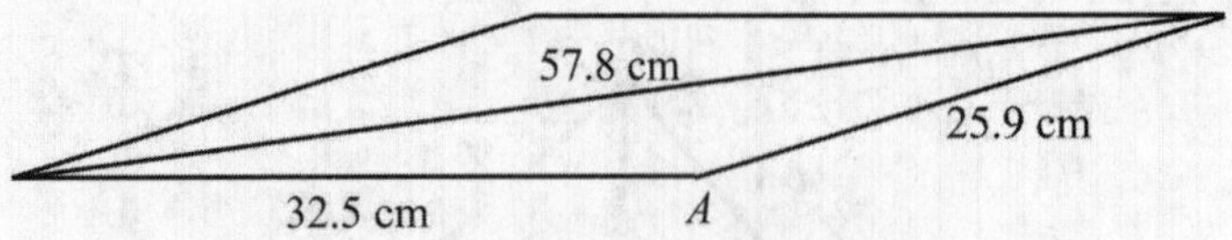

$$\cos A = \frac{25.9^2 + 32.5^2 - 57.8^2}{2(25.9)(32.5)} \approx -.95858628 \Rightarrow A \approx 163.5°$$

59. Find *x* using the law of cosines.

$$x^2 = 25^2 + 25^2 - 2(25)(25)\cos 52° \approx 480 \Rightarrow x \approx 22 \text{ ft}$$

61. Let *a* be the length of the segment from (0, 0) to (6, 8). Use the distance formula.

$$a = \sqrt{(6-0)^2 + (8-0)^2} = \sqrt{6^2 + 8^2} = \sqrt{36+64} = \sqrt{100} = 10$$

Let *b* be the length of the segment from (0, 0) to (4, 3).

$$b = \sqrt{(4-0)^2 + (3-0)^2} = \sqrt{4^2 + 3^2} = \sqrt{16+9} = \sqrt{25} = 5$$

Let *c* be the length of the segment from (4, 3) to (6, 8).

$$c = \sqrt{(6-4)^2 + (8-3)^2} = \sqrt{2^2 + 5^2} = \sqrt{4+25} = \sqrt{29}$$

$$\cos\theta = \frac{a^2 + b^2 - c^2}{2ab} \Rightarrow \cos\theta = \frac{10^2 + 5^2 - \left(\sqrt{29}\right)^2}{2(10)(5)} = \frac{100+25-29}{100} = .96 \Rightarrow \theta \approx 16.26°$$

63. Using $A = \frac{1}{2}bh \Rightarrow A = \frac{1}{2}(16)\left(3\sqrt{3}\right) = 24\sqrt{3} \approx 41.57$.

To use Heron's Formula, first find the semiperimeter, $s = \frac{1}{2}(a+b+c) = \frac{1}{2}(6+14+16) = \frac{1}{2}\cdot 36 = 18$.

Now find the area of the triangle.

$$A = \sqrt{s(s-a)(s-b)(s-c)} = \sqrt{18(18-6)(18-14)(18-16)} = \sqrt{18(12)(4)(2)} = \sqrt{1728} = 24\sqrt{3} \approx 41.57$$

Both formulas give the same area.

65. $a = 12$ m, $b = 16$ m, $c = 25$ m

$$s = \frac{1}{2}(a+b+c) = \frac{1}{2}(12+16+25) = \frac{1}{2}\cdot 53 = 26.5$$

$$A = \sqrt{s(s-a)(s-b)(s-c)} = \sqrt{26.5(26.5-12)(26.5-16)(26.5-25)} = \sqrt{26.5(14.5)(10.5)(1.5)} \approx 78 \text{ m}^2$$

(rounded to two significant digits)

67. $a = 154$ cm, $b = 179$ cm, $c = 183$ cm

$$s = \frac{1}{2}(a+b+c) = \frac{1}{2}(154+179+183) = \frac{1}{2}\cdot 516 = 258$$

$$A = \sqrt{s(s-a)(s-b)(s-c)}$$

$$= \sqrt{258(258-154)(258-179)(258-183)} = \sqrt{258(104)(79)(75)} \approx 12{,}600 \text{ cm}^2$$ (rounded to three significant digits)

69. $a = 76.3$ ft, $b = 109$ ft, $c = 98.8$ ft

$$s = \frac{1}{2}(a+b+c) = \frac{1}{2}(76.3+109+98.8) = \frac{1}{2}\cdot 284.1 = 142.05$$

$$A = \sqrt{s(s-a)(s-b)(s-c)}$$

$$= \sqrt{142.05(142.05-76.3)(142.05-109)(142.05-98.8)} = \sqrt{142.05(65.75)(33.05)(43.25)} \approx 3650 \text{ ft}^2$$

(rounded to three significant digits)

71. $AB = 22.47928$ mi, $AC = 28.14276$ mi, $A = 58.56989°$

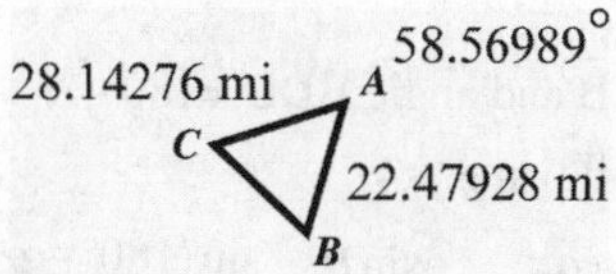

This is SAS, so use the law of cosines.

$$BC^2 = AC^2 + AB^2 - 2(AC)(AB)\cos A$$

$$BC^2 = 28.14276^2 + 22.47928^2 - 2(28.14276)(22.47928)\cos 58.56989°$$

$$BC^2 \approx 637.55393$$

$$BC \approx 25.24983$$

BC is approximately 25.24983 mi. (rounded to seven significant digits)

73. Find the area of the Bermuda Triangle using Heron's Formula.

$$s = \frac{1}{2}(a+b+c) = \frac{1}{2}(850+925+1300) = \frac{1}{2}\cdot 3075 = 1537.5$$

$$A = \sqrt{s(s-a)(s-b)(s-c)} = \sqrt{1537.5(1537.5-850)(1537.5-925)(1537.5-1300)}$$

$$= \sqrt{1537.5(687.5)(612.5)(237.5)} \approx 392{,}128.82$$

The area of the Bermuda Triangle is 392,000 mi^2. (rounded to three significant digits)

75. Perimeter: 9 + 10 + 17 = 36 feet, so the semi-perimeter is $\frac{1}{2}\cdot 36 = 18$ feet.

Use Heron's Formula to find the area.

$$A = \sqrt{s(s-a)(s-b)(s-c)} = \sqrt{18(18-9)(18-10)(18-17)} = \sqrt{18(9)(8)(1)} = \sqrt{1296} = 36 \text{ ft}$$

Since the perimeter and area both equal 36 feet, the triangle is a *perfect triangle*.

77. **(a)** Using the law of sines, we have the following.

$$\frac{\sin C}{c} = \frac{\sin A}{a} \Rightarrow \frac{\sin C}{15} = \frac{\sin 60°}{13} \Rightarrow \sin C = \frac{15\sin 60°}{13} = \frac{15}{13}\cdot\frac{\sqrt{3}}{2} \approx .99926008$$

There are two angles C between $0°$ and $180°$ that satisfy the condition. Since $\sin C \approx .99926008$, to the nearest tenth value of C is $C_1 = 87.8°$. Supplementary angles have the same sine value, so another possible value of C is $B_2 = 180° - 87.8° = 92.2°$.

(b) By the law of cosines, we have the following.

$$\cos C = \frac{a^2+b^2-c^2}{2ab} \Rightarrow \cos C = \frac{13^2+7^2-15^2}{2(13)(7)} = \frac{-7}{182} = -\frac{1}{26} \approx -.03846154 \Rightarrow C \approx 92.2°$$

(c) With the law of cosines, we are required to find the inverse cosine of a negative number; therefore; we know angle C is greater than $90°$.

79. Given point D is on side AB of triangle ABC such that CD bisects angle C, angle ACD = angle DCB.

Show that $\frac{AD}{DB}=\frac{b}{a}$.

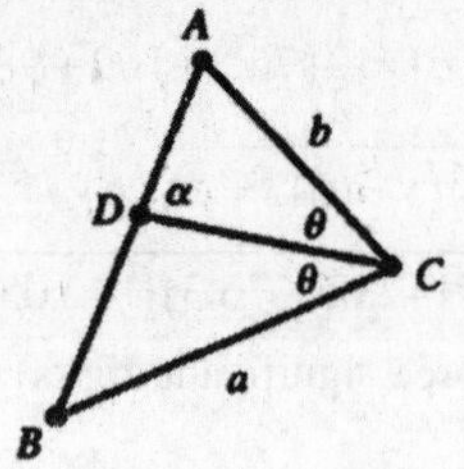

Let $\theta=$ the measure of angle ACD;

$\alpha=$ the measure of angle ADC.

Then $\theta=$ the measure of angle DCB and angle BDC $=180-\alpha$.

By the law of sines, we have the following.

$$\frac{\sin\theta}{AD}=\frac{\sin\alpha}{b}\Rightarrow\sin\theta=\frac{AD\sin\alpha}{b}\text{ and }\frac{\sin\theta}{DB}=\frac{\sin(180^\circ-\alpha)}{a}\Rightarrow\sin\theta=\frac{DB\sin(180^\circ-\alpha)}{a}$$

By substitution, we have the following.

$$\frac{AD\sin\alpha}{b}=\frac{DB\sin(180^\circ-\alpha)}{a}$$

Since $\sin\alpha=\sin(180^\circ-\alpha), \frac{AD}{b}=\frac{DB}{a}$.

Multiplying both sides by $\frac{b}{DB}$, we get $\frac{AD}{b}\cdot\frac{b}{DB}=\frac{DB}{a}\cdot\frac{b}{DB}\Rightarrow\frac{AD}{DB}=\frac{b}{a}$.

Section 8.3: Vectors, Operations, and the Dot Product

1. Equal vectors have the same magnitude and direction. Equal vectors are **m** and **p**; **n** and **r**.

3. One vector is a positive scalar multiple of another if the two vectors point in the same direction; they may have different magnitudes.

$$\mathbf{m}=1\mathbf{p};\ \mathbf{m}=2\mathbf{t};\ \mathbf{n}=1\mathbf{r};\ \mathbf{p}=2\mathbf{t}\ \text{ or }\ \mathbf{p}=1\mathbf{m};\ \mathbf{t}=\frac{1}{2}\mathbf{m};\ \mathbf{r}=1\mathbf{n};\ \mathbf{t}=\frac{1}{2}\mathbf{p}$$

5.

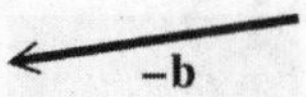

7.

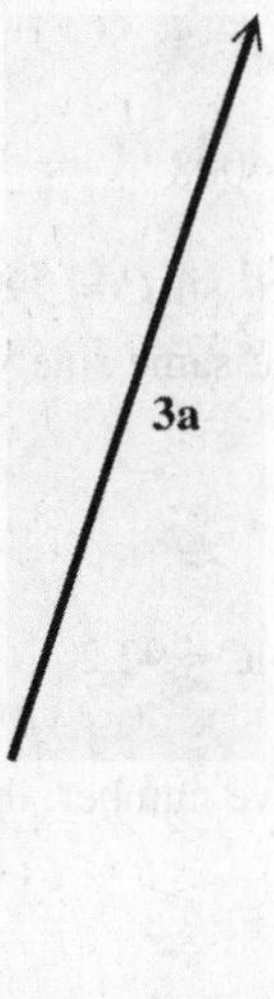

9.

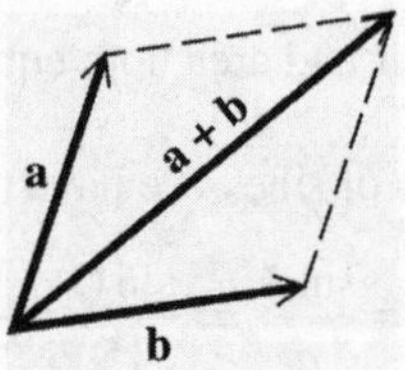

11.

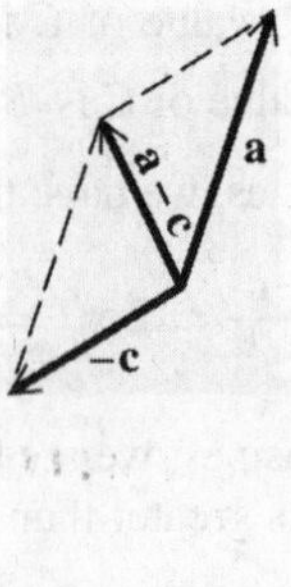

13.

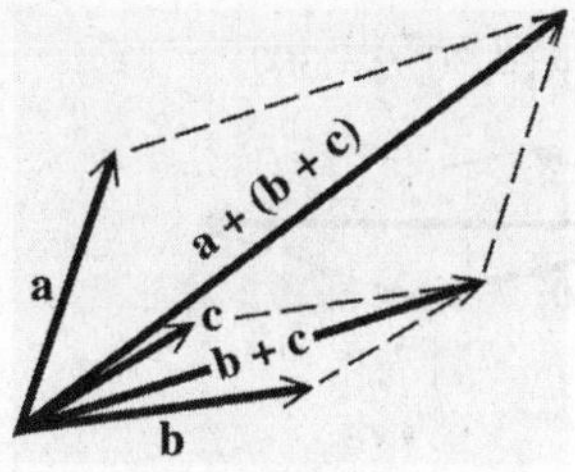

15.

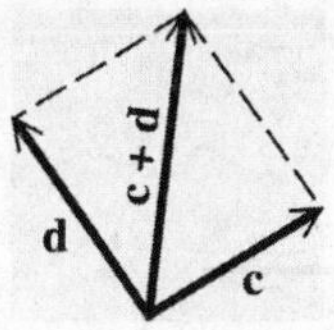

17. **a + (b + c) = (a + b) + c**

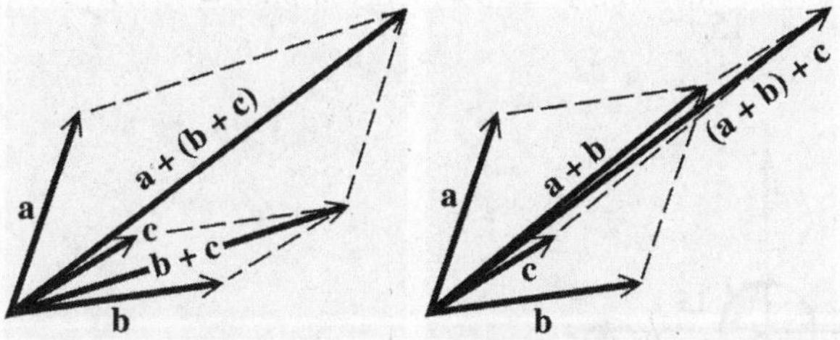

Yes, vector addition is associative.

19. Use the figure to find the components of **a** and **b**: $\mathbf{a} = \langle -8, 8 \rangle$ and $\mathbf{b} = \langle 4, 8 \rangle$.

(a) $\mathbf{a} + \mathbf{b} = \langle -8, 8 \rangle + \langle 4, 8 \rangle = \langle -8 + 4, 8 + 8 \rangle = \langle -4, 16 \rangle$

(b) $\mathbf{a} - \mathbf{b} = \langle -8, 8 \rangle - \langle 4, 8 \rangle = \langle -8 - 4, 8 - 8 \rangle = \langle -12, 0 \rangle$

(c) $-\mathbf{a} = -\langle -8, 8 \rangle = \langle 8, -8 \rangle$

21. Use the figure to find the components of **a** and **b**: $\mathbf{a} = \langle 4, 8 \rangle$ and $\mathbf{b} = \langle 4, -8 \rangle$.

(a) $\mathbf{a} + \mathbf{b} = \langle 4, 8 \rangle + \langle 4, -8 \rangle = \langle 4 + 4, 8 - 8 \rangle = \langle 8, 0 \rangle$

(b) $\mathbf{a} - \mathbf{b} = \langle 4, 8 \rangle - \langle 4, -8 \rangle = \langle 4 - 4, 8 - (-8) \rangle = \langle 0, 16 \rangle$

(c) $-\mathbf{a} = -\langle 4, 8 \rangle = \langle -4, -8 \rangle$

23. Use the figure to find the components of **a** and **b**: $\mathbf{a} = \langle -8, 4 \rangle$ and $\mathbf{b} = \langle 8, 8 \rangle$.

(a) $\mathbf{a} + \mathbf{b} = \langle -8, 4 \rangle + \langle 8, 8 \rangle = \langle -8 + 8, 4 + 8 \rangle = \langle 0, 12 \rangle$

(b) $\mathbf{a} - \mathbf{b} = \langle -8, 4 \rangle - \langle 8, 8 \rangle = \langle -8 - 8, 4 - 8 \rangle = \langle -16, -4 \rangle$

(c) $-\mathbf{a} = -\langle -8, 4 \rangle = \langle 8, -4 \rangle$

25. **(a)** $2\mathbf{a} = 2(2\mathbf{i}) = 4\mathbf{i}$

(b) $2\mathbf{a} + 3\mathbf{b} = 2(2\mathbf{i}) + 3(\mathbf{i} + \mathbf{j}) = 4\mathbf{i} + 3\mathbf{i} + 3\mathbf{j} = 7\mathbf{i} + 3\mathbf{j}$

(c) $\mathbf{b} - 3\mathbf{a} = \mathbf{i} + \mathbf{j} - 3(2\mathbf{i}) = \mathbf{i} + \mathbf{j} - 6\mathbf{i} = -5\mathbf{i} + \mathbf{j}$

27. **(a)** $2\mathbf{a} = 2\langle -1, 2 \rangle = \langle -2, 4 \rangle$

(b) $2\mathbf{a} + 3\mathbf{b} = 2\langle -1, 2 \rangle + 3\langle 3, 0 \rangle = \langle -2, 4 \rangle + \langle 9, 0 \rangle = \langle -2 + 9, 4 + 0 \rangle = \langle 7, 4 \rangle$

(c) $\mathbf{b} - 3\mathbf{a} = \langle 3, 0 \rangle - 3\langle -1, 2 \rangle = \langle 3, 0 \rangle - \langle -3, 6 \rangle = \langle 3 - (-3), 0 - 6 \rangle = \langle 6, -6 \rangle$

29. $|\mathbf{u}| = 12, |\mathbf{w}| = 20, \theta = 27°$

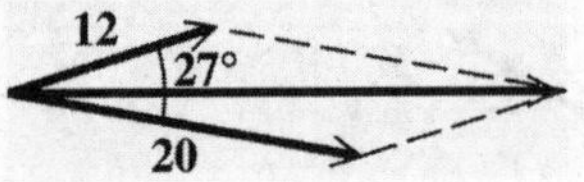

31. $|\mathbf{u}| = 20, |\mathbf{w}| = 30, \theta = 30°$

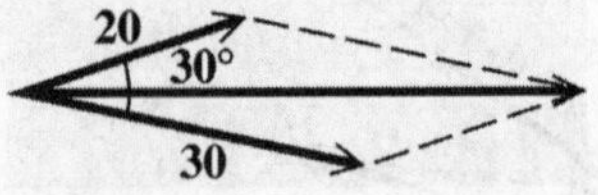

33. Magnitude: $\sqrt{15^2 + (-8)^2} = \sqrt{225 + 64} = \sqrt{289} = 17$

Angle: $\tan\theta' = \frac{b}{a} \Rightarrow \tan\theta' = \frac{-8}{15} \Rightarrow \theta' = \tan^{-1}\left(-\frac{8}{15}\right) \approx -28.1° \Rightarrow \theta = -28.1° + 360° = 331.9°$

(θ lies in quadrant IV)

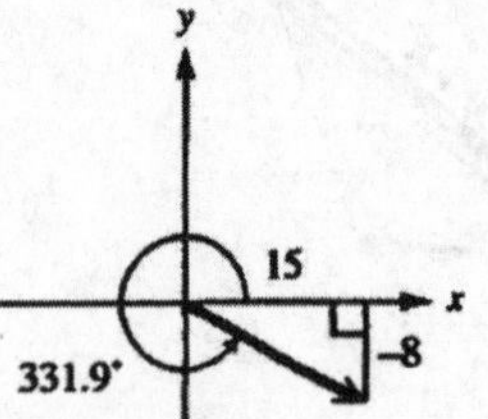

35. Magnitude: $\sqrt{(-4)^2 + (4\sqrt{3})^2} = \sqrt{16 + 48} = \sqrt{64} = 8$

Angle: $\tan\theta' = \frac{b}{a} \Rightarrow \tan\theta' = \frac{4\sqrt{3}}{-4} \Rightarrow \theta' = \tan^{-1}(-\sqrt{3}) = -60° \Rightarrow \theta = -60° + 180° = 120°$

(θ lies in quadrant II)

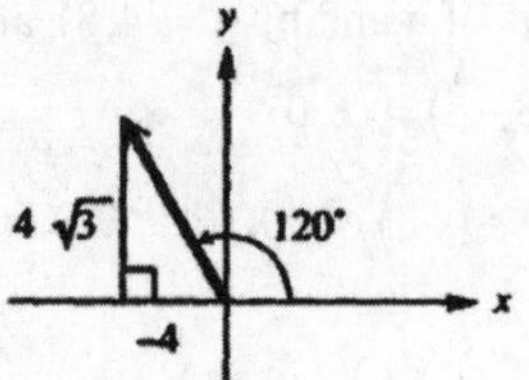

36. Magnitude: $\sqrt{(8\sqrt{2})^2 + (-8\sqrt{2})^2} = \sqrt{128 + 128} = \sqrt{256} = 16$

Angle: $\tan\theta' = \frac{b}{a} \Rightarrow \tan\theta = \frac{-8\sqrt{2}}{8\sqrt{2}} \Rightarrow \theta' = \tan^{-1}(-1) \approx -45° \Rightarrow \theta = -45° + 360° = 315°$

(θ lies in quadrant IV)

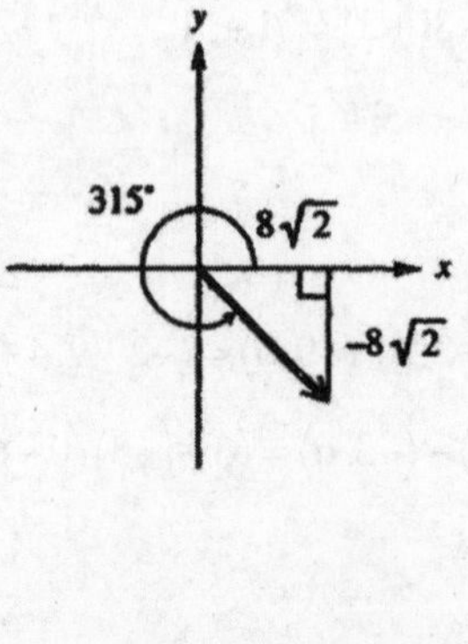

In Exercises 37 – 41, **x** is the horizontal component of **v**, and **y** is the vertical component of **v**. Thus, $|\mathbf{x}|$ is the magnitude of **x** and $|\mathbf{y}|$ is the magnitude of **y**.

37. $\alpha = 20°, |\mathbf{v}| = 50$

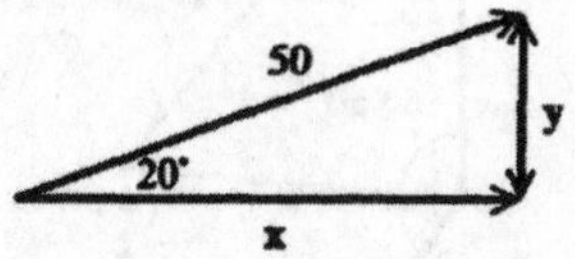

$\mathbf{x} = 50\cos 20° \approx 47 \Rightarrow |\mathbf{x}| \approx 47$

$\mathbf{y} = 50\sin 20° \approx 17 \Rightarrow |\mathbf{y}| \approx 17$

39. $\alpha = 35°50', |\mathbf{v}| = 47.8$

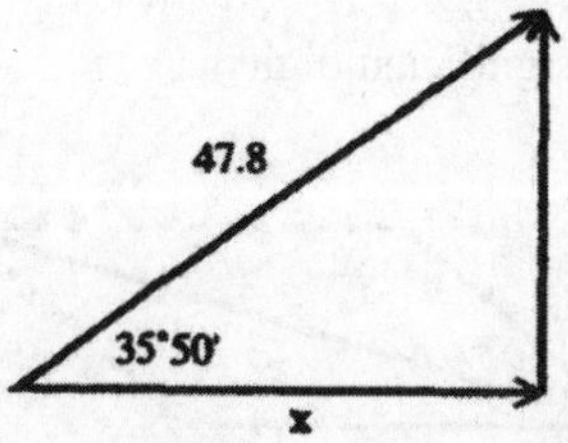

$\mathbf{x} = 47.8\cos 35°50' \approx 38.8 \Rightarrow |\mathbf{x}| \approx 38.8$

$\mathbf{y} = 47.8\sin 35°50' \approx 28.0 \Rightarrow |\mathbf{y}| \approx 28.0$

41. $\alpha = 128.5°, |\mathbf{v}| = 198$

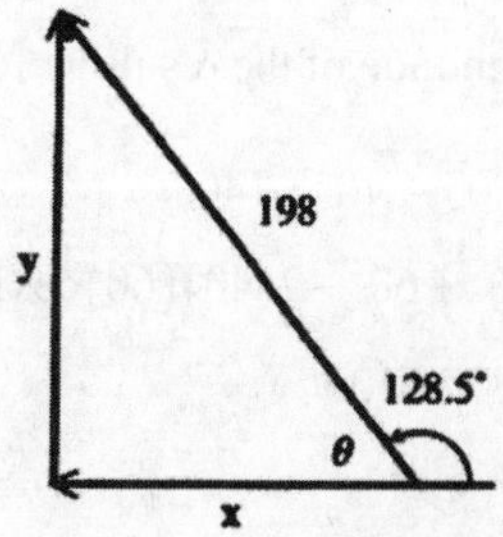

$\mathbf{x} = 198\cos 128.5° \approx -123 \Rightarrow |\mathbf{x}| \approx 123$

$\mathbf{y} = 198\sin 128.5° \approx 155 \Rightarrow |\mathbf{y}| \approx 155$

43. $\mathbf{u} = \langle a, b\rangle = \langle 5\cos(30°), 5\sin(30°)\rangle = \left\langle \frac{5\sqrt{3}}{2}, \frac{5}{2}\right\rangle$

45. $\mathbf{v} = \langle a, b\rangle = \langle 4\cos(40°), 4\sin(40°)\rangle \approx \langle 3.0642, 2.5712\rangle$

47. $\mathbf{v} = \langle a, b\rangle = \langle 5\cos(-35°), 5\sin(-35°)\rangle \approx \langle 4.0958, -2.8679\rangle$

49. Forces of 250 newtons and 450 newtons, forming an angle of 85°

$\alpha = 180° - 85° = 95°$

$|\mathbf{v}|^2 = 250^2 + 450^2 - 2(250)(450)\cos 95°$

$|\mathbf{v}|^2 \approx 284{,}610.04$

$|\mathbf{v}| \approx 533.5$

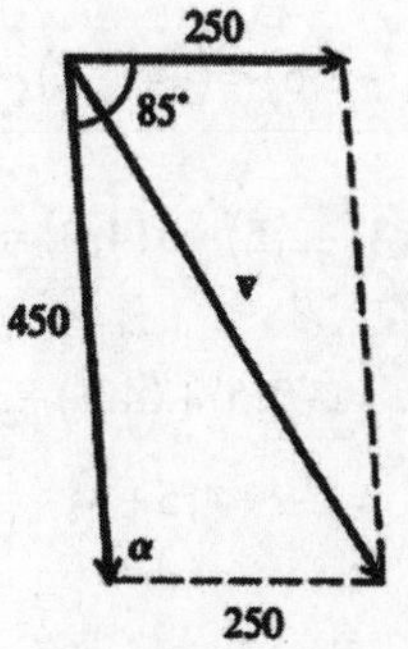

The magnitude of the resulting force is 530 newtons. (rounded to two significant digits)

51. Forces of 116 lb and 139 lb, forming an angle of 140° 50′

$\alpha = 180° - 140° 50'$

$= 179°60' - 140° 50' = 39°10'$

$|\mathbf{v}|^2 = 139^2 + 116^2 - 2(139)(116)\cos 39°10'$

$|\mathbf{v}|^2 \approx 7774.7359$

$|\mathbf{v}| \approx 88.174$

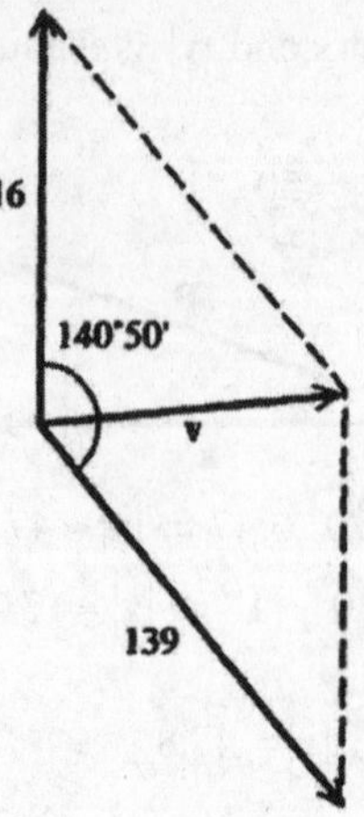

The magnitude of the resulting force is 88.2 lb. (rounded to three significant digits)

53. $\alpha = 180° - 40° = 140°$

$|\mathbf{v}|^2 = 40^2 + 60^2 - 2(40)(60)\cos 140°$

$|\mathbf{v}|^2 \approx 8877.0133$

$|\mathbf{v}| \approx 94.2$ lb

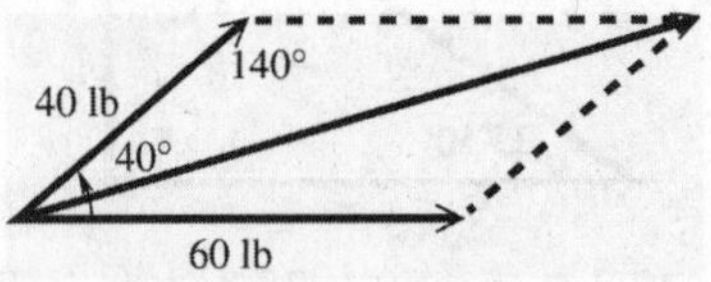

55. $\alpha = 180° - 110° = 70°$

$|\mathbf{v}|^2 = 15^2 + 25^2 - 2(15)(25)\cos 70°$

$|\mathbf{v}|^2 \approx 593.48489$

$|\mathbf{v}| \approx 24.4$ lb

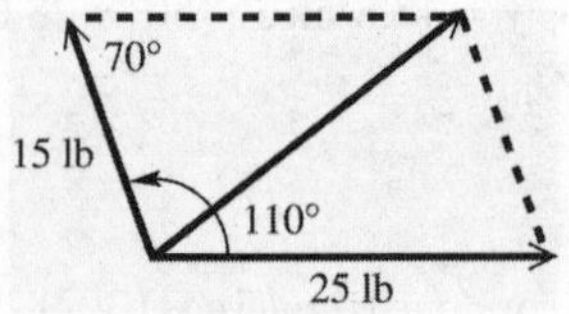

57. If $\mathbf{u} = \langle a, b\rangle$ and $\mathbf{v} = \langle c, d\rangle$, then $\mathbf{u} + \mathbf{v} = \langle a + c, b + d\rangle$.

For Exercises 59 – 65, $\mathbf{u} = \langle -2, 5\rangle$ and $\mathbf{v} = \langle 4, 3\rangle$.

59. $\mathbf{u} + \mathbf{v} = \langle -2, 5\rangle + \langle 4, 3\rangle = \langle -2 + 4, 5 + 3\rangle = \langle 2, 8\rangle$

61. $-4\mathbf{u} = -4\langle -2, 5\rangle = \langle -4(-2), -4(5)\rangle = \langle 8, -20\rangle$

63. $3\mathbf{u} - 6\mathbf{v} = 3\langle -2, 5\rangle - 6\langle 4, 3\rangle = \langle -6, 15\rangle - \langle 24, 18\rangle = \langle -6 - 24, 15 - 18\rangle = \langle -30, -3\rangle$

65. $\mathbf{u} + \mathbf{v} - 3\mathbf{u} = \langle -2, 5\rangle + \langle 4, 3\rangle - 3\langle -2, 5\rangle = \langle -2, 5\rangle + \langle 4, 3\rangle - \langle 3(-2), 3(5)\rangle = \langle -2, 5\rangle + \langle 4, 3\rangle - \langle -6, 15\rangle$

$= \langle -2 + 4, 5 + 3\rangle - \langle -6, 15\rangle = \langle 2, 8\rangle - \langle -6, 15\rangle = \langle 2 - (-6), 8 - 15\rangle = \langle 8, -7\rangle$

67. $\langle -5, 8\rangle = -5\mathbf{i} + 8\mathbf{j}$

69. $\langle 2, 0\rangle = 2\mathbf{i} + 0\mathbf{j} = 2\mathbf{i}$

71. $\langle 6, -1\rangle \cdot \langle 2, 5\rangle = 6(2)+(-1)(5) = 12-5 = 7$

73. $\langle 2, -3\rangle \cdot \langle 6, 5\rangle = 2(6)+(-3)(5) = 12-15 = -3$

75. $4\mathbf{i} = \langle 4,0\rangle; 5\mathbf{i}-9\mathbf{j} = \langle 5,-9\rangle$

$\langle 4,0\rangle \cdot \langle 5,-9\rangle = 4(5)+0(-9) = 20-0 = 20$

77. $\langle 2, 1\rangle \cdot \langle -3, 1\rangle$

$$\cos\theta = \frac{\langle 2, 1\rangle \cdot \langle -3, 1\rangle}{\sqrt{2^2+1^2}\cdot\sqrt{(-3)^2+1^2}} = \frac{-6+1}{\sqrt{5}\cdot\sqrt{10}} = \frac{-5}{5\sqrt{2}} = \frac{-1}{\sqrt{2}} = -\frac{\sqrt{2}}{2} \Rightarrow \theta = 135°$$

79. $\langle 1, 2\rangle \cdot \langle -6, 3\rangle$

$$\cos\theta = \frac{\langle 1, 2\rangle \cdot \langle -6, 3\rangle}{\sqrt{1^2+2^2}\cdot\sqrt{(-6)^2+3^2}} = \frac{-6+6}{\sqrt{5}\sqrt{45}} = \frac{0}{15} = 0 \Rightarrow \theta = 90°$$

81. First write the given vectors in component form.

$$3\mathbf{i}+4\mathbf{j} = \langle 3,4\rangle \text{ and } \mathbf{j} = \langle 0,1\rangle$$

$$\cos\theta = \frac{\langle 3, 4\rangle \cdot \langle 0, 1\rangle}{|\langle 3, 4\rangle||\langle 0, 1\rangle|} = \frac{\langle 3, 4\rangle \cdot \langle 0, 1\rangle}{\sqrt{3^2+4^2}\cdot\sqrt{0^2+1^2}} = \frac{0+4}{\sqrt{25}\cdot\sqrt{1}} = \frac{4}{5\cdot 1} = \frac{4}{5} = .8 \Rightarrow \theta = \cos^{-1}.8 \approx 36.87°$$

For Exercises 83 & 85, $\mathbf{u} = \langle -2,1\rangle$, $\mathbf{v} = \langle 3,4\rangle$, and $\mathbf{w} = \langle -5,12\rangle$.

83. $(3\mathbf{u})\cdot\mathbf{v} = (3\langle -2, 1\rangle)\cdot\langle 3, 4\rangle = \langle -6, 3\rangle \cdot \langle 3, 4\rangle = -18+12 = -6$

85. $\mathbf{u}\cdot\mathbf{v}-\mathbf{u}\cdot\mathbf{w} = \langle -2, 1\rangle \cdot \langle 3,4\rangle - \langle -2,1\rangle \cdot \langle -5, 12\rangle = (-6+4)-(10+12) = -2-22 = -24$

87. Since $\langle 1,2\rangle \cdot \langle -6,3\rangle = -6+6 = 0,$ the vectors are orthogonal.

89. Since $\langle 1,0\rangle \cdot \langle \sqrt{2},0\rangle = \sqrt{2}+0 = \sqrt{2} \neq 0,$ the vectors are not orthogonal

91. $\sqrt{5}\mathbf{i}-2\mathbf{j} = \langle \sqrt{5},-2\rangle; -5\mathbf{i}+2\sqrt{5}\mathbf{j} = \langle -5, 2\sqrt{5}\rangle$

Since $\langle \sqrt{5},-2\rangle \cdot \langle -5, 2\sqrt{5}\rangle = -5\sqrt{5}-4\sqrt{5} = -9\sqrt{5} \neq 0,$ the vectors are not orthogonal.

93. Draw a line parallel to the x-axis and the vector **u** + **v** (shown as a dashed line).
Since $\theta_1 = 110°$, its supplementary angle is 70°. Further, since $\theta_2 = 260°$, the angle α is $260° - 180° = 80°$. Then the angle CBA becomes 180 – (80 + 70) = 180 – 150 = 30°.

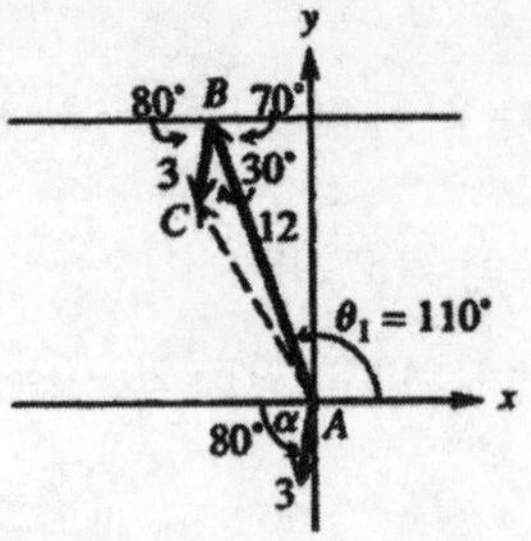

Using the law of cosines, the magnitude of **u** + **v** is the following.

$$|\mathbf{u}+\mathbf{v}|^2 = a^2 + c^2 - 2ac\cos B$$

$$|\mathbf{u}+\mathbf{v}|^2 = 3^2 + 12^2 - 2(3)(12)\cos 30° = 9 + 144 - 72\cdot\frac{\sqrt{3}}{2} = 153 - 36\sqrt{3} \approx 90.646171$$

Thus, $|\mathbf{u}+\mathbf{v}| \approx 9.5208$.
Using the law of sines, we have the following.

$$\frac{\sin A}{a} = \frac{\sin B}{b} \Rightarrow \frac{\sin A}{3} = \frac{\sin 30°}{9.5208} \Rightarrow \sin A = \frac{3\sin 30°}{9.5208} = \frac{3\cdot\frac{1}{2}}{9.5208} \approx .15754979 \Rightarrow A \approx 9.0647°$$

The direction angle of **u** + **v** is $110° + 9.0647° = 119.0647°$.

94. Since $a = 12\cos 110° \approx -4.10424172$ and $b = 12\sin 110° \approx 11.27631145$, $\langle a,b\rangle \approx \langle -4.1042, 11.2763\rangle$.

95. Since $c = 3\cos 260° \approx -.52094453$ and $d = 3\sin 260° \approx -2.95442326$, $\langle c,d\rangle \approx \langle -.5209, -2.9544\rangle$.

96. If $\mathbf{u} = \langle a,b\rangle = \langle -4.10424, 11.27631\rangle$ and $\mathbf{v} = \langle c,d\rangle = \langle -.52094, -2.95442\rangle$, then $\mathbf{u}+\mathbf{v}$ is the following.

$$\begin{aligned}\mathbf{u}+\mathbf{v} &= \langle -4.10424172 + (-.52094453), 11.27631145 + (-2.95442326)\rangle \\ &= \langle -4.62518625, 8.32188819\rangle \approx \langle -4.6252, 8.3219\rangle\end{aligned}$$

97. Magnitude: $\sqrt{(-4.62518625)^2 + 8.32188819^2} \approx 9.5208$

Angle: $\tan\theta' = \dfrac{8.32188819}{-4.625186258} \Rightarrow \theta' \approx -60.9353° \Rightarrow \theta = -60.9353° + 180° = 119.0647°$
(θ lies in quadrant II)

98. They are the same. Preference of method is an individual choice.

Section 8.4: Applications of Vectors

1. Find the direction and magnitude of the equilibrant.
Since $A = 180° - 28.2° = 151.8°$, we can use the law of cosines to find the magnitude of the resultant, **v**.

$|\mathbf{v}|^2 = 1240^2 + 1480^2 - 2(1240)(1480)\cos 151.8° \approx 6962736.2 \Rightarrow |\mathbf{v}| \approx 2639$ lb (will be rounded as 2640)

Use the law of sines to find α.

$$\frac{\sin\alpha}{1240} = \frac{\sin 151.8°}{2639} \Rightarrow \sin\alpha = \frac{1240\sin 151.8°}{2639} \approx .22203977 \Rightarrow \alpha \approx 12.8°$$

Thus, we have 2640 lb at an angle of $\theta = 180° - 12.8° = 167.2°$ with the 1480-lb force.

3. Let α = the angle between the forces.

To find α, use the law of cosines to find θ.

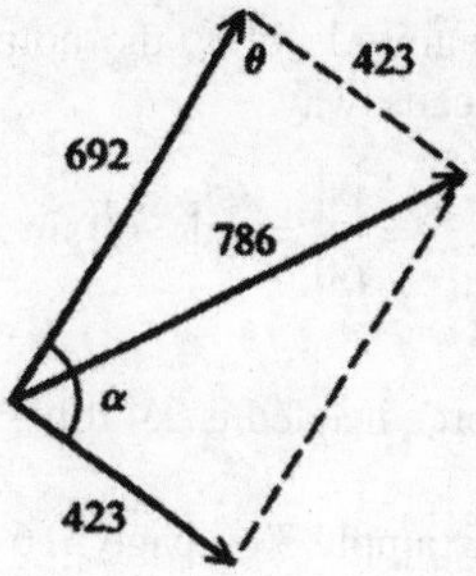

$$786^2 = 692^2 + 423^2 - 2(692)(423)\cos\theta$$

$$\cos\theta = \frac{692^2 + 423^2 - 786^2}{2(692)(423)} \approx .06832049$$

$$\theta \approx 86.1°$$

Thus, $\alpha = 180° - 86.1° = 93.9°$.

5. Use the parallelogram rule. In the figure, **x** represents the second force and **v** is the resultant.

$$\alpha = 180° - 78°50'$$
$$= 179°60' - 78°50' = 101°10'$$

and

$$\beta = 78°50' - 41°10' = 37°40'$$

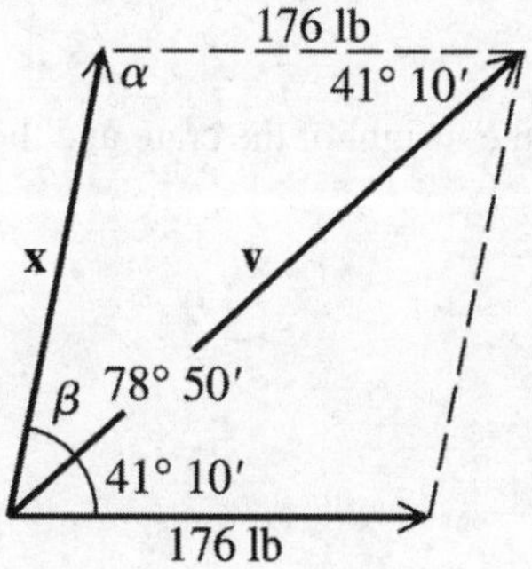

Using the law of sines, we have the following.

$$\frac{|\mathbf{x}|}{\sin 41°10'} = \frac{176}{\sin 37°40'} \Rightarrow |\mathbf{x}| = \frac{176\sin 41°10'}{\sin 37°40'} \approx 190$$

$$\frac{|\mathbf{v}|}{\sin\alpha} = \frac{176}{\sin 37°40'} \Rightarrow |\mathbf{v}| = \frac{176\sin 101°10'}{\sin 37°40'} \approx 283$$

Thus, the magnitude of the second force is about 190 lb and the magnitude of the resultant is about 283 lb.

7. Let θ = the angle that the hill makes with the horizontal.

The 80-lb downward force has a 25-lb component parallel to the hill. The two right triangles are similar and have congruent angles.

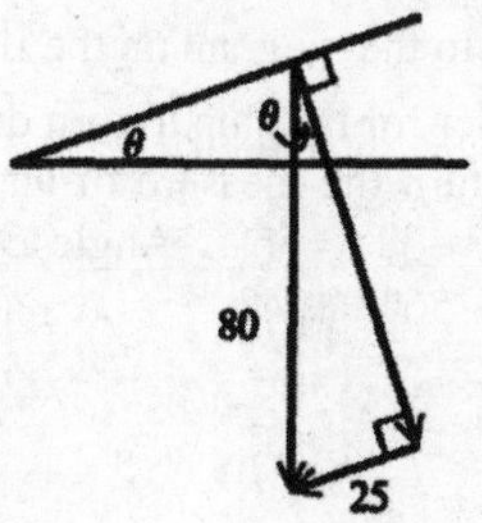

$$\sin\theta = \frac{25}{80} = \frac{5}{16} = .3125 \Rightarrow \theta \approx 18°$$

9. Find the force needed to pull a 60-ton monolith along the causeway.

The force needed to pull 60 tons is equal to the magnitude of **x**, the component parallel to the causeway.

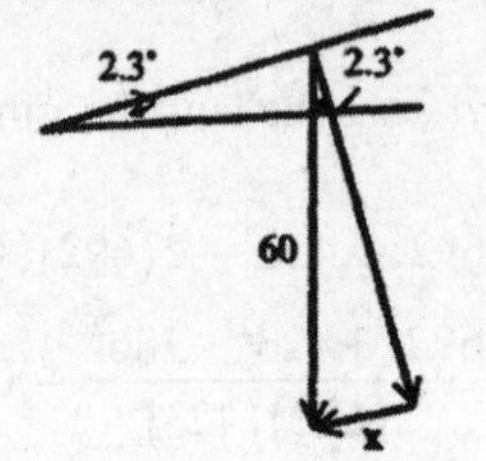

$$\sin 2.3° = \frac{|\mathbf{x}|}{60} \Rightarrow |\mathbf{x}| = 60 \sin 2.3° \approx 2.4 \text{ tons}$$

The force needed is 2.4 tons.

11. Like Example 3 on page 316 or your text, angle B equals angle θ and here the magnitude of vector **BA** represents the weight of the stump grinder. The vector **AC** equals vector **BE**, which represents the force required to hold the stump grinder on the incline. Thus, we have the following.

$$\sin B = \frac{18}{60} = \frac{3}{10} = .3 \Rightarrow B \approx 17.5°$$

13. Find the weight of the crate and the tension on the horizontal rope.

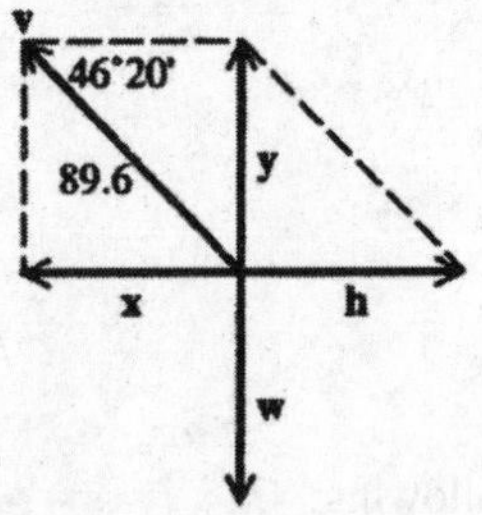

v has horizontal component **x** and vertical component **y**. The resultant **v** + **h** also has vertical component **y**. The resultant balances the weight of the crate, so its vertical component is the equilibrant of the crate's weight.

$$|\mathbf{w}| = |\mathbf{y}| = 89.6 \sin 46° 20' \approx 64.8 \text{ lb}$$

Since the crate is not moving side-to-side, **h**, the horizontal tension on the rope, is the opposite of **x**.

$$|\mathbf{h}| = |\mathbf{x}| = 89.6 \cos 46° 20' \approx 61.9 \text{ lb}$$

The weight of the crate is 64.8 lb; the tension is 61.9 lb.

15. Refer to the diagram on the right.

In order for the ship to turn due east, the ship must turn the measure of angle CAB, which is $90° - 34° = 56°$. Angle DAB is therefore $180° - 56° = 124°$.

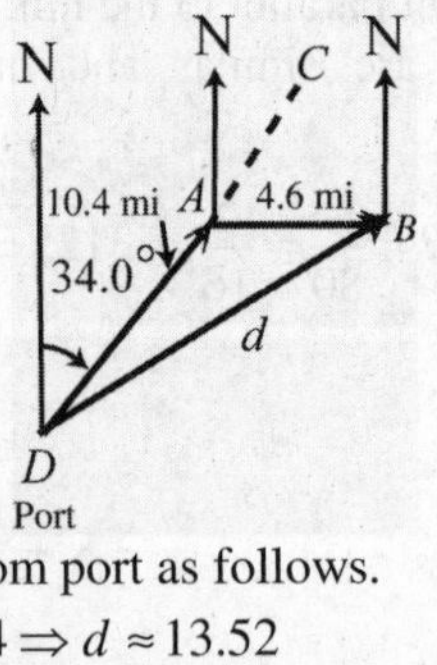

Using the law of cosines, we can solve for the distance the ship is from port as follows.

$$d^2 = 10.4^2 + 4.6^2 - 2(10.4)(4.6)\cos 124° \approx 182.824 \Rightarrow d \approx 13.52$$

Thus, the distance the ship is from port is 13.5 mi. (rounded to three significant digits)
To find the bearing, we first seek the measure of angle ADB, which we will refer to as angle D. Using the law of cosines we have the following.

$$\cos D = \frac{13.52^2 + 10.4^2 - 4.6^2}{2(13.52)(10.4)} \approx .95937073 \Rightarrow D \approx 16.4°$$

Thus, the bearing is $34.0° + D = 34.0° + 16.4° = 50.4°$.

17. Find the distance of the ship from point A.

Angle 1 = 189° − 180° = 9°

Angle 2 = 360° − 317° = 43°

Angle 1 + Angle 2 = 9° + 43° = 52°

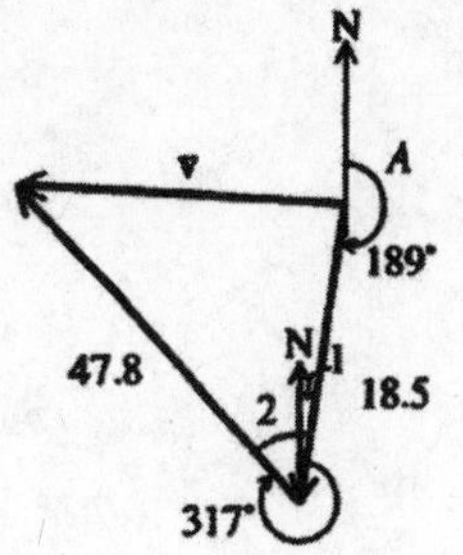

Use the law of cosines to find $|\mathbf{v}|$.

$$|\mathbf{v}|^2 = 47.8^2 + 18.5^2 - 2(47.8)(18.5)\cos 52° \approx 1538.23 \Rightarrow |\mathbf{v}| \approx 39.2 \text{ km}$$

19. Let x = be the actual speed of the motorboat;
y = the speed of the current.

$$\sin 10° = \frac{y}{20.0} \Rightarrow y = 20.0 \sin 10° \approx 3.5$$

$$\cos 10° = \frac{x}{20.0} \Rightarrow x = 20.0 \cos 10° \approx 19.7$$

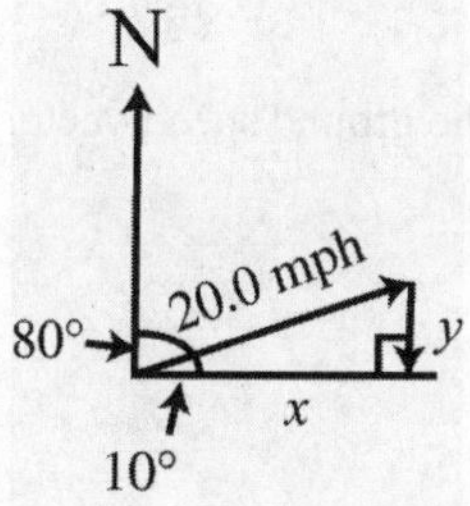

The speed of the current is 3.5 mph and the actual speed of the motorboat is 19.7 mph.

21. Let $\mathbf{v}$ = the ground speed vector.
Find the bearing and ground speed of the plane.
Angle A = 233° − 114° = 119°
Use the law of cosines to find $|\mathbf{v}|$.

$$|\mathbf{v}|^2 = 39^2 + 450^2 - 2(39)(450)\cos 119°$$

$$|\mathbf{v}|^2 \approx 221{,}037.82$$

$$|\mathbf{v}| \approx 470.1$$

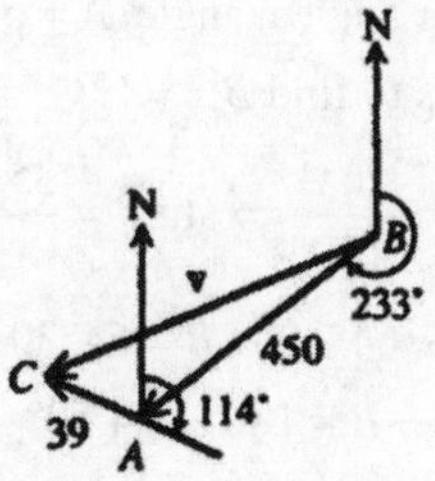

The ground speed is 470 mph. (rounded to two significant digits)
Use the law of sines to find angle B.

$$\frac{\sin B}{39} = \frac{\sin 119°}{470.1} \Rightarrow \sin B = \frac{39 \sin 119°}{470.1} \approx .07255939 \Rightarrow B \approx 4°$$

Thus, the bearing is $B + 233° = 4° + 233° = 237°$.

23. Let $|\mathbf{x}|$ = the airspeed and $|\mathbf{d}|$ = the ground speed.

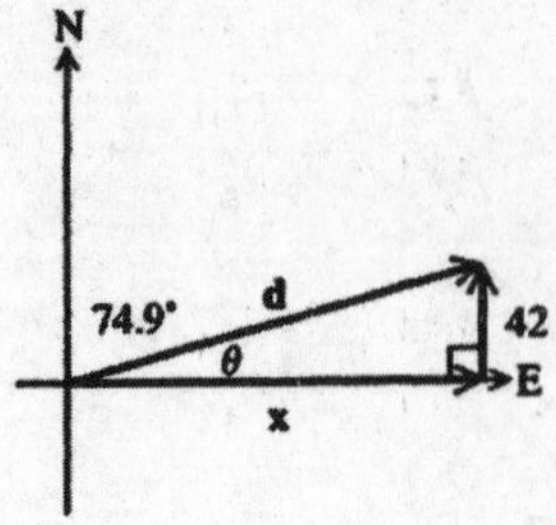

$$\theta = 90° - 74.9° = 15.1°$$

$$\frac{|\mathbf{x}|}{42} = \cot 15.1° \Rightarrow |\mathbf{x}| = 42 \cot 15.1° = \frac{42}{\tan 15.1°} \approx 156 \text{ mph}$$
$$\frac{|\mathbf{d}|}{42} = \csc 15.1° \Rightarrow |\mathbf{d}| = 42 \csc 15.1° = \frac{42}{\sin 15.1°} \approx 161 \text{ mph}$$

25. Let **c** = the ground speed vector.

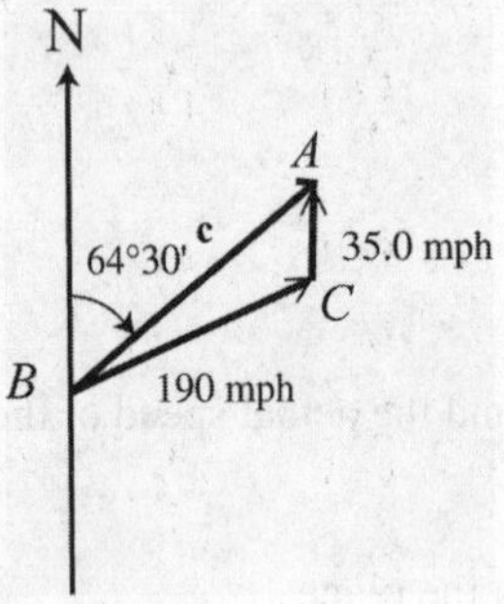

By alternate interior angles, angle $A = 64°30'$.
Use the law of sines to find B.

$$\frac{\sin B}{35.0} = \frac{\sin A}{190} \Rightarrow \sin B = \frac{35.0 \sin 64°30'}{190} \approx .16626571 \Rightarrow B \approx 9.57° \approx 9°30'$$

Thus, the bearing is $64°30' + B = 64°30' + 9°30' = 74°00'$.
Since $C = 180° - A - B = 180° - 64.50° - 9.57° = 105.93°$, we use the law of sine to find the ground speed.

$$\frac{|\mathbf{c}|}{\sin C} = \frac{35.0}{\sin B} \Rightarrow |\mathbf{c}| = \frac{35.0 \sin 105.93°}{\sin 9.57°} \approx 202 \text{ mph}$$

The bearing is $74°00'$; the ground speed is 202 mph.

27. Let **v** = the airspeed vector.

The ground speed is $\frac{400 \text{ mi}}{2.5 \text{ hr}} = 160$ mph.

angle *BAC* = 328° – 180° = 148°

Using the law of cosines to find $|\mathbf{v}|$, we have the following.

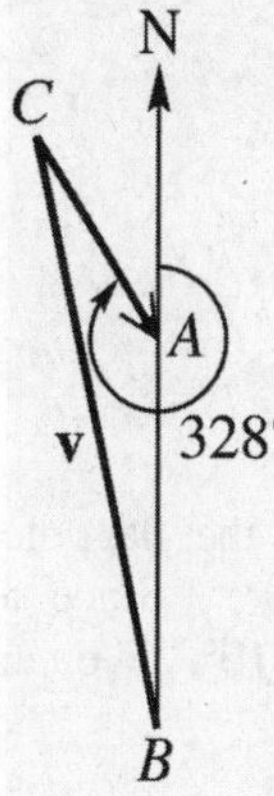

$$|\mathbf{v}|^2 = 11^2 + 160^2 - 2(11)(160)\cos 148°$$

$$|\mathbf{v}|^2 \approx 28,706.1$$

$$|\mathbf{v}| \approx 169.4$$

The airspeed must be 170 mph. (rounded to two significant digits)

Use the law of sines to find *B*.

$$\frac{\sin B}{11} = \frac{\sin 148°}{169.4} \Rightarrow \sin B = \frac{11 \sin 148°}{169.4} \Rightarrow \sin B \approx .03441034 \Rightarrow B \approx 2.0°$$

The bearing must be approximately 360° – 2.0° = 358°.

29. Find the ground speed and resulting bearing.
Angle *A* = 245° – 174° = 71°
Use the law of cosines to find $|\mathbf{v}|$.

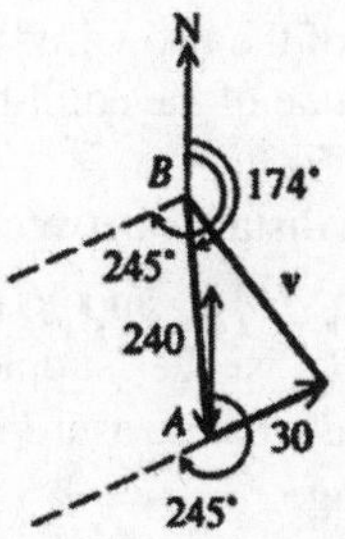

$$|\mathbf{v}|^2 = 30^2 + 240^2 - 2(30)(240)\cos 71°$$

$$|\mathbf{v}|^2 \approx 53,811.8$$

$$|\mathbf{v}| \approx 232.1$$

The ground speed is 230 km per hr. (rounded to two significant digits)
Use the law of sines to find angle *B*.

$$\frac{\sin B}{30} = \frac{\sin 71°}{230} \Rightarrow \sin B = \frac{30 \sin 71°}{230} \approx .12332851 \Rightarrow B \approx 7°$$

Thus, the bearing is $174° - B = 174° - 7° = 167°$.

31. $\mathbf{R} = \mathbf{i} - 2\mathbf{j}$ and $\mathbf{A} = .5\mathbf{i} + \mathbf{j}$

(a) Write the given vector in component form. $\mathbf{R} = \mathbf{i} - 2\mathbf{j} = \langle 1, -2 \rangle$ and $\mathbf{A} = .5\mathbf{i} + \mathbf{j} = \langle .5, 1 \rangle$

$$|\mathbf{R}| = \sqrt{1^2 + (-2)^2} = \sqrt{1+4} = \sqrt{5} \approx 2.2 \text{ and } |\mathbf{A}| = \sqrt{.5^2 + 1^2} = \sqrt{.25+1} = \sqrt{1.25} \approx 1.1$$

About 2.2 in. of rain fell. The area of the opening of the rain gauge is about 1.1 in.^{2}.

(b) $V = |\mathbf{R} \cdot \mathbf{A}| = |\langle 1, -2 \rangle \cdot \langle .5, 1 \rangle| = |.5 + (-2)| = |-1.5| = 1.5$

The volume of rain was 1.5 in.^{3}.

(c) **R** and **A** should be parallel and point in opposite directions.

Summary Exercises on Applications of Trigonometry and Vectors

1. Consider the diagram below.

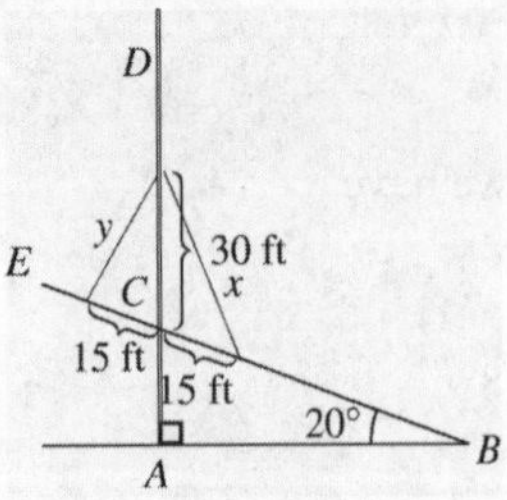

If we extend the flagpole, a right triangle *CAB* is formed. Thus, the measure of angle *BCA* is $90° - 20° = 70°$. Since angle *DCB* and *BCA* are supplementary, the measure of angle *DCB* is $180° - 70° = 110°$. We can now use the law of cosines to find the measure of the support wire on the right, *x*.

$$x^2 = 30^2 + 15^2 - 2(30)(15)\cos 110° \approx 1432.818 \approx 37.85 \text{ ft}$$

Now, to find the length of the support wire on the left, we have different ways to find it. One way would be to use the approximation for *x* and use the law of cosines. To avoid using the approximate value, we will find *y* with the same method as for *x*.

Since angle *DCB* and *DCE* are supplementary, the measure of angle *DCE* is $180° - 110° = 70°$. We can now use the law of cosines to find the measure of the support wire on the left, *y*.

$$y^2 = 30^2 + 15^2 - 2(30)(15)\cos 70° \approx 817.182 \approx 28.59 \text{ ft}$$

The length of the two wires are 28.59 ft and 37.85 ft.
The magnitude of the equilibrant force Michael must apply is 30.4 lb.

3. Let *c* be the distance between the two lighthouses.

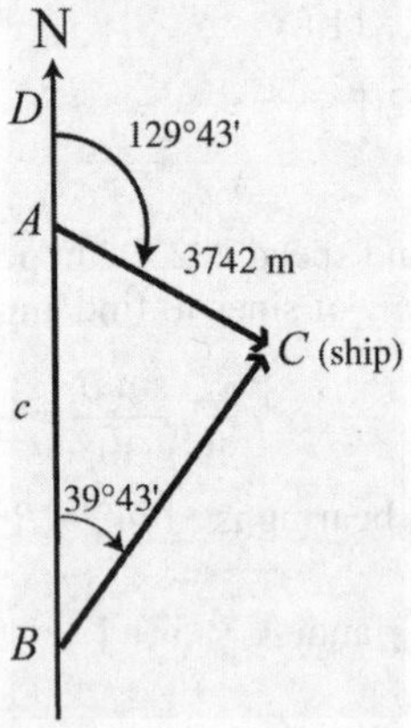

Since angle *DAC* and *CAB* form a line, angle *CAB* is the supplement of angle *DAC*. Thus, the measure of angle *CAB* is the following.

$$180° - 129°43' = 179°60' - 129°43' = 50°17'$$

Since the angles of a triangle must add up to 180°, the measure of angle *ACB* is the following.

$$180° - 39°43' - 50°17' = 180° - 90° = 90°$$

Thus, we can solve the following.

$$\cos 50°17' = \frac{3742}{c} \Rightarrow c = \frac{3742}{\cos 50°17'} \approx 5856$$

The two lighthouses are 5856 m apart.

5. Let **x** be the horizontal force.

$$\sin 40° = \frac{|\mathbf{x}|}{50} \Rightarrow |\mathbf{x}| = 50 \sin 40° \approx 32 \text{ lb}$$

7. We must find the length of *CD*

Angle *BAC* is equal to 35° - 30° = 5°.

Side *AB* = 5000 ft. Since triangle *ABC* is a right triangle, $\cos 5° = \dfrac{5000}{AC} \Rightarrow AC = \dfrac{5000}{\cos 5°} \approx 5019$ ft.

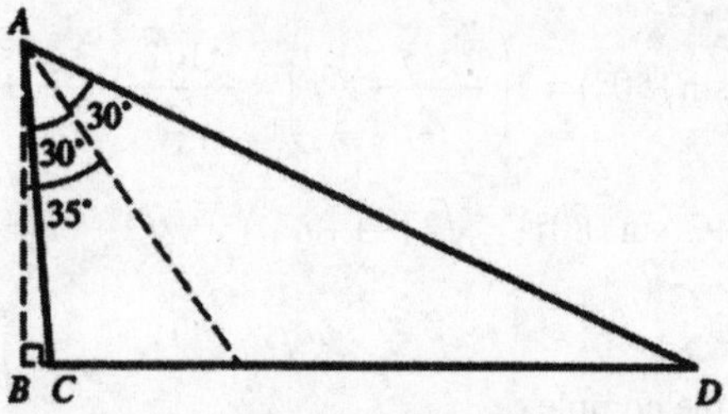

The angular coverage of the lens is 60°, so angle *CAD* = 60°. From geometry, angle *ACB* = 85°, angle *ACD* = 95°, and angle *ADC* = 25°. We now know three angles and one side in triangle *ACD* and can now use the law of sines to solve for the length of *CD*.

$$\frac{CD}{\sin 60°} = \frac{AC}{\sin 25°} \Rightarrow \frac{CD}{\sin 60°} = \frac{5019}{\sin 25°} \Rightarrow CD = \frac{5019 \sin 60°}{\sin 25°} \approx 10,285 \text{ ft}$$

Section 8.5: Trigonometric (Polar) Form of Complex Numbers; Products and Quotients

1.

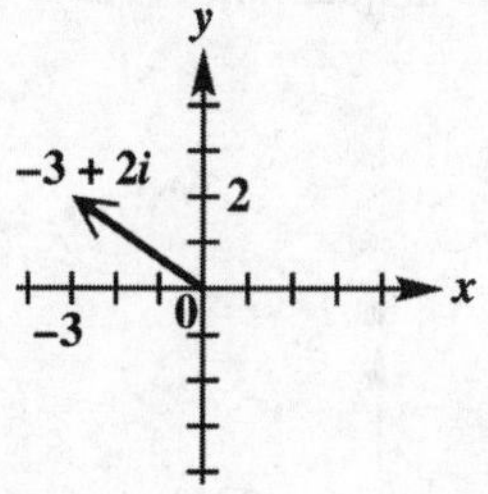

3.

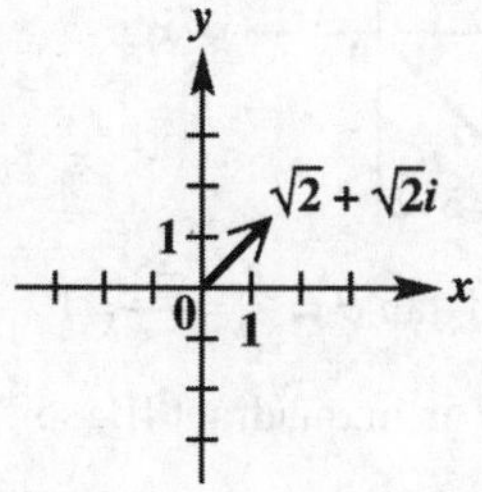

5.

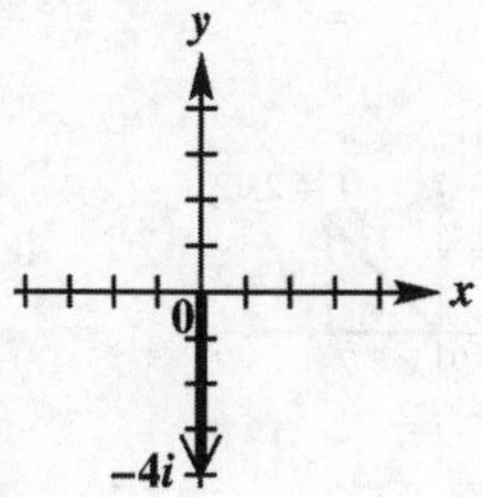

7.

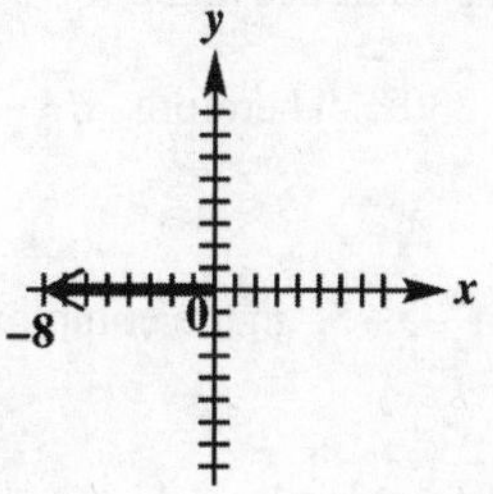

9. $1-4i$

11. $5-6i,\ -2+3i$

$(5-6i)+(-2+3i)=3-3i$

13. $-3,\ 3i$

$(-3+0i)+(0+3i)=-3+3i$

15. $7+6i,\ 3i$

$(7+6i)+(0+3i)=7+9i$

17. $10(\cos 90° + i \sin 90°) = 10(0+i) = 0+10i = 10i$

19. $4(\cos 240° + i \sin 240°) = 4\left(-\frac{1}{2} - i\frac{\sqrt{3}}{2}\right) = -2 - 2i\sqrt{3}$

21. $3 \text{ cis } 150° = 3(\cos 150° + i \sin 150°) = 3\left(-\frac{\sqrt{3}}{2} + \frac{1}{2}i\right) = -\frac{3\sqrt{3}}{2} + \frac{3}{2}i$

23. $\sqrt{2} \text{ cis } 180° = \sqrt{2}(\cos 180° + i \sin 180°) = \sqrt{2}(-1 + i \cdot 0) = -\sqrt{2} + 0i = -\sqrt{2}$

25. $\sqrt{3} - i$

Sketch a graph of $\sqrt{3} - i$ in the complex plane.

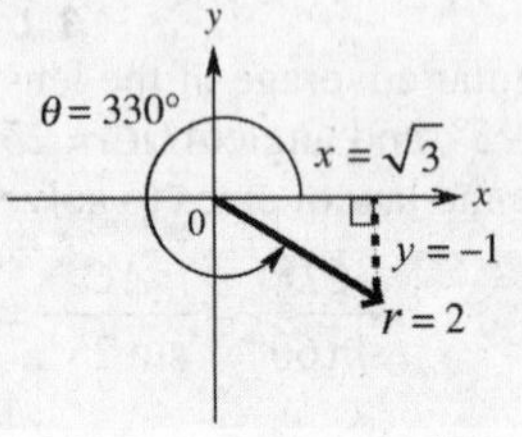

Since $x = \sqrt{3}$ and $y = -1$, $r = \sqrt{(\sqrt{3})^2 + (-1)^2} = \sqrt{3+1} = \sqrt{4} = 2$ and $\tan\theta = \frac{-1}{\sqrt{3}} = -\frac{\sqrt{3}}{3}$. Since $\tan\theta = -\frac{\sqrt{3}}{3}$, the reference angle for θ is 30°. The graph shows that θ is in quadrant IV, so $\theta = 360° - 30° = 330°$. Therefore, $\sqrt{3} - i = 2(\cos 330° + i \sin 330°)$.

27. $-5 - 5i$

Sketch a graph of $-5 - 5i$ in the complex plane.

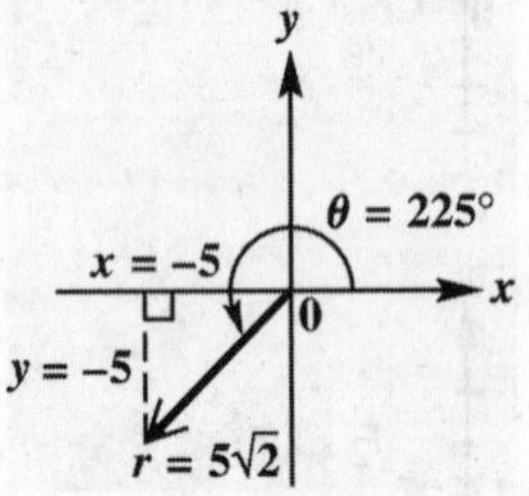

Since $x = -5$ and $y = -5$, $r = \sqrt{(-5)^2 + (-5)^2} = \sqrt{25+25} = \sqrt{50} = 5\sqrt{2}$ and $\tan\theta = \frac{y}{x} = \frac{-5}{-5} = 1$. Since $\tan\theta = 1$, the reference angle for θ is 45°. The graph shows that θ is in quadrant III, so $\theta = 180° + 45° = 225°$. Therefore, $-5 - 5i = 5\sqrt{2}(\cos 225° + i \sin 225°)$.

29. $2 + 2i$

Sketch a graph of $2 + 2i$ in the complex plane.

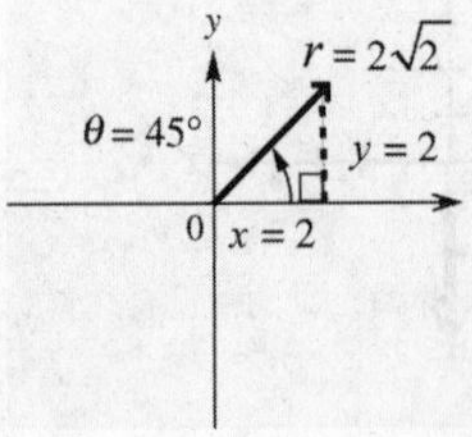

Since $x = 2$ and $y = 2$, $r = \sqrt{2^2 + 2^2} = \sqrt{4+4} = \sqrt{8} = 2\sqrt{2}$ and $\tan\theta = \frac{2}{2} = 1$. Since $\tan\theta = 1$, the reference angle for θ is 45°. The graph shows that θ is in quadrant I, so $\theta = 45°$. Therefore, $2 + 2i = 2\sqrt{2}(\cos 45° + i \sin 45°)$.

31. $5i = 0 + 5i$

$0 + 5i$ is on the positive y-axis, so $\theta = 90°$ and $x = 0,\ y = 5 \Rightarrow r = \sqrt{0^2 + 5^2} = \sqrt{0 + 25} = 5$

Thus, $5i = 5(\cos 90° + i \sin 90°)$.

33. $3(\cos 250° + i \sin 250°) = -1.0261 - 2.8191i$

35. $12i = 0 + 12i$

$x = 0,\ y = 12 \Rightarrow r = \sqrt{0^2 + 12^2} = \sqrt{0 + 144} = \sqrt{144} = 12$

0 + 12*i* is on the positive *y*-axis, so 0 = 90°.

$12i = 12(\cos 90° + i \sin 90°)$

37. $3 + 5i$

$x = 3,\ y = 5 \Rightarrow r = \sqrt{3^2 + 5^2} = \sqrt{9 + 25} = \sqrt{34}$

$\tan \theta = \frac{5}{3}$

$3 + 5i$ is in the quadrant I, so $\theta = 59.04°$.

$3 + 5i = \sqrt{34}\,(\cos 59.04° + i \sin 59.04°)$

39. Since the modulus represents the magnitude of the vector in the complex plane, $r = 1$ would represent a circle of radius one centered at the origin.

41. Since the real part of $z = x + yi$ is 1, the graph of $1 + yi$ would be the vertical line $x = 1$.

43. $z = -.2i$

$z^2 - 1 = (-.2i)^2 - 1 = .04i^2 - 1 = .04(-1) - 1 = -.04 - 1 = -1.04$

The modulus is 1.04.

$(z^2 - 1)^2 - 1 = (-1.04)^2 - 1 = 1.0816 - 1 = .0816$

The modulus is .0816.

$\left[\left(z^2 - 1\right)^2 - 1\right]^2 - 1 = (.0816)^2 - 1 = .0665856 - 1 = -.99334144$

The modulus is .99334144.

The moduli do not exceed 2. Therefore, *z* is in the Julia set.

45. $\left[2(\cos 45° + i \sin 45°)\right] \cdot \left[2(\cos 225° + i \sin 225°)\right] = 2 \cdot 2\left[\cos(45° + 225°) + i \sin(45° + 225°)\right]$

$= 4(\cos 270° + i \sin 270°) = 4(0 - i) = 0 - 4i$ or $-4i$

47. $\left[4(\cos 60° + i \sin 60°)\right] \cdot \left[6(\cos 330° + i \sin 330°)\right] = 4 \cdot 6\left[(\cos(60° + 330°) + i \sin(60° + 330°)\right]$

$= 24(\cos 390° + i \sin 390°) = 24(\cos 30° + i \sin 30°)$

$= 24\left(\frac{\sqrt{3}}{2} + i\frac{1}{2}\right) = 12\sqrt{3} + 12i$

49. $[5 \text{ cis } 90°][3 \text{ cis } 45°] = 5 \cdot 3\left[\text{cis}(90° + 45°)\right] = 15 \text{ cis } 135°$

$= 15(\cos 135° + i \sin 135°) = 15\left(-\frac{\sqrt{2}}{2} + \frac{\sqrt{2}}{2}i\right) = -\frac{15\sqrt{2}}{2} + \frac{15\sqrt{2}}{2}i$

51. $\left[\sqrt{3}\text{ cis }45°\right]\left[\sqrt{3}\text{ cis }225°\right]=\sqrt{3}\cdot\sqrt{3}\left[\text{cis}(45°+225°)\right]$

$=3\text{ cis }270°=3(\cos 270°+i\sin 270°)=3(0-i)=0-3i$ or $-3i$

53. $\dfrac{10(\cos 225°+i\sin 225°)}{5(\cos 45°+i\sin 45°)}=\dfrac{10}{5}\left[\cos(225°-45°)+i\sin(225°-45°)\right]$

$=2(\cos 180°+i\sin 180°)=2(-1+0\cdot i)=-2+0i$ or -2

55. $\dfrac{3\text{ cis }305°}{9\text{ cis }65°}=\dfrac{1}{3}\text{cis }(305°-65°)=\dfrac{1}{3}(\text{cis }240°)=\dfrac{1}{3}(\cos 240°+i\sin 240°)=\dfrac{1}{3}\left(-\dfrac{1}{2}-\dfrac{\sqrt{3}}{2}i\right)=-\dfrac{1}{6}-\dfrac{\sqrt{3}}{6}i$

57. $\dfrac{-i}{1+i}$

numerator: $-i=0-i$ and $r=\sqrt{0^2+(-1)^2}=\sqrt{0+1}=\sqrt{1}=1$

$\theta=270°$ since $\cos 270°=0$ and $\sin 270°=-1$, so $-i=1\text{ cis}270°$.

denominator: $1+i$

$r=\sqrt{1^2+1^2}=\sqrt{1+1}=\sqrt{2}$ and $\tan\theta=\dfrac{y}{x}=\dfrac{1}{1}=1$

Since x and y are both positive, θ is in quadrant I, so $\theta=45°$. Thus,

$1+i=\sqrt{2}\text{ cis }45°$

$\dfrac{-i}{1+i}=\dfrac{\text{cis }270°}{\sqrt{2}\text{ cis }45°}=\dfrac{1}{\sqrt{2}}\text{cis }(270°-45°)$

$=\dfrac{\sqrt{2}}{2}\text{ cis }225°=\dfrac{\sqrt{2}}{2}(\cos 225°+i\sin 225°)=\dfrac{\sqrt{2}}{2}\left(-\dfrac{\sqrt{2}}{2}-i\cdot\dfrac{\sqrt{2}}{2}\right)=-\dfrac{1}{2}-\dfrac{1}{2}i$

59. $\dfrac{2\sqrt{6}-2i\sqrt{2}}{\sqrt{2}-i\sqrt{6}}$

numerator: $2\sqrt{6}-2i\sqrt{2}$ and $r=\sqrt{\left(2\sqrt{6}\right)^2+\left(-2\sqrt{2}\right)^2}=\sqrt{24+8}=\sqrt{32}=4\sqrt{2}$

$\tan\theta=\dfrac{-2\sqrt{2}}{2\sqrt{6}}=-\dfrac{1}{\sqrt{3}}=-\dfrac{\sqrt{3}}{3}$

Since x is positive and y is negative, θ is in quadrant IV, so $\theta=-30°$. Thus,

$2\sqrt{6}-2i\sqrt{2}=4\sqrt{2}\text{ cis}(-30°)$.

denominator: $\sqrt{2}-i\sqrt{6}$ and $r=\sqrt{\left(\sqrt{2}\right)^2+\left(-\sqrt{6}\right)^2}=\sqrt{2+6}=\sqrt{8}=2\sqrt{2}$

$\tan\theta=\dfrac{-\sqrt{6}}{\sqrt{2}}=-\sqrt{3}$

Since x is positive and y is negative, θ is in quadrant IV, so $\theta=-60°$. Thus,

$\sqrt{2}-i\sqrt{6}=2\sqrt{2}\text{ cis}(-30°)$

$\dfrac{2\sqrt{6}-2i\sqrt{2}}{\sqrt{2}-i\sqrt{6}}=\dfrac{4\sqrt{2}\text{ cis}(-30°)}{2\sqrt{2}\text{ cis}(-60°)}$

$=\dfrac{4\sqrt{2}}{2\sqrt{2}}\text{cis}\left[-30°-(-60°)\right]=2\text{cis }30°=2(\cos 30°+i\sin 30°)=2\left(\dfrac{\sqrt{3}}{2}+i\dfrac{1}{2}\right)=\sqrt{3}+i$

61. $[2.5(\cos 35°+i\sin 35°)]\cdot[3.0(\cos 50°+i\sin 50°)]=2.5\cdot 3.0[\cos(35°+50°)+i\sin(35°+50°)]$
$=7.5(\cos 85°+i\sin 85°)\approx .6537+7.4715i$

63. $(12\text{ cis } 18.5°)(3\text{ cis } 12.5°)=12\cdot 3\text{ cis }(18.5°+12.5°)$
$=36\text{ cis } 31°=36(\cos 31°+i\sin 31°)\approx 30.8580+18.5414i$

65. $\dfrac{45(\cos 127°+i\sin 127°)}{22.5(\cos 43°+i\sin 43°)}=\dfrac{45}{22.5}[\cos(127°-43°)+i\sin(127°-43°)]$
$=2(\cos 84°+i\sin 84°)\approx .2091+1.9890i$

In Exercises 67 – 73, $w=-1+i$ and $z=-1-i$.

67. $w\cdot z=(-1+i)(-1-i)=-1(-1)+(-1)(-i)+i(-1)+i(-i)=1+i-i-i^2=1-(-1)=2$

68. $w=-1+i$:
$r=\sqrt{(-1)^2+1^2}=\sqrt{1+1}=\sqrt{2}$ and $\tan\theta=\dfrac{1}{-1}=-1$
Since x is negative and y is positive, θ is in quadrant II, so $\theta=135°$. Thus, $w=\sqrt{2}\text{ cis } 135°$.
$z=-1-i$:
$r=\sqrt{(-1)^2+(-1)^2}=\sqrt{1+1}=\sqrt{2}$ and $\tan\theta=\dfrac{-1}{-1}=1$
Since x and y are negative, θ is in quadrant III, so $\theta=225°$. Thus, $z=\sqrt{2}\text{ cis } 225°$.

69. $w\cdot z=(\sqrt{2}\text{ cis } 135°)(\sqrt{2}\text{ cis } 225°)=\sqrt{2}\cdot\sqrt{2}[\text{ cis }(135°+225°)]=2\text{ cis } 360°=2\text{ cis } 0°$

70. $2\text{ cis } 0°=2(\cos 0°+i\sin 0°)=2(1+0\cdot i)=2\cdot 1=2$; It is the same.

71. $\dfrac{w}{z}=\dfrac{-1+i}{-1-i}=\dfrac{-1+i}{-1-i}\cdot\dfrac{-1+i}{-1+i}=\dfrac{1-i-i+i^2}{1-i^2}=\dfrac{1-2i+(-1)}{1-(-1)}=\dfrac{-2i}{2}=-i$

72. $\dfrac{w}{z}=\dfrac{\sqrt{2}\text{ cis } 135°}{\sqrt{2}\text{ cis } 225°}=\dfrac{\sqrt{2}}{\sqrt{2}}\text{ cis }(135°-225°)=\text{ cis }(-90°)$

73. $\text{cis }(-90°)=\cos(-90°)+i\sin(-90°)=0+i(-1)=0-i=-i$; It is the same.

75. $E=8(\cos 20°+i\sin 20°), R=6, X_L=3,\ I=\dfrac{E}{Z}, Z=R+X_L i$
Write $Z=6+3i$ in trigonometric form.
$x=6$, and $y=3\Rightarrow r=\sqrt{6^2+3^2}=\sqrt{36+9}=\sqrt{45}=3\sqrt{5}$.
$\tan\theta=\dfrac{3}{6}=\dfrac{1}{2}$, so $\theta\approx 26.6°$. Thus, $Z=3\sqrt{5}\text{ cis } 26.6°$.
$I=\dfrac{8\text{ cis } 20°}{3\sqrt{5}\text{ cis } 26.6°}=\dfrac{8}{3\sqrt{5}}\text{ cis }(20°-26.6°)$
$=\dfrac{8\sqrt{5}}{15}\text{ cis }(-6.6°)=\dfrac{8\sqrt{5}}{15}[\cos(-6.6°)+i\sin(-6.6°)]\approx 1.18-.14i$

77. Since $Z_1 = 50+25i$ and $Z_2 = 60+20i$, we have the following.

$$\frac{1}{Z_1} = \frac{1}{50+25i}\cdot\frac{50-25i}{50-25i} = \frac{50-25i}{50^2-25^2i^2} = \frac{50-25i}{2500-625(-1)} = \frac{50-25i}{2500+625} = \frac{50-25i}{3125} = \frac{2}{125}-\frac{1}{125}i$$

and

$$\frac{1}{Z_2} = \frac{1}{60+20i}\cdot\frac{60-20i}{60-20i} = \frac{60-20i}{60^2-20^2i^2} = \frac{60-20i}{3600-400(-1)} = \frac{60-20i}{3600+400} = \frac{60-20i}{4000} = \frac{3}{200}-\frac{1}{200}i$$

and

$$\frac{1}{Z_1}+\frac{1}{Z_2} = \left(\frac{2}{125}-\frac{1}{125}i\right)+\left(\frac{3}{200}-\frac{1}{200}i\right) = \left(\frac{2}{125}+\frac{3}{200}\right)-\left(\frac{1}{125}+\frac{1}{200}\right)i$$
$$= \left(\frac{16}{1000}+\frac{15}{1000}\right)-\left(\frac{8}{1000}+\frac{5}{1000}\right)i = \frac{31}{1000}-\frac{13}{1000}i$$

$$Z = \frac{1}{\frac{1}{Z_1}+\frac{1}{Z_2}} = \frac{1}{\frac{31}{1000}-\frac{13}{1000}i} = \frac{1000}{31-13i}\cdot\frac{31+13i}{31+13i} = \frac{1000(31+13i)}{31^2-13^2i^2}$$
$$= \frac{31,000+13,000}{961-169(-1)} = \frac{31,000+13,000}{961+169} = \frac{31,000+13,000i}{1130} = \frac{3100}{113}+\frac{1300}{113}i \approx 27.43+11.5i$$

Section 8.6: Demoivre's Theorem; Powers and Roots of Complex Numbers

1. $\left[3(\cos 30°+i\sin 30°)\right]^3 = 3^3\left[\cos(3\cdot 30°)+i\sin(3\cdot 30°)\right]$
$$= 27(\cos 90°+i\sin 90°) = 27(0+1\cdot i) = 0+27i \text{ or } 27i$$

3. $(\cos 45°+i\sin 45°)^8 = \left[\cos(8\cdot 45°)+i\sin(8\cdot 45°)\right] = \cos 360°+i\sin 360° = 1+0\cdot i$ or 1

5. $\left[3\text{ cis }100°\right]^3 = 3^3\text{ cis }(3\cdot 100°)$
$$= 27\text{ cis }300° = 27(\cos 300°+i\sin 300°) = 27\left(\frac{1}{2}-\frac{\sqrt{3}}{2}i\right) = \frac{27}{2}-\frac{27\sqrt{3}}{2}i$$

7. $\left(\sqrt{3}+i\right)^5$

First write $\sqrt{3}+i$ in trigonometric form.

$$r = \sqrt{\left(\sqrt{3}\right)^2+1^2} = \sqrt{3+1} = \sqrt{4} = 2 \text{ and } \tan\theta = \frac{1}{\sqrt{3}} = \frac{\sqrt{3}}{3}$$

Because x and y are both positive, θ is in quadrant I, so $\theta = 30°$.

$$\sqrt{3}+i = 2(\cos 30°+i\sin 30°)$$
$$\left(\sqrt{3}+i\right)^5 = \left[2(\cos 30°+i\sin 30°)\right]^5 = 2^5\left[\cos(5\cdot 30°)+i\sin(5\cdot 30°)\right]$$
$$= 32(\cos 150°+i\sin 150°) = 32\left(-\frac{\sqrt{3}}{2}+i\frac{1}{2}\right) = -16\sqrt{3}+16i$$

9. $\left(2-2i\sqrt{3}\right)^4$

First write $2-2i\sqrt{3}$ in trigonometric form.

$$r=\sqrt{2^2+\left(-2\sqrt{3}\right)^2}=\sqrt{4+12}=\sqrt{16}=4 \text{ and } \tan\theta=\frac{-2\sqrt{3}}{2}=-\sqrt{3}$$

Because x is positive and y is negative, θ is in quadrant IV, so $\theta=300°$.

$$2\text{–}2i\sqrt{3}=4\left(\cos 300°+i\sin 300°\right)$$

$$\left(2\text{–}2i\sqrt{3}\right)^4=\left[4\left(\cos 300°+i\sin 300°\right)\right]^4=4^4\left[\cos\left(4\cdot 300°\right)+i\sin\left(4\cdot 300°\right)\right]$$

$$=256\left(\cos 1200°+i\sin 1200°\right)=256\left(-\frac{1}{2}+\frac{i\sqrt{3}}{2}\right)=-128+128i\sqrt{3}$$

11. $(-2-2i)^5$

First write $-2-2i$ in trigonometric form.

$$r=\sqrt{(-2)^2+(-2)^2}=\sqrt{4+4}=\sqrt{8}=2\sqrt{2} \text{ and } \tan\theta=\frac{-2}{-2}=1$$

Because x and y are both negative, θ is in quadrant III, so $\theta=225°$.

$$-2-2i=2\sqrt{2}\left(\cos 225°+i\sin 225°\right)$$

$$(-2-2i)^5=\left[2\sqrt{2}\left(\cos 225°+i\sin 225°\right)\right]^5=\left(2\sqrt{2}\right)^5\left[\cos\left(5\cdot 225°\right)+i\sin\left(5\cdot 225°\right)\right]$$

$$=32\sqrt{32}\left(\cos 1125°+i\sin 1125°\right)=128\sqrt{2}\left(\cos 45°+i\sin 45°\right)$$

$$=128\sqrt{2}\left(\frac{\sqrt{2}}{2}+\frac{\sqrt{2}}{2}i\right)=128+128i$$

13. **(a)** $\cos 0°+i\sin 0°=1\left(\cos 0°+i\sin 0°\right)$

We have $r=1$ and $\theta=0°$.

Since $r^3\left(\cos 3\alpha+i\sin 3\alpha\right)=1\left(\cos 0°+i\sin 0°\right)$, then we have the following.

$$r^3=1\Rightarrow r=1 \text{ and } 3\alpha=0°+360°\cdot k\Rightarrow\alpha=\frac{0°+360°\cdot k}{3}=0°+120°\cdot k=120°\cdot k,\ k \text{ any integer.}$$

If $k=0$, then $\alpha=0°$. If $k=1$, then $\alpha=120°$. If $k=2$, then $\alpha=240°$.

So, the cube roots are $\cos 0°+i\sin 0°$, $\cos 120°+i\sin 120°$, and $\cos 240°+i\sin 240°$.

(b)

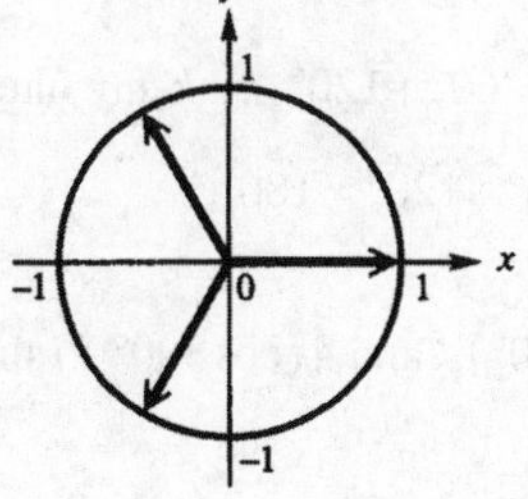

15. (a) Find the cube roots of 8 cis 60°

We have $r=8$ and $\theta=60°$.

Since $r^3(\cos 3\alpha+i\sin 3\alpha)=8(\cos 60°+i\sin 60°)$, then we have the following.

$$r^3=1\Rightarrow r=1 \text{ and } 3\alpha=60°+360°\cdot k\Rightarrow \alpha=\frac{60°+360°\cdot k}{3}=20°+120°\cdot k,\ k \text{ any integer.}$$

If $k=0$, then $\alpha=20°+0°=20°$. If $k=1$, then $\alpha=20°+120°=140°$.

If $k=2$, then $\alpha=20°+240°=260°$.

So, the cube roots are 2 cis 20°, 2 cis140°, and 2 cis 260°.

(b)

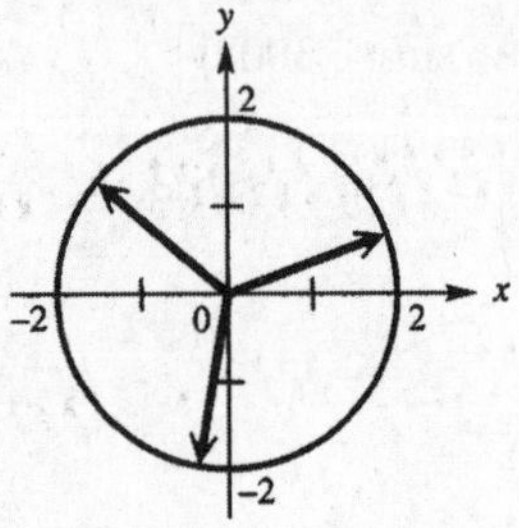

17. (a) Find the cube roots of $-8i=8(\cos 270°+i\sin 270°)$

We have $r=8$ and $\theta=270°$.

Since $r^3(\cos 3\alpha+i\sin 3\alpha)=8(\cos 270°+i\sin 270°)$, then we have the following.

$$r^3=8\Rightarrow r=2 \text{ and } 3\alpha=270°+360°\cdot k\Rightarrow \alpha=\frac{270°+360°\cdot k}{3}=90°+120°\cdot k,\ k \text{ any integer.}$$

If $k=0$, then $\alpha=90°+0°=90°$. If $k=1$, then $\alpha=90°+120°=210°$.

If $k=2$, then $\alpha=90°+240°=330°$.

So, the cube roots are $2(\cos 90°+i\sin 90°)$, $2(\cos 210°+i\sin 210°)$, and $2(\cos 330°+i\sin 330°)$.

(b)

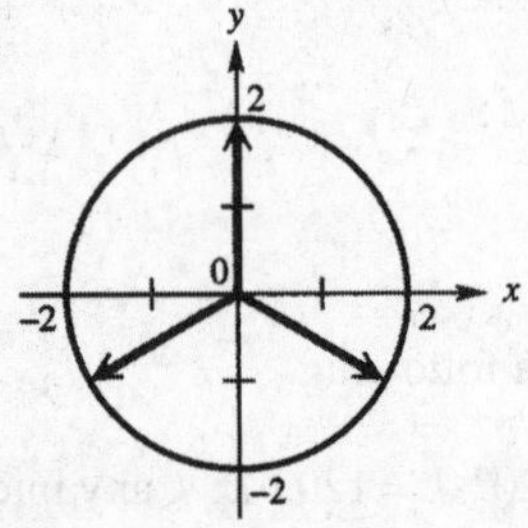

19. (a) Find the cube roots of $-64=64(\cos 180°+i\sin 180°)$

We have $r=64$ and $\theta=180°$.

Since $r^3(\cos 3\alpha+i\sin 3\alpha)=64(\cos 180°+i\sin 180°)$, then we have the following.

$$r^3=64\Rightarrow r=4 \text{ and } 3\alpha=180°+360°\cdot k\Rightarrow \alpha=\frac{180°+360°\cdot k}{3}=60°+120°\cdot k,\ k \text{ any integer.}$$

If $k=0$, then $\alpha=60°+0°=60°$. If $k=1$, then $\alpha=60°+120°=180°$.

If $k=2$, then $\alpha=60°+240°=300°$.

So, the cube roots are $4(\cos 60°+i\sin 60°)$, $4(\cos 180°+i\sin 180°)$, and $4(\cos 300°+i\sin 300°)$.

(b)

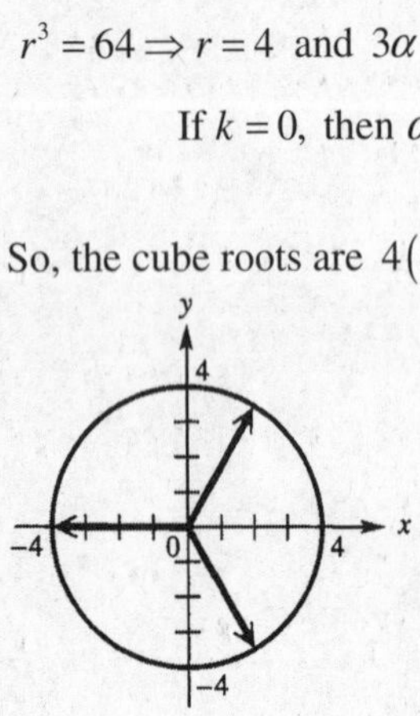

21. (a) Find the cube roots of $1+i\sqrt{3}$.

We have $r=\sqrt{1^2+(\sqrt{3})^2}=\sqrt{1+3}=\sqrt{4}=2$ and $\tan\theta=\frac{\sqrt{3}}{1}=\sqrt{3}$. Since θ is in quadrant I, $\theta=60°$.

Thus, $1+i\sqrt{3}=2\left(\frac{1}{2}+i\frac{\sqrt{3}}{2}\right)=2(\cos 60°+i\sin 60°)$.

Since $r^3(\cos 3\alpha+i\sin 3\alpha)=2(\cos 60°+i\sin 60°)$, then we have the following.

$$r^3=2\Rightarrow r=\sqrt[3]{2} \text{ and } 3\alpha=60°+360°\cdot k\Rightarrow\alpha=\frac{60°+360°\cdot k}{3}=20°+120°\cdot k,\ k \text{ any integer.}$$

If $k=0$, then $\alpha=20°+0°=20°$. If $k=1$, then $\alpha=20°+120°=140°$.

If $k=2$, then $\alpha=20°+240°=260°$.

So, the cube roots are $\sqrt[3]{2}(\cos 20°+i\sin 20°)$, $\sqrt[3]{2}(\cos 140°+i\sin 140°)$, and $\sqrt[3]{2}(\cos 260°+i\sin 260°)$.

(b)

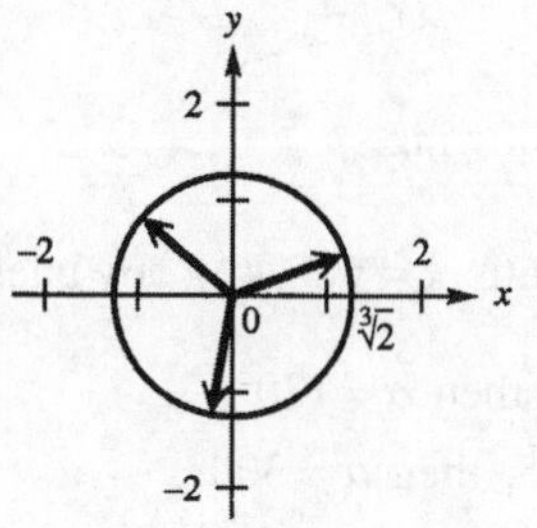

23. (a) Find the cube roots of $-2\sqrt{3}+2i$.

We have $r=\sqrt{(-2\sqrt{3})^2+2^2}=\sqrt{12+4}=\sqrt{16}=4$ and $\tan\theta=\frac{2}{-2\sqrt{3}}=-\frac{\sqrt{3}}{3}$. Since θ is in quadrant II, $\theta=150°$.

Thus, $-2\sqrt{3}+2i=4\left(-\frac{\sqrt{3}}{2}+\frac{1}{2}i\right)=4(\cos 150°+i\sin 150°)$.

Since $r^3(\cos 3\alpha+i\sin 3\alpha)=4(\cos 150°+i\sin 150°)$, then we have the following.

$$r^3=4\Rightarrow r=\sqrt[3]{4} \text{ and } 3\alpha=150°+360°\cdot k\Rightarrow\alpha=\frac{150°+360°\cdot k}{3}=50°+120°\cdot k,\ k \text{ any integer.}$$

If $k=0$, then $\alpha=50°+0°=50°$. If $k=1$, then $\alpha=50°+120°=170°$.

If $k=2$, then $\alpha=50°+240°=290°$.

So, the cube roots are $\sqrt[3]{4}(\cos 50°+i\sin 50°)$, $\sqrt[3]{4}(\cos 170°+i\sin 170°)$, and $\sqrt[3]{4}(\cos 290°+i\sin 290°)$.

(b)

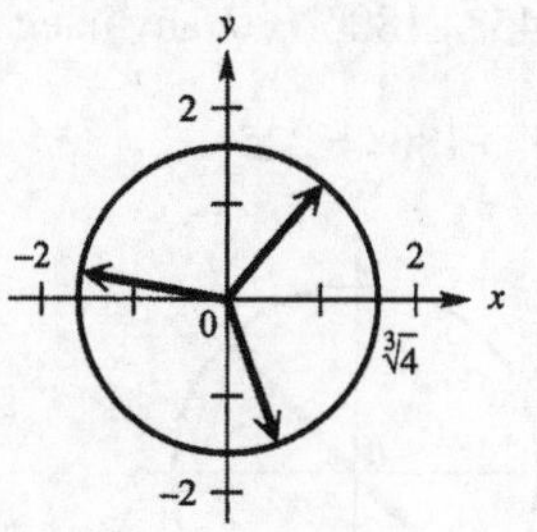

25. Find all the second (or square) roots of $1 = 1(\cos 0° + i\sin 0°)$.

Since $r^2(\cos 2\alpha + i\sin 2\alpha) = 1(\cos 0° + i\sin 0°)$, then we have the following.

$$r^2 = 1 \Rightarrow r = 1 \text{ and } 2\alpha = 0° + 360°\cdot k \Rightarrow \alpha = \frac{0° + 360°\cdot k}{2} = 0° + 180°\cdot k = 180°\cdot k,\ k \text{ any integer.}$$

If $k = 0$, then $\alpha = 0°$. If $k = 1$, then $\alpha = 180°$.

So, the second roots of 1 are
$\cos 0° + i\sin 0°$, and $\cos 180° + i\sin 180°$.
(or 1 and –1)

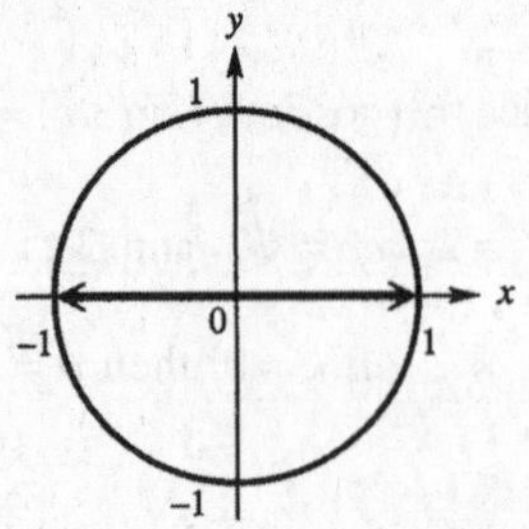

27. Find all the sixth roots of $1 = 1(\cos 0° + i\sin 0°)$.

Since $r^6(\cos 6\alpha + i\sin 6\alpha) = 1(\cos 0° + i\sin 0°)$, then we have the following.

$$r^6 = 1 \Rightarrow r = 1 \text{ and } 6\alpha = 0° + 360°\cdot k \Rightarrow \alpha = \frac{0° + 360°\cdot k}{6} = 0° + 60°\cdot k = 60°\cdot k,\ k \text{ any integer.}$$

If $k = 0$, then $\alpha = 0°$. If $k = 1$, then $\alpha = 60°$. If $k = 2$, then $\alpha = 120°$.
If $k = 3$, then $\alpha = 180°$. If $k = 4$, then $\alpha = 240°$. If $k = 5$, then $\alpha = 300°$.

So, the sixth roots of 1 are $\cos 0° + i\sin 0°$, $\cos 60° + i\sin 60°$, $\cos 120° + i\sin 120°$, $\cos 180° + i\sin 180°$,

$\cos 240° + i\sin 240°$, and $\cos 300° + i\sin 300°$. $\left(\text{or } 1, \frac{1}{2} + \frac{\sqrt{3}}{2}i, -\frac{1}{2} + \frac{\sqrt{3}}{2}i, -1, -\frac{1}{2} - \frac{\sqrt{3}}{2}i, \text{ and } \frac{1}{2} - \frac{\sqrt{3}}{2}i\right)$

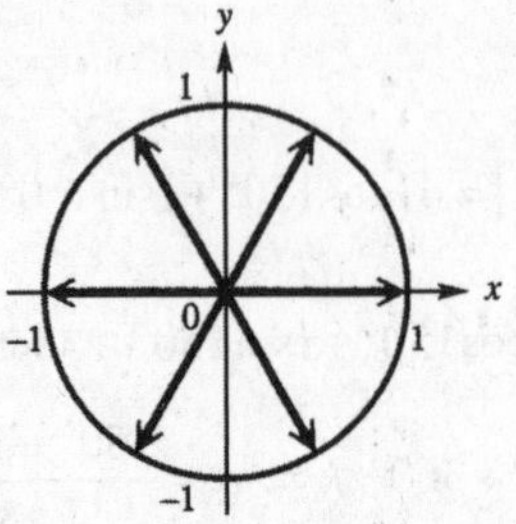

29. Find all the second (square) roots of $i = 1(\cos 90° + i\sin 90°)$.

Since $r^2(\cos 2\alpha + i\sin 2\alpha) = 1(\cos 90° + i\sin 90°)$, then we have the following.

$$r^2 = 1 \Rightarrow r = 1 \text{ and } 2\alpha = 90° + 360°\cdot k \Rightarrow \alpha = \frac{90° + 360°\cdot k}{2} = 45° + 180°\cdot k,\ k \text{ any integer.}$$

If $k = 0$, then $\alpha = 45° + 0° = 45°$. If $k = 1$, then $\alpha = 45° + 180° = 225°$.

So, the second roots of i are
$\cos 45° + i\sin 45°$, and $\cos 225° + i\sin 225°$.
$\left(\text{or } \frac{\sqrt{2}}{2} + \frac{\sqrt{2}}{2}i \text{ and } -\frac{\sqrt{2}}{2} - \frac{\sqrt{2}}{2}i\right)$

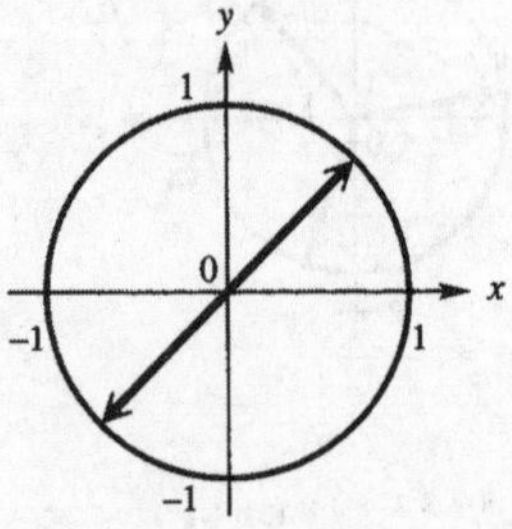

31. $x^3-1=0 \Rightarrow x^3=1$

We have $r=1$ and $\theta=0°$.

$$x^3=1=1+0i=1(\cos 0°+i\sin 0°)$$

Since $r^3(\cos 3\alpha+i\sin 3\alpha)=1(\cos 0°+i\sin 0°)$, then we have the following.

$$r^3=1 \Rightarrow r=1 \text{ and } 3\alpha=0°+360°\cdot k \Rightarrow \alpha=\frac{0°+360°\cdot k}{3}=0°+120°\cdot k=120°\cdot k, \; k \text{ any integer.}$$

If $k=0$, then $\alpha=0°$. If $k=1$, then $\alpha=120°$. If $k=2$, then $\alpha=240°$.

Solution set: $\{\cos 0°+i\sin 0°, \cos 120°+i\sin 120°, \cos 240°+i\sin 240°\}$ or $\left\{1, -\frac{1}{2}+\frac{\sqrt{3}}{2}i, -\frac{1}{2}-\frac{\sqrt{3}}{2}i\right\}$

33. $x^3+i=0 \Rightarrow x^3=-i$

We have $r=1$ and $\theta=270°$.

$$x^3=-i=0-i=1(\cos 270°+i\sin 270°)$$

Since $r^3(\cos 3\alpha+i\sin 3\alpha)=1(\cos 270°+i\sin 270°)$, then we have the following.

$$r^3=1 \Rightarrow r=1 \text{ and } 3\alpha=270°+360°\cdot k \Rightarrow \alpha=\frac{270°+360°\cdot k}{3}=90°+120°\cdot k, \; k \text{ any integer.}$$

If $k=0$, then $\alpha=90°+0°=90°$. If $k=1$, then $\alpha=90°+120°=210°$.
If $k=2$, then $\alpha=90°+240°=330°$.

Solution set: $\{\cos 90°+i\sin 90°, \cos 210°+i\sin 210°, \cos 330°+i\sin 330°\}$ or $\left\{0, -\frac{\sqrt{3}}{2}-\frac{1}{2}i, \frac{\sqrt{3}}{2}-\frac{1}{2}i\right\}$

35. $x^3-8=0 \Rightarrow x^3=8$

We have $r=8$ and $\theta=0°$.

$$x^3=8=8+0i=8(\cos 0°+i\sin 0°)$$

Since $r^3(\cos 3\alpha+i\sin 3\alpha)=8(\cos 0°+i\sin 0°)$, then we have the following.

$$r^3=8 \Rightarrow r=2 \text{ and } 3\alpha=0°+360°\cdot k \Rightarrow \alpha=\frac{0°+360°\cdot k}{3}=0°+120°\cdot k=120°\cdot k, \; k \text{ any integer.}$$

If $k=0$, then $\alpha=0°$. If $k=1$, then $\alpha=120°$. If $k=2$, then $\alpha=240°$.

Solution set: $\{2(\cos 0°+i\sin 0°), 2(\cos 120°+i\sin 120°), 2(\cos 240°+i\sin 240°)\}$ or
$\{2, -1+\sqrt{3}i, -1-\sqrt{3}i\}$

37. $x^4+1=0 \Rightarrow x^4=-1$

We have $r=1$ and $\theta=180°$.

$$x^4=-1=-1+0i=1(\cos 180°+i\sin 180°)$$

Since $r^4(\cos 4\alpha+i\sin 4\alpha)=1(\cos 180°+i\sin 180°)$, then we have the following.

$$r^4=1 \Rightarrow r=1 \text{ and } 4\alpha=180°+360°\cdot k \Rightarrow \alpha=\frac{180°+360°\cdot k}{4}=45°+90°\cdot k, \; k \text{ any integer.}$$

If $k=0$, then $\alpha=45°+0°=45°$. If $k=1$, then $\alpha=45°+90°=135°$.
If $k=2$, then $\alpha=45°+180°=225°$. If $k=3$, then $\alpha=45°+270°=315°$.

Solution set: $\{\cos 45°+i\sin 45°, \cos 135°+i\sin 135°, \cos 225°+i\sin 225°, \cos 315°+i\sin 315°\}$ or
$\left\{\frac{\sqrt{2}}{2}+\frac{\sqrt{2}}{2}i, -\frac{\sqrt{2}}{2}+\frac{\sqrt{2}}{2}i, -\frac{\sqrt{2}}{2}-\frac{\sqrt{2}}{2}i, \frac{\sqrt{2}}{2}-\frac{\sqrt{2}}{2}i\right\}$

39. $x^4 - i = 0 \Rightarrow x^4 = i$

We have $r = 1$ and $\theta = 90°$.

$$x^4 = i = 0 + i = 1(\cos 90° + i\sin 90°)$$

Since $r^4(\cos 4\alpha + i\sin 4\alpha) = 1(\cos 90° + i\sin 90°)$, then we have the following.

$$r^4 = 1 \Rightarrow r = 1 \text{ and } 4\alpha = 90° + 360° \cdot k \Rightarrow \alpha = \frac{90° + 360° \cdot k}{4} = 22.5° + 90° \cdot k, \ k \text{ any integer.}$$

If $k = 0$, then $\alpha = 22.5° + 0° = 22.5°$. If $k = 1$, then $\alpha = 22.5° + 90° = 112.5°$.
If $k = 2$, then $\alpha = 22.5° + 180° = 202.5°$. If $k = 3$, then $\alpha = 22.5° + 270° = 292.5°$.

Solution set: $\{\cos 22.5° + i\sin 22.5°, \ \cos 112.5° + i\sin 112.5°, \ \cos 202.5° + i\sin 202.5°, \ \cos 292.5° + i\sin 292.5°\}$

41. $x^3 - (4 + 4i\sqrt{3}) = 0 \Rightarrow x^3 = 4 + 4i\sqrt{3}$

We have $r = \sqrt{4^2 + (4\sqrt{3})^2} = \sqrt{16 + 48} = \sqrt{64} = 8$ and $\tan\theta = \frac{4\sqrt{3}}{4} = \sqrt{3}$. Since θ is in quadrant I, $\theta = 60°$.

$$x^3 = 4 + 4i\sqrt{3} = 8\left(\frac{1}{2} + i\frac{\sqrt{3}}{2}\right) = 8(\cos 60° + i\sin 60°)$$

Since $r^3(\cos 3\alpha + i\sin 3\alpha) = 8(\cos 60° + i\sin 60°)$, then we have the following.

$$r^3 = 8 \Rightarrow r = 2 \text{ and } 3\alpha = 60° + 360° \cdot k \Rightarrow \alpha = \frac{60° + 360° \cdot k}{3} = 20° + 120° \cdot k, \ k \text{ any integer.}$$

If $k = 0$, then $\alpha = 20° + 0° = 20°$. If $k = 1$, then $\alpha = 20° + 120° = 140°$.
If $k = 2$, then $\alpha = 20° + 240° = 260°$.

Solution set: $\{2(\cos 20° + i\sin 20°), 2(\cos 140° + i\sin 140°), 2(\cos 260° + i\sin 260°)\}$

43. $x^3 - 1 = 0 \Rightarrow (x - 1)(x^2 + x + 1) = 0$

Setting each factor equal to zero, we have the following.

$$x - 1 = 0 \Rightarrow x = 1 \text{ and } x^2 + x + 1 = 0 \Rightarrow x = \frac{-1 \pm \sqrt{1^2 - 4 \cdot 1 \cdot 1}}{2 \cdot 1} = \frac{-1 \pm \sqrt{-3}}{2} = \frac{-1 \pm i\sqrt{3}}{2} = -\frac{1}{2} \pm \frac{\sqrt{3}}{2}i$$

Thus, $x = 1, -\frac{1}{2} + \frac{\sqrt{3}}{2}i, -\frac{1}{2} - \frac{\sqrt{3}}{2}i$. We see that the solutions are the same as Exercise 31.

45. $(\cos\theta + i\sin\theta)^2 = 1^2(\cos 2\theta + i\sin 2\theta) = \cos 2\theta + i\sin 2\theta$

46. $(\cos\theta + i\sin\theta)^2 = \cos^2\theta + 2i\sin\theta\cos\theta + i^2\sin^2\theta = \cos^2\theta + 2i\sin\theta\cos\theta + (-1)\sin^2\theta$
$= \cos^2\theta + 2i\sin\theta\cos\theta - \sin^2\theta = (\cos^2\theta - \sin^2\theta) + i(2\sin\theta\cos\theta) = \cos 2\theta + i\sin 2\theta$

47. Two complex numbers $a + bi$ and $c + di$ are equal only if $a = c$ and $b = d$.
Thus, $a = c$ implies $\cos^2\theta - \sin^2\theta = \cos 2\theta$.

48. Two complex numbers $a + bi$ and $c + di$ are equal only if $a = c$ and $b = d$.
Thus, $b = d$ implies $2\sin\theta\cos\theta = \sin 2\theta$.

49. (a) If $z = 0 + 0i$, then $z = 0$, $0^2 + 0 = 0$, $0^2 + 0 = 0$, and so on. The calculations repeat as 0, 0, 0, . . ., and will never exceed a modulus of 2. The point $(0,0)$ is part of the Mandelbrot set. The pixel at the origin should be turned on.

(b) If $z = 1 - 1i$, then $(1-i)^2 + (1-i) = 1 - 3i$. The modulus of $1 - 3i$ is $\sqrt{1^2 + (-3)^2} = \sqrt{1+9} = \sqrt{10}$, which is greater than 2. Therefore, $1 - 1i$ is not part of the Mandelbrot set, and the pixel at $(1,-1)$ should be left off.

(c) If $z = -.5i$, $(-.5i)^2 - .5i = -.25 - .5i$; $(-.25 - .5i)^2 + (-.25 - .5i) = -.4375 - .25i$;

$(-.4375 - .25i)^2 + (-.4375 - .25i) = -.308593 - .03125i$;

$(-.308593 - .03125i)^2 + (-.308593 - .03125i) = -.214339 - .0119629i$;

$(-.214339 - .0119629i)^2 + (-.214339 - .0119629i) = -.16854 - .00683466i$.

This sequence appears to be approaching the origin, and no number has a modulus greater than 2. Thus, $-.5i$ is part of the Mandelbrot set, and the pixel at $(0,-.5)$ should be turned on.

51. Using the trace function, we find that the other four fifth roots of 1 are: $.30901699 + .95105652i$, $-.809017 + .58778525i$, $-.809017 - .5877853i$, $.30901699 - .9510565i$.

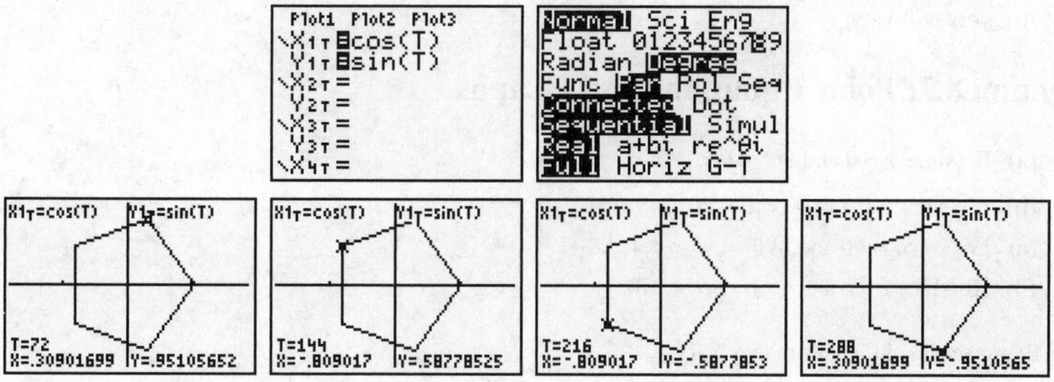

53. $2 + 2i\sqrt{3}$ is one cube root of a complex number.

$$r = \sqrt{2^2 + \left(2\sqrt{3}\right)^2} = \sqrt{4+12} = 4 \text{ and } \tan\theta = \frac{2\sqrt{3}}{2} = \sqrt{3}$$

Because x and y are both positive, θ is in quadrant I, so $\theta = 60°$.

$$2 + 2i\sqrt{3} = 4(\cos 60° + i \sin 60°)$$

$$\left(2 + 2i\sqrt{3}\right)^3 = \left[4(\cos 60° + i\sin 60°)\right]^3 = 4^3\left[\cos(3\cdot 60°) + i\sin(3\cdot 60°)\right]$$

$$= 64(\cos 180° + i\sin 180°) = 64(-1 + 0\cdot i) = -64 + 0\cdot i$$

Since the graphs of the other roots of – 64 must be equally spaced around a circle and the graphs of these roots are all on a circle that has center at the origin and radius 4, the other roots are as follows.

$$4\left[\cos(60° + 120°) + i\sin(60° + 120°)\right] = 4(\cos 180° + i\sin 180°) = 4(-1 + i\cdot 0) = -4$$

$$4\left[\cos(60° + 240°) + i\sin(60° + 240°)\right] = 4(\cos 300° + i\sin 300°) = 4\left(\frac{1}{2} - \frac{\sqrt{3}}{2}i\right) = 2 - 2i\sqrt{3}$$

55. $x^5+2+3i=0 \Rightarrow x^5=-2-3i$

$$r=\sqrt{(-2)^2+(-3)^2}=\sqrt{4+9}=\sqrt{13} \Rightarrow r^{1/n}=r^{1/5}=\left(\sqrt{13}\right)^{1/5}=13^{1/10}\approx 1.2924 \text{ and } \tan\theta=\frac{-3}{-2}=1.5$$

Since θ is in quadrant III, $\theta\approx 236.310°$ and $\alpha=\dfrac{236.310°+360°\cdot k}{5}=47.262°+72°\cdot k,$ where k is an integer.

$$x\approx 1.29239(\cos 47.262°+i\sin 47.262°), 1.29239(\cos 119.262°+i\sin 119.2622°),$$
$$1.29239(\cos 191.262°+i\sin 191.2622°), 1.29239(\cos 263.262°+i\sin 263.2622°),$$
$$1.29239(\cos 335.262°+i\sin 335.2622°)$$

Solution set: $\{.87708+.94922i, -.63173+1.1275i, -1.2675-.25240i, -.15164-1.28347i, 1.1738-.54083i\}$

57. The statement, "Every real number must have two real square roots," is false. Consider, for example, the real number –4. Its two square roots are $2i$ and $-2i$, which are not real.

59. If z is an nth root of 1, then $z^n=1$. Since $1=\frac{1}{1}=\frac{1}{z^n}=\left(\frac{1}{z}\right)^n$, then $\frac{1}{z}$ is also an nth root of 1.

61. Answers will vary.

Section 8.7: Polar Equations and Graphs

1. **(a)** II (since $r>0$ and $90°<\theta<180°$)

(b) I (since $r>0$ and $0°<\theta<90°$)

(c) IV (since $r>0$ and $-90°<\theta<0°$)

(d) III (since $r>0$ and $180°<\theta<270°$)

For Exercises 3 – 11, answers may vary.

3. **(a)**

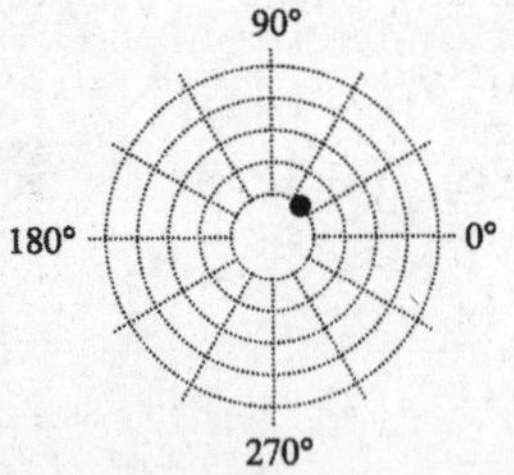

(b) Two other pairs of polar coordinates for (1, 45°) are (1, 405°) and (–1, 225°).

(c) Since $x=r\cos\theta \Rightarrow x=1\cdot\cos 45°=\frac{\sqrt{2}}{2}$ and $y=r\sin\theta \Rightarrow y=1\cdot\sin 45°=\frac{\sqrt{2}}{2}$, the point is $\left(\frac{\sqrt{2}}{2},\frac{\sqrt{2}}{2}\right)$.

5. (a)

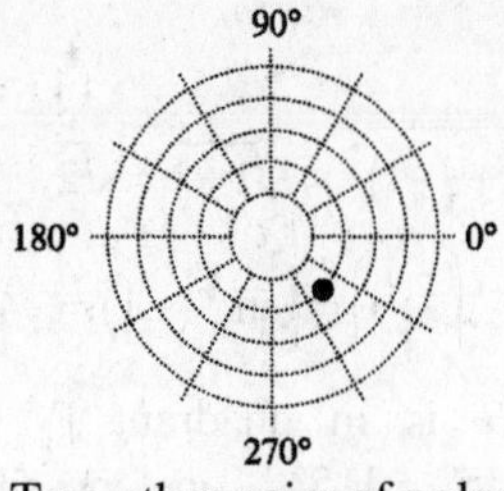

(b) Two other pairs of polar coordinates for (–2, 135°) are (–2, 495°) and (2, 315°).

(c) Since $x = r\cos\theta \Rightarrow x = (-2)\cos 135° = \sqrt{2}$ and $y = r\sin\theta \Rightarrow y = (-2)\sin 135° = \sqrt{2}$, the point is $\left(\sqrt{2}, -\sqrt{2}\right)$.

7. (a)

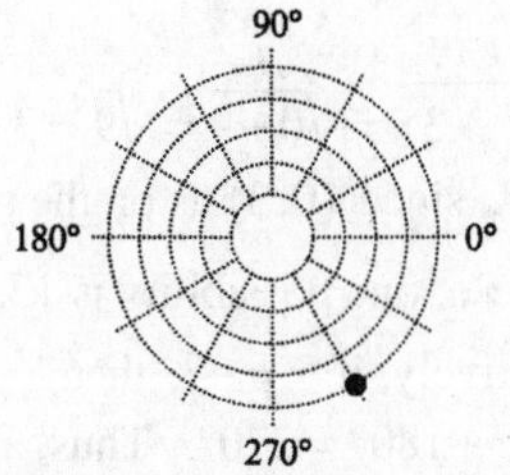

(b) Two other pairs of polar coordinates for (5, – 60°) are (5, 300°) and (–5, 120°).

(c) Since $x = r\cos\theta \Rightarrow x = 5\cos(-60°) = \dfrac{5}{2}$ and $y = r\sin\theta \Rightarrow y = 5\sin(-60°) = -\dfrac{5\sqrt{3}}{2}$, the point is $\left(\dfrac{5}{2}, -\dfrac{5\sqrt{3}}{2}\right)$.

9. (a)

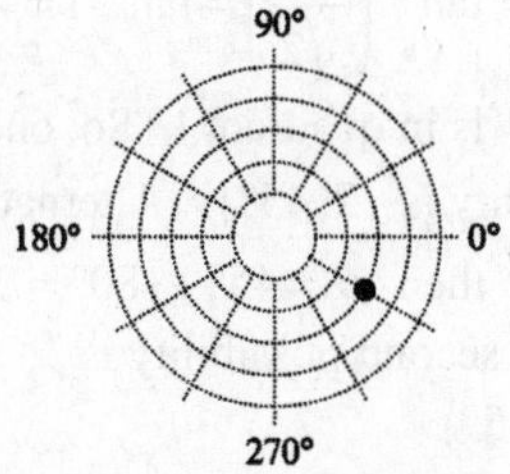

(b) Two other pairs of polar coordinates for (–3, –210°) are (–3, 150°) and (3, –30°).

(c) Since $x = r\cos\theta \Rightarrow x = (-3)\cos(-210°) = \dfrac{3\sqrt{3}}{2}$ and $y = r\sin\theta \Rightarrow y = (-3)\sin(-210°) = -\dfrac{3}{2}$, the point is $\left(\dfrac{3\sqrt{3}}{2}, -\dfrac{3}{2}\right)$.

11. (a)

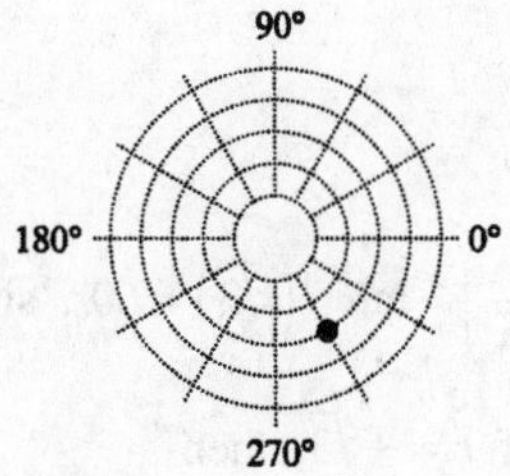

(b) Two other pairs of polar coordinates for $\left(3, \dfrac{5\pi}{3}\right)$ are $\left(3, \dfrac{11\pi}{3}\right)$ and $\left(-3, \dfrac{2\pi}{3}\right)$.

(c) Since $x = r\cos\theta \Rightarrow x = 3\cos\dfrac{5\pi}{3} = \dfrac{3}{2}$ and $y = r\sin\theta \Rightarrow y = 3\sin\dfrac{5\pi}{3} = -\dfrac{3\sqrt{3}}{2}$, the point is $\left(\dfrac{3}{2}, -\dfrac{3\sqrt{3}}{2}\right)$.

For Exercises 13 – 21, answers may vary.

13. (a)

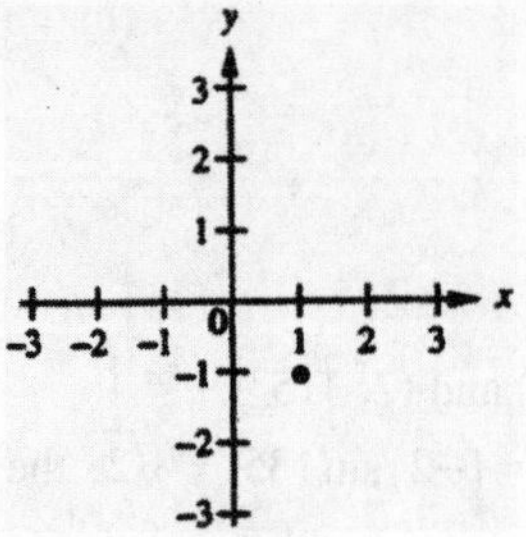

(b) $r=\sqrt{1^2+(-1)^2}=\sqrt{1+1}=\sqrt{2}$ and $\theta=\tan^{-1}\left(\frac{-1}{1}\right)=\tan^{-1}(-1)=-45°$, since θ is in quadrant IV. Since $360°-45°=315°$, one possibility is $\left(\sqrt{2},315°\right)$. Alternatively, if $r=-\sqrt{2}$, then $\theta=315°-180°=135°$. Thus, a second possibility is $\left(-\sqrt{2},135°\right)$.

15. (a)

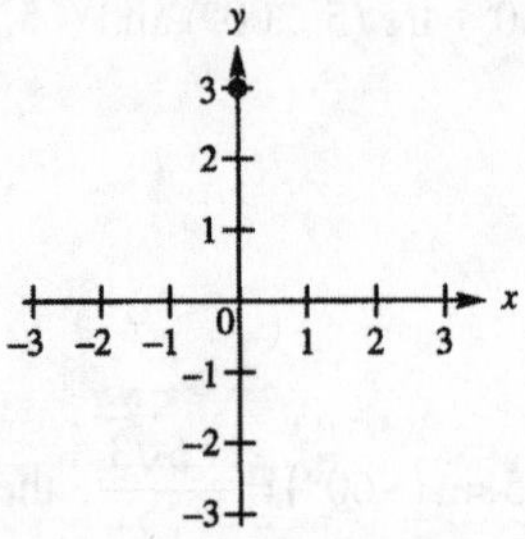

(b) $r=\sqrt{0^2+3^2}=\sqrt{0+9}=\sqrt{9}=3$ and $\theta=90°$, since $(0,3)$ is on the positive *y*-axis. So, one possibility is $(3,90°)$. Alternatively, if $r=-3$, then $\theta=90°+180°=270°$. Thus, a second possibility is $(-3,270°)$.

17. (a)

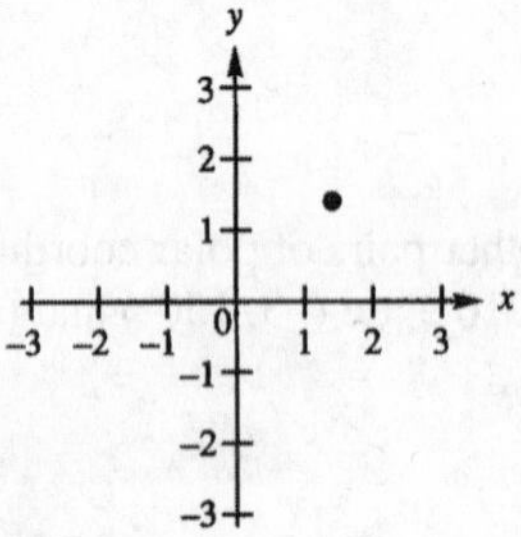

(b) $r=\sqrt{\left(\sqrt{2}\right)^2+\left(\sqrt{2}\right)^2}=\sqrt{2+2}=\sqrt{4}=2$ and $\theta=\tan^{-1}\left(\frac{\sqrt{2}}{\sqrt{2}}\right)=\tan^{-1}1=45°$, since θ is in quadrant I. So, one possibility is $(2,45°)$. Alternatively, if $r=-2$, then $\theta=45°+180°=225°$. Thus, a second possibility is $(-2,225°)$.

19. (a)

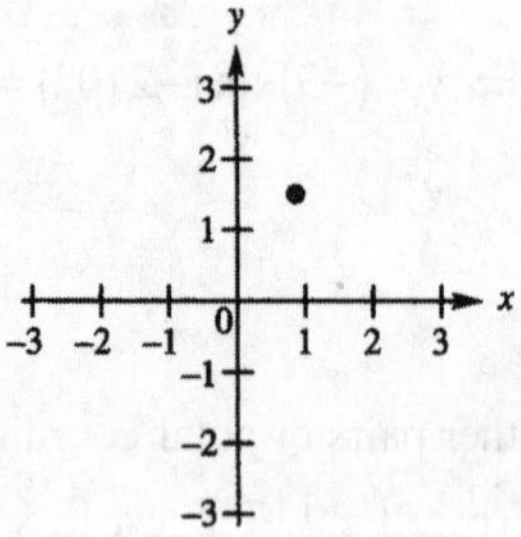

(b) $r=\sqrt{\left(\frac{\sqrt{3}}{2}\right)^2+\left(\frac{3}{2}\right)^2}=\sqrt{\frac{3}{4}+\frac{9}{4}}=\sqrt{\frac{12}{4}}=\sqrt{3}$ and $\theta=\arctan\left(\frac{3}{2}\cdot\frac{2}{\sqrt{3}}\right)=\tan^{-1}\left(\sqrt{3}\right)=60°$, since θ is in quadrant I. So, one possibility is $\left(\sqrt{3},60°\right)$. Alternatively, if $r=-\sqrt{3}$, then $\theta=60°+180°=240°$. Thus, a second possibility is $\left(-\sqrt{3},240°\right)$.

21. (a)

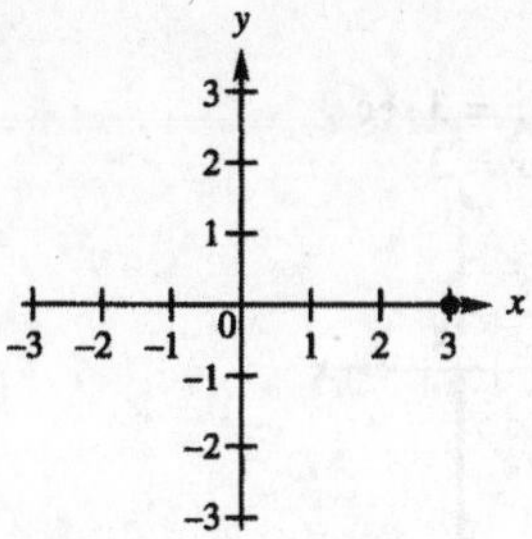

(b) $r=\sqrt{3^2+0^2}=\sqrt{9+0}=\sqrt{9}=3$ and $\theta=0°$, since $(3,0)$ is on the positive x-axis. So, one possibility is $(3,0°)$. Alternatively, if $r=-3$, then $\theta=0°+180°=180°$. Thus, a second possibility is $(-3,180°)$.

23. $x-y=4$

Using the general form for the polar equation of a line, $r=\dfrac{c}{a\cos\theta+b\sin\theta}$, with $a=1, b=-1$, and $c=4$, the polar equation is $r=\dfrac{4}{\cos\theta-\sin\theta}$.

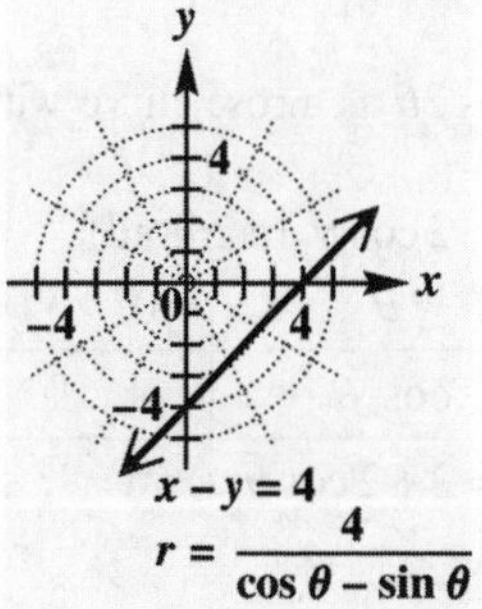

25. $x^2+y^2=16 \Rightarrow r^2=16 \Rightarrow r=\pm 4$

The equation of the circle in polar form is $r=4$ or $r=-4$.

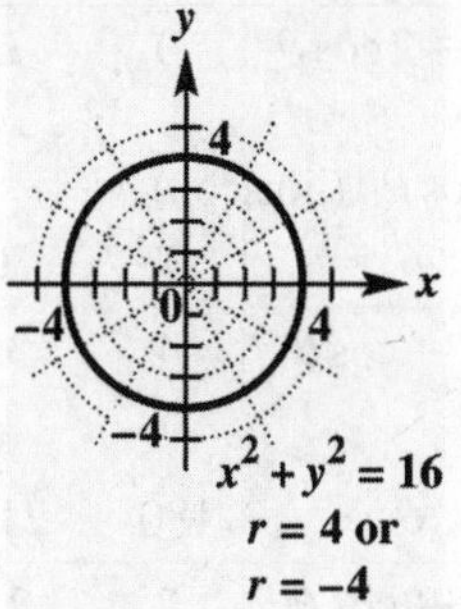

27. $2x+y=5$

Using the general form for the polar equation of a line, $r=\dfrac{c}{a\cos\theta+b\sin\theta}$, with $a=2, b=1$, and $c=5$, the polar equation is $r=\dfrac{5}{2\cos\theta+\sin\theta}$.

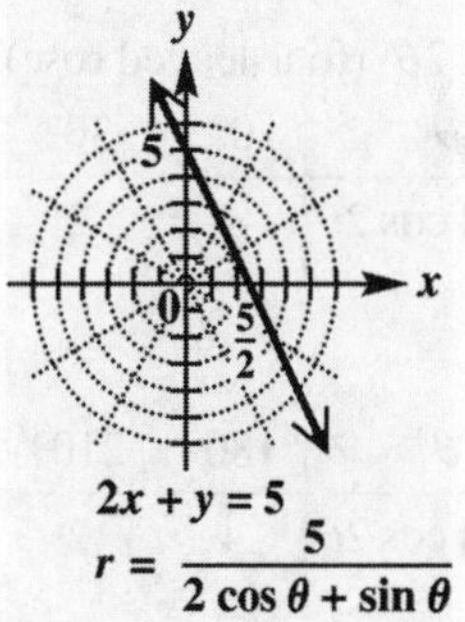

29. $r\sin\theta=k$

30. $r=\dfrac{k}{\sin\theta}$

31. $r=\dfrac{k}{\sin\theta} \Rightarrow r=k\csc\theta$

32. $y=3$

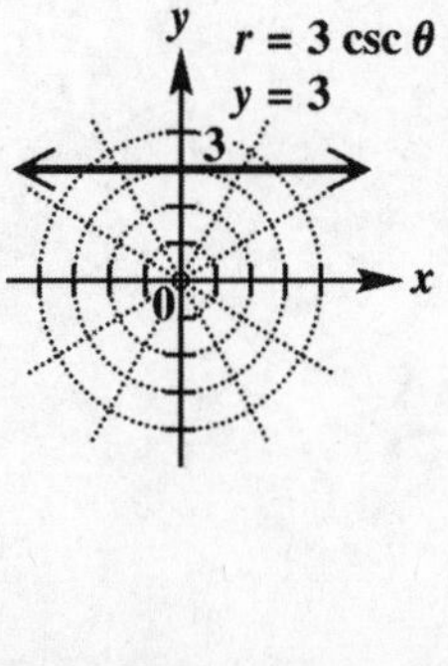

33. $r\cos\theta = k$

34. $r = \dfrac{k}{\cos\theta}$

35. $r = \dfrac{k}{\cos\theta} \Rightarrow r = k\sec\theta$

36. $x = 3$

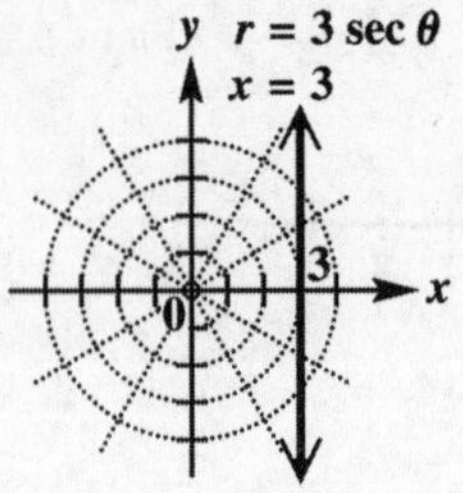

37. $r = 3$ represents the set of all points 3 units from the pole. The correct choice is C.

39. $r = \cos 2\theta$ is a rose curve with $2 \cdot 2 = 4$ petals. The correct choice is A

41. $r = 2 + 2\cos\theta$ (cardioid)

θ	0°	30°	60°	90°	120°	150°
$\cos\theta$	1	.9	.5	0	–.5	–.9
$r = 2 + 2\cos\theta$	4	3.8	3	2	1	.2

θ	180°	210°	240°	270°	300°	330°
$\cos\theta$	–1	–.9	–.5	0	.5	.9
$r = 2 + 2\cos\theta$	0	.3	1	2	3	3.7

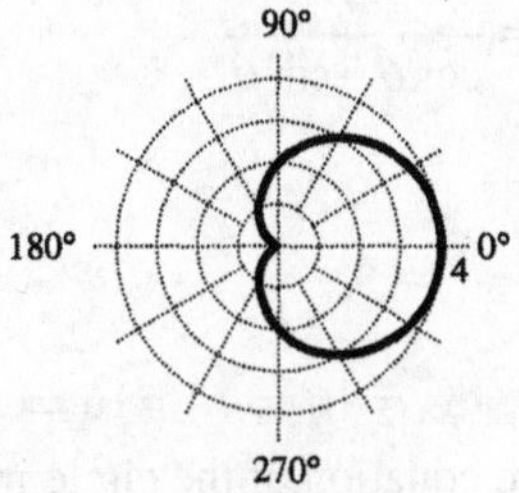

43. $r = 3 + \cos\theta$ (limaçon)

θ	0°	30°	60°	90°	120°	150°
$r = 3 + \cos\theta$	4	3.9	3.5	3	2.5	2.1

θ	180°	210°	240°	270°	300°	330°
$r = 3 + \cos\theta$	2	2.1	2.5	3	3.5	3.9

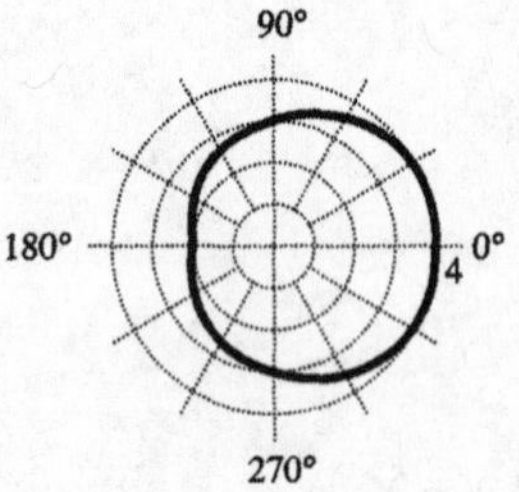

45. $r = 4\cos 2\theta$ (four-leaved rose)

θ	0°	30°	45°	60°	90°	120°	135°	150°
$r = 4\cos 2\theta$	4	2	0	–2	–4	–2	0	2

θ	180°	210°	225°	240°	270°	300°	315°	330°
$r = 4\cos 2\theta$	4	2	0	–2	–4	–2	0	2

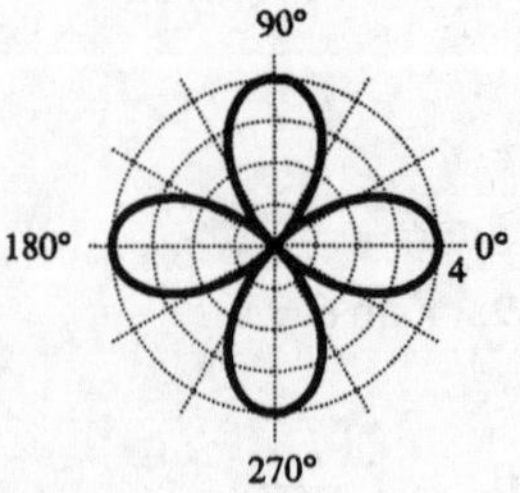

47. $r^2 = 4\cos 2\theta \Rightarrow r = \pm 2\sqrt{\cos 2\theta}$ (lemniscate)

Graph only exists for [0°, 45°], [135°, 225°], and [315°, 360°] because $\cos 2\theta$ must be positive.

θ	0°	30°	45°	135°	150°
$r = \pm 2\sqrt{\cos 2\theta}$	±2	±1.4	0	0	±1.4

θ	180°	210°	225°	315°	330°
$r = \pm 2\sqrt{\cos 2\theta}$	±2	±1.4	0	0	±1.4

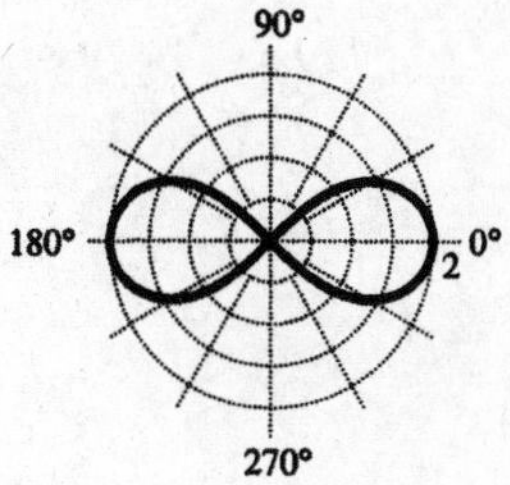

49. $r = 4 - 4\cos\theta$ (cardioid)

θ	0°	30°	60°	90°	120°	150°
$r = 4 - 4\cos\theta$	0	.5	2	4	6	7.5

θ	180°	210°	240°	270°	300°	330°
$r = 4 - 4\cos\theta$	8	7.5	6	4	2	.5

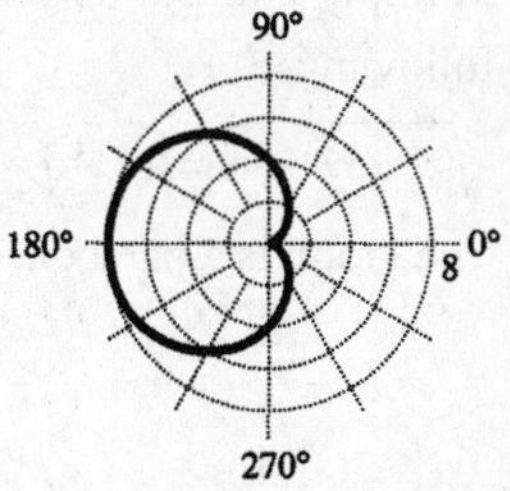

51. $r = 2\sin\theta\tan\theta$ (cissoid)

r is undefined at $\theta = 90°$ and $\theta = 270°$.

θ	0°	30°	45°	60°	90°	120°	135°	150°	180°
$r = 2\sin\theta\tan\theta$	0	.6	1.4	3	–	–3	–1.4	–.6	0

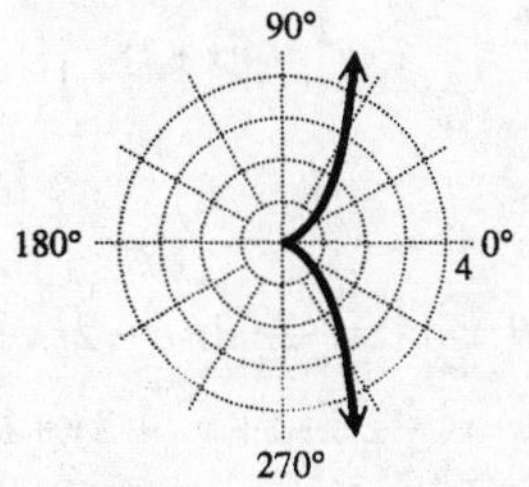

Notice that for [180°, 360°), the graph retraces the path traced for [0°, 180°).

53. $r = 2\sin\theta$

Multiply both sides by r to obtain $r^2 = 2r\sin\theta$. Since $r^2 = x^2 + y^2$ and $y = r\sin\theta$, $x^2 + y^2 = 2y$.

Complete the square on y to obtain $x^2 + y^2 - 2y + 1 = 1 \Rightarrow x^2 + (y-1)^2 = 1$.

The graph is a circle with center at $(0,1)$ and radius 1.

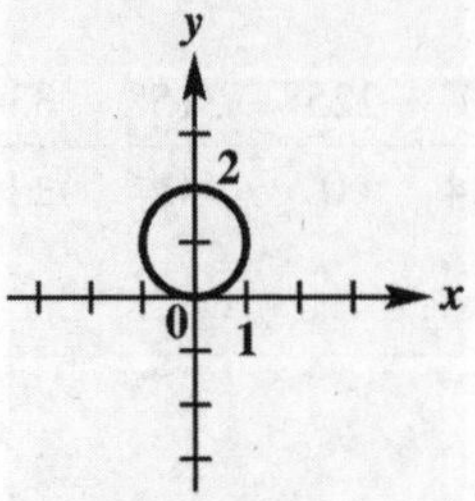

$r = 2\sin\theta$
$x^2 + (y-1)^2 = 1$

55. $r = \dfrac{2}{1-\cos\theta}$

Multiply both sides by $1 - \cos\theta$ to obtain $r - r\cos\theta = 2$. Substitute $r = \sqrt{x^2 + y^2}$ to obtain the following.

$\sqrt{x^2 + y^2} - x = 2 \Rightarrow \sqrt{x^2 + y^2} = 2 + x \Rightarrow x^2 + y^2 = (2+x)^2 \Rightarrow x^2 + y^2 = 4 + 4x + x^2 \Rightarrow y^2 = 4(1+x)$

The graph is a parabola with vertex at $(-1,0)$ and axis $y = 0$.

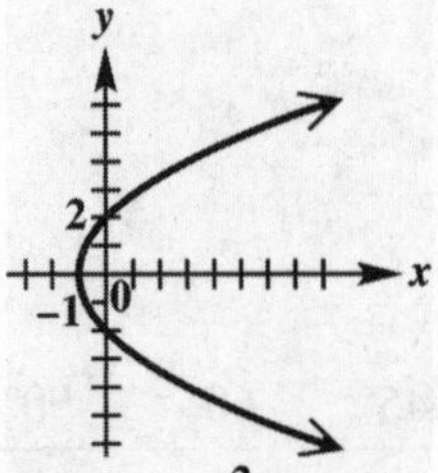

$r = \dfrac{2}{1-\cos\theta}$
$y^2 = 4(x+1)$

57. $r + 2\cos\theta = -2\sin\theta$

$$r + 2\cos\theta = -2\sin\theta \Rightarrow r^2 = -2r\sin\theta - 2r\cos\theta \Rightarrow x^2 + y^2 = -2y - 2x$$

$$x^2 + 2x + y^2 + 2y = 0 \Rightarrow x^2 + 2x + 1 + y^2 + 2y + 1 = 2 \Rightarrow (x+1)^2 + (y+1)^2 = 2$$

The graph is a circle with center $(-1,-1)$ and radius $\sqrt{2}$.

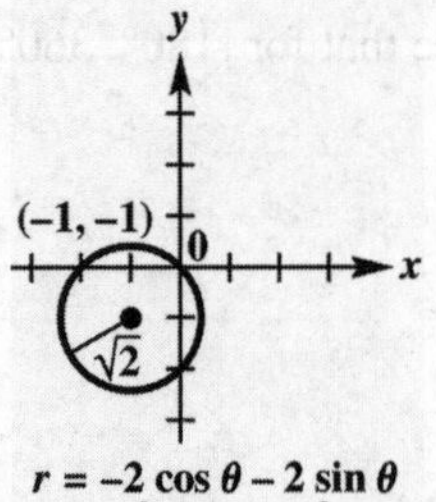

$r = -2\cos\theta - 2\sin\theta$
$(x+1)^2 + (y+1)^2 = 2$

59. $r = 2\sec\theta$

$$r = 2\sec\theta \Rightarrow r = \frac{2}{\cos\theta} \Rightarrow r\cos\theta = 2 \Rightarrow x = 2$$

The graph is a vertical line, intercepting the x-axis at 2.

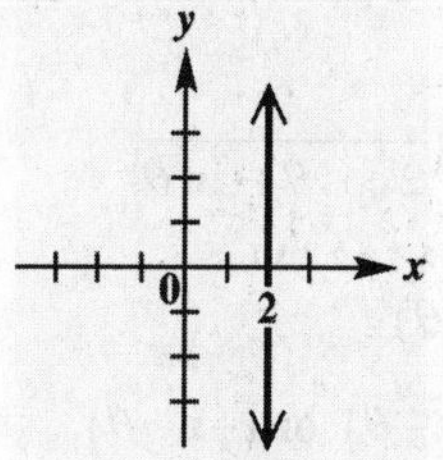

$r = 2\sec\theta$
$x = 2$

61. $r = \dfrac{2}{\cos\theta + \sin\theta}$

Using the general form for the polar equation of a line, $r = \dfrac{c}{a\cos\theta + b\sin\theta}$, with $a = 1,\ b = 1,$ and $c = 2,$ we have $x + y = 2.$

The graph is a line with intercepts $(0, 2)$ and $(2, 0)$.

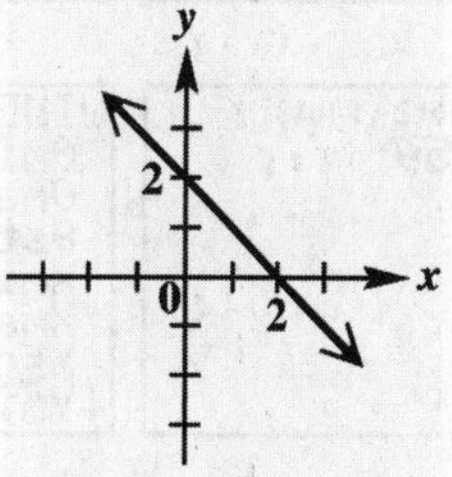

$r = \dfrac{2}{\cos\theta + \sin\theta}$
$x + y = 2$

63. Graph $r = \theta$, a spiral of Archimedes.

θ	–360°	–270°	–180°	–90°
θ (radians)	–6.3	–4.7	–3.1	–1.6
$r = \theta$	–6.3	–4.7	–3.1	–1.6

θ	0°	90°	180°	270°	360°
θ (radians)	0	1.6	3.1	4.7	6.3
$r = \theta$	0	1.6	3.1	4.7	6.3

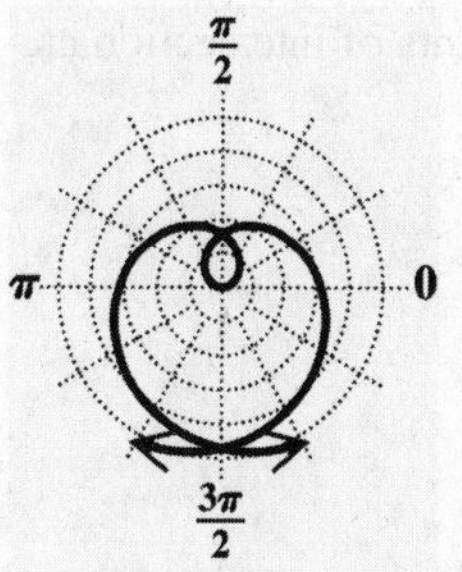

$r = \theta$

65. In rectangular coordinates, the line passes through $(1,0)$ and $(0,2)$. So $m=\dfrac{2-0}{0-1}=\dfrac{2}{-1}=-2$ and $(y-0)=-2(x-1)\Rightarrow y=-2x+2\Rightarrow 2x+y=2$. Converting to polar form $r=\dfrac{c}{a\cos\theta+b\sin\theta}$, we have: $r=\dfrac{2}{2\cos\theta+\sin\theta}$.

67. (a) $(r,-\theta)$

(b) $(r,\pi-\theta)$ or $(-r,-\theta)$

(c) $(r,\pi+\theta)$ or $(-r,\theta)$

69.

71.

73. $r=4\sin\theta,\ r=1+2\sin\theta,\ 0\le\theta<2\pi$

$$4\sin\theta=1+2\sin\theta\Rightarrow 2\sin\theta=1\Rightarrow\sin\theta=\frac{1}{2}\Rightarrow\theta=\frac{\pi}{6}\text{ or }\frac{5\pi}{6}$$

The points of intersection are $\left(4\sin\dfrac{\pi}{6},\dfrac{\pi}{6}\right)=\left(2,\dfrac{\pi}{6}\right)$ and $\left(4\sin\dfrac{5\pi}{6},\dfrac{5\pi}{6}\right)=\left(2,\dfrac{5\pi}{6}\right)$.

75. $r=2+\sin\theta,\ r=2+\cos\theta,\ 0\le\theta<2\pi$

$$2+\sin\theta=2+\cos\theta\Rightarrow\sin\theta=\cos\theta\Rightarrow\theta=\frac{\pi}{4}\text{ or }\frac{5\pi}{4}$$

$$r=2+\sin\frac{\pi}{4}=2+\frac{\sqrt{2}}{2}=\frac{4+\sqrt{2}}{2}\quad\text{and}\quad r=2+\sin\frac{5\pi}{4}=2-\frac{\sqrt{2}}{2}=\frac{4-\sqrt{2}}{2}$$

The points of intersection are $\left(\dfrac{4+\sqrt{2}}{2},\dfrac{\pi}{4}\right)$ and $\left(\dfrac{4-\sqrt{2}}{2},\dfrac{5\pi}{4}\right)$.

77. (a) Plot the following polar equations on the same polar axis in radian mode: Mercury: $r = \dfrac{.39(1-.206^2)}{1+.206\cos\theta}$; Venus: $r = \dfrac{.78(1-.007^2)}{1+.007\cos\theta}$; Earth: $r = \dfrac{1(1-.017^2)}{1+.017\cos\theta}$;

Mars: $r = \dfrac{1.52(1-.093^2)}{1+.093\cos\theta}$.

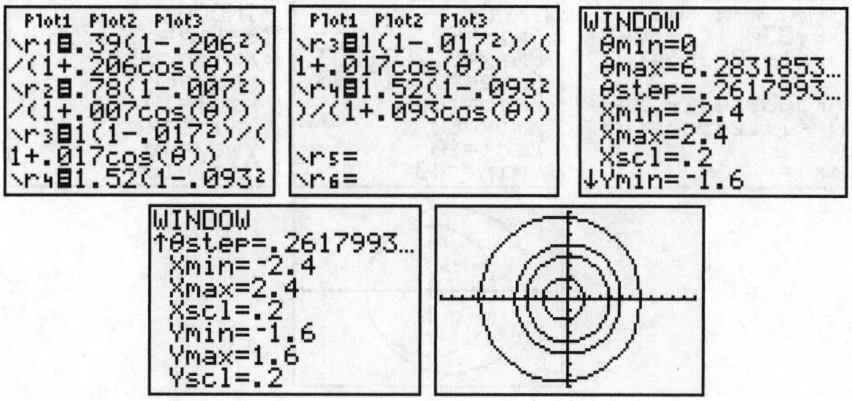

(b) Plot the following polar equations on the same polar axis: Earth: $r = \dfrac{1(1-.017^2)}{1+.017\cos\theta}$;

Jupiter: $r = \dfrac{5.2(1-.048^2)}{1+.048\cos\theta}$; Uranus: $r = \dfrac{19.2(1-.047^2)}{1+.047\cos\theta}$; Pluto: $r = \dfrac{39.4(1-.249^2)}{1+.249\cos\theta}$.

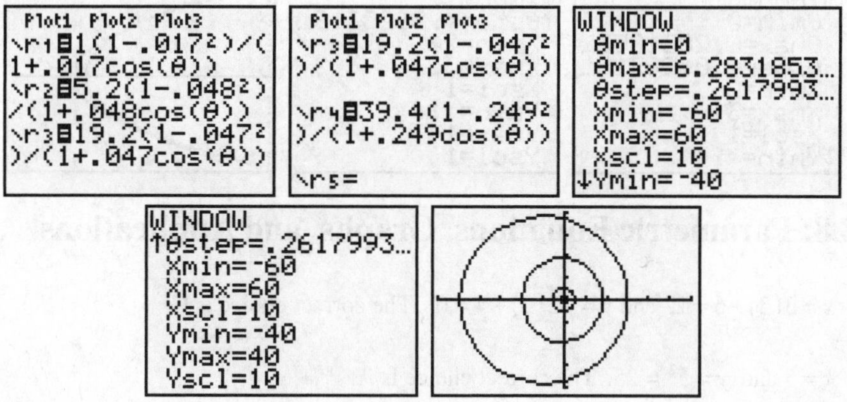

Continued on next page

77. (continued)

(c) We must determine if the orbit of Pluto is always outside the orbits of the other planets. Since Neptune is closest to Pluto, plot the orbits of Neptune and Pluto on the same polar axes.

$$\text{Neptune: } r=\frac{30.1(1-.009^2)}{1+.009\cos\theta};\ \text{Pluto: } r=\frac{39.4(1-.249^2)}{1+.249\cos\theta}$$

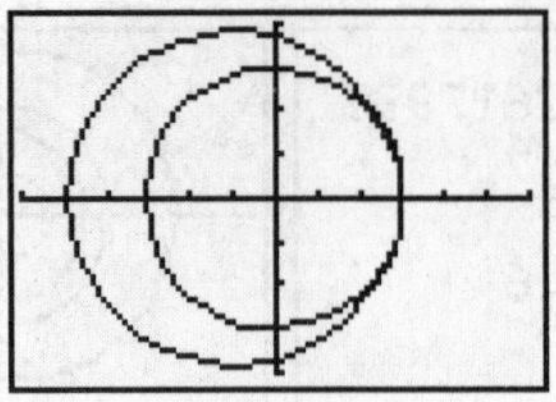

The graph shows that their orbits are very close near the polar axis.

Use ZOOM or change your window to see that the orbit of Pluto does indeed pass inside the orbit of Neptune. Therefore, there are times when Neptune, not Pluto, is the farthest planet from the sun. (However, Pluto's average distance from the sun is considerably greater than Neptune's average distance.)

Section 8.8: Parametric Equations, Graphs, and Applications

1. At $t=2$, $x=3(2)+6=12$ and $y=-2(2)+4=0$. The correct choice is C.

3. At $t=5$, $x=5$ and $y=5^2=25$. The correct choice is A.

5. **(a)** $x=t+2$, $y=t^2$, for t in $[-1, 1]$

t	$x=t+2$	$y=t^2$
-1	$-1+2=1$	$(-1)^2=1$
0	$0+2=2$	$0^2=0$
1	$1+2=3$	$1^2=1$

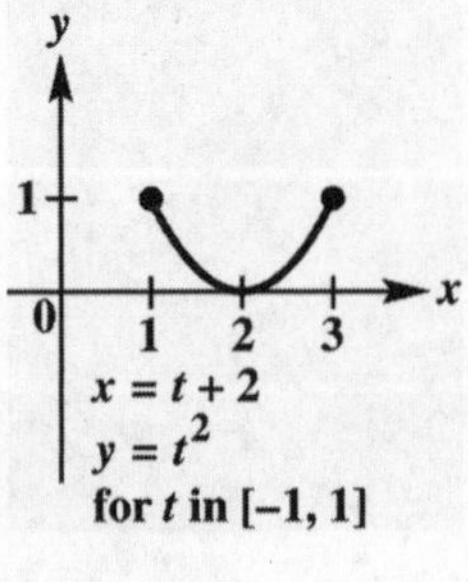

(b) $x-2=t$, therefore $y=(x-2)^2$ or $y=x^2-4x+4$. Since t is in $[-1, 1]$, x is in $[-1+2, 1+2]$ or $[1, 3]$.

7. **(a)** $x=\sqrt{t}$, $y=3t-4$, for t in [0, 4].

t	$x=\sqrt{t}$	$y=3t-4$
0	$\sqrt{0}=0$	$3(0)-4=-4$
1	$\sqrt{1}=1$	$3(1)-4=-1$
2	$\sqrt{2}=1.4$	$3(2)-4=2$
3	$\sqrt{3}=1.7$	$3(3)-4=5$
4	$\sqrt{4}=2$	$3(4)-4=8$

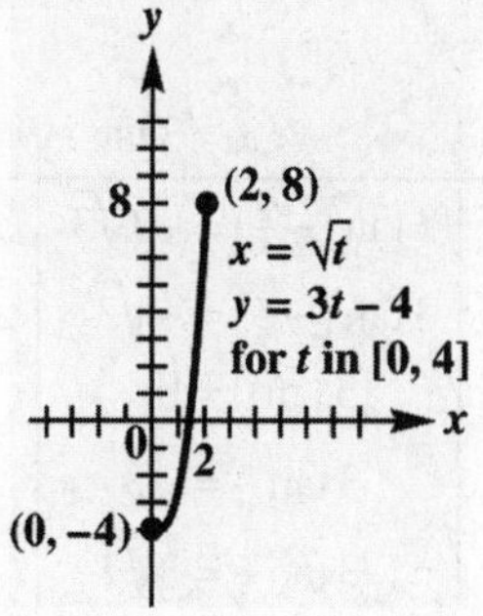

(b) $x=\sqrt{t}$, $y=3t-4$

Since $x=\sqrt{t}\Rightarrow x^2=t$, we have $y=3x^2-4$. Since t is in [0, 4], x is in $[\sqrt{0},\sqrt{4}]$ or [0, 2].

9. **(a)** $x=t^3+1$, $y=t^3-1$, for t in $(-\infty,\infty)$

t	$x=t^3+1$	$y=t^3-1$
-2	$(-2)^3+1=-7$	$(-2)^3-1=-9$
-1	$(-1)^3+1=0$	$(-1)^3-1=-2$
0	$0^3+1=1$	$0^3-1=-1$
1	$1^3+1=2$	$1^3-1=0$
2	$2^3+1=9$	$2^3-1=7$
3	$3^3+1=28$	$3^3-1=26$

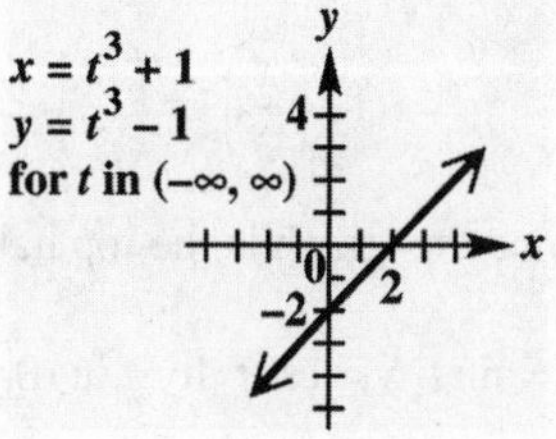

(b) Since $x=t^3+1$, we have $x-1=t^3$. Since $y=t^3-1$, we have $y=(x-1)-1=x-2$. Since t is in $(-\infty,\infty)$, x is in $(-\infty,\infty)$.

11. **(a)** $x=2\sin t$, $y=2\cos t$, for t in $[0, 2\pi]$

t	$x=2\sin t$	$y=2\cos t$
0	$2\sin 0=0$	$2\cos\theta=2$
$\frac{\pi}{6}$	$2\sin\frac{\pi}{6}=1$	$2\cos\frac{\pi}{6}=\sqrt{3}$
$\frac{\pi}{4}$	$2\sin\frac{\pi}{4}=\sqrt{2}$	$2\cos\frac{\pi}{4}=\sqrt{2}$
$\frac{\pi}{3}$	$2\sin\frac{\pi}{3}=\sqrt{3}$	$2\cos\frac{\pi}{3}=1$
$\frac{\pi}{2}$	$2\sin\frac{\pi}{2}=2$	$2\cos\frac{\pi}{2}=0$

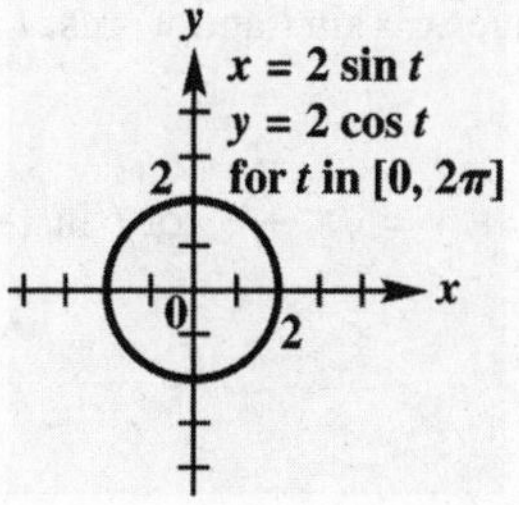

(b) Since $x=2\sin t$ and $y=2\cos t$, we have $\frac{x}{2}=\sin t$ and $\frac{y}{2}=\cos t$.

Since $\sin^2 t+\cos^2 t=1$, we have $\left(\frac{x}{2}\right)^2+\left(\frac{y}{2}\right)^2=1\Rightarrow\frac{x^2}{4}+\frac{y^2}{4}=1\Rightarrow x^2+y^2=4$. Since t is in $[0, 2\pi]$, x is in $[-2, 2]$ because the graph is a circle, centered at the origin, with radius 2.

13. (a) $x = 3\tan t,\ y = 2\sec t,$ for t in $\left(-\frac{\pi}{2}, \frac{\pi}{2}\right)$

t	$x = 3\tan t$	$y = 2\sec t$
$-\frac{\pi}{3}$	$3\tan\left(-\frac{\pi}{3}\right) = -3\sqrt{3}$	$2\sec\left(-\frac{\pi}{3}\right) = 4$
$-\frac{\pi}{6}$	$3\tan\left(-\frac{\pi}{6}\right) = -\sqrt{3}$	$2\sec\left(-\frac{\pi}{6}\right) = \frac{4\sqrt{3}}{3}$
0	$3\tan 0 = 0$	$2\sec 0 = 2$
$\frac{\pi}{6}$	$3\tan\frac{\pi}{6} = \sqrt{3}$	$2\sec\frac{\pi}{6} = \frac{4\sqrt{3}}{3}$
$\frac{\pi}{3}$	$3\tan\frac{\pi}{3} = 3\sqrt{3}$	$2\sec\frac{\pi}{3} = 4$

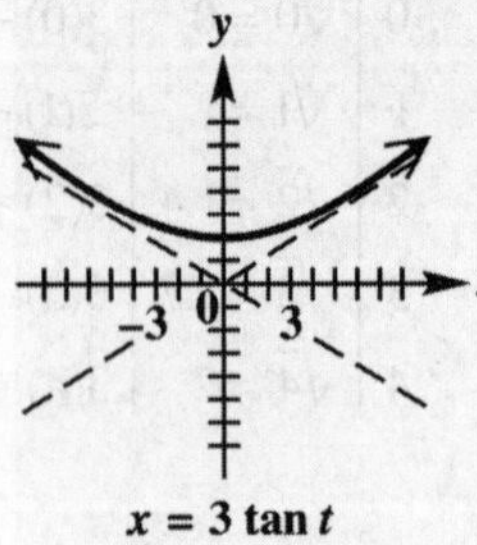

(b) Since $\frac{x}{3} = \tan t,\ \frac{y}{2} = \sec t,$ and $1 + \tan^2 t = \left(\frac{y}{2}\right)^2 = \sec^2 t,$ we have the following.

$$1 + \left(\frac{x}{3}\right)^2 = \left(\frac{y}{2}\right)^2 \Rightarrow 1 + \frac{x^2}{9} = \frac{y^2}{4} \Rightarrow y^2 = 4\left(1 + \frac{x^2}{9}\right) \Rightarrow y = 2\sqrt{1 + \frac{x^2}{9}}$$

Since this graph is the top half of a hyperbola, x is in $(-\infty, \infty)$.

15. (a) $x = \sin t,\ y = \csc t$ for t in $(0, \pi)$

Since t is in $(0, \pi)$ and $x = \sin t$, x is in $(0, 1]$.

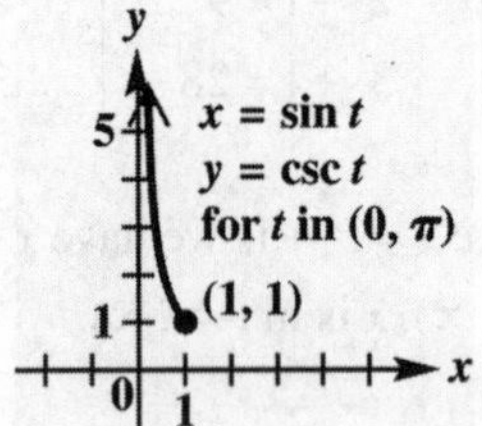

(b) Since $x = \sin t$ and $y = \csc t = \frac{1}{\sin t}$, we have $y = \frac{1}{x}$, where x is in $(0, 1]$.

17. (a) $x = t,\ y = \sqrt{t^2 + 2},$ for t in $(-\infty, \infty)$

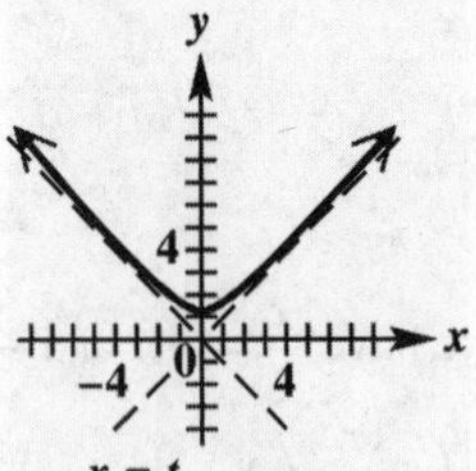

(b) Since $x = t$ and $y = \sqrt{t^2 + 2},\ y = \sqrt{x^2 + 2}.$ Since t is in $(-\infty\ \infty)$ and $x = t,\ x$ is in $(-\infty, \infty)$.

19. **(a)** $x = 2 + \sin t,\ y = 1 + \cos t,$ for t in $[0, 2\pi]$

Since this is a circle centered at $(2, 1)$ with radius 1, and t is in $[0, 2\pi]$, x is in $[1, 3]$.

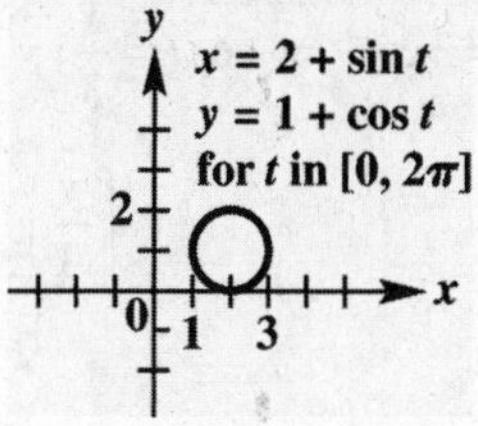

(b) Since $x = 2 + \sin t$ and $y = 1 + \cos t$, $x - 2 = \sin t$ and $y - 1 = \cos t$. Since $\sin^2 t + \cos^2 t = 1$, we have $(x-2)^2 + (y-1)^2 = 1$.

21. **(a)** $x = t + 2,\ y = \dfrac{1}{t+2}$, for $t \neq 2$

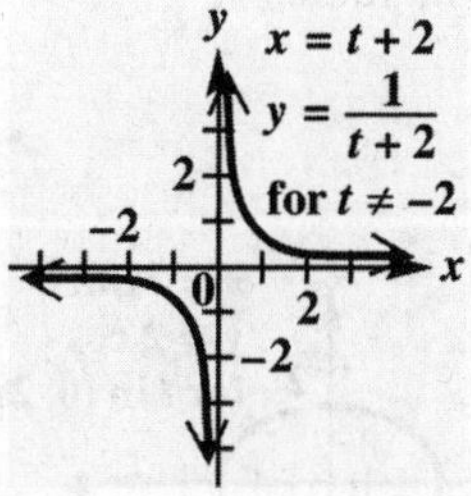

(b) Since $x = t + 2$ and $y = \dfrac{1}{t+2}$, we have $y = \dfrac{1}{x}$. Since $t \neq -2$, $x \neq -2 + 2$, $x \neq 0$. Therefore, x is in $(-\infty, 0) \cup (0, \infty)$.

23. **(a)** $x = t + 2,\ y = t - 4,$ for t in $(-\infty, \infty)$

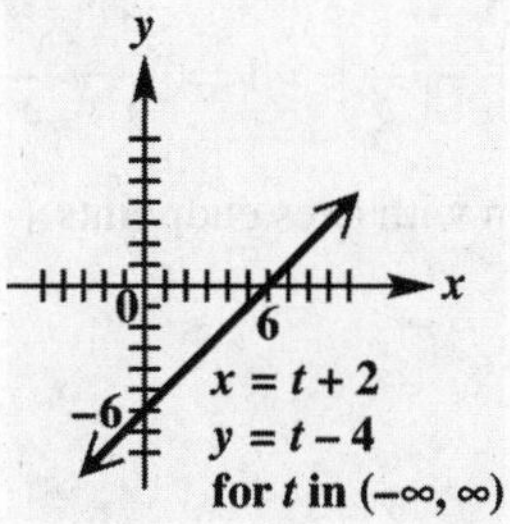

(b) Since $x = t + 2$, we have $t = x - 2$. Since $y = t - 4$, we have $y = (x-2) - 4 = x - 6$. Since t is in $(-\infty, \infty)$, x is in $(-\infty, \infty)$.

25. $x = 3\cos t,\ y = 3\sin t$

Since $x = 3\cos t \Rightarrow \cos t = \frac{x}{3}$, $y = 3\sin t \Rightarrow \sin t = \frac{y}{3}$, and $\sin^2 t + \cos^2 t = 1$, we have the following.

$$\left(\frac{y}{3}\right)^2 + \left(\frac{x}{3}\right)^2 = 1 \Rightarrow \frac{y^2}{9} + \frac{x^2}{9} = 1 \Rightarrow x^2 + y^2 = 9$$

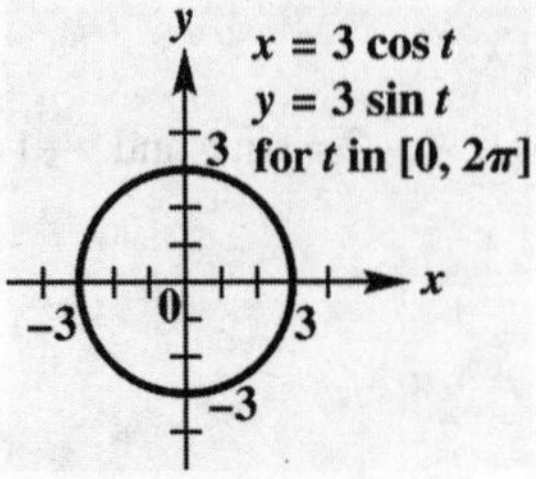

This is a circle centered at the origin with radius 3.

27. $x = 3\sin t,\ y = 2\cos t$

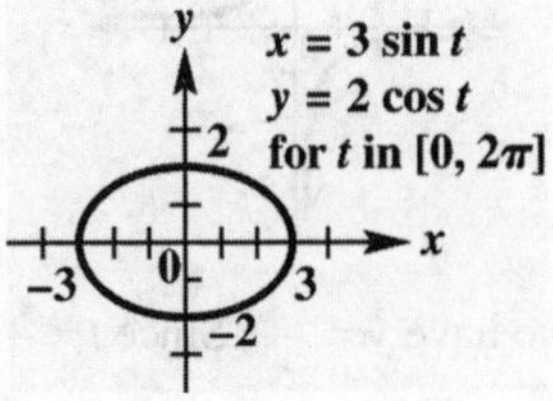

Since $x = 3\sin t \Rightarrow \sin t = \frac{x}{3}$, $y = 2\cos t \Rightarrow \cos t = \frac{y}{2}$, and $\sin^2 t + \cos^2 t = 1$, we have the following.

$$\left(\frac{x}{3}\right)^2 + \left(\frac{y}{2}\right)^2 = 1 \Rightarrow \frac{x^2}{9} + \frac{y^2}{4} = 1$$

This is an ellipse centered at the origin with axes endpoints $(-3,0), (3,0), (0,-2), (0,2)$.

In Exercises 29 & 31, answers may vary.

29. $y = (x+3)^2 - 1$

$x = t,\ y = (t+3)^2 - 1$ for t in $(-\infty, \infty)$; $x = t-3,\ y = t^2 - 1$ for t in $(-\infty, \infty)$

31. $y = x^2 - 2x + 3 = (x-1)^2 + 2$

$x = t,\ y = (t-1)^2 + 2$ for t in $(-\infty, \infty)$; $x = t+1,\ y = t^2 + 2$ for t in $(-\infty, \infty)$

33. $x = 2t - 2\sin t,\ y = 2 - 2\cos t,$ for t in $[0, 8\pi]$

t	0	$\frac{\pi}{2}$	π	$\frac{3\pi}{2}$	2π	3π	4π	5π	6π	7π	8π
$x = 2t - 2\sin t$	0	1.4	2π	11.4	4π	6π	8π	10π	12π	14π	16π
$y = 2 - 2\cos t$	0	2	4	2	0	4	0	4	0	4	0

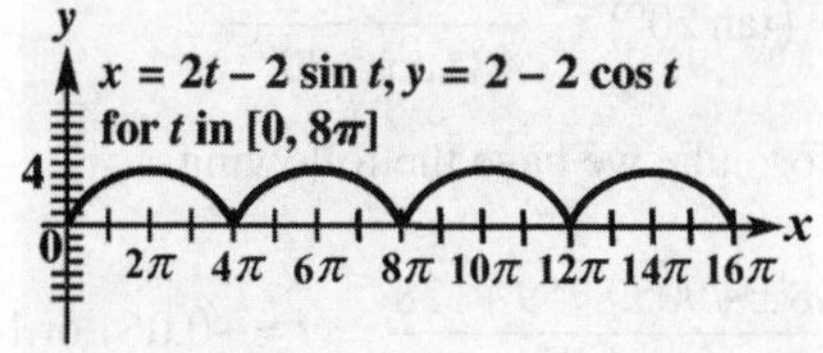

Note: The graph in the answer section of your text shows up to 8π on the x-axis.

Exercises 35 & 37 are graphed in parametric mode in the following window.

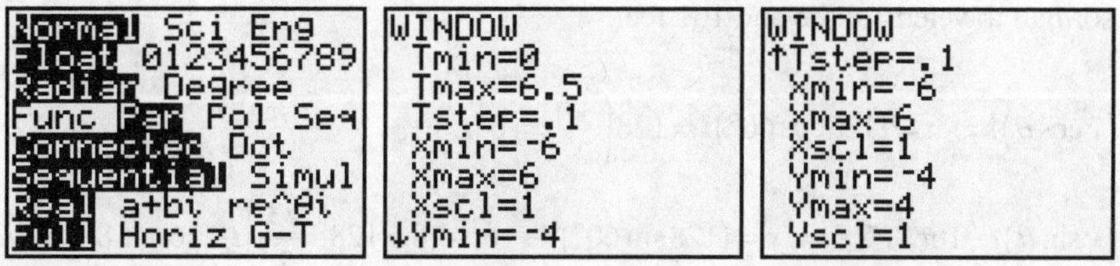

35. $x = 2\cos t,\ y = 3\sin 2t$

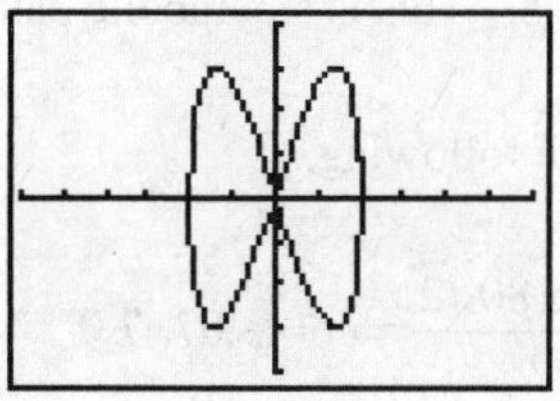

37. $x = 3\sin 4t,\ y = 3\cos 3t$

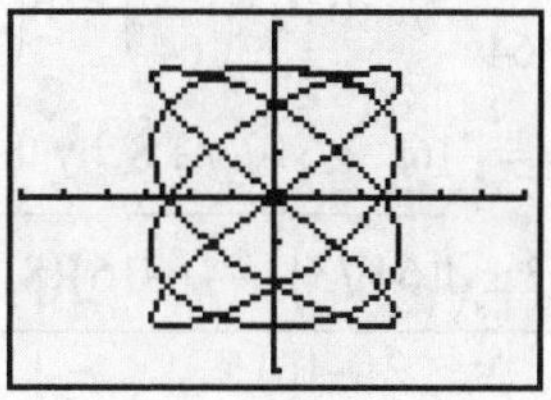

For Exercises 39 & 41, recall that the motion of a projectile (neglecting air resistance) can be modeled by: $x = (v_0 \cos\theta)t,\ y = (v_0 \sin\theta)t - 16t^2$ for t in $[0, k]$.

39. (a) $x = (v\cos\theta)t \Rightarrow x = (48\cos 60°)t = 48\left(\frac{1}{2}\right)t = 24t$

$$y = (v\sin\theta)t - 16t^2 \Rightarrow y = (48\sin 60°)t - 16t^2 = 48\cdot\frac{\sqrt{3}}{2}t - 16t^2 = -16t^2 + 24\sqrt{3}t$$

(b) $t = \frac{x}{24}$, so $y = -16\left(\frac{x}{24}\right)^2 + 24\sqrt{3}\left(\frac{x}{24}\right) = -\frac{x^2}{36} + \sqrt{3}x$

(c) $y = -16t^2 + 24\sqrt{3}t$

When the rocket is no longer in flight, $y = 0$. Solve $0 = -16t^2 + 24\sqrt{3}t \Rightarrow 0 = t\left(-16t + 24\sqrt{3}\right)$.

$$t = 0 \text{ or } -16t + 24\sqrt{3} = 0 \Rightarrow -16t = -24\sqrt{3} \Rightarrow t = \frac{24\sqrt{3}}{16} \Rightarrow t = \frac{3\sqrt{3}}{2} \approx 2.6$$

The flight time is about 2.6 seconds. The horizontal distance at $t = \frac{3\sqrt{3}}{2}$ is the following.

$$x = 24t = 24\left(\frac{3\sqrt{3}}{2}\right) \approx 62 \text{ ft}$$

41. (a) $x=(v\cos\theta)t \Rightarrow x=(88\cos 20°)t$

$y=(v\sin\theta)t-16t^2+2 \Rightarrow y=(88\sin 20°)t-16t^2+2$

(b) Since $t=\dfrac{x}{88\cos 20°}$, we have the following.

$$y=88\sin 20°\left(\frac{x}{88\cos 20°}\right)-16\left(\frac{x}{88\cos 20°}\right)^2+2=(\tan 20°)\,x-\frac{x^2}{484\cos^2 20°}+2$$

(c) Solving $0=-16t^2+(88\sin 20°)t+2$ by the quadratic formula, we have the following.

$$t=\frac{-88\sin 20° \pm\sqrt{(88\sin 20°)^2-4(-16)(2)}}{(2)(-16)}=\frac{-30.098\pm\sqrt{905.8759+128}}{-32}\Rightarrow t\approx -0.064 \text{ or } 1.9$$

Discard $t=-0.064$ since it is an unacceptable answer. At $t\approx 1.9$ sec, $x=(88\cos 20°)t\approx 161$ ft. The softball traveled 1.9 sec and 161 feet.

43. (a) $x=(v\cos\theta)t \Rightarrow x=(128\cos 60°)t=128\left(\frac{1}{2}\right)t=64t$

$y=(v\sin\theta)t-16t^2+2.5 \Rightarrow y=(128\sin 60°)t-16t^2+8=128\left(\frac{\sqrt{3}}{2}\right)t-16t^2+8=64\sqrt{3}t-16t^2+8$

Since $t=\frac{x}{64}$, $y=64\sqrt{3}\left(\frac{x}{64}\right)-16\left(\frac{x}{64}\right)^2+8=y=-\frac{1}{256}x^2+\sqrt{3}x+8$. This is a parabolic path.

(b) Solving $0=-16t^2+64\sqrt{3}t+8$ by the quadratic formula, we have the following.

$$t=\frac{-64\sqrt{3}\pm\sqrt{(64\sqrt{3})^2-4(-16)(8)}}{2(-16)}=\frac{-64\sqrt{3}\pm\sqrt{12{,}800}}{-32}=\frac{-64\sqrt{3}\pm 80\sqrt{2}}{-32}\Rightarrow t\approx -.07,\ 7.0$$

Discard $t=-.07$ since it gives an unacceptable answer. At $t\approx 7.0$ sec, $x=64t=448$ ft. The rocket traveled approximately 7 sec and 448 feet.

45. (a) $x=(v\cos\theta)t \Rightarrow x=(64\cos 60°)t=64\left(\frac{1}{2}\right)t=32t$

$y=(v\sin\theta)t-16t^2+3 \Rightarrow y=(64\sin 60°)t-16t^2+3=64\left(\frac{\sqrt{3}}{2}\right)t-16t^2+3=32\sqrt{3}t-16t^2+3$

(b) Solving $0=-16t^2+32\sqrt{3}t+3$ by the quadratic formula, we have the following.

$$t=\frac{-32\sqrt{3}\pm\sqrt{(32\sqrt{3})^2-4(-16)(3)}}{2(-16)}=\frac{-32\sqrt{3}\pm\sqrt{3264}}{-32}=\frac{-32\sqrt{3}\pm 8\sqrt{51}}{-32}\Rightarrow t\approx -.05,\ 3.52$$

Discard $t=-.07$ since it gives an unacceptable answer. At $t\approx 3.52$ sec, $x=32t\approx 112.6$ ft. The ball traveled approximately 112.6 feet.

Continued on next page

45. (continued)

(c) To find the maximum height, find the vertex of $y=-16t^2+32\sqrt{3}t+3$.

$$y=-16t^2+32\sqrt{3}t+3=-16\left(t^2-2\sqrt{3}t\right)+3=-16\left(t^2-2\sqrt{3}t+3-3\right)+3$$
$$y=-16\left(t-\sqrt{3}\right)^2+48+3=-16\left(t-\sqrt{3}\right)^2+51$$

The maximum height of 51 ft is reached at $\sqrt{3}\approx 1.73$ sec. Since $x=32t$, the ball has traveled horizontally $32\sqrt{3}\approx 55.4$ ft.

(d) To determine if the ball would clear a 5-ft-high fence that is 100 ft from the batter, we need to first determine at what time is the ball 100 ft from the batter. Since $x=32t$, the time the ball is 100 ft from the batter is $t=\dfrac{100}{32}=3.125$ sec. We next need to determine how high off the ground the ball is at this time. Since $y=32\sqrt{3}t-16t^2+3$, the height of the ball is the following.

$$y=32\sqrt{3}(3.125)-16(3.125)^2+3\approx 20.0 \text{ ft}$$

Since this height exceeds 5 ft, the ball will clear the fence.

47. (a)

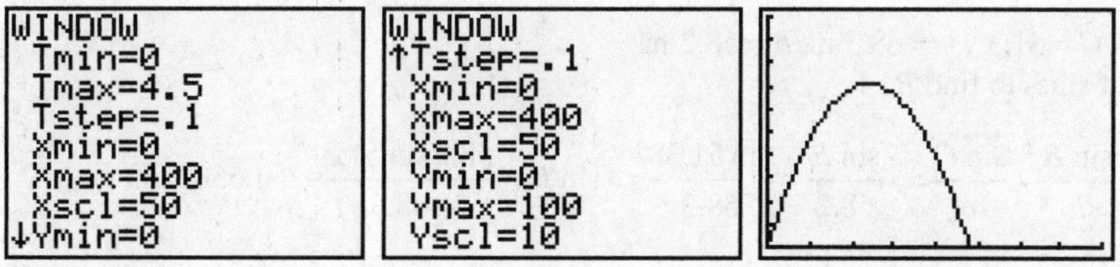

(b) $x=56.56530965t=v(\cos\theta)t\Rightarrow 56.56530965=v\cos\theta$

$y=-16t^2+67.41191099t=-16t^2+v(\sin\theta)t\Rightarrow 67.41191099=v\sin\theta$

Thus, $\dfrac{67.41191099}{56.56530965}=\dfrac{v\sin\theta}{v\cos\theta}\Rightarrow 1.1918=\tan\theta\Rightarrow\theta\approx 50.0°$.

(c) $67.41191099=v\sin 50.0°\Rightarrow v\approx 88.0$ ft/sec

Thus, the parametric equations are $x=88(\cos 50.0°)t,\ y=-16t^2+88(\sin 50.0°)t$.

For Exercises 49 & 51, many answers are possible.

49. $y=a(x-h)^2+k$

To find one parametric representation, let $x=t$. We therefore have, $y=a(t-h)^2+k$.

For another representation, let $x=t+h$. We therefore have $y=a\left(t+h-h\right)^2+k=at^2+k$.

51. $\dfrac{x^2}{a^2}+\dfrac{y^2}{b^2}=1$

To find a parametric representation, let $x=a\sin t$. We therefore have the following.

$$\frac{(a\sin t)^2}{a^2}+\frac{y^2}{b^2}=1\Rightarrow\frac{a^2\sin^2 t}{a^2}+\frac{y^2}{b^2}=1\Rightarrow\sin^2 t+\frac{y^2}{b^2}=1\Rightarrow\frac{y^2}{b^2}=1-\sin^2 t$$
$$y^2=b^2\left(1-\sin^2 t\right)\Rightarrow y^2=b^2\cos^2 t\Rightarrow y=b\cos t$$

53. To show that $r\theta = a$ is given parametrically by $x = \frac{a\cos\theta}{\theta}$, $y = \frac{a\sin\theta}{\theta}$, for θ in $(-\infty,0)\cup(0,\infty)$,

we must show that the parametric equations yield $r\theta = a$, where $r^2 = x^2 + y^2$.

$$r^2 = x^2 + y^2 \Rightarrow r^2 = \left(\frac{a\cos\theta}{\theta}\right)^2 + \left(\frac{a\sin\theta}{\theta}\right)^2 \Rightarrow r^2 = \frac{a^2\cos^2\theta}{\theta^2} + \frac{a^2\sin^2\theta}{\theta^2}$$

$$r^2 = \frac{a^2}{\theta^2}\cos^2\theta + \frac{a^2}{\theta^2}\sin^2\theta \Rightarrow r^2 = \frac{a^2}{\theta^2}\left(\cos^2\theta + \sin^2\theta\right) \Rightarrow r^2 = \frac{a^2}{\theta^2} \Rightarrow r = \pm\frac{a}{\theta} \text{ or just } r = \frac{a}{\theta}$$

This implies that the parametric equations satisfy $r\theta = a$.

55. If $x = f(t)$ is replaced by $x = c + f(t)$, the graph will be translated c units horizontally.

Chapter 8: Review Exercises

1. Find b, given $C = 74.2°$, $c = 96.3$ m, $B = 39.5°$.
Use the law of sines to find b.

$$\frac{b}{\sin B} = \frac{c}{\sin C} \Rightarrow \frac{b}{\sin 39.5°} = \frac{96.3}{\sin 74.2°} \Rightarrow b = \frac{96.3\sin 39.5°}{\sin 74.2°} \approx 63.7 \text{ m}$$

3. Find B, given $C = 51.3°$, $c = 68.3$ m, $b = 58.2$ m.
Use the law of sines to find B.

$$\frac{\sin B}{b} = \frac{\sin C}{c} \Rightarrow \frac{\sin B}{58.2} = \frac{\sin 51.3°}{68.3} \Rightarrow \sin B = \frac{58.2\sin 51.3°}{68.3} \approx .66502269$$

There are two angles B between 0° and 180° that satisfy the condition. Since $\sin B \approx .66502269$, to the nearest tenth value of B is $B_1 = 41.7°$. Supplementary angles have the same sine value, so another possible value of B is $B_2 = 180° - 41.7° = 138.3°$. This is not a valid angle measure for this triangle since $C + B_2 = 51.3° + 138.3° = 189.6° > 180°$.

Thus, $B = 41.7°$.

5. Find A, given $B = 39°50'$, $b = 268$ m, $a = 340$ m.
Use the law of sines to find A.

$$\frac{\sin A}{a} = \frac{\sin B}{b} \Rightarrow \frac{\sin A}{340} = \frac{\sin 39°50'}{268} \Rightarrow \sin A = \frac{340\sin 39°50'}{268} \approx .81264638$$

There are two angles A between 0° and 180° that satisfy the condition. Since $\sin A \approx .81264638$, to the nearest tenth value of A is $A_1 = 54.4° \approx 54°20'$. Supplementary angles have the same sine value, so another possible value of A is $A_2 = 180° - 54°20' = 179°60' - 54°20' = 125°40'$. This is a valid angle measure for this triangle since $B + A_2 = 39°50' + 125°40' = 165°30' < 180°$.

$A = 54°20'$ or $A = 125°40'$

7. No; If you are given two angles of a triangle, then the third angle is known since the sum of the measures of the three angles is 180°. Since you are also given one side, there will only be one triangle that will satisfy the conditions.

9. $a = 10, B = 30°$

(a) The value of b that forms a right triangle would yield exactly one value for A. That is, $b = 10 \sin 30° = 5$. Also, any value of b greater than or equal to 10 would yield a unique value for A.

(b) Any value of b between 5 and 10, would yield two possible values for A.

(c) If b is less than 5, then no value for A is possible.

11. Find A, given $a = 86.14$ in., $b = 253.2$ in., $c = 241.9$ in.

Use the law of cosines to find A.

$$a^2 = b^2 + c^2 - 2bc \cos A \Rightarrow \cos A = \frac{b^2 + c^2 - a^2}{2bc} = \frac{253.2^2 + 241.9^2 - 86.14^2}{2(253.2)(241.9)} \approx .94046923$$

Thus, $A \approx 19.87°$ or $19°\ 52'$.

13. Find a, given $A = 51°\ 20'$, $c = 68.3$ m, $b = 58.2$ m.
Use the law of cosines to find a.

$$a^2 = b^2 + c^2 - 2bc \cos A \Rightarrow a^2 = 58.2^2 + 68.3^2 - 2(58.2)(68.3)\cos 51°\ 20' \approx 3084.99 \Rightarrow a \approx 55.5 \text{ m}$$

15. Find a, given $A = 60°$, $b = 5$cm, $c = 21$ cm.
Use the law of cosines to find a.

$$a^2 = b^2 + c^2 - 2bc \cos A \Rightarrow a^2 = 5^2 + 21^2 - 2(5)(21)\cos 60° = 361 \Rightarrow a = 19 \text{ cm}$$

17. Solve the triangle, given $A = 25.2°$, $a = 6.92$ yd, $b = 4.82$ yd.

$$\frac{\sin B}{b} = \frac{\sin A}{a} \Rightarrow \sin B = \frac{b \sin A}{a} \Rightarrow \sin B = \frac{4.82 \sin 25.2°}{6.92} \approx .29656881$$

There are two angles B between 0° and 180° that satisfy the condition. Since $\sin B \approx .29656881$, to the nearest tenth value of B is $B_1 = 17.3°$. Supplementary angles have the same sine value, so another possible value of B is $B_2 = 180° - 17.3° = 162.7°$. This is not a valid angle measure for this triangle since $A + B_2 = 25.2° + 162.7° = 187.9° > 180°$.

$$C = 180° - A - B \Rightarrow C = 180° - 25.2° - 17.3° \Rightarrow C = 137.5°$$

Use the law of sines to find c.

$$\frac{c}{\sin C} = \frac{a}{\sin A} \Rightarrow \frac{c}{\sin 137.5°} = \frac{6.92}{\sin 25.2°} \Rightarrow c = \frac{6.92 \sin 137.5°}{\sin 25.2°} \approx 11.0 \text{ yd}$$

19. Solve the triangle, given $a = 27.6$ cm, $b = 19.8$ cm, $C = 42°\ 30'$.
This is a SAS case, so using the law of cosines.

$$c^2 = a^2 + b^2 - 2ab \cos C \Rightarrow c^2 = 27.6^2 + 19.8^2 - 2(27.6)(19.8)\cos 42°\ 30' \approx 347.985 \Rightarrow c \approx 18.65 \text{cm}$$

(will be rounded as 18.7)

Of the remaining angles A and B, B must be smaller since it is opposite the shorter of the two sides a and b. Therefore, B cannot be obtuse.

$$\frac{\sin B}{b} = \frac{\sin C}{c} \Rightarrow \frac{\sin B}{19.8} = \frac{\sin 42°30'}{18.65} \Rightarrow \sin B = \frac{19.8 \sin 42°30'}{18.65} \approx .717124859 \Rightarrow B \approx 45.8° \approx 45°50'$$

Thus, $A = 180° - B - C = 180° - 45°\ 50' - 42°\ 30' = 179°60' - 88°20' = 91°\ 40'$.

21. Given $b = 840.6$ m, $c = 715.9$ m, $A = 149.3°$, find the area.
Angle A is included between sides b and c. Thus, we have the following.

$$\mathcal{A} = \frac{1}{2}bc\sin A = \frac{1}{2}(840.6)(715.9)\sin 149.3° \approx 153{,}600 \text{ m}^2 \text{ (rounded to four significant digits)}$$

23. Given $a = .913$ km, $b = .816$ km, $c = .582$ km, find the area.
Use Heron's formula to find the area.

$$s = \frac{1}{2}(a+b+c) = \frac{1}{2}(.913+.816+.582) = \frac{1}{2}\cdot 2.311 = 1.1555$$

$$\begin{aligned}\mathcal{A} &= \sqrt{s(s-a)(s-b)(s-c)}\\ &= \sqrt{1.1555(1.1555-.913)(1.1555-.816)(1.1555-.582)}\\ &= \sqrt{1.1555(.2425)(.3395)(.5735)} \approx .234 \text{ km}^2 \text{ (rounded to three significant digits)}\end{aligned}$$

25. Since $B = 58.4°$ and $C = 27.9°$, $A = 180° - B - C = 180° - 58.4° - 27.9° = 93.7°$.
Using the law of sines, we have the following.

$$\frac{AB}{\sin C} = \frac{125}{\sin A} \Rightarrow \frac{AB}{\sin 27.9°} = \frac{125}{\sin 93.7°} \Rightarrow AB = \frac{125\sin 27.9°}{\sin 93.7°} \approx 58.61$$

The canyon is 58.6 feet across. (rounded to three significant digits)

27. Let AC = the height of the tree.
Angle $A = 90° - 8.0° = 82°$
Angle $C = 180° - B - A = 30°$
Use the law of sines to find $AC = b$.

$$\frac{b}{\sin B} = \frac{c}{\sin C}$$

$$\frac{b}{\sin 68°} = \frac{7.0}{\sin 30°}$$

$$b = \frac{7.0\sin 68°}{\sin 30°}$$

$$b \approx 12.98$$

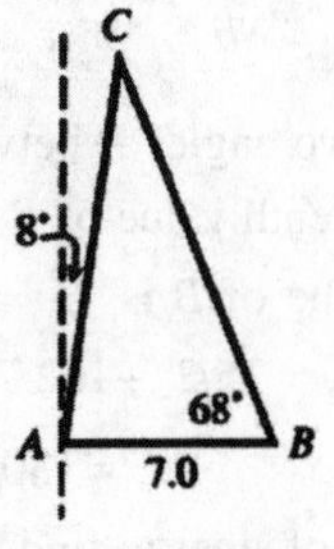

The tree is 13 meters tall. (rounded to two significant digits)

29. Let h = the height of tree.

$$\theta = 27.2° - 14.3° = 12.9°$$

$$\alpha = 90° - 27.2° = 62.8°$$

$$\frac{h}{\sin\theta} = \frac{212}{\sin\alpha}$$

$$\frac{h}{\sin 12.9°} = \frac{212}{\sin 62.8°}$$

$$h = \frac{212\sin 12.9°}{\sin 62.8°}$$

$$h \approx 53.21$$

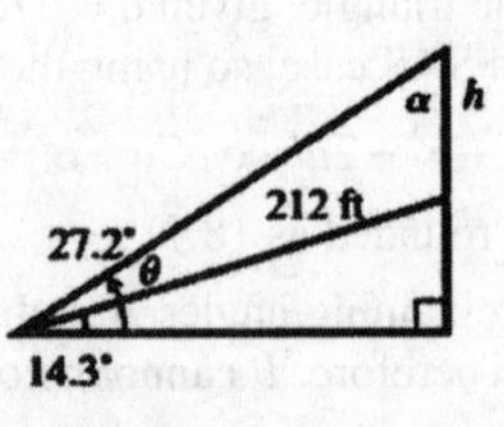

The height of the tree is 53.2 ft. (rounded to three significant digits)

31. Let x = the distance between the boats.
In 3 hours the first boat travels 3(36.2) = 108.6 km and the second travels 3(45.6)=136.8 km.
Use the law of cosines to find x.

$$x^2 = 108.6^2 + 136.8^2 - 2(108.6)(136.8)\cos 54°10' \approx 13{,}113.359 \Rightarrow x \approx 115 \text{ km}$$

They are 115 km apart.

33. Use the distance formula to find the distances between the points.
Distance between (–8, 6) and (0, 0):

$$\sqrt{(-8-0)^2+(6-0)^2} = \sqrt{(-8)^2+6^2} = \sqrt{64+36} = \sqrt{100} = 10$$

Distance between (–8, 6) and (3, 4):

$$\sqrt{(-8-3)^2+(6-4)^2} = \sqrt{(-11)^2+2^2} = \sqrt{121+4} = \sqrt{125} \approx 11.18$$

Distance between (3, 4) and (0, 0):

$$\sqrt{(3-0)^2+(4-0)^2} = \sqrt{3^2+4^2} = \sqrt{9+16} = \sqrt{25} = 5$$

$$s \approx \frac{1}{2}(10+11.18+5) = \frac{1}{2}\cdot 26.18 = 13.09$$

$$\text{A} = \sqrt{s(s-a)(s-b)(s-c)} = \sqrt{13.09(13.09-10)(13.09-11.18)(13.09-5)}$$
$$= \sqrt{13.09(3.09)(1.91)(8.09)} \approx 25 \text{ sq units (rounded to two significant digits)}$$

35. **a – b**

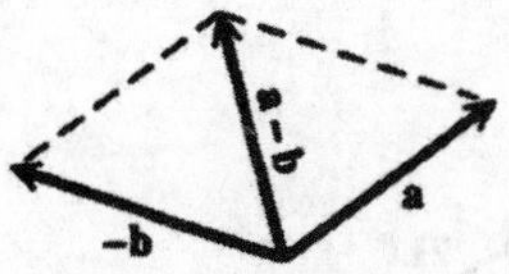

37. **(a)** true
(b) false

39.

$$\alpha = 180° - 52° = 128°$$
$$|\mathbf{v}|^2 = 100^2 + 130^2 - 2(100)(130)\cos 128°$$
$$|\mathbf{v}|^2 \approx 42907.2$$
$$|\mathbf{v}| \approx 207 \text{ lb}$$

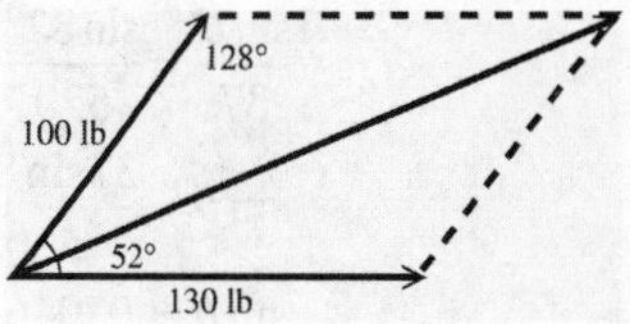

41. $|\mathbf{v}| = 964,\ \theta = 154°20'$
horizontal: $x = |\mathbf{v}|\cos\theta = 964\cos 154°\ 20' \approx 869$
vertical: $y = |\mathbf{v}|\sin\theta = 964\sin 154°\ 20' \approx 418$

43. $\mathbf{u} = \langle -9, 12\rangle$

magnitude: $|\mathbf{u}| = \sqrt{(-9)^2+12^2} = \sqrt{81+144} = \sqrt{225} = 15$

Angle: $\tan\theta' = \dfrac{b}{a} \Rightarrow \tan\theta' = \dfrac{12}{-9} \Rightarrow \theta' = \tan^{-1}\left(-\dfrac{4}{3}\right) \approx -53.1° \Rightarrow \theta = -53.1° + 180° = 126.9°$

(θ lies in quadrant II)

45. $\mathbf{a}=\langle 3,-2\rangle,\ \mathbf{b}=\langle -1,3\rangle$

$\mathbf{a}\cdot\mathbf{b}=\langle 3,-2\rangle\cdot\langle -1,3\rangle=3(-1)+(-2)\cdot 3=-3-6=-9$

$$\cos\theta=\frac{\mathbf{a}\cdot\mathbf{b}}{|\mathbf{a}||\mathbf{b}|}\Rightarrow\cos\theta=\frac{-9}{|\langle 3,-2\rangle||\langle -1,3\rangle|}$$

$$=\frac{-9}{\sqrt{3^2+(-2)^2}\sqrt{(-1)^2+3^2}}=-\frac{9}{\sqrt{9+4}\sqrt{1+9}}=-\frac{9}{\sqrt{13}\sqrt{10}}=-\frac{9}{\sqrt{130}}\approx -.78935222$$

Thus, $\theta\approx 142.1°$.

47. $|\mathbf{u}|=\sqrt{5^2+12^2}=\sqrt{169}=13$

$$\mathbf{v}=\frac{\mathbf{u}}{|\mathbf{u}|}=\frac{\langle 5,12\rangle}{13}=\left\langle\frac{5}{13},\frac{12}{13}\right\rangle$$

49. Let $|\mathbf{x}|$ be the resultant force.

$\theta=180°-15°-10°=155°$

$|\mathbf{x}|^2=12^2+18^2-2(12)(18)\cos 155°$

$|\mathbf{x}|^2\approx 859.5\Rightarrow|\mathbf{x}|\approx 29$

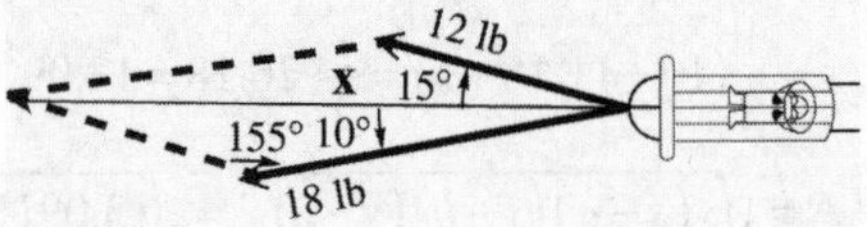

The magnitude of the resultant force on Jessie and the sled is 29 lb.

51. Let $\mathbf{v}$ = the ground speed vector.

$\alpha=212°-180°=32°$ and $\beta=50°$ because they are alternate interior angles. Angle opposite to 520 is $\alpha+\beta=82°$.

Using the law of sines, we have the following.

$$\frac{\sin\theta}{37}=\frac{\sin 82°}{520}$$

$$\sin\theta=\frac{37\sin 82°}{520}$$

$$\sin\theta\approx .07046138$$

$$\theta\approx 4°$$

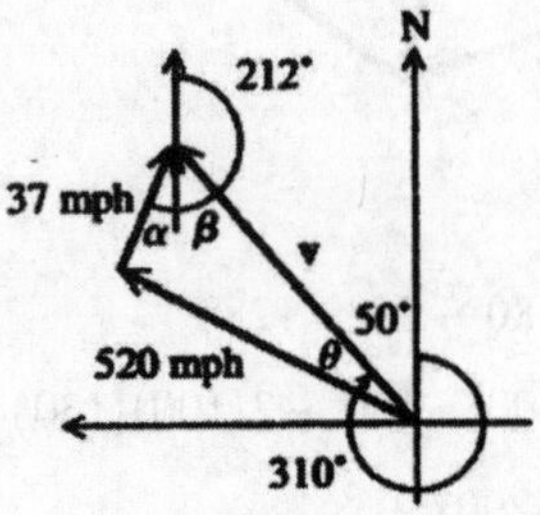

Thus, the bearing is 360° – 50° – θ = 306°. The angle opposite $\mathbf{v}$ is 180° – 82° – 4° = 94°. Using the laws of sines, we have the following.

$$\frac{|\mathbf{v}|}{\sin 94°}=\frac{520}{\sin 82°}\Rightarrow|\mathbf{v}|=\frac{520\sin 94°}{\sin 82°}\approx 524\text{ mph}$$

The pilot should fly on a bearing of 306°. Her actual speed is 524 mph.

53. Refer to the diagram below. In each of the triangles *ABP* and *PBC*, we know two angles and one side. Solve each triangle using the law of sines.

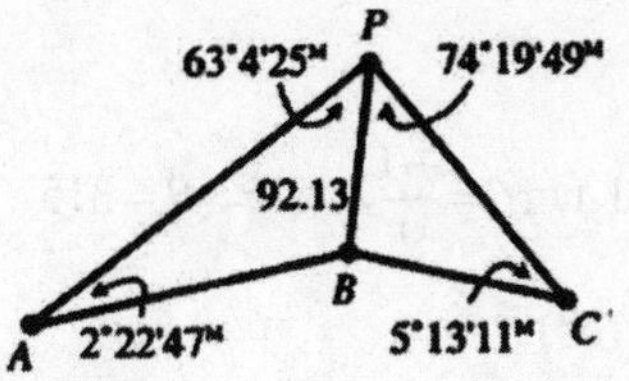

$$AB = \frac{92.13 \sin 63^\circ\ 4'\ 25''}{\sin 2^\circ\ 22'\ 47''} \approx 1978.28 \text{ ft and } BC = \frac{92.13 \sin 74^\circ\ 19'\ 49''}{\sin 5^\circ\ 13'\ 11''} \approx 975.05 \text{ ft}$$

55. $[3 \operatorname{cis} 135^\circ][2 \operatorname{cis} 105^\circ] = 3 \cdot 2 \operatorname{cis}(135^\circ + 105^\circ)$

$$= 6 \operatorname{cis} 240^\circ = 6(\cos 240^\circ + i \sin 240^\circ) = 6\left(-\frac{1}{2} - \frac{\sqrt{3}}{2} i\right) = -3 - 3\sqrt{3} i$$

57. $\dfrac{4 \operatorname{cis} 270^\circ}{2 \operatorname{cis} 90^\circ} = \dfrac{4}{2} \operatorname{cis}(270^\circ - 90^\circ) = 2 \operatorname{cis} 180^\circ = 2(\cos 180^\circ + i \sin 180^\circ) = 2(-1 + 0i) = -2 + 0i$ or -2

59. $(\cos 100^\circ + i \sin 100^\circ)^6 = \cos(6 \cdot 100^\circ) + i \sin(6 \cdot 100^\circ)$

$$= \cos 600^\circ + i \sin 600^\circ = \cos 240^\circ + i \sin 240^\circ = -\cos 60^\circ - i \sin 60^\circ = -\frac{1}{2} - \frac{\sqrt{3}}{2} i$$

61.

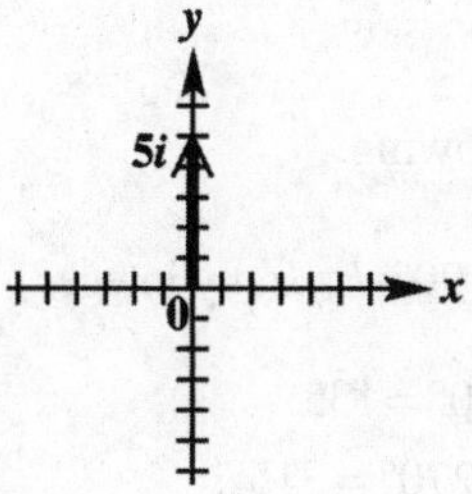

63. $-2 + 2i$

$$r = \sqrt{(-2)^2 + 2^2} = \sqrt{4+4} = \sqrt{8} = 2\sqrt{2}$$

Since θ is in quadrant II, $\tan \theta = \dfrac{2}{-2} = -1 \Rightarrow \theta = 135^\circ$. Thus, $-2 + 2i = 2\sqrt{2}(\cos 135^\circ + i \sin 135^\circ)$.

65. $2(\cos 225^\circ + i \sin 225^\circ) = 2(-\cos 45^\circ - i \sin 45^\circ) = 2\left(-\dfrac{\sqrt{2}}{2} - \dfrac{i\sqrt{2}}{2}\right) = -\sqrt{2} - i\sqrt{2}$

67. $1 - i$

$r = \sqrt{1^2 + (-1)^2} = \sqrt{1+1} = \sqrt{2}$ and $\tan \theta = \dfrac{-1}{1} = -1 \Rightarrow \theta = 315^\circ$, since θ is in quadrant IV.

Thus, $1 - i = \sqrt{2}(\cos 315^\circ + i \sin 315^\circ)$.

69. $-4i$

Since $r = 4$ and the point $(0, -4)$ intersects the negative *y*-axis, $\theta = 270^\circ$ and $-4i = 4(\cos 270^\circ + i \sin 270^\circ)$.

71. $z = x + yi$
Since the imaginary part of z is the negative of the real part of z, we are saying $y = -x$. This is a line.

73. Convert $1 - i$ to polar form

$r = \sqrt{1^2 + (-1)^2} = \sqrt{1+1} = \sqrt{2}$ and $\tan\theta = \frac{-1}{1} = -1 \Rightarrow \theta = 315°$, since θ is in quadrant IV.

Thus, $1 - i = \sqrt{2}(\cos 315° + i\sin 315°)$.

Since $r^3(\cos 3\alpha + i\sin 3\alpha) = \sqrt{2}(\cos 315° + i\sin 315°)$, then we have the following.

$$r^3 = \sqrt{2} \Rightarrow r = \sqrt[6]{2} \text{ and } 3\alpha = 315° + 360° \cdot k \Rightarrow \alpha = \frac{315° + 360° \cdot k}{3} = 105° + 120° \cdot k, \ k \text{ any integer.}$$

$$\text{If } k = 0, \text{ then } \alpha = 105° + 0° = 105°. \text{ If } k = 1, \text{ then } \alpha = 105° + 120° = 225°.$$
$$\text{If } k = 2, \text{ then } \alpha = 105° + 240° = 345°.$$

So, the cube roots of $1 - i$ are $\sqrt[6]{2}(\cos 105° + i\sin 105°)$, $\sqrt[6]{2}(\cos 225° + i\sin 225°)$, and $\sqrt[6]{2}(\cos 345° + i\sin 345°)$.

75. The number -64 has no real sixth roots because a real number raised to the sixth power will never be negative.

77. $x^4 + 16 = 0 \Rightarrow x^4 = -16$
We have, $r = 16$ and $\theta = 180°$.

$$x^4 = -16 = -16 + 0i = 16(\cos 180° + i\sin 180°)$$

Since $r^4(\cos 4\alpha + i\sin 4\alpha) = 16(\cos 180° + i\sin 180°)$, then we have the following.

$$r^4 = 16 \Rightarrow r = 2 \text{ and } 4\alpha = 180° + 360° \cdot k \Rightarrow \alpha = \frac{180° + 360° \cdot k}{4} = 45° + 90° \cdot k, \ k \text{ any integer.}$$

$$\text{If } k = 0, \text{ then } \alpha = 45° + 0° = 45°. \text{ If } k = 1, \text{ then } \alpha = 45° + 90° = 135°.$$
$$\text{If } k = 2, \text{ then } \alpha = 45° + 180° = 225°. \text{ If } k = 3, \text{ then } \alpha = 45° + 270° = 315°.$$

Solution set:
$\{2(\cos 45° + i\sin 45°), 2(\cos 135° + i\sin 135°), 2(\cos 225° + i\sin 225°), 2(\cos 315° + i\sin 315°)\}$

79. $(5, 315°)$

$$x = r\cos\theta \Rightarrow x = 5\cos 315° = 5\left(\frac{\sqrt{2}}{2}\right) = \frac{5\sqrt{2}}{2} \text{ and } y = r\sin\theta \Rightarrow y = 5\sin 315° = 5\left(-\frac{\sqrt{2}}{2}\right) = -\frac{5\sqrt{2}}{2}.$$

Thus, the rectangular coordinates are $\left(\frac{5\sqrt{2}}{2}, -\frac{5\sqrt{2}}{2}\right)$.

81. $r = 4\cos\theta$ is a circle.

θ	0°	30°	45°	60°	90°	120°	135°	150°	180°
$r = 4\cos\theta$	4	3.5	2.8	2	0	−2	−2.8	−3.5	−4

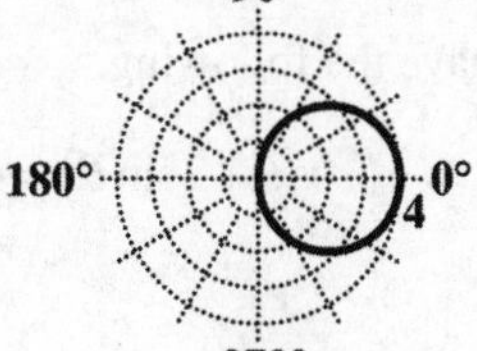

$r = 4\cos\theta$

Graph is retraced in the interval (180°, 360°).

83. $r = 2\sin 4\theta$ is an eight-leaved rose.

θ	0°	7.5°	15°	22.5°	0°	37.5°	45°
$r = 2\sin 4\theta$	0	1	$\sqrt{3}$	2	$\sqrt{3}$	1	0

θ	52.5°	60°	67.5°	75°	82.5°	90°	52.5°
$r = 2\sin 4\theta$	−1	$-\sqrt{3}$	−2	$-\sqrt{3}$	−1	0	−1

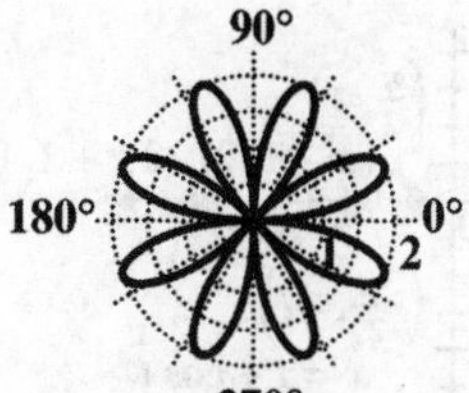

$r = 2\sin 4\theta$

The graph continues to form eight petals for the interval [0°, 360°).

85. $r = \dfrac{3}{1+\cos\theta}$

$$r = \frac{3}{1+\cos\theta} \Rightarrow r(1+\cos\theta) = 3 \Rightarrow r + r\cos\theta = 3 \Rightarrow \sqrt{x^2+y^2} + x = 3 \Rightarrow \sqrt{x^2+y^2} = 3 - x$$

$$x^2 + y^2 = (3-x)^2 \Rightarrow x^2 + y^2 = 9 - 6x + x^2 \Rightarrow y^2 = 9 - 6x \Rightarrow y^2 + 6x - 9 = 0 \Rightarrow y^2 = -6x + 9$$

$$y^2 = -6\left(x - \frac{3}{2}\right) \text{ or } y^2 + 6x - 9 = 0$$

87. $r = 2 \Rightarrow \sqrt{x^2+y^2} = 2 \Rightarrow x^2 + y^2 = 4$

89. $y = x^2 \Rightarrow r\sin\theta = r^2\cos^2\theta \Rightarrow \sin\theta = r\cos^2\theta \Rightarrow r = \dfrac{\sin\theta}{\cos^2\theta} \Rightarrow r = \dfrac{\sin\theta}{\cos\theta}\cdot\dfrac{1}{\cos\theta} = \tan\theta\sec\theta$

$$r = \tan\theta\sec\theta \text{ or } r = \frac{\tan\theta}{\cos\theta}$$

91. $x = 2$

Since $x = r\cos\theta$, we have the following.

$$x = r\cos\theta \Rightarrow r\cos\theta = 2 \Rightarrow r = \frac{2}{\cos\theta} \text{ or } r = 2\sec\theta$$

93. $x + 2y = 4$

Since $x = r\cos\theta$ and $y = r\sin\theta$, we have the following.

$$r\cos\theta + 2(r\sin\theta) = 4 \Rightarrow r(\cos\theta + 2\sin\theta) = 4 \Rightarrow r = \frac{4}{\cos\theta + 2\sin\theta}$$

95. $x = t + \cos t$, $y = \sin t$ for t in $[0, 2\pi]$

t	0	$\frac{\pi}{6}$	$\frac{\pi}{3}$	$\frac{\pi}{2}$	$\frac{3\pi}{4}$	π
$x = t + \cos t$	0	$\frac{\pi}{6} + \frac{\sqrt{3}}{2}$ ≈ 1.4	$\frac{\pi}{3} + \frac{1}{2}$ ≈ 1.5	$\frac{\pi}{2}$ ≈ 1.6	$\frac{3\pi}{4} - \frac{\sqrt{2}}{2}$ ≈ 1.6	$\pi - 1$ ≈ 2.1
$y = \sin t$	0	$\frac{1}{2} = .5$	$\frac{\sqrt{3}}{2} \approx 1.7$	1	$\frac{\sqrt{2}}{2} \approx .7$	0

t	$\frac{7\pi}{6}$	$\frac{5\pi}{4}$	$\frac{4\pi}{3}$	$\frac{3\pi}{2}$	$\frac{7\pi}{4}$	2π
$x = t + \cos t$	$\frac{7\pi}{6} - \frac{\sqrt{3}}{2}$ ≈ 2.8	$\frac{5\pi}{4} - \frac{\sqrt{2}}{2}$ ≈ 3.2	$\frac{4\pi}{3} - \frac{1}{2}$ ≈ 3.7	$\frac{3\pi}{2}$ ≈ 4.7	$\frac{7\pi}{4} + \frac{\sqrt{2}}{2}$ ≈ 6.2	$2\pi + 1$ ≈ 7.3
$y = \sin t$	$-\frac{1}{2} = -.5$	$-\frac{\sqrt{2}}{2} \approx -.7$	$-\frac{\sqrt{3}}{2} \approx -1.7$	-1	$-\frac{\sqrt{2}}{2} \approx -.7$	0

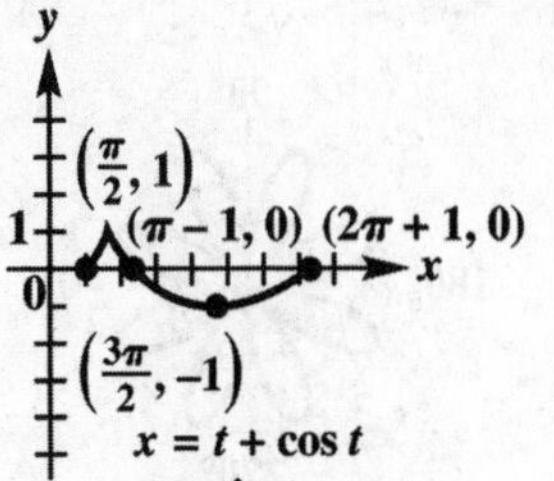

$x = t + \cos t$
$y = \sin t$
for t in $[0, 2\pi]$

97. $x = \sqrt{t-1}$, $y = \sqrt{t}$, for t in $[1, \infty)$

Since $x = \sqrt{t-1} \Rightarrow x^2 = t - 1 \Rightarrow t = x^2 + 1$, substitute $x^2 + 1$ for t in the equation for y to obtain $y = \sqrt{x^2 + 1}$. Since t is in $[1, \infty)$, x is in $[\sqrt{1-1}, \infty)$ or $[0, \infty)$.

99. $x = 5\tan t$, $y = 3\sec t$, for t in $\left(-\frac{\pi}{2}, \frac{\pi}{2}\right)$

Since $\frac{x}{5} = \tan t$, $\frac{y}{3} = \sec t$, and $1 + \tan^2 t = \sec^2 t$, we have the following.

$$1 + \left(\frac{x}{5}\right)^2 = \left(\frac{y}{3}\right)^2 \Rightarrow 1 + \frac{x^2}{25} = \frac{y^2}{9} \Rightarrow 9\left(1 + \frac{x^2}{25}\right) = y^2 \Rightarrow y = \sqrt{9\left(1 + \frac{x^2}{25}\right)} \Rightarrow y = 3\sqrt{1 + \frac{x^2}{25}}$$

y is positive since $y = 3\sec t > 0$ for t in $\left(-\frac{\pi}{2}, \frac{\pi}{2}\right)$.

Since t is in $\left(-\frac{\pi}{2}, \frac{\pi}{2}\right)$ and $x = 5\tan t$ is undefined at $-\frac{\pi}{2}$ and $\frac{\pi}{2}$, x is in $(-\infty, \infty)$.

101. The radius of the circle that has center $(3,4)$ and passes through the origin is the following.

$$r=\sqrt{(3-0)^2+(4-0)^2}=\sqrt{3^2+4^2}=\sqrt{9+16}=\sqrt{25}=5$$

Thus, the equation of this circle is $(x-3)^2+(y-4)^2=5^2$

Since $\cos^2 t+\sin^2 y=1 \Rightarrow 25\cos^2 t+25\sin^2 t=25 \Rightarrow (5\cos t)^2+(5\sin t)^2=5^2$, we can have $5\cos t=x-3$ and $5\sin t=y-4$. Thus, a pair of parametric equations can be the following.

$x=3+5\cos t$, $y=4+5\sin t$, where t in $[0, 2\pi]$

103.(a) $x=(v\cos\theta)t \Rightarrow x=(118\cos 27°)t$ and $y=(v\sin\theta)t-16t^2+h \Rightarrow y=(118\sin 27°)t-16t^2+3.2$

(b) Since $t=\dfrac{x}{118\cos 27°}$, we have the following.

$$y=118\sin 27°\cdot\frac{x}{118\cos 27°}-16\left(\frac{x}{118\cos 27°}\right)^2+3.2=3.2-\frac{4}{3481\cos^2 27°}x^2+(\tan 27°)x$$

(c) Solving $0=-16t^2+(118\sin 27°)t+3.2$ by the quadratic formula, we have the following.

$$t=\frac{-118\sin 27°\pm\sqrt{(118\sin 27°)^2-4(-16)(3.2)}}{2(-16)} \Rightarrow t\approx -.06,\ 3.406$$

Discard $t = -0.06$ sec since it is an unacceptable answer. At $t = 3.4$ sec, the baseball traveled $x=(118\cos 27°)(3.406)\approx 358$ ft.

Chapter 8: Test

1. Find C, given $A = 25.2°$, $a = 6.92$ yd, $b = 4.82$ yd.
Use the law of sines to first find the measure of angle B.

$$\frac{\sin 25.2°}{6.92}=\frac{\sin B}{4.82} \Rightarrow \sin B=\frac{4.82\sin 25.2°}{6.92}\approx .29656881 \Rightarrow B\approx 17.3°$$

Use the fact that the angles of a triangle sum to 180° to find the measure of angle C.

$$C=180-A-B=180°-25.2°-17.3°=137.5°$$

Angle C measures 137.5°.

2. Find c, given $C = 118°$, $b = 130$ km, $a = 75$ km.
Using the law of cosines to find the length of c.

$$c^2=a^2+b^2-2ab\cos C \Rightarrow c^2=75^2+130^2-2(75)(130)\cos 118°\approx 31679.70 \Rightarrow c\approx 178.0 \text{ km}$$

c is approximately 180 km. (rounded to two significant digits)

3. Find B, given $a = 17.3$ ft, $b = 22.6$ ft, $c = 29.8$ ft.
Using the law of cosines, find the measure of angle B.

$$b^2=a^2+c^2-2ac\cos B \Rightarrow \cos B=\frac{a^2+c^2-b^2}{2ac}=\frac{17.3^2+29.8^2-22.6^2}{2(17.3)(29.8)}\approx .65617605 \Rightarrow B\approx 49.0°$$

B is approximately 49.0°.

4. Find the area of triangle *ABC*, given $C = 118°$, $b = 130$ km, $a = 75$ km.

$$A = \frac{1}{2}ab\sin C = \frac{1}{2}(75)(130)\sin 118° \approx 4304.4$$

The area of the triangle is approximately 4300 km^2. (rounded to two significant digits)
(*Note*: Since *c* was found in Exercise 2, Heron's formula can also be used.)

5. Since $B > 90°$, *b* must be the longest side of the triangle.

(a) $b > 10$

(b) none

(c) $b \le 10$

6. The semi-perimeter *s* is $s = \frac{1}{2}(a+b+c) = \frac{1}{2}(22+26+40) = \frac{1}{2}\cdot 88 = 44.$

Using Heron's formula, we have the following.

$$A = \sqrt{s(s-a)(s-b)(s-c)} = \sqrt{44(44-22)(44-26)(44-40)} = \sqrt{44(22)(18)(4)} = \sqrt{69{,}696} = 264$$

The area of the triangle is 264 square units.

7. magnitude: $|\mathbf{v}| = \sqrt{(-6)^2 + 8^2} = \sqrt{36+64} = \sqrt{100} = 10$

angle: $\tan\theta' = \frac{y}{x} \Rightarrow \tan\theta' = \frac{8}{-6} = -\frac{4}{3} \approx -1.33333333 \Rightarrow \theta' \approx -53.1° \Rightarrow \theta = -53.1° + 180° = 126.9°$

(θ lies in quadrant II)

The magnitude $|\mathbf{v}|$ is 10 and $\theta = 126.9°$.

8. $\mathbf{u} = \langle -1, 3\rangle, \mathbf{v} = \langle 2, -6\rangle$

(a) $\mathbf{u}+\mathbf{v} = \langle -1, 3\rangle + \langle 2, -6\rangle = \langle -1+2, 3+(-6)\rangle = \langle 1, -3\rangle$

(b) $-3\mathbf{v} = -3\langle 2, -6\rangle = \langle -3\cdot 2, -3(-6)\rangle = \langle -6, 18\rangle$

(c) $\mathbf{u}\cdot\mathbf{v} = \langle -1, 3\rangle \cdot \langle 2, -6\rangle = -1(2) + 3(-6) = -2 - 18 = -20$

(d) $|\mathbf{u}| = \sqrt{(-1)^2 + 3^2} = \sqrt{1+9} = \sqrt{10}$

9. Given $A = 24°\ 50', B = 47°\ 20'$ and $AB = 8.4$ mi, first find the measure of angle *C*.

$C = 180° - 47°\ 20' - 24°\ 50'$
$= 179°60' - 72°\ 10'$
$= 107°\ 50'$

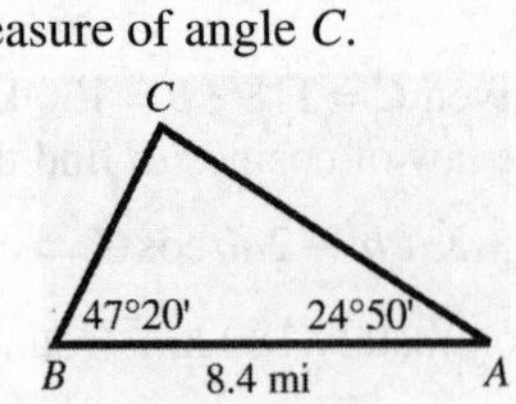

Use this information and the law of sines to find *AC*.

$$\frac{AC}{\sin 47°\ 20'} = \frac{8.4}{\sin 107°\ 50'} \Rightarrow AC = \frac{8.4\sin 47°\ 20'}{\sin 107°50'} \approx 6.49 \text{ mi}$$

Drop a perpendicular line from *C* to segment *AB*.

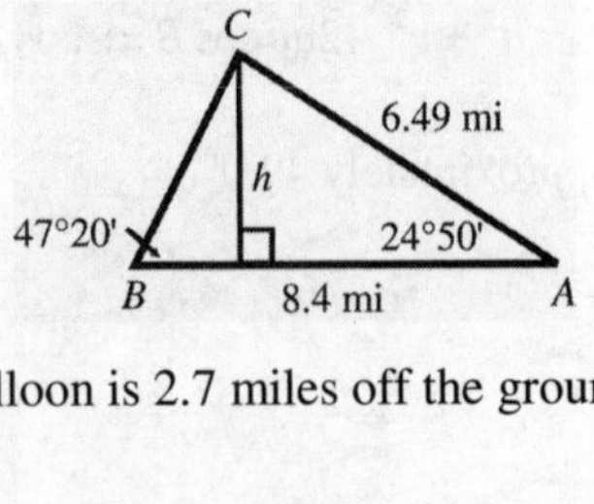

Thus, $\sin 24°50' = \frac{h}{6.49} \Rightarrow h \approx 6.49\sin 24°50' \approx 2.7$ mi. The balloon is 2.7 miles off the ground.

10. horizontal: $x=|\mathbf{v}|\cos\theta=569\cos 127.5°\approx -346$ and vertical: $y=|\mathbf{v}|\sin\theta=569\sin 127.5°\approx 451$

The vector is $\langle -346, 451\rangle$.

11. Consider the figure below.

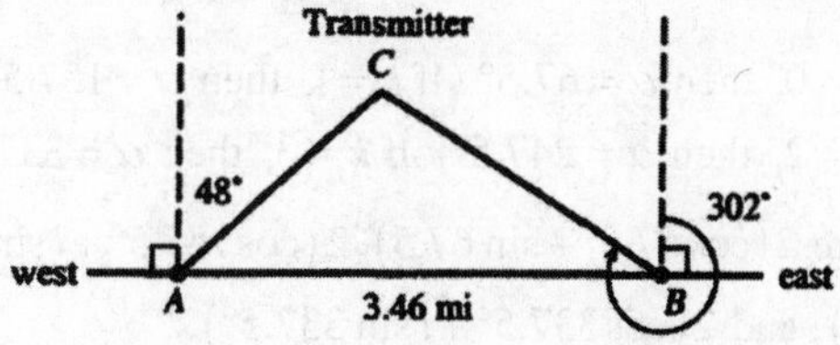

Since the bearing is 48° from A, angle A in ABC must be $90° - 48° = 42°$. Since the bearing is 302° from B, angle B in ABC must be $302° - 270° = 32°$. The angles of a triangle sum to 180°, so $C=180°-A-B=180°-42°-32°=106°$. Using the law of sines, we have the following.

$$\frac{b}{\sin B}=\frac{c}{\sin C}\Rightarrow\frac{b}{\sin 32°}=\frac{3.46}{\sin 106°}\Rightarrow b=\frac{3.46\sin 32°}{\sin 106°}\approx 1.91\text{ mi}$$

The distance from A to the transmitter is 1.91 miles. (rounded to two significant digits)

12. **(a)** $3i$

$r=\sqrt{0^2+3^2}=\sqrt{0+9}=\sqrt{9}=3$

The point $(0,3)$ is on the positive y-axis, so, $\theta=90°$. Thus, $3i=3(\cos 90°+i\sin 90°)$.

(b) $1+2i$

$r=\sqrt{1^2+2^2}=\sqrt{1+4}=\sqrt{5}$

Since θ is in quadrant I, $\theta=\tan^{-1}\left(\frac{2}{1}\right)=\tan^{-1}2\approx 63.43°$.

Thus, $1+2i=\sqrt{5}(\cos 63.43°+i\sin 63.43°)$.

(c) $-1-\sqrt{3}i$

$r=\sqrt{(-1)^2+(-\sqrt{3})^2}=\sqrt{1+3}=\sqrt{4}=2$

Since θ is in quadrant III, $\theta=\tan^{-1}\left(\frac{-\sqrt{3}}{-1}\right)=\tan^{-1}\sqrt{3}=240°$.

Thus, $-1-\sqrt{3}i=2(\cos 240°+i\sin 240°)$

13. **(a)** $3(\cos 30°+i\sin 30°)=3\left(\frac{\sqrt{3}}{2}+\frac{1}{2}i\right)=\frac{3\sqrt{3}}{2}+\frac{3}{2}i$

(b) $4\text{ cis }4°=3.06+2.57i$

(c) $3(\cos 90°+i\sin 90°)=3(0+1\cdot i)=0+3i=3i$

14. $w=8(\cos 40°+i\sin 40°), z=2(\cos 10°+i\sin 10°)$

(a) $wz=8\cdot 2[\cos(40°+10°)+i\sin(40°+10°)]=16(\cos 50°+i\sin 50°)$

(b) $\frac{w}{z}=\frac{8}{2}[\cos(40°-10°)+i\sin(40°-10°)]=4(\cos 30°+i\sin 30°)=4\left(\frac{\sqrt{3}}{2}+\frac{1}{2}i\right)=2\sqrt{3}+2i$

(c) $z^3=[2(\cos 10°+i\sin 10°)]^3$

$=2^3(\cos 3\cdot 10°+i\sin 3\cdot 10°)=8(\cos 30°+i\sin 30°)=8\left(\frac{\sqrt{3}}{2}+\frac{1}{2}i\right)=4\sqrt{3}+4i$

15. Find all the fourth roots of $-16i = 16(\cos 270° + i\sin 270°)$.

Since $r^4(\cos 4\alpha + i\sin 4\alpha) = 16(\cos 270° + i\sin 270°)$, then we have the following.

$$r^4 = 16 \Rightarrow r = 2 \text{ and } 4\alpha = 270° + 360°\cdot k \Rightarrow \alpha = \frac{270° + 360°\cdot k}{4} = 67.5° + 90°\cdot k,\ k \text{ any integer.}$$

If $k = 0$, then $\alpha = 67.5°$. If $k = 1$, then $\alpha = 157.5°$.

If $k = 2$, then $\alpha = 247.5°$. If $k = 3$, then $\alpha = 337.5°$.

The fourth roots of $-16i$ are $2(\cos 67.5° + \sin 67.5), 2(\cos 157.5° + i\sin 157.5°)$, $2(\cos 247.5° + i\sin 247.5°)$, and $2(\cos 337.5° + i\sin 337.5°)$.

For Exercise 16, answers may vary.

16. (a) $(0,5)$

$r = \sqrt{0^2 + 5^2} = \sqrt{0+25} = \sqrt{25} = 5$

The point $(0,5)$ is on the positive y-axis. Thus, $\theta = 90°$. One possibility is (5, 90°).

Alternatively, if $\theta = 90° - 360° = -270°$, a second possibility is (5, –270°).

(b) $(-2,-2)$

$r = \sqrt{(-2)^2 + (-2)^2} = \sqrt{4+4} = \sqrt{8} = 2\sqrt{2}$

Since θ is in quadrant III, $\theta = \tan^{-1}\left(\frac{-2}{-2}\right) = \tan^{-1} 1 = 225°$. One possibility is $\left(2\sqrt{2}, 225°\right)$.

Alternatively, if $\theta = 225° - 360° = -135°$, a second possibility is $\left(2\sqrt{2}, -135°\right)$.

17. (a) $(3, 315°)$

$$x = r\cos\theta \Rightarrow x = 3\cos 315° = 3\cdot\frac{\sqrt{2}}{2} = \frac{3\sqrt{2}}{2} \text{ and } y = r\sin\theta \Rightarrow y = 3\sin 315° = 3\left(-\frac{\sqrt{2}}{2}\right) = \frac{-3\sqrt{2}}{2}$$

The rectangular coordinates are $\left(\frac{3\sqrt{2}}{2}, \frac{-3\sqrt{2}}{2}\right)$.

(b) $(-4, 90°)$

$x = r\cos\theta \Rightarrow x = -4\cos 90° = 0$ and $y = r\sin\theta \Rightarrow y = -4\sin 90° = -4$

The rectangular coordinates are $(0,-4)$.

18. $r = 1 - \cos\theta$ is a cardioid.

θ	0°	30°	45°	60°	90°	135°
$r = 1 - \cos\theta$	0	.1	.3	.5	1	1.7

θ	180°	225°	270°	315°	360°
$r = 1 - \cos\theta$	2	1.7	1	.3	0

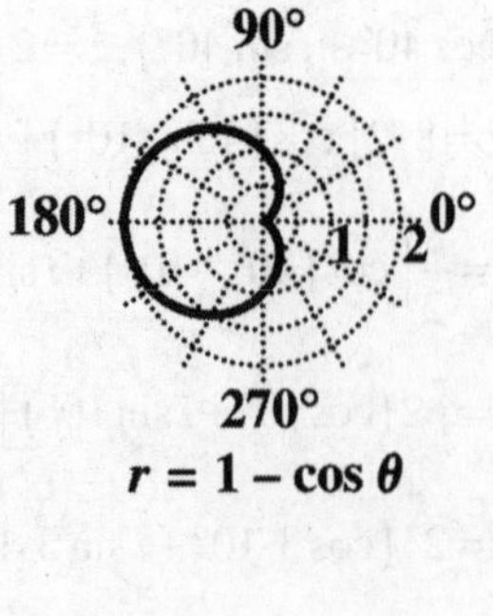

r = 1 – cos θ

19. $r = 3\cos 3\theta$ is a three-leaved rose.

θ	0°	30°	45°	60°	90°	120°	135°	150°	180°
$r = 3\cos 3\theta$	3	0	−2.1	−3	0	3	2.1	0	−3

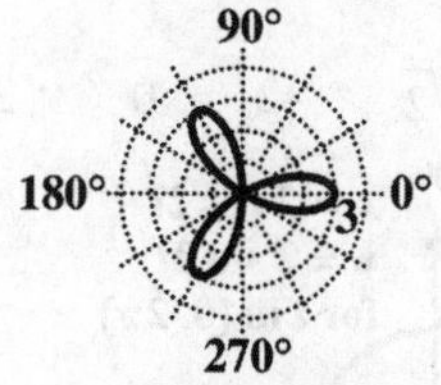

r = 3 cos 3θ

Graph is retraced in the interval (180°, 360°).

20. (a) Since $r = \dfrac{4}{2\sin\theta - \cos\theta} = \dfrac{4}{-1\cdot\cos\theta + 2\sin\theta}$, we can use the general form for the polar equation of a line, $r = \dfrac{c}{a\cos\theta + b\sin\theta}$, with $a = -1$, $b = 2$, and $c = 4$, we have the following.

$$-x + 2y = 4 \text{ or } x - 2y = -4$$

The graph is a line with intercepts $(-4, 0)$ and $(0, 2)$.

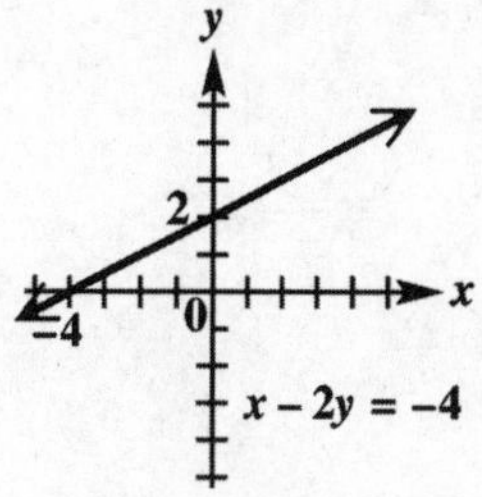

(b) $r = 6$ represents the equation of a circle centered at the origin with radius 6, namely $x^2 + y^2 = 36$.

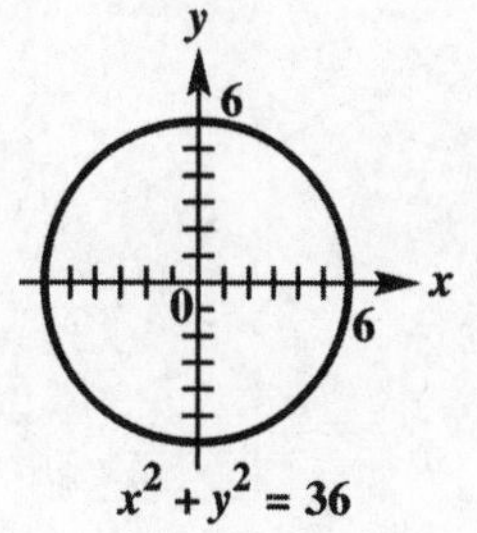

21. $x = 4t - 3$, $y = t^2$ for t in [−3, 4]

t	x	y
−3	−15	9
−1	−7	1
0	−3	0
1	1	1
2	5	4
4	13	16

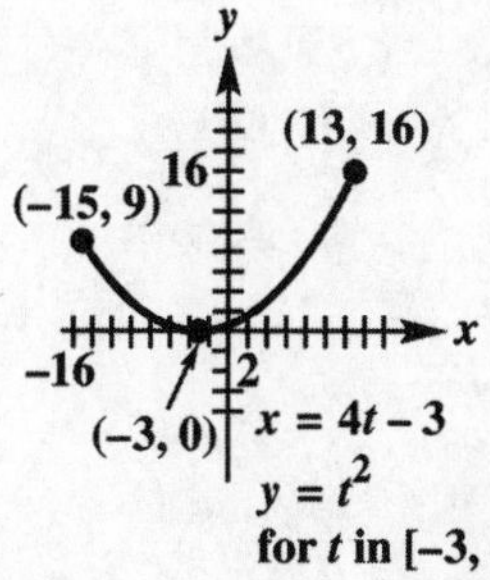

Since $x = 4t - 3 \Rightarrow t = \dfrac{x+3}{4}$ and $y = t^2$ we have $y = \left(\dfrac{x+3}{4}\right)^2 = \dfrac{1}{4}(x+3)^2$, where x is in [−15, 13]

22. $x = 2\cos 2t$, $y = 2\sin 2t$ for t in $[0, 2\pi]$

t	0	$\frac{\pi}{8}$	$\frac{\pi}{4}$	$\frac{3\pi}{8}$	$\frac{\pi}{2}$	$\frac{5\pi}{8}$	$\frac{3\pi}{4}$	π	$\frac{5\pi}{4}$	$\frac{3\pi}{2}$	$\frac{7\pi}{4}$	2π
x	2	$\sqrt{2}$	0	$-\sqrt{2}$	-2	$-\sqrt{2}$	0	2	0	-2	0	2
y	0	$\sqrt{2}$	2	$\sqrt{2}$	0	$-\sqrt{2}$	-2	0	2	0	-2	0

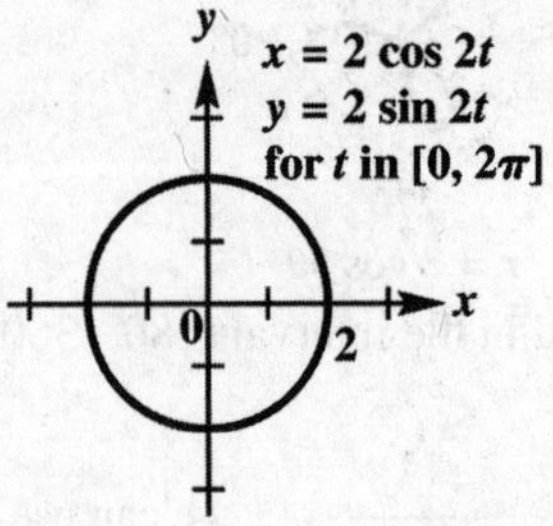

Since $x = 2\cos 2t \Rightarrow \cos 2t = \frac{x}{2}$, $y = 2\sin 2t \Rightarrow \sin 2t = \frac{y}{2}$, and $\cos^2(2t) + \sin^2(2t) = 1$, we have $\left(\frac{x}{2}\right)^2 + \left(\frac{y}{2}\right)^2 = 1 \Rightarrow \frac{x^2}{4} + \frac{y^2}{4} = 1 \Rightarrow x^2 + y^2 = 4$, where x is in $[-1, 1]$.

Chapter 9
SYSTEMS AND MATRICES

Section 9.1: Systems of Linear Equations

1. The two graphs meet at the approximate point (2002, 3.3). Thus, in approximately 2002 both projections produce the same level of migration.

3. The point where the graphs meet, (2002, 3.3 million), is the solution of the system.

5. t would represent time in years and y would represent number of migrants.

7. $4x + 3y = -13$ (1)
$-x + y = 5$ (2)

Solve equation (2) for y.

$$-x+y=5 \quad (2)$$
$$y=x+5 \quad (3)$$

Replace y with $x+5$ in equation (1), and solve for x.

$$4x+3y=-13 \Rightarrow 4x+3(x+5)=-13 \Rightarrow 4x+3x+15=-13 \Rightarrow 7x+15=-13 \Rightarrow 7x=-28 \Rightarrow x=-4$$

Replace x with -4 in equation (3) to obtain $y=-4+5=1$.

Check:

$4x+3y=-13$ (1)	$-x+y=5$ (2)
$4(-4)+3(1)=-13$?	$-(-4)+1=5$?
$-16+3=-13$	$4+1=5$
$-13=-13$ True	$5=5$ True

Solution set: $\{(-4,1)\}$

9. $x - 5y = 8$ (1)
$x = 6y$ (2)

Replace x with $6y$ in equation (1), and solve for y.

$$x-5y=8 \Rightarrow 6y-5y=8 \Rightarrow y=8$$

Replace y with 8 in equation (2) to obtain $x = 6(8) = 48$.

Check:

$x-5y=8$ (1)	$x=6y$ (2)
$48-5(8)=8$?	$48=6(8)$?
$48-40=8$	$48=48$ True
$8=8$ True	

Solution set: $\{(48,8)\}$

11. $8x-10y=-22$ (1)

$3x+\quad y=\quad 6$ (2)

Solve equation (2) for *y*.

$$3x+y=6 \quad (2)$$
$$y=-3x+6 \quad (3)$$

Replace *y* with $-3x+6$ in equation (1), and solve for *x*.

$$8x-10y=-22 \Rightarrow 8x-10(-3x+6)=-22$$
$$8x+30x-60=-22$$
$$38x-60=-22 \Rightarrow 38x=38 \Rightarrow x=1$$

Replace *x* with 1 in equation (3) to obtain $y=-3(1)+6=3$.

Check: $8x-10y=-22$ (1)	$3x+y=6$ (2)
$8(1)-10(3)=-22$?	$3(1)+3=6$?
$8-30=-22$	$3+3=6$
$-22=-22$ True	$6=6$ True

Solution set: $\{(1,3)\}$

13. $7x-y=-10$ (1)

$3y-x=\ 10$ (2)

Solve equation (1) for *y*.

$$7x-y=-10 \quad (1)$$
$$y=7x+10 \quad (3)$$

Replace *y* with $7x+10$ in equation (2), and solve for *x*.

$$3y-x=10 \Rightarrow 3(7x+10)-x=10$$
$$21x+30-x=10$$
$$20x+30=10$$
$$20x=-20 \Rightarrow x=-1$$

Replace *x* with -1 in equation (3) to obtain $y=7(-1)+10=3$.

Check: $7x-y=-10$ (1)	$3y-x=10$ (2)
$7(-1)-3=-10$?	$3(3)-(-1)=10$?
$-7-3=-10$	$9+1=10$
$-10=-10$ True	$10=10$ True

Solution set: $\{(-1,3)\}$

15. $-2x=6y+18$ (1)

$-29=5y-3x$ (2)

Solve equation (1) for *x*.

$$-2x=6y+18 \quad (1)$$
$$x=-3y-9 \quad (3)$$

Replace *x* with $-3y-9$ in equation (2), and solve for *y*.

$$-29=5y-3(-3y-9)$$
$$-29=5y+9y+27 \Rightarrow -29=14y+27$$
$$-56=14y \Rightarrow -4=y$$

Replace *y* with -4 in equation (3) to obtain $x=-3(-4)-9=12-9=3$.

Check: $-2x=6y+18$ (1)	$-29=5y-3x$ (2)
$-2(3)=6(-4)+18$?	$-29=5(-4)-3(3)$?
$-6=-24+18$	$-29=-20-9$
$-6=-6$ True	$-29=-29$ True

Solution set: $\{(3,-4)\}$

17. $3y = 5x + 6 \quad (1)$

$x + y = 2 \quad (2)$

Solve equation (2) for y. (You could solve equation (2) for x just as easily.)

$$x + y = 2 \quad (2)$$
$$y = 2 - x \quad (3)$$

Replace y with $2 - x$ in equation (1), and solve for x.

$$3y = 5x + 6 \Rightarrow 3(2 - x) = 5x + 6 \Rightarrow 6 - 3x = 5x + 6 \Rightarrow 6 = 8x + 6 \Rightarrow 0 = 8x \Rightarrow 0 = x$$

Replace x with 0 in equation (3) to obtain $y = 2 - 0 = 2$.

Check:

$3y = 5x + 6 \quad (1)$	$x + y = 2 \quad (2)$
$3(2) = 5(0) + 6 \quad ?$	$0 + 2 = 2 \quad ?$
$6 = 0 + 6$	$2 = 2$ True
$6 = 6$ True	

Solution set: $\{(0, 2)\}$

19. $3x - y = -4 \quad (1)$

$x + 3y = 12 \quad (2)$

Multiply equation (2) by –3 and add the result to equation (1).

$$\begin{array}{r} 3x - y = -4 \\ \underline{-3x - 9y = -36} \\ -10y = -40 \Rightarrow y = 4 \end{array}$$

Substitute 4 for y in equation (2) and solve for x.

$$x + 3(4) = 12 \Rightarrow x + 12 = 12 \Rightarrow x = 0$$

Check:

$3x - y = -4 \quad (1)$	$x + 3y = 12 \quad (2)$
$3(0) - 4 = -4 \quad ?$	$0 + 3(4) = 12 \quad ?$
$0 - 4 = -4$	$0 + 12 = 12$
$-4 = -4$ True	$12 = 12$ True

Solution set: $\{(0, 4)\}$

21. $2x - 3y = -7 \; (1)$

$5x + 4y = 17 \; (2)$

Multiply equation (1) by 4 and equation (2) by 3 and then add the resulting equations.

$$\begin{array}{r} 8x - 12y = -28 \\ \underline{15x + 12y = 51} \\ 23x \quad = 23 \Rightarrow x = 1 \end{array}$$

Substitute 1 for x in equation (2) and solve for y.

$$5(1) + 4y = 17 \Rightarrow 5 + 4y = 17 \Rightarrow 4y = 12 \Rightarrow y = 3$$

Check:

$2x - 3y = -7 \quad (1)$	$5x + 4y = 17 \quad (2)$
$2(1) - 3(3) = -7 \quad ?$	$5(1) + 4(3) = 17 \quad ?$
$2 - 9 = -7$	$5 + 12 = 17$
$-7 = -7$ True	$17 = 17$ True

Solution set: $\{(1, 3)\}$

23. $5x+7y=6$ (1)
$10x-3y=46$ (2)

Multiply equation (1) by –2 and add to equation (2).

$$\begin{array}{r} -10x-14y=-12 \\ 10x-\ \ 3y=\ \ 46 \\ \hline -17y=\ \ 34 \Rightarrow y=-2 \end{array}$$

Substitute –2 for y in equation (2) and solve for x.

$$\begin{aligned} 10x-3(-2)&=46 \\ 10x+6&=46 \\ 10x&=40 \\ x&=4 \end{aligned}$$

Check:

$5x+7y=6$ (1)	$10x-3y=46$ (2)
$5(4)+7(-2)=6$?	$10(4)-3(-2)=46$?
$20-14=6$	$40+6=46$
$6=6$ True	$46=46$ True

Solution set: $\{(4,-2)\}$

25. $6x+7y+2=0$ (1)
$7x-6y-26=0$ (2)

Multiply equation (1) by 6 and equation (2) by 7 and then add the resulting equations.

$$\begin{array}{l} 36x+42y+\ 12=0 \\ 49x-42y-182=0 \\ \hline 85x\qquad -170=0 \Rightarrow 85x=170 \Rightarrow x=2 \end{array}$$

Substitute 2 for x in equation (1).

$$\begin{aligned} 6(2)+7y+2&=0 \\ 12+7y+2&=0 \\ 7y+14&=0 \\ 7y&=-14 \Rightarrow y=-2 \end{aligned}$$

Check:

$6x+7y+2=0$ (1)	$7x-6y-26=0$ (2)
$6(2)+7(-2)+2=0$?	$7(2)-6(-2)-26=0$?
$12-14+2=0$	$14+12-26=0$
$0=0$ True	$0=0$ True

Solution set: $\{(2,-2)\}$

27. $\frac{x}{2}+\frac{y}{3}=4$ (1)
$\frac{3x}{2}+\frac{3y}{2}=15$ (2)

To clear denominators, multiply equation (1) by 6 and equation (2) by 2.

$$6\left(\tfrac{x}{2}+\tfrac{y}{3}\right)=6(4)$$
$$2\left(\tfrac{3x}{2}+\tfrac{3y}{2}\right)=2(15)$$

This gives the system

$$\begin{aligned} 3x+2y&=24 \quad (3) \\ 3x+3y&=30 \quad (4). \end{aligned}$$

Multiply equation (3) by –1 and add to equation (4).

$$\begin{array}{r} -3x-2y=-24 \\ 3x+3y=\ \ 30 \\ \hline y=\ \ \ 6 \end{array}$$

Substitute 6 for y in equation (1).

$$\tfrac{x}{2}+\tfrac{6}{3}=4 \Rightarrow \tfrac{x}{2}+2=4 \Rightarrow \tfrac{x}{2}=2 \Rightarrow x=4$$

Continued on next page

27. (continued)

Check:

$\frac{x}{2}+\frac{y}{3}=4$ (1)	$\frac{3x}{2}+\frac{3y}{2}=15$ (2)
$\frac{4}{2}+\frac{6}{3}=4$?	$\frac{3(4)}{2}+\frac{3(6)}{2}=15$?
$2+2=4$	$6+9=15$
$4=4$ True	$15=15$ True

Solution set: $\{(4,6)\}$

29. $\frac{2x-1}{3}+\frac{y+2}{4}=4\ (1)$

$\frac{x+3}{2}-\frac{x-y}{3}=3\ (2)$

Multiply equation (1) by 12 and equation (2) by 6 to clear denominators. Also, remove parentheses and combine like terms.

$$12\left(\frac{2x-1}{3}+\frac{y+2}{4}\right)=12(4)\Rightarrow 4(2x-1)+3(y+2)=48\Rightarrow 8x-4+3y+6=48\Rightarrow 8x+3y=46\ (3)$$

$$6\left(\frac{x+3}{2}-\frac{x-y}{3}\right)=6(3)\Rightarrow 3(x+3)-2(x-y)=18\Rightarrow 3x+9-2x+2y=18\Rightarrow x+2y=9\ (4)$$

Multiply equation (4) by –8 and then add the result to equation (3).

$$\begin{array}{r} 8x+3y=46 \\ -8x-16y=-72 \\ \hline -13y=-26\Rightarrow y=2 \end{array}$$

Substitute 2 for *y* into equation (4) and solve for *x*.

$$\begin{aligned} x+2(2)&=9 \\ x+4&=9 \\ x&=5 \end{aligned}$$

Check:

$\frac{2x-1}{3}+\frac{y+2}{4}=4$ (1)	$\frac{x+3}{2}-\frac{x-y}{3}=3$ (2)
$\frac{2(5)-1}{3}+\frac{2+2}{4}=4$?	$\frac{5+3}{2}-\frac{5-2}{3}=3$?
$\frac{10-1}{3}+\frac{4}{4}=4$	$\frac{8}{2}-\frac{3}{3}=3$
$\frac{9}{3}+1=4$	$4-1=3$
$3+1=4$	$3=3$ True
$4=4$ True	

Solution set: $\{(5,2)\}$

31. $9x-5y=1\ (1)$

$-18x+10y=1\ (2)$

Multiply equation (1) by 2 and add the result to equation (2).

$$\begin{array}{r} 18x-10y=2 \\ -18x+10y=1 \\ \hline 0=3 \end{array}$$

This is a false statement. The solution set is $\varnothing$, and the system is inconsistent.

33. $4x - y = 9$ (1)

$-8x + 2y = -18$ (2)

Multiply equation (1) by 2 and add the result to equation (2).

$$\begin{aligned} 8x - 2y &= 18 \\ -8x + 2y &= -18 \\ \hline 0 &= 0 \end{aligned}$$

This is a true statement. There are infinitely many solutions. We will now express the solution set with y as the arbitrary variable. Solve equation (1) for x.

$$4x - y = 9 \Rightarrow 4x = y + 9 \Rightarrow x = \tfrac{y+9}{4}$$

Solution set: $\left\{\left(\frac{y+9}{4}, y\right)\right\}$

35. $5x - 5y - 3 = 0$ (1)

$x - y - 12 = 0$ (2)

Multiply equation (2) by –5 and then add the resulting equations.

$$\begin{aligned} 5x - 5y - 3 &= 0 \\ -5x + 5y + 60 &= 0 \\ \hline 57 &= 0 \end{aligned}$$

This is a false statement. The solution set is $\varnothing$, and the system is inconsistent.

37. $7x + 2y = 6$ (1)

$14x + 4y = 12$ (2)

Multiply equation (1) by –2 and add the result to equation (2).

$$\begin{aligned} -14x - 4y &= -12 \\ 14x + 4y &= 12 \\ \hline 0 &= 0 \end{aligned}$$

This is a true statement. There are infinitely many solutions. We will express the solution set with y as the arbitrary variable. Solve equation (1) for x.

$$7x + 2y = 6 \Rightarrow 7x = 6 - 2y \Rightarrow x = \tfrac{6-2y}{7}$$

Solution set: $\left\{\left(\frac{6-2y}{7}, y\right)\right\}$

39. $4x - 5y = -11$

$$-5y = -4x - 11$$

$$y = \tfrac{4}{5}x + \tfrac{11}{5}$$

$$2x + y = 5$$

$$y = -2x + 5$$

Screen A is the correct choice.

41. Solve each equation for y.

$$\sqrt{3}x - y = 5 \Rightarrow -y = -\sqrt{3}x + 5 \Rightarrow y = \sqrt{3}x - 5 \text{ and } 100x + y = 9 \Rightarrow y = 9 - 100x$$

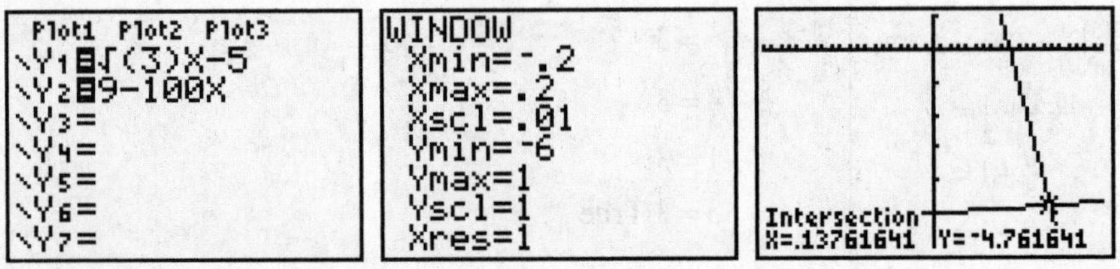

Solution set: $\{(.138, -4.762)\}$

43. Solve each equation for y.

$$.2x + \sqrt{2}y = 1 \Rightarrow \sqrt{2}y = 1 - .2x \Rightarrow y = \tfrac{1-.2x}{\sqrt{2}} \text{ and } \sqrt{5}x + .7y = 1 \Rightarrow .7y = 1 - \sqrt{5}x \Rightarrow y = \tfrac{1-\sqrt{5}x}{.7}$$

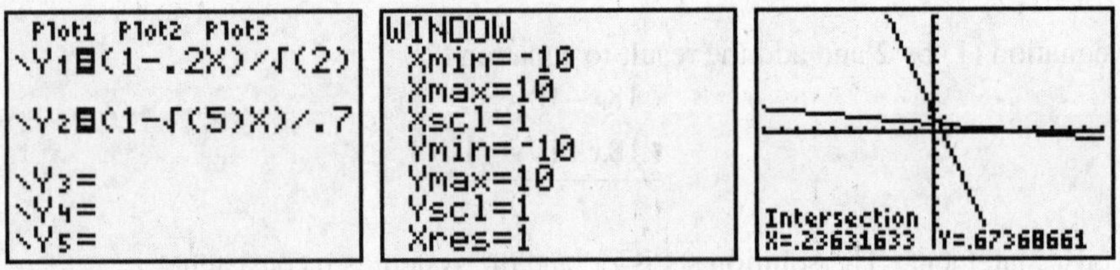

Solution set: $\{(.236, .674)\}$

45. $x-2y=3 \quad (1)$
$-2x+4y=k \quad (2)$

Multiply equation (1) by 2 and add the result to equation (2).

$$\begin{array}{r} 2x-4y=6 \\ \underline{-2x+4y=k} \\ 0=6+k \end{array}$$

The system will have no solution when $6+k \neq 0 \Rightarrow k \neq -6$.

The system will have infinitely many solutions when $6+k=0 \Rightarrow k=-6$.

47. $x+y+z=2 \quad (1)$
$2x+y-z=5 \quad (2)$
$x-y+z=-2 \quad (3)$

Eliminate z by adding equations (1) and (2) to get $3x+2y=7$ (4).

Eliminate z by adding equations (2) and (3) to get $3x=3 \Rightarrow x=1$ (5).

Using $x=1$, find y from equation (4) by substitution.

$$3(1)+2y=7 \Rightarrow 3+2y=7 \Rightarrow 2y=4 \Rightarrow y=2$$

Substitute 1 for x and 2 for y in equation (1) to find z.

$$1+2+z=2 \Rightarrow 3+z=2 \Rightarrow z=-1$$

Verify that the ordered triple $(1, 2, -1)$ satisfies all three equations.

Check: $x+y+z=2$ (1)	$2x+y-z=5$ (2)	$x-y+z=-2$ (3)
$1+2+(-1)=2$?	$2(1)+2-(-1)=5$?	$1-2+(-1)=-2$?
$2=2$ True	$2+2+1=5$	$-1-1=-2$
	$5=5$ True	$-2=-2$ True

Solution set: $\{(1, 2, -1)\}$

49. $x+3y+4z=14 \quad (1)$
$2x-3y+2z=10 \quad (2)$
$3x-y+z=9 \quad (3)$

Eliminate y by adding equations (1) and (2) to get $3x+6z=24$ (4).

Multiply equation (3) by 3 and add the result to equation (1).

$$\begin{array}{r} x+3y+4z=14 \\ \underline{9x-3y+3z=27} \\ 10x+\quad 7z=41 \ (5) \end{array}$$

Multiply equation (4) by 10 and equation (5) by -3 and add in order to eliminate y.

$$\begin{array}{r} 30x+60z=240 \\ \underline{-30x-21z=-123} \\ 39z=117 \Rightarrow z=3 \end{array}$$

Using $z=3$, find x from equation (5) by substitution.

$$10x+7(3)=41 \Rightarrow 10x+21=41 \Rightarrow 10x=20 \Rightarrow x=2$$

Substitute 2 for x and 3 for z in equation (1) to find y.

$$2+3y+4(3)=14 \Rightarrow 3y=0 \Rightarrow y=0$$

Verify that the ordered triple $(2,0,3)$ satisfies all three equations.

Continued on next page

49. (continued)

Check:

$x+3y+4z=14$ (1)	$2x-3y+2z=10$ (2)	$3x-y+z=9$ (3)
$2+3(0)+4(3)=14$?	$2(2)-3(0)+2(3)=10$?	$3(2)-0+3=9$?
$2+0+12=14$	$4-0+6=10$	$6-0+3=9$
$14=14$ True	$10=10$ True	$9=9$ True

Solution set: $\{(2,0,3)\}$

51. $x+4y-z=6$ (1)
$2x-y+z=3$ (2)
$3x+2y+3z=16$ (3)

Eliminate z by adding equations (1) and (2) to get $3x+3y=9$ or $x+y=3$ (4).

Multiply equation (1) by 3 and add the result to equation (3).

$$\begin{array}{l} 3x+12y-3z=18 \\ \underline{3x+\ 2y+3z=16} \\ 6x+14y \qquad\ =34 \quad (5) \end{array}$$

Multiply equation (4) by –6 and then add the result to equation (5) in order to eliminate x.

$$\begin{array}{l} -6x-\ 6y=-18 \\ \underline{6x+14y=\ 34} \\ \qquad\ 8y=\ 16 \Rightarrow y=2 \end{array}$$

Using $y=2$, find x from equation (4) by substitution.

$$x+2=3 \Rightarrow x=1$$

Substitute 1 for x and 2 for y in equation (1) to find z.

$$1+4(2)-z=6 \Rightarrow 1+8-z=6 \Rightarrow 9-z=6 \Rightarrow -z=-3 \Rightarrow z=3$$

Verify that the ordered triple $(1,2,3)$ satisfies all three equations.

Check:

$x+4y-z=6$ (1)	$2x-y+z=3$ (2)	$3x+2y+3z=16$ (3)
$1+4(2)-3=6$?	$2(1)-2+3=3$?	$3(1)+2(2)+3(3)=16$?
$1+8-3=6$	$2-2+3=3$	$3+4+9=16$
$6=6$ True	$3=3$ True	$16=16$ True

Solution set: $\{(1,2,3)\}$

53. $x-3y-2z=-3$ (1)
$3x+2y-z=12$ (2)
$-x-y+4z=3$ (3)

Eliminate x by adding equations (1) and (3) to get $-4y+2z=0$ (4).

Eliminate x by multiplying equation (3) by 3 and add to equation (2).

$$\begin{array}{l} -3x-3y+12z=9 \\ \underline{3x+2y-\ \ z=12} \\ \qquad -y+11z=21 \quad (5) \end{array}$$

Multiply equation (5) by –4 and add to equation (4) in order to eliminate y.

$$\begin{array}{l} -4y+\ 2z=\ 0 \\ \underline{4y-44z=-84} \\ \qquad -42z=-84 \Rightarrow z=2 \end{array}$$

Using $z=2$, find y from equation (4) by substitution.

$$-4y+2(2)=0 \Rightarrow -4y+4=0 \Rightarrow -4y=-4 \Rightarrow y=1$$

Substitute 1 for y and 2 for z in equation (1) to find x.

$$x-3(1)-2(2)=-3 \Rightarrow x-3-4=-3 \Rightarrow x-7=-3 \Rightarrow x=4$$

Continued on next page

53. (continued)

Verify that the ordered triple $(4,1,2)$ satisfies all three equations.

Check:

$x-3y-2z=-3$ (1)	$3x+2y-z=12$ (2)	$-x-y+4z=3$ (3)
$4-3(1)-2(2)=-3$?	$3(4)+2(1)-2=12$?	$-4-1+4(2)=3$?
$4-3-4=-3$	$12+2-2=12$	$-4-1+8=3$
$-3=-3$ True	$12=12$ True	$3=3$ True

Solution set: $\{(4,1,2)\}$

55. $2x+6y-z=6$ (1)
$4x-3y+5z=-5$ (2)
$6x+9y-2z=11$ (3)

Eliminate y by multiplying equation (2) by 2 and add to equation (1).

$$\begin{aligned} 2x+6y-z&=6\\ 8x-6y+10z&=-10\\ \hline 10x+9z&=-4 \quad (4)\end{aligned}$$

Eliminate y by multiplying equation (2) by 3 and add to equation (3).

$$\begin{aligned} 6x+9y-2z&=11\\ 12x-9y+15z&=-15\\ \hline 18x+13z&=-4 \quad (5)\end{aligned}$$

Multiply equation (4) by 9 and equation (5) by -5 and add in order to eliminate x.

$$\begin{aligned} 90x+81z&=-36\\ -90x-65z&=20\\ \hline 16z&=-16\Rightarrow z=-1\end{aligned}$$

Using $z=-1$, find x from equation (4) by substitution.

$$10x+9(-1)=-4\Rightarrow 10x-9=-4$$
$$10x=5\Rightarrow x=\tfrac{1}{2}$$

Substitute $\frac{1}{2}$ for x and -1 for z in equation (1) to find y.

$$2\left(\tfrac{1}{2}\right)+6y-(-1)=6\Rightarrow 1+6y+1=6\Rightarrow 6y+2=6\Rightarrow 6y=4\Rightarrow y=\tfrac{2}{3}$$

Verify that the ordered triple $\left(\frac{1}{2},\frac{2}{3},-1\right)$ satisfies all three equations.

Check:

$2x+6y-z=6$ (1)	$4x-3y+5z=-5$ (2)	$6x+9y-2z=11$ (3)
$2\left(\frac{1}{2}\right)+6\left(\frac{2}{3}\right)-(-1)=6$?	$4\left(\frac{1}{2}\right)-3\left(\frac{2}{3}\right)+5(-1)=-5$?	$6\left(\frac{1}{2}\right)+9\left(\frac{2}{3}\right)-2(-1)=11$?
$1+4+1=6$	$2-2-5=-5$	$3+6+2=11$
$6=6$ True	$-5=-5$ True	$11=11$ True

Solution set: $\left\{\left(\frac{1}{2},\frac{2}{3},-1\right)\right\}$

57. $2x-3y+2z\ \ -3=0\ (1)$

$4x+8y+\ \ z\ \ -2=0\ (2)$

$-x-7y+3z-14=0\ (3)$

Eliminate x by multiplying equation (3) by 2 and add to equation (1).

$$\begin{array}{r} 2x-\ 3y+2z-\ 3=0 \\ -2x-14y+6z-28=0 \\ \hline -17y+8z-31\ =0\ (4) \end{array}$$

Eliminate x by multiplying equation (3) by 4 and add to equation (2).

$$\begin{array}{r} 4x+\ 8y+\ \ z-\ \ 2=0 \\ -4x-28y+12z-56=0 \\ \hline -20y+13z-58\ =0\ (5) \end{array}$$

Multiply equation (5) by 17, equation (4) by −20, and add in order to eliminate y.

$$\begin{array}{r} 340y-160z+620=0 \\ -340y+221z-986=0 \\ \hline 61z-366=0\Rightarrow z=6 \end{array}$$

Using $z=6$, find y from equation (5) by substitution.

$$-20y+13(6)-58=0\Rightarrow -20y+78-58=0$$
$$-20y+20=0\Rightarrow -20y=-20\Rightarrow y=1$$

Substitute 1 for y and 6 for z in equation (1) to find x.

$$2x-3(1)+2(6)-3=0\Rightarrow 2x-3+12-3=0\Rightarrow 2x+6=0\Rightarrow 2x=-6\Rightarrow x=-3$$

Verify that the ordered triple $(-3,1,6)$ satisfies all three equations.

Check:

$2x-3y+2z-3=0\ \ (1)$	$4x+8y+z-2=0\ \ (2)$	$-x-7y+3z-14=0\ \ (3)$
$2(-3)-3(1)+2(6)-3=0\ \ ?$	$4(-3)+8(1)+6-2=0$	$-(-3)-7(1)+3(6)-14=0\ \ ?$
$-6-3+12-3=0$	$-12+8+6-2=0\ \ ?$	$3-7+18-14=0$
$0=0$ True	$0=0$ True	$0=0$ True

Solution set: $\{(-3,1,6)\}$

59. $x-2y+3z=6\ (1)$

$2x-\ \ y+2z=5\ (2)$

Multiply equation (2) by −2 and add to equation (1) in order to eliminate y.

$$\begin{array}{r} x-\ 2y+3z=\ \ \ 6 \\ -4x+2y-4z=-10 \\ \hline -3x\qquad\ -z=\ -4\ (3) \end{array}$$

Solve equation (3) for z.

$$-3x-z=-4\Rightarrow -z=3x-4\Rightarrow z=-3x+4$$

Express y in terms of x by solving equation (1) for y and substituting $-3x+4$ for z.

$$x-2y+3z=6\Rightarrow -2y=-x-3z+6\Rightarrow y=\frac{-x-3z+6}{-2}=\frac{x+3z-6}{2}$$

$$y=\frac{x+3(-3x+4)-6}{2}=\frac{x-9x+12-6}{2}=\frac{-8x+6}{2}=-4x+3$$

With x arbitrary, the solution set is of the form $\{(x,-4x+3,-3x+4)\}$.

61. $5x-4y+z=\ 9$ (1)

$x+\ y\ \ \ \ =15$ (2)

Multiply equation (2) by 4 and add to equation (1) in order to eliminate *y*.

$$\begin{array}{l} 5x-4y+z=\ 9 \\ \underline{4x+4y\ \ \ \ \ \ =60} \\ 9x\ \ \ \ \ \ \ \ +z=69\ (3) \end{array}$$

Solve equation (3) for *z*.

$$9x+z=69 \Rightarrow z=-9x+69$$

Express *y* in terms of *x* by solving equation (1) for *y* and substituting $-9x+69$ for *z*.

$$5x-4y+z=9 \Rightarrow -4y=-5x-z+9 \Rightarrow y=\frac{-5x-z+9}{-4}=\frac{5x+z-9}{4}$$

$$y=\frac{5x+(-9x+69)-9}{4}=\frac{-4x+60}{4}=-x+15$$

With *x* arbitrary, the solution set is of the form $\{(x,-x+15,-9x+69)\}$.

63. $3x+4y-z=13$ (1)

$x+\ y+2z=15$ (2)

Multiply equation (2) by -4 and add to equation (1) in order to eliminate *y*.

$$\begin{array}{l} 3x+4y-\ z=\ 13 \\ \underline{-4x-4y-8z=-60} \\ -x\ \ \ \ \ \ \ \ -9z=-47\ (3) \end{array}$$

Solve equation (3) for *z*.

$$-x-9z=-47 \Rightarrow -9z=-47+x \Rightarrow z=\frac{-47+x}{-9}=\frac{47-x}{9}$$

Express *y* in terms of *x* by solving equation (2) for *y* and substituting $\frac{47-x}{9}$ for *z*.

$$x+y+2z=15 \Rightarrow y=-x-2z+15 \Rightarrow y=-x-2\left(\tfrac{47-x}{9}\right)+15$$

$$y=\frac{-9x-2(47-x)+135}{9}=\frac{-9x-94+2x+135}{9}=\frac{41-7x}{9}$$

With *x* arbitrary, the solution set is of the form $\left\{\left(x,\frac{41-7x}{9},\frac{47-x}{9}\right)\right\}$.

65. $3x+\ 5y-\ z=-2$ (1)

$4x-\ \ \ y+2z=\ 1$ (2)

$-6x-10y+2z=\ 0$ (3)

Multiply equation (1) by 2 and add the result to equation (3).

$$\begin{array}{r} 6x+10y-2z=-4 \\ \underline{-6x-10y+2z=\ 0} \\ 0=-4 \end{array}$$

We obtain a false statement. The solution set is $\varnothing$, and the system is inconsistent.

67.
$$\begin{aligned} 5x - 4y + z &= 0 \quad (1) \\ x + y \quad &= 0 \quad (2) \\ -10x + 8y - 2z &= 0 \quad (3) \end{aligned}$$

Multiply equation (2) by 4 and add the result to equation (1) in order to eliminate y.

$$\begin{aligned} 5x - 4y + z &= 0 \\ 4x + 4y \quad &= 0 \\ \hline 9x \quad + z &= 0 \quad (4) \end{aligned}$$

Multiply equation (2) by -8 and add the result to equation (3) in order to eliminate y.

$$\begin{aligned} -8x - 8y \quad &= 0 \\ -10x + 8y - 2z &= 0 \\ \hline -18x \quad - 2z &= 0 \quad (5) \end{aligned}$$

Multiply equation (4) by 2 and add the result to equation (5).

$$\begin{aligned} 18x + 2z &= 0 \\ -18x - 2z &= 0 \\ \hline 0 &= 0 \end{aligned}$$

This is a true statement and the system has infinitely many solutions.
Solve equation (4) for x.

$$9x + z = 0 \Rightarrow 9x = -z \Rightarrow x = -\tfrac{z}{9}$$

Express y in terms of z by solving equation (1) for y and substituting $-\frac{z}{9}$ for x.

$$5x - 4y + z = 0 \Rightarrow -4y = -5x - z \Rightarrow y = \tfrac{-5x-z}{-4} = \tfrac{5x+z}{4}$$

$$y = \frac{5\left(-\frac{z}{9}\right)+z}{4} = \frac{-5z+9z}{36} = \frac{4z}{36} = \frac{z}{9}$$

With z arbitrary, the solution set is of the form $\left\{\left(-\frac{z}{9}, \frac{z}{9}, z\right)\right\}$.

69.
$$\begin{aligned} \tfrac{2}{x} + \tfrac{1}{y} &= \tfrac{3}{2} \quad (1) \\ \tfrac{3}{x} - \tfrac{1}{y} &= 1 \quad (2) \end{aligned}$$

Let $\frac{1}{x} = t$ and $\frac{1}{y} = u$. With these substitutions, the system becomes

$$\begin{aligned} 2t + u &= \tfrac{3}{2} \ (3) \\ 3t - u &= 1. \ (4) \end{aligned}$$

Add these equations, eliminating u, and solve for t.

$$5t = \tfrac{5}{2} \Rightarrow t = \tfrac{1}{2}$$

Substitute $\frac{1}{2}$ for t in equation (3) and solve for u.

$$2\left(\tfrac{1}{2}\right) + u = \tfrac{3}{2} \Rightarrow 1 + u = \tfrac{3}{2} \Rightarrow u = \tfrac{1}{2}$$

Now find the values of x and y, the variables in the original system. So, $\frac{1}{x} = t$, $tx = 1$, and $x = \frac{1}{t}$.
Likewise $y = \frac{1}{u}$.

$$x = \frac{1}{t} = \frac{1}{\frac{1}{2}} = 2 \text{ and } y = \frac{1}{u} = \frac{1}{\frac{1}{2}} = 2$$

Solution set: $\{(2, 2)\}$

71. $\frac{2}{x}+\frac{1}{y}=11$ (1)

$\frac{3}{x}-\frac{5}{y}=10$ (2)

Let $\frac{1}{x}=t$ and $\frac{1}{y}=u$. With these substitutions, the system becomes

$$2t+u=11 \quad (3)$$
$$3t-5u=10. \quad (4)$$

Multiply equation (3) by 5 and add to equation (4), eliminating *u*, and solve for *t*.

$$\begin{aligned} 10t+5u&=55 \\ 3t-5u&=10 \\ \hline 13t\qquad&=65 \Rightarrow t=5 \end{aligned}$$

Substitute 5 for *t* in equation (3) and solve for *u*.

$$2(5)+u=11 \Rightarrow 10+u=11 \Rightarrow u=1$$

Now find the values of *x* and *y*, the variables in the original system. So, $x=\frac{1}{t}=\frac{1}{5}$ and $y=\frac{1}{u}=\frac{1}{1}=1$.

Solution set: $\left\{\left(\frac{1}{5},1\right)\right\}$

73. $\frac{2}{x}+\frac{3}{y}-\frac{2}{z}=-1$ (1)

$\frac{8}{x}-\frac{12}{y}+\frac{5}{z}=5$ (2)

$\frac{6}{x}+\frac{3}{y}-\frac{1}{z}=1$ (3)

Let $\frac{1}{x}=t$, $\frac{1}{y}=u$, and $\frac{1}{z}=v$. With these substitutions, the system becomes

$$2t+3u-2v=-1 \quad (4)$$
$$8t-12u+5v=5 \quad (5)$$
$$6t+3u-v=1 \quad (6)$$

Eliminate *v* by multiplying equation (6) by 5 and add to equation (5).

$$\begin{aligned} 8t-12u+5v&=5 \\ 30t+15u-5v&=5 \\ \hline 38t+3u\qquad&=10 \quad (7) \end{aligned}$$

Eliminate *v* by multiplying equation (6) by −2 and add to equation (4).

$$\begin{aligned} 2t+3u-2v&=-1 \\ -12t-6u+2v&=-2 \\ \hline -10t-3u\qquad&=-3 \quad (8) \end{aligned}$$

Add equations (7) and (8) in order to eliminate *u*.

$$\begin{aligned} 38t+3u&=10 \\ -10t-3u&=-3 \\ \hline 28t\qquad&=7 \Rightarrow t=\tfrac{1}{4} \end{aligned}$$

Using $t=\frac{1}{4}$, find *u* from equation (7) by substitution.

$$38\left(\tfrac{1}{4}\right)+3u=10 \Rightarrow \tfrac{19}{2}+3u=10 \Rightarrow 3u=\tfrac{20}{2}-\tfrac{19}{2}=\tfrac{1}{2} \Rightarrow u=\tfrac{1}{6}$$

Substitute $\frac{1}{4}$ for *t* and $\frac{1}{6}$ for *u* in equation (4) to find *v*.

$$2\left(\tfrac{1}{4}\right)+3\left(\tfrac{1}{6}\right)-2v=-1 \Rightarrow \tfrac{1}{2}+\tfrac{1}{2}-2v=-1 \Rightarrow 1-2v=-1 \Rightarrow -2v=-2 \Rightarrow v=1$$

Now find the values of *x*, *y*, and *z*, the variables in the original system. So, $x=\frac{1}{t}=\frac{1}{\frac{1}{4}}=4$, $y=\frac{1}{u}=\frac{1}{\frac{1}{6}}=6$, and $z=\frac{1}{v}=\frac{1}{1}=1$.

Solution set: $\{(4,6,1)\}$

75. Answers will vary.

(a)
$$\begin{aligned} x+\ \ y+\ z&=4\\ x+2y+\ z&=5\\ 2x-\ \ y+3z&=4 \end{aligned}$$

This system has exactly one solution, namely (4, 1, –1). (There are other equations that would do the same.)

(b)
$$\begin{aligned} x+y+\ z&=4\\ x+y+\ z&=5\\ 2x-y+3z&=4 \end{aligned}$$

This system has no solution, since no ordered triple can satisfy the first two equations simultaneously. (There are other equations that would do the same.)

(c)
$$\begin{aligned} x+\ \ y+\ z&=4\\ 2x+2y+2z&=8\\ 2x-\ \ y+3z&=4 \end{aligned}$$

This system has infinitely many solutions, since all the ordered triples that satisfy the first equation will also satisfy the second equation. (There are other equations that would do the same.)

77. Since $y=ax^2+b+c$ and the parabola passes through the points (2, 3), (–1, 0), and (–2, 2), we have the following equations.

$$3=a(2)^2+b(2)+c \quad \Rightarrow 4a+2b+c=3\ (1)$$
$$0=a(-1)^2+b(-1)+c\Rightarrow\ a-\ b+c=0\ (2)$$
$$2=a(-2)^2+b(-2)+c\Rightarrow 4a-2b+c=2\ (3)$$

Multiply equation (2) by –1 and add the result to equation (1) in order to eliminate *c*.

$$\begin{aligned} 4a+2b+c&=3\\ -a+\ b-c&=0\\ \hline 3a+3b\quad\ &=3\ \ (4) \end{aligned}$$

Multiplying equation (4) by –1 and then adding the result to equation (5).

$$\begin{aligned} -3a-3b&=-3\\ 3a-\ \ b&=\ 2\\ \hline -4b&=-1\Rightarrow b=\tfrac{1}{4} \end{aligned}$$

Multiply equation (2) by –1 and add the result to equation (3) in order to eliminate *c*.

$$\begin{aligned} -a+\ b-c&=0\\ 4a-2b+c&=2\\ \hline 3a-\ b\quad\ &=2\ \ (5) \end{aligned}$$

Substitute this value into equation (5).

$3a-\frac{1}{4}=2\Rightarrow 3a=\frac{8}{4}+\frac{1}{4}=\frac{9}{4}\Rightarrow a=\frac{3}{4}$

Substitute $a=\frac{3}{4}$ and $b=\frac{1}{4}$ into equation (1) in order to solve for *c*.

$$4\left(\tfrac{3}{4}\right)+2\left(\tfrac{1}{4}\right)+c=3$$
$$3+\tfrac{1}{2}+c=3\Rightarrow c=-\tfrac{1}{2}$$

The equation of the parabola is $y=\frac{3}{4}x^2+\frac{1}{4}x-\frac{1}{2}$.

79. Since $y = ax + b$ and the line passes through the points $(2,5)$ and $(-1,-4)$, we have the equations $5 = a(2) + b$ and $-4 = a(-1) + b$.

This becomes the following system.

$$\begin{aligned} 2a + b &= 5 \quad (1) \\ -a + b &= -4. \quad (2) \end{aligned}$$

Multiply equation (2) by –1 and add the result to equation (1) in order to eliminate b.

$$\begin{array}{r} 2a + b = 5 \\ \underline{a - b = 4} \\ 3a \quad = 9 \Rightarrow a = 3 \end{array}$$

Substitute this value into equation (1).

$$2(3) + b = 5 \Rightarrow 6 + b = 5 \Rightarrow b = -1$$

The equation is $y = 3x - 1$.

81. Since $y = ax^2 + bx + c$ and the parabola passes through the points $(-2,-3.75)$, $(4,-3.75)$, and $(-1,-1.25)$, we have the following equations.

$$\begin{aligned} -3.75 &= a(-2)^2 + b(-2) + c \Rightarrow 4a - 2b + c = -3.75 \quad (1) \\ -3.75 &= a(4)^2 + b(4) + c \Rightarrow 16a + 4b + c = -3.75 \quad (2) \\ -1.25 &= a(-1)^2 + b(-1) + c \Rightarrow a - b + c = -1.25 \quad (3) \end{aligned}$$

Multiply equation (2) by –1 and add the result to equation (1) in order to eliminate c.

$$\begin{array}{r} 4a - 2b + c = -3.75 \\ \underline{-16a - 4b - c = 3.75} \\ -12a - 6b \quad = 0 \text{ or } 2a + b = 0 \quad (4) \end{array}$$

Multiply equation (2) by –1 and add the result to equation (3) in order to eliminate c.

$$\begin{array}{r} -16a - 4b - c = 3.75 \\ \underline{a - b + c = -1.25} \\ -15a - 5b \quad = 2.50 \text{ or } -3a - b = .5 \quad (5) \end{array}$$

Add equations (4) and (5) in order to solve for b.

$$\begin{array}{r} 2a + b = 0 \\ \underline{-3a - b = .5} \\ -a \quad = .5 \Rightarrow a = -.5 \end{array}$$

Substitute $a = -.5$ into equation (4) in order to solve for b.

$$2(-.5) + b = 0 \Rightarrow -1 + b = 0 \Rightarrow b = 1$$

Substitute $a = -.5$ and $b = 1$ into equation (3) in order to solve for c.

$$\begin{aligned} -.5 - 1 + c &= -1.25 \\ -1.5 + c &= -1.25 \Rightarrow c = .25 \end{aligned}$$

The equation of the parabola is $y = -.5x^2 + x + .25$ or $y = -\frac{1}{2}x^2 + x + \frac{1}{4}$.

83. Since $x^2+y^2+ax+by+c=0$ and the circle passes through the points $(-1,3)$, $(6,2)$, and $(-2,-4)$, we have the following equations.

$$(-1)^2+3^2+a(-1)+b(3)+c=0 \Rightarrow -a+3b+c=-10 \quad (1)$$
$$6^2+2^2+a(6)+b(2)+c=0 \Rightarrow 6a+2b+c=-40 \quad (2)$$
$$(-2)^2+(-4)^2+a(-2)+b(-4)+c=0 \Rightarrow -2a-4b+c=-20 \quad (3)$$

Multiply equation (1) by –2 and adding the result to equation (3) in order to eliminate *a*.

$$\begin{array}{r} 2a-6b-2c=\ \ 20 \\ -2a-4b+\ c=-20 \\ \hline -10b-\ c=\ \ 0\ (4) \end{array}$$

Multiply equation (1) by 6 and adding the result to equation (2) in order to eliminate *a*

$$\begin{array}{r} -6a+18b+6c=-60 \\ 6a+\ 2b+\ c=-40 \\ \hline 20b+7c=-100\ (5) \end{array}$$

Multiply equation (4) by 7 and adding the result to equation (5) in order to eliminate *c*

$$\begin{array}{r} -70b-7c=\ \ 0 \\ 20b+7c=-100 \\ \hline -50b\ \ =-100 \Rightarrow b=2 \end{array}$$

We substitute this value into equation (4) in order to solve for *c*.

$$-10(2)-c=0 \Rightarrow -20-c=0 \Rightarrow -20=c$$

Substitute $b=2$ and $c=-20$ into equation (1).

$$-a+3(2)-20=-10 \Rightarrow -a+6-20=-10 \Rightarrow -a-14=-10 \Rightarrow -a=4 \Rightarrow a=-4$$

The equation of the circle is $x^2+y^2-4x+2y-20=0$.

85. Since $x^2+y^2+ax+by+c=0$ and the circle passes through the points (2, 1), (–1, 0), and (3, 3), we have the following equations.

$$2^2+1^2+a(2)+b(1)+c=0 \Rightarrow 2a+b+c=-5 \quad (1)$$
$$(-1)^2+0^2+a(-1)+b(0)+c=0 \Rightarrow -a+c=-1 \quad (2)$$
$$3^2+3^2+a(3)+b(3)+c=0 \Rightarrow 3a+3b+c=-18 \quad (3)$$

Multiply equation (1) by –3 and add the result to equation (3) in order to eliminate *b*.

$$\begin{array}{r} -6a-3b-3c=\ \ 15 \\ 3a+3b\ +c=-18 \\ \hline -3a-\ \ 2c=\ -3\ \ (4) \end{array}$$

Multiply equation (2) by 2 and add the result to equation (4) in order to eliminate *c*

$$\begin{array}{r} -2a+2c=-2 \\ -3a-2c=-3 \\ \hline -5a\ \ =-5 \Rightarrow a=1 \end{array}$$

We substitute this value into equation (2) in order to solve for *c*.

$$-1+c=-1 \Rightarrow c=0$$

Substitute $a=1$ and $c=0$ into equation (1).

$$2(1)+b+0=-5 \Rightarrow 2+b=-5 \Rightarrow b=-7$$

The equation of the circle is $x^2+y^2+x-7y=0$.

87. (a) Since $C = at^2 + bt + c$ and we have the ordered pairs (0, 318), (20, 341), and (40, 371), we have the following equations.

$$318 = a(0)^2 + b(0) + c \Rightarrow \qquad c = 318 \; (1)$$
$$341 = a(20)^2 + b(20) + c \Rightarrow 400a + 20b + c = 341 \; (2)$$
$$371 = a(40)^2 + b(40) + c \Rightarrow 1600a + 40b + c = 371 \; (3)$$

Since c = 318, we substitute this value into equations (2) and (3) to obtain the following system.

$$400a + 20b + 318 = 341 \Rightarrow 400a + 20b = 23 \; (4)$$
$$1600a + 40b + 318 = 371 \Rightarrow 1600a + 40b = 53 \; (5)$$

Multiply equation (4) by –2 and add the result to equation (5) in order to eliminate b.

$$-800a - 40b = -46$$
$$1600a + 40b = 53$$
$$800a \quad = 7 \Rightarrow a = \tfrac{7}{800}$$

Substitute $a = \frac{7}{800}$ into equation (5) in order to solve for b.

$$1600\left(\tfrac{7}{800}\right) + 40b = 53$$
$$14 + 40b = 53$$
$$40b = 39 \Rightarrow b = \tfrac{39}{40}$$

The constants are $a = \frac{7}{800}$, $b = \frac{39}{40}$, and $c = 318$ and the relationship is $C = \frac{7}{800}t^2 + \frac{39}{40}t + 318$.

(b) Since t = 0 corresponds to 1962, the amount of carbon dioxide will be double its 1962 level when $\frac{7}{800}t^2 + \frac{39}{40}t + 318 = 2(318)$. Solve this equation.

$$\tfrac{7}{800}t^2 + \tfrac{39}{40}t + 318 = 2(318) \Rightarrow \tfrac{7}{800}t^2 + \tfrac{39}{40}t - 318 = 0 \Rightarrow 7t^2 + 780t - 254{,}400 = 0$$

Use the quadratic formula, where $a = 7, b = 780$, and $c = -254{,}400$.

$$t = \frac{-780 \pm \sqrt{780^2 - 4(7)(-254{,}400)}}{2(7)} = \frac{-780 \pm \sqrt{608{,}400 + 7{,}123{,}200}}{14} = \frac{-780 \pm \sqrt{7{,}731{,}600}}{14}$$
$$t = \frac{-780 - \sqrt{7{,}731{,}600}}{14} \approx -254.3 \text{ or } t = \frac{-780 + \sqrt{7{,}731{,}600}}{14} \approx 142.9$$

We reject the first proposed solution because time cannot be negative. If t is approximately 142.9 then the year is $1962 + 142.9 = 2104.9$ (near the end of 2104).

89. Let $x =$ the deficit in billions of dollars for New York.
$y =$ the deficit in billions of dollars for California.

We have the following system of equations.

$$y = 3x - 1 \; (1)$$
$$x + y = 47 \; (2)$$

Replace y with $3x - 1$ in equation (2), and solve for x.

$$x + y = 47 \Rightarrow x + (3x - 1) = 47$$
$$4x - 1 = 47 \Rightarrow 4x = 48 \Rightarrow x = 12$$

Replace x with 12 in equation (1) to obtain $y = 3(12) - 1 = 36 - 1 = 35$.

California had a deficit of \$35 billion and New York had a deficit of \$12 billion.

91. Let x = the number of \$3.00 gallons;
y = the number of \$4.50 gallons;
z = the number of \$9.00 gallons.

We have the following equations.

$$\begin{aligned} x+\quad y+\ z &= 300 \quad (1) \\ 2x = y \Rightarrow 2x-\quad y \qquad &= \ \ 0 \quad (2) \\ 3.00x+4.50y+9.00z = 6.00(300) \Rightarrow 3x+4.5y+9z &= 1800 \quad (3) \end{aligned}$$

Multiply equation (1) by –9 and add to equation (3) in order to eliminate z.

$$\begin{array}{r} -9x-\ \ 9y-9z = -2700 \\ 3x+4.5y+9z = \ \ 1800 \\ \hline -6x-4.5y \qquad = -900\ (4) \end{array}$$

Multiply equation (2) by 3 and add to equation (4) in order to eliminate x.

$$\begin{array}{r} 6x-\ \ 3y = \qquad 0 \\ -6x-4.5y = -900 \\ \hline -7.5y = -900 \Rightarrow y = 120 \end{array}$$

Substitute this value into equation (2) to solve for x.

$$2x-120=0 \Rightarrow 2x=120 \Rightarrow x=60$$

Substitute $x=60$ and $y=120$ into equation (1) and solve for y.

$$60+120+z=300 \Rightarrow 180+z=300 \Rightarrow z=120$$

She should use 60 gal of the \$3.00 water, 120 gal of the \$4.50 water, and 120 gal of the \$9.00 water.

93. Let x = the length of the shortest side;
y = the length of the medium side;
z = the length of the longest side.

We have the following equations.

$$\begin{aligned} x+y+z &= 59 \quad (1) \\ z=y+11 \Rightarrow \quad -y+z &= 11 \quad (2) \\ y=x+3 \Rightarrow -x+y \qquad &= \ 3 \quad (3) \end{aligned}$$

Add equations (1) and (3) together in order to eliminate x.

$$\begin{array}{r} x+y+z = 59 \\ -x+y \qquad = \ \ 3 \\ \hline 2y+z = 62\ (4) \end{array}$$

Multiply equation (2) by 2 and then add the result to equation (4) to solve for z.

$$\begin{array}{r} -2y+2z = 22 \\ 2y+\ \ z = 62 \\ \hline 3z = 84 \Rightarrow z = 28 \end{array}$$

Substitute this value into equation (2) in order to solve for y.

$$-y+28=11 \Rightarrow -y=-17 \Rightarrow y=17$$

Substitute $y=17$ into equation (3) in order to solve for x.

$$-x+17=3 \Rightarrow -x=-14 \Rightarrow x=14$$

The lengths of the sides of the triangle are 14 inches, 17 inches, and 28 inches.
Note: $14+17+28=59$

95. Let x = the amount invested in real estate (at 3%);
y = the amount invested in a money market account (at 2.5%);
z = the amount invested in CDs (at 1.5%).

Completing the table we have the following.

	Amount Invested	Rate (as a decimal)	Annual Interest
Real Estate	x	.03	$.03x$
Money Market	y	.025	$.025y$
CDs	z	.015	$.015z$

We have the following equations.

$$x+y+z=200{,}000 \quad (1)$$
$$z=x+y-80{,}000 \Rightarrow x+y-z=80{,}000 \quad (2)$$
$$.03x+.025y+.015z=4900 \Rightarrow 30x+25y+15z=4{,}900{,}000 \quad (3)$$

Add equations (1) and (2) in order to eliminate z.

$$\begin{aligned} x+y+z&=200{,}000 \\ x+y-z&=80{,}000 \\ \hline 2x+2y&=280{,}000 \text{ or } x+y=140{,}000 \ (4) \end{aligned}$$

Multiply equation (2) by 15 and add the result to equation (3) in order to eliminate z.

$$\begin{aligned} 15x+15y-15z&=1{,}200{,}000 \\ 30x+25y+15z&=4{,}900{,}000 \\ \hline 45x+40y&=6{,}100{,}000 \text{ or } 9x+8y=1{,}220{,}000 \ (5) \end{aligned}$$

Multiply equation (4) by -8 and add the result to equation (5).

$$\begin{aligned} -8x-8y&=-1{,}120{,}000 \\ 9x+8y&=1{,}220{,}000 \\ \hline x&=100{,}000 \end{aligned}$$

Substitute this value into equation (4) in order to solve for y.

$$100{,}000+y=140{,}000 \Rightarrow y=40{,}000$$

Substitute $x=100{,}000$ and $y=40{,}000$ into equation (1) in order to solve for z.

$$100{,}000+40{,}000+z=200{,}000 \Rightarrow 140{,}000+z=200{,}000 \Rightarrow z=60{,}000$$

The amounts invested were \$100,000 at 3% (real estate), \$40,000 at 2.5% (money market), and \$60,000 at 1.5% (CDs).

97. $p=16-\frac{5}{4}q$

(a) $p=16-\frac{5}{4}(0)=16-0=16$

The price is \$16.

(b) $p=16-\frac{5}{4}(4)=16-5=16-5=11$

The price is \$11.

(c) $p=16-\frac{5}{4}(8)=16-10=6$

The price is \$6.

98. $p=16-\frac{5}{4}q$

(a) $6=16-\frac{5}{4}q$

$-10=-\frac{5}{4}q \Rightarrow -40=-5q \Rightarrow 8=q$

The demand is 8 units.

(b) $11=16-\frac{5}{4}q$

$-5=-\frac{5}{4}q \Rightarrow -20=-5q \Rightarrow 4=q$

The demand is 4 units.

(c) $16=16-\frac{5}{4}q \Rightarrow 0=-\frac{5}{4}q \Rightarrow 0=q$

The demand is 0 units.

99. See answer to Exercise 101.

100. $p = \frac{3}{4}q$

(a) $0 = \frac{3}{4}q \Rightarrow 0 = q$

(b) $10 = \frac{3}{4}q \Rightarrow 40 = 3q \Rightarrow q = \frac{40}{3}$

(b) $20 = \frac{3}{4}q \Rightarrow 80 = 3q \Rightarrow q = \frac{80}{3}$

101.

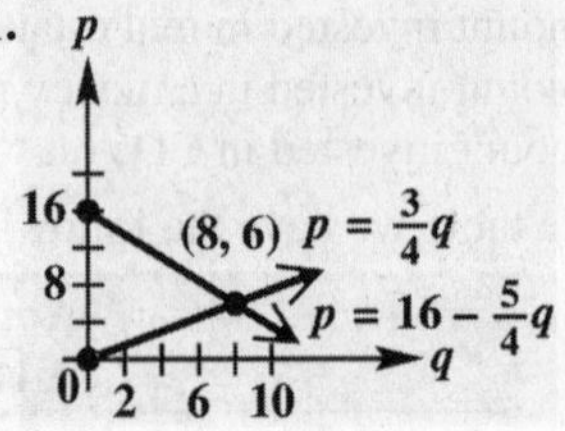

102. To find the equilibrium supply, solve the following system.

$$p = 16 - \tfrac{5}{4}q \quad (1)$$
$$p = \tfrac{3}{4}q. \quad (2)$$

Replace p with $16 - \frac{5}{4}q$ in equation (2), and solve for q. The value of q will give the equilibrium supply.

$$16 - \tfrac{5}{4}q = \tfrac{3}{4}q$$
$$4\left(\tfrac{3}{4}q\right) = 4\left(16 - \tfrac{5}{4}q\right)$$
$$3q = 64 - 5q$$
$$8q = 64$$
$$q = 8$$

The equilibrium supply is 8.
To find p, substitute $q = 8$ into equation (2).

$$p = \tfrac{3}{4}(8) = 6$$

The equilibrium price is \$6.

103.
$$25x + 40y + 20z = 2200 \quad (4)$$
$$4x + 2y + 3z = 280 \quad (5)$$
$$3x + 2y + z = 180 \quad (6)$$

Eliminate z by multiplying equation (6) by -3 and add to equation (5).

$$\begin{array}{r} -9x - 6y - 3z = -540 \\ 4x + 2y + 3z = 280 \\ \hline -5x - 4y \quad = -260 \quad (7) \end{array}$$

Eliminate z by multiplying equation (6) by -20 and add to equation (4).

$$\begin{array}{r} -60x - 40y - 20z = -3600 \\ 25x + 40y + 20z = 2200 \\ \hline -35x \quad = -1400 \Rightarrow x = 40 \end{array}$$

Substitute this value in equation (7) in order to solve for y.

$$-5(40) - 4y = -260 \Rightarrow -200 - 4y = -260 \Rightarrow -4y = -60 \Rightarrow y = 15$$

Substitute $x = 40$ and $y = 15$ into equation (6) to solve for z.

$$3(40) + 2(15) + z = 180 \Rightarrow 120 + 30 + z = 180 \Rightarrow 150 + z = 180 \Rightarrow z = 30$$

Solution set: $\{(40, 15, 30)\}$

Section 9.2: Matrix Solution of Linear Systems

Connections (page 807)

1. $T(n) = \frac{2}{3}n^3 + \frac{3}{2}n^2 - \frac{7}{6}n$

Continuing in this manner we have the following.

n	T
3	28
6	191
10	805
29	17,487
100	681,550
200	5,393,100
400	42,906,200
1000	668,165,500
5000	8.3×10^{10}
10,000	6.7×10^{11}
100,000	6.7×10^{14}

2. Using the tables he would have to do 17,487 operations. Yes, this is too many to do by hand.

3. If the number of variables doubles, the number of operations increases by a factor of 8. 100 variables require 681,550 operations and 200 variables requires 5,393,100 operations.

$$\text{The ratio } \frac{5{,}393{,}100}{681{,}550} \approx 7.91 \approx 8.$$

4. A system of 100,000 variables has 6.7×10^{14} operations. If a Cray-T90 does 60 billion = 6×10^{10} operations per second, then the system would take $\frac{6.7\times10^{14}}{6\times10^{10}} \approx 11{,}166.67$ sec. Since there are 3600 seconds in 1 hr, the system would take $\frac{11{,}166.67}{3600} \approx 3.1$ hr.

Exercises

1. $\begin{bmatrix} 2 & 4 \\ 4 & 7 \end{bmatrix}$; -2 times row 1 added to row 2

$$\begin{bmatrix} 2 & 4 \\ 4+(-2)(2) & 7+(-2)(4) \end{bmatrix} = \begin{bmatrix} 2 & 4 \\ 0 & -1 \end{bmatrix}$$

3. $\begin{bmatrix} 1 & 5 & 6 \\ -2 & 3 & -1 \\ 4 & 7 & 0 \end{bmatrix}$; 2 times row 1 added to row 2

$$\begin{bmatrix} 1 & 5 & 6 \\ -2+2(1) & 3+2(5) & -1+2(6) \\ 4 & 7 & 0 \end{bmatrix} = \begin{bmatrix} 1 & 5 & 6 \\ 0 & 13 & 11 \\ 4 & 7 & 0 \end{bmatrix}$$

5. $2x+3y=11$
   $x+2y=8$

The augmented matrix is $\left[\begin{array}{cc|c} 2 & 3 & 11 \\ 1 & 2 & 8 \end{array}\right]$. The size is 2×3.

7. $\begin{aligned} 2x+\ y+\ z-3&=0 \\ 3x-4y+2z+7&=0 \\ x+\ y+\ z-2&=0 \end{aligned}$

Each equation of a linear system must have the constant term isolated on one side of the equal sign.

Rewriting this system, we have $\begin{aligned} 2x+\ y+\ z&=\ 3 \\ 3x-4y+2z&=-7 \\ x+\ y+\ z&=\ 2. \end{aligned}$ The augmented matrix is $\left[\begin{array}{ccc|c} 2 & 1 & 1 & 3 \\ 3 & -4 & 2 & -7 \\ 1 & 1 & 1 & 2 \end{array}\right]$. The size is 3×4.

9. $\left[\begin{array}{ccc|c} 3 & 2 & 1 & 1 \\ 0 & 2 & 4 & 22 \\ -1 & -2 & 3 & 15 \end{array}\right]$ is associated with the system $\begin{aligned} 3x+2y+z&=1 \\ 2y+4z&=22 \\ -x-2y+3z&=15. \end{aligned}$

11. $\left[\begin{array}{ccc|c} 1 & 0 & 0 & 2 \\ 0 & 1 & 0 & 3 \\ 0 & 0 & 1 & -2 \end{array}\right]$ is associated with the system $\begin{aligned} x&=\ 2 \\ y&=\ 3 \\ z&=-2. \end{aligned}$

13. $\left[\begin{array}{ccc|c} 1 & 1 & 0 & 3 \\ 0 & 2 & 1 & -4 \\ 1 & 0 & -1 & 5 \end{array}\right]$ is associated with the system $\begin{aligned} x+y&=\ 3 \\ 2y+z&=-4 \\ x-z&=\ 5. \end{aligned}$

15. $\begin{aligned} x+y&=5 \\ x-y&=-1 \end{aligned}$; This system has the augmented matrix $\left[\begin{array}{cc|c} 1 & 1 & 5 \\ 1 & -1 & -1 \end{array}\right]$.

$$\left[\begin{array}{cc|c} 1 & 1 & 5 \\ 0 & -2 & -6 \end{array}\right] -1R1+R2 \Rightarrow \left[\begin{array}{cc|c} 1 & 1 & 5 \\ 0 & 1 & 3 \end{array}\right] -\tfrac{1}{2}R2 \Rightarrow \left[\begin{array}{cc|c} 1 & 0 & 2 \\ 0 & 1 & 3 \end{array}\right] -1R2+R1$$

Solution set: $\{(2,3)\}$

17. $\begin{aligned} 3x+2y&=-9 \\ 2x-5y&=-6 \end{aligned}$; This system has the augmented matrix $\left[\begin{array}{cc|c} 3 & 2 & -9 \\ 2 & -5 & -6 \end{array}\right]$.

$$\left[\begin{array}{cc|c} 1 & 7 & -3 \\ 2 & -5 & -6 \end{array}\right] -1R2+R1 \left[\begin{array}{cc|c} 1 & 7 & -3 \\ 0 & -19 & 0 \end{array}\right] -2R1+R2 \Rightarrow \left[\begin{array}{cc|c} 1 & 7 & -3 \\ 0 & 1 & 0 \end{array}\right] -\tfrac{1}{19}R2 \Rightarrow \left[\begin{array}{cc|c} 1 & 0 & -3 \\ 0 & 1 & 0 \end{array}\right] -7R2+R1$$

Solution set: $\{(-3,0)\}$

19. $\begin{aligned} 6x+y-5&=0 \\ 5x+y-3&=0 \end{aligned}$; Rewrite the system as $\begin{aligned} 6x+y&=5 \\ 5x+y&=3. \end{aligned}$ The augmented matrix is $\left[\begin{array}{cc|c} 6 & 1 & 5 \\ 5 & 1 & 3 \end{array}\right]$.

$$\left[\begin{array}{cc|c} 1 & \frac{1}{6} & \frac{5}{6} \\ 5 & 1 & 3 \end{array}\right] \tfrac{1}{6}R1 \Rightarrow \left[\begin{array}{cc|c} 1 & \frac{1}{6} & \frac{5}{6} \\ 0 & \frac{1}{6} & -\frac{7}{6} \end{array}\right] -5R1+R2 \Rightarrow \left[\begin{array}{cc|c} 1 & \frac{1}{6} & \frac{5}{6} \\ 0 & 1 & -7 \end{array}\right] 6R2 \Rightarrow \left[\begin{array}{cc|c} 1 & 0 & 2 \\ 0 & 1 & -7 \end{array}\right] -\tfrac{1}{6}R2+R1$$

or

$$\left[\begin{array}{cc|c} 1 & 0 & 2 \\ 5 & 1 & 3 \end{array}\right] -1R2+R1 \Rightarrow \left[\begin{array}{cc|c} 1 & 0 & 2 \\ 0 & 1 & -7 \end{array}\right] -5R1+R2$$

Solution set: $\{(2,-7)\}$

21. $\begin{aligned} 2x - y &= 6 \\ 4x - 2y &= 0 \end{aligned}$; This system has the augmented matrix $\left[\begin{array}{cc|c} 2 & -1 & 6 \\ 4 & -2 & 0 \end{array}\right]$.

$$\left[\begin{array}{cc|c} 1 & -\frac{1}{2} & 3 \\ 4 & -2 & 0 \end{array}\right]\begin{array}{l} \frac{1}{2}\text{R1} \\ \end{array} \Rightarrow \left[\begin{array}{cc|c} 1 & -\frac{1}{2} & 3 \\ 0 & 0 & -12 \end{array}\right]\begin{array}{l} \\ -4\text{R1}+\text{R2} \end{array}$$

The second row of the augmented matrix corresponds to the equation $0x + 0y = -12$, which has no solution. Thus, the solution set is $\varnothing$.

23. $\begin{aligned} x + y - 5z &= -18 \\ 3x - 3y + z &= 6 \\ x + 3y - 2z &= -13 \end{aligned}$; This system has the augmented matrix $\left[\begin{array}{ccc|c} 1 & 1 & -5 & -18 \\ 3 & -3 & 1 & 6 \\ 1 & 3 & -2 & -13 \end{array}\right]$.

$$\left[\begin{array}{ccc|c} 1 & 1 & -5 & -18 \\ 0 & -6 & 16 & 60 \\ 1 & 3 & -2 & -13 \end{array}\right]\begin{array}{l} \\ -3\text{R1}+\text{R2} \\ \\ \end{array} \Rightarrow \left[\begin{array}{ccc|c} 1 & 1 & -5 & -18 \\ 0 & -6 & 16 & 60 \\ 0 & 2 & 3 & 5 \end{array}\right]\begin{array}{l} \\ \\ -1\text{R1}+\text{R3} \end{array} \Rightarrow \left[\begin{array}{ccc|c} 1 & 1 & -5 & -18 \\ 0 & 1 & -\frac{8}{3} & -10 \\ 0 & 2 & 3 & 5 \end{array}\right]\begin{array}{l} \\ -\frac{1}{6}\text{R2} \\ \\ \end{array}$$

$$\left[\begin{array}{ccc|c} 1 & 0 & -\frac{7}{3} & -8 \\ 0 & 1 & -\frac{8}{3} & -10 \\ 0 & 2 & 3 & 5 \end{array}\right]\begin{array}{l} -1\text{R2}+\text{R1} \\ \\ \\ \end{array} \Rightarrow \left[\begin{array}{ccc|c} 1 & 0 & -\frac{7}{3} & -8 \\ 0 & 1 & -\frac{8}{3} & -10 \\ 0 & 0 & \frac{25}{3} & 25 \end{array}\right]\begin{array}{l} \\ \\ -2\text{R2}+\text{R3} \end{array} \Rightarrow \left[\begin{array}{ccc|c} 1 & 0 & -\frac{7}{3} & -8 \\ 0 & 1 & -\frac{8}{3} & -10 \\ 0 & 0 & 1 & 3 \end{array}\right]\begin{array}{l} \\ \\ \frac{3}{25}\text{R3} \end{array}$$

$$\left[\begin{array}{ccc|c} 1 & 0 & 0 & -1 \\ 0 & 1 & -\frac{8}{3} & -10 \\ 0 & 0 & 1 & 3 \end{array}\right]\begin{array}{l} \frac{7}{3}\text{R3}+\text{R1} \\ \\ \\ \end{array} \Rightarrow \left[\begin{array}{ccc|c} 1 & 0 & 0 & -1 \\ 0 & 1 & 0 & -2 \\ 0 & 0 & 1 & 3 \end{array}\right]\begin{array}{l} \\ \frac{8}{3}\text{R3}+\text{R2} \\ \\ \end{array}$$

Solution set: $\{(-1,-2,3)\}$

25. $\begin{aligned} x + y - z &= 6 \\ 2x - y + z &= -9 \\ x - 2y + 3z &= 1 \end{aligned}$; This system has the augmented matrix $\left[\begin{array}{ccc|c} 1 & 1 & -1 & 6 \\ 2 & -1 & 1 & -9 \\ 1 & -2 & 3 & 1 \end{array}\right]$.

$$\left[\begin{array}{ccc|c} 1 & 1 & -1 & 6 \\ 0 & -3 & 3 & -21 \\ 1 & -2 & 3 & 1 \end{array}\right]\begin{array}{l} \\ -2\text{R1}+\text{R2} \\ \\ \end{array} \Rightarrow \left[\begin{array}{ccc|c} 1 & 1 & -1 & 6 \\ 0 & -3 & 3 & -21 \\ 0 & -3 & 4 & -5 \end{array}\right]\begin{array}{l} \\ \\ -1\text{R1}+\text{R3} \end{array} \Rightarrow \left[\begin{array}{ccc|c} 1 & 1 & -1 & 6 \\ 0 & 1 & -1 & 7 \\ 0 & -3 & 4 & -5 \end{array}\right]\begin{array}{l} \\ -\frac{1}{3}\text{R2} \\ \\ \end{array}$$

$$\left[\begin{array}{ccc|c} 1 & 0 & 0 & -1 \\ 0 & 1 & -1 & 7 \\ 0 & -3 & 4 & -5 \end{array}\right]\begin{array}{l} -1\text{R2}+\text{R1} \\ \\ \\ \end{array} \Rightarrow \left[\begin{array}{ccc|c} 1 & 0 & 0 & -1 \\ 0 & 1 & -1 & 7 \\ 0 & 0 & 1 & 16 \end{array}\right]\begin{array}{l} \\ \\ 3\text{R2}+\text{R3} \end{array} \Rightarrow \left[\begin{array}{ccc|c} 1 & 0 & 0 & -1 \\ 0 & 1 & 0 & 23 \\ 0 & 0 & 1 & 16 \end{array}\right]\begin{array}{l} \\ \text{R3}+\text{R2} \\ \\ \end{array}$$

Solution set: $\{(-1,23,16)\}$

27. $\begin{aligned} x - z &= -3 \\ y + z &= 9 \\ x + z &= 7 \end{aligned}$; This system has the augmented matrix $\left[\begin{array}{ccc|c} 1 & 0 & -1 & -3 \\ 0 & 1 & 1 & 9 \\ 1 & 0 & 1 & 7 \end{array}\right]$.

$$\left[\begin{array}{ccc|c} 1 & 0 & -1 & -3 \\ 0 & 1 & 1 & 9 \\ 0 & 0 & 2 & 10 \end{array}\right]\begin{array}{l} \\ \\ -1\text{R1}+\text{R3} \end{array} \Rightarrow \left[\begin{array}{ccc|c} 1 & 0 & -1 & -3 \\ 0 & 1 & 1 & 9 \\ 0 & 0 & 1 & 5 \end{array}\right]\begin{array}{l} \\ \\ \frac{1}{2}\text{R3} \end{array}$$

$$\left[\begin{array}{ccc|c} 1 & 0 & 0 & 2 \\ 0 & 1 & 1 & 9 \\ 0 & 0 & 1 & 5 \end{array}\right]\begin{array}{l} \text{R3}+\text{R1} \\ \\ \\ \end{array} \Rightarrow \left[\begin{array}{ccc|c} 1 & 0 & 0 & 2 \\ 0 & 1 & 0 & 4 \\ 0 & 0 & 1 & 5 \end{array}\right]\begin{array}{l} \\ -1\text{R3}+\text{R2} \\ \\ \end{array}$$

Solution set: $\{(2,4,5)\}$

29. $\begin{aligned} y&=-2x-2z+1\\ x&=-2y-z+2\\ z&=x-y \end{aligned}$; Rewrite the system as $\begin{aligned} 2x+y+2z&=1\\ x+2y+z&=2\\ x-y-z&=0. \end{aligned}$ The augmented matrix is $\left[\begin{array}{ccc|c} 2 & 1 & 2 & 1\\ 1 & 2 & 1 & 2\\ 1 & -1 & -1 & 0 \end{array}\right]$.

$$\left[\begin{array}{ccc|c} 1 & 2 & 1 & 2\\ 2 & 1 & 2 & 1\\ 1 & -1 & -1 & 0 \end{array}\right] \begin{matrix} \\ \text{R1}\leftrightarrow\text{R2} \\ \\ \end{matrix} \Rightarrow \left[\begin{array}{ccc|c} 1 & 2 & 1 & 2\\ 0 & -3 & 0 & -3\\ 1 & -1 & -1 & 0 \end{array}\right] \begin{matrix} \\ -2\text{R1}+\text{R2} \\ \\ \end{matrix} \Rightarrow \left[\begin{array}{ccc|c} 1 & 2 & 1 & 2\\ 0 & -3 & 0 & -3\\ 0 & -3 & -2 & -2 \end{array}\right] \begin{matrix} \\ \\ -1\text{R1}+\text{R3} \end{matrix}$$

$$\left[\begin{array}{ccc|c} 1 & 2 & 1 & 2\\ 0 & 1 & 0 & 1\\ 0 & -3 & -2 & -2 \end{array}\right] \begin{matrix} \\ -\frac{1}{3}\text{R2} \\ \\ \end{matrix} \Rightarrow \left[\begin{array}{ccc|c} 1 & 0 & 1 & 0\\ 0 & 1 & 0 & 1\\ 0 & -3 & -2 & -2 \end{array}\right] \begin{matrix} -2\text{R2}+\text{R1} \\ \\ \\ \end{matrix} \Rightarrow \left[\begin{array}{ccc|c} 1 & 0 & 1 & 0\\ 0 & 1 & 0 & 1\\ 0 & 0 & -2 & 1 \end{array}\right] \begin{matrix} \\ \\ 3\text{R2}+\text{R3} \end{matrix}$$

$$\left[\begin{array}{ccc|c} 1 & 0 & 1 & 0\\ 0 & 1 & 0 & 1\\ 0 & 0 & 1 & -\frac{1}{2} \end{array}\right] \begin{matrix} \\ \\ -\frac{1}{2}\text{R3} \end{matrix} \Rightarrow \left[\begin{array}{ccc|c} 1 & 0 & 0 & \frac{1}{2}\\ 0 & 1 & 0 & 1\\ 0 & 0 & 1 & -\frac{1}{2} \end{array}\right] \begin{matrix} -1\text{R3}+\text{R1} \\ \\ \\ \end{matrix}$$

Solution set: $\left\{\left(\frac{1}{2},1,-\frac{1}{2}\right)\right\}$

31. $\begin{aligned} 2x-y+3z&=0\\ x+2y-z&=5\\ 2y+z&=1 \end{aligned}$; This system has the augmented matrix $\left[\begin{array}{ccc|c} 2 & -1 & 3 & 0\\ 1 & 2 & -1 & 5\\ 0 & 2 & 1 & 1 \end{array}\right]$.

$$\left[\begin{array}{ccc|c} 1 & 2 & -1 & 5\\ 2 & -1 & 3 & 0\\ 0 & 2 & 1 & 1 \end{array}\right] \begin{matrix} \text{R1}\leftrightarrow\text{R2} \\ \\ \\ \end{matrix} \Rightarrow \left[\begin{array}{ccc|c} 1 & 2 & -1 & 5\\ 0 & -5 & 5 & -10\\ 0 & 2 & 1 & 1 \end{array}\right] \begin{matrix} \\ -2\text{R1}+\text{R2} \\ \\ \end{matrix} \Rightarrow \left[\begin{array}{ccc|c} 1 & 2 & -1 & 5\\ 0 & 1 & -1 & 2\\ 0 & 2 & 1 & 1 \end{array}\right] \begin{matrix} \\ -\frac{1}{5}\text{R2} \\ \\ \end{matrix}$$

$$\left[\begin{array}{ccc|c} 1 & 0 & 1 & 1\\ 0 & 1 & -1 & 2\\ 0 & 2 & 1 & 1 \end{array}\right] \begin{matrix} -2\text{R2}+\text{R1} \\ \\ \\ \end{matrix} \Rightarrow \left[\begin{array}{ccc|c} 1 & 0 & 1 & 1\\ 0 & 1 & -1 & 2\\ 0 & 0 & 3 & -3 \end{array}\right] \begin{matrix} \\ \\ -2\text{R2}+\text{R3} \end{matrix} \Rightarrow \left[\begin{array}{ccc|c} 1 & 0 & 1 & 1\\ 0 & 1 & -1 & 2\\ 0 & 0 & 1 & -1 \end{array}\right] \begin{matrix} \\ \\ \frac{1}{3}\text{R3} \end{matrix}$$

$$\left[\begin{array}{ccc|c} 1 & 0 & 0 & 2\\ 0 & 1 & -1 & 2\\ 0 & 0 & 1 & -1 \end{array}\right] \begin{matrix} -1\text{R3}+\text{R1} \\ \\ \\ \end{matrix} \Rightarrow \left[\begin{array}{ccc|c} 1 & 0 & 0 & 2\\ 0 & 1 & 0 & 1\\ 0 & 0 & 1 & -1 \end{array}\right] \begin{matrix} \\ \text{R3}+\text{R2} \\ \\ \end{matrix}$$

Solution set: $\{(2,1,-1)\}$

33. $\begin{aligned} 3x+\ 5y-z+2&=0\\ 4x-\ y+2z-1&=0\\ -6x-10y+2z\ &=0 \end{aligned}$; Rewrite the system as $\begin{aligned} 3x+\ 5y-\ z&=-2\\ 4x-\ y+2z&=\ 1\\ -6x-10y+2z&=\ 0. \end{aligned}$

The augmented matrix is $\left[\begin{array}{ccc|c} 3 & 5 & -1 & -2\\ 4 & -1 & 2 & 1\\ -6 & -10 & 2 & 0 \end{array}\right]$.

$$\left[\begin{array}{ccc|c} 1 & \frac{5}{3} & -\frac{1}{3} & -\frac{2}{3}\\ 4 & -1 & 2 & 1\\ -6 & -10 & 2 & 0 \end{array}\right] \begin{matrix} \frac{1}{3}\text{R1} \\ \\ \\ \end{matrix} \Rightarrow \left[\begin{array}{ccc|c} 1 & \frac{5}{3} & -\frac{1}{3} & -\frac{2}{3}\\ 0 & -\frac{23}{3} & \frac{10}{3} & \frac{11}{3}\\ -6 & -10 & 2 & 0 \end{array}\right] \begin{matrix} \\ -4\text{R1}+\text{R2} \\ \\ \end{matrix} \Rightarrow \left[\begin{array}{ccc|c} 1 & \frac{5}{3} & -\frac{1}{3} & -\frac{2}{3}\\ 0 & -\frac{23}{3} & \frac{10}{3} & \frac{11}{3}\\ 0 & 0 & 0 & -4 \end{array}\right] \begin{matrix} \\ \\ 6\text{R1}+\text{R3} \end{matrix}$$

The last row indicates that there is no solution. The solution set is $\varnothing$.

35. $\begin{aligned} x-8y+z&=4 \\ 3x-y+2z&=-1 \end{aligned}$ This system has the augmented matrix $\left[\begin{array}{ccc|c} 1 & -8 & 1 & 4 \\ 3 & -1 & 2 & -1 \end{array}\right]$.

$$\left[\begin{array}{ccc|c} 1 & -8 & 1 & 4 \\ 0 & 23 & -1 & -13 \end{array}\right] -3\text{R1}+\text{R2} \Rightarrow \left[\begin{array}{ccc|c} 1 & -8 & 1 & 4 \\ 0 & 1 & -\frac{1}{23} & -\frac{13}{23} \end{array}\right] \tfrac{1}{23}\text{R2} \Rightarrow \left[\begin{array}{ccc|c} 1 & 0 & \frac{15}{23} & -\frac{12}{23} \\ 0 & 1 & -\frac{1}{23} & -\frac{13}{23} \end{array}\right] 8\text{R2}+\text{R1}$$

The equations that correspond to the final matrix are

$$x+\tfrac{15}{23}z=-\tfrac{12}{23} \text{ and } y-\tfrac{1}{23}z=-\tfrac{13}{23}.$$

This system has infinitely many solutions. We will express the solution set with z as the arbitrary variable. Therefore, $x=-\frac{15}{23}z-\frac{12}{23}$ and $y=\frac{1}{23}z-\frac{13}{23}$.

Solution set: $\left\{\left(-\frac{15}{23}z-\frac{12}{23}, \frac{1}{23}z-\frac{13}{23}, z\right)\right\}$

37. $\begin{aligned} x-y+2z+w&=4 \\ y+z&=3 \\ z-w&=2 \\ x-y&=0 \end{aligned}$; This system has the augmented matrix $\left[\begin{array}{cccc|c} 1 & -1 & 2 & 1 & 4 \\ 0 & 1 & 1 & 0 & 3 \\ 0 & 0 & 1 & -1 & 2 \\ 1 & -1 & 0 & 0 & 0 \end{array}\right]$

$$\left[\begin{array}{cccc|c} 1 & -1 & 2 & 1 & 4 \\ 0 & 1 & 1 & 0 & 3 \\ 0 & 0 & 1 & -1 & 2 \\ 0 & 0 & -2 & -1 & -4 \end{array}\right] -1\text{R1}+\text{R4} \Rightarrow \left[\begin{array}{cccc|c} 1 & 0 & 3 & 1 & 7 \\ 0 & 1 & 1 & 0 & 3 \\ 0 & 0 & 1 & -1 & 2 \\ 0 & 0 & -2 & -1 & -4 \end{array}\right] \begin{matrix}\text{R2}+\text{R1}\\ \\ \\ \\ \end{matrix} \Rightarrow \left[\begin{array}{cccc|c} 1 & 0 & 0 & 4 & 1 \\ 0 & 1 & 1 & 0 & 3 \\ 0 & 0 & 1 & -1 & 2 \\ 0 & 0 & -2 & -1 & -4 \end{array}\right] \begin{matrix}-3\text{R3}+\text{R1}\\ \\ \\ \\ \end{matrix}$$

$$\left[\begin{array}{cccc|c} 1 & 0 & 0 & 4 & 1 \\ 0 & 1 & 0 & 1 & 1 \\ 0 & 0 & 1 & -1 & 2 \\ 0 & 0 & -2 & -1 & -4 \end{array}\right] \begin{matrix} \\ -1\text{R3}+\text{R2}\\ \\ \\ \end{matrix} \Rightarrow \left[\begin{array}{cccc|c} 1 & 0 & 0 & 4 & 1 \\ 0 & 1 & 0 & 1 & 1 \\ 0 & 0 & 1 & -1 & 2 \\ 0 & 0 & 0 & -3 & 0 \end{array}\right] 2\text{R3}+\text{R4} \Rightarrow \left[\begin{array}{cccc|c} 1 & 0 & 0 & 4 & 1 \\ 0 & 1 & 0 & 1 & 1 \\ 0 & 0 & 1 & -1 & 2 \\ 0 & 0 & 0 & 1 & 0 \end{array}\right] -\tfrac{1}{3}\text{R4}$$

$$\left[\begin{array}{cccc|c} 1 & 0 & 0 & 0 & 1 \\ 0 & 1 & 0 & 1 & 1 \\ 0 & 0 & 1 & -1 & 2 \\ 0 & 0 & 0 & 1 & 0 \end{array}\right] \begin{matrix}-4\text{R4}+\text{R1}\\ \\ \\ \\ \end{matrix} \Rightarrow \left[\begin{array}{cccc|c} 1 & 0 & 0 & 0 & 1 \\ 0 & 1 & 0 & 0 & 1 \\ 0 & 0 & 1 & -1 & 2 \\ 0 & 0 & 0 & 1 & 0 \end{array}\right] \begin{matrix} \\ -1\text{R4}+\text{R2}\\ \\ \\ \end{matrix} \Rightarrow \left[\begin{array}{cccc|c} 1 & 0 & 0 & 0 & 1 \\ 0 & 1 & 0 & 0 & 1 \\ 0 & 0 & 1 & 0 & 2 \\ 0 & 0 & 0 & 1 & 0 \end{array}\right] \begin{matrix} \\ \\ \text{R4}+\text{R3}\\ \\ \end{matrix}$$

Solution set: $\{(1,1,2,0)\}$

39. $\begin{aligned} x+3y-2z-w&=9 \\ 4x+y+z+2w&=2 \\ -3x-y+z-w&=-5 \\ x-y-3z-2w&=2 \end{aligned}$; This system has the augmented matrix $\left[\begin{array}{cccc|c} 1 & 3 & -2 & -1 & 9 \\ 4 & 1 & 1 & 2 & 2 \\ -3 & -1 & 1 & -1 & -5 \\ 1 & -1 & -3 & -2 & 2 \end{array}\right]$.

$$\left[\begin{array}{cccc|c} 1 & 3 & -2 & -1 & 9 \\ 0 & -11 & 9 & 6 & -34 \\ -3 & -1 & 1 & -1 & -5 \\ 1 & -1 & -3 & -2 & 2 \end{array}\right] \begin{matrix} \\ -4\text{R1}+\text{R2}\\ \\ \\ \end{matrix} \Rightarrow \left[\begin{array}{cccc|c} 1 & 3 & -2 & -1 & 9 \\ 0 & -11 & 9 & 6 & -34 \\ 0 & 8 & -5 & -4 & 22 \\ 1 & -1 & -3 & -2 & 2 \end{array}\right] \begin{matrix} \\ \\ 3\text{R1}+\text{R3}\\ \\ \end{matrix}$$

$$\left[\begin{array}{cccc|c} 1 & 3 & -2 & -1 & 9 \\ 0 & -11 & 9 & 6 & -34 \\ 0 & 8 & -5 & -4 & 22 \\ 0 & -4 & -1 & -1 & -7 \end{array}\right] -1\text{R1}+\text{R4} \Rightarrow \left[\begin{array}{cccc|c} 1 & 3 & -2 & -1 & 9 \\ 0 & 1 & -\frac{9}{11} & -\frac{6}{11} & \frac{34}{11} \\ 0 & 8 & -5 & -4 & 22 \\ 0 & -4 & -1 & -1 & -7 \end{array}\right] \begin{matrix} \\ -\frac{1}{11}\text{R2}\\ \\ \\ \end{matrix}$$

Continued on next page

39. (continued)

$$\left[\begin{array}{cccc|c} 1 & 0 & \frac{5}{11} & \frac{7}{11} & -\frac{3}{11} \\ 0 & 1 & -\frac{9}{11} & -\frac{6}{11} & \frac{34}{11} \\ 0 & 8 & -5 & -4 & 22 \\ 0 & -4 & -1 & -1 & -7 \end{array}\right]\begin{matrix} -3R2+R1 \\ \\ \\ \\ \end{matrix} \Rightarrow \left[\begin{array}{cccc|c} 1 & 0 & \frac{5}{11} & \frac{7}{11} & -\frac{3}{11} \\ 0 & 1 & -\frac{9}{11} & -\frac{6}{11} & \frac{34}{11} \\ 0 & 0 & \frac{17}{11} & \frac{4}{11} & -\frac{30}{11} \\ 0 & -4 & -1 & -1 & -7 \end{array}\right]\begin{matrix} \\ \\ -8R2+R3 \\ \\ \end{matrix}$$

$$\left[\begin{array}{cccc|c} 1 & 0 & \frac{5}{11} & \frac{7}{11} & -\frac{3}{11} \\ 0 & 1 & -\frac{9}{11} & -\frac{6}{11} & \frac{34}{11} \\ 0 & 0 & \frac{17}{11} & \frac{4}{11} & -\frac{30}{11} \\ 0 & 0 & -\frac{47}{11} & -\frac{35}{11} & \frac{59}{11} \end{array}\right]\begin{matrix} \\ \\ \\ 4R2+R4 \end{matrix} \Rightarrow \left[\begin{array}{cccc|c} 1 & 0 & \frac{5}{11} & \frac{7}{11} & -\frac{3}{11} \\ 0 & 1 & -\frac{9}{11} & -\frac{6}{11} & \frac{34}{11} \\ 0 & 0 & 1 & \frac{4}{17} & -\frac{30}{17} \\ 0 & 0 & -\frac{47}{11} & -\frac{35}{11} & \frac{59}{11} \end{array}\right]\begin{matrix} \\ \\ \frac{11}{17}R3 \\ \\ \end{matrix}$$

$$\left[\begin{array}{cccc|c} 1 & 0 & 0 & \frac{9}{17} & \frac{9}{17} \\ 0 & 1 & -\frac{9}{11} & -\frac{6}{11} & \frac{34}{11} \\ 0 & 0 & 1 & \frac{4}{17} & -\frac{30}{17} \\ 0 & 0 & -\frac{47}{11} & -\frac{35}{11} & \frac{59}{11} \end{array}\right]\begin{matrix} -\frac{5}{11}R3+R1 \\ \\ \\ \\ \end{matrix} \Rightarrow \left[\begin{array}{cccc|c} 1 & 0 & 0 & \frac{9}{17} & \frac{9}{17} \\ 0 & 1 & 0 & -\frac{6}{17} & \frac{28}{71} \\ 0 & 0 & 1 & \frac{4}{17} & -\frac{30}{17} \\ 0 & 0 & -\frac{47}{11} & -\frac{35}{11} & \frac{59}{11} \end{array}\right]\begin{matrix} \\ \frac{9}{11}R3+R2 \\ \\ \\ \end{matrix}$$

$$\left[\begin{array}{cccc|c} 1 & 0 & 0 & \frac{9}{17} & \frac{9}{17} \\ 0 & 1 & 0 & -\frac{6}{17} & \frac{28}{17} \\ 0 & 0 & 1 & \frac{4}{17} & -\frac{30}{17} \\ 0 & 0 & 0 & -\frac{37}{17} & -\frac{37}{17} \end{array}\right]\begin{matrix} \\ \\ \\ \frac{47}{11}R3+R4 \end{matrix} \Rightarrow \left[\begin{array}{cccc|c} 1 & 0 & 0 & \frac{9}{17} & \frac{9}{17} \\ 0 & 1 & 0 & -\frac{6}{17} & \frac{28}{17} \\ 0 & 0 & 1 & \frac{4}{17} & -\frac{30}{17} \\ 0 & 0 & 0 & 1 & 1 \end{array}\right]\begin{matrix} \\ \\ \\ -\frac{17}{37}R4 \end{matrix}$$

$$\left[\begin{array}{cccc|c} 1 & 0 & 0 & 0 & 0 \\ 0 & 1 & 0 & -\frac{6}{17} & \frac{28}{17} \\ 0 & 0 & 1 & \frac{4}{17} & -\frac{30}{17} \\ 0 & 0 & 0 & 1 & 1 \end{array}\right]\begin{matrix} -\frac{9}{17}R4+R1 \\ \\ \\ \\ \end{matrix} \Rightarrow \left[\begin{array}{cccc|c} 1 & 0 & 0 & 0 & 0 \\ 0 & 1 & 0 & 0 & 2 \\ 0 & 0 & 1 & \frac{4}{17} & -\frac{30}{17} \\ 0 & 0 & 0 & 1 & 1 \end{array}\right]\begin{matrix} \\ \frac{6}{17}R4+R2 \\ \\ \\ \end{matrix}$$

$$\left[\begin{array}{cccc|c} 1 & 0 & 0 & 0 & 0 \\ 0 & 1 & 0 & 0 & 2 \\ 0 & 0 & 1 & 0 & -2 \\ 0 & 0 & 0 & 1 & 1 \end{array}\right]\begin{matrix} \\ \\ -\frac{4}{17}R4+R3 \\ \\ \end{matrix}$$

Solution set: $\{(0,2,-2,1)\}$

41. $\begin{aligned} .3x+2.7y-\sqrt{2}z &= 3 \\ \sqrt{7}x-20y+12z &= -2 \\ 4x+\sqrt{3}y-1.2z &= \frac{3}{4} \end{aligned}$; This system has the augmented matrix $\left[\begin{array}{ccc|c} .3 & 2.7 & -\sqrt{2} & 3 \\ \sqrt{7} & -20 & 12 & -2 \\ 4 & \sqrt{3} & -1.2 & \frac{3}{4} \end{array}\right]$.

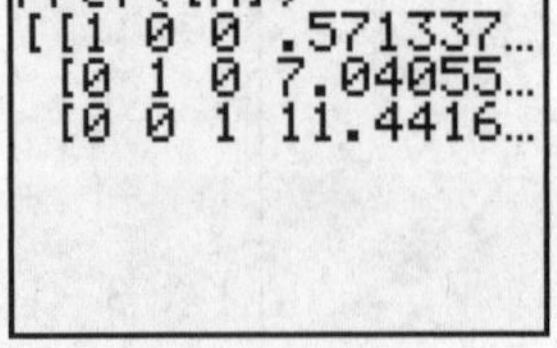

Using a graphing calculator capable of performing row operations, we obtain the approximate solution set.

Solution set: {(.571, 7.041, 11.442)}.

43. $2x+3y=5 \Rightarrow 3y=5-2x \Rightarrow y=\frac{5-2x}{3}$

$-3x+5y=22 \Rightarrow 5y=3x+22 \Rightarrow y=\frac{3x+22}{5}$

$2x+y=-1 \Rightarrow y=2x-1$

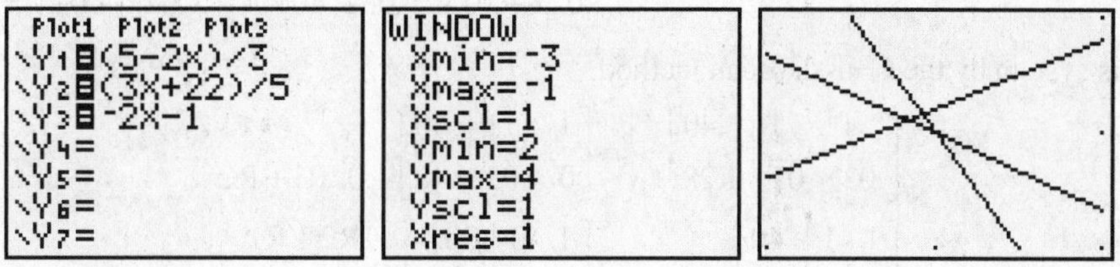

There are no solutions since the three lines do not intersect.

45. $\dfrac{1}{(x-1)(x+1)}=\dfrac{A}{x-1}+\dfrac{B}{x+1}$

If we add the rational expression on the right, we get the following.

$$\frac{1}{(x-1)(x+1)}=\frac{A(x+1)}{(x-1)(x+1)}+\frac{B(x-1)}{(x-1)(x+1)} \Rightarrow \frac{1}{(x-1)(x+1)}=\frac{A(x+1)+B(x-1)}{(x-1)(x+1)}$$

Since the denominators are equal, the numerators must be equal. Thus we have the equation $1=A(x+1)+B(x-1)$.

$$1=A(x+1)+B(x-1) \Rightarrow 1=Ax+A+Bx-B$$
$$1=(A-B)+(Ax+Bx) \Rightarrow 1=(A-B)+(A+B)x$$

Equating the coefficients of like powers of x gives the following system of equations.

$$A+B=0$$
$$A-B=1$$

Solve this system by the Gauss-Jordan method.

$$\left[\begin{array}{cc|c}1&1&0\\1&-1&1\end{array}\right] \Rightarrow \left[\begin{array}{cc|c}1&1&0\\0&-2&1\end{array}\right]\begin{array}{l}\\-\text{R1}+\text{R2}\end{array} \Rightarrow \left[\begin{array}{cc|c}1&1&0\\0&1&-\frac{1}{2}\end{array}\right]\begin{array}{l}\\-\frac{1}{2}\text{R2}\end{array} \Rightarrow \left[\begin{array}{cc|c}1&0&\frac{1}{2}\\0&1&-\frac{1}{2}\end{array}\right]\begin{array}{l}-1\text{R2}+\text{R1}\\ \\\end{array}$$

Thus, $A=\frac{1}{2}$ and $B=-\frac{1}{2}$.

47. $\dfrac{x}{(x-a)(x+a)}=\dfrac{A}{x-a}+\dfrac{B}{x+a}$

If we add the rational expression on the right, we get the following.

$$\frac{x}{(x-a)(x+a)}=\frac{A(x+a)}{(x-a)(x+a)}+\frac{B(x-a)}{(x-a)(x+a)} \Rightarrow \frac{x}{(x-a)(x+a)}=\frac{A(x+a)+B(x-a)}{(x-a)(x+a)}$$

Since the denominators are equal, the numerators must be equal. Thus we have the equation $x=A(x+a)+B(x-a)$.

$$x=A(x+a)+B(x-a) \Rightarrow x=Ax+Aa+Bx-Ba \Rightarrow x=(A+B)x+(A-B)a$$

Equating the coefficients of like powers of x gives the following system of equations.

$$A+B=1$$
$$A-B=0$$

Solve this system by the Gauss-Jordan method.

$$\left[\begin{array}{cc|c}1&1&1\\1&-1&0\end{array}\right] \Rightarrow \left[\begin{array}{cc|c}1&1&1\\0&-2&-1\end{array}\right]\begin{array}{l}\\-\text{R1}+\text{R2}\end{array} \Rightarrow \left[\begin{array}{cc|c}1&1&1\\0&1&\frac{1}{2}\end{array}\right]\begin{array}{l}\\-\frac{1}{2}\text{R2}\end{array} \Rightarrow \left[\begin{array}{cc|c}1&0&\frac{1}{2}\\0&1&\frac{1}{2}\end{array}\right]\begin{array}{l}-1\text{R2}+\text{R1}\\ \\\end{array}$$

Thus, $A=\frac{1}{2}$ and $B=\frac{1}{2}$.

49. Let x = number of cubic centimeters of the 2% solution;
y = number of cubic centimeters of the 7% solution.

From the information we can write the system $\begin{aligned} x+\quad y&=40 \\ .02x+.07y&=.032(40) \end{aligned}$ or $\begin{aligned} x+\quad y&=40 \\ .02x+.07y&=1.28 \end{aligned}$.

Solve this system by the Gauss-Jordan method.

$$\left[\begin{array}{cc|c} 1 & 1 & 40 \\ .02 & .07 & 1.28 \end{array}\right] \Rightarrow \left[\begin{array}{cc|c} 1 & 1 & 40 \\ 0 & .05 & .48 \end{array}\right] -.02\text{R1}+\text{R2}$$

$$\left[\begin{array}{cc|c} 1 & 1 & 40 \\ 0 & 1 & 9.6 \end{array}\right] \tfrac{1}{.05}\text{R2} \Rightarrow \left[\begin{array}{cc|c} 1 & 0 & 30.4 \\ 0 & 1 & 9.6 \end{array}\right] \begin{array}{l} -1\text{R2}+\text{R1} \\ \end{array}$$

From the final matrix, $x=30.4$ and $y=9.6$, so the chemist should mix 30.4 cm^3 of the 2% solution with 9.6 cm^3 of the 7% solution.

51. Answers will vary.

If the condition that correlates to the third row in the augmented matrix, $\left[\begin{array}{ccc|c} 1 & 1 & 1 & 25{,}000 \\ 8 & 10 & 9 & 222{,}000 \\ -1 & 2 & 0 & 4000 \end{array}\right]$, was dropped, then that row would be dropped. We would have $\left[\begin{array}{ccc|c} 1 & 1 & 1 & 25{,}000 \\ 8 & 10 & 9 & 222{,}000 \end{array}\right]$.

Solve by the Gauss-Jordan method.

$$\left[\begin{array}{ccc|c} 1 & 1 & 1 & 25{,}000 \\ 8 & 10 & 9 & 222{,}000 \end{array}\right] -8\text{R1}+\text{R2} \Rightarrow \left[\begin{array}{ccc|c} 1 & 1 & 1 & 25{,}000 \\ 0 & 2 & 1 & 22{,}000 \end{array}\right] -8\text{R1}+\text{R2}$$

$$\left[\begin{array}{ccc|c} 1 & 1 & 1 & 25{,}000 \\ 0 & 1 & \frac{1}{2} & 11{,}000 \end{array}\right] \tfrac{1}{2}\text{R2} \Rightarrow \left[\begin{array}{ccc|c} 1 & 0 & \frac{1}{2} & 14{,}000 \\ 0 & 1 & \frac{1}{2} & 11{,}000 \end{array}\right] \begin{array}{l} -1\text{R1}+\text{R2} \\ \end{array}$$

We can see it is not possible to find a unique solution.

53. Let x = number of grams of food A;
y = number of grams of food B;
z = number of grams of food C.
Completing the table we have the following.

				Total
Food Group	A	B	C	
Grams/Meal	x	y	z	400

From the information given in the exercise, we can write the system.

$$\begin{aligned} x+\ y+z&=400 \\ x=\tfrac{1}{3}y \Rightarrow 3x-\ y\quad &= 0 \\ x+z=2y \Rightarrow x-2y+z&= 0 \end{aligned}$$

This system has the augmented matrix $\left[\begin{array}{ccc|c} 1 & 1 & 1 & 400 \\ 3 & -1 & 0 & 0 \\ 1 & -2 & 1 & 0 \end{array}\right]$.

Continued on next page

53. (continued)

Solve by the Gauss-Jordan method.

$$\left[\begin{array}{rrr|r} 1 & 1 & 1 & 400 \\ 0 & -4 & -3 & -1200 \\ 1 & -2 & 1 & 0 \end{array}\right] \begin{array}{l} \\ -3\text{R1}+\text{R2} \\ \\ \end{array} \Rightarrow \left[\begin{array}{rrr|r} 1 & 1 & 1 & 400 \\ 0 & -4 & -3 & -1200 \\ 0 & -3 & 0 & -400 \end{array}\right] \begin{array}{l} \\ \\ -1\text{R1}+\text{R3} \end{array} \Rightarrow \left[\begin{array}{rrr|r} 1 & 1 & 1 & 400 \\ 0 & 1 & \frac{3}{4} & 300 \\ 0 & -3 & 0 & -400 \end{array}\right] \begin{array}{l} \\ -\frac{1}{4}\text{R2} \\ \\ \end{array}$$

$$\left[\begin{array}{rrr|r} 1 & 0 & \frac{1}{4} & 100 \\ 0 & 1 & \frac{3}{4} & 300 \\ 0 & -3 & 0 & -400 \end{array}\right] \begin{array}{l} -1\text{R2}+\text{R1} \\ \\ \\ \end{array} \Rightarrow \left[\begin{array}{rrr|r} 1 & 0 & \frac{1}{4} & 100 \\ 0 & 1 & \frac{3}{4} & 300 \\ 0 & 0 & \frac{9}{4} & 500 \end{array}\right] \begin{array}{l} \\ \\ 3\text{R2}+\text{R3} \end{array} \Rightarrow \left[\begin{array}{rrr|r} 1 & 0 & \frac{1}{4} & 100 \\ 0 & 1 & \frac{3}{4} & 300 \\ 0 & 0 & 1 & \frac{2000}{9} \end{array}\right] \begin{array}{l} \\ \\ \frac{4}{9}\text{R3} \end{array}$$

$$\left[\begin{array}{rrr|r} 1 & 0 & 0 & \frac{400}{9} \\ 0 & 1 & \frac{3}{4} & 300 \\ 0 & 0 & 1 & \frac{2000}{9} \end{array}\right] \begin{array}{l} -\frac{1}{4}\text{R3}+\text{R1} \\ \\ \\ \end{array} \Rightarrow \left[\begin{array}{rrr|r} 1 & 0 & 0 & \frac{400}{9} \\ 0 & 1 & 0 & \frac{400}{3} \\ 0 & 0 & 1 & \frac{2000}{9} \end{array}\right] \begin{array}{l} \\ -\frac{3}{4}\text{R3}+\text{R2} \\ \\ \end{array}$$

From the final matrix, we have $x = \frac{400}{9} \approx 44.4$, $y = \frac{400}{3} \approx 133.3$, and $z = \frac{2000}{9} \approx 222.2$. The diet should include 44.4 g of food A, 133.3 g of food B, and 222.2 g of food C.

55. (a) For the 65 or older group:

With $x = 0$ representing 2000 and $x = 50$ represent 2050, we have information that correlates to the points (0, .124) and (50, .203).

$$m = \frac{.203 - .124}{50 - 0} = \frac{.079}{50} = .00158$$

Since we have the point (0, .124), the equation in slope-intercept form is $y = .00158x + .124$.

For the 25-34 group:

With $x = 0$ representing 2000 and $x = 50$ represent 2050, we have information that correlates to the points (0, .142) and (50, .125).

$$m = \frac{.125 - .142}{50 - 0} = \frac{-.017}{50} = -.000340 \text{ (three significant figures)}$$

Since we have the point (0, .142), the equation in slope-intercept form is $y = -.000340x + .142$.

(b) We need to solve the following system.

$$y = .00158x + .124 \quad \Rightarrow -.00158x + y = .124 \Rightarrow 158x - 100{,}000y = -12{,}400$$
$$y = -.000340x + .142 \Rightarrow .000340x + y = .142 \Rightarrow 34x + 100{,}000y = 14{,}200$$

This system has the augmented matrix $\left[\begin{array}{rr|r} 158 & -100{,}000 & -12{,}400 \\ 34 & 100{,}000 & 14{,}200 \end{array}\right]$.

Solve by the Gauss-Jordan method.

$$\left[\begin{array}{rr|r} 1 & -\frac{50{,}000}{79} & -\frac{6200}{79} \\ 34 & 100{,}000 & 14{,}200 \end{array}\right] \begin{array}{l} \frac{1}{158}\text{R1} \\ \\ \end{array} \Rightarrow \left[\begin{array}{rr|r} 1 & -\frac{50{,}000}{79} & -\frac{6200}{79} \\ 0 & \frac{9{,}600{,}000}{79} & \frac{1{,}332{,}600}{79} \end{array}\right] \begin{array}{l} \\ -34\text{R1}+\text{R2} \end{array}$$

$$\left[\begin{array}{rr|r} 1 & -\frac{50{,}000}{79} & -\frac{6200}{79} \\ 0 & 1 & \frac{2221}{16{,}000} \end{array}\right] \begin{array}{l} \\ \frac{79}{9{,}600{,}000}\text{R1}+\text{R2} \end{array} \Rightarrow \left[\begin{array}{rr|r} 1 & 0 & \frac{75}{8} \\ 0 & 1 & \frac{2221}{16{,}000} \end{array}\right] \begin{array}{l} \frac{50{,}000}{79}\text{R2}+\text{R1} \\ \\ \end{array}$$

The solution set is $\left(\frac{75}{8}, \frac{2221}{16{,}000}\right)$. $x = \frac{75}{8} = 9.375$ represents the year 2009 and $y = \frac{2221}{16{,}000} \approx 13.9\%$.

57. (a) A height of 6′11″ is 83″.

If $W = 7.46H - 374$, then $W = 7.46(83) - 374 = 245.18$.

Using the first equation, the predicted weight is approximately 245 pounds.

If $W = 7.93H - 405$, then $W = 7.93(83) - 405 = 253.19$.

Using the second equation, the predicted weight is approximately 253 pounds.

(b) For the first model $W = 7.46H - 374$, a 1-inch increase in height results in a 7.46-pound increase in weight.

For the second model $W = 7.93H - 405$, a 1-inch increase in height results in a 7.93-pound increase in weight.

In each case, the change is given by the slope of the line that is the graph of the given equation.

(c) $W - 7.46H = -374$

$W - 7.93H = -405$

This system has the augmented matrix $\left[\begin{array}{cc|c} 1 & -7.46 & -374 \\ 1 & -7.93 & -405 \end{array}\right]$.

Solve this system by the Gauss-Jordan method.

$$\left[\begin{array}{cc|c} 1 & -7.46 & -374 \\ 0 & -.47 & -31 \end{array}\right]\begin{array}{l} \\ -1R1+R2 \end{array} \Rightarrow \left[\begin{array}{cc|c} 1 & -7.46 & -374 \\ 0 & 1 & 65.957 \end{array}\right]\begin{array}{l} \\ -\frac{1}{.47}R2 \end{array} \Rightarrow \left[\begin{array}{cc|c} 1 & 0 & 118.043 \\ 0 & 1 & 65.957 \end{array}\right]\begin{array}{l} 7.46R2+R1 \\ \end{array}$$

From the last matrix, we have $W \approx 118$ and $H \approx 66$.

The two models agree at a height of 66 inches and a weight of 118 pounds.

59. $F = a + bA + cP + dW$

Substituting the values, we have the following system of equations.

$a + 871b + 11.5c + 3d = 239$
$a + 847b + 12.2c + 2d = 234$
$a + 685b + 10.6c + 5d = 192$
$a + 969b + 14.2c + 1d = 343.$

60. The augmented matrix is $\left[\begin{array}{cccc|c} 1 & 871 & 11.5 & 3 & 239 \\ 1 & 847 & 12.2 & 2 & 234 \\ 1 & 685 & 10.6 & 5 & 192 \\ 1 & 969 & 14.2 & 1 & 343 \end{array}\right]$.

$$\left[\begin{array}{cccc|c} 1 & 871 & 11.5 & 3 & 239 \\ 1 & 847 & 12.2 & 2 & 234 \\ 1 & 685 & 10.6 & 5 & 192 \\ 1 & 969 & 14.2 & 1 & 343 \end{array}\right] \Rightarrow \left[\begin{array}{cccc|c} 1 & 871 & 11.5 & 3 & 239 \\ 0 & -24 & .7 & -1 & -5 \\ 1 & 685 & 10.6 & 5 & 192 \\ 1 & 969 & 14.2 & 1 & 343 \end{array}\right]\begin{array}{l} \\ -1R1+R2 \\ -1R1+R3 \\ \\ \end{array}$$

$$\left[\begin{array}{cccc|c} 1 & 871 & 11.5 & 3 & 239 \\ 0 & -24 & .7 & -1 & -5 \\ 0 & -186 & -.9 & 2 & -47 \\ 1 & 969 & 14.2 & 1 & 343 \end{array}\right]\begin{array}{l} \\ \\ -1R1+R3 \\ \\ \end{array} \Rightarrow \left[\begin{array}{cccc|c} 1 & 871 & 11.5 & 3 & 239 \\ 0 & -24 & .7 & -1 & -5 \\ 0 & -186 & -.9 & 2 & -47 \\ 0 & 98 & 2.7 & -2 & 104 \end{array}\right]\begin{array}{l} \\ \\ \\ -1R1+R4 \end{array}$$

$$\left[\begin{array}{cccc|c} 1 & 871 & 11.5 & 3 & 239 \\ 0 & 1 & -\frac{7}{240} & \frac{1}{24} & \frac{5}{24} \\ 0 & -186 & -.9 & 2 & -47 \\ 0 & 98 & 2.7 & -2 & 104 \end{array}\right]\begin{array}{l} \\ -\frac{1}{24}R2 \\ \\ \\ \end{array} \Rightarrow \left[\begin{array}{cccc|c} 1 & 0 & \frac{8857}{240} & -\frac{799}{24} & \frac{1381}{24} \\ 0 & 1 & -\frac{7}{240} & \frac{1}{24} & \frac{5}{24} \\ 0 & -186 & -.9 & 2 & -47 \\ 0 & 98 & 2.7 & -2 & 104 \end{array}\right]\begin{array}{l} -871R2+R1 \\ \\ \\ \\ \end{array}$$

Continued on next page

60. (continued)

$$\left[\begin{array}{cccc|c} 1 & 0 & \frac{8857}{240} & -\frac{799}{24} & \frac{1381}{24} \\ 0 & 1 & -\frac{7}{240} & \frac{1}{24} & \frac{5}{24} \\ 0 & 0 & -\frac{253}{40} & \frac{39}{4} & -\frac{33}{4} \\ 0 & 98 & 2.7 & -2 & 104 \end{array}\right] 186R2+R3 \Rightarrow \left[\begin{array}{cccc|c} 1 & 0 & \frac{8857}{240} & -\frac{799}{24} & \frac{1381}{24} \\ 0 & 1 & -\frac{7}{240} & \frac{1}{24} & \frac{5}{24} \\ 0 & 0 & -\frac{253}{40} & \frac{39}{4} & -\frac{33}{4} \\ 0 & 0 & \frac{667}{120} & -\frac{73}{12} & \frac{1003}{12} \end{array}\right] -98R2+R4$$

$$\left[\begin{array}{cccc|c} 1 & 0 & \frac{8857}{240} & -\frac{799}{24} & \frac{1381}{24} \\ 0 & 1 & -\frac{7}{240} & \frac{1}{24} & \frac{5}{24} \\ 0 & 0 & 1 & -\frac{390}{253} & \frac{30}{23} \\ 0 & 0 & \frac{667}{120} & -\frac{73}{12} & \frac{1003}{12} \end{array}\right] -\frac{40}{253}R3 \Rightarrow \left[\begin{array}{cccc|c} 1 & 0 & 0 & \frac{35{,}819}{1518} & \frac{649}{69} \\ 0 & 1 & -\frac{7}{240} & \frac{1}{24} & \frac{5}{24} \\ 0 & 0 & 1 & -\frac{390}{253} & \frac{30}{23} \\ 0 & 0 & \frac{667}{120} & -\frac{73}{12} & \frac{1003}{12} \end{array}\right] -\frac{8857}{240}R3+R1$$

$$\left[\begin{array}{cccc|c} 1 & 0 & 0 & \frac{35{,}819}{1518} & \frac{649}{69} \\ 0 & 1 & 0 & -\frac{5}{1518} & \frac{17}{69} \\ 0 & 0 & 1 & -\frac{390}{253} & \frac{30}{23} \\ 0 & 0 & \frac{667}{120} & -\frac{73}{12} & \frac{1003}{12} \end{array}\right] \frac{7}{240}R3+R2 \Rightarrow \left[\begin{array}{cccc|c} 1 & 0 & 0 & \frac{35{,}819}{1518} & \frac{649}{69} \\ 0 & 1 & 0 & -\frac{5}{1518} & \frac{17}{69} \\ 0 & 0 & 1 & -\frac{390}{253} & \frac{30}{23} \\ 0 & 0 & 0 & \frac{82}{33} & \frac{229}{3} \end{array}\right] -\frac{667}{120}R3+R4$$

$$\left[\begin{array}{cccc|c} 1 & 0 & 0 & \frac{35{,}819}{1518} & \frac{649}{69} \\ 0 & 1 & 0 & -\frac{5}{1518} & \frac{17}{69} \\ 0 & 0 & 1 & -\frac{390}{253} & \frac{30}{23} \\ 0 & 0 & 0 & 1 & \frac{2519}{82} \end{array}\right] \frac{33}{82}R4 \Rightarrow \left[\begin{array}{cccc|c} 1 & 0 & 0 & 0 & -\frac{117{,}335}{164} \\ 0 & 1 & 0 & -\frac{5}{1518} & \frac{17}{69} \\ 0 & 0 & 1 & -\frac{390}{253} & \frac{30}{23} \\ 0 & 0 & 0 & 1 & \frac{2519}{82} \end{array}\right] -\frac{35819}{1518}R4+R1$$

$$\left[\begin{array}{cccc|c} 1 & 0 & 0 & 0 & -\frac{117{,}335}{164} \\ 0 & 1 & 0 & 0 & \frac{57}{164} \\ 0 & 0 & 1 & -\frac{390}{253} & \frac{30}{23} \\ 0 & 0 & 0 & 1 & \frac{2519}{82} \end{array}\right] \frac{5}{1518}R4+R2 \Rightarrow \left[\begin{array}{cccc|c} 1 & 0 & 0 & 0 & -\frac{117{,}335}{164} \\ 0 & 1 & 0 & 0 & \frac{57}{164} \\ 0 & 0 & 1 & 0 & \frac{1995}{41} \\ 0 & 0 & 0 & 1 & \frac{2519}{82} \end{array}\right] \frac{390}{253}R4+R3$$

We obtain $a = -\frac{117{,}335}{164} \approx -715.457$, $b = \frac{57}{164} \approx .34756$, $c = \frac{1995}{41} \approx 48.6585$, and $d = \frac{2519}{82} \approx 30.71951$.

61. Using these values, $F = -714.457 + .34756A + 48.6585P + 30.71951W$

62. Using $A = 960$, $P = 12.6$, and $W = 3$ we obtain the following.

$$F = -715.457 + .34756(960) + 48.6585(12.6) + 30.71951(3) = 323.45623 \approx 323$$

Therefore, the predicted fawn count is approximately 323, which is just slightly higher than the actual value of 320.

Section 9.3: Determinant Solution of Linear Systems

1. $\begin{vmatrix} -5 & 9 \\ 4 & -1 \end{vmatrix} = -5(-1) - 4\cdot 9 = 5 - 36 = -31$

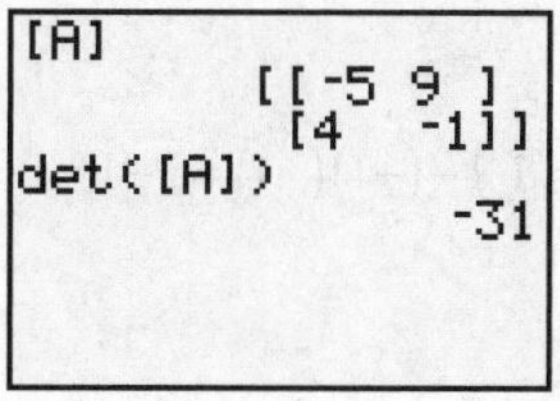

3. $\begin{vmatrix} -1 & -2 \\ 5 & 3 \end{vmatrix} = -1\cdot 3 - 5(-2) = -3 - (-10) = 7$

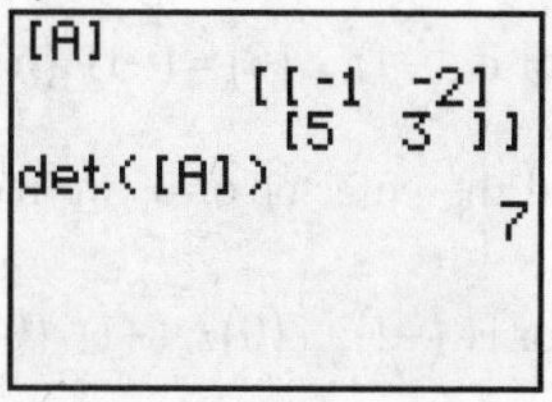

5. $\begin{vmatrix} 9 & 3 \\ -3 & -1 \end{vmatrix} = 9(-1)-(-3)\cdot 3 = -9-(-9) = 0$

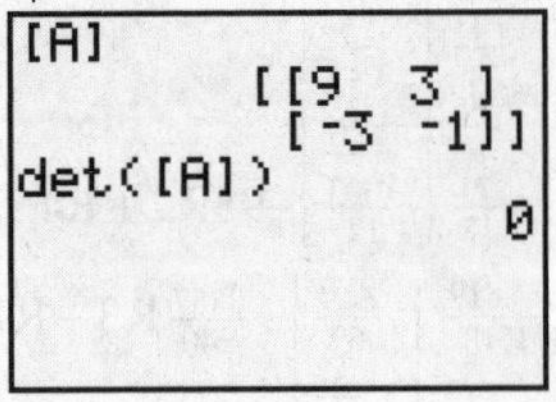

7. $\begin{vmatrix} 3 & 4 \\ 5 & -2 \end{vmatrix} = 3(-2)-5\cdot 4 = -6-20 = -26$

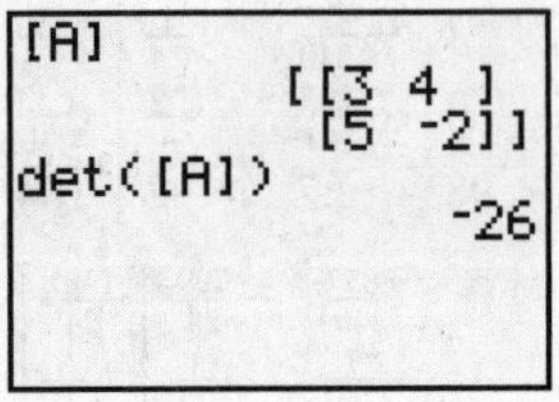

9. $\begin{vmatrix} -7 & 0 \\ 3 & 0 \end{vmatrix} = -7\cdot 0 - 3\cdot 0 = 0-0 = 0$

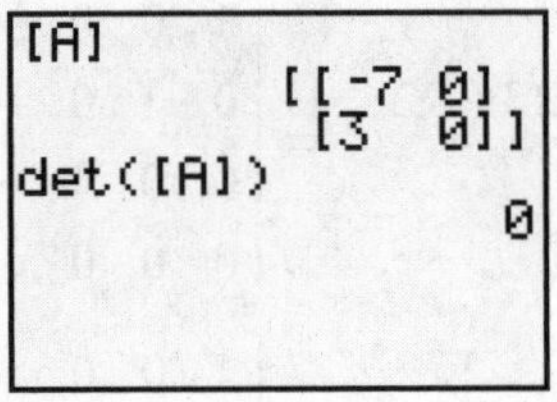

11. $\begin{vmatrix} -2 & 0 & 1 \\ 1 & 2 & 0 \\ 4 & 2 & 1 \end{vmatrix}$

To find the cofactor of 1, we have $i=2, j=1, M_{21} = \begin{vmatrix} 0 & 1 \\ 2 & 1 \end{vmatrix} = 0\cdot 1 - 2\cdot 1 = 0-2 = -2$. Thus, the cofactor is $(-1)^{2+1}(-2) = (-1)^3(-2) = (-1)(-2) = 2$.

To find the cofactor of 2, we have $i=2, j=2, M_{22} = \begin{vmatrix} -2 & 1 \\ 4 & 1 \end{vmatrix} = -2\cdot 1 - 4\cdot 1 = -2-4 = -6$. Thus, the cofactor is $(-1)^{2+2}(-6) = (-1)^4(-6) = 1(-6) = -6$.

To find the cofactor of 0, we have $i=2, j=3, M_{23} = \begin{vmatrix} -2 & 0 \\ 4 & 2 \end{vmatrix} = -2\cdot 2 - 4\cdot 0 = -4-0 = -4$. Thus, the cofactor is $(-1)^{2+3}(-4) = (-1)^5(-4) = (-1)(-4) = 4$.

13. $\begin{vmatrix} 1 & 2 & -1 \\ 2 & 3 & -2 \\ -1 & 4 & 1 \end{vmatrix}$

To find the cofactor of 2, we have $i=2, j=1, M_{21} = \begin{vmatrix} 2 & -1 \\ 4 & 1 \end{vmatrix} = 2\cdot 1 - 4(-1) = 2-(-4) = 6$. Thus, the cofactor is $(-1)^{2+1}(6) = (-1)^3(6) = (-1)(6) = -6$.

To find the cofactor of 3, we have $i=2, j=2, M_{22} = \begin{vmatrix} 1 & -1 \\ -1 & 1 \end{vmatrix} = 1\cdot 1 - (-1)(-1) = 1-1 = 0$. Thus, the cofactor is $(-1)^{2+2}(0) = (-1)^4(0) = 1(0) = 0$.

To find the cofactor of -2, we have $i=2, j=3, M_{23} = \begin{vmatrix} 1 & 2 \\ -1 & 4 \end{vmatrix} = 1\cdot 4 - (-1)\cdot 2 = 4-(-2) = 6$. Thus, the cofactor is $(-1)^{2+3}(6) = (-1)^5(6) = (-1)(6) = -6$.

For Exercises 15 – 27, an answer can be arrived at by expanding on any row or column as noted on page 816 of your text. In the solutions, we will expand on a row or column that allows a minimum number of calculations. Any row or column containing zero, will reduce the number of calculations as noted in the same paragraph.

15. $\begin{vmatrix} 4 & -7 & 8 \\ 2 & 1 & 3 \\ -6 & 3 & 0 \end{vmatrix}$

If we expand by the third row, we will need to find $a_{31} \cdot A_{31} + a_{32} \cdot A_{32} + a_{33} \cdot A_{33}$. However, we do not need to calculate A_{33}, since $a_{33} = 0$.

$$A_{31} = (-1)^{3+1} \begin{vmatrix} -7 & 8 \\ 1 & 3 \end{vmatrix} = (-1)^4 (-7 \cdot 3 - 1 \cdot 8) = 1(-21-8) = 1(-29) = -29$$

$$A_{32} = (-1)^{3+2} \begin{vmatrix} 4 & 8 \\ 2 & 3 \end{vmatrix} = (-1)^5 (4 \cdot 3 - 2 \cdot 8) = -1(12-16) = -1(-4) = 4$$

$$a_{31} \cdot A_{31} + a_{32} \cdot A_{32} + a_{33} \cdot A_{33} = a_{31} \cdot A_{31} + a_{32} \cdot A_{32} + 0 \cdot A_{33} = -6(-29) + 3(4) + 0 = 174 + 12 = 186$$

17. $\begin{vmatrix} 1 & 2 & 0 \\ -1 & 2 & -1 \\ 0 & 1 & 4 \end{vmatrix}$

If we expand by the third row, we will need to find $a_{31} \cdot A_{31} + a_{32} \cdot A_{32} + a_{33} \cdot A_{33}$. However, we do not need to calculate A_{31}, since $a_{31} = 0$.

$$A_{32} = (-1)^{3+2} \begin{vmatrix} 1 & 0 \\ -1 & -1 \end{vmatrix} = (-1)^5 [1(-1) - (-1) \cdot 0] = -1(-1-0) = -1(-1) = 1$$

$$A_{33} = (-1)^{3+3} \begin{vmatrix} 1 & 2 \\ -1 & 2 \end{vmatrix} = (-1)^6 [1 \cdot 2 - (-1) \cdot 2] = 1[2-(-2)] = 1(4) = 4$$

$$a_{31} \cdot A_{31} + a_{32} \cdot A_{32} + a_{33} \cdot A_{33} = 0 \cdot A_{31} + a_{32} \cdot A_{32} + a_{33} \cdot A_{33} = 0 + 1(1) + 4(4) = 1 + 16 = 17$$

For Exercises 19 – 27, we will use the sign checkerboard as described in the margin of page 816 in calculations.

19. $\begin{vmatrix} 10 & 2 & 1 \\ -1 & 4 & 3 \\ -3 & 8 & 10 \end{vmatrix}$

If we expand by the first row, we will need to find $a_{11} \cdot M_{11} - a_{12} \cdot M_{12} + a_{13} \cdot M_{13}$.

$$M_{11} = \begin{vmatrix} 4 & 3 \\ 8 & 10 \end{vmatrix} = 4 \cdot 10 - 8 \cdot 3 = 40 - 24 = 16, \quad M_{12} = \begin{vmatrix} -1 & 3 \\ -3 & 10 \end{vmatrix} = -1 \cdot 10 - (-3) \cdot 3 = -10 - (-9) = -1, \text{ and}$$

$$M_{13} = \begin{vmatrix} -1 & 4 \\ -3 & 8 \end{vmatrix} = -1 \cdot 8 - (-3) \cdot 4 = -8 - (-12) = 4$$

$$a_{11} \cdot M_{11} - a_{12} \cdot M_{12} + a_{13} \cdot M_{13}. = 10 \cdot 16 - 2(-1) + 1 \cdot 4 = 160 - (-2) + 4 = 166$$

21. $\begin{vmatrix} 1 & -2 & 3 \\ 0 & 0 & 0 \\ 1 & 10 & -12 \end{vmatrix}$

If we expand by the second row, we will need to find $-a_{21} \cdot M_{21} + a_{22} \cdot M_{22} - a_{23} \cdot M_{23}$. Since $a_{21} = a_{22} = a_{23} = 0$, the result will be zero.

23. $\begin{vmatrix} 3 & 3 & -1 \\ 2 & 6 & 0 \\ -6 & -6 & 2 \end{vmatrix}$

If we expand by the second row, we will need to find $-a_{21} \cdot M_{21} + a_{22} \cdot M_{22} - a_{23} \cdot M_{23}$. However, we do not need to calculate M_{23}, since $a_{23} = 0$.

$$M_{21} = \begin{vmatrix} 3 & -1 \\ -6 & 2 \end{vmatrix} = 3 \cdot 2 - (-6)(-1) = 6 - 6 = 0 \text{ and } M_{22} = \begin{vmatrix} 3 & -1 \\ -6 & 2 \end{vmatrix} = 3 \cdot 2 - (-6)(-1) = 6 - 6 = 0$$

$$a_{21} \cdot M_{21} - a_{22} \cdot M_{22} + a_{23} \cdot M_{23} = a_{21} \cdot M_{21} - a_{22} \cdot M_{22} + 0 \cdot M_{23} = 2 \cdot 0 - 6 \cdot 0 + 0 = 0 - 0 = 0$$

25. $\begin{vmatrix} 1 & 0 & 0 \\ 0 & 1 & 0 \\ 0 & 0 & 1 \end{vmatrix}$

If we expand by the first row, we will need to find $a_{11} \cdot M_{11} - a_{12} \cdot M_{12} + a_{13} \cdot M_{13}$. However, we do not need to calculate M_{12} or M_{13}, since $a_{12} = a_{13} = 0$.

$$M_{11} = \begin{vmatrix} 1 & 0 \\ 0 & 1 \end{vmatrix} = 1 \cdot 1 - 0 \cdot 0 = 1 - 0 = 1$$

$$a_{11} \cdot M_{11} - a_{12} \cdot M_{12} + a_{13} \cdot M_{13} = a_{11} \cdot M_{11} - 0 \cdot M_{12} + 0 \cdot M_{13} = 1 \cdot 1 - 0 + 0 = 1$$

27. $\begin{vmatrix} -2 & 0 & 1 \\ 0 & 1 & 0 \\ 0 & 0 & -1 \end{vmatrix}$

If we expand by the first column, we will need to find $a_{11} \cdot M_{11} - a_{21} \cdot M_{21} + a_{31} \cdot M_{31}$. However, we do not need to calculate M_{21} or M_{31}, since $a_{21} = a_{31} = 0$.

$$M_{11} = \begin{vmatrix} 1 & 0 \\ 0 & -1 \end{vmatrix} = 1(-1) - 0 \cdot 0 = -1 - 0 = -1$$

$$a_{11} \cdot M_{11} - a_{21} \cdot M_{21} + a_{31} \cdot M_{31} = a_{11} \cdot M_{11} - 0 \cdot M_{21} + 0 \cdot M_{31} = -2(-1) - 0 + 0 = 2$$

29. $\begin{vmatrix} .4 & -.8 & .6 \\ .3 & .9 & .7 \\ 3.1 & 4.1 & -2.8 \end{vmatrix}$

The determinant is −5.5.

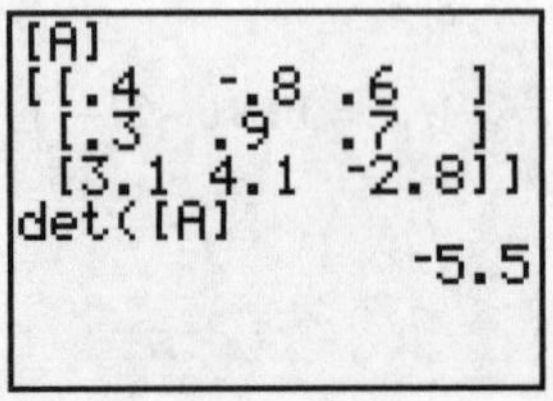

31. $\begin{vmatrix} x & 2 & 1 \\ -1 & x & 4 \\ -2 & 0 & 5 \end{vmatrix}$

If we expand by the third row, we will need to find $a_{31} \cdot M_{31} - a_{32} \cdot M_{32} + a_{33} \cdot M_{33}$. However, we do not need to calculate M_{32}, since $a_{32} = 0$.

$$M_{31} = \begin{vmatrix} 2 & 1 \\ x & 4 \end{vmatrix} = 2 \cdot 4 - x \cdot 1 = 8 - x \text{ and } M_{33} = \begin{vmatrix} x & 2 \\ -1 & x \end{vmatrix} = x \cdot x - (-1) \cdot 2 = x^2 + 2$$

$$\begin{aligned} a_{31} \cdot M_{31} - a_{32} \cdot M_{32} + a_{33} \cdot M_{33} &= a_{31} \cdot M_{31} - 0 \cdot M_{32} + a_{33} \cdot M_{33} \\ &= -2(8 - x) - 0 + 5(x^2 + 2) = -16 + 2x + 5x^2 + 10 = 5x^2 + 2x - 6 \end{aligned}$$

32. The equation is $5x^2 + 2x - 6 = 45$, which is a quadratic equation.

33. $5x^2 + 2x - 6 = 45$

Rewriting the equation in standard form we have $5x^2 + 2x - 51 = 0$.

Solve this equation by factoring.

$$(5x + 17)(x - 3) = 0$$

$$5x + 17 = 0 \quad \text{or} \quad x - 3 = 0$$

$$x = -\tfrac{17}{5} = -3.4 \qquad x = 3$$

Solution set: $\{-3.4, 3\}$

34. If $x = -3.4$, the determinant becomes $\begin{vmatrix} -3.4 & 2 & 1 \\ -1 & -3.4 & 4 \\ -2 & 0 & 5 \end{vmatrix}$. If we expand by the third row, we will need to find $a_{31} \cdot M_{31} - a_{32} \cdot M_{32} + a_{33} \cdot M_{33}$. However, we do not need to calculate M_{32}, since $a_{32} = 0$.

$$M_{31} = \begin{vmatrix} 2 & 1 \\ -3.4 & 4 \end{vmatrix} = 2 \cdot 4 - (-3.4) \cdot 1 = 8 - (-3.4) = 11.4$$

$$M_{33} = \begin{vmatrix} -3.4 & 2 \\ -1 & -3.4 \end{vmatrix} = (-3.4)(-3.4) - (-1) \cdot 2 = 11.56 + 2 = 13.56$$

$$\begin{aligned} a_{31} \cdot M_{31} - a_{32} \cdot M_{32} + a_{33} \cdot M_{33} &= a_{31} \cdot M_{31} - 0 \cdot M_{32} + a_{33} \cdot M_{33} \\ &= -2 \cdot 11.4 - 0 + 5 \cdot 13.56 = -22.8 + 67.8 = 45 \end{aligned}$$

If $x = 3$, the determinant becomes $\begin{vmatrix} 3 & 2 & 1 \\ -1 & 3 & 4 \\ -2 & 0 & 5 \end{vmatrix}$.

Since $M_{31} = \begin{vmatrix} 2 & 1 \\ 3 & 4 \end{vmatrix} = 2 \cdot 4 - 3 \cdot 1 = 8 - 3 = 5$ and $M_{33} = \begin{vmatrix} 3 & 2 \\ -1 & 3 \end{vmatrix} = 3 \cdot 3 - (-1) \cdot 2 = 9 + 2 = 11$, we have $a_{31} \cdot M_{31} - a_{32} \cdot M_{32} + a_{33} \cdot M_{33} = a_{31} \cdot M_{31} - 0 \cdot M_{32} + a_{33} \cdot M_{33} = -2 \cdot 5 - 0 + 5 \cdot 11 = -10 + 55 = 45$.

35. To solve the equation $\begin{vmatrix} 5 & x \\ -3 & 2 \end{vmatrix} = 6$, we need to solve $5 \cdot 2 - (-3) \cdot x = 6$.

$$5 \cdot 2 - (-3) \cdot x = 6 \Rightarrow 10 + 3x = 6 \Rightarrow 3x = -4 \Rightarrow x = -\frac{4}{3}$$

Verifying $\begin{vmatrix} 5 & -\frac{4}{3} \\ -3 & 2 \end{vmatrix} = 6$, we have $5 \cdot 2 - (-3)\left(-\frac{4}{3}\right) = 10 - 4 = 6$.

Solution set: $\left\{-\frac{4}{3}\right\}$

37. To solve the equation $\begin{vmatrix} x & 3 \\ x & x \end{vmatrix} = 4$, we need to solve $x \cdot x - 3x = 4$.

$$x \cdot x - 3x = 4 \Rightarrow x^2 - 3x = 4 \Rightarrow x^2 - 3x - 4 = 0 \Rightarrow (x+1)(x-4) = 0$$

$$x + 1 = 0 \quad \text{or} \quad x - 4 = 0$$

$$x = -1 \qquad\qquad x = 4$$

Verify $x = -1$.

$$\begin{vmatrix} -1 & 3 \\ -1 & -1 \end{vmatrix} = -1(-1) - (-1) \cdot 3 = 1 - (-3) = 4$$

Verify $x = 4$.

$$\begin{vmatrix} 4 & 3 \\ 4 & 4 \end{vmatrix} = 4 \cdot 4 - 4 \cdot 3 = 16 - 12 = 4$$

Solution set: $\{-1, 4\}$

39. To solve the equation $\begin{vmatrix} -2 & 0 & 1 \\ -1 & 3 & x \\ 5 & -2 & 0 \end{vmatrix} = 3$, expand by the first row. In order to do this, we will need to find $a_{11} \cdot M_{11} - a_{12} \cdot M_{12} + a_{13} \cdot M_{13}$. However, we do not need to calculate M_{12}, since $a_{12} = 0$.

$$M_{11} = \begin{vmatrix} 3 & x \\ -2 & 0 \end{vmatrix} = 3 \cdot 0 - (-2) \cdot x = 0 - (-2x) = 2x$$

$$M_{13} = \begin{vmatrix} -1 & 3 \\ 5 & -2 \end{vmatrix} = (-1)(-2) - 5 \cdot 3 = 2 - 15 = -13$$

$$\begin{aligned} a_{11} \cdot M_{11} - a_{12} \cdot M_{12} + a_{13} \cdot M_{13} &= a_{11} \cdot M_{11} - 0 \cdot M_{12} + a_{13} \cdot M_{13} \\ &= -2(2x) - 0 + 1(-13) = -4x + (-13) = -4x - 13 \end{aligned}$$

Set this equal to 3 and solve to get $-4x - 13 = 3 \Rightarrow -4x = 16 \Rightarrow x = -4$.

Verify $\begin{vmatrix} -2 & 0 & 1 \\ -1 & 3 & -4 \\ 5 & -2 & 0 \end{vmatrix} = 3$.

Since $M_{11} = \begin{vmatrix} 3 & -4 \\ -2 & 0 \end{vmatrix} = 3 \cdot 0 - (-2)(-4) = 0 - 8 = -8$ and $M_{13} = \begin{vmatrix} -1 & 3 \\ 5 & -2 \end{vmatrix} = -13$, we have

$$a_{11} \cdot M_{11} - a_{12} \cdot M_{12} + a_{13} \cdot M_{13} = a_{11} \cdot M_{11} - 0 \cdot M_{12} + a_{13} \cdot M_{13} = -2(-8) - 0 + 1(-13) = 16 + (-13) = 3.$$

Solution set: $\{-4\}$

41. To solve the equation $\begin{vmatrix} 5 & 3x & -3 \\ 0 & 2 & -1 \\ 4 & -1 & x \end{vmatrix} = -7$, expand by the second row. We will need to find

$-a_{21} \cdot M_{21} + a_{22} \cdot M_{22} - a_{23} \cdot M_{23}$. However, we do not need to calculate M_{21}, since $a_{21} = 0$.

$M_{22} = \begin{vmatrix} 5 & -3 \\ 4 & x \end{vmatrix} = 5x - 4(-3) = 5x - (-12) = 5x + 12$ and $M_{23} = \begin{vmatrix} 5 & 3x \\ 4 & -1 \end{vmatrix} = 5(-1) - 4 \cdot 3x = -5 - 12x$

$$\begin{aligned} -a_{21} \cdot M_{21} + a_{22} \cdot M_{22} - a_{23} \cdot M_{23} &= -0 \cdot M_{21} + a_{22} \cdot M_{22} - a_{23} \cdot M_{23} = 0 + 2(5x+12) - (-1)(-5-12x) \\ &= 2(5x+12) + (-5-12x) = 10x + 24 - 5 - 12x = 19 - 2x \end{aligned}$$

Set this equal to -7 and solve to get $19 - 2x = -7 \Rightarrow -2x = -26 \Rightarrow x = 13$.

Verify $\begin{vmatrix} 5 & 3(13) & -3 \\ 0 & 2 & -1 \\ 4 & -1 & 13 \end{vmatrix} = \begin{vmatrix} 5 & 39 & -3 \\ 0 & 2 & -1 \\ 4 & -1 & 13 \end{vmatrix} = -7$.

Since $M_{22} = \begin{vmatrix} 5 & -3 \\ 4 & 13 \end{vmatrix} = 5 \cdot 13 - 4(-3) = 65 - (-12) = 77$ and $M_{23} = \begin{vmatrix} 5 & 39 \\ 4 & -1 \end{vmatrix} = 5(-1) - 4 \cdot 39 = -5 - 156 = -161$,

we have the following.

$$\begin{aligned} -a_{21} \cdot M_{21} + a_{22} \cdot M_{22} - a_{23} \cdot M_{23} &= -0 \cdot M_{21} + a_{22} \cdot M_{22} - a_{23} \cdot M_{23} \\ &= 0 + 2 \cdot 77 - (-1)(-161) = 154 - 161 = -7 \end{aligned}$$

Solution set: $\{13\}$

43. $P(0,0), Q(0,2), R(1,4)$

Find $D = \frac{1}{2}\begin{vmatrix} x_1 & y_1 & 1 \\ x_2 & y_2 & 1 \\ x_3 & y_3 & 1 \end{vmatrix}$, where $P = (x_1, y_1) = (0,0), Q(x_2, y_2) = (0,2)$, and $R = (x_3, y_3) = (1,4)$.

Expanding by the first row, we have the following.

$$D = \frac{1}{2}\begin{vmatrix} 0 & 0 & 1 \\ 0 & 2 & 1 \\ 1 & 4 & 1 \end{vmatrix} = \frac{1}{2}\left[0\begin{vmatrix} 2 & 1 \\ 4 & 1 \end{vmatrix} - 0\begin{vmatrix} 0 & 1 \\ 1 & 1 \end{vmatrix} + 1\begin{vmatrix} 0 & 2 \\ 1 & 4 \end{vmatrix}\right]$$

$$= \tfrac{1}{2}[0(2-4) - 0(0-1) + 1(0-2)] = \tfrac{1}{2}[0(-2) - 0(-1) + 1(-2)] = \tfrac{1}{2}[0 - 0 + (-2)] = \tfrac{1}{2}(-2) = -1$$

Area of triangle $= |D| = |-1| = 1$.

45. $P(2,5), Q(-1,3),\ R(4,0)$

Find $D = \frac{1}{2}\begin{vmatrix} x_1 & y_1 & 1 \\ x_2 & y_2 & 1 \\ x_3 & y_3 & 1 \end{vmatrix}$, where $P = (x_1, y_1) = (2,5), Q(x_2, y_2) = (-1,3)$, and $R = (x_3, y_3) = (4,0)$.

Expanding by the third row, we have the following.

$$D = \frac{1}{2}\begin{vmatrix} 2 & 5 & 1 \\ -1 & 3 & 1 \\ 4 & 0 & 1 \end{vmatrix} = \frac{1}{2}\left[4\begin{vmatrix} 5 & 1 \\ 3 & 1 \end{vmatrix} - 0\begin{vmatrix} 2 & 1 \\ -1 & 1 \end{vmatrix} + 1\begin{vmatrix} 2 & 5 \\ -1 & 3 \end{vmatrix}\right]$$

$$= \tfrac{1}{2}\left[4(5-3) - 0(2+1) + 1(6+5)\right] = \tfrac{1}{2}\left[4(2) - 0(3) + 1(11)\right] = \tfrac{1}{2}(8 - 0 + 11) = \tfrac{1}{2}(19) = \tfrac{19}{2} = 9.5$$

Area of triangle $= |D| = |9.5| = 9.5$.

47. $(101.3, 52.7), (117.2, 253.9), (313.1, 301.6)$

Label the points as follows.

$P = (x_1, y_1) = (101.3, 52.7), Q(x_2, y_2) = (117.2, 253.9)$, and $R = (x_3, y_3) = (313.1, 301.6)$.

Since $D = \frac{1}{2}\begin{vmatrix} x_1 & y_1 & 1 \\ x_2 & y_2 & 1 \\ x_3 & y_3 & 1 \end{vmatrix} = \frac{1}{2}\begin{vmatrix} 101.3 & 52.7 & 1 \\ 117.2 & 253.9 & 1 \\ 313.1 & 301.6 & 1 \end{vmatrix}$, we will enter the 3×3 as $\begin{bmatrix} 101.3 & 52.7 & 1 \\ 117.2 & 253.9 & 1 \\ 313.1 & 301.6 & 1 \end{bmatrix}$ and perform the calculations as shown below.

Area of triangular lot is $|-19{,}328.325|$ ft^2 or approximately 19,328.3 ft^2.

49. $\begin{vmatrix} 1 & 0 & 0 \\ 1 & 0 & 1 \\ 3 & 0 & 0 \end{vmatrix}$

By Theorem 1, the determinant is 0 since every entry in column 2 is 0.

51. $\begin{vmatrix} 6 & 8 & -12 \\ -1 & 0 & 2 \\ 4 & 0 & -8 \end{vmatrix}$

Given $\begin{bmatrix} 6 & 8 & -12 \\ -1 & 0 & 2 \\ 4 & 0 & -8 \end{bmatrix}$, add 2 times column 1 to column 3 to obtain $\begin{bmatrix} 6 & 8 & 0 \\ -1 & 0 & 0 \\ 4 & 0 & 0 \end{bmatrix}$. By Theorem 6 the following statement is true.

$$\begin{vmatrix} 6 & 8 & -12 \\ -1 & 0 & 2 \\ 4 & 0 & -8 \end{vmatrix} = \begin{vmatrix} 6 & 8 & 0 \\ -1 & 0 & 0 \\ 4 & 0 & 0 \end{vmatrix}$$

By Theorem 1, the determinant is 0 since every entry in column 3 is 0.

53. $\begin{vmatrix} -4 & 1 & 4 \\ 2 & 0 & 1 \\ 0 & 2 & 4 \end{vmatrix}$

Since $\begin{bmatrix} -4 & 1 & 4 \\ 2 & 0 & 1 \\ 0 & 2 & 4 \end{bmatrix} \Rightarrow \begin{bmatrix} 0 & 1 & 6 \\ 2 & 0 & 1 \\ 0 & 2 & 4 \end{bmatrix} \begin{matrix} 2R2+R1 \\ \\ \\ \end{matrix}$, by Theorem 6 we have the following.

$$\begin{vmatrix} -4 & 1 & 4 \\ 2 & 0 & 1 \\ 0 & 2 & 4 \end{vmatrix} = \begin{vmatrix} 0 & 1 & 6 \\ 2 & 0 & 1 \\ 0 & 2 & 4 \end{vmatrix}$$

Expanding by the first column, we have the following.

$$\begin{vmatrix} 0 & 1 & 6 \\ 2 & 0 & 1 \\ 0 & 2 & 4 \end{vmatrix} = 0\begin{vmatrix} 0 & 1 \\ 2 & 4 \end{vmatrix} - 2\begin{vmatrix} 1 & 6 \\ 2 & 4 \end{vmatrix} + 0\begin{vmatrix} 1 & 6 \\ 0 & 1 \end{vmatrix}$$
$$= 0 - 2(4-12) + 0 = --2(-8) = 16$$

As noted on page 816 of the next, the array of signs can be extended for determinants of 4×4 matrices. For Exercises 55 – 57, use the following array of signs.

$$\underline{For\, 4\times4\, matrices}$$
$$\begin{matrix} + & - & + & - \\ - & + & - & + \\ + & - & + & - \\ - & + & - & + \end{matrix}$$

Like previous exercises, you can arrive at a solution by expanding on any row or column. We will also use determinant theorems to reduce the number of calculations.

55. $\begin{vmatrix} 3 & -6 & 5 & -1 \\ 0 & 2 & -1 & 3 \\ -6 & 4 & 2 & 0 \\ -7 & 3 & 1 & 1 \end{vmatrix}$

Add 3 times row 1 to row 2 and add row 1 to row 4 to obtain $\begin{vmatrix} 3 & -6 & 5 & -1 \\ 0 & 2 & -1 & 3 \\ -6 & 4 & 2 & 0 \\ -7 & 3 & 1 & 1 \end{vmatrix} = \begin{vmatrix} 3 & -6 & 5 & -1 \\ 9 & -16 & 14 & 0 \\ -6 & 4 & 2 & 0 \\ -4 & -3 & 6 & 0 \end{vmatrix}$.

Expanding by the fourth column, we have the following.

$$\begin{vmatrix} 3 & -6 & 5 & -1 \\ 9 & -16 & 14 & 0 \\ -6 & 4 & 2 & 0 \\ -4 & -3 & 6 & 0 \end{vmatrix} = -(-1)\begin{vmatrix} 9 & -16 & 14 \\ -6 & 4 & 2 \\ -4 & -3 & 6 \end{vmatrix} = \begin{vmatrix} 9 & -16 & 14 \\ -6 & 4 & 2 \\ -4 & -3 & 6 \end{vmatrix}$$

Adding -7 times row 2 to row 1 and -3 times row 2 added to row 3 we have the following.

$$\begin{vmatrix} 9 & -16 & 14 \\ -6 & 4 & 2 \\ -4 & -3 & 6 \end{vmatrix} = \begin{vmatrix} 51 & -44 & 0 \\ -6 & 4 & 2 \\ 14 & -15 & 0 \end{vmatrix}$$

Expanding by the third column, we have $-2\begin{vmatrix} 51 & -44 \\ 14 & -15 \end{vmatrix} = -2(-765+616) = -2(-149) = 298$

57. $\begin{vmatrix} 4 & 0 & 0 & 2 \\ -1 & 0 & 3 & 0 \\ 2 & 4 & 0 & 1 \\ 0 & 0 & 1 & 2 \end{vmatrix}$

Expanding by the second column, we have the following.

$$\begin{vmatrix} 4 & 0 & 0 & 2 \\ -1 & 0 & 3 & 0 \\ 2 & 4 & 0 & 1 \\ 0 & 0 & 1 & 2 \end{vmatrix} = -4\begin{vmatrix} 4 & 0 & 2 \\ -1 & 3 & 0 \\ 0 & 1 & 2 \end{vmatrix}$$

Using the definition of the determinant on page 814 of your text, we have the following.

$$-4\begin{vmatrix} 4 & 0 & 2 \\ -1 & 3 & 0 \\ 0 & 1 & 2 \end{vmatrix} = -4\left(\left[4(3)(2)+0(0)(0)+2(-1)(1)\right]-\left[0(3)(2)+1(0)(4)+2(-1)(0)\right]\right)$$

$$= -4\left[(24+0-2)-(0+0+0)\right] = -4(22-0) = -4(22) = -88$$

$4x+3y-2z=1$

59. For $7x-4y+3z=2$, we have the following.
$-2x+y-8z=0$

$$D=\begin{vmatrix}4&3&-2\\7&-4&3\\-2&1&-8\end{vmatrix}, D_x=\begin{vmatrix}1&3&-2\\2&-4&3\\0&1&-8\end{vmatrix}, D_y=\begin{vmatrix}4&1&-2\\7&2&3\\-2&0&-8\end{vmatrix}, \text{ and } D_z=\begin{vmatrix}4&3&1\\7&-4&2\\-2&1&0\end{vmatrix}$$

(a) D **(c)** C
(b) A **(d)** B

61. $x+y=4$
$2x-y=2$

Since $D=\begin{vmatrix}1&1\\2&-1\end{vmatrix}=1(-1)-2(1)=-1-2=-3$, $D_x=\begin{vmatrix}4&1\\2&-1\end{vmatrix}=4(-1)-2(1)=-4-2=-6$, and

$D_y=\begin{vmatrix}1&4\\2&2\end{vmatrix}=1(2)-2(4)=2-8=-6$, we have $x=\frac{D_x}{D}=\frac{-6}{-3}=2$ and $y=\frac{D_y}{D}=\frac{-6}{-3}=2$.

Solution set: $\{(2,2)\}$

63. $4x+3y=-7$
$2x+3y=-11$

Since $D=\begin{vmatrix}4&3\\2&3\end{vmatrix}=4(3)-2(3)=12-6=6$, $D_x=\begin{vmatrix}-7&3\\-11&3\end{vmatrix}=-7(3)-(-11)(3)=-21+33=12$, and

$D_y=\begin{vmatrix}4&-7\\2&-11\end{vmatrix}=4(-11)-2(-7)=-44+14=-30$, we have $x=\frac{D_x}{D}=\frac{12}{6}=2$ and $y=\frac{D_y}{D}=\frac{-30}{6}=-5$.

Solution set: $\{(2,-5)\}$

65. $5x+4y=10$
$3x-7y=6$

Since $D=\begin{vmatrix}5&4\\3&-7\end{vmatrix}=5(-7)-3(4)=-35-12=-47$, $D_x=\begin{vmatrix}10&4\\6&-7\end{vmatrix}=10(-7)-6(4)=-70-24=-94$,

and $D_y=\begin{vmatrix}5&10\\3&6\end{vmatrix}=5(6)-3(10)=30-30=0$, we have $x=\frac{D_x}{D}=\frac{-94}{-47}=2$ and $y=\frac{D_y}{D}=\frac{0}{-47}=0$.

Solution set: $\{(2,0)\}$

67. $1.5x+3y=5$ (1)
$2x+4y=3$ (2)

$$D=\begin{vmatrix}1.5&3\\2&4\end{vmatrix}=(1.5)(4)-2(3)=6-6=0$$

Because $D=0$, Cramer's rule does not apply. To determine whether the system is inconsistent or has infinitely many solutions, use the elimination method.

$6x+12y=20$ Multiply equation (1) by 4.
$-6x-12y=-9$ Multiply equation (2) by -3.
$0=11$ False

The system is inconsistent.
Solution set: $\emptyset$

69. $3x+2y=4\,(1)$
$6x+4y=8\,(2)$

$$D=\begin{vmatrix}3 & 2\\ 6 & 4\end{vmatrix}=3(4)-6(2)=12-12=0$$

Because $D = 0$, Cramer's rule does not apply. To determine whether the system is inconsistent or has infinitely many solutions, use the elimination method.

$$\begin{aligned} -6x-4y &= -8 \quad \text{Multiply equation (1) by } -2.\\ 6x+4y &= \ \ 8 \\ \hline 0 &= \ \ 0 \quad \text{True}\end{aligned}$$

This shows that equations (1) and (2) are dependent. To write the solution set with y as the arbitrary variable, solve equation (1) for x in terms of y.

$$3x+2y=4 \Rightarrow 3x=4-2y \Rightarrow x=\tfrac{4-2y}{3}$$

Solution set: $\left\{\left(\tfrac{4-2y}{3}, y\right)\right\}$

71. $\frac{1}{2}x+\frac{1}{3}y=2$
$\frac{3}{2}x-\frac{1}{2}y=-12$

$$D=\begin{vmatrix}\frac{1}{2} & \frac{1}{3}\\ \frac{3}{2} & -\frac{1}{2}\end{vmatrix}=\tfrac{1}{2}\left(-\tfrac{1}{2}\right)-\tfrac{3}{2}\left(\tfrac{1}{3}\right)=-\tfrac{1}{4}-\tfrac{1}{2}=-\tfrac{1}{4}-\tfrac{2}{4}=-\tfrac{3}{4}$$

$$D_x=\begin{vmatrix}2 & \frac{1}{3}\\ -12 & -\frac{1}{2}\end{vmatrix}=2\left(-\tfrac{1}{2}\right)-(-12)\left(\tfrac{1}{3}\right)=-1+4=3 \text{ and } D_y=\begin{vmatrix}\frac{1}{2} & 2\\ \frac{3}{2} & -12\end{vmatrix}=\tfrac{1}{2}(-12)-\tfrac{3}{2}(2)=-6-3=-9$$

Thus, we have $x=\frac{D_x}{D}=\frac{3}{-\frac{3}{4}}=3\left(-\frac{4}{3}\right)=-4$ and $y=\frac{D_y}{D}=\frac{-9}{-\frac{3}{4}}=-9\left(-\frac{4}{3}\right)=12$.

Solution set: $\{(-4,12)\}$

In Exercises 73 – 83, we will be using the Determinant Theorems on page 822 of your text to reduce the number of calculations necessary in simplifying determinants.

73.
$$\begin{aligned} 2x-\ \ y+4z+\ 2&=0 \\ 3x+2y-\ \ z+\ 3&=0 \\ x+4y+2z-17&=0 \end{aligned} \Rightarrow \begin{aligned} 2x-\ \ y+4z&=-2 \\ 3x+2y-z&=-3 \\ x+4y+2z&=17 \end{aligned}$$

Adding 2 times row 1 to row 2 and 4 times row 1 to row 3 we have $D=\begin{vmatrix}2 & -1 & 4\\ 3 & 2 & -1\\ 1 & 4 & 2\end{vmatrix}=\begin{vmatrix}2 & -1 & 4\\ 7 & 0 & 7\\ 9 & 0 & 18\end{vmatrix}$.

Expanding by column two, we have $D=-(-1)\begin{vmatrix}7 & 7\\ 9 & 18\end{vmatrix}=126-63=63$.

Adding 2 times row 1 to row 2 and 4 times row 1 to row 3, we have $D_x=\begin{vmatrix}-2 & -1 & 4\\ -3 & 2 & -1\\ 17 & 4 & 2\end{vmatrix}=\begin{vmatrix}-2 & -1 & 4\\ -7 & 0 & 7\\ 9 & 0 & 18\end{vmatrix}$.

Continued on next page

73. (continued)

Expanding about column two, we have $D_x = -(-1)\begin{vmatrix} -7 & 7 \\ 9 & 18 \end{vmatrix} = -126 - 63 = -189.$

Adding column 2 to column 1, we have $D_y = \begin{vmatrix} 2 & -2 & 4 \\ 3 & -3 & -1 \\ 1 & 17 & 2 \end{vmatrix} = \begin{vmatrix} 0 & -2 & 4 \\ 0 & -3 & -1 \\ 18 & 17 & 2 \end{vmatrix}.$

Expanding by column one, we have $D_y = 18\begin{vmatrix} -2 & 4 \\ -3 & -1 \end{vmatrix} = 18(2+12) = 18(14) = 252.$

Adding column 3 to column 1, we have $D_z = \begin{vmatrix} 2 & -1 & -2 \\ 3 & 2 & -3 \\ 1 & 4 & 17 \end{vmatrix} = \begin{vmatrix} 0 & -1 & -2 \\ 0 & 2 & -3 \\ 18 & 4 & 17 \end{vmatrix}.$

Expanding by column one we have $D_z = 18\begin{vmatrix} -1 & -2 \\ 2 & -3 \end{vmatrix} = 18(3+4) = 18(7) = 126.$

Thus, we have $x = \frac{D_x}{D} = \frac{-189}{63} = -3,\ y = \frac{D_y}{D} = \frac{252}{63} = 4,$ and $z = \frac{D_z}{D} = \frac{126}{63} = 2.$

Solution set: $\{(-3, 4, 2)\}$

75. $4x - 3y + z = -1$
$5x + 7y + 2z = -2$
$3x - 5y - z = 1$

Adding row 3 to row 1 and 2 times row 3 to row 2, we have $D = \begin{vmatrix} 4 & -3 & 1 \\ 5 & 7 & 2 \\ 3 & -5 & -1 \end{vmatrix} = \begin{vmatrix} 7 & -8 & 0 \\ 11 & -3 & 0 \\ 3 & -5 & -1 \end{vmatrix}.$

Expanding by column three, we have $D = -1\begin{vmatrix} 7 & -8 \\ 11 & -3 \end{vmatrix} = -1(-21+88) = -1(67) = -67.$

Adding column 1 to column 3 we have $D_x = \begin{vmatrix} -1 & -3 & 1 \\ -2 & 7 & 2 \\ 1 & -5 & -1 \end{vmatrix} = \begin{vmatrix} -1 & 3 & 0 \\ -2 & 7 & 0 \\ 1 & -5 & 0 \end{vmatrix}.$

Since we have a column of zeros, $D_x = 0.$

Adding column 2 to column 3, we have $D_y = \begin{vmatrix} 4 & -1 & 1 \\ 5 & -2 & 2 \\ 3 & 1 & -1 \end{vmatrix} = \begin{vmatrix} 4 & -1 & 0 \\ 5 & -2 & 0 \\ 3 & 1 & 0 \end{vmatrix}.$

Since we have a column of zeros, $D_y = 0.$

Adding row 3 to row 1 and 2 times row 3 to row 2, we have $D_z = \begin{vmatrix} 4 & -3 & -1 \\ 5 & 7 & -2 \\ 3 & -5 & 1 \end{vmatrix} = \begin{vmatrix} 7 & -8 & 0 \\ 11 & -3 & 0 \\ 3 & -5 & 1 \end{vmatrix}.$

Expanding by the third column, we have $D_z = 1\begin{vmatrix} 7 & -8 \\ 11 & -3 \end{vmatrix} = -21 + 88 = 67.$

Thus, we have $x = \frac{D_x}{D} = \frac{0}{-67} = 0,\ y = \frac{D_y}{D} = \frac{0}{-67} = 0,$ and $z = \frac{D_z}{D} = \frac{67}{-67} = -1.$

Solution set: $\{(0, 0, -1)\}$

77. $x+2y+3z=4 \quad (1)$
$4x+3y+2z=1 \quad (2)$
$-x-2y-3z=0 \quad (3)$

Adding row 1 to row 3, we have $D=\begin{vmatrix}1 & 2 & 3\\ 4 & 3 & 2\\ -1 & -2 & -3\end{vmatrix}=\begin{vmatrix}1 & 2 & 3\\ 4 & 3 & 2\\ 0 & 0 & 0\end{vmatrix}$.

Since we have a row of zeros, $D=0$ and we cannot use Cramer's rule.
Using the elimination method, we can add equations (1) and (3).

$$\begin{array}{r} x+2y+3z=4\\ -x-2y-3z=0\\ \hline 0=4 \text{ False}\end{array}$$

The system is inconsistent.
Solution set: $\varnothing$

79. $-2x-2y+3z=4 \quad (1)$
$5x+7y-z=2 \quad (2)$
$2x+2y-3z=-4 \quad (3)$

Adding row 1 to row 3, we have $D=\begin{vmatrix}-2 & -2 & 3\\ 5 & 7 & -1\\ 2 & 2 & -3\end{vmatrix}=\begin{vmatrix}-2 & -2 & 3\\ 5 & 7 & -1\\ 0 & 0 & 0\end{vmatrix}$.

Since we have a row of zeros, $D=0$ and we cannot use Cramer's rule.
Using the elimination method, we can add equations (1) and (3).

$$\begin{array}{r} -2x-2y+3z=4\\ 2x+2y-3z=-4\\ \hline 0=0 \text{ True}\end{array}$$

This system will have infinitely many solutions.
Solve the system made up of equations (2) and (3) in terms of the arbitrary variable z. To eliminate x, multiply equation (2) by -2 and equation (3) by 5 and add the results.

$$\begin{array}{r} -10x-14y+2z=-4\\ 10x+10y-15z=-20\\ \hline -4y-13z=-24\end{array}$$

Solve for y in terms of z.

$$-4y-13z=-24 \Rightarrow -4y=-24+13z \Rightarrow y=\frac{-24+13z}{-4} \Rightarrow y=\frac{24-13z}{4}$$

Now, express x also in terms of z by solving equation (3) for x and substituting $\frac{24-13z}{4}$ for y in the result.

$$2x+2y-3z=-4 \Rightarrow 2x=-2y+3z-4 \Rightarrow x=\frac{-2y+3z-4}{2}$$

$$x=\frac{-2\left(\frac{24-13z}{4}\right)+3z-4}{2}=\frac{\frac{-24+13z}{2}+3z-4}{2}=\frac{-24+13z+6z-8}{4}=\frac{-32+19z}{4}$$

Solution set (with z arbitrary): $\left\{\left(\frac{-32+19z}{4}, \frac{24-13z}{4}, z\right)\right\}$

81. $5x - y = -4$
$3x + 2z = 4$
$4y + 3z = 22$

Adding 4 times row 1 to row 3, we have $D = \begin{vmatrix} 5 & -1 & 0 \\ 3 & 0 & 2 \\ 0 & 4 & 3 \end{vmatrix} = \begin{vmatrix} 5 & -1 & 0 \\ 3 & 0 & 2 \\ 20 & 0 & 3 \end{vmatrix}$.

Expanding by column two, we have $D = -(-1)\begin{vmatrix} 3 & 2 \\ 20 & 3 \end{vmatrix} = 9 - 40 = -31$.

Adding 4 times row 1 to row 3, we have $D_x = \begin{vmatrix} -4 & -1 & 0 \\ 4 & 0 & 2 \\ 22 & 4 & 3 \end{vmatrix} = \begin{vmatrix} -4 & -1 & 0 \\ 4 & 0 & 2 \\ 6 & 0 & 3 \end{vmatrix}$.

Expand by column two, we have $D_x = -(-1)\begin{vmatrix} 4 & 2 \\ 6 & 3 \end{vmatrix} = 12 - 12 = 0$.

Adding column 2 to column 1, we have $D_y = \begin{vmatrix} 5 & -4 & 0 \\ 3 & 4 & 2 \\ 0 & 22 & 3 \end{vmatrix} = \begin{vmatrix} 1 & -4 & 0 \\ 7 & 4 & 2 \\ 22 & 22 & 3 \end{vmatrix}$.

Adding 4 times column 1 to column 2, we now have $D_y = \begin{vmatrix} 1 & 0 & 0 \\ 7 & 32 & 2 \\ 22 & 110 & 3 \end{vmatrix}$.

Expanding by row one, we have $D_y = 1\begin{vmatrix} 32 & 2 \\ 110 & 3 \end{vmatrix} = 96 - 220 = -124$.

Adding 4 times row 1 to row 3, we have $D_z = \begin{vmatrix} 5 & -1 & -4 \\ 3 & 0 & 4 \\ 0 & 4 & 22 \end{vmatrix} = \begin{vmatrix} 5 & -1 & -4 \\ 3 & 0 & 4 \\ 20 & 0 & 6 \end{vmatrix}$.

Expanding by column two ,we have $D_z = -(-1)\begin{vmatrix} 3 & 4 \\ 20 & 6 \end{vmatrix} = 18 - 80 = -62$.

Thus, we have $x = \frac{D_x}{D} = \frac{0}{-31} = 0$, $y = \frac{D_y}{D} = \frac{-124}{-31} = 4$, and $z = \frac{D_z}{D} = \frac{-62}{-31} = 2$.

Solution set: $\{(0,4,2)\}$

83. $x + 2y = 10$
$3x + 4z = 7$
$-y - z = 1$

Adding -3 times row 1 to row 2, we have $D = \begin{vmatrix} 1 & 2 & 0 \\ 3 & 0 & 4 \\ 0 & -1 & -1 \end{vmatrix} = \begin{vmatrix} 1 & 2 & 0 \\ 0 & -6 & 4 \\ 0 & -1 & -1 \end{vmatrix}$.

Expanding by column one, we have $D = 1\begin{vmatrix} -6 & 4 \\ -1 & -1 \end{vmatrix} = 6 + 4 = 10$.

Continued on next page

83. (continued)

Adding column 1 to column 2 and column 1 to column 3, we have $D_x = \begin{vmatrix} 10 & 2 & 0 \\ 7 & 0 & 4 \\ 1 & -1 & -1 \end{vmatrix} = \begin{vmatrix} 10 & 12 & 10 \\ 7 & 7 & 11 \\ 1 & 0 & 0 \end{vmatrix}$.

Expanding by row three, we have $D_x = 1\begin{vmatrix} 12 & 10 \\ 7 & 11 \end{vmatrix} = 132 - 70 = 62$.

Adding column 2 to column 3, we have $D_y = \begin{vmatrix} 1 & 10 & 0 \\ 3 & 7 & 4 \\ 0 & 1 & -1 \end{vmatrix} = \begin{vmatrix} 1 & 10 & 10 \\ 3 & 7 & 11 \\ 0 & 1 & 0 \end{vmatrix}$.

Expanding by row three, we have $D_y = -1\begin{vmatrix} 1 & 10 \\ 3 & 11 \end{vmatrix} = -1(11-30) = -1(-19) = 19$.

Adding column 3 to column 2, we have $D_z = \begin{vmatrix} 1 & 2 & 10 \\ 3 & 0 & 7 \\ 0 & -1 & 1 \end{vmatrix} = \begin{vmatrix} 1 & 12 & 10 \\ 3 & 7 & 7 \\ 0 & 0 & 1 \end{vmatrix}$.

Expanding by row three, we have $D_z = 1\begin{vmatrix} 1 & 12 \\ 3 & 7 \end{vmatrix} = 7 - 36 = -29$.

Thus, we have $x = \frac{D_x}{D} = \frac{62}{10} = \frac{31}{5}$, $y = \frac{D_y}{D} = \frac{19}{10}$, and $z = \frac{D_z}{D} = \frac{-29}{10} = -\frac{29}{10}$.

Solution set: $\left\{\left(\frac{31}{5}, \frac{19}{10}, -\frac{29}{10}\right)\right\}$

85. $\frac{\sqrt{3}}{2}(W_1 + W_2) = 100$

$W_1 - W_2 = 0$

Using the distributive property, we have the following system.

$$\frac{\sqrt{3}}{2}W_1 + \frac{\sqrt{3}}{2}W_2 = 100$$
$$W_1 - W_2 = 0$$

Using Cramer's rule, we have $D = \begin{vmatrix} \frac{\sqrt{3}}{2} & \frac{\sqrt{3}}{2} \\ 1 & -1 \end{vmatrix} = -\frac{\sqrt{3}}{2} - \frac{\sqrt{3}}{2} = -\sqrt{3}$, $D_{W_1} = \begin{vmatrix} 100 & \frac{\sqrt{3}}{2} \\ 0 & -1 \end{vmatrix} = -100 - 0 = -100$,

and $D_{W_2} = \begin{vmatrix} \frac{\sqrt{3}}{2} & 100 \\ 1 & 0 \end{vmatrix} = 0 - 100 = -100$. This yields the following solution.

$$W_1 = \frac{D_{W_1}}{D} = \frac{-100}{-\sqrt{3}} = \frac{100}{\sqrt{3}} = \frac{100\sqrt{3}}{3} \approx 58 \text{ and } W_2 = \frac{D_{W_2}}{D} = \frac{-100}{-\sqrt{3}} \approx 58$$

Both W_1 and W_2 are approximately 58 lb.

87. $bx + y = a^2$
$ax + y = b^2$

Using Cramer's rule, we have $D = \begin{vmatrix} b & 1 \\ a & 1 \end{vmatrix} = b - a$, $D_x = \begin{vmatrix} a^2 & 1 \\ b^2 & 1 \end{vmatrix} = a^2 - b^2$, and $D_y = \begin{vmatrix} b & a^2 \\ a & b^2 \end{vmatrix} = b^3 - a^3$.

$$x = \frac{D_x}{D} = \frac{a^2 - b^2}{b - a} = \frac{(a+b)(a-b)}{b-a} = \frac{(a+b)(a-b)}{-(a-b)} = -(a+b) = -a - b$$

$$y = \frac{D_y}{D} = \frac{b^3 - a^3}{b - a} = \frac{(b-a)(b^2 + ab + a^2)}{b-a} = b^2 + ab + a^2$$

Solution set: $\{(-a-b, a^2 + ab + b^2)\}$

89. $b^2 x + a^2 y = b^2$
$ax + by = a$

Using Cramer's rule, we have $D = \begin{vmatrix} b^2 & a^2 \\ a & b \end{vmatrix} = b^3 - a^3$, $D_x = \begin{vmatrix} b^2 & a^2 \\ a & b \end{vmatrix} = b^3 - a^3$, and

$D_y = \begin{vmatrix} b^2 & b^2 \\ a & a \end{vmatrix} = ab^2 - ab^2 = 0.$

$$x = \frac{D_x}{D} = \frac{b^3 - a^3}{b^3 - a^3} = 1$$

$$y = \frac{D_y}{D} = \frac{0}{b^3 - a^3} = 0$$

Note: In order for $D \neq 0$, we also assumed $a \neq b$.

Solution set: $\{(1,0)\}$

Section 9.4: Partial Fractions

1. $$\frac{5}{3x(2x+1)} = \frac{A}{3x} + \frac{B}{2x+1}$$

Multiply both sides by $3x(2x+1)$ to get $5 = A(2x+1) + B(3x)$. (1)
First substitute 0 for x to get $5 = A(2\cdot 0+1) + B(3\cdot 0) \Rightarrow A = 5$.

Replace A with 5 in equation (1) and substitute $-\frac{1}{2}$ for x to get the following.

$$5 = 5\left[2\left(-\tfrac{1}{2}\right)+1\right] + B\left[3\left(-\tfrac{1}{2}\right)\right] \Rightarrow 5 = 5(-1+1) - \tfrac{3}{2}B$$

$$5 = 5(0) - \tfrac{3}{2}B \Rightarrow 5 = -\tfrac{3}{2}B \Rightarrow -\tfrac{10}{3} = B$$

Thus, we have $\dfrac{5}{3x(2x+1)} = \dfrac{5}{3x} + \dfrac{-\frac{10}{3}}{2x+1} \Rightarrow \dfrac{5}{3x(2x+1)} = \dfrac{5}{3x} + \dfrac{-10}{3(2x+1)}$.

3. $\dfrac{4x+2}{(x+2)(2x-1)}=\dfrac{A}{x+2}+\dfrac{B}{2x-1}$

Multiply both sides by $(x+2)(2x-1)$ to get $4x+2=A(2x-1)+B(x+2)$. (1)

First substitute -2 for x to get the following.

$$4(-2)+2=A[2(-2)-1]+B(-2+2)\Rightarrow -8+2=A(-4-1)+B(0)=-6=-5A\Rightarrow A=\tfrac{6}{5}$$

Replace A with $\frac{6}{5}$ in equation (1) and substitute $\frac{1}{2}$ for x to get the following.

$$4\cdot\tfrac{1}{2}+2=\tfrac{6}{5}\left(2\cdot\tfrac{1}{2}-1\right)+B\left(\tfrac{1}{2}+2\right)\Rightarrow 2+2=\tfrac{6}{5}(1-1)+B\cdot\tfrac{5}{2}\Rightarrow 4=\tfrac{6}{5}(0)+\tfrac{5}{2}B\Rightarrow 4=\tfrac{5}{2}B\Rightarrow B=\tfrac{8}{5}$$

Thus, we have $\dfrac{4x+2}{(x+2)(2x-1)}=\dfrac{\frac{6}{5}}{(x+2)}+\dfrac{\frac{8}{5}}{(2x-1)}\Rightarrow\dfrac{4x+2}{(x+2)(2x-1)}=\dfrac{6}{5(x+2)}+\dfrac{8}{5(2x-1)}$.

5. $\dfrac{x}{x^2+4x-5}=\dfrac{x}{(x+5)(x-1)}=\dfrac{A}{x+5}+\dfrac{B}{x-1}$

Multiply both sides by $(x+5)(x-1)$ to get $x=A(x-1)+B(x+5)$. (1)

First substitute -5 for x to get

$$-5=A(-5-1)+B(-5+5)\Rightarrow -5=A(-6)+B(0)\Rightarrow -5=-6A\Rightarrow A=\tfrac{5}{6}.$$

Replace A with $\frac{5}{6}$ in equation (1) and substitute 1 for x to get

$$1=\tfrac{5}{6}(1-1)+B(1+5)\Rightarrow 1=\tfrac{5}{6}(0)+B(6)\Rightarrow 1=6B\Rightarrow B=\tfrac{1}{6}.$$

Thus, we have $\dfrac{x}{(x+5)(x-1)}=\dfrac{\frac{5}{6}}{x+5}+\dfrac{\frac{1}{6}}{x-1}=\dfrac{5}{6(x+5)}+\dfrac{1}{6(x-1)}$.

7. $\dfrac{2x}{(x+1)(x+2)^2}=\dfrac{A}{x+1}+\dfrac{B}{x+2}+\dfrac{C}{(x+2)^2}$

Multiply both sides by $(x+1)(x+2)^2$ to get $2x=A(x+2)^2+B(x+1)(x+2)+C(x+1)$. (1)

First substitute -1 for x to get the following.

$$2(-1)=A(-1+2)^2+B(-1+1)(-1+2)+C(-1+1)\Rightarrow -2=A(1)^2+B(0)(1)+C(0)\Rightarrow -2=A$$

Replace A with -2 in equation (1) and substitute -2 for x to get the following.

$$2(-2)=-2(-2+2)^2+B(-2+1)(-2+2)+C(-2+1)\Rightarrow -4=0+0-C\Rightarrow C=4$$

$$2x=-2(x+2)^2+B(x+1)(x+2)+4(x+1)\ (2)$$

Now substitute 0 (arbitrary choice) for x in equation (2) to get the following.

$$2(0)=-2(0+2)^2+B(0+1)(0+2)+4(0+1)\Rightarrow 0=-2(2)^2+B(1)(2)+4(1)$$
$$0=-2(4)+2B+4\Rightarrow 0=-8+2B+4\Rightarrow 0=-4+2B\Rightarrow 4=2B\Rightarrow B=2$$

Thus we have $\dfrac{2x}{(x+1)(x+2)^2}=\dfrac{-2}{x+1}+\dfrac{2}{x+2}+\dfrac{4}{(x+2)^2}$.

9. $\dfrac{4}{x(1-x)}=\dfrac{A}{x}+\dfrac{B}{1-x}$

Multiply both sides by $x(1-x)$ to get $4=A(1-x)+Bx.$ (1)

First substitute 0 for x to get the following.

$$4=A(1-0)+B(0)\Rightarrow 4=A+0\Rightarrow A=4$$

Replace A with 4 in equation (1) and substitute 1 for x to get the following.

$$4=4(1-1)+B(1)\Rightarrow 4=0+B\Rightarrow B=4$$

Thus, we have $\dfrac{4}{x(1-x)}=\dfrac{4}{x}+\dfrac{4}{1-x}.$

11. $\dfrac{2x+1}{(x+2)^3}=\dfrac{A}{x+2}+\dfrac{B}{(x+2)^2}+\dfrac{C}{(x+2)^3}$

Multiply both sides by $(x+2)^3$ to get $2x+1=A(x+2)^2+B(x+2)+C.$ (1)

First substitute -2 for x to get the following.

$$2(-2)+1=A(-2+2)^2+B(-2+2)+C\Rightarrow -4+1=0+0+C\Rightarrow C=-3$$

Replace C with -3 in equation (1) and substitute 0 (arbitrary choice) for x to get the following.

$$2(0)+1=A(0+2)^2+B(0+2)-3\Rightarrow 1=4A+2B-3\Rightarrow 4A+2B=4\Rightarrow 2A+B=2 \text{ (3)}$$

Replace C with -3 in equation (1) and substitute -1 (arbitrary choice) for x to get the following.

$$2(-1)+1=A(-1+2)^2+B(-1+2)-3\Rightarrow -1=A+B-3\Rightarrow A+B=2 \text{ (4)}$$

Solve the system of equations by multiplying equation (4) by -1 and adding to equation 3.

$$\begin{array}{r} 2A+B=\ \ 2 \\ \underline{-A-B=-2} \\ A\qquad=\ \ 0 \end{array}$$

Substituting 0 for A in equation (4) we obtain $0+B=2\Rightarrow B=2.$

Thus, we have $\dfrac{2x+1}{(x+2)^3}=\dfrac{0}{x+2}+\dfrac{2}{(x+2)^2}+\dfrac{-3}{(x+2)^3}=\dfrac{2}{(x+2)^2}+\dfrac{-3}{(x+2)^3}.$

13. $\dfrac{x^2}{x^2+2x+1}$

This is not a proper fraction; the numerator has degree greater than or equal to that of the denominator. Divide the numerator by the denominator.

$$\begin{array}{r} 1 \\ x^2+2x+1\overline{\big)\, x^2\qquad\quad} \\ \underline{x^2+2x+1} \\ -2x-1 \end{array}$$

Find the partial fraction decomposition for $\dfrac{-2x-1}{x^2+2x+1}=\dfrac{-2x-1}{(x+1)^2}.$

Continued on next page

13. (continued)

$$\frac{-2x-1}{(x+1)^2}=\frac{A}{x+1}+\frac{B}{(x+1)^2}$$

Multiply both sides by $(x+1)^2$ to get $-2x-1=A(x+1)+B$. (1)

First substitute -1 for x to get the following.

$$-2(-1)-1=A(-1+1)+B\Rightarrow 2-1=0+B\Rightarrow 1=B$$

Replace B with 1 in equation (1) and substitute 2 (arbitrary choice) for x to get the following.

$$-2(2)-1=A(2+1)+1\Rightarrow -5=3A+1\Rightarrow -6=3A\Rightarrow A=-2$$

Thus, we have $\dfrac{x^2}{x^2+2x+1}=1+\dfrac{-2}{x+1}+\dfrac{1}{(x+1)^2}$.

15. $\dfrac{2x^5+3x^4-3x^3-2x^2+x}{2x^2+5x+2}$

The degree of the numerator is greater than the degree of the denominator, so first find the quotient.

$$\begin{array}{r|l} & x^3-x^2 \\ \hline 2x^2+5x+2 & 2x^5+3x^4-3x^3-2x^2+x \\ & 2x^5+5x^4+2x^3 \\ \hline & -2x^4-5x^3-2x^2+x \\ & -2x^4-5x^3-2x^2 \\ \hline & x \end{array}$$

Find the partial fraction decomposition for $\dfrac{x}{2x^2+5x+2}=\dfrac{x}{(2x+1)(x+2)}$.

$$\frac{x}{(2x+1)(x+2)}=\frac{A}{2x+1}+\frac{B}{x+2}$$

Multiply both sides by $(2x+1)(x+2)$ to get $x=A(x+2)+B(2x+1)$. (1)

First substitute $-\frac{1}{2}$ for x to get the following.

$$-\tfrac{1}{2}=A\left(-\tfrac{1}{2}+2\right)+B\left[2\left(-\tfrac{1}{2}\right)+1\right]\Rightarrow -\tfrac{1}{2}=A\left(\tfrac{3}{2}\right)+B(0)\Rightarrow -\tfrac{1}{2}=\tfrac{3}{2}A\Rightarrow A=-\tfrac{1}{3}$$

Replace A with $-\frac{1}{3}$ in equation (1) and substitute -2 for x to get the following.

$$-2=-\tfrac{1}{3}(-2+2)+B\left[2(-2)+1\right]\Rightarrow -2=-\tfrac{1}{3}(0)+B(-3)\Rightarrow -2=-3B\Rightarrow B=\tfrac{2}{3}$$

Thus, we have $\dfrac{2x^5+3x^4-3x^3-2x^2+x}{2x^2+5x+2}=x^3-x^2+\dfrac{-1}{3(2x+1)}+\dfrac{2}{3(x+2)}$.

17. $\dfrac{x^3+4}{9x^3-4x}$

Find the quotient since the degrees of the numerator and denominator are the same.

$$\begin{array}{r} \tfrac{1}{9} \\ 9x^3-4x\overline{\big)\,x^3+0x^2+0x+4} \\ \underline{x^3 \qquad\quad -\tfrac{4}{9}x} \\ \tfrac{4}{9}x+4 \end{array}$$

Find the partial fraction decomposition for $\dfrac{\frac{4}{9}x+4}{9x^3-4x}$.

$$\frac{\frac{4}{9}x+4}{9x^3-4x}=\frac{\frac{4}{9}x+4}{x\left(9x^2-4\right)}=\frac{\frac{4}{9}x+4}{x(3x+2)(3x-2)}=\frac{A}{x}+\frac{B}{3x+2}+\frac{C}{3x-2}$$

Multiply both sides of $\dfrac{\frac{4}{9}x+4}{9x^3-4x}=\dfrac{A}{x}+\dfrac{B}{3x+2}+\dfrac{C}{3x-2}$ by $x(3x+2)(3x-2)$ to get the following.

$$\tfrac{4}{9}x+4=A(3x+2)(3x-2)+Bx(3x-2)+Cx(3x+2)\ (1)$$

First substitute 0 for x to get the following.

$$\tfrac{4}{9}(0)+4=A[3(0)+2][3(0)-2]+B(0)[3(0)-2]+C(0)[3(0)+2]$$
$$0+4=A(2)(-2)+0+0\Rightarrow 4=-4A\Rightarrow A=-1$$

Replace A with -1 in equation (1) and substitute $-\frac{2}{3}$ for x to get the following.

$$\tfrac{4}{9}\left(-\tfrac{2}{3}\right)+4=-\left[3\left(-\tfrac{2}{3}\right)+2\right]\left[3\left(-\tfrac{2}{3}\right)-2\right]+B\left(-\tfrac{2}{3}\right)\left[3\left(-\tfrac{2}{3}\right)-2\right]+C\left(-\tfrac{2}{3}\right)\left[3\left(-\tfrac{2}{3}\right)+2\right]$$
$$-\tfrac{8}{27}+4=0+B\left(-\tfrac{2}{3}\right)(-4)+0\Rightarrow\tfrac{100}{27}=\tfrac{8}{3}B\Rightarrow B=\tfrac{25}{18}$$
$$\tfrac{4}{9}x+4=-(3x+2)(3x-2)+\tfrac{25}{18}x(3x-2)+Cx(3x+2)\ (2)$$

Substitute $\frac{2}{3}$ in equation (2) for x to get the following.

$$\tfrac{4}{9}\left(\tfrac{2}{3}\right)+4=-\left[3\left(\tfrac{2}{3}\right)+2\right]\left[3\left(\tfrac{2}{3}\right)-2\right]+\tfrac{25}{18}\left(\tfrac{2}{3}\right)\left[3\left(\tfrac{2}{3}\right)-2\right]+C\left(\tfrac{2}{3}\right)\left[3\left(\tfrac{2}{3}\right)+2\right]$$
$$\tfrac{8}{27}+4=0+0+C\left(\tfrac{2}{3}\right)(4)\Rightarrow\tfrac{116}{27}=\tfrac{8}{3}C\Rightarrow C=\tfrac{29}{18}$$

Thus, we have $\dfrac{x^3+4}{9x^3-4x}=\dfrac{1}{9}+\dfrac{-1}{x}+\dfrac{25}{18(3x+2)}+\dfrac{29}{18(3x-2)}$.

19. $\dfrac{-3}{x^2(x^2+5)} = \dfrac{A}{x} + \dfrac{B}{x^2} + \dfrac{Cx+D}{x^2+5}$

We will be using Method 2 (similar to Example 4) in this solution.

Multiply both sides by $x^2(x^2+5)$ to get the following.

$$-3 = Ax(x^2+5) + B(x^2+5) + (Cx+D)x^2$$

Distributing and combining like terms on the right side of the equation, we have the following.

$$-3 = Ax(x^2+5) + B(x^2+5) + (Cx+D)x^2$$

$$-3 = Ax^3 + 5Ax + Bx^2 + 5B + Cx^3 + Dx^2$$

$$-3 = (A+C)x^3 + (B+D)x^2 + (5A)x + 5B$$

Equate the coefficients of like powers of x on the two sides of the equation.

For the x^3 – term, we have $0 = A + C$.

For the x^2 – term, we have $0 = B + D$.

For the x – term, we have $0 = 5A \Rightarrow A = 0$.

For the constant term, we have $-3 = 5B \Rightarrow B = -\frac{3}{5}$.

Since $A = 0$ and $0 = A + C$, we have $C = 0$.

Since $B = -\frac{3}{5}$ and $0 = B + D$, we have $D = \frac{3}{5}$.

Thus, we have $\dfrac{-3}{x^2(x^2+5)} = \dfrac{-3}{5x^2} + \dfrac{3}{5(x^2+5)}$.

21. $\dfrac{3x-2}{(x+4)(3x^2+1)} = \dfrac{A}{x+4} + \dfrac{Bx+C}{3x^2+1}$

We will be using Method 1 (similar to Example 3) in this solution.

Multiply both sides by $(x+4)(3x^2+1)$ to get the following.

$$3x - 2 = A(3x^2+1) + (Bx+C)(x+4) \quad (1)$$

First substitute –4 for x to get the following.

$$3(-4) - 2 = A\left[3(-4)^2+1\right] + \left[B(-4)+C\right](-4+4)$$

$$-12 - 2 = A(48+1) + 0 \Rightarrow -14 = 49A \Rightarrow -\tfrac{14}{49} = A \Rightarrow A = -\tfrac{2}{7}$$

Replace A with $-\frac{2}{7}$ in equation (1) and substitute 0 for x to get the following.

$$3(0) - 2 = -\tfrac{2}{7}\left[3(0)^2+1\right] + \left[B(0)+C\right](0+4) \Rightarrow -2 = -\tfrac{2}{7} + 4C \Rightarrow -\tfrac{12}{7} = 4C \Rightarrow C = -\tfrac{3}{7}$$

$$3x - 2 = -\tfrac{2}{7}(3x^2+1) + (Bx - \tfrac{3}{7})(x+4) \quad (2)$$

Substitute 1 (arbitrary value) in equation (2) for x to get the following.

$$3(1) - 2 = -\tfrac{2}{7}\left[3(1)^2+1\right] + \left[B(1) - \tfrac{3}{7}\right](1+4)$$

$$3 - 2 = -\tfrac{2}{7}(4) + \left[B - \tfrac{3}{7}\right](5) \Rightarrow 1 = -\tfrac{8}{7} + 5B - \tfrac{15}{7} \Rightarrow 1 = 5B - \tfrac{23}{7} \Rightarrow \tfrac{30}{7} = 5B \Rightarrow B = \tfrac{6}{7}$$

Thus, we have $\dfrac{3x-2}{(x+4)(3x^2+1)} = \dfrac{-\frac{2}{7}}{x+4} + \dfrac{\frac{6}{7}x + \left(-\frac{3}{7}\right)}{3x^2+1} = \dfrac{-2}{7(x+4)} + \dfrac{6x-3}{7(3x^2+1)}$.

23. $\dfrac{1}{x(2x+1)(3x^2+4)}=\dfrac{A}{x}+\dfrac{B}{2x+1}+\dfrac{Cx+D}{3x^2+4}$

We will be using Method 2 (similar to Example 4) in this solution.

Multiply both sides by $x(2x+1)(3x^2+4)$ to get the following.

$$1=A(2x+1)(3x^2+4)+Bx(3x^2+4)+(Cx+D)(x)(2x+1)$$

Expanding and combining like terms on the right side of the equation, we have the following.

$$1=A(2x+1)(3x^2+4)+Bx(3x^2+4)+(Cx+D)(x)(2x+1)$$
$$1=A(6x^3+3x^2+8x+4)+B(3x^3+4x)+C(2x^3+x^2)+D(2x^2+x)$$
$$1=6Ax^3+3Ax^2+8Ax+4A+3Bx^3+4Bx+2Cx^3+Cx^2+2Dx^2+Dx$$
$$1=(6A+3B+2C)x^3+(3A+C+2D)x^2+(8A+4B+D)x+4A$$

Equate the coefficients of like powers of x on the two sides of the equation.

For the x^3- term, we have $0=6A+3B+2C.$

For the x^2- term, we have $0=3A+C+2D.$

For the $x-$ term, we have $0=8A+4B+D.$

For the constant term, we have $1=4A.$

If we use the Gauss-Jordan method, we begin with the following augmented matrix.

$$\left[\begin{array}{cccc|c} 6 & 3 & 2 & 0 & 0 \\ 3 & 0 & 1 & 2 & 0 \\ 8 & 4 & 0 & 1 & 0 \\ 4 & 0 & 0 & 0 & 1 \end{array}\right]$$

$$\left[\begin{array}{cccc|c} 6 & 3 & 2 & 0 & 0 \\ 3 & 0 & 1 & 2 & 0 \\ 8 & 4 & 0 & 1 & 0 \\ 1 & 0 & 0 & 0 & \frac{1}{4} \end{array}\right]\begin{array}{l} \\ \\ \\ \frac{1}{4}\text{R4} \end{array} \Rightarrow \left[\begin{array}{cccc|c} 1 & 0 & 0 & 0 & \frac{1}{4} \\ 3 & 0 & 1 & 2 & 0 \\ 8 & 4 & 0 & 1 & 0 \\ 6 & 3 & 2 & 0 & 0 \end{array}\right]\begin{array}{l} \text{R1}\leftrightarrow\text{R4} \\ \\ \\ \\ \end{array} \Rightarrow \left[\begin{array}{cccc|c} 1 & 0 & 0 & 0 & \frac{1}{4} \\ 0 & 0 & 1 & 2 & -\frac{3}{4} \\ 0 & 4 & 0 & 1 & -2 \\ 0 & 3 & 2 & 0 & -\frac{3}{2} \end{array}\right]\begin{array}{l} \\ -3\text{R1}+\text{R2} \\ -8\text{R1}+\text{R3} \\ -6\text{R1}+\text{R4} \end{array}$$

$$\left[\begin{array}{cccc|c} 1 & 0 & 0 & 0 & \frac{1}{4} \\ 0 & 0 & 1 & 2 & -\frac{3}{4} \\ 0 & 1 & 0 & \frac{1}{4} & -\frac{1}{2} \\ 0 & 3 & 2 & 0 & -\frac{3}{2} \end{array}\right]\begin{array}{l} \\ \\ \frac{1}{4}\text{R3} \\ \\ \end{array} \Rightarrow \left[\begin{array}{cccc|c} 1 & 0 & 0 & 0 & \frac{1}{4} \\ 0 & 1 & 0 & \frac{1}{4} & -\frac{1}{2} \\ 0 & 0 & 1 & 2 & -\frac{3}{4} \\ 0 & 3 & 2 & 0 & -\frac{3}{2} \end{array}\right]\begin{array}{l} \\ \text{R2}\leftrightarrow\text{R3} \\ \\ \\ \end{array} \Rightarrow \left[\begin{array}{cccc|c} 1 & 0 & 0 & 0 & \frac{1}{4} \\ 0 & 1 & 0 & \frac{1}{4} & -\frac{1}{2} \\ 0 & 0 & 1 & 2 & -\frac{3}{4} \\ 0 & 0 & 2 & -\frac{3}{4} & 0 \end{array}\right]\begin{array}{l} \\ \\ \\ -3\text{R2}+\text{R4} \end{array}$$

$$\left[\begin{array}{cccc|c} 1 & 0 & 0 & 0 & \frac{1}{4} \\ 0 & 1 & 0 & \frac{1}{4} & -\frac{1}{2} \\ 0 & 0 & 1 & 2 & -\frac{3}{4} \\ 0 & 0 & 0 & -\frac{19}{4} & \frac{3}{2} \end{array}\right]\begin{array}{l} \\ \\ \\ -2\text{R3}+\text{R4} \end{array} \Rightarrow \left[\begin{array}{cccc|c} 1 & 0 & 0 & 0 & \frac{1}{4} \\ 0 & 1 & 0 & \frac{1}{4} & -\frac{1}{2} \\ 0 & 0 & 1 & 2 & -\frac{3}{4} \\ 0 & 0 & 0 & 1 & -\frac{6}{19} \end{array}\right]\begin{array}{l} \\ \\ \\ -\frac{4}{19}\text{R4} \end{array} \Rightarrow \left[\begin{array}{cccc|c} 1 & 0 & 0 & 0 & \frac{1}{4} \\ 0 & 1 & 0 & 0 & -\frac{8}{19} \\ 0 & 0 & 1 & 0 & -\frac{9}{76} \\ 0 & 0 & 0 & 1 & -\frac{6}{19} \end{array}\right]\begin{array}{l} \\ -\frac{1}{4}\text{R4}+\text{R2} \\ -2\text{R4}+\text{R3} \\ \\ \end{array}$$

Thus, we have $\dfrac{1}{x(2x+1)(3x^2+4)}=\dfrac{\frac{1}{4}}{x}+\dfrac{-\frac{8}{19}}{2x+1}+\dfrac{-\frac{9}{76}x+\left(-\frac{6}{19}\right)}{3x^2+4}=\dfrac{\frac{1}{4}}{x}+\dfrac{-\frac{8}{19}}{2x+1}+\dfrac{-\frac{9}{76}x-\frac{24}{76}}{3x^2+4}$

$$=\frac{1}{4x}+\frac{-8}{19(2x+1)}+\frac{-9x-24}{76(3x^2+4)}.$$

25. $\frac{3x-1}{x(2x^2+1)^2}=\frac{A}{x}+\frac{Bx+C}{2x^2+1}+\frac{Dx+E}{(2x^2+1)^2}$

Multiply both sides by $x(2x^2+1)^2$ to get the following.

$$3x-1=A(2x^2+1)^2+(Bx+C)(x)(2x^2+1)+(Dx+E)x$$

Expanding and combining like terms on the right side of the equation, we have the following.

$$3x-1=A(2x^2+1)^2+(Bx+C)(x)(2x^2+1)+(Dx+E)x$$
$$3x-1=A(4x^4+4x^2+1)+B(2x^4+x^2)+C(2x^3+x)+Dx^2+Ex$$
$$3x-1=4Ax^4+4Ax^2+A+2Bx^4+Bx^2+2Cx^3+Cx+Dx^2+Ex$$
$$3x-1=(4A+2B)x^4+2Cx^3+(4A+B+D)x^2+(C+E)x+A$$

Equate the coefficients of like powers of x on the two sides of the equation.

For the x^4 – term, we have $0=4A+2B$.

For the x^3 – term, we have $0=2C\Rightarrow C=0$.

For the x^2 – term, we have $0=4A+B+D$.

For the x – term, we have $3=C+E$.

For the constant term, we have $-1=A$.

Since $A=-1$ and $0=4A+2B$, we have $B=2$.

Since $A=-1$, $B=2$ and $0=4A+B+D$, we have $D=2$.

Since $C=0$ and $3=C+E$, we have $E=3$.

Thus, we have $\frac{3x-1}{x(2x^2+1)^2}=\frac{-1}{x}+\frac{2x+0}{2x^2+1}+\frac{2x+3}{(2x^2+1)^2}=\frac{-1}{x}+\frac{2x}{2x^2+1}+\frac{2x+3}{(2x^2+1)^2}$.

27. $\frac{-x^4-8x^2+3x-10}{(x+2)(x^2+4)^2}=\frac{A}{x+2}+\frac{Bx+C}{x^2+4}+\frac{Dx+E}{(x^2+4)^2}$

Multiply both sides by $(x+2)(x^2+4)^2$ to get the following.

$$-x^4-8x^2+3x-10=A(x^2+4)^2+(Bx+C)(x+2)(x^2+4)+(Dx+E)(x+2) \quad (1)$$

We can combine Methods 1 and 2 by first doing a substitution then expanding and combining like terms on the right side of the equation.

Substitute -2 in equation (1) for x to get the following.

$$-(-2)^4-8(-2)^2+3(-2)-10=A\left[(-2)^2+4\right]^2+\left[B(-2)+C\right](-2+2)\left[(-2)^2+4\right]+\left[D(-2)+E\right](-2+2)$$
$$-16-32+(-6)-10=A(4+4)^2+0+0\Rightarrow -64=64A\Rightarrow A=-1$$

Substituting -1 for A in equation (1) and expanding and combining like terms, we have the following.

$$-x^4-8x^2+3x-10=-1(x^2+4)^2+(Bx+C)(x+2)(x^2+4)+(Dx+E)(x+2)$$
$$-x^4-8x^2+3x-10=-1(x^4+8x^2+16)+(Bx+C)(x^3+2x^2+4x+8)+D(x^2+2x)+E(x+2)$$
$$-x^4-8x^2+3x-10=-x^4-8x^2-16+Bx^4+2Bx^3+4Bx^2+8Bx+Cx^3+2Cx^2+4Cx+8C+Dx^2+2Dx+Ex+2E$$
$$-x^4-8x^2+3x-10=(-1+B)x^4+(2B+C)x^3+(-8+4B+2C+D)x^2+(8B+4C+2D+E)x+(-16+8C+2E)$$

Continued on next page

27. (continued)

Equate the coefficients of like powers of x on the two sides of the equation.

For the x^4 – term, we have $-1=-1+B \Rightarrow B=0.$

For the x^3 – term, we have $0=2B+C.$

For the x^2 – term, we have $-8=-8+4B+2C+D \Rightarrow 0=4B+2C+D.$

For the x – term, we have $3=8B+4C+2D+E.$

For the constant term, we have $-10=-16+8C+2E \Rightarrow 6=8C+2E.$

Since $B=0$ and $0=2B+C,$ we have $C=0.$

Since $B=0,\ C=0,$ and $0=4B+2C+D,$ we have $D=0.$

Since $C=0$ and $6=8C+2E,$ we have $E=3.$

Thus we have, $\dfrac{-x^4-8x^2+3x-10}{(x+2)(x^2+4)^2}=\dfrac{-1}{x+2}+\dfrac{0\cdot x+0}{x^2+4}+\dfrac{0\cdot x+3}{(x^2+4)^2}=\dfrac{-1}{x+2}+\dfrac{3}{(x^2+4)^2}.$

29. $\dfrac{5x^5+10x^4-15x^3+4x^2+13x-9}{x^3+2x^2-3x}$

Since the degree of the numerator is higher than the degree of the denominator, first find the quotient.

$$\begin{array}{r} 5x^2 \\ x^3+2x^2-3x \overline{\smash{)}\ 5x^5+10x^4-15x^3+4x^2+13x-9} \\ \underline{5x^5+10x^4-15x^3} \\ 4x^2+13x-9 \end{array}$$

Find the partial fraction decomposition of $\dfrac{4x^2+13x-9}{x^3+2x^2-3x}.$

$$\frac{4x^2+13x-9}{x^3+2x^2-3x}=\frac{4x^2+13x-9}{x(x^2+2x-3)}=\frac{4x^2+13x-9}{x(x+3)(x-1)}=\frac{A}{x}+\frac{B}{x+3}+\frac{C}{x-1}$$

Multiply by $x(x+3)(x-1)$ to obtain $4x^2+13x-9=A(x+3)(x-1)+Bx(x-1)+Cx(x+3).$ (1)

First substitute 0 for x in equation (1) to get the following.

$$4(0)^2+13(0)-9=A(0+3)(0-1)+B(0)(0-1)+C(0)(0+3) \Rightarrow -9=-3A \Rightarrow A=3$$

Replace A with 3 in equation (1) and substitute -3 for x to get the following.

$$4(-3)^2+13(-3)-9=3(-3+3)(-3-1)+B(-3)(-3-1)+C(-3)(-3+3) \Rightarrow -12=12B \Rightarrow B=-1$$

$$4x^2+13x-9=3(x+3)(x-1)-x(x-1)+Cx(x+3) \quad (2)$$

Now substitute 1 (arbitrary choice) for x in equation (2) to get the following.

$$4(1)^2+13(1)-9=3(1+3)(1-1)-1(1-1)+C(1)(1+3) \Rightarrow 8=4C \Rightarrow C=2$$

Thus, we have $\dfrac{5x^5+10x^4-15x^3+4x^2+13x-9}{x^3+2x^2-3x}=5x^2+\dfrac{3}{x}+\dfrac{-1}{x+3}+\dfrac{2}{x-1}.$

31. $\dfrac{4x^2-3x-4}{x^3+x^2-2x}=\dfrac{2}{x}+\dfrac{-1}{x-1}+\dfrac{3}{x+2}$; The graphs coincide; correct.

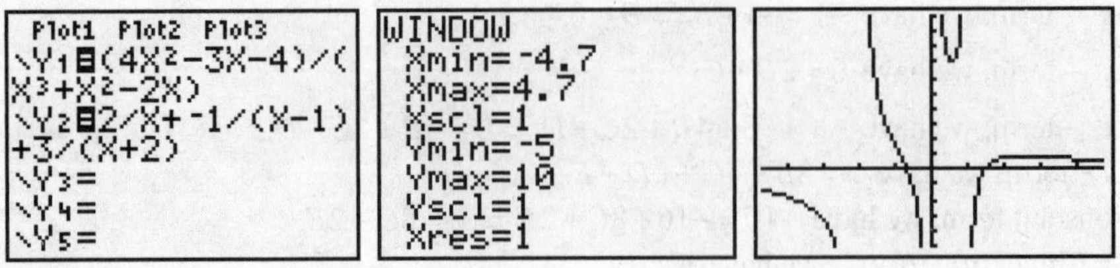

33. $\dfrac{x^3-2x}{\left(x^2+2x+2\right)^2}=\dfrac{x-2}{x^2+2x+2}+\dfrac{2}{\left(x^2+2x+2\right)^2}$; The graphs do not coincide; not correct.

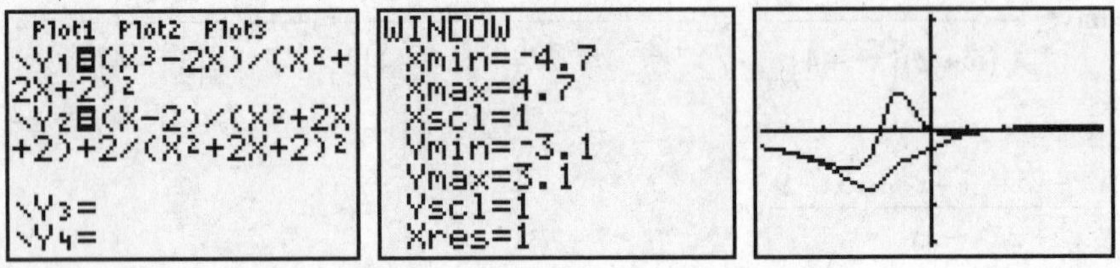

Section 9.5: Nonlinear Systems of Equations

1. The system is $\begin{aligned} x^2 &= y-1 \\ y &= 3x+5 \end{aligned}$ and the proposed solution set is $\{(-1,2),(4,17)\}$.

Check $(-1,2)$.

$$\begin{aligned} x^2 &= y-1 & y &= 3x+5 \\ (-1)^2 &= 2-1\ ? & 2 &= 3(-1)+5\ ? \\ 1 &= 1 & 2 &= -3+5 \\ & & 2 &= 2 \end{aligned}$$

Check $(4,17)$.

$$\begin{aligned} x^2 &= y-1 & y &= 3x+5 \\ 4^2 &= 17-1\ ? & 17 &= 3(4)+5\ ? \\ 16 &= 16 & 17 &= 12+5 \\ & & 17 &= 17 \end{aligned}$$

Both solutions are valid.

3. The system is $\begin{aligned} x^2+y^2 &= 5 \\ -3x+4y &= 2 \end{aligned}$ and the proposed solution set is $\left\{(-2,-1),\left(\frac{38}{25},\frac{41}{25}\right)\right\}$.

Check $(-2,-1)$.

$$\begin{aligned} x^2+y^2 &= 5 & -3x+4y &= 2 \\ (-2)^2+(-1)^2 &= 5\ ? & -3(-2)+4(-1) &= 2\ ? \\ 4+1 &= 5 & 6+(-4) &= 2 \\ 5 &= 5 & 2 &= 2 \end{aligned}$$

Check $\left(\frac{38}{25},\frac{41}{25}\right)$.

$$\begin{aligned} x^2+y^2 &= 5 & -3x+4y &= 2 \\ \left(\tfrac{38}{25}\right)^2+\left(\tfrac{41}{25}\right)^2 &= 5\ ? & -3\left(\tfrac{38}{25}\right)+4\left(\tfrac{41}{25}\right) &= 2\ ? \\ \tfrac{1444}{625}+\tfrac{1681}{625} &= 5 & -\tfrac{114}{25}+\tfrac{164}{25} &= 2 \\ \tfrac{3125}{625} &= 5 & \tfrac{50}{25} &= 2 \\ 5 &= 5 & 2 &= 2 \end{aligned}$$

Both solutions are valid.

5. The system is $\begin{aligned} y &= \log x \\ x^2 - y^2 &= 4 \end{aligned}$ and the proposed approximate solution set is $\{(2.0232821, .30605644)\}$.

To show this, we will recreate the solution with the graphing calculator. In order to get $x^2 - y^2 = 4$ to be displayed, solve for y and enter the relation as two functions.

$$x^2 - y^2 = 4 \Rightarrow y^2 = x^2 - 4 \Rightarrow y = \pm\sqrt{x^2 - 4}$$

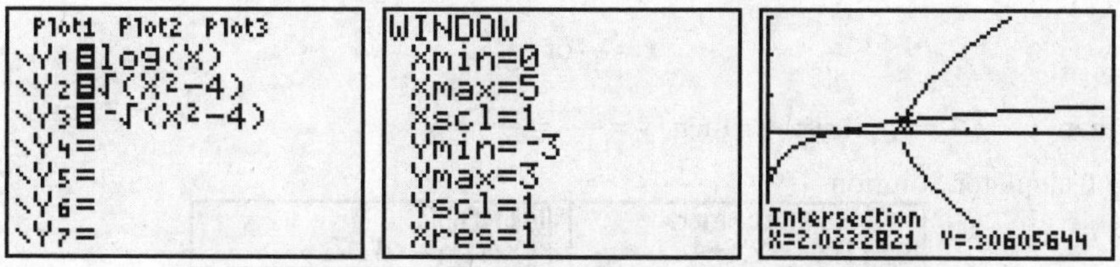

7. The system $\begin{aligned} x^2 - y &= 4 \\ x + y &= -2 \end{aligned}$ cannot have more than two solutions because a parabola and a line cannot intersect in more than two points.

In the solutions to Exercises 9 – 13, we will include both the algebraic solution and graphing calculator solution (like Example 1), for Exercises 15 – 41, we will include just the algebraic solution. Also, in the solutions to Exercises 9 – 41, we will omit the checking of solutions. Recall, though, when checking elements of the solution set, substitute the ordered pair(s) into both equations of the system.

9. $x^2 - y = 0$ (1)
$x + y = 2$ (2)

Algebraic Solution:
Solving equation (2) for *y*, we have $y = 2 - x$.
Substitute this result into equation (1).

$$2 - x = x^2 \Rightarrow x^2 + x - 2 = 0 \Rightarrow (x+2)(x-1) = 0$$
$$x = -2 \text{ or } x = 1$$

If $x = -2$, then $y = 2-(-2) = 4$. If $x = 1$, then $y = 2 - 1 = 1$.

Graphing Calculator Solution
$x^2 - y = 0 \Rightarrow y = x^2$ and $x + y = 2 \Rightarrow y = 2 - x$

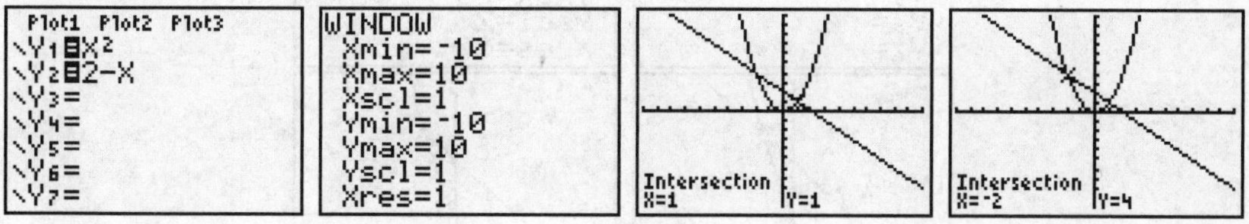

Solution set: $\{(1,1),(-2,4)\}$

11. $y = x^2 - 2x + 1$ (1)
$x - 3y = -1$ (2)

Algebraic Solution:

Solving equation (2) for y, we have $y = \frac{x+1}{3}$.

Substitute this result into equation (1).

$$\frac{x+1}{3} = x^2 - 2x + 1 \Rightarrow x + 1 = 3x^2 - 6x + 3 \Rightarrow 3x^2 - 7x + 2 = 0 \Rightarrow (3x-1)(x-2) = 0$$

$$x = \frac{1}{3} \text{ or } x = 2$$

If $x = 2$, then $y = \frac{2+1}{3} = 1$. If $x = \frac{1}{3}$, then $y = \frac{\frac{1}{3}+1}{3} = \frac{1+3}{9} = \frac{4}{9}$.

Graphing Calculator Solution

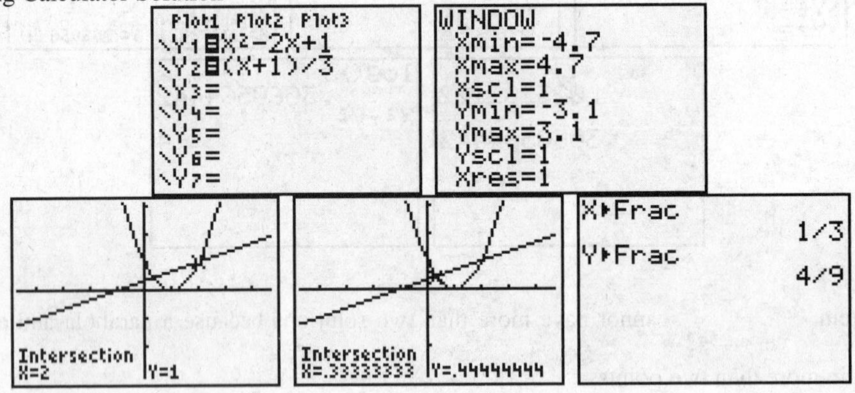

Solution set: $\left\{(2,1), \left(\frac{1}{3}, \frac{4}{9}\right)\right\}$

13. $y = x^2 + 4x$ (1)
$2x - y = -8$ (2)

Algebraic Solution:

Solving equation (2) for y, we have $y = 2x + 8$.

Substitute this result into equation (1).

$$2x + 8 = x^2 + 4x \Rightarrow x^2 + 2x - 8 = 0 \Rightarrow (x+4)(x-2) = 0$$

$$x = -4 \text{ or } x = 2$$

If $x = -4$, then $y = 2(-4) + 8 = 0$. If $x = 2$, then $y = 2(2) + 8 = 12$.

Graphing Calculator Solution

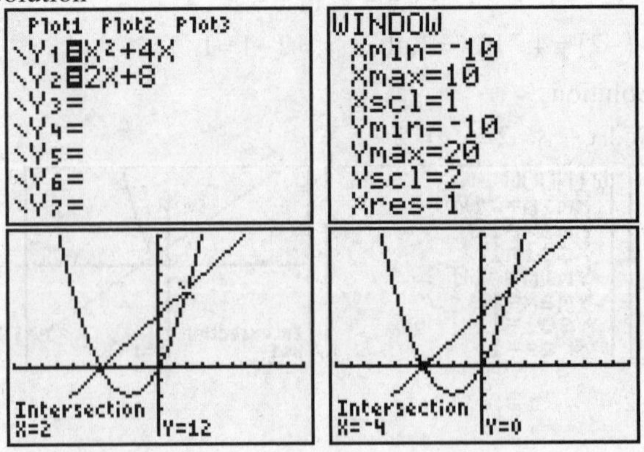

Solution set: $\{(2,12), (-4,0)\}$

15. $3x^2 + 2y^2 = 5$ (1)

$x - y = -2$ (2)

Solving equation (2) for *y*, we have $y = x + 2$.

Substitute this result into equation (1).

$$3x^2 + 2(x+2)^2 = 5 \Rightarrow 3x^2 + 2\left(x^2 + 4x + 4\right) = 5 \Rightarrow 3x^2 + 2x^2 + 8x + 8 = 5$$

$$5x^2 + 8x + 3 = 0 \Rightarrow (5x+3)(x+1) = 0$$

$$x = -\tfrac{3}{5} \text{ or } x = -1$$

If $x = -\frac{3}{5}$, then $y = -\frac{3}{5} + 2 = -\frac{3}{5} + \frac{10}{5} = \frac{7}{5}$. If $x = -1$, then $y = -1 + 2 = 1$.

Solution set: $\left\{\left(-\frac{3}{5}, \frac{7}{5}\right), (-1, 1)\right\}$

17. $x^2 + y^2 = 8$ (1)

$x^2 - y^2 = 0$ (2)

Using the elimination method, we add equations (1) and (2).

$$\begin{array}{rl} x^2 + y^2 &= 8 \\ x^2 - y^2 &= 0 \\ \hline 2x^2 \quad\quad &= 8 \Rightarrow x^2 = 4 \Rightarrow x = \pm 2 \end{array}$$

Find *y* by substituting back into equation (2).

If $x = 2$, then $2^2 - y^2 = 0 \Rightarrow 4 - y^2 = 0 \Rightarrow y^2 = 4 \Rightarrow y = \pm 2$.

If $x = -2$, then $(-2)^2 - y^2 = 0 \Rightarrow 4 - y^2 = 0 \Rightarrow y^2 = 4 \Rightarrow y = \pm 2$.

Solution set: $\{(2,2), (2,-2), (-2,2), (-2,-2)\}$

19. $5x^2 - y^2 = 0$ (1)

$3x^2 + 4y^2 = 0$ (2)

Using the elimination method, we multiply equation (1) by 4 and add to equation (2).

$$\begin{array}{rl} 20x^2 - 4y^2 &= 0 \\ 3x^2 + 4y^2 &= 0 \\ \hline 23x^2 \quad\quad &= 0 \Rightarrow x^2 = 0 \Rightarrow x = 0 \end{array}$$

Find *y* by substituting back into equation (1).

If $x = 0$, then $5(0)^2 - y^2 = 0 \Rightarrow 0 - y^2 = 0 \Rightarrow y^2 = 0 \Rightarrow y = 0$.

Solution set: $\{(0,0)\}$

21. $3x^2 + y^2 = 3$ (1)

$4x^2 + 5y^2 = 26$ (2)

Using the elimination method, we multiply equation (1) by -5 and add to equation (2).

$$\begin{array}{r} -15x^2 - 5y^2 = -15 \\ 4x^2 + 5y^2 = 26 \\ \hline -11x^2 \quad = 11 \Rightarrow x^2 = -1 \Rightarrow x = \pm i \end{array}$$

Find y by substituting back into equation (1).

If $x = i$, then $3(i)^2 + y^2 = 3 \Rightarrow 3(-1) + y^2 = 3 \Rightarrow -3 + y^2 = 3 \Rightarrow y^2 = 6 \Rightarrow y = \pm\sqrt{6}$.

If $x = -i$, then $3(-i)^2 + y^2 = 3 \Rightarrow 3(-1) + y^2 = 3 \Rightarrow -3 + y^2 = 3 \Rightarrow y^2 = 6 \Rightarrow y = \pm\sqrt{6}$.

Solution set: $\{(i, \sqrt{6}), (-i, \sqrt{6}), (i, -\sqrt{6}), (-i, -\sqrt{6})\}$

23. $2x^2 + 3y^2 = 5$ (1)

$3x^2 - 4y^2 = -1$ (2)

Using the elimination method, we multiply equation (1) by 4 and equation (2) by 3 and then add the resulting equations.

$$\begin{array}{r} 8x^2 + 12y^2 = 20 \\ 9x^2 - 12y^2 = -3 \\ \hline 17x^2 \quad = 17 \Rightarrow x^2 = 1 \Rightarrow x = \pm 1 \end{array}$$

Find y by substituting back into equation (1).

If $x = 1$, then $2(1)^2 + 3y^2 = 5 \Rightarrow 2 + 3y^2 = 5 \Rightarrow 3y^2 = 3 \Rightarrow y^2 = 1 \Rightarrow y = \pm 1$.

If $x = -1$, then $2(-1)^2 + 3y^2 = 5 \Rightarrow 2 + 3y^2 = 5 \Rightarrow 3y^2 = 3 \Rightarrow y^2 = 1 \Rightarrow y = \pm 1$.

Solution set: $\{(1, -1), (-1, 1), (1, 1), (-1, -1)\}$

25. $2x^2 + 2y^2 = 20$ (1)

$4x^2 + 4y^2 = 30$ (2)

Using the elimination method, we multiply equation (1) by -2 and add to equation (2).

$$\begin{array}{r} -4x^2 - 4y^2 = -40 \\ 4x^2 + 4y^2 = 30 \\ \hline 0 = -10 \end{array}$$

This is a false statement.
Solution set: $\varnothing$

27. $2x^2 - 3y^2 = 8$ (1)

$6x^2 + 5y^2 = 24$ (2)

Using the elimination method, we multiply equation (1) by -3 and add to equation (2).

$$\begin{array}{r} -6x^2 + 9y^2 = -24 \\ 6x^2 + 5y^2 = 24 \\ \hline 14y^2 = 0 \Rightarrow y^2 = 0 \Rightarrow y = 0 \end{array}$$

Find x by substituting back into equation (2).

If $y = 0$, then $6x^2 + 5(0)^2 = 24 \Rightarrow 6x^2 + 0 = 24 \Rightarrow x^2 = 4 \Rightarrow x = \pm 2$.

Solution set: $\{(2, 0), (-2, 0)\}$

29. $xy = -15 \quad (1)$

$4x + 3y = 3 \quad (2)$

Solving equation (1) for y, we have $y = -\frac{15}{x}$.

Substitute this result into equation (2).

$$4x + 3\left(-\frac{15}{x}\right) = 3 \Rightarrow 4x^2 - 45 = 3x \Rightarrow 4x^2 - 3x - 45 = 0 \Rightarrow (x+3)(4x-15) = 0$$

$$x = -3 \text{ or } x = \frac{15}{4}$$

If $x = -3$, then $y = -\frac{15}{-3} = 5$. If $x = \frac{15}{4}$, then $y = -\frac{15}{\frac{15}{4}} = -4$.

Solution set: $\left\{(-3, 5), \left(\frac{15}{4}, -4\right)\right\}$

31. $2xy + 1 = 0 \; (1)$

$x + 16y = 2 \; (2)$

Solving equation (2) for x, we have $x = 2 - 16y$.

Substitute this result into equation (1).

$$2(-16y + 2)y + 1 = 0 \Rightarrow -32y^2 + 4y + 1 = 0 \Rightarrow 32y^2 - 4y - 1 = 0 \Rightarrow (8y+1)(4y-1) = 0$$

$$y = -\frac{1}{8} \text{ or } y = \frac{1}{4}$$

If $y = -\frac{1}{8}$, then $x = 2 - 16\left(-\frac{1}{8}\right) = 2 + 2 = 4$. If $y = \frac{1}{4}$, then $x = 2 - 16\left(\frac{1}{4}\right) = 2 - 4 = -2$.

Solution set: $\left\{\left(4, -\frac{1}{8}\right), \left(-2, \frac{1}{4}\right)\right\}$

33. $x^2 + 4y^2 = 25 \; (1)$

$xy = 6 \quad (2)$

Solving equation (2) for x, we have $x = \frac{6}{y}$.

Substitute this result into equation (1).

$$\left(\frac{6}{y}\right)^2 + 4y^2 = 25 \Rightarrow \frac{36}{y^2} + 4y^2 = 25 \Rightarrow 36 + 4y^4 = 25y^2 \Rightarrow 4y^4 - 25y^2 + 36 = 0 \Rightarrow \left(y^2 - 4\right)\left(4y^2 - 9\right) = 0$$

$$y^2 = 4 \quad \text{or} \quad y^2 = \frac{9}{4}$$

$$y = \pm 2 \qquad y = \pm\frac{3}{2}$$

If $y = 2$, then $x = \frac{6}{2} = 3$. If $y = -2$, then $x = \frac{6}{-2} = -3$.

If $y = \frac{3}{2}$, then $x = \frac{6}{\frac{3}{2}} = 4$. If $y = -\frac{3}{2}$, then $x = \frac{6}{-\frac{3}{2}} = -4$.

Solution set: $\left\{(3, 2), (-3, -2), \left(4, \frac{3}{2}\right), \left(-4, -\frac{3}{2}\right)\right\}$

35. $x^2 - xy + y^2 = 5$ (1)

$2x^2 + xy - y^2 = 10$ (2)

Using the elimination method, we add equations (1) and (2).

$$\begin{array}{r} x^2 - xy + y^2 = 5 \\ 2x^2 + xy - y^2 = 10 \\ \hline 3x^2 \qquad\quad = 15 \Rightarrow x^2 = 5 \Rightarrow x = \pm\sqrt{5} \end{array}$$

Find y by substituting back into equation (1).

If $x = \sqrt{5}$, then $\left(\sqrt{5}\right)^2 - \sqrt{5}y + y^2 = 5 \Rightarrow 5 - \sqrt{5}y + y^2 = 5 \Rightarrow y^2 - \sqrt{5}y = 0 \Rightarrow y\left(y - \sqrt{5}\right) = 0.$ Thus, we have $y = 0$ or $y = \sqrt{5}$.

If $x = -\sqrt{5}$, then $\left(-\sqrt{5}\right)^2 - \left(-\sqrt{5}\right)y + y^2 = 5 \Rightarrow 5 + \sqrt{5}y + y^2 = 5 \Rightarrow y^2 + \sqrt{5}y = 0 \Rightarrow y\left(y + \sqrt{5}\right) = 0.$

Thus, we have $y = 0$ or $y = -\sqrt{5}$.

Solution set: $\left\{\left(\sqrt{5}, 0\right), \left(-\sqrt{5}, 0\right), \left(\sqrt{5}, \sqrt{5}\right), \left(-\sqrt{5}, -\sqrt{5}\right)\right\}$

37. $x^2 + 2xy - y^2 = 14$ (1)

$x^2 - y^2 = -16$ (2)

This system can be solved using a combination of the elimination and substitution methods.
Using the elimination method, multiply equation (2) by -1 and add to equation (1).

$$\begin{array}{r} x^2 + 2xy - y^2 = 14 \\ -x^2 + \qquad\quad y^2 = 16 \\ \hline 2xy \qquad = 30 \Rightarrow xy = 15 \,(3) \end{array}$$

Solve equation (3) for y.

$$xy = 15 \Rightarrow y = \tfrac{15}{x} \,(4)$$

Find x by substituting equation (4) into equation (2).

$$x^2 - \left(\tfrac{15}{x}\right)^2 = -16 \Rightarrow x^2 - \tfrac{225}{x^2} = -16 \Rightarrow x^4 - 225 = -16x^2 \Rightarrow x^4 + 16x^2 - 225 = 0 \Rightarrow \left(x^2 - 9\right)\left(x^2 + 25\right) = 0$$

$$x^2 = 9 \quad \text{or} \quad x^2 = -25$$

$$x = \pm 3 \qquad x = \pm 5i$$

If $x = 3$, then $y = \frac{15}{3} = 5$. If $x = -3$, then $y = \frac{15}{-3} = -5$.

If $x = 5i$, then $y = \frac{15}{5i} = \frac{3}{i} = -3i$. If $x = -5i$, then $y = \frac{15}{-5i} = -\frac{3}{i} = 3i$.

Solution set: $\{(3,5), (-3,-5), (5i,-3i), (-5i,3i)\}$

39. $x = |y|$ (1)

$x^2 + y^2 = 18$ (2)

If $x = |y|$, then $x^2 = y^2$ since $|y|^2 = y^2$. Substitute $x^2 = y^2$ into equation (2).

$$y^2 + y^2 = 18 \Rightarrow 2y^2 = 18 \Rightarrow y^2 = 9 \Rightarrow y = \pm 3$$

If $y = 3$, then $x = |y| = |3| = 3$. If $y = -3$, then $x = |y| = |-3| = 3$.

Solution set: $\{(3,-3), (3,3)\}$

41. $2x^2 - y^2 = 4 \quad (1)$

$|x| = |y| \qquad (2)$

Since $|x|^2 = x^2$ and $|y|^2 = y^2$, we substitute $y^2 = x^2$ into equation (1) and solve for x.

$$2x^2 - x^2 = 4 \Rightarrow x^2 = 4 \Rightarrow x = \pm 2$$

By substituting these values back into equation (2) we have the following.

If $x = 2$, then $|2| = |y| \Rightarrow 2 = |y| \Rightarrow y = \pm 2$. If $x = -2$, then $|-2| = |y| \Rightarrow 2 = |y| \Rightarrow y = \pm 2$.

Solution set: $\{(2,2),(-2,-2),(2,-2),(-2,2)\}$

43. $y = \log(x+5)$

$y = x^2$

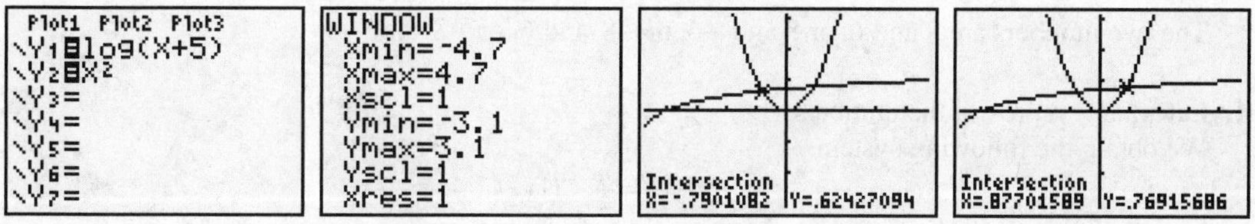

Solution set: $\{(-.79,.62),(.88,.77)\}$

45. $y = e^{x+1}$

$2x + y = 3 \Rightarrow y = 3 - 2x$

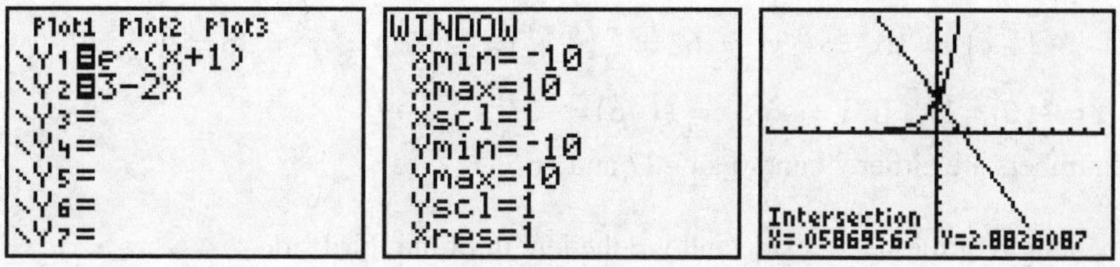

Solution set: $\{(.06,2.88)\}$

47. Let x and y represent the numbers.

We obtain the following system.

$$x + y = 17 \ (1)$$
$$xy = 42 \ (2)$$

Solving equation (1) for y we have $y = 17 - x$. (3)

Substituting this into equation (2) we have $x(17 - x) = 42$.

Solving this equation for x we have the following.

$$x(17-x) = 42 \Rightarrow 17x - x^2 = 42 \Rightarrow 0 = x^2 - 17x + 42 \Rightarrow (x-3)(x-14) = 0$$
$$x = 3 \text{ or } x = 14$$

Using equation (3), if $x = 3$ then $3 + y = 17 \Rightarrow y = 14$. If $x = 14$, then $14 + y = 17 \Rightarrow y = 3$.

The two numbers are 14 and 3.

49. Let x and y represent the numbers.
We obtain the following system.

$$x^2 + y^2 = 100 \ (1)$$
$$x^2 - y^2 = 28 \ (2)$$

Adding equations (1) and (2) in order to eliminate y^2, we have $2x^2 = 128$.
Solving this equation for x we have the following.

$$2x^2 = 128 \Rightarrow x^2 = 64 \Rightarrow x = \pm 8$$

Using equation (1), if $x = 8$ then $8^2 + y^2 = 100 \Rightarrow 64 + y^2 = 100 \Rightarrow y^2 = 36 \Rightarrow y = \pm 6$.

If $x = -8$ then $(-8)^2 + y^2 = 100 \Rightarrow 64 + y^2 = 100 \Rightarrow y^2 = 36 \Rightarrow y = \pm 6$.

The two numbers are 8 and 6, or 8 and −6, or −8 and 6, or −8 and −6.

51. Let x and y represent the numbers.
We obtain the following system.

$$\frac{x}{y} = \frac{9}{2} \quad (1)$$
$$xy = 162 \ (2)$$

Solve equation (1) for x.

$$y\left(\frac{x}{y}\right) = y\left(\frac{9}{2}\right) \Rightarrow x = \frac{9}{2}y$$

Substitute $\frac{9}{2}y$ for x in equation (2) and solve for y.

$$\left(\frac{9}{2}y\right)y = 162 \Rightarrow \frac{9}{2}y^2 = 162 \Rightarrow \frac{2}{9}\left(\frac{9}{2}y^2\right) = \frac{2}{9}(162) \Rightarrow y^2 = 36 \Rightarrow y = \pm 6$$

If $y = 6$, $x = \frac{9}{2}(6) = 27$. If $y = -6$, $x = \frac{9}{2}(-6) = -27$.
The two numbers are either 27 and 6, or −27 and −6.

53. Let x = the length of the second side and y = the length of the third side.
We obtain the following system.

$$x^2 + y^2 = 13^2 = 169 \quad (1)$$
$$x = y + 7 \quad (2)$$

Substitute $y + 7$ for x in equation (1) and solve for y.

$$(y+7)^2 + y^2 = 169 \Rightarrow y^2 + 14y + 49 + y^2 = 169 \Rightarrow 2y^2 + 14y - 120 = 0$$
$$y^2 + 7y - 60 = 0 \Rightarrow (y+12)(y-5) = 0$$
$$y = -12 \text{ or } y = 5$$

We disregard the negative solution since a length cannot be negative. If $y = 5$, then $x = 5 + 7 = 12$.
The lengths of the two shorter sides are 5 m and 12 m.

55. If the system formed by the following equations has a solution, the line and the circle intersect.

$$3x - 2y = 9 \ (1)$$
$$x^2 + y^2 = 25 \ (2)$$

Solving equation (1) for x we have $3x = 9 + 2y \Rightarrow x = \frac{9+2y}{3}$. (3)

Substituting into equation (3) into equation (2) we have $\left(\frac{9+2y}{3}\right)^2 + y^2 = 25$.

Continued on next page

55. (continued)
Solving this equation for y we have the following.

$$\left(\frac{9+2y}{3}\right)^2+y^2=25\Rightarrow\frac{(9+2y)^2}{9}+y^2=25\Rightarrow(9+2y)^2+9y^2=225\Rightarrow81+36y+4y^2+9y^2=225$$

$$13y^2+36y+81=225\Rightarrow13y^2+36y-144=0$$

Using the quadratic formula where $a=13, b=36,$ and $c=-144,$ we have the following.

$$y=\frac{-36\pm\sqrt{(36)^2-4(13)(-144)}}{2(13)}=\frac{-36\pm\sqrt{1296+7488}}{26}=\frac{-36\pm\sqrt{8784}}{26}$$

$$y=\frac{-36-\sqrt{8784}}{26}\approx-4.989 \text{ and } y=\frac{-36+\sqrt{8784}}{26}\approx2.220$$

If $y=\frac{-36+\sqrt{8784}}{26}$, then $x=\frac{9+2\left(\frac{-36+\sqrt{8784}}{26}\right)}{3}=\frac{234+2\left(-36+\sqrt{8784}\right)}{78}=\frac{162+2\sqrt{8784}}{78}\approx4.480.$

If $y=\frac{-36-\sqrt{8784}}{26}$, then $x=\frac{9+2\left(\frac{-36-\sqrt{8784}}{26}\right)}{3}=\frac{234+2\left(-36-\sqrt{8784}\right)}{78}=\frac{162-2\sqrt{8784}}{78}\approx-.326$

Thus, the circle and line do intersect, in fact twice, at approximately (4.48, 2.22) and (–.326, – 4.99).

57. We must first find the solution to the following system.

$$y=x^2 \quad (1)$$
$$x^2+y^2=90 \quad (2)$$

Substitute y for x^2 in equation (2) and solve for y.

$$y+y^2=90\Rightarrow y^2+y-90=0\Rightarrow(y+10)(y-9)=0$$
$$y=-10 \text{ or } y=9$$

If $y=-10,$ then $-10=x^2\Rightarrow x=\pm i\sqrt{10}.$ Since we are seeking points of intersection, we reject these nonreal solutions. If $y=9$, then $9=x^2\Rightarrow x=\pm3.$

The two points of intersection of the two graphs are (3, 9) and (–3, 9). The slope of the line through these two points is $m=\frac{9-9}{-3-3}=0,$ so this is the horizontal line with equation $y=9.$

59. Let x represent the length and width of the square base, and let y represent the height.
Using the formula for the volume of a box, $V=LWH,$ we have the equation $x^2y=360.$ (1)
Since the height is 4 ft greater than both the length and width we have the equation $y=x+4.$ (2)
Since the surface area consists of a square base and four rectangular sides we have the equation $x^2+4xy=276.$ (3)
Substituting equation (2) into equation (3) we have $x^2+4x(x+4)=276.$
Solving this equation for x we have the following.

$$x^2+4x(x+4)=276\Rightarrow x^2+4x^2+16x=276\Rightarrow5x^2+16x=276$$
$$5x^2+16x-276=0\Rightarrow(5x+46)(x-6)=0$$
$$x=-\tfrac{46}{5} \text{ or } x=6$$

We disregard the negative solution since a length (or width) cannot be negative. If x = 6, then $y=6+4=10.$
Thus, the length, which is equal to the width, is 6 ft and the height is 10 ft.
Note: Since $6^2(10)=360,$ the conditions for the volume are satisfied.

61. The system is $\begin{aligned} x^2y &= 75 \\ x^2+4xy &= 85 \end{aligned}$

The first possible solution is $x = 5$ and $y = 3$.

$$\begin{aligned} x^2y &= 75 \\ 5^2\cdot 3 &= 75 \ ? \\ 25\cdot 3 &= 75 \\ 75 &= 75 \text{ True} \end{aligned} \qquad \begin{aligned} x^2+4xy &= 85 \\ 5^2+4\cdot 5\cdot 3 &= 85 \ ? \\ 25+60 &= 85 \\ 85 &= 85 \text{ True} \end{aligned}$$

Thus, the solution length = width = 5 in. and height = 3 in. is valid.

Ideally we should check the exact values in the system in order to determine if the approximate dimensions are valid. From Example 6 we have $x = \frac{-5+\sqrt{5^2-4(1)(-60)}}{2(1)} = \frac{-5+\sqrt{25+240}}{2} = \frac{-5+\sqrt{265}}{2}$. The corresponding y-value would be $y = \frac{75}{x^2} = \frac{75}{\left(\frac{-5+\sqrt{265}}{2}\right)^2} = \frac{75}{\frac{(-5+\sqrt{265})^2}{4}} = \frac{300}{\left(-5+\sqrt{265}\right)^2}$.

The second possible solution is $x = \frac{-5+\sqrt{265}}{2}$ and $y = \frac{300}{\left(-5+\sqrt{265}\right)^2}$.

$$\begin{aligned} x^2y &= 75 \\ \left(\frac{-5+\sqrt{265}}{2}\right)^2\cdot\frac{300}{\left(-5+\sqrt{265}\right)^2} &= 75 \ ? \\ \frac{\left(-5+\sqrt{265}\right)^2}{4}\cdot\frac{300}{\left(-5+\sqrt{265}\right)^2} &= 75 \\ 75 &= 75 \text{ True} \end{aligned}$$

$$\begin{aligned} x^2+4xy &= 85 \\ \frac{\left(-5+\sqrt{265}\right)^2}{4}+\frac{600}{-5+\sqrt{265}} &= 85 \ ? \\ \frac{\left(-5+\sqrt{265}\right)^3+2400}{4\left(-5+\sqrt{265}\right)} &= 85 \\ \frac{\left(-5+\sqrt{265}\right)^2\left(-5+\sqrt{265}\right)+2400}{4\left(-5+\sqrt{265}\right)} &= 85 \\ \frac{\left(25-10\sqrt{265}+265\right)\left(-5+\sqrt{265}\right)+2400}{4\left(-5+\sqrt{265}\right)} &= 85 \\ \frac{\left(290-10\sqrt{265}\right)\left(-5+\sqrt{265}\right)+2400}{4\left(-5+\sqrt{265}\right)} &= 85 \\ \frac{\left(-1450+340\sqrt{265}-2650\right)+2400}{4\left(-5+\sqrt{265}\right)} &= 85 \\ \frac{-4100+340\sqrt{265}+2400}{4\left(-5+\sqrt{265}\right)} &= 85 \\ \frac{-1700+340\sqrt{265}}{4\left(-5+\sqrt{265}\right)} &= 85 \\ \frac{340\left(-5+\sqrt{265}\right)}{4\left(-5+\sqrt{265}\right)} &= 85 \\ 85 &= 85 \text{ True} \end{aligned}$$

63. supply: $p=\sqrt{.1q+9}-2$

demand: $p=\sqrt{25-.1q}$

(a) Equilibrium occurs when supply = demand, so solve the system formed by the supply and demand equations. This system can be solved by substitution. Substitute $\sqrt{.1q+9}-2$ for p in the demand equation and solve the resulting equation for q.

$$\sqrt{.1q+9}-2=\sqrt{25-.1q}\Rightarrow\left(\sqrt{.1q+9}-2\right)^2=\left(\sqrt{25-.1q}\right)^2$$

$$.1q+9-4\sqrt{.1q+9}+4=25-.1q\Rightarrow .2q-12=4\sqrt{.1q+9}\Rightarrow(.2q-12)^2=\left(4\sqrt{.1q+9}\right)^2$$

$$.04q^2-4.8q+144=16(.1q+9)\Rightarrow .04q^2-4.8q+144=1.6q+144$$

$$.04q^2-6.4q=0\Rightarrow .04q(q-160)=0$$

$$q=0 \text{ or } q=160$$

Disregard an equilibrium demand of 0. The equilibrium demand is 160 units.

(b) Substitute 160 for q in either equation and solve for p.

$$p=\sqrt{.1(160)+9}-2=\sqrt{16+9}-2=\sqrt{25}-2=5-2=3$$

The equilibrium price is \$3.

65. (a) The emission of carbon is increasing with time. The carbon emissions from the former USSR and Eastern Europe have surpassed the emissions of Western Europe.

(b) They were equal in 1963 when the levels were approximately 400 million metric tons.

(c)

$$W=E$$

$$375(1.008)^{(t-1950)}=260(1.038)^{(t-1950)}$$

$$\ln\left[375(1.008)^{(t-1950)}\right]=\ln\left[260(1.038)^{(t-1950)}\right]$$

$$\ln 375+(t-1950)\ln 1.008=\ln 260+(t-1950)\ln 1.038$$

$$\ln 375-\ln 260=(t-1950)\ln 1.038-(t-1950)\ln 1.008$$

$$\ln 375-\ln 260=(\ln 1.038-\ln 1.008)\cdot(t-1950)$$

$$\frac{\ln 375-\ln 260}{\ln 1.038-\ln 1.008}=t-1950\Rightarrow t=1950+\frac{\ln 375-\ln 260}{\ln 1.038-\ln 1.008}\approx 1962.49$$

If t is approximately 1962.49, $W=375(1.008)^{(1962.49-1950)}\approx 414.24$.

In 1962, the emission levels were equal and were approximately 414 million metric tons.

66. Shift the graph of $y=|x|$ one unit to the right to obtain the graph of $y=|x-1|$.

67. Shift the graph of $y=x^2$ four units down to obtain the graph of $y=x^2-4$.

68. If $x-1\ge 0\ (x\ge 1)$, $|x-1|=x-1$. If $x-1<0\ (x<1)$, $|x-1|=-(x-1)=1-x$.

Therefore, $y=\begin{cases}x-1 & \text{if } x\ge 1\\ 1-x & \text{if } x<1.\end{cases}$

69. $x^2-4=x-1$ if $x\ge 1$ and $x^2-4=1-x$ if $x<1$

70. $x^2-4=x-1$ if $x\geq 1$

$x^2-x-3=0$

Solve by the quadratic formula where $a=1, b=-1$, and $c=-3$.

$$x=\frac{-(-1)\pm\sqrt{(-1)^2-4(1)(-3)}}{2(1)}=\frac{1\pm\sqrt{1+12}}{2}=\frac{1\pm\sqrt{13}}{2}$$

If $\frac{1+\sqrt{13}}{2}\approx 2.3\geq 1$, but $\frac{1-\sqrt{13}}{2}\approx -1.3<1$. Therefore, $x=\frac{1+\sqrt{13}}{2}$.

$x^2-4=1-x$ if $x<1$

$x^2+x-5=0$

Solve by the quadratic formula where $a=1, b=1$, and $c=-5$.

$$x=\frac{-1\pm\sqrt{1^2-4(1)(-5)}}{2(1)}=\frac{-1\pm\sqrt{1+20}}{2}=\frac{-1\pm\sqrt{21}}{2}$$

If $\frac{-1-\sqrt{21}}{2}\approx -2.8<1$, but $\frac{-1+\sqrt{21}}{2}\approx 1.8>1$, Therefore, $x=\frac{-1-\sqrt{21}}{2}$.

71. If $y=|x-1|$ and $x=\frac{1+\sqrt{13}}{2}$, then $y=\left|\frac{1+\sqrt{13}}{2}-1\right|=\left|\frac{1+\sqrt{13}}{2}-\frac{2}{2}\right|=\left|\frac{-1+\sqrt{13}}{2}\right|=\frac{-1+\sqrt{13}}{2}$.

If $y=1-x$ and $x=\frac{-1-\sqrt{21}}{2}$, then $y=1-\left(\frac{-1-\sqrt{21}}{2}\right)=\frac{2}{2}+\frac{1+\sqrt{21}}{2}=\frac{3+\sqrt{21}}{2}$.

Solution set: $\left\{\left(\frac{1+\sqrt{13}}{2},\frac{-1+\sqrt{13}}{2}\right),\left(\frac{-1-\sqrt{21}}{2},\frac{3+\sqrt{21}}{2}\right)\right\}$

Summary Exercises on Systems of Equations

As noted on page 841 of the text, different methods of solving equations have been introduced. In the solutions to these exercises, we will present the solution using one method (or combination of methods). In general, the nonlinear systems cannot use the matrix, Gauss-Jordan, Cramer's rule methods. Only the methods of substitution or elimination should be considered for such systems.

1. $2x+5y=4$

$3x-2y=-13$

Since $D=\begin{vmatrix}2 & 5\\ 3 & -2\end{vmatrix}=2(-2)-3(5)=-4-15=-19$, $D_x=\begin{vmatrix}4 & 5\\ -13 & -2\end{vmatrix}=4(-2)-(-13)(5)=-8-(-65)=57$,

and $D_y=\begin{vmatrix}2 & 4\\ 3 & -13\end{vmatrix}=2(-13)-3(4)=-26-12=-38$, we have $x=\frac{D_x}{D}=\frac{57}{-19}=-3$ and $y=\frac{D_y}{D}=\frac{-38}{-19}=2$.

Solution set: $\{(-3,2)\}$

3. $2x^2+\ y^2=5$ (1)

$3x^2+2y^2=10$ (2)

Using the elimination method, we add -2 times equation (1) to equation (2).

$$\begin{aligned}-4x^2-2y^2&=-10\\ 3x^2+2y^2&=\ 10\\ \hline -x^2\qquad\quad &=\ 0\Rightarrow x^2=0\Rightarrow x=0\end{aligned}$$

If $x=0$, then $2(0)^2+y^2=5\Rightarrow 0+y^2=5\Rightarrow y^2=5\Rightarrow y=\pm\sqrt{5}$.

Solution set: $\{(0,\sqrt{5}),(0,-\sqrt{5})\}$

5. $6x - y = 5 \; (1)$

$xy = 4 \quad (2)$

Solving equation (2) for *y*, we have $y = \frac{4}{x}$.

Substitute this result into equation (1).

$$6x - \tfrac{4}{x} = 5 \Rightarrow 6x^2 - 4 = 5x \Rightarrow 6x^2 - 5x - 4 = 0 \Rightarrow (2x+1)(3x-4) = 0$$

$$x = -\tfrac{1}{2} \text{ or } x = \tfrac{4}{3}$$

If $x = \frac{4}{3}$, then $y = \frac{4}{\frac{4}{3}} = 3$. If $x = -\frac{1}{2}$, then $y = \frac{4}{-\frac{1}{2}} = -8$.

Solution set: $\left\{\left(\frac{4}{3}, 3\right), \left(-\frac{1}{2}, -8\right)\right\}$

7. $x + 2y + z = 5 \; (1)$

$y + 3z = 9 \quad (2)$

This system has infinitely many solutions. We will express the solution set with *z* as the arbitrary variable. Solving equation (2) for *y*, we have $y = 9 - 3z$. Substituting *y* (in terms of *z*) into equation (1) and solving for *x* we have the following.

$$x + 2(9 - 3z) + z = 5 \Rightarrow x + 18 - 6z + z = 5 \Rightarrow x + 18 - 5z = 5 \Rightarrow x = -13 + 5z$$

Solution set: $\{(-13 + 5z, 9 - 3z, z)\}$

9. $\begin{aligned} 3x + 6y - 9z &= 1 \\ 2x + 4y - 6z &= 1 \\ 3x + 4y + 5z &= 0 \end{aligned}$; This system has the augmented matrix $\left[\begin{array}{ccc|c} 3 & 6 & -9 & 1 \\ 2 & 4 & -6 & 1 \\ 3 & 4 & 5 & 0 \end{array}\right]$.

$$\left[\begin{array}{ccc|c} 2 & 4 & -6 & 1 \\ 3 & 6 & -9 & 1 \\ 3 & 4 & 5 & 0 \end{array}\right] \begin{matrix} \text{R1} \leftrightarrow \text{R2} \\ \\ \\ \end{matrix} \Rightarrow \left[\begin{array}{ccc|c} 1 & 2 & -3 & \frac{1}{2} \\ 3 & 6 & -9 & 1 \\ 3 & 4 & 5 & 0 \end{array}\right] \begin{matrix} \frac{1}{2}\text{R1} \\ \\ \\ \end{matrix} \Rightarrow \left[\begin{array}{ccc|c} 1 & 2 & -3 & \frac{1}{2} \\ 0 & 0 & 0 & -\frac{1}{2} \\ 0 & -2 & 14 & -\frac{3}{2} \end{array}\right] \begin{matrix} \\ -3\text{R1}+\text{R2} \\ -3\text{R1}+\text{R3} \end{matrix}$$

The second row of the augmented matrix corresponds to the statement $0 = -\frac{1}{2}$. This is a false statement. Thus the solution set is $\varnothing$.

11. $x^2 + y^2 = 4 \; (1)$

$y = x + 6 \quad (2)$

Substitute equation (1) into equation (2).

$$x^2 + (x+6)^2 = 4 \Rightarrow x^2 + x^2 + 12x + 36 = 4 \Rightarrow 2x^2 + 12x + 36 = 4$$

$$2x^2 + 12x + 32 = 0 \Rightarrow x^2 + 6x + 16 = 0$$

Using the quadratic formula where $a = 1, b = 6,$ and $c = 16,$ we have the following.

$$x = \frac{-6 \pm \sqrt{6^2 - 4(1)(16)}}{2(1)} = \frac{-6 \pm \sqrt{36 - 64}}{2} = \frac{-6 \pm \sqrt{-28}}{2} = \frac{-6 \pm 2i\sqrt{7}}{2} = -3 \pm i\sqrt{7}$$

If $x = -3 + i\sqrt{7}$, then $y = -3 + i\sqrt{7} + 6 = 3 + i\sqrt{7}$. If $x = -3 - i\sqrt{7}$, then $y = -3 - i\sqrt{7} + 6 = 3 - i\sqrt{7}$.

Solution set: $\left\{\left(-3 + i\sqrt{7}, 3 + i\sqrt{7}\right), \left(-3 - i\sqrt{7}, 3 - i\sqrt{7}\right)\right\}$

13. $y+1=x^2+2x \quad (1)$

$y+2x=4 \quad (2)$

Solving equation (2) for *y*, we have $y=4-2x$.

Substitute this result into equation (1).

$$4-2x+1=x^2+2x \Rightarrow 5-2x=x^2+2x \Rightarrow 0=x^2+4x-5 \Rightarrow (x+5)(x-1)=0$$

$$x=-5 \text{ or } x=1$$

If $x=-5$, then $y=4-2(-5)=4+10=14$. If $x=1$, then $y=4-2(1)=4-2=2$.

Solution set: $\{(1,2),(-5,14)\}$

15. $\begin{aligned} 2x+3y+4z&=3 \\ -4x+2y-6z&=2 \\ 4x+3z&=0 \end{aligned}$; This system has the augmented matrix $\left[\begin{array}{ccc|c} 2 & 3 & 4 & 3 \\ -4 & 2 & -6 & 2 \\ 4 & 0 & 3 & 0 \end{array}\right]$.

$$\left[\begin{array}{ccc|c} 1 & \frac{3}{2} & 2 & \frac{3}{2} \\ -4 & 2 & -6 & 2 \\ 4 & 0 & 3 & 0 \end{array}\right]\begin{matrix}\frac{1}{2}\text{R1} \\ \\ \\ \end{matrix} \Rightarrow \left[\begin{array}{ccc|c} 1 & \frac{3}{2} & 2 & \frac{3}{2} \\ 0 & 8 & 2 & 8 \\ 0 & -6 & -5 & -6 \end{array}\right]\begin{matrix} \\ 4\text{R1+R2} \\ -4\text{R1+R3} \end{matrix} \Rightarrow \left[\begin{array}{ccc|c} 1 & \frac{3}{2} & 2 & \frac{3}{2} \\ 0 & 1 & \frac{1}{4} & 1 \\ 0 & -6 & -5 & -6 \end{array}\right]\begin{matrix} \\ \frac{1}{8}\text{R2} \\ \\ \end{matrix}$$

$$\left[\begin{array}{ccc|c} 1 & 0 & \frac{13}{8} & 0 \\ 0 & 1 & \frac{1}{4} & 1 \\ 0 & 0 & -\frac{7}{2} & 0 \end{array}\right]\begin{matrix} -\frac{3}{2}\text{R2+R1} \\ \\ 6\text{R2+R3} \end{matrix} \Rightarrow \left[\begin{array}{ccc|c} 1 & 0 & \frac{13}{8} & 0 \\ 0 & 1 & \frac{1}{4} & 1 \\ 0 & 0 & 1 & 0 \end{array}\right]\begin{matrix} \\ \\ -\frac{2}{7}\text{R3} \end{matrix} \Rightarrow \left[\begin{array}{ccc|c} 1 & 0 & 0 & 0 \\ 0 & 1 & 0 & 1 \\ 0 & 0 & 1 & 0 \end{array}\right]\begin{matrix} -\frac{13}{8}\text{R3+R1} \\ -\frac{1}{4}\text{R3+R2} \\ \\ \end{matrix}$$

Solution set: $\{(0,1,0)\}$

17. $-5x+2y+z=5 \ (1)$

$-3x-2y-z=3 \ (2)$

$-x+6y \quad =1 \ (3)$

Add equations (1) and (2) in order to eliminate *z* to obtain $-8x=8$ or $x=-1$.

Substitute $x=-1$ into equation (3) to solve for *y*.

$$-(-1)+6y=1 \Rightarrow 1+6y=1 \Rightarrow 6y=0 \Rightarrow y=0$$

Substitute $x=-1$ and $y=0$ into equation (1) to solve for *z*.

$$-5(-1)+2(0)+z=5 \Rightarrow 5+0+z=5 \Rightarrow 5+z=5 \Rightarrow z=0$$

Solution set: $\{(-1,0,0)\}$

19. $2x^2+\ y^2=9 \quad (1)$

$3x\ -2y\ =-6 \ (2)$

Solving equation (2) for *x*, we have $3x=2y-6 \Rightarrow x=\frac{2y-6}{3}$.

Substitute this result into equation (1).

$$2\left(\frac{2y-6}{3}\right)^2+y^2=9 \Rightarrow 2\cdot\frac{(2y-6)^2}{9}+y^2=9 \Rightarrow 2\cdot(2y-6)^2+9y^2=81 \Rightarrow 2\left(4y^2-24y+36\right)+9y^2=81$$

$$8y^2-48y+72+9y^2=81 \Rightarrow 17y^2-48y+72=81$$

$$17y^2-48y-9=0 \Rightarrow (y-3)(17y+3)=0$$

$$y=3 \text{ or } y=-\frac{3}{17}$$

If $y=3$, then $x=\frac{2(3)-6}{3}=\frac{6-6}{3}=\frac{0}{3}=0$. If $y=-\frac{3}{17}$, then $x=\frac{2\left(-\frac{3}{17}\right)-6}{3}=\frac{2(-3)-102}{51}=\frac{-6-102}{51}=\frac{-108}{51}=-\frac{36}{17}$.

Solution set: $\left\{(0,3),\left(-\frac{36}{17},-\frac{3}{17}\right)\right\}$

21.

$$\begin{aligned} x+y-\ z&=\ 0 \ (1)\\ 2y-\ z&=\ 1 \ (2)\\ 2x+3y-4z&=-4 \ (3)\end{aligned}$$

Add –2 times equation (1) to equation (3) in order to eliminate *x*.

$$\begin{aligned} -2x-2y+2z&=\ 0\\ 2x+3y-4z&=-4\\ \hline y-2z&=-4 \ (4)\end{aligned}$$

Add –2 times equation (4) to equation (2) in order to eliminate *y* and solve for *z*.

$$\begin{aligned} 2y-\ z&=1\\ -2y+4z&=8\\ \hline 3z&=9 \Rightarrow z=3\end{aligned}$$

Substitute 3 for *z* in equation (4) to obtain $y-2(3)=-4 \Rightarrow y-6=-4 \Rightarrow y=2.$

Substitute 3 for *z* and 2 for *y* in equation (1) to obtain $x+2-3=0 \Rightarrow x-1=0 \Rightarrow x=1.$

Solution set: $\{(1,2,3)\}$

23.

$$\begin{aligned} 4x-\ z&=-6 \ (1)\\ \tfrac{3}{5}y+\tfrac{1}{2}z&=\ 0 \ (2)\\ \tfrac{1}{3}x+\tfrac{2}{3}z&=-5 \ (3)\end{aligned}$$

Before applying one of the methods, it would be helpful to clear the fractions in equations (2) and (3) by multiplying equation (2) by 10 and equation (3) by 3 to obtain the following.

$$\begin{aligned} 6y+5z&=\ 0 \ \ (4)\\ x+2z&=-15 \ (5)\end{aligned}$$

The system formed by equations (1), (4), and (5) can be represented by the following augmented matrix.

$$\left[\begin{array}{ccc|c} 4 & 0 & -1 & -6\\ 0 & 6 & 5 & 0\\ 1 & 0 & 2 & -15\end{array}\right]$$

$$\left[\begin{array}{ccc|c} 1 & 0 & 2 & -15\\ 0 & 6 & 5 & 0\\ 4 & 0 & -1 & -6\end{array}\right]\begin{array}{l}\text{R1}\leftrightarrow\text{R3}\\ \\ \\ \end{array} \Rightarrow \left[\begin{array}{ccc|c} 1 & 0 & 2 & -15\\ 0 & 6 & 5 & 0\\ 0 & 0 & -9 & 54\end{array}\right]\begin{array}{l} \\ \\ -4\text{R1}+\text{R3}\end{array} \Rightarrow \left[\begin{array}{ccc|c} 1 & 0 & 2 & -15\\ 0 & 1 & \frac{5}{6} & 0\\ 0 & 0 & -9 & 54\end{array}\right]\begin{array}{l} \\ \frac{1}{6}\text{R2}\\ \\ \end{array}$$

$$\left[\begin{array}{ccc|c} 1 & 0 & 2 & -15\\ 0 & 1 & \frac{5}{6} & 0\\ 0 & 0 & 1 & -6\end{array}\right]\begin{array}{l} \\ \\ -\frac{1}{9}\text{R3}\end{array} \Rightarrow \left[\begin{array}{ccc|c} 1 & 0 & 0 & -3\\ 0 & 1 & 0 & 5\\ 0 & 0 & 1 & -6\end{array}\right]\begin{array}{l} -2\text{R3}+\text{R1}\\ -\frac{5}{6}\text{R3}+\text{R2}\\ \\ \end{array}$$

Solution set: $\{(-3,5,-6)\}$

25. $x^2+3y^2=28\,(1)$

$y-x=-2\,(2)$

Solving equation (2) for *y*, we have $y=x-2$.

Substitute this result into equation (1) and solve for *y*.

$$x^2+3(x-2)^2=28\Rightarrow x^2+3\left(x^2-4x+4\right)=28\Rightarrow x^2+3x^2-12x+12=28\Rightarrow 4x^2-12x+12=28$$

$$4x^2-12x-16=0\Rightarrow x^2-3x-4=0\Rightarrow (x+1)(x-4)=0$$

$$x=-1 \text{ or } x=4$$

If $x=-1$, then $y=-1-2=-3$. If $x=4$, then $y=4-2=2$.

Solution set: $\{(4,2),(-1,-3)\}$

27. $2x^2+3y^2=20\ (1)$

$x^2+4y^2=5\ \ (2)$

Using the elimination method, we add -2 times equation (2) to equation (1).

$$\begin{aligned}2x^2+3y^2&=20\\ -2x^2-8y^2&=-10\\ \hline -5y^2=10\Rightarrow y^2&=-2\Rightarrow y=\pm i\sqrt{2}\end{aligned}$$

Find *x* by substituting back into equation (2).

If $y=i\sqrt{2}$, then $x^2+4\left(i\sqrt{2}\right)^2=5\Rightarrow x^2+4(-1)(2)=5\Rightarrow x^2-8=5\Rightarrow x^2=13\Rightarrow x=\pm\sqrt{13}$.

If $y=-i\sqrt{2}$, then $x^2+4\left(-i\sqrt{2}\right)^2=5\Rightarrow x^2+4(-1)(2)=5\Rightarrow x^2-8=5\Rightarrow x^2=13\Rightarrow x=\pm\sqrt{13}$.

Solution set: $\left\{\left(\sqrt{13},i\sqrt{2}\right),\left(-\sqrt{13},i\sqrt{2}\right),\left(\sqrt{13},-i\sqrt{2}\right),\left(-\sqrt{13},-i\sqrt{2}\right)\right\}$

29.
$$\begin{aligned}x+2z&=9\\ y+\ z&=1\\ 3x-2y&=9\end{aligned}$$

Adding -3 times row 1 to row 3, we have $D=\begin{vmatrix}1&0&2\\0&1&1\\3&-2&0\end{vmatrix}=\begin{vmatrix}1&0&2\\0&1&1\\0&-2&-6\end{vmatrix}$.

Expanding by column one, we have $D=1\cdot\begin{vmatrix}1&1\\-2&-6\end{vmatrix}=-6+2=-4$.

Adding 2 times row 2 to row 3, we have $D_x=\begin{vmatrix}9&0&2\\1&1&1\\9&-2&0\end{vmatrix}=\begin{vmatrix}9&0&2\\1&1&1\\11&0&2\end{vmatrix}$.

Expanding by column two, we have $D_x=1\cdot\begin{vmatrix}9&2\\11&2\end{vmatrix}=18-22=-4$.

Continued on next page

29. (continued)

Adding -3 times row 1 to row 3 we have $D_y = \begin{vmatrix} 1 & 9 & 2 \\ 0 & 1 & 1 \\ 3 & 9 & 0 \end{vmatrix} = \begin{vmatrix} 1 & 9 & 2 \\ 0 & 1 & 1 \\ 0 & -18 & -6 \end{vmatrix}$.

Expanding by column one, we have $D_y = 1 \cdot \begin{vmatrix} 1 & 1 \\ -18 & -6 \end{vmatrix} = -6 + 18 = 12.$

Adding -3 times row 1 to row 3, we have $D_z = \begin{vmatrix} 1 & 0 & 9 \\ 0 & 1 & 1 \\ 3 & -2 & 9 \end{vmatrix} = \begin{vmatrix} 1 & 0 & 9 \\ 0 & 1 & 1 \\ 0 & -2 & -18 \end{vmatrix}$.

Expanding by column one, we have $D_z = 1 \cdot \begin{vmatrix} 1 & 1 \\ -2 & -18 \end{vmatrix} = -18 + 2 = -16.$

Thus, we have $x = \frac{D_x}{D} = \frac{-4}{-4} = 1$, $y = \frac{D_y}{D} = \frac{12}{-4} = -3$, and $z = \frac{D_z}{D} = \frac{-16}{-4} = 4$.

Solution set: $\{(1, -3, 4)\}$

31. $\begin{aligned} -x + y \quad &= -1 \\ x + \quad z &= 4 \\ 6x - 3y + 2z &= 10 \end{aligned}$; This system has the augmented matrix $\left[\begin{array}{ccc|c} -1 & 1 & 0 & -1 \\ 1 & 0 & 1 & 4 \\ 6 & -3 & 2 & 10 \end{array}\right]$.

$$\left[\begin{array}{ccc|c} 1 & -1 & 0 & 1 \\ 1 & 0 & 1 & 4 \\ 6 & -3 & 2 & 10 \end{array}\right] \begin{matrix} -1\text{R1} \\ \\ \\ \end{matrix} \Rightarrow \left[\begin{array}{ccc|c} 1 & -1 & 0 & 1 \\ 0 & 1 & 1 & 3 \\ 0 & 3 & 2 & 4 \end{array}\right] \begin{matrix} \\ -1\text{R1}+\text{R2} \\ -6\text{R1}+\text{R3} \end{matrix} \Rightarrow \left[\begin{array}{ccc|c} 1 & 0 & 1 & 4 \\ 0 & 1 & 1 & 3 \\ 0 & 0 & -1 & -5 \end{array}\right] \begin{matrix} \text{R2}+\text{R1} \\ \\ -3\text{R2}+\text{R3} \end{matrix}$$

$$\left[\begin{array}{ccc|c} 1 & 0 & 1 & 4 \\ 0 & 1 & 1 & 3 \\ 0 & 0 & 1 & 5 \end{array}\right] \begin{matrix} \\ \\ -1\text{R3} \end{matrix} \Rightarrow \left[\begin{array}{ccc|c} 1 & 0 & 0 & -1 \\ 0 & 1 & 0 & -2 \\ 0 & 0 & 1 & 5 \end{array}\right] \begin{matrix} -1\text{R3}+\text{R1} \\ -1\text{R3}+\text{R2} \\ \\ \end{matrix}$$

Solution set: $\{(-1, -2, 5)\}$

33. $xy = -3 \quad (1)$
$x + y = -2 \quad (2)$
Solving equation (1) for y, we have $y = -\frac{3}{x}$.
Substitute this result into equation (2).

$$x + \left(-\tfrac{3}{x}\right) = -2 \Rightarrow x^2 - 3 = -2x \Rightarrow x^2 + 2x - 3 = 0 \Rightarrow (x+3)(x-1) = 0$$

$$x = -3 \text{ or } x = 1$$

If $x = -3$, then $y = -\frac{3}{-3} = 1$. If $x = 1$, then $y = -\frac{3}{1} = -3$.
Solution set: $\{(1, -3), (-3, 1)\}$

35. $y = x^2 + 6x + 9 \, (1)$
$x + y = 3 \quad (2)$
Solve equation (2) for y to obtain $x + y = 3 \Rightarrow y = 3 - x$. (3)
Substitute equation (3) into equation (1) and solve for x.

$$3 - x = x^2 + 6x + 9 \Rightarrow 0 = x^2 + 7x + 6 \Rightarrow (x+6)(x+1) = 0$$

$$x = -6 \text{ or } x = -1$$

If $x = -6$, then $y = 3 - (-6) = 9$. If $x = -1$, then $y = 3 - (-1) = 4$.

Solution set: $\{(-6, 9), (-1, 4)\}$

37.
$$\begin{aligned} 2x-3y \quad &= -2 \quad (1) \\ x+\ y-4z &= -16 \quad (2) \\ 3x-2y+\ z &= 7 \quad (3) \end{aligned}$$

Add 4 times equation (3) to equation (2) in order to eliminate *z*.

$$\begin{array}{rl} x+\ y-4z &= -16 \\ 12x-8y+4z &= 28 \\ \hline 13x-7y \quad &= 12 \quad (4) \end{array}$$

Add 3 times equation (4) to -7 times equation (1) in order to eliminate *y* and solve for *x*.

$$\begin{array}{rl} -14x+21y &= 14 \\ 39x-21y &= 36 \\ \hline 25x \quad &= 50 \Rightarrow x=2 \end{array}$$

Substitute 2 for *x* in equation (4) to obtain $13(2)-7y=12 \Rightarrow 26-7y=12 \Rightarrow -7y=-14 \Rightarrow y=2.$

Substitute 2 for *x* and 2 for *y* in equation (2) to obtain the following.

$$2+2-4z=-16 \Rightarrow 4-4z=-16 \Rightarrow -4z=-20 \Rightarrow z=5.$$

Solution set: $\{(2,2,5)\}$

Section 9.6: Systems of Inequalities and Linear Programming

1. $x+2y \le 6$

The boundary is the line $x+2y=6$, which can be graphed using the *x*-intercept 6 and *y*-intercept 3. The boundary is included in the graph, so draw a solid line. Solving for *y*, we have the following.

$$x+2y \le 6 \Rightarrow 2y \le -x+6 \Rightarrow y \le -\tfrac{1}{2}x+3$$

Since *y* is *less than* or equal to $-\frac{1}{2}x+3$, the graph of the solution set is the line and the half-plane *below* the boundary.

We also can use (0, 0) as a test point. Since $0+2(0) \le 6 \Rightarrow 0 \le 6$ is a true statement, shade line and the side of the graph containing the test point (0,0) (the half-plane below the boundary).

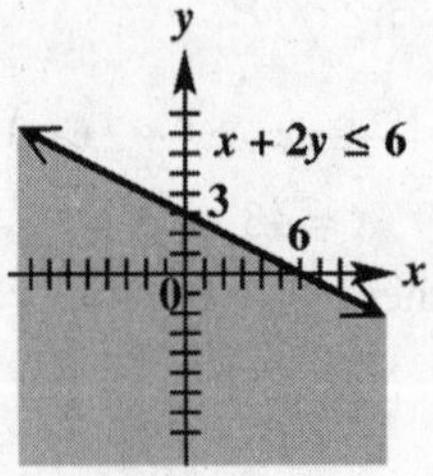

3. $2x+3y \ge 4$

The boundary is the line $2x+3y=4$, which can be graphed using the *x*-intercept 2 and *y*-intercept $\frac{4}{3}$. The boundary is included in the graph, so draw a solid line. Solving for y, we have the following.

$$2x+3y \ge 4 \Rightarrow 3y \ge -2x+4 \Rightarrow y \ge -\frac{2}{3}x+\frac{4}{3}$$

Since *y* is *greater than* or equal to $-\frac{2}{3}x+\frac{4}{3}$, the graph of the solution set is the line and the half-plane *above* the boundary.

We also can use (0, 0) as a test point. Since $2(0)+3(0) \ge 4 \Rightarrow 0 \ge 4$ is a false statement, shade the line and the side of the graph not containing the test point (0,0) (the half-plane above the boundary).

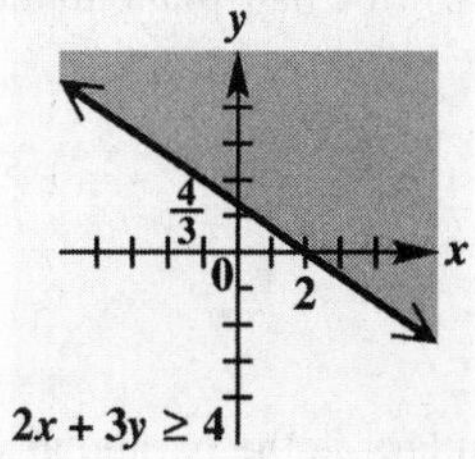

5. $3x-5y>6$

The boundary is the line $3x-5y=6$, which can be graphed using the *x*-intercept 2 and *y*-intercept $-\frac{6}{5}$. The boundary is not included in the graph, so draw a dashed line. Solving for *y*, we have the following.

$$3x-5y>6 \Rightarrow -5y>-3x+6 \Rightarrow y<\frac{3}{5}x-\frac{6}{5}$$

Since y is *less than* $\frac{3}{5}x-\frac{6}{5}$, the graph of the solution set is the half-plane *below* the boundary.

We also can use (0, 0) as a test point. Since $3(0)-5(0)>6 \Rightarrow 0>6$ is a false statement, shade the side of the graph not containing the test point (0, 0) (the half-plane below the boundary).

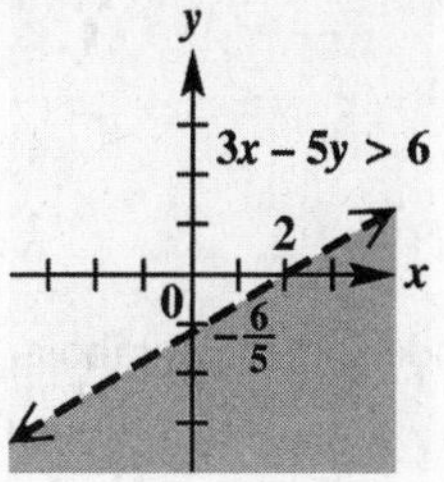

7. $5x \le 4y-2$

The boundary is the line $5x=4y-2$, which can be graphed using the *x*-intercept $-\frac{2}{5}$ and *y*-intercept $\frac{1}{2}$. The boundary is included in the graph, so draw a solid line. Solving for *y*, we have the following.

$$5x \le 4y-2 \Rightarrow -4y \le -5x-2 \Rightarrow y \ge \frac{5}{4}x+\frac{1}{2}$$

Since *y* is *greater than* or equal to $\frac{5}{4}x+\frac{1}{2}$, the graph of the solution set is the line and the half-plane *above* the boundary.

We also can use (0, 0) as a test point. Since $5(0) \le 4(0)-2 \Rightarrow 0 \le -2$ is a false statement, shade the line and the side of the graph not containing the test point (0, 0) (the half-plane above the boundary).

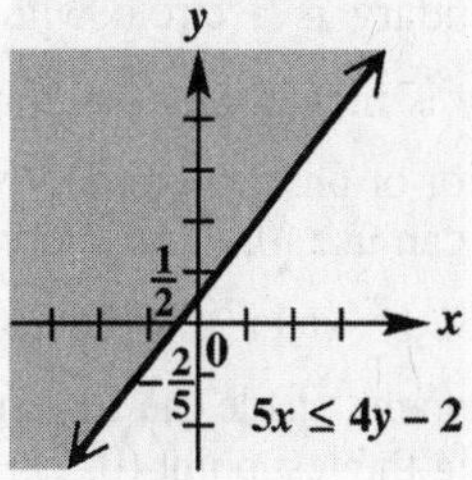

9. $x \le 3$

The boundary is the vertical line $x = 3$, which intersects the x-axis at 3. The boundary is included in the graph, so draw a solid line. Since $x \le 3$, it can easily be determined that we should shade to the left of the boundary.

We also can use (0, 0) as a test point. Since $0 \le 3$ is a true statement, shade the line and the side of the graph containing the test point (0, 0) (the half-plane to the left of the boundary).

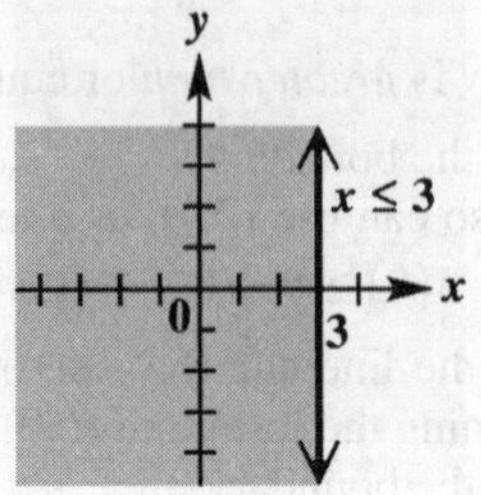

11. $y < 3x^2 + 2$

The boundary is the parabola $y = 3x^2 + 2$, which opens upwards. It has vertex $(0,2)$, y-intercept 2, and no x-intercepts. Since the inequality symbol is <, draw a dashed curve. Since y is *less than* $3x^2 + 2$, the graph of the solution set is the half-plane *below* the boundary.

We also can use (0, 0) as a test point. Since $0 < 3(0)^2 + 2 \Rightarrow 0 < 2$ is a true statement, shade the region of the graph containing the test point (0, 0).

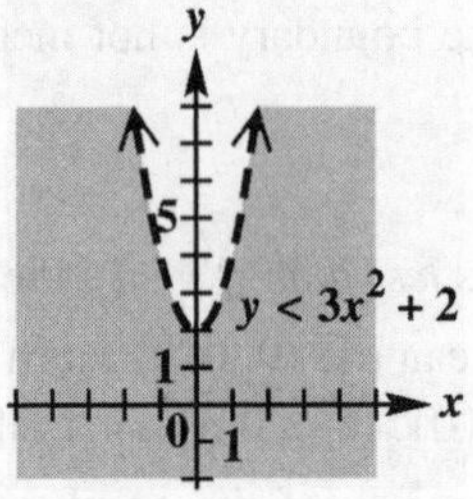

13. $y > (x-1)^2 + 2$

The boundary is the parabola $y = (x-1)^2 + 2$, which opens upwards. It has vertex $(1,2)$, y-intercept 3, and no x-intercepts. Since the inequality symbol is >, draw a dashed curve. Since y is *greater than* $(x-1)^2 + 2$, the graph of the solution set is the half-plane *above* the boundary.

We also can use (0, 0) as a test point. Since $0 > (0-1)^2 + 2 \Rightarrow 0 > 3$ is a false statement, shade the region of the graph not containing the test point (0, 0).

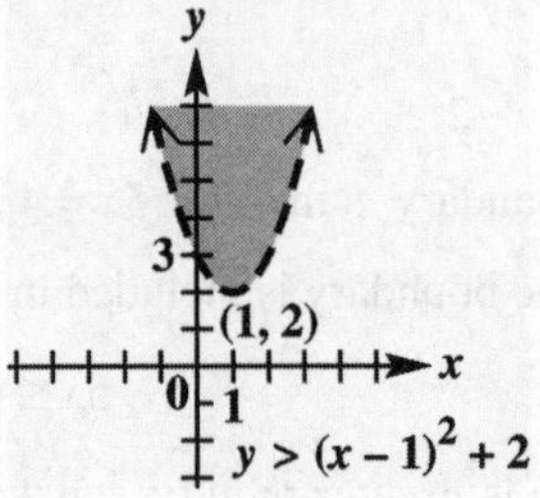

15. $x^2 + (y+3)^2 \le 16$

The boundary is a circle with center (0, –3) and radius 4. Draw a solid circle to show that the boundary is included in the graph. Since $x^2 + (y+3)^2 \le 16$, it can easily be determined that points in the interior or on the boundary would satisfy this relation.

We also can use (0, 0) as a test point. Since we have $0^2 + (0+3)^2 \le 16 \Rightarrow 9 \le 16$ is a true statement, shade the region of the graph containing the test point (0, 0).

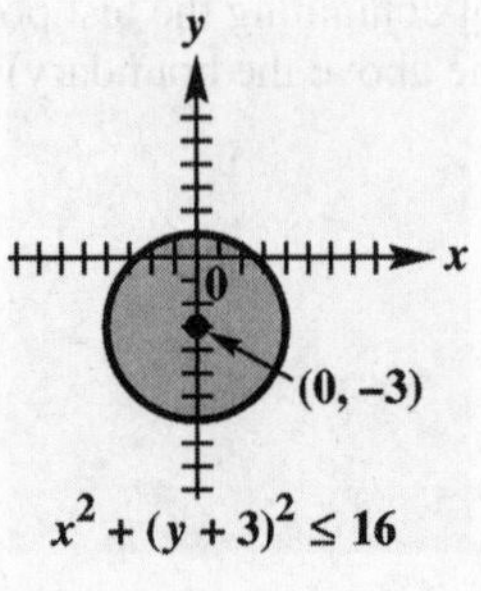

17. If an inequality is a "strict" inequality $(< \text{ or } >)$, then the boundary is not included and is represented by a dashed line. If an inequality is a "nonstrict" or "weak" inequality $(\leq \text{ or } \geq)$, then the boundary is included and is represented by a solid line.

19. $Ax + By \geq C, B > 0$
Solving for y we have the following.

$$Ax + By \geq C \Rightarrow By \geq -Ax + C \Rightarrow y \geq -\frac{A}{B}x + \frac{C}{B}$$

Since $B > 0$, the inequality symbol was not reversed when both sides are divided by B.
Since $y \geq -\frac{A}{B}x + \frac{C}{B}$, you would shade above the line.

21. The graph of $(x-5)^2 + (y-2)^2 = 4$ is a circle with center (5, 2) and radius $r = \sqrt{4} = 2$. The graph of $(x-5)^2 + (y-2)^2 < 4$ is the region in the interior of this circle. The correct response is B.

23. The graph of $y \leq 3x - 6$ is the region below the line with slope 3 and y-intercept -6. This is graph C.

25. The graph of $y \leq -3x - 6$ is the region below the line with slope -3 and y-intercept -6. This is graph A.

27. $x + y \geq 0$
$2x - y \geq 3$
Graph $x + y = 0$ as a solid line through the origin with a slope of -1. Shade the region above this line. Graph $2x - y = 3$ as a solid line with x-intercept $\frac{3}{2}$ and y-intercept -3. Shade the region below this line. To find where the boundaries of the two lines intersect, solve the system $\begin{aligned} x + y &= 0 \; (1) \\ 2x - y &= 3 \; (2) \end{aligned}$ by adding the two equations together to obtain $3x = 3 \Rightarrow x = 1$. Substituting this value into equation (1), we obtain $1 + y = 0 \Rightarrow y = -1$. Thus, the boundaries intersect at $(1, -1)$. The solution set is the common region, which is shaded in the final graph.

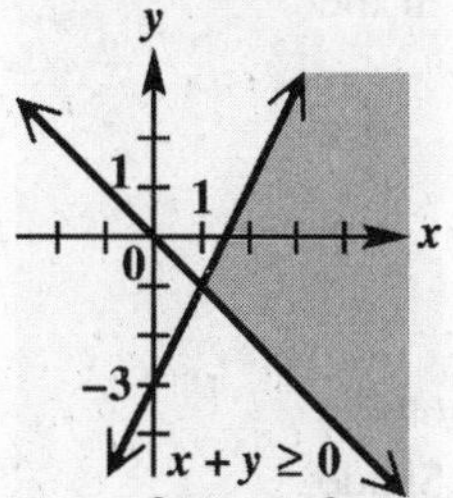

For Exercises 29 – 53, we will omit finding the points in which the boundaries intersect.

29. $2x + y > 2$
$x - 3y < 6$

Graph $2x + y = 2$ as a dashed line with y-intercept 2 and x-intercept 1. Shade the region above this line. Graph $x - 3y = 6$ as a dashed line with y-intercept -2 and x-intercept 6. Shade the region above this line. The solution set is the common region, which is shaded in the final graph.

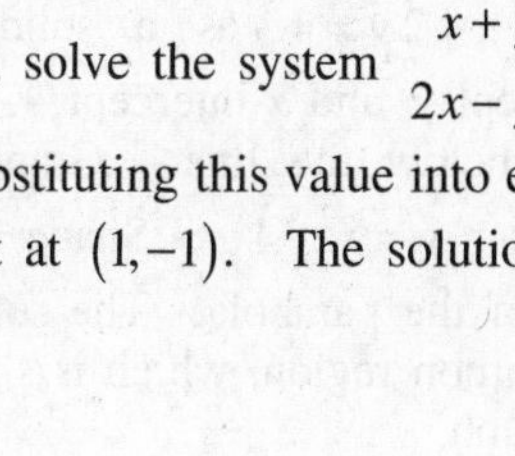

31. $3x+5y\leq 15$

$x-3y\geq 9$

Graph $3x + 5y = 15$ as a solid line with y-intercept 3 and x-intercept 5. Shade the region below this line. Graph $x - 3y = 9$ as a solid line with y-intercept -3 and x-intercept 9. Shade the region below this line. The solution set is the common region, which is shaded in the final graph.

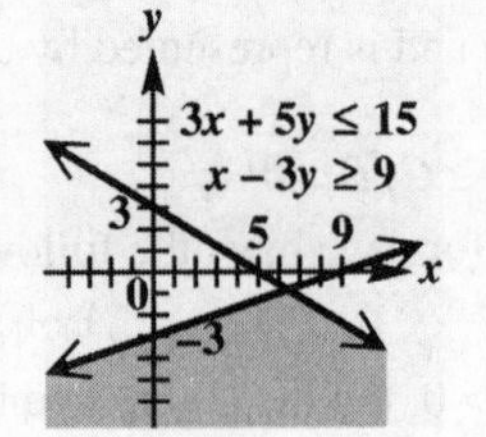

33. $4x-3y\leq 12$

$y\leq x^2$

Graph $4x - 3y = 12$ as a solid line with y-intercept -4 and x-intercept 3. Shade the region above this line. Graph the solid parabola $y = x^2$. Shade the region outside of this parabola. The solution set is the intersection of these two regions, which is shaded in the final graph.

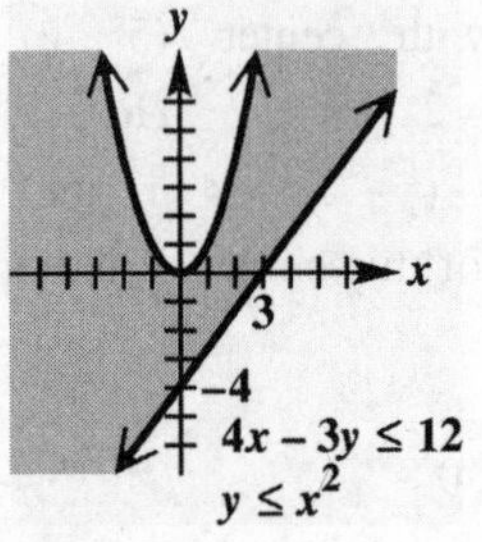

35. $x+2y\leq 4$

$y\geq x^2-1$

Graph $x+2y=4$ as a solid line with y-intercept 2 and x-intercept 4. Shade the region below the line. Graph the solid parabola $y=x^2-1$. Shade the region inside of the parabola. The solution set is the common region, which is shaded in the final graph.

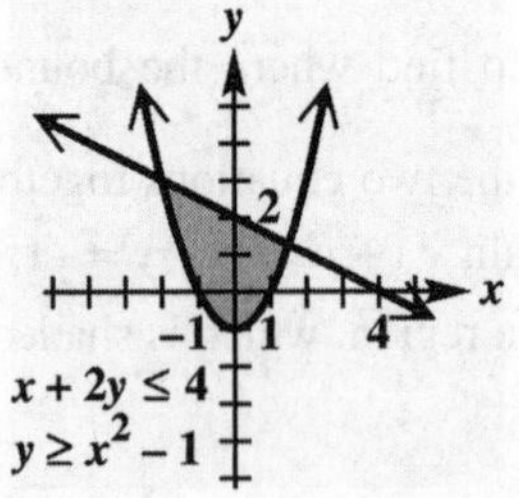

37. $y\leq (x+2)^2$

$y\geq -2x^2$

Graph $y=(x+2)^2$ as a solid parabola opening up with a vertex at (–2, 0). Shade the region below the parabola. Graph $y=-2x^2$ as a solid parabola opening down with a vertex at the origin. Shade the region above the parabola. The solution set is the intersection of these two regions, which is shaded in the final graph.

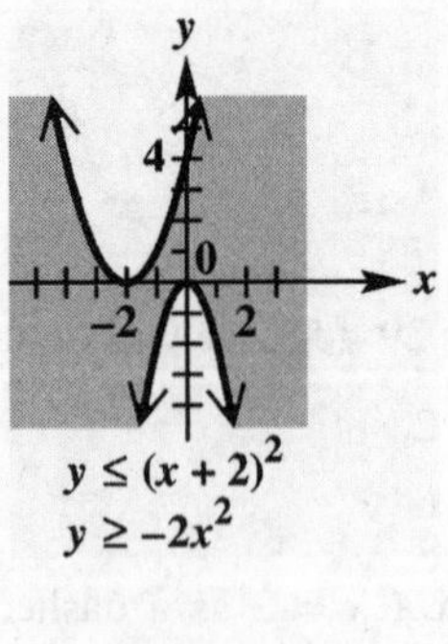

39. $x + y \le 36$

$-4 \le x \le 4$

Graph $x + y = 36$ as a solid line with y-intercept 36 and x-intercept 36. Shade the region below this line. Graph the vertical lines $x = -4$ and $x = 4$ as solid lines. Shade the region between these lines. The solution set is the intersection of these two regions, which is shaded in the final graph.

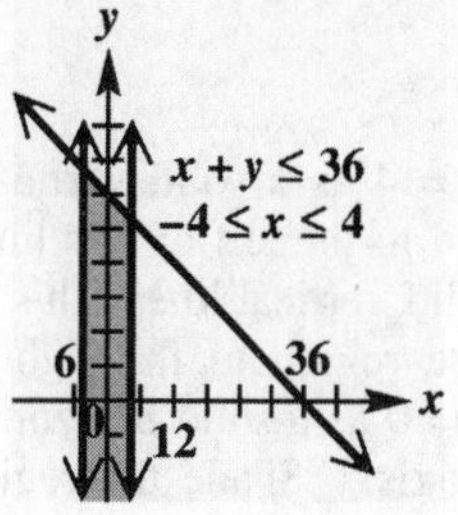

41. $y \ge x^2 + 4x + 4$

$y < -x^2$

Graph the solid parabola $y = x^2 + 4x + 4$ or $y = (x+2)^2$, which has vertex (–2, 0) and opens upward. Shade the region inside of this parabola. Graph the dashed parabola $y = -x^2$, which has vertex (0, 0) and opens downward. Shade the region inside this parabola. These two regions have no points in common, so the system has no solution.

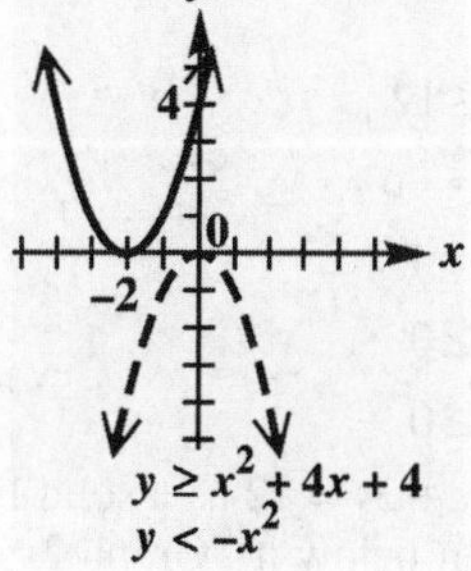

43. $3x - 2y \ge 6$

$x + y \le -5$

$y \le 4$

Graph $3x - 2y = 6$ as a solid line and shade the region below it. Graph $x + y = -5$ as a solid line and shade the region below it. Graph $y = 4$ as a solid horizontal line and shade the region below it. The solution set is the intersection of these three regions, which is shaded in the final graph.

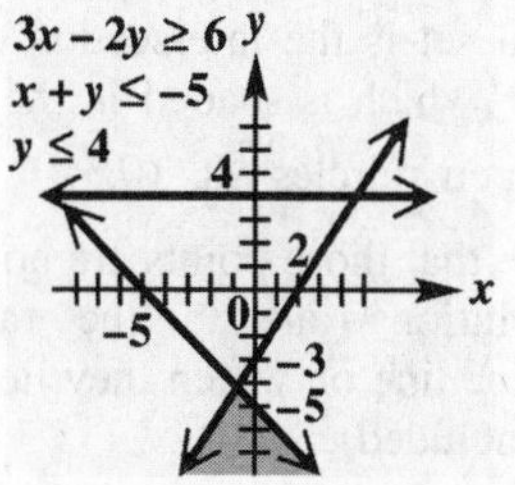

45. $-2 < x < 2$

$y > 1$

$x - y > 0$

Graph the vertical lines $x = -2$ and $x = 2$ as a dashed line. Shade the region between the two lines. Graph the horizontal line $y = 1$ as a dashed line. Shade the region above the line. Graph the line $x - y = 0$ as a dashed line through the origin with a slope of 1. Shade the region below this line. The solution set is the intersection of these three regions, which is shaded in the final graph.

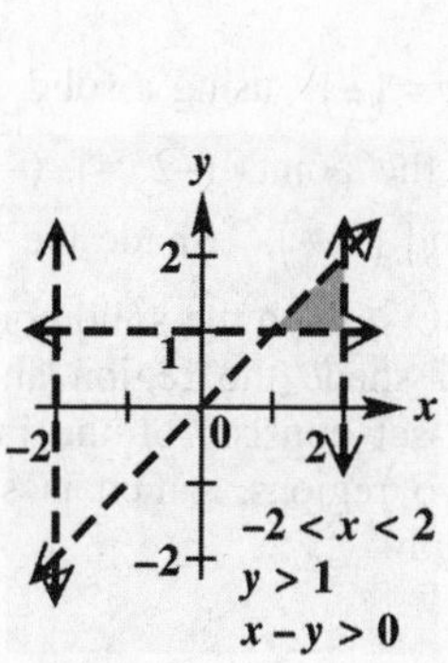

47. $x \le 4$
$x \ge 0$
$y \ge 0$
$x + 2y \ge 2$

Graph $x = 4$ as a solid vertical line. Shade the region to the left of this line. Graph $x = 0$ as a solid vertical line. (This is the y-axis.) Shade the region to the right of this line. Graph $y = 0$ as a solid horizontal line. (This is the x-axis.) Shade the region above the line. Graph $x + 2y = 2$ as a solid line with x-intercept 2 and y-intercept 1. Shade the region above the line. The solution set is the intersection of these four regions, which is shaded in the final graph.

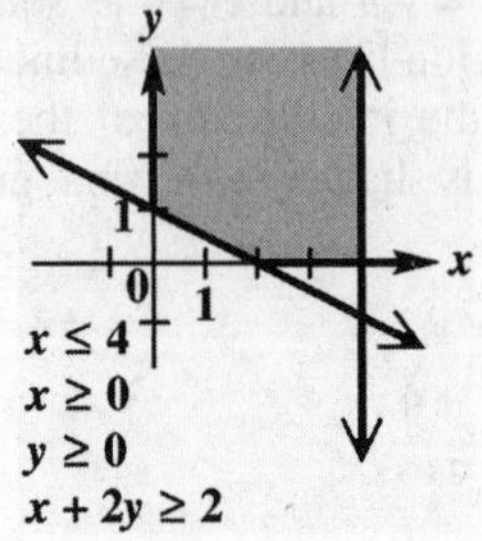

49. $2x + 3y \le 12$
$2x + 3y > -6$
$3x + y < 4$
$x \ge 0$
$y \ge 0$

Graph $2x + 3y = 12$ as a solid line and shade the region below it. Graph $2x + 3y = 6$ as a dashed line and shade the region above it. Graph $3x + y = 4$ as a dashed line and shade the region below it. $x = 0$ is the y-axis. Shade the region to the right of it. $y = 0$ is the x-axis. Shade the region above it. The solution set is the intersection of these five regions, which is shaded in the final graph. The open circles at (0, 4) and $\left(\frac{4}{3}, 0\right)$ indicate that those points are not included in the solution (due to the fact that the boundary line on which they lie, $3x + y = 4$, is not included).

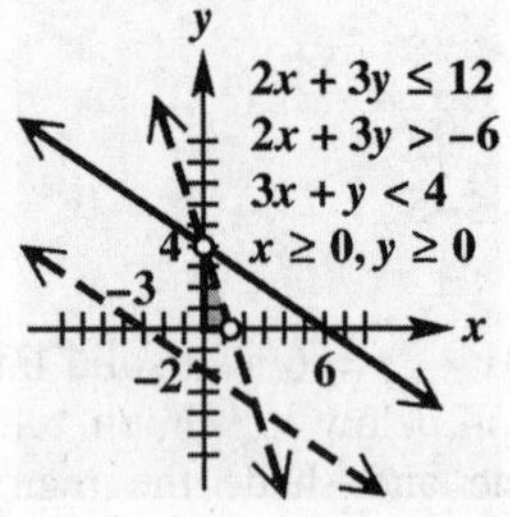

51. $y \le \left(\frac{1}{2}\right)^x$
$y \ge 4$

Graph $y = \left(\frac{1}{2}\right)^x$ using a solid curve passing through the points (–2, 4), (–1, 2), (0, 1), $\left(1, \frac{1}{2}\right)$, and $\left(2, \frac{1}{4}\right)$. Shade the region below this curve. Graph the solid horizontal line $y = 4$ and shade the region above it. The solution set consists of the intersection of these two regions, which is shaded in the final graph.

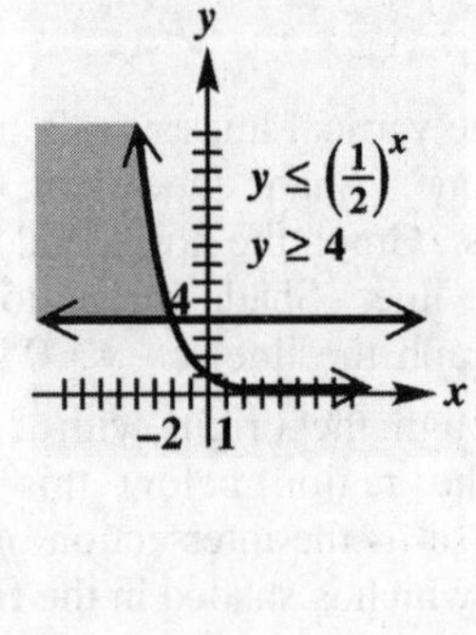

53. $y \le \log x$
$y \ge |x-2|$

Graph $y = \log x$ using a solid curve because $y \le \log x$ is a nonstrict inequality. (Recall that "log x" means $\log_{10} x$.) This graph contains the points $(.1,-1)$, $(1,0)$, and $(10,1)$. Use a calculator to approximate other points on the graph, such as $(2,.30)$ and $(4,.60)$. Because the symbol is $\le$, shade the region *below* the curve.

Now graph $y = |x-2|$. Make this boundary solid because $y \ge |x-2|$ is also a nonstrict inequality. This graph can be obtained by translating the graph of $y = |x|$ to the right 2 units. It contains points $(0,2)$, $(2,0)$, and $(4,2)$. Because the symbol is $\ge$, shade the region *above* the absolute value graph. The solution set is the intersection of the two regions, which is shaded in the final graph.

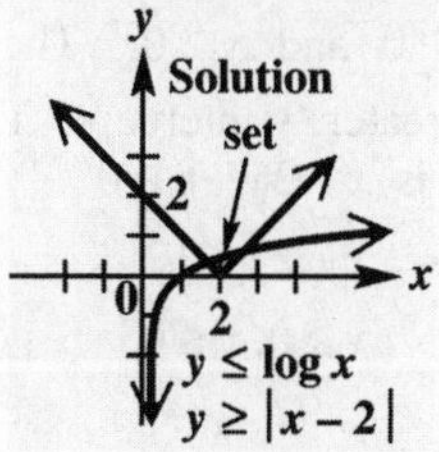

55. $y \ge x$
$y \le 2x-3$

The graph is the region above the line $y = x$ and below the line $y = 2x-3$. This is graph A.

57. $x^2 + y^2 \le 16$
$y \ge 0$

The graph is the region inside the circle $x^2 + y^2 = 16$ and above the horizontal line $y = 0$. This is graph B.

59. $3x + 2y \ge 6$

Solving the inequality for y we have $3x+2y \ge 6 \Rightarrow 2y \ge -3x+6 \Rightarrow y \ge -\frac{3}{2}x+3$.

Enter $Y_1 = (-3/2)x + 3$ and use a graphing calculator to shade the region above the line. Notice the icon to the left of Y_1.

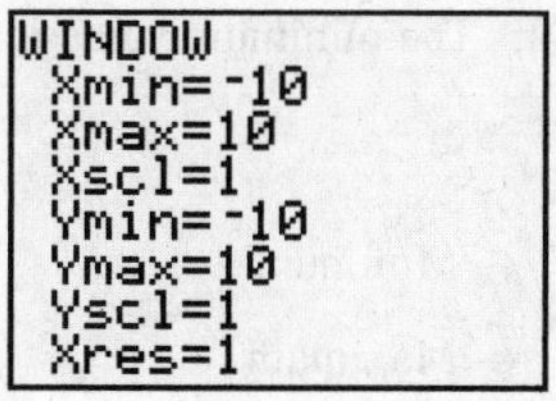

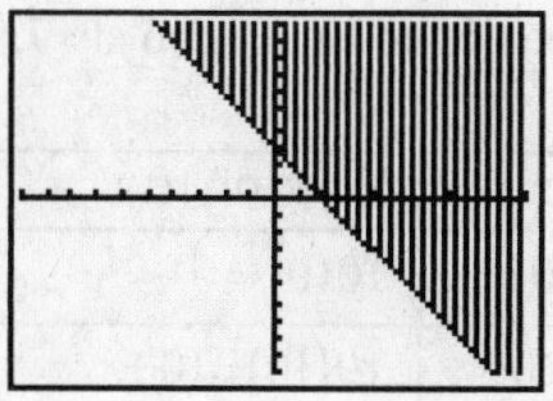

61. $x + y \geq 2$

$x + y \leq 6$

Solving each inequality for *y*, we have $y = -x + 2$ and $y = -x + 6$. Enter $Y_1 = -x + 2$ and $Y_2 = -x + 6$ and use the graphing calculator to shade the region above the graph of $y_1 = -x + 2$ and below the graph of $y_2 = -x + 6$.

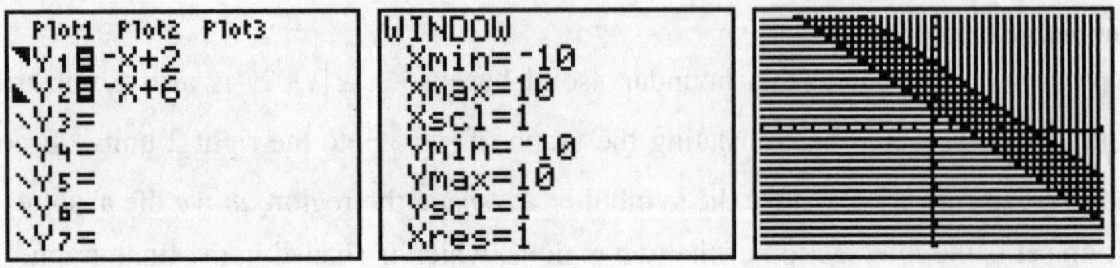

63. Since we are in the first quadrant, $x \geq 0$ and $y \geq 0$. The lines $x + 2y - 8 = 0$ and $x + 2y = 12$ are parallel, with $x + 2y = 12$ having the greater *y*-intercept. Therefore, we must shade below $x + 2y = 12$ and above $x + 2y - 8 = 0$. The system is $x + 2y - 8 \geq 0$

$x + 2y \leq 12$

$x \geq 0,\ y \leq 0.$

65.

Point	Value of $3x + 5y$	
$(1,1)$	$3(1) + 5(1) = 8$	← Minimum
$(2,7)$	$3(2)+5(7)=41$	
$(5,10)$	$3(5)+5(10)=65$	← Maximum
$(6,3)$	$3(6)+5(3)=33$	

The maximum value is 65 at $(5,10)$. The minimum value is 8 at (1, 1).

67.

Point	Value of $3x + 5y$	
$(1,0)$	$3(1) + 5(0) = 3$	← Minimum
$(1,10)$	$3(1)+5(10)=53$	
$(7,9)$	$3(7)+5(9)=66$	← Maximum
$(7,6)$	$3(7)+5(6)=51$	

The maximum value is 66 at $(7,9)$. The minimum value is 3 at $(1,0)$.

69.

Point	Value of $10y$	
$(1,0)$	$10(0) = 0$	← Minimum
$(1,10)$	$10(10)=100$	← Maximum
$(7,9)$	$10(9)=90$	
$(7,6)$	$10(6)=60$	

The maximum value is 100 at $(1,10)$. The minimum value is 0 at $(1,0)$.

71. Let x = the number of Brand X pills;
y = the number of Brand Y pills.
The following table is helpful in organizing the information.

	Number of Brand X pills (x)	Number of Brand Y pills (y)	Restrictions
Vitamin A	3000	1000	At least 6000
Vitamin C	45	50	At least 195
Vitamin D	75	200	At least 600

We have $3000x + 1000y \geq 6000$

$$45x + 50y \geq 195$$
$$75x + 200y \geq 600$$
$$x \geq 0,\ y \geq 0.$$

Graph $3000x + 1000y = 6000$ as a solid line with x-intercept 2 and y-intercept 6. Shade the region above the line. Graph $45x + 50y = 195$ as a solid line with x-intercept $4.\overline{3}$ and y-intercept 3.9. Shade the region above the line. Graph $75x + 200y = 600$ as a solid line with x-intercept 8 and y-intercept 3. Shade the region above the line. Graph $x = 0$ (the y-axis) as a solid line and shade the region to the right of it. Graph $y = 0$(the x-axis) as a solid line and shade the region above it. The region of feasible solutions is the intersection of these five regions.

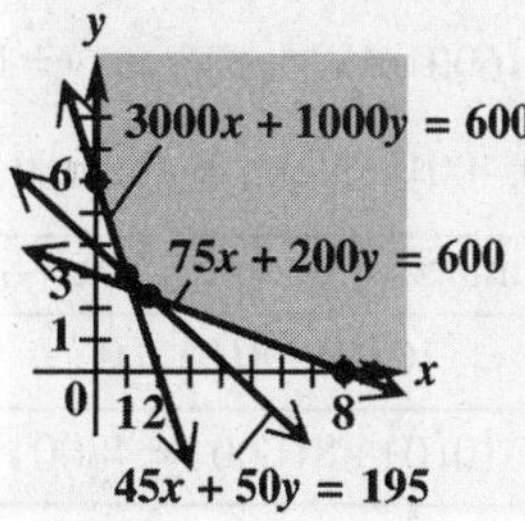

73. (a) Let x = number of cartons of food;
and y = number of cartons of clothing.
The following table is helpful in organizing the information.

	Number of cartons of food (x)	Number of cartons of clothing (y)	Restrictions
Weight	40	10	Cannot Exceed 16,000
Volume	20	30	No more than 18,000

We have $40x + 10y \leq 16{,}000$ Maximize objective function, number of people $= 10x + 8y$.

$$20x + 30y \leq 18{,}000$$
$$x \geq 0,\ y \geq 0.$$

Find the region of feasible solutions by graphing the system of inequalities that is made up of the constraints. To graph $40x + 10y \leq 16{,}000$, draw the line with x-intercept 400 and y-intercept 1600 as a solid line. Because the test point $(0,0)$ satisfies this inequality, shade the region *below* the line.

To graph $20x + 30y \leq 18{,}000$, draw the line with x-intercept 900 and y-intercept 600 as a solid line. Because the test point $(0,0)$ satisfies this inequality, shade the region *below* the line.

The constraints $x \geq 0$ and $y \geq 0$ restrict the graph to the first quadrant. The graph of the feasible region is the intersection of the regions that are the graphs of the individual constraints.

Continued on next page

73. (a) (continued)

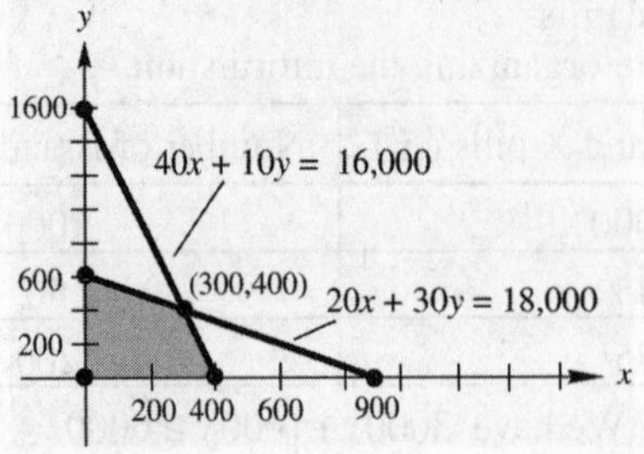

From the graph, observe that three are the vertices are $(0,0),(0,600)$, and $(400,0)$. The fourth vertex is the intersection point of the lines $40x+10y=16,000$ and $20x+30y=18,000$. To find this point, solve the system $40x+10y=16,000$

$$20x+30y=18,000.$$

The first equation can be written as $4x+y=1600 \Rightarrow y=1600-4x$. Substituting this equation into $20x+30y=18,000$, we have the following.

$$20x+30(1600-4x)=18,000 \Rightarrow 20x+48,000-120x=18,000$$

$$48,000-100x=18,000 \Rightarrow -100x=-30,000 \Rightarrow x=300$$

Substituting $x=300$ into $y=1600-4x$, we have $y=1600-4(300)=1600-1200=400$.

Thus, the fourth vertex is $(300,400)$. Next, evaluate the objective function at each vertex.

Point	Number of people $=10x+8y$	
$(0,0)$	$10(0)+8(0)=0$	
$(0,600)$	$10(0)+8(600)=4800$	
$(300,400)$	$10(300)+8(400)=6200$	← Maximum
$(400,0)$	$10(400)+8(0)=4000$	

The maximum value of $10x+8y$ occurs at $(300,400)$, so they should send 300 cartons of food and 400 cartons of clothes to maximize the number of people helped.

(b) The maximum number of people helped is 6200.

75. Let x = number of cabinet A
and y = number of cabinet B.
The cost constraint is $10x+20y\le 140$. The space constraint is $6x+8y\le 72$. Since the numbers of cabinets cannot be negative, we also have $x\ge 0$ and $y\ge 0$. We want to maximize the objective function, storage capacity $=8x+12y$.

Find the region of feasible solutions by graphing the system of inequalities that is made up of the constraints. To graph $10x+20y\le 140$, draw the line with x-intercept 14 and y-intercept 7 as a solid line. Because the test point $(0,0)$ satisfies this inequality, shade the region *below* the line.

To graph $6x+8y\le 72$, draw the line with x-intercept 12 and y-intercept 9 as a solid line. Because the test point $(0,0)$ satisfies this inequality, shade the region *below* the line.

The constraints $x\ge 0$ and $y\ge 0$ restrict the graph to the first quadrant. The graph of the feasible region is the intersection of the regions that are the graphs of the individual constraints.

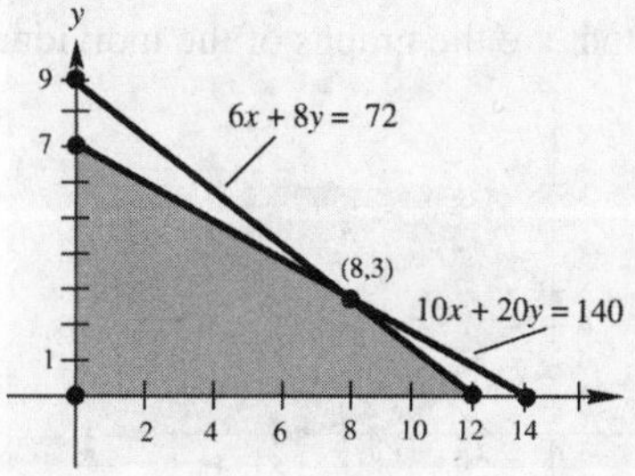

From the graph, observe that three vertices are $(0,0),(0,7)$, and $(12,0)$. The fourth vertex is the intersection point of the lines $10x+20y=140$ and $6x+8y=72$. To find this point, solve the system

$$\begin{aligned}10x+20y&=140\\ 6x+\ 8y&=72.\end{aligned}$$

The first equation can be written as $x+2y=14\Rightarrow x=14-2y$. Substituting this equation into $6x+8y=72$, we have the following.

$$6(14-2y)+8y=72\Rightarrow 84-12y+8y=72\Rightarrow 84-4y=72\Rightarrow -4y=-12\Rightarrow y=3$$

Substituting $y=3$ into $x=14-2y$, we have $x=14-2(3)=14-6=8$.

Thus, the fourth vertex is $(8,3)$. Next, evaluate the objective function at each vertex.

Point	Storage Capacity $=8x+12y$	
$(0,0)$	$8(0)+12(0)=0$	
$(0,7)$	$8(0)+12(7)=84$	
$(8,3)$	$8(8)+12(3)=100$	← Maximum
$(12,0)$	$8(12)+12(0)=96$	

The maximum value of $8x+12y$ occurs at $(8,3)$, so the office manager should buy 8 of cabinet A and 3 of cabinet B for a total storage capacity of 100 ft^3.

77. Let $x =$ number of servings of product A;
and $y =$ number of servings of product B.
The Supplement I constraint is $3x+2y \ge 15$. The Supplement II constraint is $2x+4y \ge 15$. Since the numbers of servings cannot be negative, we also have $x \ge 0$ and $y \ge 0$. We want to minimize the objective function, cost $= .25x + .40y$.

Find the region of feasible solutions by graphing the system of inequalities that is made up of the constraints. To graph $3x+2y \ge 15$, draw the line with x-intercept 5 and y-intercept $\frac{15}{2} = 7\frac{1}{2}$ as a solid line. Because the test point $(0,0)$ does not satisfy this inequality, shade the region *above* the line.

To graph $2x+4y \ge 15$, draw the line with x-intercept $\frac{15}{2} = 7\frac{1}{2}$ and y-intercept $\frac{15}{4} = 3\frac{3}{4}$ as a solid line. Because the test point $(0,0)$ does not satisfy this inequality, shade the region *above* the line.

The constraints $x \ge 0$ and $y \ge 0$ restrict the graph to the first quadrant. The graph of the feasible region is the intersection of the regions that are the graphs of the individual constraints.

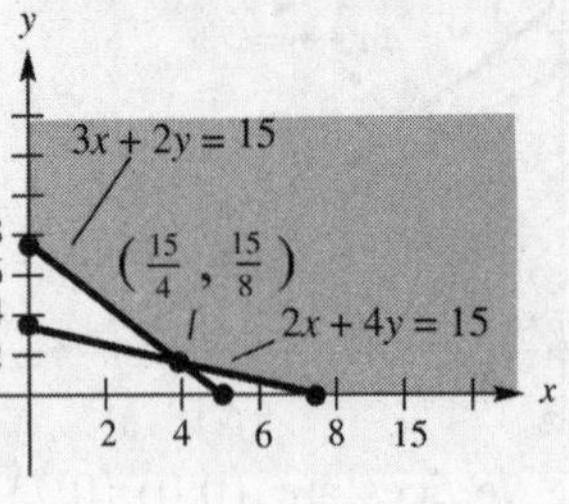

From the graph, observe that two vertices are $\left(0, \frac{15}{2}\right)$ and $\left(\frac{15}{2}, 0\right)$. The third vertex is the intersection point of the lines $3x+2y=15$ and $2x+4y=15$. To find this point, solve the system

$$\begin{aligned} 3x+2y&=15 \\ 2x+4y&=15. \end{aligned}$$

Multiply the first equation by –2 and add it to the second equation.

$$\begin{aligned} -6x-4y &= -30 \\ 2x+4y &= 15 \\ \hline -4x \quad &= -15 \Rightarrow x = \tfrac{15}{4} \end{aligned}$$

Substituting this equation into $2x+4y=15$, we have the following.

$$2\left(\tfrac{15}{4}\right)+4y=15 \Rightarrow \tfrac{15}{2}+4y=15 \Rightarrow 15+8y=30 \Rightarrow 8y=15 \Rightarrow y=\tfrac{15}{8}$$

Thus, the third vertex is $\left(\frac{15}{4}, \frac{15}{8}\right)$. Next, evaluate the objective function at each vertex.

Point	Cost $= .25x + .40y$	
$\left(0, \frac{15}{2}\right)$	$.25(0)+.40\left(\frac{15}{2}\right)=3.00$	
$\left(\frac{15}{4}, \frac{15}{8}\right)$	$.25\left(\frac{15}{4}\right)+.40\left(\frac{15}{8}\right)=1.69$	← Minimum
$\left(\frac{15}{2}, 0\right)$	$.25\left(\frac{15}{2}\right)+.40(0)=1.88$	

The minimum cost is \$1.69 for $\frac{15}{4} = 3\frac{3}{4}$ servings of *A* and $\frac{15}{8} = 1\frac{7}{8}$ servings of *B*.

Section 9.7: Properties of Matrices

1. $\begin{bmatrix} -3 & a \\ b & 5 \end{bmatrix} = \begin{bmatrix} c & 0 \\ 4 & d \end{bmatrix}$

Since corresponding elements are equal, we have the following.

$$a = 0, b = 4, c = -3, d = 5$$

3. $\begin{bmatrix} x+2 & y-6 \\ z-3 & w+5 \end{bmatrix} = \begin{bmatrix} -2 & 8 \\ 0 & 3 \end{bmatrix}$

Since corresponding elements are equal, we have the following.

$$x+2=-2 \Rightarrow x=-4$$
$$y-6=8 \Rightarrow y=14$$
$$z-3=0 \Rightarrow z=3$$
$$w+5=3 \Rightarrow w=-2$$

5. $\begin{bmatrix} 0 & 5 & x \\ -1 & 3 & y+2 \\ 4 & 1 & z \end{bmatrix} = \begin{bmatrix} 0 & w+3 & 6 \\ -1 & 3 & 0 \\ 4 & 1 & 8 \end{bmatrix}$

Since corresponding elements are equal, we have the following.

$$x = 6$$
$$y+2=0 \Rightarrow y=-2$$
$$z = 8$$
$$w+3=5 \Rightarrow w=2$$

7. Since $\begin{bmatrix} x & y & z \end{bmatrix}$ is a 1×3 matrix and $\begin{bmatrix} 21 & 6 \end{bmatrix}$ is a 1×2 matrix, the statement cannot be true, hence we cannot find values of *x*, *y*, and *z*.

9. $\begin{bmatrix} -7+z & 4r & 8s \\ 6p & 2 & 5 \end{bmatrix} + \begin{bmatrix} -9 & 8r & 3 \\ 2 & 5 & 4 \end{bmatrix} = \begin{bmatrix} 2 & 36 & 27 \\ 20 & 7 & 12a \end{bmatrix} \Rightarrow \begin{bmatrix} -16+z & 12r & 8s+3 \\ 6p+2 & 7 & 9 \end{bmatrix} = \begin{bmatrix} 2 & 36 & 27 \\ 20 & 7 & 12a \end{bmatrix}$

Since corresponding elements are equal, we have the following.

$-16+z=2 \Rightarrow z=18,\ 12r=36 \Rightarrow r=3,\ 8s+3=27 \Rightarrow s=3,\ 6p+2=20 \Rightarrow p=3,\ 9=12a \Rightarrow a=\frac{3}{4}$

Thus, $z = 18$, $r = 3$, $s = 3$, $p = 3$, and $a = \frac{3}{4}$.

11. A 3×8 matrix has <u>8</u> columns and <u>3</u> rows.

13. $\begin{bmatrix} -4 & 8 \\ 2 & 3 \end{bmatrix}$

This matrix has 2 rows and 2 columns, so it is a 2×2 square matrix.

15. $\begin{bmatrix} -6 & 8 & 0 & 0 \\ 4 & 1 & 9 & 2 \\ 3 & -5 & 7 & 1 \end{bmatrix}$

This matrix has 3 rows and 4 columns, so it is a 3×4 matrix.

17. $\begin{bmatrix} 2 \\ 4 \end{bmatrix}$

This matrix has 2 rows and 1 column, so it is a 2×1 column matrix.

19. Answers will vary.

21. $\begin{bmatrix} -4 & 3 \\ 12 & -6 \end{bmatrix} + \begin{bmatrix} 2 & -8 \\ 5 & 10 \end{bmatrix} = \begin{bmatrix} -4+2 & 3+(-8) \\ 12+5 & -6+10 \end{bmatrix} = \begin{bmatrix} -2 & -5 \\ 17 & 4 \end{bmatrix}$

23. $\begin{bmatrix} 6 & -9 & 2 \\ 4 & 1 & 3 \end{bmatrix} + \begin{bmatrix} -8 & 2 & 5 \\ 6 & -3 & 4 \end{bmatrix} = \begin{bmatrix} 6+(-8) & -9+2 & 2+5 \\ 4+6 & 1+(-3) & 3+4 \end{bmatrix} = \begin{bmatrix} -2 & -7 & 7 \\ 10 & -2 & 7 \end{bmatrix}$

25. Since $\begin{bmatrix} 2 & 4 & 6 \end{bmatrix}$ is a 1×3 matrix and $\begin{bmatrix} -2 \\ -4 \\ -6 \end{bmatrix}$ is a 3×1 matrix, $\begin{bmatrix} 2 & 4 & 6 \end{bmatrix} + \begin{bmatrix} -2 \\ -4 \\ -6 \end{bmatrix}$ cannot be simplified.

27. $\begin{bmatrix} -6 & 8 \\ 0 & 0 \end{bmatrix} - \begin{bmatrix} 0 & 0 \\ -4 & -2 \end{bmatrix} = \begin{bmatrix} -6-0 & 8-0 \\ 0-(-4) & 0-(-2) \end{bmatrix} = \begin{bmatrix} -6 & 8 \\ 4 & 2 \end{bmatrix}$

29. $\begin{bmatrix} 12 \\ -1 \\ 3 \end{bmatrix} - \begin{bmatrix} 8 \\ 4 \\ -1 \end{bmatrix} = \begin{bmatrix} 12-8 \\ -1-4 \\ 3-(-1) \end{bmatrix} = \begin{bmatrix} 4 \\ -5 \\ 4 \end{bmatrix}$

31. Since $\begin{bmatrix} -4 & 3 \end{bmatrix}$ is a 1×2 matrix and $\begin{bmatrix} 5 & 8 & 2 \end{bmatrix}$ is a 1×3 matrix, $\begin{bmatrix} -4 & 3 \end{bmatrix} - \begin{bmatrix} 5 & 8 & 2 \end{bmatrix}$ cannot be simplified.

33. $\begin{bmatrix} 1 & -4 \\ 2 & -3 \\ -8 & 4 \end{bmatrix} - \begin{bmatrix} -6 & 9 \\ -2 & 5 \\ -7 & -12 \end{bmatrix} = \begin{bmatrix} 1-(-6) & -4-9 \\ 2-(-2) & -3-6 \\ -8-(-7) & 4-(-12) \end{bmatrix} = \begin{bmatrix} 7 & -13 \\ 4 & -8 \\ -1 & 16 \end{bmatrix}$

35. $\begin{bmatrix} 3x+y & x-2y & 2x \\ 5x & 3y & x+y \end{bmatrix} + \begin{bmatrix} 2x & 3y & 5x+y \\ 3x+2y & x & 2x \end{bmatrix} = \begin{bmatrix} (3x+y)+2x & (x-2y)+3y & 2x+(5x+y) \\ 5x+(3x+2y) & 3y+x & (x+y)+2x \end{bmatrix}$

$= \begin{bmatrix} 5x+y & x+y & 7x+y \\ 8x+2y & x+3y & 3x+y \end{bmatrix}$

In Exercises 37–39, $A = \begin{bmatrix} -2 & 4 \\ 0 & 3 \end{bmatrix}$ and $B = \begin{bmatrix} -6 & 2 \\ 4 & 0 \end{bmatrix}$.

37. $2A = 2\begin{bmatrix} -2 & 4 \\ 0 & 3 \end{bmatrix} = \begin{bmatrix} 2(-2) & 2(4) \\ 2(0) & 2(3) \end{bmatrix} = \begin{bmatrix} -4 & 8 \\ 0 & 6 \end{bmatrix}$

39. $\frac{3}{2}B = \frac{3}{2}\begin{bmatrix} -6 & 2 \\ 4 & 0 \end{bmatrix} = \begin{bmatrix} \frac{3}{2}(-6) & \frac{3}{2}(2) \\ \frac{3}{2}(4) & \frac{3}{2}(0) \end{bmatrix} = \begin{bmatrix} -9 & 3 \\ 6 & 0 \end{bmatrix}$

41. $2A - B = 2\begin{bmatrix} -2 & 4 \\ 0 & 3 \end{bmatrix} - \begin{bmatrix} -6 & 2 \\ 4 & 0 \end{bmatrix} = \begin{bmatrix} -4 & 8 \\ 0 & 6 \end{bmatrix} - \begin{bmatrix} -6 & 2 \\ 4 & 0 \end{bmatrix} = \begin{bmatrix} -4-(-6) & 8-2 \\ 0-4 & 6-0 \end{bmatrix} = \begin{bmatrix} 2 & 6 \\ -4 & 6 \end{bmatrix}$

43. $-A + \frac{1}{2}B = -\begin{bmatrix} -2 & 4 \\ 0 & 3 \end{bmatrix} + \frac{1}{2}\begin{bmatrix} -6 & 2 \\ 4 & 0 \end{bmatrix} = \begin{bmatrix} 2 & -4 \\ 0 & -3 \end{bmatrix} + \begin{bmatrix} -3 & 1 \\ 2 & 0 \end{bmatrix} = \begin{bmatrix} 2+(-3) & -4+1 \\ 0+2 & -3+0 \end{bmatrix} = \begin{bmatrix} -1 & -3 \\ 2 & -3 \end{bmatrix}$

45. AB can be calculated and the result will be a 2×5 matrix.

Matrix A Matrix B

2×3 3×5

matches

size of AB

2×5

47. BA cannot be calculated.

Matrix B Matrix A

3×5 2×3

different

49. BC can be calculated and the result will be a 3×2 matrix.

Matrix B Matrix C

3×5 5×2

matches

size of CA

3×2

51. A 2×2 matrix multiplied by a 2×1 matrix results in a 2×1 matrix.

$$\begin{bmatrix}1 & 2\\3 & 4\end{bmatrix}\begin{bmatrix}-1\\7\end{bmatrix}=\begin{bmatrix}1(-1)+2(7)\\3(-1)+4(7)\end{bmatrix}=\begin{bmatrix}-1+14\\-3+28\end{bmatrix}=\begin{bmatrix}13\\25\end{bmatrix}$$

53. A 2×3 matrix multiplied by a 3×1 matrix results in a 2×1 matrix.

$$\begin{bmatrix}3 & -4 & 1\\5 & 0 & 2\end{bmatrix}\begin{bmatrix}-1\\4\\2\end{bmatrix}=\begin{bmatrix}3(-1)+(-4)(4)+1(2)\\5(-1)+0(4)+2(2)\end{bmatrix}=\begin{bmatrix}-3+(-16)+2\\-5+0+4\end{bmatrix}=\begin{bmatrix}-17\\-1\end{bmatrix}$$

55. A 2×2 matrix multiplied by a 2×2 matrix results in a 2×2 matrix.

$$\begin{bmatrix}5 & 2\\-1 & 4\end{bmatrix}\begin{bmatrix}3 & -2\\1 & 0\end{bmatrix}=\begin{bmatrix}5(3)+2(1) & 5(-2)+2(0)\\-1(3)+4(1) & -1(-2)+4(0)\end{bmatrix}=\begin{bmatrix}15+2 & -10+0\\-3+4 & 2+0\end{bmatrix}=\begin{bmatrix}17 & -10\\1 & 2\end{bmatrix}$$

57. A 2×3 matrix multiplied by a 3×2 matrix results in a 2×2 matrix.

$$\begin{bmatrix}2 & 2 & -1\\3 & 0 & 1\end{bmatrix}\begin{bmatrix}0 & 2\\-1 & 4\\0 & 2\end{bmatrix}=\begin{bmatrix}2(0)+2(-1)+(-1)(0) & 2(2)+2(4)+(-1)(2)\\3(0)+0(-1)+1(0) & 3(2)+0(4)+1(2)\end{bmatrix}$$

$$=\begin{bmatrix}0+(-2)+0 & 4+8+(-2)\\0+0+0 & 6+0+2\end{bmatrix}=\begin{bmatrix}-2 & 10\\0 & 8\end{bmatrix}$$

59. $\begin{bmatrix}-3 & 0 & 2 & 1\\4 & 0 & 2 & 6\end{bmatrix}\begin{bmatrix}-4 & 2\\0 & 1\end{bmatrix}$

A 2×4 matrix cannot be multiplied by a 2×2 matrix because the number of columns of the first matrix (four) is not equal to the number of rows of the second matrix (two).

61. A 1×3 matrix multiplied by a 3×3 matrix results in a 1×3 matrix.

$$\begin{bmatrix}-2 & 4 & 1\end{bmatrix}\begin{bmatrix}3 & -2 & 4\\2 & 1 & 0\\0 & -1 & 4\end{bmatrix}=\begin{bmatrix}-2(3)+4(2)+1(0) & -2(-2)+4(1)+1(-1) & -2(4)+4(0)+1(4)\end{bmatrix}$$

$$=\begin{bmatrix}-6+8+0 & 4+4+(-1) & -8+0+4\end{bmatrix}=\begin{bmatrix}2 & 7 & -4\end{bmatrix}$$

63. A 3×3 matrix multiplied by a 3×3 matrix results in a 3×3 matrix.

$$\begin{bmatrix}-2&-3&-4\\2&-1&0\\4&-2&3\end{bmatrix}\begin{bmatrix}0&1&4\\1&2&-1\\3&2&-2\end{bmatrix}$$

$$=\begin{bmatrix}-2(0)+(-3)(1)+(-4)(3)&-2(1)+(-3)(2)+(-4)(2)&-2(4)+(-3)(-1)+(-4)(-2)\\2(0)+(-1)(1)+0(3)&2(1)+(-1)(2)+0(2)&2(4)+(-1)(-1)+0(-2)\\4(0)+(-2)(1)+3(3)&4(1)+(-2)(2)+3(2)&4(4)+(-2)(-1)+3(-2)\end{bmatrix}$$

$$=\begin{bmatrix}0+(-3)+(-12)&-2+(-6)+(-8)&-8+3+8\\0+(-1)+0&2+(-2)+0&8+1+0\\0+(-2)+9&4+(-4)+6&16+2+(-6)\end{bmatrix}=\begin{bmatrix}-15&-16&3\\-1&0&9\\7&6&12\end{bmatrix}$$

In Exercises 65–71, $A=\begin{bmatrix}4&-2\\3&1\end{bmatrix}$, $B=\begin{bmatrix}5&1\\0&-2\\3&7\end{bmatrix}$ and $C=\begin{bmatrix}-5&4&1\\0&3&6\end{bmatrix}$.

65. A 3×2 matrix multiplied by a 2×2 matrix results in a 3×2 matrix.

$$BA=\begin{bmatrix}5&1\\0&-2\\3&7\end{bmatrix}\begin{bmatrix}4&-2\\3&1\end{bmatrix}=\begin{bmatrix}5(4)+1(3)&5(-2)+1(1)\\0(4)+(-2)(3)&0(-2)+(-2)(1)\\3(4)+7(3)&3(-2)+7(1)\end{bmatrix}=\begin{bmatrix}20+3&-10+1\\0+(-6)&0+(-2)\\12+21&-6+7\end{bmatrix}=\begin{bmatrix}23&-9\\-6&-2\\33&1\end{bmatrix}$$

67. A 3×2 matrix multiplied by a 2×3 matrix results in a 3×3 matrix.

$$BC=\begin{bmatrix}5&1\\0&-2\\3&7\end{bmatrix}\begin{bmatrix}-5&4&1\\0&3&6\end{bmatrix}=\begin{bmatrix}5(-5)+1(0)&5(4)+1(3)&5(1)+1(6)\\0(-5)+(-2)(0)&0(4)+(-2)(3)&0(1)+(-2)(6)\\3(-5)+7(0)&3(4)+7(3)&3(1)+7(6)\end{bmatrix}$$

$$=\begin{bmatrix}-25+0&20+3&5+6\\0+0&0+(-6)&0+(-12)\\-15+0&12+21&3+42\end{bmatrix}=\begin{bmatrix}-25&23&11\\0&-6&-12\\-15&33&45\end{bmatrix}$$

69. $AB=\begin{bmatrix}4&-2\\3&1\end{bmatrix}\begin{bmatrix}5&1\\0&-2\\3&7\end{bmatrix}$ is the product of a 2×2 matrix multiplied by a 3×2 matrix, which is not possible.

71. Since $A^2=AA$, we are finding the product of two 2×2 matrices, which results in a 2×2 matrix.

$$A^2=\begin{bmatrix}4&-2\\3&1\end{bmatrix}\begin{bmatrix}4&-2\\3&1\end{bmatrix}=\begin{bmatrix}4(4)+(-2)(3)&4(-2)+(-2)(1)\\3(4)+1(3)&3(-2)+1(1)\end{bmatrix}=\begin{bmatrix}16+(-6)&-8+(-2)\\12+3&-6+1\end{bmatrix}=\begin{bmatrix}10&-10\\15&-5\end{bmatrix}$$

73. Since the answers to 65 and 69 are not equal, $BA\neq AB$.
Since the answers to 67 and 68 are not equal, $BC\neq CB$.
Since the answers to 66 and 70 are not equal, $AC\neq CA$.
No, matrix multiplication is not commutative.

75. $A=\begin{bmatrix}3 & 4\\ -2 & 1\end{bmatrix}$ and $B=\begin{bmatrix}6 & 0\\ 5 & -2\end{bmatrix}$

$$AB=\begin{bmatrix}3 & 4\\ -2 & 1\end{bmatrix}\begin{bmatrix}6 & 0\\ 5 & -2\end{bmatrix}=\begin{bmatrix}3(6)+4(5) & 3(0)+4(-2)\\ -2(6)+1(5) & -2(0)+1(-2)\end{bmatrix}=\begin{bmatrix}18+20 & 0+(-8)\\ -12+5 & 0+(-2)\end{bmatrix}=\begin{bmatrix}38 & -8\\ -7 & -2\end{bmatrix}$$

$$BA=\begin{bmatrix}6 & 0\\ 5 & -2\end{bmatrix}\begin{bmatrix}3 & 4\\ -2 & 1\end{bmatrix}=\begin{bmatrix}6(3)+0(-2) & 6(4)+0(1)\\ 5(3)+(-2)(-2) & 5(4)+(-2)(1)\end{bmatrix}=\begin{bmatrix}18+0 & 24+0\\ 15+4 & 20+(-2)\end{bmatrix}=\begin{bmatrix}18 & 24\\ 19 & 18\end{bmatrix}$$

Note: $AB \neq BA$

77. $A=\begin{bmatrix}0 & 1 & -1\\ 0 & 1 & 0\\ 0 & 0 & 1\end{bmatrix}$ and $B=\begin{bmatrix}1 & 0 & 0\\ 0 & 1 & 0\\ 0 & 0 & 1\end{bmatrix}$

$$AB=\begin{bmatrix}0 & 1 & -1\\ 0 & 1 & 0\\ 0 & 0 & 1\end{bmatrix}\begin{bmatrix}1 & 0 & 0\\ 0 & 1 & 0\\ 0 & 0 & 1\end{bmatrix}=\begin{bmatrix}0(1)+1(0)+(-1)(0) & 0(0)+1(1)+(-1)(0) & 0(0)+1(0)+(-1)(1)\\ 0(1)+1(0)+0(0) & 0(0)+1(1)+0(0) & 0(0)+1(0)+0(1)\\ 0(1)+0(0)+1(0) & 0(0)+0(1)+1(0) & 0(0)+0(0)+1(1)\end{bmatrix}$$

$$=\begin{bmatrix}0+0+0 & 0+1+0 & 0+0+(-1)\\ 0+0+0 & 0+1+0 & 0+0+0\\ 0+0+0 & 0+0+0 & 0+0+1\end{bmatrix}=\begin{bmatrix}0 & 1 & -1\\ 0 & 1 & 0\\ 0 & 0 & 1\end{bmatrix}$$

$$BA=\begin{bmatrix}1 & 0 & 0\\ 0 & 1 & 0\\ 0 & 0 & 1\end{bmatrix}\begin{bmatrix}0 & 1 & -1\\ 0 & 1 & 0\\ 0 & 0 & 1\end{bmatrix}=\begin{bmatrix}1(0)+0(0)+0(0) & 1(1)+0(1)+0(0) & 1(-1)+0(0)+0(1)\\ 0(0)+1(0)+0(0) & 0(1)+1(1)+0(0) & 0(-1)+1(0)+0(1)\\ 0(0)+0(0)+1(0) & 0(1)+0(1)+1(0) & 0(-1)+0(0)+1(1)\end{bmatrix}$$

$$=\begin{bmatrix}0+0+0 & 1+0+0 & -1+0+0\\ 0+0+0 & 0+1+0 & 0+0+0\\ 0+0+0 & 0+0+0 & 0+0+1\end{bmatrix}=\begin{bmatrix}0 & 1 & -1\\ 0 & 1 & 0\\ 0 & 0 & 1\end{bmatrix}$$

Note: $AB = BA = A$

79. In Exercise 77, $AB = A$ and $BA = A$. For this pair of matrices, B acts in the same way for multiplication as the number 1 acts for multiplication of real numbers.

81. **(a)** The sales figure information may be written as the 3×3 matrix where column 1 represents nonfat, column 2 represents regular, and column 3 represents supercreamy.

$$\begin{matrix}\text{Location I}\\ \text{Location II}\\ \text{Location III}\end{matrix}\begin{bmatrix}50 & 100 & 30\\ 10 & 90 & 50\\ 60 & 120 & 40\end{bmatrix}.$$

(b) The income per gallon information may be written as the 3×1 matrix $\begin{bmatrix}12\\ 10\\ 15\end{bmatrix}$.

Note: If the matrix in part (a) had been written with its rows and columns interchanged, then this income per gallon information would be written instead as a 1×3 matrix.

(c) $\begin{bmatrix}50 & 100 & 30\\ 10 & 90 & 50\\ 60 & 120 & 40\end{bmatrix}\begin{bmatrix}12\\ 10\\ 15\end{bmatrix}=\begin{bmatrix}2050\\ 1770\\ 2520\end{bmatrix}$; Note: This result may be written as a 1×3 matrix instead.

(d) $2050 + 1770 + 2520 = 6340$; The total daily income from the three locations is \$6340.

83. (a) $j_1 = 690, s_p = 210, a_1 = 2100$

1st year: $j_2 = .33a_1 = .33(2100) = 693;\ s_2 = .18j_1 = .18(690) \approx 124$

$a_2 = .71s_1 + .94a_1 = .71(210) + .94(2100) \approx 2123$

$j_2 + s_2 + a_2 = 693 + 124 + 2123 = 2940$

2nd year: $j_3 = .33a_2 = .33(2123) \approx 700;\ s_3 = .18j_2 = .18(693) \approx 125$

$a_3 = .71s_2 + .94a_2 = .71(124) + .94(2123) \approx 2084$

$j_3 + s_3 + a_3 = 700 + 125 + 2084 = 2909$

3rd year: $j_4 = .33a_3 = .33(2084) \approx 687;\ s_4 = .18j_3 = .18(700) = 126$

$a_4 = .72s_3 + .94a_3 = .71(125) + .94(2084) = 2048$

$j_3 + s_3 + a_3 = 687 + 126 + 2048 = 2861$

4th year: $j_5 = .33a_4 = .33(2048) \approx 676;\ s_5 = .18j_4 = .18(687) \approx 124$

$a_5 = .72s_4 + .94a_4 = .71(126) + .94(2048) = 2014$

$j_5 + s_5 + a_5 = 686 + 124 + 2048 = 2814$

5th year: $j_6 = .33a_5 = .33(2014) \approx 664;\ s_6 = .18j_5 = .18(676) \approx 122$

$a_6 = .72s_5 + .94a_5 = .71(124) + .94(2014) \approx 1981$

$j_6 + s_6 + a_6 = 664 + 122 + 1981 = 2767$

(b) There will be extinction of the northern spotted owl because given the population of one year, the next year always has less of a population.

(c) $j_1 = 690, s_1 = 210, a_1 = 2100$

1st year: $j_2 = .33a_1 = .33(2100) = 693;\ s_2 = .3j_1 = .3(690) = 207$

$a_2 = .71s_1 + .94a_1 = .71(210) + .94(2100) \approx 2123$

$j_2 + s_2 + a_2 = 693 + 207 + 2123 = 3023$

2nd year: $j_3 = .33a_2 = .33(2123) \approx 701;\ s_3 = .3j_2 = .3(693) \approx 208$

$a_3 = .71s_2 + .94a_2 = .71(207) = .94(2123) \approx 2143$

$j_3 + s_3 + a_3 = 701 + 208 + 2143 = 3052$

3rd year: $j_4 = .33a_3 = .33(2143) \approx 707;\ s_4 = .3j_3 = .3(701) = 210$

$a_4 = .71s_3 + .94a_3 = .71(208) + .94(2143) \approx 2162$

$j_4 + s_4 + a_4 = 707 + 210 + 2162 = 3079$

4th year: $j_5 = .33a_4 = .33(2162) \approx 714;\ s_5 = .3j_4 = .3(707) \approx 212$

$a_5 = .72s_4 + .94a_4 = .71(210) + .94(2162) \approx 2181$

$j_5 + s_5 + a_5 = 714 + 212 + 2181 = 3107$

5th year: $j_6 = .71s_5 = .33a_5 = .33(2181) \approx 720;\ s_6 = .3j_5 = .3(714) \approx 214$

$a_6 = .71s_5 + .94a_5 = .71(212) + .94(2181) = 2201$

$j_6 + s_6 + a_6 = 720 + 214 + 2201 = 3135$

85. Expanding $\begin{vmatrix} -x & 0 & .33 \\ .18 & -x & 0 \\ 0 & .71 & .94-x \end{vmatrix}$ by row one we have the following.

$$-x\begin{vmatrix} -x & 0 \\ .71 & .94-x \end{vmatrix} - 0 + .33\begin{vmatrix} .18 & -x \\ 0 & .71 \end{vmatrix} = -x\left[-x(.94-x)-.71(0)\right]+.33\left[(.18)(.71)-0(-x)\right]$$
$$= -x\left(-.94x+x^2-0\right)+.33(.1278-0) = .94x^2-x^3+.042174$$

Thus, the polynomial is $-x^3+.94x^2+.042174$. Evaluating this polynomial with $x=.98359$, we have $-(.98359)^3+.94(.98359)^2+.042174 \approx .0000029$. Thus $.98359$ is an approximate zero.

In Exercises 87 – 93, $A=\begin{bmatrix} a_{11} & a_{12} \\ a_{21} & a_{22} \end{bmatrix}$, $B=\begin{bmatrix} b_{11} & b_{12} \\ b_{21} & b_{22} \end{bmatrix}$, and $C=\begin{bmatrix} c_{11} & c_{12} \\ c_{21} & c_{22} \end{bmatrix}$.

87. $A+B=B+A$

$$A+B=\begin{bmatrix} a_{11} & a_{12} \\ a_{21} & a_{22} \end{bmatrix}+\begin{bmatrix} b_{11} & b_{12} \\ b_{21} & b_{22} \end{bmatrix}=\begin{bmatrix} a_{11}+b_{11} & a_{12}+b_{12} \\ a_{21}+b_{21} & a_{22}+b_{22} \end{bmatrix}=\begin{bmatrix} b_{11}+a_{11} & b_{12}+a_{12} \\ b_{21}+a_{21} & b_{22}+a_{22} \end{bmatrix}=B+A$$

89. $$(AB)C=\left(\begin{bmatrix} a_{11} & a_{12} \\ a_{21} & a_{22} \end{bmatrix}\begin{bmatrix} b_{11} & b_{12} \\ b_{21} & b_{22} \end{bmatrix}\right)C=\begin{bmatrix} a_{11}b_{11}+a_{12}b_{21} & a_{11}b_{12}+a_{12}b_{22} \\ a_{21}b_{11}+a_{22}b_{21} & a_{21}b_{12}+a_{22}b_{22} \end{bmatrix}\begin{bmatrix} c_{11} & c_{12} \\ c_{21} & c_{22} \end{bmatrix}$$
$$=\begin{bmatrix} (a_{11}b_{11}+a_{12}b_{21})c_{11}+(a_{11}b_{12}+a_{12}b_{22})c_{21} & (a_{11}b_{11}+a_{12}b_{21})c_{12}+(a_{11}b_{12}+a_{12}b_{22})c_{22} \\ (a_{21}b_{11}+a_{22}b_{21})c_{11}+(a_{21}b_{12}+a_{22}b_{22})c_{21} & (a_{21}b_{11}+a_{22}b_{21})c_{12}+(a_{21}b_{12}+a_{22}b_{22})c_{22} \end{bmatrix}$$
$$=\begin{bmatrix} a_{11}b_{11}c_{11}+a_{12}b_{21}c_{11}+a_{11}b_{12}c_{21}+a_{12}b_{22}c_{21} & a_{11}b_{11}c_{12}+a_{12}b_{21}c_{12}+a_{11}b_{12}c_{22}+a_{12}b_{22}c_{22} \\ a_{21}b_{11}c_{11}+a_{22}b_{21}c_{11}+a_{21}b_{12}c_{21}+a_{22}b_{22}c_{21} & a_{21}b_{11}c_{12}+a_{22}b_{21}c_{12}+a_{21}b_{12}c_{22}+a_{22}b_{22}c_{22} \end{bmatrix}$$
$$A(BC)=A\left(\begin{bmatrix} b_{11} & b_{12} \\ b_{21} & b_{22} \end{bmatrix}\begin{bmatrix} c_{11} & c_{12} \\ c_{21} & c_{22} \end{bmatrix}\right)=\begin{bmatrix} a_{11} & a_{12} \\ a_{21} & a_{22} \end{bmatrix}\begin{bmatrix} b_{11}c_{11}+b_{12}c_{21} & b_{11}c_{12}+b_{12}c_{22} \\ b_{21}c_{11}+b_{22}c_{21} & b_{21}c_{12}+b_{22}c_{22} \end{bmatrix}$$
$$=\begin{bmatrix} a_{11}(b_{11}c_{11}+b_{12}c_{21})+a_{12}(b_{21}c_{11}+b_{22}c_{21}) & a_{11}(b_{11}c_{12}+b_{12}c_{22})+a_{12}(b_{21}c_{12}+b_{22}c_{22}) \\ a_{21}(b_{11}c_{11}+b_{12}c_{21})+a_{22}(b_{21}c_{11}+b_{22}c_{21}) & a_{21}(b_{11}c_{12}+b_{12}c_{22})+a_{22}(b_{21}c_{12}+b_{22}c_{22}) \end{bmatrix}$$
$$=\begin{bmatrix} a_{11}b_{11}c_{11}+a_{11}b_{12}c_{21}+a_{12}b_{21}c_{11}+a_{12}b_{22}c_{21} & a_{11}b_{11}c_{12}+a_{11}b_{12}c_{22}+a_{12}b_{21}c_{12}+a_{12}b_{22}c_{22} \\ a_{21}b_{11}c_{11}+a_{21}b_{12}c_{21}+a_{22}b_{21}c_{11}+a_{22}b_{22}c_{21} & a_{21}b_{11}c_{12}+a_{21}b_{12}c_{22}+a_{22}b_{21}c_{12}+a_{22}b_{22}c_{22} \end{bmatrix}$$
$$=\begin{bmatrix} a_{11}b_{11}c_{11}+a_{12}b_{21}c_{11}+a_{11}b_{12}c_{21}+a_{12}b_{22}c_{21} & a_{11}b_{11}c_{12}+a_{12}b_{21}c_{12}+a_{11}b_{12}c_{22}+a_{12}b_{22}c_{22} \\ a_{21}b_{11}c_{11}+a_{22}b_{21}c_{11}+a_{21}b_{12}c_{21}+a_{22}b_{22}c_{21} & a_{21}b_{11}c_{12}+a_{22}b_{21}c_{12}+a_{21}b_{12}c_{22}+a_{22}b_{22}c_{22} \end{bmatrix}$$

Since the final matrix for $(AB)C$ and $A(BC)$ are the same, we have obtained the desired results.

91. $c(A+B)=cA+cB$, for any real number c.

$$c(A+B)=c\left(\begin{bmatrix} a_{11} & a_{12} \\ a_{21} & a_{22} \end{bmatrix}+\begin{bmatrix} b_{11} & b_{12} \\ b_{21} & b_{22} \end{bmatrix}\right)=c\begin{bmatrix} a_{11}+b_{11} & a_{12}+b_{12} \\ a_{21}+b_{21} & a_{22}+b_{22} \end{bmatrix}=\begin{bmatrix} c(a_{11}+b_{11}) & c(a_{12}+b_{12}) \\ c(a_{21}+b_{21}) & c(a_{22}+b_{22}) \end{bmatrix}$$
$$=\begin{bmatrix} c\cdot a_{11}+c\cdot b_{11} & c\cdot a_{12}+c\cdot b_{12} \\ c\cdot a_{21}+c\cdot b_{21} & c\cdot a_{22}+c\cdot b_{22} \end{bmatrix}=\begin{bmatrix} c\cdot a_{11} & c\cdot a_{12} \\ c\cdot a_{21} & c\cdot a_{22} \end{bmatrix}+\begin{bmatrix} c\cdot b_{11} & c\cdot b_{12} \\ c\cdot b_{21} & c\cdot b_{22} \end{bmatrix}$$
$$=c\begin{bmatrix} a_{11} & a_{12} \\ a_{21} & a_{22} \end{bmatrix}+c\begin{bmatrix} b_{11} & b_{12} \\ b_{21} & b_{22} \end{bmatrix}=cA+cB$$

93. $c(A)d=(cd)A$, for any real numbers c and d.

$$c(A)d=\left(c\begin{bmatrix}a_{11} & a_{12}\\ a_{21} & a_{22}\end{bmatrix}\right)d=\begin{bmatrix}c\cdot a_{11} & c\cdot a_{12}\\ c\cdot a_{21} & c\cdot a_{22}\end{bmatrix}d=\begin{bmatrix}c\cdot a_{11}\cdot d & c\cdot a_{12}\cdot d\\ c\cdot a_{21}\cdot d & c\cdot a_{22}\cdot d\end{bmatrix}=\begin{bmatrix}c\cdot d\cdot a_{11} & c\cdot d\cdot a_{12}\\ c\cdot d\cdot a_{21} & c\cdot d\cdot a_{22}\end{bmatrix}$$

$$=\begin{bmatrix}(cd)\cdot a_{11} & (cd)\cdot a_{12}\\ (cd)\cdot a_{21} & (cd)\cdot a_{22}\end{bmatrix}=(cd)\begin{bmatrix}a_{11} & a_{12}\\ a_{21} & a_{22}\end{bmatrix}=(cd)A$$

Section 9.8: Matrix Inverses

1. $A=\begin{bmatrix}-2 & 4 & 0\\ 3 & 5 & 9\\ 0 & 8 & -6\end{bmatrix}$ and $I_3=\begin{bmatrix}1 & 0 & 0\\ 0 & 1 & 0\\ 0 & 0 & 1\end{bmatrix}$

$$I_3A=\begin{bmatrix}1 & 0 & 0\\ 0 & 1 & 0\\ 0 & 0 & 1\end{bmatrix}\begin{bmatrix}-2 & 4 & 0\\ 3 & 5 & 9\\ 0 & 8 & -6\end{bmatrix}=\begin{bmatrix}1(-2)+0(3)+0(0) & 1(4)+0(5)+0(8) & 1(0)+0(9)+0(-6)\\ 0(-2)+1(3)+0(0) & 0(4)+1(5)+0(8) & 0(0)+1(9)+0(-6)\\ 0(-2)+0(3)+1(0) & 0(4)+0(5)+1(8) & 0(0)+0(9)+1(-6)\end{bmatrix}$$

$$=\begin{bmatrix}-2+0+0 & 4+0+0 & 0+0+0\\ 0+3+0 & 0+5+0 & 0+9+0\\ 0+0+0 & 0+0+8 & 0+0+(-6)\end{bmatrix}=\begin{bmatrix}-2 & 4 & 0\\ 3 & 5 & 9\\ 0 & 8 & -6\end{bmatrix}$$

3. $\begin{bmatrix}5 & 7\\ 2 & 3\end{bmatrix}\begin{bmatrix}3 & -7\\ -2 & 5\end{bmatrix}=\begin{bmatrix}5(3)+7(-2) & 5(-7)+7(5)\\ 2(3)+3(-2) & 2(-7)+3(5)\end{bmatrix}=\begin{bmatrix}15+(-14) & -35+35\\ 6+(-6) & (-14)+15\end{bmatrix}=\begin{bmatrix}1 & 0\\ 0 & 1\end{bmatrix}$

$\begin{bmatrix}3 & -7\\ -2 & 5\end{bmatrix}\begin{bmatrix}5 & 7\\ 2 & 3\end{bmatrix}=\begin{bmatrix}3(5)+(-7)(2) & 3(7)+(-7)(3)\\ (-2)(5)+5(2) & (-2)(7)+5(3)\end{bmatrix}=\begin{bmatrix}15+(-14) & 21+(-21)\\ (-10)+10 & (-14)+15\end{bmatrix}=\begin{bmatrix}1 & 0\\ 0 & 1\end{bmatrix}$

Since the products obtained by multiplying the matrices in either order are both the 2×2 identity matrix, the given matrices are inverses of each other.

5. $\begin{bmatrix}-1 & 2\\ 3 & -5\end{bmatrix}\begin{bmatrix}-5 & -2\\ -3 & -1\end{bmatrix}=\begin{bmatrix}-1(-5)+2(-3) & -1(-2)+2(-1)\\ 3(-5)+(-5)(-3) & 3(-2)+(-5)(-1)\end{bmatrix}=\begin{bmatrix}5+(-6) & 2+(-2)\\ -15+15 & -6+5\end{bmatrix}=\begin{bmatrix}-1 & 0\\ 0 & -1\end{bmatrix}$

Since this product is not the 2×2 identity matrix, the given matrices are not inverses of each other.

7. $\begin{bmatrix}0 & 1 & 0\\ 0 & 0 & -2\\ 1 & -1 & 0\end{bmatrix}\begin{bmatrix}1 & 0 & 1\\ 1 & 0 & 0\\ 0 & -1 & 0\end{bmatrix}=\begin{bmatrix}0(1)+1(1)+0(0) & 0(0)+1(0)+0(-1) & 0(1)+1(0)+0(0)\\ 0(1)+0(1)+(-2)(0) & 0(0)+0(0)+(-2)(-1) & 0(1)+0(0)+(-2)(0)\\ 1(1)+(-1)(1)+0(0) & 1(0)+(-1)(0)+0(-1) & 1(1)+(-1)(0)+0(0)\end{bmatrix}$

$$=\begin{bmatrix}0+1+0 & 0+0+0 & 0+0+0\\ 0+0+0 & 0+0+2 & 0+0+0\\ 1+(-1)+0 & 0+0+0 & 1+0+0\end{bmatrix}=\begin{bmatrix}1 & 0 & 0\\ 0 & 2 & 0\\ 0 & 0 & 1\end{bmatrix}$$

Since this product is not the 3×3 identity matrix, the given matrices are not inverses of each other.

9. $\begin{bmatrix} -1 & -1 & -1 \\ 4 & 5 & 0 \\ 0 & 1 & -3 \end{bmatrix}\begin{bmatrix} 15 & 4 & -5 \\ -12 & -3 & 4 \\ -4 & -1 & 1 \end{bmatrix}$

$$= \begin{bmatrix} -1(15)+(-1)(-12)+(-1)(-4) & -1(4)+(-1)(-3)+(-1)(-1) & -1(-5)+(-1)(4)+(-1)(1) \\ 4(15)+5(-12)+0(-4) & 4(4)+5(-3)+0(-1) & 4(-5)+5(4)+0(1) \\ 0(15)+1(-12)+(-3)(-4) & 0(4)+1(-3)+(-3)(-1) & 0(-5)+1(4)+(-3)(1) \end{bmatrix}$$

$$= \begin{bmatrix} -15+12+4 & -4+3+1 & 5+(-4)+(-1) \\ 60+(-60)+0 & 16+(-15)+0 & -20+20+0 \\ 0+(-12)+12 & 0+(-3)+3 & 0+4+(-3) \end{bmatrix} = \begin{bmatrix} 1 & 0 & 0 \\ 0 & 1 & 0 \\ 0 & 0 & 1 \end{bmatrix} = I_3$$

$\begin{bmatrix} 15 & 4 & -5 \\ -12 & -3 & 4 \\ -4 & -1 & 1 \end{bmatrix}\begin{bmatrix} -1 & -1 & -1 \\ 4 & 5 & 0 \\ 0 & 1 & -3 \end{bmatrix}$

$$= \begin{bmatrix} 15(-1)+4(4)+(-5)(0) & 15(-1)+4(5)+(-5)(1) & 15(-1)+4(0)+(-5)(-3) \\ -12(-1)+(-3)(4)+4(0) & -12(-1)+(-3)(5)+4(1) & -12(-1)+(-3)(0)+4(-3) \\ -4(-1)+(-1)(4)+1(0) & -4(-1)+(-1)(5)+1(1) & -4(-1)+(-1)(0)+1(-3) \end{bmatrix}$$

$$= \begin{bmatrix} -15+16+0 & -15+20+(-5) & -15+0+15 \\ 12+(-12)+0 & 12+(-15)+4 & 12+0+(-12) \\ 4+(-4)+0 & 4+(-5)+1 & 0+4+(-3) \end{bmatrix} = \begin{bmatrix} 1 & 0 & 0 \\ 0 & 1 & 0 \\ 0 & 0 & 1 \end{bmatrix} = I_3$$

The given matrices are inverses of each other.

11. Find the inverse of $A = \begin{bmatrix} -1 & 2 \\ -2 & -1 \end{bmatrix}$, if it exists. Since $[A \mid I_2] = \left[\begin{array}{cc|cc} -1 & 2 & 1 & 0 \\ -2 & -1 & 0 & 1 \end{array}\right]$, we have

$$\left[\begin{array}{cc|cc} 1 & -2 & -1 & 0 \\ -2 & -1 & 0 & 1 \end{array}\right]\begin{matrix} -1\text{R1} \\ \end{matrix} \Rightarrow \left[\begin{array}{cc|cc} 1 & -2 & -1 & 0 \\ 0 & -5 & -2 & 1 \end{array}\right]\begin{matrix} \\ 2\text{R1}+\text{R2} \end{matrix}$$

$$\left[\begin{array}{cc|cc} 1 & -2 & -1 & 0 \\ 0 & 1 & \frac{2}{5} & -\frac{1}{5} \end{array}\right]\begin{matrix} \\ -\frac{1}{5}\text{R2} \end{matrix} \Rightarrow \left[\begin{array}{cc|cc} 1 & 0 & -\frac{1}{5} & -\frac{2}{5} \\ 0 & 1 & \frac{2}{5} & -\frac{1}{5} \end{array}\right]\begin{matrix} 2\text{R2}+\text{R1} \\ \end{matrix}.$$

Thus, $A^{-1} = \begin{bmatrix} -\frac{1}{5} & -\frac{2}{5} \\ \frac{2}{5} & -\frac{1}{5} \end{bmatrix}$.

13. Find the inverse of $A = \begin{bmatrix} -1 & -2 \\ 3 & 4 \end{bmatrix}$, if it exists. Since $[A \mid I_2] = \left[\begin{array}{cc|cc} -1 & -2 & 1 & 0 \\ 3 & 4 & 0 & 1 \end{array}\right]$, we have

$$\left[\begin{array}{cc|cc} -1 & -2 & 1 & 0 \\ 0 & -2 & 3 & 1 \end{array}\right]\begin{matrix} \\ 3\text{R1}+\text{R2} \end{matrix} \Rightarrow \left[\begin{array}{cc|cc} 1 & 2 & -1 & 0 \\ 0 & -2 & 3 & 1 \end{array}\right]\begin{matrix} -1\text{R1} \\ \end{matrix}$$

$$\left[\begin{array}{cc|cc} 1 & 0 & 2 & 1 \\ 0 & -2 & 3 & 1 \end{array}\right]\begin{matrix} \text{R2}+\text{R1} \\ \end{matrix} \Rightarrow \left[\begin{array}{cc|cc} 1 & 0 & 2 & 1 \\ 0 & 1 & -\frac{3}{2} & -\frac{1}{2} \end{array}\right]\begin{matrix} \\ -\frac{1}{2}\text{R2} \end{matrix}.$$

Thus, $A^{-1} = \begin{bmatrix} 2 & 1 \\ -\frac{3}{2} & -\frac{1}{2} \end{bmatrix}$.

15. Find the inverse of $\begin{bmatrix} 5 & 10 \\ -3 & -6 \end{bmatrix}$, if it exists. Since $\left[A|I_2\right] = \left[\begin{array}{cc|cc} 5 & 10 & 1 & 0 \\ -3 & -6 & 0 & 1 \end{array}\right]$, we have

$$\left[\begin{array}{cc|cc} 1 & 2 & \frac{1}{5} & 0 \\ -3 & -6 & 0 & 1 \end{array}\right] \begin{matrix} \frac{1}{5}\text{R1} \\ \end{matrix} \Rightarrow \left[\begin{array}{cc|cc} 1 & 2 & \frac{1}{5} & 0 \\ 0 & 0 & \frac{3}{5} & 1 \end{array}\right] \begin{matrix} \\ 3\text{R1}+\text{R2} \end{matrix}$$

At this point, the matrix should be changed so that the second-row, second-column element will be 1. Since that element is now 0, the desired transformation cannot be completed. Therefore, the inverse of the given matrix does not exist.

17. Find the inverse of $A = \begin{bmatrix} 1 & 0 & 1 \\ 0 & -1 & 0 \\ 2 & 1 & 1 \end{bmatrix}$, if it exists. Since $\left[A|I_3\right] = \left[\begin{array}{ccc|ccc} 1 & 0 & 1 & 1 & 0 & 0 \\ 0 & -1 & 0 & 0 & 1 & 0 \\ 2 & 1 & 1 & 0 & 0 & 1 \end{array}\right]$ we have

$$\left[\begin{array}{ccc|ccc} 1 & 0 & 1 & 1 & 0 & 0 \\ 0 & -1 & 0 & 0 & 1 & 0 \\ 0 & 1 & -1 & -2 & 0 & 1 \end{array}\right] \begin{matrix} \\ \\ -2\text{R1}+\text{R3} \end{matrix} \Rightarrow \left[\begin{array}{ccc|ccc} 1 & 0 & 1 & 1 & 0 & 0 \\ 0 & 1 & 0 & 0 & -1 & 0 \\ 0 & 0 & -1 & -2 & 1 & 1 \end{array}\right] \begin{matrix} \\ -1\text{R2} \\ \text{R2}+\text{R3} \end{matrix}$$

$$\left[\begin{array}{ccc|ccc} 1 & 0 & 1 & 1 & 0 & 0 \\ 0 & 1 & 0 & 0 & -1 & 0 \\ 0 & 0 & 1 & 2 & -1 & -1 \end{array}\right] \begin{matrix} \\ \\ -1\text{R3} \end{matrix} \Rightarrow \left[\begin{array}{ccc|ccc} 1 & 0 & 0 & -1 & 1 & 1 \\ 0 & 1 & 0 & 0 & -1 & 0 \\ 0 & 0 & 1 & 2 & -1 & -1 \end{array}\right] \begin{matrix} -1\text{R3}+\text{R1} \\ \\ \\ \end{matrix}.$$

Thus, $A^{-1} = \begin{bmatrix} -1 & 1 & 1 \\ 0 & -1 & 0 \\ 2 & -1 & -1 \end{bmatrix}$.

19. Find the inverse of $A = \begin{bmatrix} 1 & 3 & 3 \\ 1 & 4 & 3 \\ 1 & 3 & 4 \end{bmatrix}$, if it exists. Since $\left[A|I_3\right] = \left[\begin{array}{ccc|ccc} 1 & 3 & 3 & 1 & 0 & 0 \\ 1 & 4 & 3 & 0 & 1 & 0 \\ 1 & 3 & 4 & 0 & 0 & 1 \end{array}\right]$, we have

$$\left[\begin{array}{ccc|ccc} 1 & 3 & 3 & 1 & 0 & 0 \\ 0 & 1 & 0 & -1 & 1 & 0 \\ 0 & 0 & 1 & -1 & 0 & 1 \end{array}\right] \begin{matrix} \\ -1\text{R1}+\text{R2} \\ -1\text{R1}+\text{R3} \end{matrix} \Rightarrow \left[\begin{array}{ccc|ccc} 1 & 0 & 3 & 4 & -3 & 0 \\ 0 & 1 & 0 & -1 & 1 & 0 \\ 0 & 0 & 1 & -1 & 0 & 1 \end{array}\right] \begin{matrix} -3\text{R2}+\text{R1} \\ \\ \\ \end{matrix}$$

$$\left[\begin{array}{ccc|ccc} 1 & 0 & 0 & 7 & -3 & -3 \\ 0 & 1 & 0 & -1 & 1 & 0 \\ 0 & 0 & 1 & -1 & 0 & 1 \end{array}\right] \begin{matrix} -3\text{R3}+\text{R1} \\ \\ \\ \end{matrix}.$$

Thus, $A^{-1} = \begin{bmatrix} 7 & -3 & -3 \\ -1 & 1 & 0 \\ -1 & 0 & 1 \end{bmatrix}$.

21. Find the inverse of $A=\begin{bmatrix} 2 & 2 & -4 \\ 2 & 6 & 0 \\ -3 & -3 & 5 \end{bmatrix}$, if it exists. Since $\left[A\,|\,I_3\right]=\left[\begin{array}{ccc|ccc} 2 & 2 & -4 & 1 & 0 & 0 \\ 2 & 6 & 0 & 0 & 1 & 0 \\ -3 & -3 & 5 & 0 & 0 & 1 \end{array}\right]$,

$$\left[\begin{array}{ccc|ccc} 1 & 1 & -2 & \frac{1}{2} & 0 & 0 \\ 2 & 6 & 0 & 0 & 1 & 0 \\ -3 & -3 & 5 & 0 & 0 & 1 \end{array}\right]\begin{array}{l} \frac{1}{2}\text{R1} \\ \\ \\ \end{array} \Rightarrow \left[\begin{array}{ccc|ccc} 1 & 1 & -2 & \frac{1}{2} & 0 & 0 \\ 0 & 4 & 4 & -1 & 1 & 0 \\ 0 & 0 & -1 & \frac{3}{2} & 0 & 1 \end{array}\right]\begin{array}{l} \\ -2\text{R1}+\text{R2} \\ 3\text{R1}+\text{R3} \end{array}$$

$$\left[\begin{array}{ccc|ccc} 1 & 1 & -2 & \frac{1}{2} & 0 & 0 \\ 0 & 1 & 1 & -\frac{1}{4} & \frac{1}{4} & 0 \\ 0 & 0 & -1 & \frac{3}{2} & 0 & 1 \end{array}\right]\begin{array}{l} \\ \frac{1}{4}\text{R2} \\ \\ \end{array} \Rightarrow \left[\begin{array}{ccc|ccc} 1 & 0 & -3 & \frac{3}{4} & -\frac{1}{4} & 0 \\ 0 & 1 & 1 & -\frac{1}{4} & \frac{1}{4} & 0 \\ 0 & 0 & -1 & \frac{3}{2} & 0 & 1 \end{array}\right]\begin{array}{l} -1\text{R2}+\text{R1} \\ \\ \\ \end{array} \quad \backslash$$

$$\left[\begin{array}{ccc|ccc} 1 & 0 & -3 & \frac{3}{4} & -\frac{1}{4} & 0 \\ 0 & 1 & 1 & -\frac{1}{4} & \frac{1}{4} & 0 \\ 0 & 0 & 1 & -\frac{3}{2} & 0 & -1 \end{array}\right]\begin{array}{l} \\ \\ -1\text{R3} \end{array} \Rightarrow \left[\begin{array}{ccc|ccc} 1 & 0 & 0 & -\frac{15}{4} & -\frac{1}{4} & -3 \\ 0 & 1 & 0 & \frac{5}{4} & \frac{1}{4} & 1 \\ 0 & 0 & 1 & -\frac{3}{2} & 0 & -1 \end{array}\right]\begin{array}{l} 3\text{R3}+\text{R1} \\ -1\text{R3}+\text{R2}. \\ \\ \end{array}$$

Thus, $A^{-1}=\begin{bmatrix} -\frac{15}{4} & -\frac{1}{4} & -3 \\ \frac{5}{4} & \frac{1}{4} & 1 \\ -\frac{3}{2} & 0 & -1 \end{bmatrix}$.

23. Find the inverse of $A=\begin{bmatrix} 1 & 1 & 0 & 2 \\ 2 & -1 & 1 & -1 \\ 3 & 3 & 2 & -2 \\ 1 & 2 & 1 & 0 \end{bmatrix}$, if it exists.

$$\left[A\,|\,I_4\right]=\left[\begin{array}{cccc|cccc} 1 & 1 & 0 & 2 & 1 & 0 & 0 & 0 \\ 2 & -1 & 1 & -1 & 0 & 1 & 0 & 0 \\ 3 & 3 & 2 & -2 & 0 & 0 & 1 & 0 \\ 1 & 2 & 1 & 0 & 0 & 0 & 0 & 1 \end{array}\right] \Rightarrow \left[\begin{array}{cccc|cccc} 1 & 1 & 0 & 2 & 1 & 0 & 0 & 0 \\ 0 & -3 & 1 & -5 & -2 & 1 & 0 & 0 \\ 0 & 0 & 2 & -8 & -3 & 0 & 1 & 0 \\ 0 & 1 & 1 & -2 & -1 & 0 & 0 & 1 \end{array}\right]\begin{array}{l} \\ -2\text{R1}+\text{R2} \\ -3\text{R1}+\text{R3} \\ -1\text{R1}+\text{R4} \end{array}$$

$$\Rightarrow \left[\begin{array}{cccc|cccc} 1 & 1 & 0 & 2 & 1 & 0 & 0 & 0 \\ 0 & 1 & -\frac{1}{3} & \frac{5}{3} & \frac{2}{3} & -\frac{1}{3} & 0 & 0 \\ 0 & 0 & 2 & -8 & -3 & 0 & 1 & 0 \\ 0 & 1 & 1 & -2 & -1 & 0 & 0 & 1 \end{array}\right]\begin{array}{l} \\ -\frac{1}{3}\text{R2} \\ \\ \\ \end{array} \Rightarrow \left[\begin{array}{cccc|cccc} 1 & 0 & \frac{1}{3} & \frac{1}{3} & \frac{1}{3} & \frac{1}{3} & 0 & 0 \\ 0 & 1 & -\frac{1}{3} & \frac{5}{3} & \frac{2}{3} & -\frac{1}{3} & 0 & 0 \\ 0 & 0 & 2 & -8 & -3 & 0 & 1 & 0 \\ 0 & 0 & \frac{4}{3} & -\frac{11}{3} & -\frac{5}{3} & \frac{1}{3} & 0 & 1 \end{array}\right]\begin{array}{l} -1\text{R2}+\text{R1} \\ \\ \\ -1\text{R2}+\text{R4} \end{array}$$

$$\Rightarrow \left[\begin{array}{cccc|cccc} 1 & 0 & \frac{1}{3} & \frac{1}{3} & \frac{1}{3} & \frac{1}{3} & 0 & 0 \\ 0 & 1 & -\frac{1}{3} & \frac{5}{3} & \frac{2}{3} & -\frac{1}{3} & 0 & 0 \\ 0 & 0 & 1 & -4 & -\frac{3}{2} & 0 & \frac{1}{2} & 0 \\ 0 & 0 & \frac{4}{3} & -\frac{11}{3} & -\frac{5}{3} & \frac{1}{3} & 0 & 1 \end{array}\right]\begin{array}{l} \\ \\ \frac{1}{2}\text{R3} \\ \\ \end{array} \Rightarrow \left[\begin{array}{cccc|cccc} 1 & 0 & 0 & \frac{5}{3} & \frac{5}{6} & \frac{1}{3} & -\frac{1}{6} & 0 \\ 0 & 1 & 0 & \frac{1}{3} & \frac{1}{6} & -\frac{1}{3} & \frac{1}{6} & 0 \\ 0 & 0 & 1 & -4 & -\frac{3}{2} & 0 & \frac{1}{2} & 0 \\ 0 & 0 & 0 & \frac{5}{3} & \frac{1}{3} & \frac{1}{3} & -\frac{2}{3} & 1 \end{array}\right]\begin{array}{l} -\frac{1}{3}\text{R3}+\text{R1} \\ \frac{1}{3}\text{R3}+\text{R2} \\ \\ -\frac{4}{3}\text{R3}+\text{R4} \end{array}$$

$$\Rightarrow \left[\begin{array}{cccc|cccc} 1 & 0 & 0 & \frac{5}{3} & \frac{5}{6} & \frac{1}{3} & -\frac{1}{6} & 0 \\ 0 & 1 & 0 & \frac{1}{3} & \frac{1}{6} & -\frac{1}{3} & \frac{1}{6} & 0 \\ 0 & 0 & 1 & -4 & -\frac{3}{2} & 0 & \frac{1}{2} & 0 \\ 0 & 0 & 0 & 1 & \frac{1}{5} & \frac{1}{5} & -\frac{2}{5} & \frac{3}{5} \end{array}\right]\begin{array}{l} \\ \\ \\ \frac{3}{5}\text{R4} \end{array} \Rightarrow \left[\begin{array}{cccc|cccc} 1 & 0 & 0 & 0 & \frac{1}{2} & 0 & \frac{1}{2} & -1 \\ 0 & 1 & 0 & 0 & \frac{1}{10} & -\frac{2}{5} & \frac{3}{10} & -\frac{1}{5} \\ 0 & 0 & 1 & 0 & -\frac{7}{10} & \frac{4}{5} & -\frac{11}{10} & \frac{12}{5} \\ 0 & 0 & 0 & 1 & \frac{1}{5} & \frac{1}{5} & -\frac{2}{5} & \frac{3}{5} \end{array}\right]\begin{array}{l} -\frac{5}{3}\text{R4}+\text{R1} \\ -\frac{1}{3}\text{R4}+\text{R2} \\ 4\text{R4}+\text{R3} \\ \\ \end{array}$$

Thus, $A^{-1}=\begin{bmatrix} \frac{1}{2} & 0 & \frac{1}{2} & -1 \\ \frac{1}{10} & -\frac{2}{5} & \frac{3}{10} & -\frac{1}{5} \\ -\frac{7}{10} & \frac{4}{5} & -\frac{11}{10} & \frac{12}{5} \\ \frac{1}{5} & \frac{1}{5} & -\frac{2}{5} & \frac{3}{5} \end{bmatrix}$.

25. Since $A^{-1}=\begin{bmatrix}5 & -9\\ -1 & 2\end{bmatrix}$, we need to find A, where $A=\left(A^{-1}\right)^{-1}$.

$$\left[A^{-1}|I_2\right]=\left[\begin{array}{cc|cc}5 & -9 & 1 & 0\\ -1 & 2 & 0 & 1\end{array}\right]\Rightarrow\left[\begin{array}{cc|cc}1 & -\frac{9}{5} & \frac{1}{5} & 0\\ -1 & 2 & 0 & 1\end{array}\right]\tfrac{1}{5}\text{R1}\Rightarrow\left[\begin{array}{cc|cc}1 & -\frac{9}{5} & \frac{1}{5} & 0\\ 0 & \frac{1}{5} & \frac{1}{5} & 1\end{array}\right]1\text{R1}+\text{R2}$$

$$\left[\begin{array}{cc|cc}1 & -\frac{9}{5} & \frac{1}{5} & 0\\ 0 & 1 & 1 & 5\end{array}\right]5\text{R2}\Rightarrow\left[\begin{array}{cc|cc}1 & 0 & 2 & 9\\ 0 & 1 & 1 & 5\end{array}\right]\tfrac{9}{5}\text{R2}+\text{R1}$$

Thus, $A=\begin{bmatrix}2 & 9\\ 1 & 5\end{bmatrix}$.

27. If $A=\begin{bmatrix}a & b\\ c & d\end{bmatrix}$, then $ad-bc=ad-cb$ is the determinant of matrix A.

28. If $A^{-1}=\begin{bmatrix}\frac{d}{ad-bc} & \frac{-b}{ad-bc}\\ \frac{-c}{ad-bc} & \frac{a}{ad-bc}\end{bmatrix}$, then $A^{-1}=\begin{bmatrix}\frac{d}{|A|} & \frac{-b}{|A|}\\ \frac{-c}{|A|} & \frac{a}{|A|}\end{bmatrix}$.

29. $A^{-1}=\begin{bmatrix}\frac{d}{|A|} & \frac{-b}{|A|}\\ \frac{-c}{|A|} & \frac{a}{|A|}\end{bmatrix}=\begin{bmatrix}\frac{1}{|A|}d & \frac{1}{|A|}(-b)\\ \frac{1}{|A|}(-c) & \frac{1}{|A|}a\end{bmatrix}=\frac{1}{|A|}\begin{bmatrix}d & -b\\ -c & a\end{bmatrix}$

30. Given $A=\begin{bmatrix}a & b\\ c & d\end{bmatrix}$, switch entries a_{11} and a_{22} (a and d, respectively). Then negate entries a_{12} and a_{21} (b and c, respectively). Finally, multiply the matrix by $\frac{1}{|A|}$ to obtain $A^{-1}=\frac{1}{|A|}\begin{bmatrix}d & -b\\ -c & a\end{bmatrix}$.

31. Given $A=\begin{bmatrix}4 & 2\\ 7 & 3\end{bmatrix}$, $|A|=12-14=-2$. Thus $A^{-1}=\frac{1}{-2}\begin{bmatrix}3 & -2\\ -7 & 4\end{bmatrix}=\begin{bmatrix}-\frac{3}{2} & 1\\ \frac{7}{2} & -2\end{bmatrix}$.

32. The inverse of a 2×2 matrix A does not exist if the determinant of A has the value zero.

33. $-x+y=1$
$2x-y=1$

Given $A=\begin{bmatrix}-1 & 1\\ 2 & -1\end{bmatrix}$, $X=\begin{bmatrix}x\\ y\end{bmatrix}$, and $B=\begin{bmatrix}1\\ 1\end{bmatrix}$, find A^{-1}. Since $\left[A|I_2\right]=\left[\begin{array}{cc|cc}-1 & 1 & 1 & 0\\ 2 & -1 & 0 & 1\end{array}\right]$,

$$\left[\begin{array}{cc|cc}1 & -1 & -1 & 0\\ 2 & -1 & 0 & 1\end{array}\right]-1\text{R1}\Rightarrow\left[\begin{array}{cc|cc}1 & -1 & -1 & 0\\ 0 & 1 & 2 & 1\end{array}\right]-2\text{R1}+\text{R2}\Rightarrow\left[\begin{array}{cc|cc}1 & 0 & 1 & 1\\ 0 & 1 & 2 & 1\end{array}\right]\text{R2}+\text{R1}.$$

Thus, $A^{-1}=\begin{bmatrix}1 & 1\\ 2 & 1\end{bmatrix}$.

$$X=A^{-1}B=\begin{bmatrix}1 & 1\\ 2 & 1\end{bmatrix}\begin{bmatrix}1\\ 1\end{bmatrix}=\begin{bmatrix}1(1)+1(1)\\ 2(1)+1(1)\end{bmatrix}=\begin{bmatrix}1+1\\ 2+1\end{bmatrix}=\begin{bmatrix}2\\ 3\end{bmatrix}$$

Solution set: $\{(2,3)\}$

35. $2x-y=-8$
$3x+y=-2$

Given $A=\begin{bmatrix}2 & -1\\ 3 & 1\end{bmatrix}, X=\begin{bmatrix}x\\ y\end{bmatrix},$ and $B=\begin{bmatrix}-8\\ -2\end{bmatrix}$, find A^{-1}. We will use the relation given on the bottom of page 875 to calculate A^{-1} in the solution to this exercise.

If $A=\begin{bmatrix}a & b\\ c & d\end{bmatrix}$, then $A^{-1}=\begin{bmatrix}\frac{d}{ad-bc} & \frac{-b}{ad-bc}\\ \frac{-c}{ad-bc} & \frac{a}{ad-bc}\end{bmatrix}$. Thus we have the following.

$$A^{-1}=\begin{bmatrix}\frac{1}{2(1)-(-1)(3)} & \frac{1}{2(1)-(-1)(3)}\\ \frac{-3}{2(1)-(-1)(3)} & \frac{2}{2(1)-(-1)(3)}\end{bmatrix}=\begin{bmatrix}\frac{1}{2-(-3)} & \frac{1}{2-(-3)}\\ \frac{-3}{2-(-3)} & \frac{2}{2-(-3)}\end{bmatrix}=\begin{bmatrix}\frac{1}{5} & \frac{1}{5}\\ -\frac{3}{5} & \frac{2}{5}\end{bmatrix}$$

$$X=A^{-1}B=\begin{bmatrix}\frac{1}{5} & \frac{1}{5}\\ -\frac{3}{5} & \frac{2}{5}\end{bmatrix}\begin{bmatrix}-8\\ -2\end{bmatrix}=\begin{bmatrix}\frac{1}{5}(-8)+\frac{1}{5}(-2)\\ -\frac{3}{5}(-8)+\frac{2}{5}(-2)\end{bmatrix}=\begin{bmatrix}-\frac{8}{5}+\left(-\frac{2}{5}\right)\\ \frac{24}{5}+\left(-\frac{4}{5}\right)\end{bmatrix}=\begin{bmatrix}-\frac{10}{5}\\ \frac{20}{5}\end{bmatrix}=\begin{bmatrix}-2\\ 4\end{bmatrix}$$

Solution set: $\{(-2,4)\}$

37. $2x+3y=-10$
$3x+4y=-12$

Given $A=\begin{bmatrix}2 & 3\\ 3 & 4\end{bmatrix}, X=\begin{bmatrix}x\\ y\end{bmatrix}$, and $B=\begin{bmatrix}-10\\ -12\end{bmatrix}$, find A^{-1}. Since $\left[A|I_2\right]=\left[\begin{array}{cc|cc}2 & 3 & 1 & 0\\ 3 & 4 & 0 & 1\end{array}\right]$,

$$\left[\begin{array}{cc|cc}1 & \frac{3}{2} & \frac{1}{2} & 0\\ 3 & 4 & 0 & 1\end{array}\right]\begin{matrix}\frac{1}{2}\text{R1}\\ \\ \end{matrix}\Rightarrow\left[\begin{array}{cc|cc}1 & \frac{3}{2} & \frac{1}{2} & 0\\ 0 & -\frac{1}{2} & -\frac{3}{2} & 1\end{array}\right]\begin{matrix}\\ -3\text{R1}+\text{R2}\end{matrix}$$

$$\left[\begin{array}{cc|cc}1 & \frac{3}{2} & \frac{1}{2} & 0\\ 0 & 1 & 3 & -2\end{array}\right]\begin{matrix}\\ -2\text{R2}\end{matrix}\Rightarrow\left[\begin{array}{cc|cc}1 & 0 & -4 & 3\\ 0 & 1 & 3 & -2\end{array}\right]\begin{matrix}-\frac{3}{2}\text{R2}+\text{R1}\\ \\ \end{matrix}.\ \text{Thus, } A^{-1}=\begin{bmatrix}-4 & 3\\ 3 & -2\end{bmatrix}.$$

$$X=A^{-1}B=\begin{bmatrix}-4 & 3\\ 3 & -2\end{bmatrix}\begin{bmatrix}-10\\ -12\end{bmatrix}=\begin{bmatrix}-4(-10)+3(-12)\\ 3(-10)+(-2)(-12)\end{bmatrix}=\begin{bmatrix}40+(-36)\\ -30+24\end{bmatrix}=\begin{bmatrix}4\\ -6\end{bmatrix}$$

Solution set: $\{(4,-6)\}$

39. $6x+9y=3$
$-8x+3y=6$

Given $A=\begin{bmatrix}6 & 9\\ -8 & 3\end{bmatrix}, X=\begin{bmatrix}x\\ y\end{bmatrix}$, and $B=\begin{bmatrix}3\\ 6\end{bmatrix}$, find A^{-1}. We will use the results of the Relating Concepts exercises to calculate A^{-1} in the solution to this exercise.

If $A=\begin{bmatrix}a & b\\ c & d\end{bmatrix}$, then $A^{-1}=\frac{1}{ad-bc}\begin{bmatrix}d & -b\\ -c & a\end{bmatrix}$. Thus we have the following.

$$A^{-1}=\frac{1}{6(3)-9(-8)}\begin{bmatrix}3 & -9\\ 8 & 6\end{bmatrix}=\frac{1}{18-(-72)}\begin{bmatrix}3 & -9\\ 8 & 6\end{bmatrix}=\frac{1}{90}\begin{bmatrix}3 & -9\\ 8 & 6\end{bmatrix}=\begin{bmatrix}\frac{3}{90} & \frac{-9}{90}\\ \frac{8}{90} & \frac{6}{90}\end{bmatrix}=\begin{bmatrix}\frac{1}{30} & -\frac{1}{10}\\ \frac{4}{45} & \frac{1}{15}\end{bmatrix}$$

$$X=A^{-1}B=\begin{bmatrix}\frac{1}{30} & -\frac{1}{10}\\ \frac{4}{45} & \frac{1}{15}\end{bmatrix}\begin{bmatrix}3\\ 6\end{bmatrix}=\begin{bmatrix}\frac{1}{30}(3)+\left(-\frac{1}{10}\right)(6)\\ \frac{4}{45}(3)+\frac{1}{15}(6)\end{bmatrix}=\begin{bmatrix}\frac{1}{10}+\left(-\frac{6}{10}\right)\\ \frac{4}{15}+\frac{2}{5}\end{bmatrix}=\begin{bmatrix}-\frac{5}{10}\\ \frac{4}{15}+\frac{6}{15}\end{bmatrix}=\begin{bmatrix}-\frac{1}{2}\\ \frac{10}{15}\end{bmatrix}=\begin{bmatrix}-\frac{1}{2}\\ \frac{2}{3}\end{bmatrix}$$

Solution set: $\left\{\left(-\frac{1}{2},\frac{2}{3}\right)\right\}$

41. $.2x + .3y = -1.9$
$.7x - .2y = 4.6$

Given $A = \begin{bmatrix} .2 & .3 \\ .7 & -.2 \end{bmatrix}$, $X = \begin{bmatrix} x \\ y \end{bmatrix}$, and $B = \begin{bmatrix} -1.9 \\ 4.6 \end{bmatrix}$, find A^{-1}. Since $\left[A \mid I_2\right] = \left[\begin{array}{cc|cc} .2 & .3 & 1 & 0 \\ .7 & -.2 & 0 & 1 \end{array}\right]$,

$$\left[\begin{array}{cc|cc} 1 & 1.5 & 5 & 0 \\ .7 & -.2 & 0 & 1 \end{array}\right]\begin{matrix} 5\text{R1} \\ \end{matrix} \Rightarrow \left[\begin{array}{cc|cc} 1 & 1.5 & 5 & 0 \\ 0 & -1.25 & -3.5 & 1 \end{array}\right]\begin{matrix} \\ -.7\text{R1}+\text{R2} \end{matrix}$$

$$\left[\begin{array}{cc|cc} 1 & 1.5 & 5 & 0 \\ 0 & 1 & 2.8 & -.8 \end{array}\right]\begin{matrix} \\ \frac{1}{-1.25}\text{R2} \end{matrix} \Rightarrow \left[\begin{array}{cc|cc} 1 & 0 & .8 & 1.2 \\ 0 & 1 & 2.8 & -.8 \end{array}\right]\begin{matrix} -1.5\text{R2}+\text{R1} \\ \end{matrix}. \quad \text{Thus, } A^{-1} = \begin{bmatrix} .8 & 1.2 \\ 2.8 & -.8 \end{bmatrix}.$$

$$X = A^{-1}B = \begin{bmatrix} .8 & 1.2 \\ 2.8 & -.8 \end{bmatrix}\begin{bmatrix} -1.9 \\ 4.6 \end{bmatrix} = \begin{bmatrix} .8(-1.9)+1.2(4.6) \\ 2.8(-1.9)+(-.8)(4.6) \end{bmatrix} = \begin{bmatrix} -1.52+5.52 \\ -5.32+(-3.68) \end{bmatrix} = \begin{bmatrix} 4 \\ -9 \end{bmatrix}$$

Solution set: $\{(4,-9)\}$

43. $x + y + z = 6$
$2x + 3y - z = 7$
$3x - y - z = 6$

Given $A = \begin{bmatrix} 1 & 1 & 1 \\ 2 & 3 & -1 \\ 3 & -1 & -1 \end{bmatrix}$, $X = \begin{bmatrix} x \\ y \\ z \end{bmatrix}$, and $B = \begin{bmatrix} 6 \\ 7 \\ 6 \end{bmatrix}$, find A^{-1}. Since $\left[A \mid I_3\right] = \left[\begin{array}{ccc|ccc} 1 & 1 & 1 & 1 & 0 & 0 \\ 2 & 3 & -1 & 0 & 1 & 0 \\ 3 & -1 & -1 & 0 & 0 & 1 \end{array}\right]$,

$$\left[\begin{array}{ccc|ccc} 1 & 1 & 1 & 1 & 0 & 0 \\ 0 & 1 & -3 & -2 & 1 & 0 \\ 0 & -4 & -4 & -3 & 0 & 1 \end{array}\right]\begin{matrix} \\ -2\text{R1}+\text{R2} \\ -3\text{R1}+\text{R3} \end{matrix} \Rightarrow \left[\begin{array}{ccc|ccc} 1 & 0 & 4 & 3 & -1 & 0 \\ 0 & 1 & -3 & -2 & 1 & 0 \\ 0 & 0 & -16 & -11 & 4 & 1 \end{array}\right]\begin{matrix} -\text{R2}+\text{R1} \\ \\ 4\text{R2}+\text{R3} \end{matrix}$$

$$\left[\begin{array}{ccc|ccc} 1 & 0 & 4 & 3 & -1 & 0 \\ 0 & 1 & -3 & -2 & 1 & 0 \\ 0 & 0 & 1 & \frac{11}{16} & -\frac{1}{4} & -\frac{1}{16} \end{array}\right]\begin{matrix} \\ \\ -\frac{1}{16}\text{R3} \end{matrix} \Rightarrow \left[\begin{array}{ccc|ccc} 1 & 0 & 0 & \frac{1}{4} & 0 & \frac{1}{4} \\ 0 & 1 & 0 & \frac{1}{16} & \frac{1}{4} & -\frac{3}{16} \\ 0 & 0 & 1 & \frac{11}{16} & -\frac{1}{4} & -\frac{1}{16} \end{array}\right]\begin{matrix} -4\text{R3}+\text{R1} \\ 3\text{R3}+\text{R2}. \\ \end{matrix} \text{ Thus, } A^{-1} = \begin{bmatrix} \frac{1}{4} & 0 & \frac{1}{4} \\ \frac{1}{16} & \frac{1}{4} & -\frac{3}{16} \\ \frac{11}{16} & -\frac{1}{4} & -\frac{1}{16} \end{bmatrix}.$$

$$X = A^{-1}B = \begin{bmatrix} \frac{1}{4} & 0 & \frac{1}{4} \\ \frac{1}{16} & \frac{1}{4} & -\frac{3}{16} \\ \frac{11}{16} & -\frac{1}{4} & -\frac{1}{16} \end{bmatrix}\begin{bmatrix} 6 \\ 7 \\ 6 \end{bmatrix} = \begin{bmatrix} \frac{1}{4}(6)+0(7)+\frac{1}{4}(6) \\ \frac{1}{16}(6)+\frac{1}{4}(7)+\left(-\frac{3}{16}\right)(6) \\ \frac{11}{16}(6)+\left(-\frac{1}{4}\right)(7)+\left(-\frac{1}{16}\right)(6) \end{bmatrix} = \begin{bmatrix} \frac{3}{2}+0+\frac{3}{2} \\ \frac{3}{8}+\frac{7}{4}+\left(-\frac{9}{8}\right) \\ \frac{33}{8}+\left(-\frac{7}{4}\right)+\left(-\frac{3}{8}\right) \end{bmatrix}$$

$$= \begin{bmatrix} \frac{6}{2} \\ \frac{7}{4}+\left(-\frac{6}{8}\right) \\ \frac{30}{8}+\left(-\frac{7}{4}\right) \end{bmatrix} = \begin{bmatrix} 3 \\ \frac{7}{4}+\left(-\frac{3}{4}\right) \\ \frac{15}{4}+\left(-\frac{7}{4}\right) \end{bmatrix} = \begin{bmatrix} 3 \\ \frac{4}{4} \\ \frac{8}{4} \end{bmatrix} = \begin{bmatrix} 3 \\ 1 \\ 2 \end{bmatrix}$$

Solution set: $\{(3,1,2)\}$

45. $x+3y+3z=1$
$x+4y+3z=0$
$x+3y+4z=-1$

We have $A=\begin{bmatrix}1&3&3\\1&4&3\\1&3&4\end{bmatrix}, X=\begin{bmatrix}x\\y\\z\end{bmatrix}, B=\begin{bmatrix}1\\0\\-1\end{bmatrix}$, and $A^{-1}=\begin{bmatrix}7&-3&-3\\-1&1&0\\-1&0&1\end{bmatrix}$ (From Exercise 19).

$$X=A^{-1}B=\begin{bmatrix}7&-3&-3\\-1&1&0\\-1&0&1\end{bmatrix}\begin{bmatrix}1\\0\\-1\end{bmatrix}=\begin{bmatrix}7(1)+(-3)(0)+(-3)(-1)\\-1(1)+1(0)+0(-1)\\-1(1)+0(0)+1(-1)\end{bmatrix}=\begin{bmatrix}7+0+3\\-1+0+0\\-1+0+(-1)\end{bmatrix}=\begin{bmatrix}10\\-1\\-2\end{bmatrix}$$

Solution set: $\{(10,-1,-2)\}$

47. $2x+2y-4z=12$
$2x+6y=16$
$-3x-3y+5z=-20$

We have $A=\begin{bmatrix}2&2&-4\\2&6&0\\-3&-3&5\end{bmatrix}, X=\begin{bmatrix}x\\y\\z\end{bmatrix}, B=\begin{bmatrix}12\\16\\-20\end{bmatrix}$, and $A^{-1}=\begin{bmatrix}-\frac{15}{4}&-\frac{1}{4}&-3\\\frac{5}{4}&\frac{1}{4}&1\\-\frac{3}{2}&0&-1\end{bmatrix}$ (From Exercise 21).

$$X=A^{-1}B=\begin{bmatrix}-\frac{15}{4}&-\frac{1}{4}&-3\\\frac{5}{4}&\frac{1}{4}&1\\-\frac{3}{2}&0&-1\end{bmatrix}\begin{bmatrix}12\\16\\-20\end{bmatrix}=\begin{bmatrix}-\frac{15}{4}(12)+(-\frac{1}{4})(16)+(-3)(-20)\\\frac{5}{4}(12)+\frac{1}{4}(16)+1(-20)\\-\frac{3}{2}(12)+0(16)+(-1)(-20)\end{bmatrix}=\begin{bmatrix}-45+(-4)+60\\15+4+(-20)\\-18+0+20\end{bmatrix}=\begin{bmatrix}11\\-1\\2\end{bmatrix}$$

Solution set: $\{(11,-1,2)\}$

49. $x+y+2w=3$
$2x-y+z-w=3$
$3x+3y+2z-2w=5$
$x+2y+z=3$

We have $A=\begin{bmatrix}1&1&0&2\\2&-1&1&-1\\3&3&2&-2\\1&2&1&0\end{bmatrix}, X=\begin{bmatrix}x\\y\\z\\w\end{bmatrix}, B=\begin{bmatrix}3\\3\\5\\3\end{bmatrix}$, and $A^{-1}=\begin{bmatrix}\frac{1}{2}&0&\frac{1}{2}&-1\\\frac{1}{10}&-\frac{2}{5}&\frac{3}{10}&-\frac{1}{5}\\-\frac{7}{10}&\frac{4}{5}&-\frac{11}{10}&\frac{12}{5}\\\frac{1}{5}&\frac{1}{5}&-\frac{2}{5}&\frac{3}{5}\end{bmatrix}$ (From Exercise 23).

$$X=A^{-1}B=\begin{bmatrix}\frac{1}{2}&0&\frac{1}{2}&-1\\\frac{1}{10}&-\frac{2}{5}&\frac{3}{10}&-\frac{1}{5}\\-\frac{7}{10}&\frac{4}{5}&-\frac{11}{10}&\frac{12}{5}\\\frac{1}{5}&\frac{1}{5}&-\frac{2}{5}&\frac{3}{5}\end{bmatrix}\begin{bmatrix}3\\3\\5\\3\end{bmatrix}=\begin{bmatrix}\frac{1}{2}(3)+0(3)+\frac{1}{2}(5)+(-1)(3)\\\frac{1}{10}(3)+(-\frac{2}{5})(3)+\frac{3}{10}(5)+(-\frac{1}{5})(3)\\-\frac{7}{10}(3)+\frac{4}{5}(3)+(-\frac{11}{10})(5)+\frac{12}{5}(3)\\\frac{1}{5}(3)+\frac{1}{5}(3)+(-\frac{2}{5})(5)+\frac{3}{5}(3)\end{bmatrix}$$

$$=\begin{bmatrix}\frac{3}{2}+0+\frac{5}{2}+(-3)\\\frac{3}{10}+(-\frac{6}{5})+\frac{3}{2}+(-\frac{3}{5})\\-\frac{21}{10}+\frac{12}{5}+(-\frac{11}{2})+\frac{36}{5}\\\frac{3}{5}+\frac{3}{5}+(-2)+\frac{9}{5}\end{bmatrix}=\begin{bmatrix}\frac{8}{2}+(-3)\\\frac{3}{10}+(-\frac{9}{5})+\frac{3}{2}\\-\frac{21}{10}+(-\frac{11}{2})+\frac{48}{5}\\(-2)+\frac{15}{5}\end{bmatrix}=\begin{bmatrix}4+(-3)\\\frac{3}{10}+(-\frac{18}{10})+\frac{15}{10}\\-\frac{21}{10}+(-\frac{55}{10})+\frac{96}{10}\\(-2)+3\end{bmatrix}=\begin{bmatrix}1\\\frac{0}{10}\\\frac{20}{10}\\1\end{bmatrix}=\begin{bmatrix}1\\0\\2\\1\end{bmatrix}$$

Solution set: $\{(1,0,2,1)\}$

51. (a) $602.7 = a + 5.543b + 37.14c$

$656.7 = a + 6.933b + 41.30c$

$778.5 = a + 7.638b + 45.62c$

(b) $A = \begin{bmatrix} 1 & 5.543 & 37.14 \\ 1 & 6.933 & 41.30 \\ 1 & 7.638 & 45.62 \end{bmatrix}$, $X = \begin{bmatrix} a \\ b \\ c \end{bmatrix}$ and $B = \begin{bmatrix} 602.7 \\ 656.7 \\ 778.5 \end{bmatrix}$

Using a graphing calculator with matrix capabilities, we obtain the following.

$X = A^{-1}B$ or $\begin{bmatrix} a \\ b \\ c \end{bmatrix} = \begin{bmatrix} -490.547375 \\ -89 \\ 42.71875 \end{bmatrix}$. Thus, $a \bullet -490.547$, $b = -89$, $c = 42.71875$.

(c) $S = -490.547 - 89A + 42.71875B$

(d) If $A = 7.752$ and $B = 47.38$, the predicted value of S is given by the following.

$$S = -490.547 - 89(7.752) + 42.71875(47.38) = 843.539375 \approx 843.5$$

The predicted value is approximately 843.5.

(e) If $A = 8.9$ and $B = 66.25$, the predicted value of S is given by the following.

$$S = -490.547 - 89(8.9) + 42.71875(66.25) = 1547.470188 \approx 1547.5$$

The predicted value is approximately 1547.5.

Using only three consecutive years to forecast six years into the future, it is probably not very accurate.

53. Answers will vary.

55. Given $A = \begin{bmatrix} \frac{2}{3} & .7 \\ 22 & \sqrt{3} \end{bmatrix}$, we obtain $A^{-1} \approx \begin{bmatrix} -.1215875322 & .0491390161 \\ 1.544369078 & -.046799063 \end{bmatrix}$ using a graphing calculator.

57. Given $A = \begin{bmatrix} \frac{1}{2} & \frac{1}{4} & \frac{1}{3} \\ 0 & \frac{1}{4} & \frac{1}{3} \\ \frac{1}{2} & \frac{1}{2} & \frac{1}{3} \end{bmatrix}$, we obtain $A^{-1} = \begin{bmatrix} 2 & -2 & 0 \\ -4 & 0 & 4 \\ 3 & 3 & -3 \end{bmatrix}$ using a graphing calculator.

59. $2.1x + y = \sqrt{5}$

$\sqrt{2}x - 2y = 5$

Given $A = \begin{bmatrix} 2.1 & 1 \\ \sqrt{2} & -2 \end{bmatrix}$, $X = \begin{bmatrix} x \\ y \end{bmatrix}$, and $B = \begin{bmatrix} \sqrt{5} \\ 5 \end{bmatrix}$, using a graphing calculator, we have

$X = A^{-1}B = \begin{bmatrix} 1.68717058 \\ -1.306990242 \end{bmatrix}$. Thus, the solution set is $\{(1.68717058, -1.306990242)\}$.

61. $(\log 2)x+(\ln 3)y+(\ln 4)z=1$
$(\ln 3)x+(\log 2)y+(\ln 8)z=5$
$(\log 12)x+(\ln 4)y+(\ln 8)z=9$

Given $A=\begin{bmatrix} \log 2 & \ln 3 & \ln 4 \\ \ln 3 & \log 2 & \ln 8 \\ \log 12 & \ln 4 & \ln 8 \end{bmatrix}, X=\begin{bmatrix} x \\ y \\ z \end{bmatrix}$, and $B=\begin{bmatrix} 1 \\ 5 \\ 9 \end{bmatrix}$, using a graphing calculator, we have

$$X=A^{-1}B=\begin{bmatrix} 13.58736702 \\ 3.929011993 \\ -5.342780076 \end{bmatrix}.$$

Solution set: $\{(13.58736702, 3.929011993, -5.342780076)\}$

63. Answers will vary.

65. Let $A=\begin{bmatrix} 1 & 0 \\ 1 & 1 \end{bmatrix}$ and $B=\begin{bmatrix} 1 & 1 \\ 0 & 1 \end{bmatrix}$. (Other answers are possible.)

$$AB=\begin{bmatrix} 1 & 0 \\ 1 & 1 \end{bmatrix}\begin{bmatrix} 1 & 1 \\ 0 & 1 \end{bmatrix}=\begin{bmatrix} 1(1)+0(0) & 1(1)+0(1) \\ 1(1)+1(0) & 1(1)+1(1) \end{bmatrix}=\begin{bmatrix} 1+0 & 1+0 \\ 1+0 & 1+1 \end{bmatrix}=\begin{bmatrix} 1 & 1 \\ 1 & 2 \end{bmatrix}$$

Find $(AB)^{-1}$. Since $\left[AB|I_2\right]=\left[\begin{array}{cc|cc} 1 & 1 & 1 & 0 \\ 1 & 2 & 0 & 1 \end{array}\right]$,

$$\left[\begin{array}{cc|cc} 1 & 1 & 1 & 0 \\ 0 & 1 & -1 & 1 \end{array}\right]\begin{matrix} \\ -\text{R1}+\text{R2} \end{matrix} \Rightarrow \left[\begin{array}{cc|cc} 1 & 0 & 2 & -1 \\ 0 & 1 & -1 & 1 \end{array}\right]\begin{matrix} -\text{R2}+\text{R1} \\ \\ \end{matrix}.$$

Thus, $(AB)^{-1}=\begin{bmatrix} 2 & -1 \\ -1 & 1 \end{bmatrix}$.

Now find A^{-1}. Since $\left[A|I_2\right]=\left[\begin{array}{cc|cc} 1 & 0 & 1 & 0 \\ 1 & 1 & 0 & 1 \end{array}\right] \Rightarrow \left[\begin{array}{cc|cc} 1 & 0 & 1 & 0 \\ 0 & 1 & -1 & 1 \end{array}\right]\begin{matrix} \\ -\text{R1}+\text{R2} \end{matrix}$. Thus, $A^{-1}=\begin{bmatrix} 1 & 0 \\ -1 & 1 \end{bmatrix}$.

Now find B^{-1}. Since $\left[B|I_2\right]=\left[\begin{array}{cc|cc} 1 & 1 & 1 & 0 \\ 0 & 1 & 0 & 1 \end{array}\right] \Rightarrow \left[\begin{array}{cc|cc} 1 & 0 & 1 & -1 \\ 0 & 1 & 0 & 1 \end{array}\right]\begin{matrix} -\text{R2}+\text{R1} \\ \\ \end{matrix}$. Thus, $B^{-1}=\begin{bmatrix} 1 & -1 \\ 0 & 1 \end{bmatrix}$.

Now find $A^{-1}B^{-1}$.

$$A^{-1}B^{-1}=\begin{bmatrix} 1 & 0 \\ -1 & 1 \end{bmatrix}\begin{bmatrix} 1 & -1 \\ 0 & 1 \end{bmatrix}=\begin{bmatrix} 1(1)+0(0) & 1(-1)+0(1) \\ -1(1)+1(0) & -1(-1)+1(1) \end{bmatrix}=\begin{bmatrix} 1+0 & -1+0 \\ -1+0 & 1+1 \end{bmatrix}=\begin{bmatrix} 1 & -1 \\ -1 & 2 \end{bmatrix}$$

Thus $(AB)^{-1}\neq A^{-1}B^{-1}$.

67. Given $A=\begin{bmatrix} a & 0 & 0 \\ 0 & b & 0 \\ 0 & 0 & c \end{bmatrix}$, and since a, b, and c are all nonzero, $\frac{1}{a}, \frac{1}{b}$, and $\frac{1}{c}$ all exist.

Thus, $\left[A|I\right]=\left[\begin{array}{ccc|ccc} a & 0 & 0 & 1 & 0 & 0 \\ 0 & b & 0 & 0 & 1 & 0 \\ 0 & 0 & c & 0 & 0 & 1 \end{array}\right] \Rightarrow \left[\begin{array}{ccc|ccc} 1 & 0 & 0 & \frac{1}{a} & 0 & 0 \\ 0 & 1 & 0 & 0 & \frac{1}{b} & 0 \\ 0 & 0 & 1 & 0 & 0 & \frac{1}{c} \end{array}\right] \begin{matrix} \frac{1}{a}\text{R1} \\ \frac{1}{b}\text{R2} \\ \frac{1}{c}\text{R3} \end{matrix}$ and $A^{-1}=\begin{bmatrix} \frac{1}{a} & 0 & 0 \\ 0 & \frac{1}{b} & 0 \\ 0 & 0 & \frac{1}{c} \end{bmatrix}$.

69. Find the inverses of I_n, $-A$, and kA.

I_n is its own inverse, since $I_n \cdot I_n = I_n$.

The inverse of $-A$ is $-\left(A^{-1}\right)$, since $(-A)\left[-\left(A^{-1}\right)\right]=(-1)(-1)\left(A\cdot A^{-1}\right)=I_n$.

The inverse of kA (k a scalar) is $\frac{1}{k}A^{-1}$, since $(kA)\left(\frac{1}{k}A^{-1}\right)=\left(k\cdot\frac{1}{k}\right)\left(A\cdot A^{-1}\right)=I_n$.

Chapter 9: Review Exercises

1. $2x+6y=6$ (1)
$5x+9y=9$ (2)

Solving equation (1) for x, we have $2x+6y=6 \Rightarrow 2x=6-6y \Rightarrow x=3-3y$ (3). Substituting equation (3) into equation (2) and solving for y, we have the following.

$$5(3-3y)+9y=9 \Rightarrow 15-15y+9y=9 \Rightarrow 15-6y=9 \Rightarrow -6y=-6 \Rightarrow y=1$$

Substituting 1 for y in equation (3), we have $x=3-3(1)=3-3=0$.

Solution set: $\{(0,1)\}$

3. $x+5y=9$ (1)
$2x+10y=18$ (2)

Multiply equation (1) by -2 and add the resulting equation to equation (2).

$$\begin{array}{r} -2x-10y=-18 \\ 2x+10y=\ \ 18 \\ \hline 0=0 \end{array}$$

This is a true statement and implies that the system has infinitely many solutions. Solving equation (1) for x we have $x=9-5y$. Given y as an arbitrary value, the solution set is $\{(9-5y, y)\}$.

5. $y=-x+3$ (1)
$2x+2y=1$ (2)

Substituting equation (1) into equation (2), we have $2x+2(-x+3)=1$. Solving for x we have $2x+2(-x+3)=1 \Rightarrow 2x+(-2x)+6=1 \Rightarrow 6=1$. This is a false statement and the solution is inconsistent. Thus, the solution set is $\varnothing$.

7. $3x-2y=0\ (1)$

$9x+8y=7\ (2)$

Multiply equation (1) by –3 and add the result to equation (2).

$$\begin{array}{r} -9x+6y=0 \\ \underline{9x+8y=7} \\ 14y=7 \Rightarrow y=\frac{1}{2} \end{array}$$

Substituting $\frac{1}{2}$ for y in equation (1) and solving for x, we have the following.

$$3x-2\left(\tfrac{1}{2}\right)=0 \Rightarrow 3x-1=0$$
$$3x=1 \Rightarrow x=\tfrac{1}{3}$$

Solution set: $\left\{\left(\frac{1}{3},\frac{1}{2}\right)\right\}$

9. $2x-5y+3z=-1\ (1)$

$x+4y-2z=9\ \ (2)$

$-x+2y+4z=5\ \ (3)$

First, we eliminate x. Multiply equation (2) by –2 and add the result to equation (1).

$$\begin{array}{r} 2x-5y+3z=-1 \\ \underline{-2x-8y+4z=-18} \\ -13y+7z=-19\ (4) \end{array}$$

Next, add equations (2) and (3) to obtain $6y+2z=14\ (5)$.

Now, we solve the system $\begin{array}{r} -13y+7z=-19\ (4) \\ 6y+2z=\ \ 14\ (5) \end{array}$.

Multiply equation (4) by 2, multiply equation (5) by –7, and add the resulting equations.

$$\begin{array}{r} -26y+14z=-38 \\ \underline{-42y-14z=-98} \\ -68y \qquad =-136 \Rightarrow y=2 \end{array}$$

Substituting this value into equation (4), we have $-13(2)+7z=-19 \Rightarrow -26+7z=-19 \Rightarrow 7z=7 \Rightarrow z=1$.

Substituting 2 for y and 1 for z in equation (2), we have $x+4(2)-2(1)=9 \Rightarrow x+8-2=9 \Rightarrow x=3$.

Solution set: $\{(3,2,1)\}$

11. $5x-y=26\ (1)$

$4y+3z=-4\ (2)$

$3x+3z=15\ \ (3)$

Multiply equation (2) by –1 and add the result to equation (3) in order to eliminate z.

$$\begin{array}{r} -4y-3z=4 \\ \underline{3x \qquad +3z=15} \\ 3x-4y \qquad =19\ (4) \end{array}$$

Multiply equation (1) by –4 and add the result to equation (4).

$$\begin{array}{r} -20x+4y=-104 \\ \underline{3x-4y=\ \ \ 19} \\ -17x \qquad =-85 \Rightarrow x=5 \end{array}$$

Substitute 5 for x in equation (1) and solve for y to obtain $5(5)-y=26 \Rightarrow 25-y=26 \Rightarrow y=-1$.

Substitute 5 for x equation (3) and solve for z to obtain $3(5)+3z=15 \Rightarrow 15+3z=15 \Rightarrow 3z=0 \Rightarrow z=0$.

Solution set: $\{(5,-1,0)\}$

13. One possible answer is $\begin{array}{l} x+y=2 \\ x+y=3. \end{array}$

15. Let x = amount of rice;
and y = amount of soybeans.
We get the following system of equations. The first equation relates protein and the second relates calories.

$$\begin{aligned} 15x+22.5y&=9.5\ (1) \\ 810x+270y&=324\ (2) \end{aligned}$$

Multiply equation (1) by –12 and add the result to equation (2).

$$\begin{array}{rl} -180x-270y &= -114 \\ 810x+270y &= 324 \\ \hline 630x \qquad &= 210 \Rightarrow x=\frac{1}{3} \end{array}$$

Substitute $\frac{1}{3}$ for x in equation (1) and solve for y.

$$15\left(\tfrac{1}{3}\right)+22.5y=9.5 \Rightarrow 5+22.5y=9.5 \Rightarrow 22.5y=4.5 \Rightarrow y=.20=\tfrac{1}{5}$$

$\frac{1}{3}$ cup of rice and $\frac{1}{5}$ cup of soybeans should be used.

17. Let x = the number of blankets,
y = the number of rugs,
and z = the number of skirts.
The following table is helpful in organizing the information.

	Number of blankets (x)	Number of rugs (y)	Number of skirts (z)	Available
Spinning yarn	24	30	12	306
Dying	4	5	3	59
Weaving	15	18	9	201

We have the following system of equations.

$$\begin{aligned} 24x+30y+12z=306 &\Rightarrow 4x+5y+2z=51\ (1) \\ 4x+\ 5y+\ 3z&=59\ (2) \\ 15x+18y+\ 9z=201 &\Rightarrow 5x+6y+3z=67\ (3) \end{aligned}$$

Multiply equation (1) by –1 and add the result to equation (2).

$$\begin{array}{rl} -4x-5y-2z &= -51 \\ 4x+5y+3z &= 59 \\ \hline z &= 8 \end{array}$$

Substitute 8 for z in equations (1) and (3) and simplify.

$$4x+5y+2(8)=51 \Rightarrow 4x+5y+16=51 \Rightarrow 4x+5y=35\ (4)$$
$$5x+6y+3(8)=67 \Rightarrow 5x+6y+24=67 \Rightarrow 5x+6y=43\ (5)$$

Multiply equation (4) by 5 and equation (5) by – 4 and add the results.

$$\begin{array}{rl} 20x+25y &= 175 \\ -20x-24y &= -172 \\ \hline y &= 3 \end{array}$$

Substituting 3 for y in equation (4) and solving for x, we obtain the following.

$$4x+5(3)=35 \Rightarrow 4x+15=35 \Rightarrow 4x=20 \Rightarrow x=5$$

5 blankets, 3 rugs, and 8 skirts can be made.

19. $H = .491x + .468y + 11.2$

$H = -.981x + 1.872y + 26.4$

Substitute $H = 180$ and solve each equation for y so they can be entered into the graphing calculator.

$$180 = .491x + .468y + 11.2 \Rightarrow 168.8 - .491x = .468y \Rightarrow y = \frac{168.8 - .491x}{.468}$$

$$180 = -.981x + 1.872y + 26.4 \Rightarrow 153.6 + .981x = 1.872y \Rightarrow y = \frac{153.6 + .981x}{1.872}$$

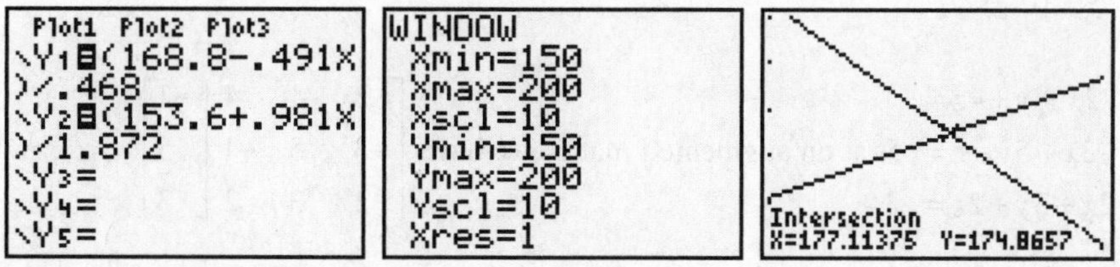

Thus, we have $x \approx 177.1$ and $y \approx 174.9$.

21. Since $y = ax^2 + bx + c$ and the points $(1,-2.3), (2,-1.3)$, and $(3,4.5)$ are on the parabola, we have the following system of equations.

$$-2.3 = a(1)^2 + b(1) + c \Rightarrow a + b + c = -2.3 \ (1)$$

$$-1.3 = a(2)^2 + b(2) + c \Rightarrow 4a + 2b + c = -1.3 \ (2)$$

$$4.5 = a(3)^2 + b(3) + c \Rightarrow 9a + 3b + c = 4.5 \ (3)$$

First, eliminate c by multiplying equation (1) by –1 and adding the result to equation (2).

$$\begin{array}{l} -a - \ \ b - c = \ \ 2.3 \\ \underline{4a + 2b + c = -1.3} \\ 3a + \ \ b \ \ \ \ \ \ \ = \ \ 1 \ (4) \end{array}$$

Next, multiply equation (2) by –1 and add to equation (3).

$$\begin{array}{l} -4a - 2b - c = 1.3 \\ \underline{\ \ 9a + 3b + c = 4.5} \\ \ \ 5a + \ \ b \ \ \ \ \ \ \ = 5.8 \ (5) \end{array}$$

Next, eliminate b by multiplying equation (4) by –1 and adding the result to equation (5).

$$\begin{array}{l} -3a - b = -1 \\ \underline{\ \ 5a + b = 5.8} \\ \ \ 2a \ \ \ \ \ \ \ = 4.8 \Rightarrow a = 2.4 \end{array}$$

Substitute this value into equation (4) to obtain $3(2.4) + b = 1 \Rightarrow 7.2 + b = 1 \Rightarrow b = -6.2.$

Substitute 2.4 for a and –6.2 for b into equation (1) in order to solve for c.

$$(2.4) + (-6.2) + c = -2.3 \Rightarrow -3.8 + c = -2.3 \Rightarrow c = 1.5$$

The equation of the parabola is $y = 2.4x^2 - 6.2x + 1.5$ or $Y_1 = 2.4X^2 - 6.2X + 1.5$.

23. $3x - 4y + z = 2 \ (1)$

$2x + y = 1 \ (2)$

Solving equation (2) for y, we obtain $y = 1 - 2x$. Substitute $1 - 2x$ for y in equation (1) and solve for z.

$$3x - 4(1 - 2x) + z = 2 \Rightarrow 3x - 4 + 8x + z = 2 \Rightarrow 11x + z = 6 \Rightarrow z = 6 - 11x$$

Solution set: $\{(x, 1 - 2x, 6 - 11x)\}$

25. Writing $\begin{aligned} 5x+2y&=-10 \\ 3x-5y&=-6 \end{aligned}$ as an augmented matrix we have $\left[\begin{array}{cc|c} 5 & 2 & -10 \\ 3 & -5 & -6 \end{array}\right]$.

$$\left[\begin{array}{cc|c} 1 & \frac{2}{5} & -2 \\ 3 & -5 & -6 \end{array}\right]\begin{array}{l} \frac{1}{5}\text{R1} \\ \end{array} \Rightarrow \left[\begin{array}{cc|c} 1 & \frac{2}{5} & -2 \\ 0 & -\frac{31}{5} & 0 \end{array}\right]\begin{array}{l} \\ -3\text{R1}+\text{R2} \end{array} \Rightarrow \left[\begin{array}{cc|c} 1 & \frac{2}{5} & -2 \\ 0 & 1 & 0 \end{array}\right]\begin{array}{l} \\ -\frac{5}{31}\text{R2} \end{array} \Rightarrow \left[\begin{array}{cc|c} 1 & 0 & -2 \\ 0 & 1 & 0 \end{array}\right]\begin{array}{l} -\frac{2}{5}\text{R2}+\text{R1} \\ \end{array}$$

Solution set: $\{(-2,0)\}$

27. Writing $\begin{aligned} 2x-y+4z&=-1 \\ -3x+5y-z&=5 \\ 2x+3y+2z&=3 \end{aligned}$ as an augmented matrix we have $\left[\begin{array}{ccc|c} 2 & -1 & 4 & -1 \\ -3 & 5 & -1 & 5 \\ 2 & 3 & 2 & 3 \end{array}\right]$.

$$\left[\begin{array}{ccc|c} 1 & -\frac{1}{2} & 2 & -\frac{1}{2} \\ -3 & 5 & -1 & 5 \\ 2 & 3 & 2 & 3 \end{array}\right]\begin{array}{l} \frac{1}{2}\text{R1} \\ \\ \end{array} \Rightarrow \left[\begin{array}{ccc|c} 1 & -\frac{1}{2} & 2 & -\frac{1}{2} \\ 0 & \frac{7}{2} & 5 & \frac{7}{2} \\ 0 & 4 & -2 & 4 \end{array}\right]\begin{array}{l} \\ 3\text{R1}+\text{R2} \\ -2\text{R1}+\text{R3} \end{array} \Rightarrow \left[\begin{array}{ccc|c} 1 & -\frac{1}{2} & 2 & -\frac{1}{2} \\ 0 & 1 & \frac{10}{7} & 1 \\ 0 & 4 & -2 & 4 \end{array}\right]\begin{array}{l} \\ \frac{2}{7}\text{R2} \\ \end{array}$$

$$\left[\begin{array}{ccc|c} 1 & 0 & \frac{19}{7} & 0 \\ 0 & 1 & \frac{10}{7} & 1 \\ 0 & 0 & -\frac{54}{7} & 0 \end{array}\right]\begin{array}{l} \frac{1}{2}\text{R2}+\text{R1} \\ \\ -4\text{R2}+\text{R3} \end{array} \Rightarrow \left[\begin{array}{ccc|c} 1 & 0 & \frac{19}{7} & 0 \\ 0 & 1 & \frac{10}{7} & 1 \\ 0 & 0 & 1 & 0 \end{array}\right]\begin{array}{l} \\ \\ -\frac{7}{54}\text{R2} \end{array} \Rightarrow \left[\begin{array}{ccc|c} 1 & 0 & 0 & 0 \\ 0 & 1 & 0 & 1 \\ 0 & 0 & 1 & 0 \end{array}\right]\begin{array}{l} -\frac{19}{7}\text{R3}+\text{R1} \\ -\frac{10}{7}\text{R3}+\text{R2} \\ \end{array}$$

Solution set: $\{(0,1,0)\}$

29. Let x = number of pounds of \$4.60 tea;
and y = the number of pounds of \$5.75 tea;
and z = the number of pounds of \$6.50 tea.

From the information in the exercise, we obtain the system $\begin{aligned} x+y+z&=20 \\ 4.6x+5.75y+6.5z&=20(5.25) \\ x&=y+z \end{aligned}$.

Rewriting the system, we have $\begin{aligned} x+y+z&=20 \\ 4.6x+5.75y+6.5z&=105 \\ x-y-z&=0 \end{aligned}$.

With an augmented matrix of $\left[\begin{array}{ccc|c} 1 & 1 & 1 & 20 \\ 4.6 & 5.75 & 6.5 & 105 \\ 1 & -1 & -1 & 0 \end{array}\right]$, we solve by the Gauss-Jordan method.

$$\left[\begin{array}{ccc|c} 1 & 1 & 1 & 20 \\ 0 & 1.15 & 1.9 & 13 \\ 0 & -2 & -2 & -20 \end{array}\right]\begin{array}{l} \\ -4.6\text{R1}+\text{R2} \\ -1\text{R1}+\text{R3} \end{array} \Rightarrow \left[\begin{array}{ccc|c} 1 & 1 & 1 & 20 \\ 0 & 1 & \frac{38}{23} & \frac{260}{23} \\ 0 & -2 & -2 & -20 \end{array}\right]\begin{array}{l} \\ \frac{20}{23}\text{R2} \\ \end{array} \Rightarrow \left[\begin{array}{ccc|c} 1 & 0 & -\frac{15}{23} & \frac{200}{23} \\ 0 & 1 & \frac{38}{23} & \frac{260}{23} \\ 0 & 0 & \frac{30}{23} & \frac{60}{23} \end{array}\right]\begin{array}{l} -1\text{R2}+\text{R1} \\ \\ 2\text{R2}+\text{R3} \end{array}$$

$$\left[\begin{array}{ccc|c} 1 & 0 & -\frac{15}{23} & \frac{200}{23} \\ 0 & 1 & \frac{38}{23} & \frac{260}{23} \\ 0 & 0 & 1 & 2 \end{array}\right]\begin{array}{l} \\ \\ \frac{23}{30}\text{R3} \end{array} \Rightarrow \left[\begin{array}{ccc|c} 1 & 0 & 0 & 10 \\ 0 & 1 & 0 & 8 \\ 0 & 0 & 1 & 2 \end{array}\right]\begin{array}{l} \frac{15}{23}\text{R3}+\text{R1} \\ -\frac{38}{23}\text{R3}+\text{R2} \\ \end{array}$$

From the final matrix, we have $x = 10$, $y = 8$, and $z = 2$. Therefore, 10 lb of \$4.60 tea, 8 lb of \$5.75 tea, and 2 lb of \$6.50 tea should be used.

31. $y = .11x + 2.9$ (1)

$y = .19x + 1.4$ (2)

The given system can be solved by substitution. Substitute equation (1) into equation (2) to obtain $.11x + 2.9 = .19x + 1.4$. Solving this equation, we have $1.5 = .08x \Rightarrow x = 18.75$.

Since $x = 0$ corresponds 1960, $x = 18.75$ implies during 1978 the male and female enrollments were the same. The enrollment of males in this year is $y = .11(18.75) + 2.9 = 4.9625$ million. The enrollment of females in this year (which is the same as the males) is $y = .19(18.75) + 1.4 = 4.9625$ million. The total enrollment was therefore approximately 10 million.

33. $\begin{vmatrix} -1 & 8 \\ 2 & 9 \end{vmatrix} = -1(9) - 2(8) = -9 - 16 = -25$

35. Expanding $\begin{vmatrix} -1 & 2 & 3 \\ 4 & 0 & 3 \\ 5 & -1 & 2 \end{vmatrix}$ by the second column, we have the following.

$$-2\begin{vmatrix} 4 & 3 \\ 5 & 2 \end{vmatrix} + 0\begin{vmatrix} -1 & 3 \\ 5 & 2 \end{vmatrix} - (-1)\begin{vmatrix} -1 & 3 \\ 4 & 3 \end{vmatrix} = -2[4(2) - 5(3)] + 0 + [(-1)(3) - (4)(3)]$$

$$= -2(8 - 15) + (-3 - 12) = -2(-7) + (-15) = 14 - 15 = -1$$

37. $\begin{vmatrix} 3x & 7 \\ -x & 4 \end{vmatrix} = 8 \Rightarrow 12x - (-7x) = 8 \Rightarrow 19x = 8 \Rightarrow x = \frac{8}{19}$

Solution set: $\left\{\frac{8}{19}\right\}$

39. $3x + 7y = 2$

$5x - y = -22$

Since $D = \begin{vmatrix} 3 & 7 \\ 5 & -1 \end{vmatrix} = 3(-1) - 5(7) = -3 - 35 = -38$, $D_x = \begin{vmatrix} 2 & 7 \\ -22 & -1 \end{vmatrix} = 2(-1) - (-22)(7) = -2 - (-154) = 152$,

and $D_y = \begin{vmatrix} 3 & 2 \\ 5 & -22 \end{vmatrix} = 3(-22) - 5(2) = -66 - 10 = -76$, we have $x = \frac{D_x}{D} = \frac{152}{-38} = -4$ and $y = \frac{D_y}{D} = \frac{-76}{-38} = 2$.

Solution set: $\{(-4, 2)\}$

41. Given $\begin{aligned} 6x + y &= -3 \quad (1) \\ 12x + 2y &= 1 \quad (2) \end{aligned}$, we have $D = \begin{vmatrix} 6 & 1 \\ 12 & 2 \end{vmatrix} = 6(2) - 12(1) = 12 - 12 = 0$.

Because $D = 0$, Cramer's rule does not apply. To determine whether the system is inconsistent or has infinitely many solutions, use the elimination method.

$$\begin{aligned} -12x - 2y &= 6 \quad \text{Multiply equation (1) by } -2. \\ 12x + 2y &= 1 \\ \hline 0 &= 7 \quad \text{False} \end{aligned}$$

The system is inconsistent. Thus the solution set is $\emptyset$.

43. $x+\ y=-1$

$2y+\ z=5$

$3x-2z=-28$

Adding –3 times row 1 to row 3, we have $D=\begin{vmatrix}1&1&0\\0&2&1\\3&0&-2\end{vmatrix}=\begin{vmatrix}1&1&0\\0&2&1\\0&-3&-2\end{vmatrix}$.

Expanding by column one, we have $D=\begin{vmatrix}2&1\\-3&-2\end{vmatrix}=-4-(-3)=-1.$

Adding –2 times row 1 to row 2, we have $D_x=\begin{vmatrix}-1&1&0\\5&2&1\\-28&0&-2\end{vmatrix}=\begin{vmatrix}-1&1&0\\7&0&1\\-28&0&-2\end{vmatrix}$.

Expanding about column two, we have $D_x=-(1)\begin{vmatrix}7&1\\-28&-2\end{vmatrix}=-\left[-14-(-28)\right]=-14.$

Adding 2 times row 2 to row 3, we have $D_y=\begin{vmatrix}1&-1&0\\0&5&1\\3&-28&-2\end{vmatrix}=\begin{vmatrix}1&-1&0\\0&5&1\\3&-18&0\end{vmatrix}$.

Expanding by column three, we have $D_y=-(1)\begin{vmatrix}1&-1\\3&-18\end{vmatrix}=-1\left[-18-(-3)\right]=-(-15)=15.$

Adding –3 times row 1 to row 3, we have $D_z=\begin{vmatrix}1&1&-1\\0&2&5\\3&0&-28\end{vmatrix}=\begin{vmatrix}1&1&-1\\0&2&5\\0&-3&-25\end{vmatrix}$.

Expanding by column one, we have $D_z=1\begin{vmatrix}2&5\\-3&-25\end{vmatrix}=-50-(-15)=-35.$

Thus, we have $x=\frac{D_x}{D}=\frac{-14}{-1}=14,\ y=\frac{D_y}{D}=\frac{15}{-1}=-15,$ and $z=\frac{D_z}{D}=\frac{-35}{-1}=35.$

Solution set: $\{(14,-15,35)\}$

45. $\dfrac{2}{3x^2-5x+2}=\dfrac{2}{(x-1)(3x-2)}=\dfrac{A}{x-1}+\dfrac{B}{3x-2}$

Multiply both sides by $(x-1)(3x-2)$ to get $2=A(3x-2)+B(x-1)$. (1)

First substitute 1 for x to get $2=A\left[3(1)-2\right]+B(1-1)\Rightarrow 2=A(1)+B(0)\Rightarrow A=2.$

Replace A with 2 in equation (1) and substitute $\frac{2}{3}$ for x to get

$$2=2\left[3\left(\tfrac{2}{3}\right)-2\right]+B\left(\tfrac{2}{3}-1\right)\Rightarrow 2=2(0)+B\left(-\tfrac{1}{3}\right)\Rightarrow 2=-\tfrac{1}{3}B\Rightarrow B=-6.$$

Thus, we have $\dfrac{2}{3x^2-5x+2}=\dfrac{2}{x-1}+\dfrac{-6}{3x-2}$ or $\dfrac{2}{x-1}-\dfrac{6}{3x-2}$.

47. $\dfrac{5-2x}{\left(x^2+2\right)(x-1)}=\dfrac{A}{x-1}+\dfrac{Bx+C}{x^2+2}$

Multiply both sides by $\left(x^2+2\right)(x-1)$ to get the following.

$$5-2x=A\left(x^2+2\right)+(Bx+C)(x-1)\ (1)$$

First substitute 1 for x to get the following.

$$5-2(1)=A\left(1^2+2\right)+\left[B(1)+C\right](1-1)\Rightarrow 5-2=A(1+2)+0\Rightarrow 3=3A\Rightarrow A=1$$

Replace A with 1 in equation (1) and substitute 0 for x to get the following.

$$5-2(0)=\left(0^2+2\right)+\left[B(0)+C\right](0-1)\Rightarrow 5-0=(0+2)+C(-1)\Rightarrow 5=2-C\Rightarrow 3=-C\Rightarrow C=-3$$

$$5-2x=\left(x^2+2\right)+(Bx-3)(x-1)\ (2)$$

Substitute 2 (arbitrary value) in equation (2) for x to get the following.

$$5-2(2)=\left(2^2+2\right)+\left[B(2)-3\right](2-1)$$

$$5-4=(4+2)+(2B-3)(1)\Rightarrow 1=6+2B-3\Rightarrow 1=3+2B\Rightarrow -2=2B\Rightarrow B=-1$$

Thus, we have $\dfrac{5-2x}{\left(x^2+2\right)(x-1)}=\dfrac{1}{x-1}+\dfrac{(-1)x+(-3)}{x^2+2}$ or $\dfrac{1}{x-1}-\dfrac{x+3}{x^2+2}$.

49. $y=2x+10\ (1)$

$x^2+y=13\ (2)$

Substituting equation (1) into equation (2), we have $x^2+(2x+10)=13$. Solving for x we get the following.

$$x^2+(2x+10)=13\Rightarrow x^2+2x-3=0\Rightarrow\Rightarrow (x+3)(x-1)=0$$

$$x=-3 \text{ or } x=1$$

For each value of x, use equation (1) to find the corresponding value of y.
If $x=-3,\ y=2(-3)+10=-6+10=4$. If $x=1,\ y=2(1)+10=2+10=12$.

Solution set: $\{(-3,4),(1,12)\}$

51. $x^2+y^2=17\,(1)$

$2x^2-y^2=31\,(2)$

Add equations (1) and (2) to obtain $3x^2=48\Rightarrow x^2=16\Rightarrow x=\pm 4$.
For each value of x, use equation (1) to find the corresponding value of y.

If $x=-4$, $(-4)^2+y^2=17\Rightarrow 16+y^2=17\Rightarrow y^2=1\Rightarrow y=\pm 1$.

If $x=4$, $4^2+y^2=17\Rightarrow 16+y^2=17\Rightarrow y^2=1\Rightarrow y=\pm 1$.

Solution set: $\{(-4,1),(-4,-1),(4,-1),(4,1)\}$

53. $xy = -10$ (1)

$x + 2y = 1$ (2)

Solving equation (2) for x, we have $x = 1 - 2y$ (3). Substituting this expression into equation (1), we obtain $(1-2y)y = -10$. Solving for y we have the following.

$$(1-2y)y = -10 \Rightarrow y - 2y^2 = -10 \Rightarrow 0 = 2y^2 - y - 10 \Rightarrow (y+2)(2y-5) = 0$$

$$y = -2 \text{ or } y = \tfrac{5}{2}$$

For each value of y, use equation (3) to find the corresponding value of x.

If $y = -2$, $x = 1 - 2(-2) = 1 - (-4) = 5$. If $y = \frac{5}{2}$, $x = 1 - 2\left(\frac{5}{2}\right) = 1 - 5 = -4$.

Solution set: $\left\{(5,-2), \left(-4, \frac{5}{2}\right)\right\}$

55. $x^2 + 2xy + y^2 = 4$ (1)

$x - 3y = -2$ (2)

Solving equation (2) for x, we have $x = 3y - 2$ (3). Substituting this expression into equation (1), we obtain $(3y-2)^2 + 2(3y-2)y + y^2 = 4$. Solving for x we have the following.

$$(3y-2)^2 + 2(3y-2)y + y^2 = 4 \Rightarrow 9y^2 - 12y + 4 + 6y^2 - 4y + y^2 = 4$$

$$16y^2 - 16y + 4 = 4 \Rightarrow 16y^2 - 16y = 0 \Rightarrow y^2 - y = 0 \Rightarrow y(y-1) = 0$$

$$y = 0 \text{ or } y = 1$$

For each value of y, use equation (3) to find the corresponding value of x.

If $y = 0$, $x = 3(0) - 2 = 0 - 2 = -2$. If $y = 1$, $x = 3(1) - 2 = 3 - 2 = 1$.

Solution set: $\{(-2,0), (1,1)\}$

57. $3x - y = b$ (1)

$x^2 + y^2 = 25$ (2)

Solving equation (1) for y we have $y = 3x - b$. Substitute this expression into equation (2).

$$x^2 + (3x-b)^2 = 25 \Rightarrow x^2 + 9x^2 - 6bx + b^2 = 25$$

$$10x^2 - 6bx + \left(b^2 - 25\right) = 0$$

We solve this quadratic equation for x by using the quadratic formula, $x = \dfrac{-b \pm \sqrt{b^2 - 4ac}}{2a}$, with $a = 10$, $b = -6b$, and $c = b^2 - 25$.

$$x = \frac{-(-6b) \pm \sqrt{(-6b)^2 - 4(10)\left(b^2 - 25\right)}}{2(10)} = \frac{6b \pm \sqrt{36b^2 - 40\left(b^2 - 25\right)}}{20} = \frac{6b \pm \sqrt{36b^2 - 40b^2 + 1000}}{20}$$

$$= \frac{6b \pm \sqrt{1000 - 4b^2}}{20} = \frac{6b \pm \sqrt{4\left(250 - b^2\right)}}{20} = \frac{6b \pm 2\sqrt{250 - b^2}}{20}$$

In order for there to be only one solution (the line touches the circle in one point),

$250 - b^2 = 0 \Rightarrow b^2 = 250 \Rightarrow b = \pm\sqrt{250} \Rightarrow b = \pm 5\sqrt{10}$.

59. $x+y\le 6$

$2x-y\ge 3$

Graph the solid line $x+y=6$, which has x-intercept 6 and y-intercept 6. Since $x+y\le 6 \Rightarrow y\le -x+6$, shade the region below this line. Graph the solid line $2x-y=3$, which has x-intercept $\frac{3}{2}$ and y-intercept -3. Since $2x-y\ge 3\Rightarrow \ -y\ge -2x+3\Rightarrow y\le 2x-3$, shade the region below this line. The solution set is the intersection of these two regions, which is shaded in the final graph.

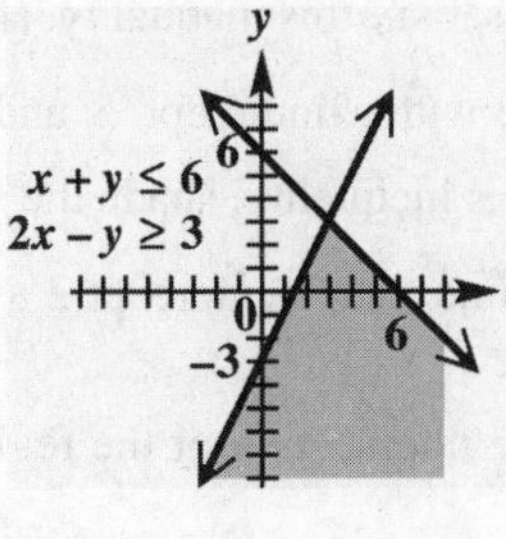

61. Find $x\ge 0$ and $y\ge 0$ such that $\begin{matrix}3x+2y\le 12\\5x+y\ge 5\end{matrix}$ and $2x+4y$ is maximized. To graph $3x+2y\le 12$, draw the line with x-intercept 4 and y-intercept 6 as a solid line. Because the test point $(0,0)$ satisfies this inequality, shade the region *below* the line. To graph $5x+y\ge 5$, draw the line with x-intercept 1 and y-intercept 5 as a solid line. Because the test point $(0,0)$ does not satisfy this inequality, shade the region *above* the line. The constraints $x\ge 0$ and $y\ge 0$ restrict the graph to the first quadrant. The graph of the feasible region is the intersection of the regions that are the graphs of the individual constraints. The four vertices are $(1,0),(4,0),(0,5),$ and $(0,6)$.

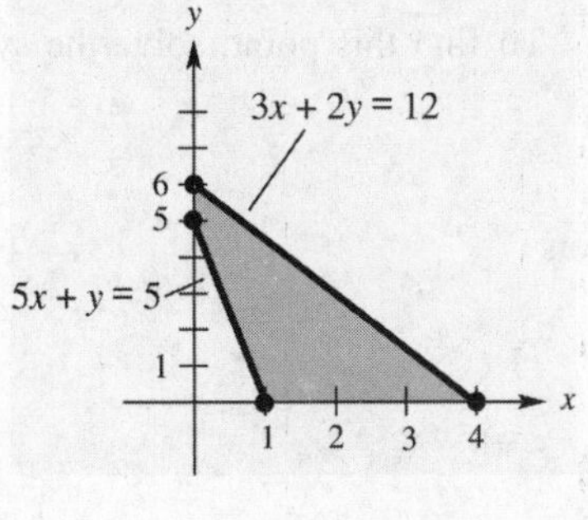

Point	Value of $2x+4y$	
$(1,0)$	$2(1)+4(0)=2$	
$(4,0)$	$2(4)+4(0)=8$	
$(0,5)$	$2(0)+4(5)=20$	
$(0,6)$	$2(0)+4(6)=24$	← Maximum

The maximum value is 24, which occurs at $(0,6)$.

63. Let $x =$ number of servings of food A;
and $y =$ number of servings of food B.
The protein constraint is $2x+6y \geq 30$. The fat constraint is $4x+2y \geq 20$. Also, $y \geq 2$ and since the numbers of servings cannot be negative, we also have $x \geq 0$. We want to minimize the objective function, cost $= .18x + .12y$.

Find the region of feasible solutions by graphing the system of inequalities that is made up of the constraints. To graph $2x+6y \geq 30$, draw the line with x-intercept 15 and y-intercept 5 as a solid line. Because the test point $(0,0)$ does not satisfy this inequality, shade the region *above* the line.

To graph $4x+2y \geq 20$, draw the line with x-intercept 5 and y-intercept 10 as a solid line. Because the test point $(0,0)$ does not satisfy this inequality, shade the region *above* the line.

To graph $y \geq 2$, draw the horizontal line with y-intercept 2 as a solid line and shade the region *above* the line.

The graph of the feasible region is the intersection of the regions that are the graphs of the individual constraints.

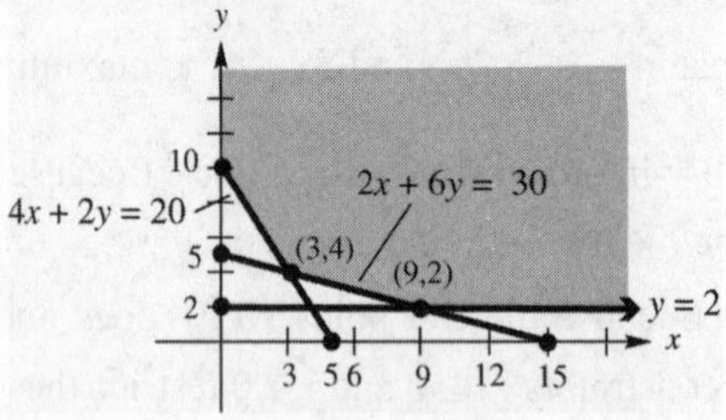

From the graph, observe that one vertex is $(0,10)$. The second occurs when $y = 2$ and $2x+6y=30 \Rightarrow 2x+6(2)=30 \Rightarrow 2x=18 \Rightarrow x=9$. Thus, $(9,2)$ is a vertex. The third vertex is the intersection point of the lines $2x+6y=30$ and $4x+2y=20$. To find this point, solve the system

$$2x+6y=30$$
$$4x+2y=20.$$

Multiply the first equation by –2 and add it to the second equation.

$$\begin{aligned} -4x-12y &= -60 \\ 4x+\ 2y &= \ 20 \\ \hline -10y &= -40 \Rightarrow y=4 \end{aligned}$$

Substituting 4 for y into $2x+6y=30$, we have the following.

$$2x+6(4)=30 \Rightarrow 2x+24=30 \Rightarrow 2x=6 \Rightarrow x=3$$

Thus, the third vertex is $(3,4)$. Next, evaluate the objective function at each vertex.

Point	Cost $= .18x + .12y$	
$(0,10)$	$.18(0)+.12(10)=1.20$	
$(3,4)$	$.18(3)+.12(4)=1.02$	← Minimum
$(9,2)$	$.18(9)+.12(2)=1.86$	

The minimum cost of \$1.02 per serving will be produced by 3 units of food A and 4 units of food B.

65. $\begin{bmatrix} 5 & x+2 \\ -6y & z \end{bmatrix} = \begin{bmatrix} a & 3x-1 \\ 5y & 9 \end{bmatrix}$

$a = 5; x+2 = 3x-1 \Rightarrow 3 = 2x \Rightarrow x = \frac{3}{2}; -6y = 5y \Rightarrow 0 = 11y \Rightarrow y = 0; z = 9$

Thus, $a = 5$, $x = \frac{3}{2}$, $y = 0$, and $z = 9$.

67. $\begin{bmatrix} 3 \\ 2 \\ 5 \end{bmatrix} - \begin{bmatrix} 8 \\ -4 \\ 6 \end{bmatrix} + \begin{bmatrix} 1 \\ 0 \\ 2 \end{bmatrix} = \begin{bmatrix} 3-8 \\ 2-(-4) \\ 5-6 \end{bmatrix} + \begin{bmatrix} 1 \\ 0 \\ 2 \end{bmatrix} = \begin{bmatrix} -5 \\ 6 \\ -1 \end{bmatrix} + \begin{bmatrix} 1 \\ 0 \\ 2 \end{bmatrix} = \begin{bmatrix} -5+1 \\ 6+0 \\ -1+2 \end{bmatrix} = \begin{bmatrix} -4 \\ 6 \\ 1 \end{bmatrix}$

69. $\begin{bmatrix} 2 & 5 & 8 \\ 1 & 9 & 2 \end{bmatrix} - \begin{bmatrix} 3 & 4 \\ 7 & 1 \end{bmatrix}$

This operation is not possible because one matrix is 2 3 3 and the other 2 3 2. Matrices of different sizes cannot be added or subtracted.

71. $\begin{bmatrix} -1 & 0 \\ 2 & 5 \end{bmatrix} \begin{bmatrix} -3 & 4 \\ 2 & 8 \end{bmatrix} = \begin{bmatrix} -1(-3)+0(2) & -1(4)+0(8) \\ 2(-3)+5(2) & 2(4)+5(8) \end{bmatrix} = \begin{bmatrix} 3+0 & -4+0 \\ -6+10 & 8+40 \end{bmatrix} = \begin{bmatrix} 3 & -4 \\ 4 & 48 \end{bmatrix}$

73. The product of a 2×3 matrix and a 3×2 matrix is a 2×2 matrix.

$$\begin{bmatrix} 3 & 2 & -1 \\ 4 & 0 & 6 \end{bmatrix} \begin{bmatrix} -2 & 0 \\ 0 & 2 \\ 3 & 1 \end{bmatrix} = \begin{bmatrix} 3(-2)+2(0)+(-1)(3) & 3(0)+2(2)+(-1)(1) \\ 4(-2)+0(0)+6(3) & 4(0)+0(2)+6(1) \end{bmatrix}$$

$$= \begin{bmatrix} -6+0-3 & 0+4-1 \\ -8+0+18 & 0+0+6 \end{bmatrix} = \begin{bmatrix} -9 & 3 \\ 10 & 6 \end{bmatrix}$$

75. The product of a 3×3 matrix and a 3×3 matrix is a 3×3 matrix.

$$\begin{bmatrix} -2 & 5 & 5 \\ 0 & 1 & 4 \\ 3 & -4 & -1 \end{bmatrix} \begin{bmatrix} 1 & 0 & -1 \\ -1 & 0 & 0 \\ 1 & 1 & -1 \end{bmatrix}$$

$$= \begin{bmatrix} -2(1)+5(-1)+5(1) & -2(0)+5(0)+5(1) & -2(-1)+5(0)+5(-1) \\ 0(1)+1(-1)+4(1) & 0(0)+1(0)+4(1) & 0(-1)+1(0)+4(-1) \\ 3(1)+(-4)(-1)+(-1)(1) & 3(0)+(-4)(0)+(-1)(1) & 3(-1)+(-4)(0)+(-1)(-1) \end{bmatrix}$$

$$= \begin{bmatrix} -2+(-5)+5 & 0+0+5 & 2+0+(-5) \\ 0+(-1)+4 & 0+0+4 & 0+0+(-4) \\ 3+4+(-1) & 0+0+(-1) & -3+0+1 \end{bmatrix} = \begin{bmatrix} -2 & 5 & -3 \\ 3 & 4 & -4 \\ 6 & -1 & -2 \end{bmatrix}$$

77. Find the inverse of $A = \begin{bmatrix} 2 & 1 \\ 5 & 3 \end{bmatrix}$, if it exists. We have $[A|I_2] = \left[\begin{array}{cc|cc} 2 & 1 & 1 & 0 \\ 5 & 3 & 0 & 1 \end{array}\right]$, which yields

$$\left[\begin{array}{cc|cc} 1 & \frac{1}{2} & \frac{1}{2} & 0 \\ 5 & 3 & 0 & 1 \end{array}\right] \begin{matrix} \frac{1}{2}\text{R1} \\ \end{matrix} \Rightarrow \left[\begin{array}{cc|cc} 1 & \frac{1}{2} & \frac{1}{2} & 0 \\ 0 & \frac{1}{2} & -\frac{5}{2} & 1 \end{array}\right] \begin{matrix} \\ -5\text{R1}+\text{R2} \end{matrix}$$

$$\left[\begin{array}{cc|cc} 1 & \frac{1}{2} & \frac{1}{2} & 0 \\ 0 & 1 & -5 & 2 \end{array}\right] \begin{matrix} \\ 2\text{R2} \end{matrix} \Rightarrow \left[\begin{array}{cc|cc} 1 & 0 & 3 & -1 \\ 0 & 1 & -5 & 2 \end{array}\right] \begin{matrix} -\frac{1}{2}\text{R2}+\text{R1} \\ \end{matrix}. \text{ Thus, } A^{-1} = \begin{bmatrix} 3 & -1 \\ -5 & 2 \end{bmatrix}.$$

79. Find the inverse of $A=\begin{bmatrix}2 & -1 & 0\\ 1 & 0 & 1\\ 1 & -2 & 0\end{bmatrix}$ if it exists. We have $\left[A\,|\,I_3\right]=\left[\begin{array}{ccc|ccc}2 & -1 & 0 & 1 & 0 & 0\\ 1 & 0 & 1 & 0 & 1 & 0\\ 1 & -2 & 0 & 0 & 0 & 1\end{array}\right]$.

$$\left[\begin{array}{ccc|ccc}1 & 0 & 1 & 0 & 1 & 0\\ 2 & -1 & 0 & 1 & 0 & 0\\ 1 & -2 & 0 & 0 & 0 & 1\end{array}\right]\begin{matrix}\text{R1}\leftrightarrow\text{R2}\\ \\ \\ \end{matrix} \Rightarrow \left[\begin{array}{ccc|ccc}1 & 0 & 1 & 0 & 1 & 0\\ 0 & -1 & -2 & 1 & -2 & 0\\ 0 & -2 & -1 & 0 & -1 & 1\end{array}\right]\begin{matrix}\\ -2\text{R1}+\text{R2}\\ -1\text{R1}+\text{R3}\end{matrix}$$

$$\left[\begin{array}{ccc|ccc}1 & 0 & 1 & 0 & 1 & 0\\ 0 & 1 & 2 & -1 & 2 & 0\\ 0 & -2 & -1 & 0 & -1 & 1\end{array}\right]\begin{matrix}\\ -1\text{R2}\\ \\ \end{matrix} \Rightarrow \left[\begin{array}{ccc|ccc}1 & 0 & 1 & 0 & 1 & 0\\ 0 & 1 & 2 & -1 & 2 & 0\\ 0 & 0 & 3 & -2 & 3 & 1\end{array}\right]\begin{matrix}\\ \\ 2\text{R2}+\text{R3}\end{matrix}$$

$$\left[\begin{array}{ccc|ccc}1 & 0 & 1 & 0 & 1 & 0\\ 0 & 1 & 2 & -1 & 2 & 0\\ 0 & 0 & 1 & -\frac{2}{3} & 1 & \frac{1}{3}\end{array}\right]\begin{matrix}\\ \\ \frac{1}{3}\text{R3}\end{matrix} \Rightarrow \left[\begin{array}{ccc|ccc}1 & 0 & 0 & \frac{2}{3} & 0 & -\frac{1}{3}\\ 0 & 1 & 0 & \frac{1}{3} & 0 & -\frac{2}{3}\\ 0 & 0 & 1 & -\frac{2}{3} & 1 & \frac{1}{3}\end{array}\right]\begin{matrix}-1\text{R3}+\text{R1}\\ -2\text{R3}+\text{R2}\\ \\ \end{matrix}$$

Thus, $A^{-1}=\begin{bmatrix}\frac{2}{3} & 0 & -\frac{1}{3}\\ \frac{1}{3} & 0 & -\frac{2}{3}\\ -\frac{2}{3} & 1 & \frac{1}{3}\end{bmatrix}$.

81. Given $\begin{aligned}3x+2y+\ z&=-5\\ x-\ y+3z&=-5\\ 2x+3y+\ z&=0\end{aligned}$ we have $A=\begin{bmatrix}3 & 2 & 1\\ 1 & -1 & 3\\ 2 & 3 & 1\end{bmatrix}$, $X=\begin{bmatrix}x\\ y\\ z\end{bmatrix}$, and $B=\begin{bmatrix}-5\\ -5\\ 0\end{bmatrix}$. Finding A^{-1}, we have

$$\left[A\,|\,I_3\right]=\left[\begin{array}{ccc|ccc}3 & 2 & 1 & 1 & 0 & 0\\ 1 & -1 & 3 & 0 & 1 & 0\\ 2 & 3 & 1 & 0 & 0 & 1\end{array}\right] \Rightarrow \left[\begin{array}{ccc|ccc}1 & -1 & 3 & 0 & 1 & 0\\ 3 & 2 & 1 & 1 & 0 & 0\\ 2 & 3 & 1 & 0 & 0 & 1\end{array}\right]\begin{matrix}\text{R1}\leftrightarrow\text{R2}\\ \\ \\ \end{matrix}$$

$$\left[\begin{array}{ccc|ccc}1 & -1 & 3 & 0 & 1 & 0\\ 0 & 5 & -8 & 1 & -3 & 0\\ 0 & 5 & -5 & 0 & -2 & 1\end{array}\right]\begin{matrix}\\ -3\text{R1}+\text{R2}\\ -2\text{R1}+\text{R2}\end{matrix} \Rightarrow \left[\begin{array}{ccc|ccc}1 & -1 & 3 & 0 & 1 & 0\\ 0 & 1 & -\frac{8}{5} & \frac{1}{5} & -\frac{3}{5} & 0\\ 0 & 5 & -5 & 0 & -2 & 1\end{array}\right]\begin{matrix}\\ \frac{1}{5}\text{R2}\\ \\ \end{matrix}$$

$$\left[\begin{array}{ccc|ccc}1 & 0 & \frac{7}{5} & \frac{1}{5} & \frac{2}{5} & 0\\ 0 & 1 & -\frac{8}{5} & \frac{1}{5} & -\frac{3}{5} & 0\\ 0 & 0 & 3 & -1 & 1 & 1\end{array}\right]\begin{matrix}\text{R2}+\text{R1}\\ \\ -5\text{R2}+\text{R3}\end{matrix} \Rightarrow \left[\begin{array}{ccc|ccc}1 & 0 & \frac{7}{5} & \frac{1}{5} & \frac{2}{5} & 0\\ 0 & 1 & -\frac{8}{5} & \frac{1}{5} & -\frac{3}{5} & 0\\ 0 & 0 & 1 & -\frac{1}{3} & \frac{1}{3} & \frac{1}{3}\end{array}\right]\begin{matrix}\\ \\ \frac{1}{3}\text{R3}\end{matrix}$$

$$\left[\begin{array}{ccc|ccc}1 & 0 & 0 & \frac{2}{3} & -\frac{1}{15} & -\frac{7}{15}\\ 0 & 1 & 0 & -\frac{1}{3} & -\frac{1}{15} & \frac{8}{15}\\ 0 & 0 & 1 & -\frac{1}{3} & \frac{1}{3} & \frac{1}{3}\end{array}\right]\begin{matrix}-\frac{7}{5}\text{R3}+\text{R1}\\ \frac{8}{5}\text{R3}+\text{R2}.\\ \\ \end{matrix}$$

Thus, $A^{-1}=\begin{bmatrix}\frac{2}{3} & -\frac{1}{15} & -\frac{7}{15}\\ -\frac{1}{3} & -\frac{1}{15} & \frac{8}{15}\\ -\frac{1}{3} & \frac{1}{3} & \frac{1}{3}\end{bmatrix}$. Finally, we need to find $X=A^{-1}B$.

$$X=A^{-1}B=\begin{bmatrix}\frac{2}{3} & -\frac{1}{15} & -\frac{7}{15}\\ -\frac{1}{3} & -\frac{1}{15} & \frac{8}{15}\\ -\frac{1}{3} & \frac{1}{3} & \frac{1}{3}\end{bmatrix}\begin{bmatrix}-5\\ -5\\ 0\end{bmatrix}$$

$$=\begin{bmatrix}\frac{2}{3}(-5)+\left(-\frac{1}{15}\right)(-5)+\left(-\frac{7}{15}\right)(0)\\ -\frac{1}{3}(-5)+\left(-\frac{1}{15}\right)(-5)+\frac{8}{15}(0)\\ -\frac{1}{3}(-5)+\frac{1}{3}(-5)+\frac{1}{3}(0)\end{bmatrix}=\begin{bmatrix}-\frac{10}{3}+\frac{1}{3}+0\\ \frac{5}{3}+\frac{1}{3}+0\\ \frac{5}{3}+\left(-\frac{5}{3}\right)+0\end{bmatrix}=\begin{bmatrix}-\frac{9}{3}\\ \frac{6}{3}\\ 0\end{bmatrix}=\begin{bmatrix}-3\\ 2\\ 0\end{bmatrix}$$

Solution set: $\{(-3,2,0)\}$

Chapter 9: Test

1. $3x - y = 9 \quad (1)$

$x + 2y = 10 \quad (2)$

Solving equation (2) for *x*, we obtain *x* = 10 – 2*y* (3). Substituting this result into equation (1) and solving for *y*, we obtain $3(10-2y) - y = 9 \Rightarrow 30 - 6y - y = 9 \Rightarrow -7y = -21 \Rightarrow y = 3$. Substituting *y* = 3 back into equation (3) in order to find *x*, we obtain $x = 10 - 2(3) = 10 - 6 = 4$.

Solution set: $\{(4,3)\}$

2. $6x + 9y = -21 \quad (1)$

$4x + 6y = -14 \quad (2)$

Solving equation (1) for *x*, we obtain $6x = -9y - 21 \Rightarrow x = \frac{-9y-21}{6} \Rightarrow x = \frac{-3y-7}{2}$ (3). Substituting this result into equation (2) and solving for *y*, we obtain the following.

$$4\left(\frac{-3y-7}{2}\right) + 6y = -14 \Rightarrow 2(-3y-7) + 6y = -14 \Rightarrow -6y - 14 + 6y = -14 \Rightarrow -14 = -14$$

This true statement implies there are infinitely many solutions. We can represent the solution set with *y* as the arbitrary variable.

Solution set: $\left\{\left(\frac{-3y-7}{2},\, y\right)\right\}$

3. $\frac{1}{4}x - \frac{1}{3}y = -\frac{5}{12} \quad (1)$

$\frac{1}{10}x + \frac{1}{5}y = \frac{1}{2} \quad (2)$

To eliminate fractions, multiply equation (1) by 12 and equation (2) by 10.

$$3x - 4y = -5 \quad (3)$$
$$x + 2y = 5 \quad (4)$$

Multiply equation (4) by 2 and add the result to equation (3).

$$\begin{array}{l} 3x - 4y = -5 \\ \underline{2x + 4y = 10} \\ 5x \qquad = 5 \Rightarrow x = 1 \end{array}$$

Substituting *x* = 1 in equation (4) to find *y*, we obtain $1 + 2y = 5 \Rightarrow 2y = 4 \Rightarrow y = 2$.

Solution set: $\{(1,2)\}$

4. $x - 2y = 4 \quad (1)$

$-2x + 4y = 6 \quad (2)$

Multiply equation (1) by 2 and add the result to equation (2).

$$\begin{array}{r} 2x - 4y = 8 \\ \underline{-2x + 4y = 6} \\ 0 = 14 \end{array}$$

The system is inconsistent. The solution set is $\emptyset$.

5. $2x+y+z=3$ (1)

$x+2y-z=3$ (2)

$3x-y+z=5$ (3)

Eliminate z first by adding equations (1) and (2) to obtain $3x+3y=6$ (4). Add equations (2) and (3) to eliminate z and obtain $4x+y=8$ (5). Multiply equation (5) by -3 and add the results to equation (4).

$$\begin{array}{rl} 3x+3y= & 6 \\ -12x-3y= & -24 \\ \hline -9x \quad = & -18 \Rightarrow x=2 \end{array}$$

Substituting $x=2$ in equation (5) to find y, we have $4(2)+y=8 \Rightarrow 8+y=8 \Rightarrow y=0.$

Substituting $x=2$ and $y=0$ in equation (1) to find z, we have $2(2)+0+z=3 \Rightarrow z=-1.$

Solution set: $\{(2,0,-1)\}$

6. Writing $\begin{array}{l} 3x-2y=13 \\ 4x-\ y=19 \end{array}$ as an augmented matrix, we have $\left[\begin{array}{cc|c} 3 & -2 & 13 \\ 4 & -1 & 19 \end{array}\right]$.

$$\left[\begin{array}{cc|c} 1 & -\frac{2}{3} & \frac{13}{3} \\ 4 & -1 & 19 \end{array}\right]\tfrac{1}{3}\text{R1} \Rightarrow \left[\begin{array}{cc|c} 1 & -\frac{2}{3} & \frac{13}{3} \\ 0 & \frac{5}{3} & \frac{5}{3} \end{array}\right]-4\text{R1}+\text{R2} \Rightarrow \left[\begin{array}{cc|c} 1 & -\frac{2}{3} & \frac{13}{3} \\ 0 & 1 & 1 \end{array}\right]\tfrac{3}{5}\text{R2} \Rightarrow \left[\begin{array}{cc|c} 1 & 0 & 5 \\ 0 & 1 & 1 \end{array}\right]\tfrac{2}{3}\text{R2}+\text{R1}$$

Solution set $\{(5,1)\}$

7. Writing $\begin{array}{l} 3x-4y+2z=15 \\ 2x-\ y+\ z=13 \\ \ x+2y-\ z=5 \end{array}$ as an augmented matrix, we have $\left[\begin{array}{ccc|c} 3 & -4 & 2 & 15 \\ 2 & -1 & 1 & 13 \\ 1 & 2 & -1 & 5 \end{array}\right]$.

$$\left[\begin{array}{ccc|c} 1 & 2 & -1 & 5 \\ 2 & -1 & 1 & 13 \\ 3 & -4 & 2 & 15 \end{array}\right]\begin{array}{l}\text{R1}\leftrightarrow\text{R3} \\ \\ \\ \end{array} \Rightarrow \left[\begin{array}{ccc|c} 1 & 2 & -1 & 5 \\ 0 & -5 & 3 & 3 \\ 0 & -10 & 5 & 0 \end{array}\right]\begin{array}{l} \\ -2\text{R1}+\text{R2} \\ -3\text{R1}+\text{R3} \end{array}$$

$$\left[\begin{array}{ccc|c} 1 & 2 & -1 & 5 \\ 0 & 1 & -\frac{3}{5} & -\frac{3}{5} \\ 0 & -10 & 5 & 0 \end{array}\right]\begin{array}{l} \\ -\frac{1}{5}\text{R2} \\ \\ \end{array} \Rightarrow \left[\begin{array}{ccc|c} 1 & 0 & \frac{1}{5} & \frac{31}{5} \\ 0 & 1 & -\frac{3}{5} & -\frac{3}{5} \\ 0 & 0 & -1 & -6 \end{array}\right]\begin{array}{l} -2\text{R2}+\text{R1} \\ \\ 10\text{R2}+\text{R3} \end{array}$$

$$\left[\begin{array}{ccc|c} 1 & 0 & \frac{1}{5} & \frac{31}{5} \\ 0 & 1 & -\frac{3}{5} & -\frac{3}{5} \\ 0 & 0 & 1 & 6 \end{array}\right]\begin{array}{l} \\ \\ -1\text{R3} \end{array} \Rightarrow \left[\begin{array}{ccc|c} 1 & 0 & 0 & 5 \\ 0 & 1 & 0 & 3 \\ 0 & 0 & 1 & 6 \end{array}\right]\begin{array}{l} -\frac{1}{5}\text{R3}+\text{R1} \\ \frac{3}{5}\text{R3}+\text{R2} \\ \\ \end{array}$$

Solution set: $\{(5,3,6)\}$

8. Since $y=ax^2+bx+c$, and the points $(1,5),(2,3)$, and $(4,11)$ are on the graph, we have the following equations which are then simplified.

$$5=a(1)^2+b(1)+c \Rightarrow \quad a+\ b+c=5 \quad (1)$$
$$3=a(2)^2+b(2)+c \Rightarrow \ 4a+2b+c=3 \quad (2)$$
$$11=a(4)^2+b(4)+c \Rightarrow 16a+4b+c=11 \quad (3)$$

Continued on next page

8. (continued)
First, eliminate c by adding –1 times equation (1) to equation (2).

$$\begin{array}{r} -a-\ \ b-c=-5 \\ 4a+2b+c=\ \ 3 \\ \hline 3a+\ \ b\ \ \ \ \ \ \ =-2\ (4) \end{array}$$

Eliminating c again by adding –1 times equation (1) to equation (3), we have the following.

$$\begin{array}{r} -a-\ \ b-c=-5 \\ 16a+4b+c=11 \\ \hline 15a+3b\ \ \ \ \ \ =\ 6\ (5) \end{array}$$

Next, eliminate b by adding –3 times equation (4) to equation (5).

$$\begin{array}{l} -9a-3b=6 \\ 15a+3b\ =6 \\ \hline 6a\ \ \ \ \ \ \ \ =12\Rightarrow a=2 \end{array}$$

Substituting this value into equation (4), we obtain $3(2)+b=-2\Rightarrow 6+b=-2\Rightarrow b=-8$.

Substituting 2 for a and –8 for b into equation (1), we have $2+(-8)+c=5\Rightarrow -6+c=5\Rightarrow c=11$.

The equation of the parabola is $y=2x^2-8x+11$.

9. Let x = number of units from Toronto;
and y = number of units from Montreal;
and z = number of units from Ottawa.

$$\begin{array}{rl} x+y+z=100 & \text{Total units} \\ 80x+50y+65z=5990 & \text{Total cost} \\ x=z & \text{Toronto units} = \text{Ottawa units} \end{array}$$

Multiply the first equation by –50 and add to the second equation.

$$\begin{array}{r} -50x-50y-50z=-5000 \\ 80x+50y+65z=\ \ 5990 \\ \hline 30x\ \ \ \ \ \ \ \ \ \ \ +15z=\ \ \ 990 \end{array}$$

Substitute x for z in this equation to obtain $30x+15x=990\Rightarrow 45x=990\Rightarrow x=22$. If x = 22, then $z=22$. Substitute 22 for x and for z in the first equation and solve for y to obtain the following.

$$22+y+22=100\Rightarrow y=56$$

22 units from Toronto, 56 units from Montreal, and 22 units from Ottawa are ordered.

10. $\begin{vmatrix} 6 & 8 \\ 2 & -7 \end{vmatrix}=6(-7)-2(8)=-58$

11. $\begin{vmatrix} 2 & 0 & 8 \\ -1 & 7 & 9 \\ 12 & 5 & -3 \end{vmatrix}$

This determinant may be evaluated by expanding about any row or any column. If we expand by the first row, we have the following.

$$\begin{vmatrix} 2 & 0 & 8 \\ -1 & 7 & 9 \\ 12 & 5 & -3 \end{vmatrix}=2\begin{vmatrix} 7 & 9 \\ 5 & -3 \end{vmatrix}-0\begin{vmatrix} -1 & 9 \\ 12 & -3 \end{vmatrix}+8\begin{vmatrix} -1 & 7 \\ 12 & 5 \end{vmatrix}=2[7(-3)-5(9)]-0+8[(-1)(5)-12(7)]$$

$$=2(-21-45)+8(-5-84)=2(-66)+8(-89)=-132-712=-844$$

12. $2x-3y=-33$
$4x+5y=11$

$$D=\begin{vmatrix}2 & -3\\ 4 & 5\end{vmatrix}=2(5)-4(-3)=10-(-12)=22;\ D_x=\begin{vmatrix}-33 & -3\\ 11 & 5\end{vmatrix}=-33(5)-11(-3)=-165-(-33)=-132;$$

$$D_y=\begin{vmatrix}2 & -33\\ 4 & 11\end{vmatrix}=2(11)-4(-33)=22-(-132)=154;\ x=\frac{D_x}{D}=\frac{-132}{22}=-6;\ y=\frac{D_y}{D}=\frac{154}{22}=7$$

Solution set: $\{(-6,7)\}$

13. $x+y-z=-4$
$2x-3y-z=5$
$x+2y+2z=3$

Adding column 3 to columns 1 and 2, we have $D=\begin{vmatrix}1 & 1 & -1\\ 2 & -3 & -1\\ 1 & 2 & 2\end{vmatrix}=\begin{vmatrix}0 & 0 & -1\\ 1 & -4 & -1\\ 3 & 4 & 2\end{vmatrix}$.

Expanding by row one, we have $D=-1\begin{vmatrix}1 & -4\\ 3 & 4\end{vmatrix}=-[4-(-12)]=-16.$

Adding –1 times row 1 to row 2 and 2 times row 1 to row 3, we have the following.

$$D_x=\begin{vmatrix}-4 & 1 & -1\\ 5 & -3 & -1\\ 3 & 2 & 2\end{vmatrix}=\begin{vmatrix}-4 & 1 & -1\\ 9 & -4 & 0\\ -5 & 4 & 0\end{vmatrix}$$

Expanding by column three, we have $D_x=-1\begin{vmatrix}9 & -4\\ -5 & 4\end{vmatrix}=-(36-20)=-16.$

Adding –1 times row 1 to row 2 and 2 times row 1 to row 3, we have the following.

$$D_y=\begin{vmatrix}1 & -4 & -1\\ 2 & 5 & -1\\ 1 & 3 & 2\end{vmatrix}=\begin{vmatrix}1 & -4 & -1\\ 1 & 9 & 0\\ 3 & -5 & 0\end{vmatrix}.$$

Expanding by column three, we have $D_y=-1\begin{vmatrix}1 & 9\\ 3 & -5\end{vmatrix}=-1(-5-27)=-(-32)=32.$

Adding –2 times row 1 to row 2 and -1 times row 1 to row 3, we have $D_z=\begin{vmatrix}1 & 1 & -4\\ 2 & -3 & 5\\ 1 & 2 & 3\end{vmatrix}=\begin{vmatrix}1 & 1 & -4\\ 0 & -5 & 13\\ 0 & 1 & 7\end{vmatrix}$.

Expanding by column one, we have $D_z=1\begin{vmatrix}-5 & 13\\ 1 & 7\end{vmatrix}=1(-35-13)=-48.$

Thus we have $x=\frac{D_x}{D}=\frac{-16}{-16}=1,\ y=\frac{D_y}{D}=\frac{32}{-16}=-2,$ and $z=\frac{D_z}{D}=\frac{-48}{-16}=3.$
Solution set: $\{(1,-2,3)\}$

14. $\frac{x+2}{x^3+x^2+x}=\frac{x+2}{x\left(x^2+x+1\right)}=\frac{x+2}{x(x+1)^2}=\frac{A}{x}+\frac{B}{x+1}+\frac{C}{(x+1)^2}$

Multiply both sides by $x(x+1)^2$ to get $x+2=A(x+1)^2+Bx(x+1)+Cx$ (1). Substituting 0 for x in equation (1), we get $0+2=A(0+1)^2+B(0)(0+1)+C(0)\Rightarrow A=2$.
Substituting 2 for A and –1 for x in equation (1), we get the following.

$$-1+2=2(-1+1)^2+B(-1)(-1+1)+C(-1)\Rightarrow 1=-C\Rightarrow C=-1$$

We now have $x+2=2(x+1)^2+Bx(x+1)+(-1)x$ (2). Now substitute 1 for x (arbitrary choice) in equation (2) to obtain the following.

$$1+2=2(1+1)^2+B(1)(1+1)+(-1)(1)\Rightarrow 3=2(4)+2B-1$$

$$3=8+2B-1\Rightarrow 3=7+2B\Rightarrow -4=2B\Rightarrow B=-2$$

Thus, $\frac{x+2}{x^3+x^2+x}=\frac{x+2}{x\left(x^2+x+1\right)}=\frac{x+2}{x(x+1)^2}=\frac{2}{x}+\frac{-2}{x+1}+\frac{-1}{(x+1)^2}$.

15. Yes: the system will have exactly one solution if the line is tangent to the circle.

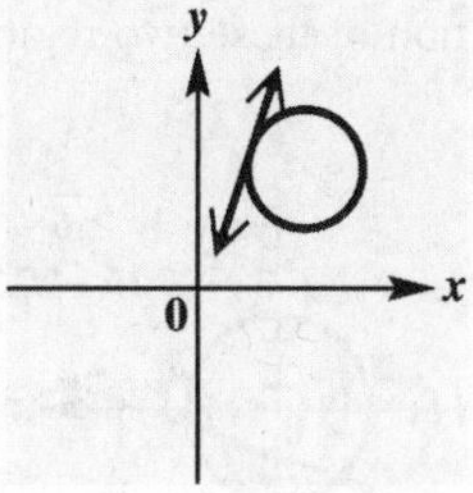

16. $2x^2+y^2=6$ (1)
$x^2-4y^2=-15$ (2)
Multiply equation (1) by 4 and add to equation (2), then solve for x.

$$\begin{aligned} 8x^2+4y^2 &= 24\\ x^2-4y^2 &= -15\\ \hline 9x^2 \quad &= 9\Rightarrow x^2=1\Rightarrow x=\pm 1\end{aligned}$$

Substitute these values into equation (1) and solve for y.
If $x=1$, then $2(1)^2+y^2=6\Rightarrow 2+y^2=6\Rightarrow y^2=4\Rightarrow y=\pm 2$.
If $x=-1$, then $2(-1)^2+y^2=6\Rightarrow 2+y^2=6\Rightarrow y^2=4\Rightarrow y=\pm 2$.
Solution set: $\{(1,2),(-1,2),(1,-2),(-1,-2)\}$

17. $x^2+y^2=25$ (1)
$x+y=7$ (2)
Solving equation (2) for x, we have $x=7-y$ (3). Substituting this result into equation (1), we have

$$(7-y)^2+y^2=25\Rightarrow 49-14y+y^2+y^2=25\Rightarrow 2y^2-14y+24=0$$

$$y^2-7y+12=0\Rightarrow(y-3)(y-4)=0$$

$$y=3 \text{ or } y=4$$

Substitute these values into equation (3) and solve for x.
If $y=3$, $x=7-3=4$. If $y=4$, $x=7-4=3$.
Solution set: $\{(3,4),(4,3)\}$

18. Let x and y be the numbers.

$$x+y=-1 \quad (1)$$
$$x^2+y^2=61 \quad (2)$$

Solving equation (1) for y, we have $y=-x-1$ (3). Substituting this result into equation (2), we have

$$x^2+(-x-1)^2=61 \Rightarrow x^2+x^2+2x+1=61 \Rightarrow 2x^2+2x-60=0$$
$$x^2+x-30=0 \Rightarrow (x+6)(x-5)=0$$
$$x=-6 \text{ or } x=5$$

Substitute these values in equation (3) to find the corresponding values of y.
If $x=-6,\ y=-(-6)-1=6-1=5.$ If $x=5,\ y=-5-1=-6.$
The same pair of numbers results from both cases. The numbers are 5 and – 6.

19. $x-3y\ge 6$
$y^2\le 16-x^2$

Graph $x-3y=6$ as a solid line with x-intercept 6 and y-intercept of –2. Because the test point $(0,0)$ does not satisfies this inequality, shade the region *below* the line. Graph $y^2=16-x^2$ or $x^2+y^2=16$ as a solid circle with a center at the origin and radius 4. Shade the region, which is the interior of the circle. The solution set is the intersection of these two regions, which is the region shaded in the final graph.

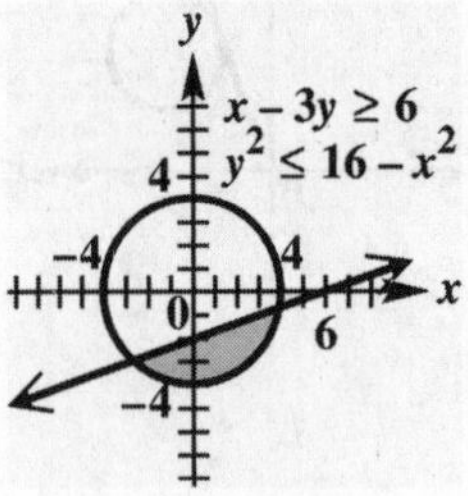

20. Find $x\ge 0$ and $y\ge 0$ such that
$x+2y\le 24$
$3x+4y\le 60$
and $2x+3y$ is maximized.

Find the region of feasible solutions by graphing the system of inequalities that is made up of the constraints. To graph $x+2y\le 24$, draw the line with x-intercept 24 and y-intercept 12 as a solid line. Because the test point $(0,0)$ satisfies this inequality, shade the region *below* the line.

To graph $3x+4y\le 60$, draw the line with x-intercept 20 and y-intercept 15 as a solid line. Because the test point $(0,0)$ satisfies this inequality, shade the region *below* the line.

The constraints $x\ge 0$ and $y\ge 0$ restrict the graph to the first quadrant. The graph of the feasible region is the intersection of the regions that are the graphs of the individual constraints.

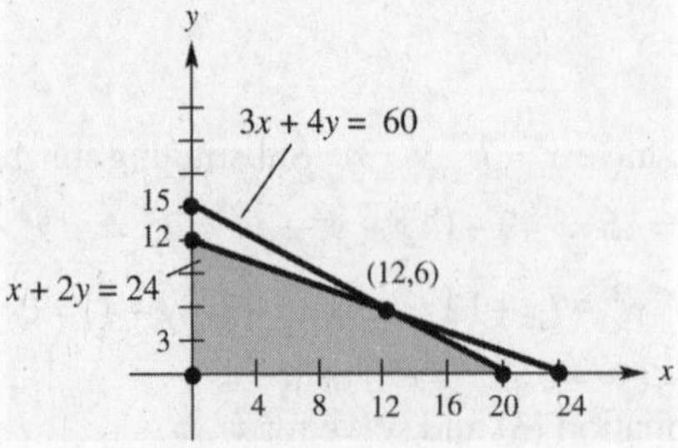

Continued on next page

20. (continued)

From the graph, observe that three vertices are $(0,0),(0,12)$, and $(20,0)$. A fourth vertex is the intersection point of the lines $x+y=24$ and $3x+4y=60$. To find this point, solve the system

$$\begin{aligned} x+2y&=24 \quad (1) \\ 3x+4y&=60 \quad (2) \end{aligned}.$$

To eliminate x, multiply equation (1) by –3 and add the result to equation (2).

$$\begin{aligned} -3x-6y&=-72 \\ 3x+4y&=\ \ 60 \\ \hline -2y&=-12 \Rightarrow y=6 \end{aligned}$$

Substituting this value into equation (1), we obtain $x+2(6)=24 \Rightarrow x+12=24 \Rightarrow x=12$.

The fourth vertex is $(12,6)$. Next, evaluate the objective function at each vertex.

Point	Profit $=2x+3y$.	
$(0,0)$	$2(0)+3(0)=0$	
$(0,12)$	$2(0)+3(12)=36$	
$(20,0)$	$2(20)+3(0)=40$	
$(12,6)$	$2(12)+3(6)=42$	← Maximum

The maximum value is 42 at (12, 6).

21. Let x = the number of VIP rings;
and y = the number of SST rings.

The constraints are $x+y\le 24$ Maximize profit function, profit $=30x+40y$.

$$3x+2y\le 60$$
$$x\ge 0,\ y\ge 0.$$

Find the region of feasible solutions by graphing the system of inequalities that is made up of the constraints. To graph $x+y\le 24$, draw the line with x-intercept 24 and y-intercept 24 as a solid line. Because the test point $(0,0)$ satisfies this inequality, shade the region *below* the line.

To graph $3x+2y\le 60$, draw the line with x-intercept 20 and y-intercept 30 as a solid line. Because the test point $(0,0)$ satisfies this inequality, shade the region *below* the line.

The constraints $x\ge 0$ and $y\ge 0$ restrict the graph to the first quadrant. The graph of the feasible region is the intersection of the regions that are the graphs of the individual constraints.

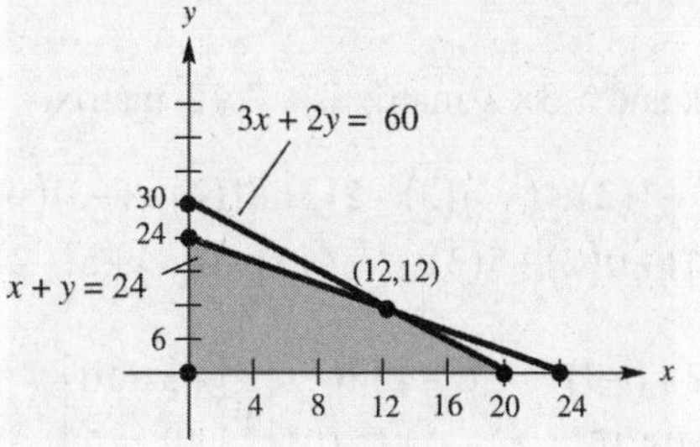

From the graph, observe that three vertices are $(0,0),(20,0)$, and $(0,24)$. A fourth vertex is the intersection point of the lines $x+y=24$ and $3x+2y=60$. To find this point, solve the system

$$\begin{aligned} x+\ y&=24 \\ 3x+2y&=60. \end{aligned}$$

Continued on next page

21. (continued)
The first equation can be written as $x = 24 - y$. Substituting this equation into $3x + 2y = 60$, we have the following.

$$3(24-y)+ y = 60 \Rightarrow 72-3y+2y = 60 \Rightarrow 72-y = 60 \Rightarrow -y = -12 \Rightarrow y = 12$$

Substituting $y = 12$ into $x = 24 - y$, we have $x = 24 - 12 = 12$.

Thus, the four vertex is $(12,12)$. Next, evaluate the objective function at each vertex.

Point	Profit $= 30x + 40y$.	
$(0,0)$	$30(0)+40(0)=0$	
$(20,0)$	$30(20)+40(0)=600$	
$(0,24)$	$30(0)+40(24)=960$	← Maximum
$(12,12)$	$30(12)+40(12)=840$	

0 VIP rings and 24 SST rings should be made daily for a daily profit of \$960.

22. $\begin{bmatrix} 5 & x+6 \\ 0 & 4 \end{bmatrix} = \begin{bmatrix} y-2 & 4-x \\ 0 & w+7 \end{bmatrix}$

All corresponding elements, position by position, of the two matrices must be equal.
$x+6 = 4-x \Rightarrow 2x = -2 \Rightarrow x = -1;\ 5 = y-2 \Rightarrow y = 7; 4 = w+7 \Rightarrow w = -3$
Thus, $x = -1$, $y = 7$, and $w = -3$.

23. $$3\begin{bmatrix} 2 & 3 \\ 1 & -4 \\ 5 & 9 \end{bmatrix} - \begin{bmatrix} -2 & 6 \\ 3 & -1 \\ 0 & 8 \end{bmatrix} = \begin{bmatrix} 3(2) & 3(3) \\ 3(1) & 3(-4) \\ 3(5) & 3(9) \end{bmatrix} - \begin{bmatrix} -2 & 6 \\ 3 & -1 \\ 0 & 8 \end{bmatrix} = \begin{bmatrix} 6 & 9 \\ 3 & -12 \\ 15 & 27 \end{bmatrix} + \begin{bmatrix} 2 & -6 \\ -3 & 1 \\ 0 & -8 \end{bmatrix}$$

$$= \begin{bmatrix} 6+2 & 9+(-6) \\ 3+(-3) & -12+1 \\ 15+0 & 27+(-8) \end{bmatrix} = \begin{bmatrix} 8 & 3 \\ 0 & -11 \\ 15 & 19 \end{bmatrix}$$

24. $\begin{bmatrix} 1 \\ 2 \end{bmatrix} + \begin{bmatrix} 4 \\ -6 \end{bmatrix} + \begin{bmatrix} 2 & 8 \\ -7 & 5 \end{bmatrix}$

The first two matrices are 2 3 1 and the third is 2 3 2. Only matrices of the same size can be added, so it is not possible to find this sum.

25. The product of a 2×3 matrix and a 3×2 matrix is a 2×2 matrix.

$$\begin{bmatrix} 2 & 1 & -3 \\ 4 & 0 & 5 \end{bmatrix}\begin{bmatrix} 1 & 3 \\ 2 & 4 \\ 3 & -2 \end{bmatrix} = \begin{bmatrix} 2(1)+1(2)+(-3)(3) & 2(3)+1(4)+(-3)(-2) \\ 4(1)+0(2)+5(3) & 4(3)+0(4)+5(-2) \end{bmatrix}$$

$$= \begin{bmatrix} 2+2+(-9) & 6+4+6 \\ 4+0+15 & 12+0+(-10) \end{bmatrix} = \begin{bmatrix} -5 & 16 \\ 19 & 2 \end{bmatrix}$$

26. $\begin{bmatrix} 2 & -4 \\ 3 & 5 \end{bmatrix}\begin{bmatrix} 4 \\ 2 \\ 7 \end{bmatrix}$

The first matrix is 2 3 2 and the second is 1 3 3. The first matrix has two columns and the second has one row, so it is not possible to find this product.

27. There are associative, distributive, and identity properties that apply to multiplication of matrices, but matrix multiplication is not commutative. The correct choice is A.

28. Find the inverse of $A=\begin{bmatrix}-8 & 5\\ 3 & -2\end{bmatrix}$, if it exists. The augmented matrix is $\left[A|I_2\right]=\left[\begin{array}{cc|cc}-8 & 5 & 1 & 0\\ 3 & -2 & 0 & 1\end{array}\right]$.

$$\left[\begin{array}{cc|cc}1 & -\frac{5}{8} & -\frac{1}{8} & 0\\ 3 & -2 & 0 & 1\end{array}\right]\begin{matrix}-\frac{1}{8}\text{R1}\\ \\ \end{matrix} \Rightarrow \left[\begin{array}{cc|cc}1 & -\frac{5}{8} & -\frac{1}{8} & 0\\ 0 & -\frac{1}{8} & \frac{3}{8} & 1\end{array}\right]\begin{matrix}\\ -3\text{R1+R2}\end{matrix}$$

$$\left[\begin{array}{cc|cc}1 & -\frac{5}{8} & -\frac{1}{8} & 0\\ 0 & 1 & -3 & -8\end{array}\right]\begin{matrix}\\ -8\text{R2}\end{matrix} \Rightarrow \left[\begin{array}{cc|cc}1 & 0 & -2 & -5\\ 0 & 1 & -3 & -8\end{array}\right]\begin{matrix}\frac{5}{8}\text{R2+R1}\\ \\ \end{matrix}$$

Thus, $A^{-1}=\begin{bmatrix}-2 & -5\\ -3 & -8\end{bmatrix}$.

29. Find the inverse of $A=\begin{bmatrix}4 & 12\\ 2 & 6\end{bmatrix}$, if it exists. The augmented matrix is $\left[A|I_2\right]=\left[\begin{array}{cc|cc}4 & 12 & 1 & 0\\ 2 & 6 & 0 & 1\end{array}\right]$.

$$\left[\begin{array}{cc|cc}1 & 3 & \frac{1}{4} & 0\\ 2 & 6 & 0 & 1\end{array}\right]\begin{matrix}\frac{1}{4}\text{R1}\\ \\ \end{matrix} \Rightarrow \left[\begin{array}{cc|cc}1 & 3 & \frac{1}{4} & 0\\ 0 & 0 & -\frac{1}{2} & 1\end{array}\right]\begin{matrix}\\ -2\text{R1}+\text{R2}\end{matrix}$$

The second row, second column element is now 0, so the desired transformation cannot be completed. Therefore, the inverse of the given matrix does not exist.

30. Find the inverse of $A=\begin{bmatrix}1 & 3 & 4\\ 2 & 7 & 8\\ -2 & -5 & -7\end{bmatrix}$, if it exists. Performing row operations on the augmented matrix, we have the following.

$$\left[A|I_3\right]=\left[\begin{array}{ccc|ccc}1 & 3 & 4 & 1 & 0 & 0\\ 2 & 7 & 8 & 0 & 1 & 0\\ -2 & -5 & -7 & 0 & 0 & 1\end{array}\right] \Rightarrow \left[\begin{array}{ccc|ccc}1 & 3 & 4 & 1 & 0 & 0\\ 0 & 1 & 0 & -2 & 1 & 0\\ 0 & 1 & 1 & 2 & 0 & 1\end{array}\right]\begin{matrix}\\ -2\text{R1}+\text{R2}\\ 2\text{R1}+\text{R3}\end{matrix}$$

$$\left[\begin{array}{ccc|ccc}1 & 0 & 4 & 7 & -3 & 0\\ 0 & 1 & 0 & -2 & 1 & 0\\ 0 & 0 & 1 & 4 & -1 & 1\end{array}\right]\begin{matrix}-3\text{R2+R1}\\ \\ -1\text{R2}+\text{R3}\end{matrix} \Rightarrow \left[\begin{array}{ccc|ccc}1 & 0 & 0 & -9 & 1 & -4\\ 0 & 1 & 0 & -2 & 1 & 0\\ 0 & 0 & 1 & 4 & -1 & 1\end{array}\right]\begin{matrix}-4\text{R3}+\text{R1}\\ \\ \\ \end{matrix}$$

Thus, $A^{-1}=\begin{bmatrix}-9 & 1 & -4\\ -2 & 1 & 0\\ 4 & -1 & 1\end{bmatrix}$.

31. The system $\begin{matrix}2x+y=-6\\ 3x-y=-29\end{matrix}$ yields the matrix equation $AX = B$ where $A=\begin{bmatrix}2 & 1\\ 3 & -1\end{bmatrix}$, $X=\begin{bmatrix}x\\ y\end{bmatrix}$, and $B=\begin{bmatrix}-6\\ -29\end{bmatrix}$. Find A^{-1}. The augmented matrix is $\left[A|I_2\right]=\left[\begin{array}{cc|cc}2 & 1 & 1 & 0\\ 3 & -1 & 0 & 1\end{array}\right]$.

Continued on next page

31. (continued)

$$\left[\begin{array}{cc|cc} 1 & \frac{1}{2} & \frac{1}{2} & 0 \\ 3 & -1 & 0 & 1 \end{array}\right]\tfrac{1}{2}\text{R1} \Rightarrow \left[\begin{array}{cc|cc} 1 & \frac{1}{2} & \frac{1}{2} & 0 \\ 0 & -\frac{5}{2} & -\frac{3}{2} & 1 \end{array}\right]-3\text{R1}+\text{R2}$$

$$\left[\begin{array}{cc|cc} 1 & 0 & \frac{1}{5} & \frac{1}{5} \\ 0 & -\frac{5}{2} & -\frac{3}{2} & 1 \end{array}\right]\tfrac{1}{5}\text{R2}+\text{R1} \Rightarrow \left[\begin{array}{cc|cc} 1 & 0 & \frac{1}{5} & \frac{1}{5} \\ 0 & 1 & \frac{3}{5} & -\frac{2}{5} \end{array}\right]-\tfrac{2}{5}\text{R2}$$

Thus, $A^{-1} = \begin{bmatrix} \frac{1}{5} & \frac{1}{5} \\ \frac{3}{5} & -\frac{2}{5} \end{bmatrix}$. Since $X = A^{-1}B$, we have the following.

$$A^{-1}B = \begin{bmatrix} \frac{1}{5} & \frac{1}{5} \\ \frac{3}{5} & -\frac{2}{5} \end{bmatrix}\begin{bmatrix} -6 \\ -29 \end{bmatrix} = \begin{bmatrix} \frac{1}{5}(-6)+\frac{1}{5}(-29) \\ \frac{3}{5}(-6)+\left(-\frac{2}{5}\right)(-29) \end{bmatrix} = \begin{bmatrix} -\frac{6}{5}+\left(-\frac{29}{5}\right) \\ -\frac{18}{5}+\frac{58}{5} \end{bmatrix} = \begin{bmatrix} -\frac{35}{5} \\ \frac{40}{5} \end{bmatrix} = \begin{bmatrix} -7 \\ 8 \end{bmatrix}$$

Solution set: $\{(-7,8)\}$

32. The system $\begin{aligned} x+y&=5 \\ y-2z&=23 \\ x+3z&=-27 \end{aligned}$ yields the matrix equation $AX = B$ where $A = \begin{bmatrix} 1 & 1 & 0 \\ 0 & 1 & -2 \\ 1 & 0 & 3 \end{bmatrix}$,

$X = \begin{bmatrix} x \\ y \\ z \end{bmatrix}$, and $B = \begin{bmatrix} 5 \\ 23 \\ -27 \end{bmatrix}$. Find A^{-1}. The augmented matrix is $[A|I_3] = \left[\begin{array}{ccc|ccc} 1 & 1 & 0 & 1 & 0 & 0 \\ 0 & 1 & -2 & 0 & 1 & 0 \\ 1 & 0 & 3 & 0 & 0 & 1 \end{array}\right]$.

$$\left[\begin{array}{ccc|ccc} 1 & 1 & 0 & 1 & 0 & 0 \\ 0 & 1 & -2 & 0 & 1 & 0 \\ 0 & -1 & 3 & -1 & 0 & 1 \end{array}\right]\begin{matrix} \\ \\ -\text{R1}+\text{R3} \end{matrix} \Rightarrow \left[\begin{array}{ccc|ccc} 1 & 0 & 2 & 1 & -1 & 0 \\ 0 & 1 & -2 & 0 & 1 & 0 \\ 0 & 0 & 1 & -1 & 1 & 1 \end{array}\right]\begin{matrix} -1\text{R2}+\text{R1} \\ \\ \text{R2}+\text{R3} \end{matrix}$$

$$\left[\begin{array}{ccc|ccc} 1 & 0 & 0 & 3 & -3 & -2 \\ 0 & 1 & 0 & -2 & 3 & 2 \\ 0 & 0 & 1 & -1 & 1 & 1 \end{array}\right]\begin{matrix} -2\text{R3}+\text{R1} \\ 2\text{R3}+\text{R2} \\ \\ \end{matrix}$$

Thus, $A^{-1} = \begin{bmatrix} 3 & -3 & -2 \\ -2 & 3 & 2 \\ -1 & 1 & 1 \end{bmatrix}$. Since $X = A^{-1}B$, we have the following.

$$A^{-1}B = \begin{bmatrix} 3 & -3 & -2 \\ -2 & 3 & 2 \\ -1 & 1 & 1 \end{bmatrix}\begin{bmatrix} 5 \\ 23 \\ -27 \end{bmatrix} = \begin{bmatrix} 3(5)+(-3)(23)+(-2)(-27) \\ -2(5)+3(23)+2(-27) \\ -1(5)+1(23)+1(-27) \end{bmatrix} = \begin{bmatrix} 15+(-69)+54 \\ -10+(69)+(-54) \\ -5+23+(-27) \end{bmatrix} = \begin{bmatrix} 0 \\ 5 \\ -9 \end{bmatrix} = X$$

Solution set: $\{(0,5,-9)\}$

Chapter 10

ANALYTIC GEOMETRY

Section 10.1: Parabolas

1. **(a)** The relation $y+2=(x-4)^2$ has vertex $(4,-2)$ and opens up, so the correct choice is D.

(b) The relation $y+4=(x-2)^2$ has vertex $(2,-4)$ and opens up, so the correct choice is B.

(c) The relation $y+2=-(x-4)^2$ has vertex $(4,-2)$ and opens down, so the correct choice is C.

(d) The relation $y+4=-(x-2)^2$ has vertex $(2,-4)$ and opens down, so the correct choice is A.

(e) The relation $x+2=(y-4)^2$ has vertex $(-2,4)$ and opens to the right, so the correct choice is F.

(f) The relation $x+4=(y-2)^2$ has vertex $(-4,2)$ and opens to the right, so the correct choice is H.

(g) The relation $x+2=-(y-4)^2$ has vertex $(-2,4)$ and opens to the left, so the correct choice is E.

(h) The relation $x+4=-(y-2)^2$ has vertex $(-4,2)$ and opens to the left, so the correct choice is G.

3. $x=-y^2 \Rightarrow x=-1(y-0)^2+0 \Rightarrow x-0=-1(y-0)^2$

The vertex is $(0,0)$. The graph opens to the left and has the same shape as $x=y^2$. The domain is $(-\infty,0]$. The range is $(-\infty,\infty)$. The graph is symmetric about its axis, the horizontal line $y=0$ (the x-axis). Use the vertex and axis and plot a few additional points.

x	y
−4	2
−1	1
0	0
−1	−1
−4	−2

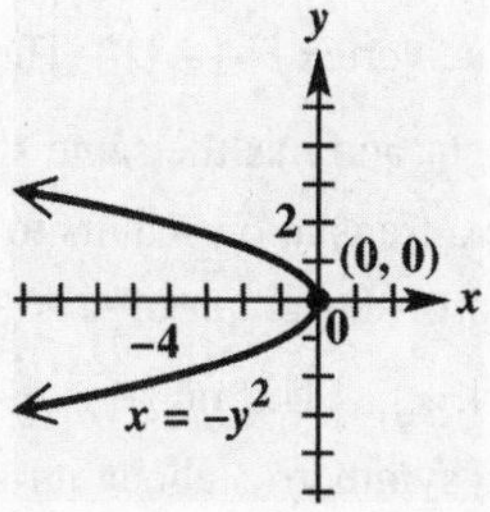

5. $x=(y-3)^2 \Rightarrow x-0=(y-3)^2$

The vertex is $(0,3)$. The graph opens to the right and has the same shape as $x=y^2$. It is a translation 3 units up of the graph of $x=y^2$. The domain is $[0,\infty)$. The range is $(-\infty,\infty)$. The graph is symmetric about its axis, the horizontal line $y=3$. Use the vertex and axis and plot a few additional points.

x	y
4	1
1	2
0	3
1	4
4	5

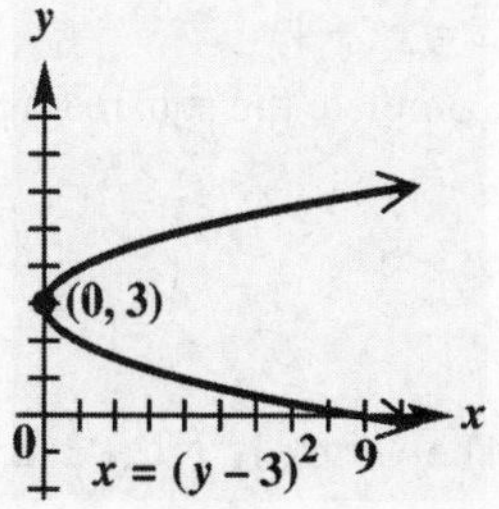

7. $x-2=(y-4)^2$

The vertex is $(2,4)$. The graph opens to the right and has the same shape as $x=y^2$. It is a translation 2 units to the right and 4 units up of the graph of $x=y^2$. The domain is $[2,\infty)$. The range is $(-\infty,\infty)$. The graph is symmetric about its axis, the horizontal line $y=4$. Use the vertex and axis and plot a few additional points.

x	y
6	6
3	5
2	4
3	3
6	2

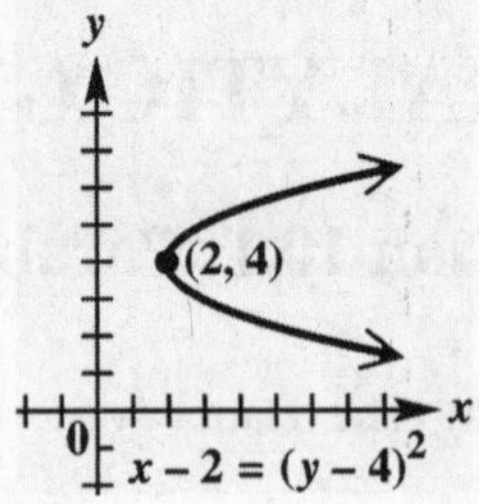

9. $x-2=-3(y-1)^2$

The vertex is $(2,1)$. The graph opens to the left and has the same shape as $x=-3y^2$. It is a translation 1 unit up and 2 units to the right of the graph of $x=-3y^2$. The domain is $(-\infty,2]$. The range is $(-\infty,\infty)$. The graph is symmetric about its axis, the horizontal line $y=1$. Use the vertex and axis and plot a few additional points.

x	y
−10	3
−1	2
2	1
−1	0
−10	−1

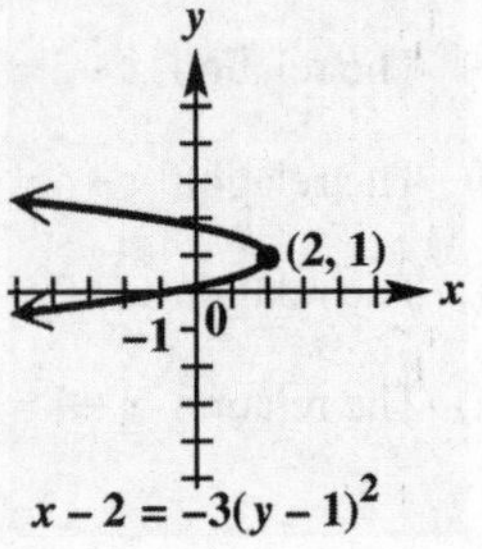

11. $x-4=\frac{1}{2}(y-1)^2$

The vertex is $(4,1)$. The graph opens to the right and has the same shape as $x=\frac{1}{2}y^2$. It is a translation 4 units to the right and 1 unit up of the graph of $x=\frac{1}{2}y^2$. The domain is $[4,\infty)$. The range is $(-\infty,\infty)$. The graph is symmetric about its axis, the horizontal line $y=1$. Use the vertex and axis and plot a few additional points.

x	y
6	3
4.5	2
4	1
4.5	0
6	−1

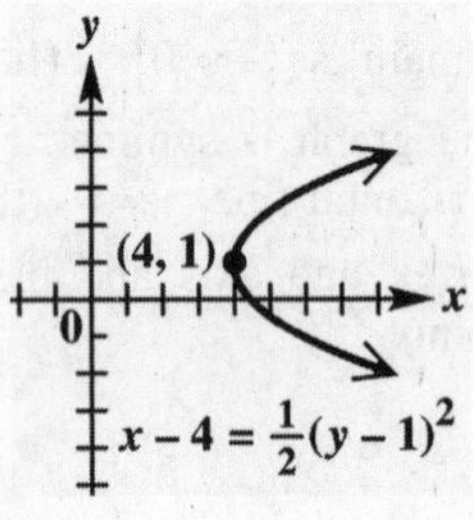

13. $x=y^2+4y+2$

Complete the square on y to find the vertex and the axis.

$$x=y^2+4y+2\Rightarrow x=\left(y^2+4y\quad\right)+2\Rightarrow x=\left(y^2+4y+4-4\right)+2$$

$$x=\left(y^2+4y+4\right)-4+2\Rightarrow x=(y+2)^2-2\Rightarrow x-(-2)=\left[y-(-2)\right]^2$$

The vertex is $(-2,-2)$. The graph opens to the right and has the same shape as $x=y^2$, translated 2 units to the left and 2 units down. The domain is $[-2,\infty)$. The range is $(-\infty,\infty)$. The graph is symmetric about its axis, the horizontal line $y=-2$. Use the vertex and axis and plot a few additional points.

Continued on next page

13. (continued)

x	y
2	0
–1	–1
–2	–2
–1	–3
2	–4

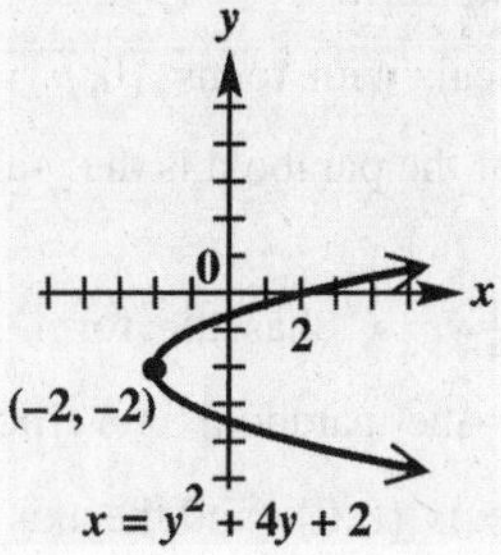

15. $x = -4y^2 - 4y + 3$

Complete the square on y to find the vertex and the axis.

$$x = -4y^2 - 4y + 3 \Rightarrow x = -4\left(y^2 + y \qquad\right) + 3 \Rightarrow x = -4\left(y^2 + y + \tfrac{1}{4} - \tfrac{1}{4}\right) + 3$$

$$x = -4\left(y^2 + y + \tfrac{1}{4}\right) - 4\left(-\tfrac{1}{4}\right) + 3 \Rightarrow x = -4\left(y^2 + y + \tfrac{1}{4}\right) + 1 + 3 \Rightarrow x = -4\left(y + \tfrac{1}{2}\right)^2 + 4$$

$$x - 4 = -4\left[y - \left(-\tfrac{1}{2}\right)\right]^2$$

The vertex is $\left(4, -\frac{1}{2}\right)$. The graph opens to the left and has the same shape as $x = -4y^2$. translated 4 units to the right and $\frac{1}{2}$ unit down. The domain is $(-\infty, 4]$. The range is $(-\infty, \infty)$. The graph is symmetric about its axis, the horizontal line $y = -\frac{1}{2}$. Use the vertex and axis and plot a few additional points.

x	y
–12	$1\frac{1}{2}$
0	$\frac{1}{2}$
4	$-\frac{1}{2}$
0	$-1\frac{1}{2}$
–12	$-2\frac{1}{2}$

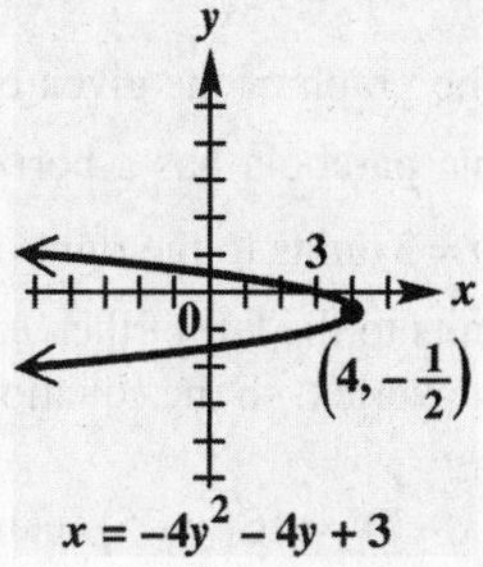

17. $2x = y^2 - 4y + 6 \Rightarrow x = \frac{1}{2}y^2 - 2y + 3$

Complete the square on y to find the vertex and the axis.

$$x = \tfrac{1}{2}y^2 - 2y + 3 \Rightarrow x = \tfrac{1}{2}\left(y^2 - 4y \qquad\right) + 3 \Rightarrow x = \tfrac{1}{2}\left(y^2 - 4y + 4 - 4\right) + 3$$

$$x = \tfrac{1}{2}\left(y^2 - 4y + 4\right) + \tfrac{1}{2}(-4) + 3 \Rightarrow x = \tfrac{1}{2}\left(y^2 - 4y + 4\right) - 2 + 3 \Rightarrow x = \tfrac{1}{2}(y - 2)^2 + 1$$

$$x - 1 = \tfrac{1}{2}(y - 2)^2$$

The vertex is $(1, 2)$. The graph opens to the right and has the same shape as $x = \frac{1}{2}y^2$, translated 1 unit to the right and 2 units up. The domain is $[1, \infty)$. The range is $(-\infty, \infty)$. The graph is symmetric about its axis, the horizontal line $y = 2$. Use the vertex and axis and plot a few additional points.

x	y
3	4
1.5	3
1	2
1.5	1
3	0

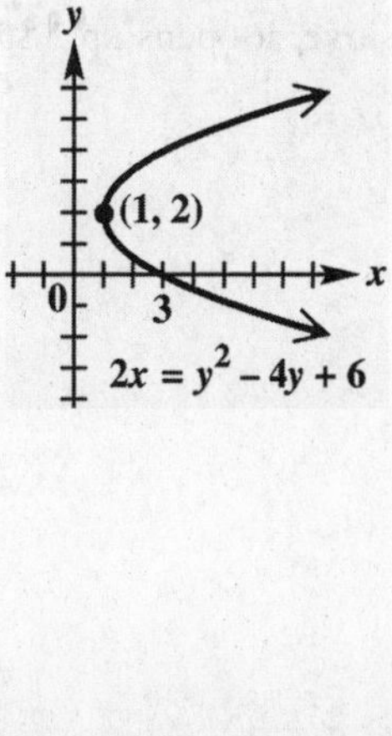

19. The equation $x^2 = 24y$ has the form $x^2 = 4py$, so $4p = 24$, from which $p = 6$. Since the x-term is squared, the parabola is vertical, with focus $(0, p) = (0, 6)$ and directrix, $y = -p$, is $y = -6$. The vertex is $(0, 0)$, and the axis of the parabola is the y-axis.

21. The equation $y = -4x^2 \Rightarrow -\frac{1}{4}y = x^2$ has the form $x^2 = 4py$, so $4p = -\frac{1}{4}$, from which $p = -\frac{1}{16}$. Since the x-term is squared, the parabola is vertical, with focus $(0, p) = \left(0, -\frac{1}{16}\right)$ and directrix, $y = -p$, is $y = \frac{1}{16}$. The vertex is $(0, 0)$, and the axis of the parabola is the y-axis.

23. The equation $y^2 = -4x$ has the form $y^2 = 4px$, so $4p = -4$, from which $p = -1$. Since the y-term is squared, the parabola is horizontal, with focus $(p, 0) = (-1, 0)$ and directrix, $x = -p$, is $x = 1$. The vertex is $(0, 0)$, and the axis of the parabola is the x-axis.

25. The equation $x = -32y^2 \Rightarrow -\frac{1}{32}x = y^2$ has the form $y^2 = 4px$, so $4p = -\frac{1}{32}$, from which $p = -\frac{1}{128}$. Since the y-term is squared, the parabola is horizontal, with focus $(p, 0) = \left(-\frac{1}{128}, 0\right)$ and directrix, $x = -p$, is $x = \frac{1}{128}$. The vertex is $(0, 0)$, and the axis of the parabola is the x-axis.

27. $(y-3)^2 = 12(x-1)$ has the form $(y-k)^2 = 4p(x-h)$, with $h = 1, k = 3$, and $4p = 12$, so $p = 3$. The graph of the given equation is a parabola with vertical axis. The vertex (h, k) is $(1, 3)$. Because this parabola has a horizontal axis and $p > 0$, the parabola opens right, so the focus is the distance $p = 3$ units to the right of the vertex. Thus the focus is $(4, 3)$. The directrix is the vertical line $p = 3$ units to the left of the vertex, so the directrix is the line $x = -2$. The axis is the horizontal line through the vertex, so the equation of the axis is $y = 3$.

29. $(x-7)^2 = 16(y+5)$ can be written as $(x-7)^2 = 16\left[y-(-5)\right]$. Thus, the parabola has the form $(x-h)^2 = 4p(y-k)$, with $h = 7, k = -5$, and $4p = 16$, so $p = 4$. The graph of the given equation is a parabola with vertical axis. The vertex (h, k) is $(7, -5)$. Because this parabola has a vertical axis and $p > 0$, the parabola opens up, so the focus is the distance $p = 4$ units above the vertex. Thus, the focus is $(7, -1)$. The directrix is the horizontal line $p = 4$ units below the vertex, so the directrix is the line $y = -9$. The axis is the vertical line through the vertex, so the equation of the axis is $x = 7$.

31. A parabola with focus $(5, 0)$ and vertex at the origin is a horizontal parabola. The equation has the form $y^2 = 4px$. Since $p = 5$ is positive, it opens to the right. Substituting 5 for p, we find that an equation for this parabola is $y^2 = 4(5)x \Rightarrow y^2 = 20x$.

33. A parabola with focus $\left(0, \frac{1}{4}\right)$ and vertex at the origin is a vertical parabola. The equation has the form $x^2 = 4py$. Since $p = \frac{1}{4}$ is positive, it opens up. Substituting $\frac{1}{4}$ for p, we find that an equation for this parabola is $x^2 = 4\left(\frac{1}{4}\right)y \Rightarrow x^2 = y$.

35. A parabola passing through $\left(\sqrt{3},3\right)$, opening up, and vertex at the origin has an equation of the form $x^2 = 4py$. Use this equation with the coordinates of the point $\left(\sqrt{3},3\right)$ to find the value of p.

$$x^2 = 4py \Rightarrow \left(\sqrt{3}\right)^2 = 4p \cdot 3 \Rightarrow 3 = 12p \Rightarrow \tfrac{1}{4} = p$$

Thus, an equation of the parabola is $x^2 = 4\left(\tfrac{1}{4}\right)y \Rightarrow x^2 = y.$

37. A parabola through $(3,2)$, symmetric with respect to the x-axis, and vertex at the origin has a horizontal axis (x-axis) and the equation is of the form $y^2 = 4px$. Use this equation with the coordinates of the point $(3,2)$ to find the value of p.

$$y^2 = 4px \Rightarrow 2^2 = 4p \cdot 3 \Rightarrow 4 = 12p \Rightarrow p = \tfrac{1}{3}$$

Thus, an equation for the parabola is $y^2 = 4\left(\tfrac{1}{3}\right)x \Rightarrow y^2 = \tfrac{4}{3}x.$

39. The vertex is $(4,3)$ and the focus is $(4,5)$.
Since the focus is above the vertex, the axis is vertical and the parabola opens upward. The distance between the vertex and the focus is 5 – 3 = 2. Since the parabola opens upward, choose $p = 2$. The equation will have the form $(x-h)^2 = 4p(y-k)$. Substitute $p = 2$, $h = 4$, and $k = 3$ to find the required equation.

$$(x-h)^2 = 4p(y-k) \Rightarrow (x-4)^2 = 4(2)(y-3) \Rightarrow (x-4)^2 = 8(y-3)$$

41. The vertex is $(-5,6)$ and focus is $(2,6)$.
Since the focus is to the right of the vertex, the axis is horizontal and the parabola opens to the right. The distance between the vertex and the focus is 2 – (–5) = 7. Since the parabola opens to the right, choose $p = 7$. The equation will have the form $(y-k)^2 = 4p(x-h)$. Substitute $p = 7$, $h = -5$, and $k = 6$.

$$(y-k)^2 = 4p(x-h) \Rightarrow (y-6)^2 = 4(7)\left[x-(-5)\right] \Rightarrow (y-6)^2 = 28(x+5)$$

43. Complete the square on y.

$$x = 3y^2 + 6y - 4 \Rightarrow 3\left(y^2 + 2y \qquad\right) - 4 = x \Rightarrow 3\left(y^2 + 2y + 1 - 1\right) - 4 = x$$

$$3\left(y^2 + 2y + 1\right) + 3(-1) - 4 = x \Rightarrow 3(y+1)^2 - 7 = x \Rightarrow 3(y+1)^2 = x + 7$$

$$(y+1)^2 = \tfrac{x+7}{3} \Rightarrow y + 1 = \pm\sqrt{\tfrac{x+7}{3}} \Rightarrow y = -1 \pm \sqrt{\tfrac{x+7}{3}}$$

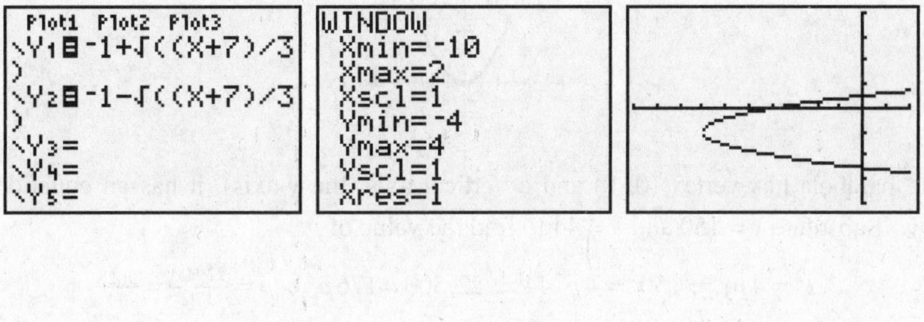

45. Solving for y we have $-(y+1)^2 = x+2 \Rightarrow (y+1)^2 = -x-2 \Rightarrow y+1 = \pm\sqrt{-x-2} \Rightarrow y = -1 \pm \sqrt{-x-2}.$

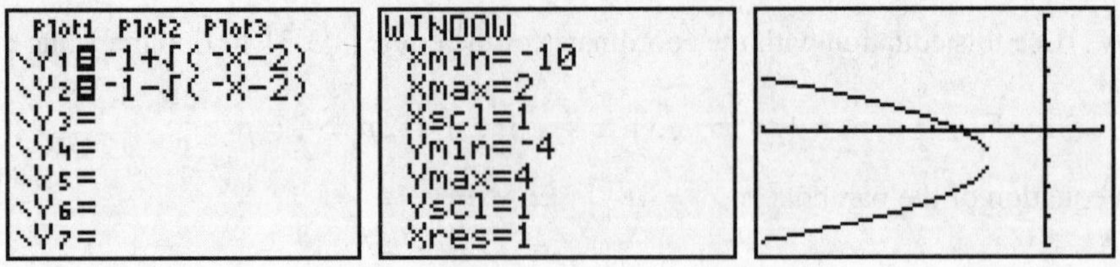

47. The equation is of the form $x = ay^2 + by + c$.

Substituting $x = -5$, $y = 1$, we get $-5 = a(1)^2 + b(1) + c \Rightarrow -5 = a + b + c.$ (1)

Substituting $x = -14$, $y = -2$, we get $-14 = a(-2)^2 + b(-2) + c \Rightarrow -14 = 4a - 2b + c.$ (2)

Substituting $x = -10$, $y = 2$, we get $-10 = a(2)^2 + b(2) + c \Rightarrow -10 = 4a + 2b + c.$ (3)

48. The following is the system of three equations.

$$a + b + c = -5 \ (1)$$
$$4a - 2b + c = -14 \ (2)$$
$$4a + 2b + c = -10 \ (3)$$

Adding equations (2) and (3), we obtain $8a + 2c = -24$ or $4a + c = -12.$ (4).

Adding 2 times equation (1) to equation (2), we obtain the following.

$$\begin{array}{rl} 2a + 2b + 2c &= -10 \\ 4a - 2b + \ \ c &= -14 \\ \hline 6a \qquad\quad + 3c &= -24 \Rightarrow 2a + c = -8 \ (5) \end{array}$$

Add –1 times equation (4) to equation (5).

$$\begin{array}{rl} -4a - c &= 12 \\ 2a + c &= -8 \\ \hline -2a \quad &= 4 \Rightarrow a = -2 \end{array}$$

Substitute $a = -2$ into equation (5) to obtain $2(-2) + c = -8 \Rightarrow -4 + c = -8 \Rightarrow c = -4.$.

Substitute $a = -2$ and $c = -4$ into equation (1) to obtain $-2 + b - 4 = -5 \Rightarrow b - 6 = -5 \Rightarrow b = 1.$

Solution set: $\{(-2, 1, -4)\}$

49. Since $a = -2 < 0$, the parabola opens to the left.

50. Substituting $a = -2$, $b = 1$, and $c = -4$, the equation of the parabola is $x = -2y^2 + y - 4$.

51. Sketch a cross-section of the dish. Place this parabola on a coordinate system with the vertex at the origin. (This solution will show that the focus lies outside of the dish.)

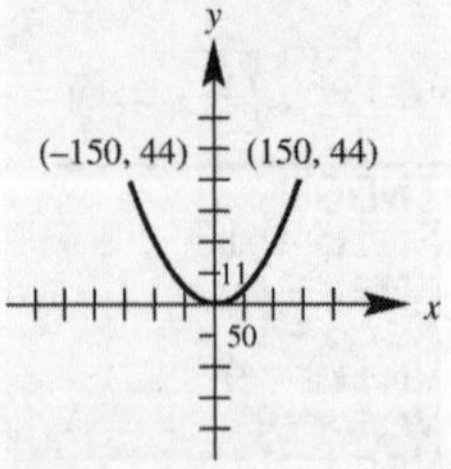

Since the parabola has vertex (0, 0) and a vertical axis (the y-axis), it has an equation of the form $x^2 = 4py$. Substitute $x = 150$ and $y = 44$ to find the value of p.

$$x^2 = 4py \Rightarrow 150^2 = 4p \cdot 44 \Rightarrow 22{,}500 = 176p \Rightarrow p = \frac{22{,}500}{176} = \frac{5625}{44}$$

The required equation is $x^2 = 4\left(\frac{5625}{44}\right)y \Rightarrow x^2 = \frac{5625}{11}y \Rightarrow y = \frac{11}{5625}x^2$.

Since $p = \frac{5625}{44} \approx 127.8$, the receiver should be placed approximately 127.8 ft from the vertex.

53. Place the parabola that represents the arch on a coordinate system with the center of the bottom of the arch at the origin. Then the vertex will be $(0,12)$ and the points $(-6,0)$ and $(6,0)$ will also be on the parabola. Because the axis of the parabola is the y-axis and the vertex is $(0,12)$, the equation will have the form $x^2 = 4p(y-12)$. Use the coordinates of the point $(6,0)$ to find the value of p.

$$x^2 = 4p(y-12) \Rightarrow 6^2 = 4p(0-12) \Rightarrow 36 = -48p \Rightarrow p = \frac{36}{-48} \Rightarrow p = -\frac{3}{4}$$

Thus, the equation of the parabola is $x^2 = 4\left(-\frac{3}{4}\right)(y-12)$ or $x^2 = -3(y-12)$.
Now find the x-coordinate of point whose y-coordinate is 9 and whose x-coordinate is positive.

$$x^2 = -3(y-12) \Rightarrow x^2 = -3(9-12) \Rightarrow x^2 = 9 \Rightarrow x = \sqrt{9} = 3$$

From the symmetry of the parabola, we see that the width of the arch 9 ft up is 2(3 ft) = 6 ft.

55. (a) Locate the cannon at the origin. With $v = 252.982$, the equation becomes the following.

$$y = x - \frac{32}{v^2}x^2 \Rightarrow y = x - \frac{32}{252.982^2}x^2 \Rightarrow y \approx x - \frac{1}{2000}x^2$$

Complete the square on x.

$$y = x - \frac{1}{2000}x^2 \Rightarrow y = -\frac{1}{2000}\left(x^2 - 2000x \qquad\right) \Rightarrow y = -\frac{1}{2000}\left(x^2 - 2000x + 1{,}000{,}000 - 1{,}000{,}000\right)$$

$$y = -\frac{1}{2000}\left(x^2 - 2000x + 1{,}000{,}000\right) + \left(-\frac{1}{2000}\right)(-1{,}000{,}000) \Rightarrow y = -\frac{1}{2000}(x-1000)^2 + 500$$

$$y - 500 = -\frac{1}{2000}(x-1000)^2$$

Thus, the vertex of the parabola is located at $(1000,500)$. Because of symmetry, the shell then travels an additional 1000 feet for a maximum distance of 2000 feet.

(b) The envelope parabola has x-intercepts located at $(-2000, 0)$ and $(2000, 0)$. The vertex is easily found to be located at $(0,1000)$. Because the axis of the parabola is the y-axis and it opens down, the equation is of the form $x^2 = 4p(y-1000)$. Use the coordinates of the point $(2000,0)$ to find the value of p.

$$2000^2 = 4p(0-1000) \Rightarrow 4{,}000{,}000 = -4000p \Rightarrow p = -1000$$

The equation of the parabola is the following.

$$x^2 = 4(-1000)(y-1000) \Rightarrow x^2 = -4000(y-1000) \Rightarrow y - 1000 = -.00025x^2 \Rightarrow y = 1000 - .0025x^2$$

(c) Using the equation of the envelope parabola in part (b), we calculate the maximum possible height of a shell when x is 1500 feet.

$$y = 1000 - .00025x^2 \Rightarrow y = 1000 - .00025(1500)^2 \Rightarrow y = 1000 - .00025(2{,}250{,}000)$$

$$y = 1000 - 562.5 \Rightarrow y = 437.5$$

If the helicopter flies at a height of 450 feet, a shell fired by the cannon would never reach the helicopter.

57. (a) $y = \frac{19}{11}x - \frac{g}{3872}x^2$

For the moon, $g = 5.2$, so the equation is $y = \frac{19}{11}x - \frac{5.2}{3872}x^2$.

For Mars, $g = 12.6$, so the equation is $y = \frac{19}{11}x - \frac{12.6}{3872}x^2$.

Graph both equations on the same screen.

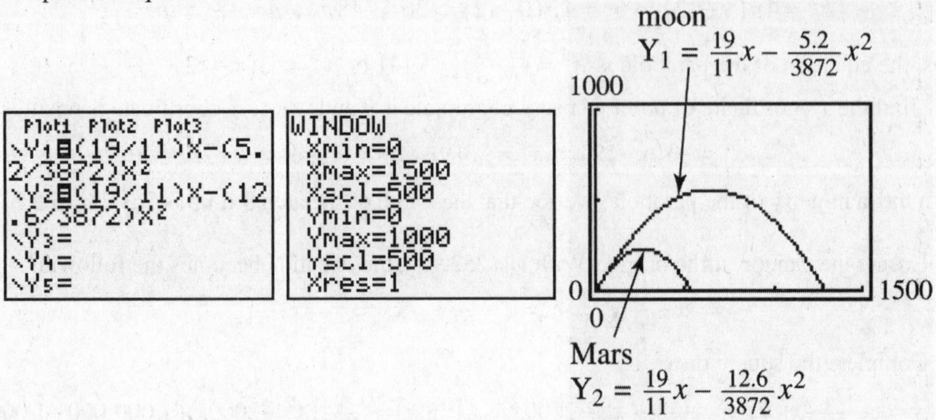

(b) Using the "maximum" option in the CALC menu, we see that the ball reaches a maximum height of $y \approx 229$ ft on Mars and $y \approx 555$ ft on the moon.

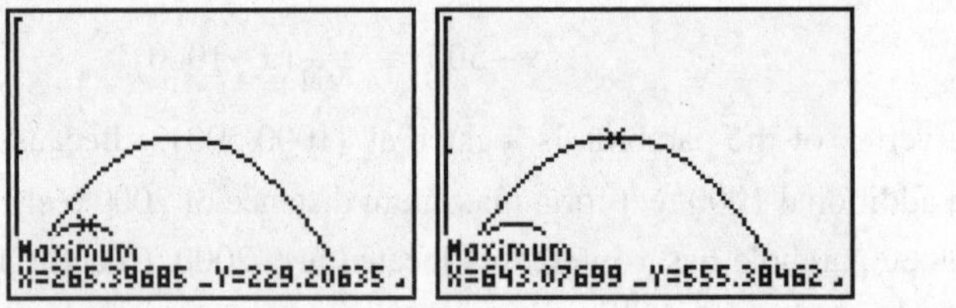

59. Answers will vary.

The proof is similar to the proof given on page 895 for a parabola that opens up (which also applied to parabolas opening down).

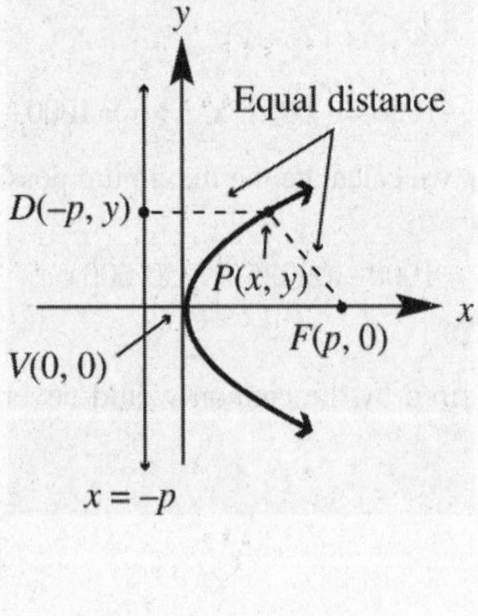

$$d(P,F) = d(P,D)$$
$$\sqrt{(x-p)^2 + (y-0)^2} = \sqrt{(x-(-p))^2 + (y-y)^2}$$
$$\sqrt{(x-p)^2 + y^2} = \sqrt{(x+p)^2}$$
$$x^2 - 2xp + p^2 + y^2 = x^2 + 2xp + p^2$$
$$-2xp + y^2 = 2xp$$
$$y^2 = 4px$$

Section 10.2: Ellipses

1. **(a)** $36x^2+9y^2=324 \Rightarrow \frac{x^2}{9}+\frac{y^2}{36}=1 \Rightarrow \frac{x^2}{3^2}+\frac{y^2}{6^2}=1$

This ellipse has endpoints of the minor axis of $(\pm 3,0)$, which are also x-intercepts. It also has vertices of $(0,\pm 6)$, which are also y-intercepts. The correct choice is A.

(b) $9x^2+36y^2=324 \Rightarrow \frac{x^2}{36}+\frac{y^2}{9}=1 \Rightarrow \frac{x^2}{6^2}+\frac{y^2}{3^2}=1$

This ellipse has vertices of $(\pm 6,0)$, which are also x-intercepts. It also has endpoints of the minor axis of $(0,\pm 3)$, which are also y-intercepts. The correct choice is C

(c) $\frac{x^2}{25}=1-\frac{y^2}{16} \Rightarrow \frac{x^2}{25}+\frac{y^2}{16}=1 \Rightarrow \frac{x^2}{5^2}+\frac{y^2}{4^2}=1$

This ellipse has vertices of $(\pm 5,0)$, which are also x-intercepts. It also has endpoints of the minor axis of $(0,\pm 4)$, which are also y-intercepts. The correct choice is D

(d) $\frac{x^2}{16}=1-\frac{y^2}{25} \Rightarrow \frac{x^2}{16}+\frac{y^2}{25}=1 \Rightarrow \frac{x^2}{4^2}+\frac{y^2}{5^2}=1$

This ellipse has endpoints of the minor axis of $(\pm 4,0)$, which are also x-intercepts. It also has vertices of $(0,\pm 5)$, which are also y-intercepts. The correct choice is B

3. $\frac{x^2}{25}+\frac{y^2}{9}=1$

The graph is an ellipse with center (0, 0). Rewriting the given equation, we have $\frac{x^2}{5^2}+\frac{y^2}{3^2}=1$. Since $5>3$, we have $a = 5$ and $b = 3$, and the major axis is horizontal. Thus, the vertices are (–5, 0) and (5, 0). The endpoints of the minor axis are (0, –3) and (0, 3). The domain is [–5, 5]. The range is [–3, 3]. To find the foci we need to find c such that $c^2=a^2-b^2$.

$$c^2=a^2-b^2 \Rightarrow c^2=25-9$$

$$c^2=16 \Rightarrow c=4$$

Since the major axis lies on the x-axis, the foci are (–4, 0) and (4, 0).

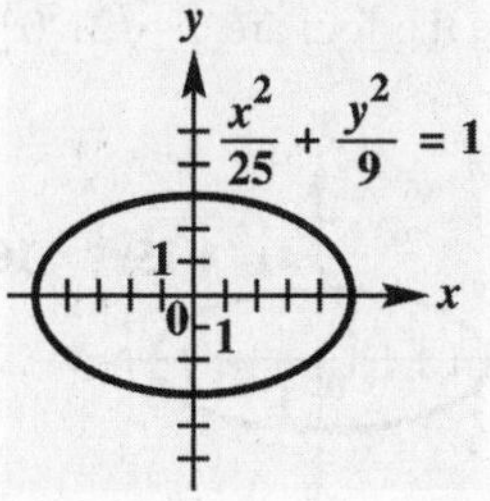

5. $\frac{x^2}{9}+y^2=1$

Rewriting the equation, we have $\frac{x^2}{3^2}+\frac{y^2}{1^2}=1$. The center is (0, 0). Since 3 > 1, we have $a = 3$ and $b = 1$, and the major axis is horizontal. The vertices are (–3, 0) and (3, 0). The endpoints of the minor axis are (0, –1) and (0, 1). The domain is [–3, 3]. The range is [–1, 1]. To find the foci, we need to find c such that $c^2=a^2-b^2$.

$$c^2=a^2-b^2 \Rightarrow c^2=9-1 \Rightarrow c^2=8 \Rightarrow c=\sqrt{8}=2\sqrt{2}$$

Since the major axis lies on the x-axis, the foci are $(-2\sqrt{2},\ 0)$ and $(2\sqrt{2},\ 0)$.

Continued on next page

5. (continued)

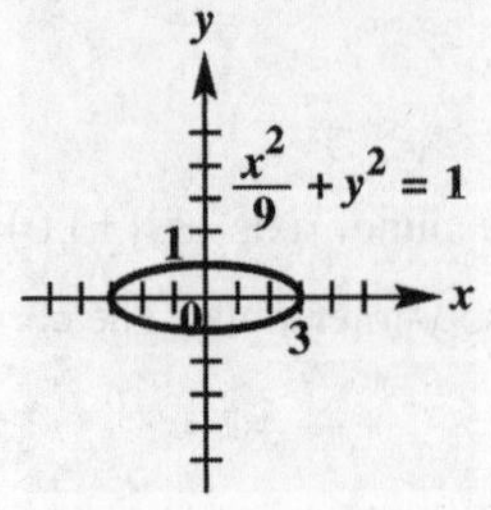

7. $9x^2+y^2=81$

Rewriting the equation, we have $\frac{x^2}{9}+\frac{y^2}{81}=1$ or $\frac{x^2}{3^2}+\frac{y^2}{9^2}=1$. The center is (0, 0). Since 9 > 3, we have $a = 9$ and $b = 3$, and the major axis is vertical. The vertices are (0, –9) and (0, 9). The endpoints of the minor axis are (–3, 0) and (3, 0). The domain is [–3, 3]. The range is [–9, 9]. To find the foci, we need to find c such that $c^2=a^2-b^2$.

$$c^2=a^2-b^2 \Rightarrow c^2=81-9 \Rightarrow c^2=72 \Rightarrow c=\sqrt{72}=6\sqrt{2}$$

Since the major axis lies on the y-axis, the foci are $\left(0,-6\sqrt{2}\right)$ and $\left(0,6\sqrt{2}\right)$.

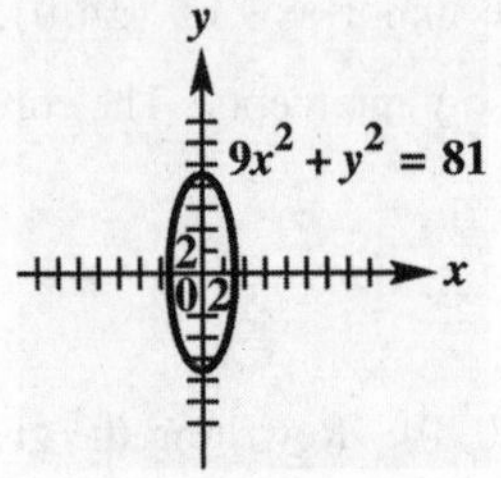

9. $4x^2+25y^2=100$

Rewriting the equation, we have $\frac{x^2}{25}+\frac{y^2}{4}=1$ or $\frac{x^2}{5^2}+\frac{y^2}{2^2}=1$. The center is (0, 0). Since 5 > 2, we have $a = 5$ and $b = 2$, and the major axis is horizontal. The vertices are (–5, 0) and (5, 0). The endpoints of the minor axis are (0, –2) and (0, 2). The domain is [–5, 5]. The range is [–2, 2]. To find the foci, we need to find c such that $c^2=a^2-b^2$.

$$c^2=a^2-b^2 \Rightarrow c^2=25-4 \Rightarrow c^2=21 \Rightarrow c=\sqrt{21}$$

Since the major axis lies on the x-axis, the foci are $\left(-\sqrt{21},0\right)$ and $\left(\sqrt{21},0\right)$.

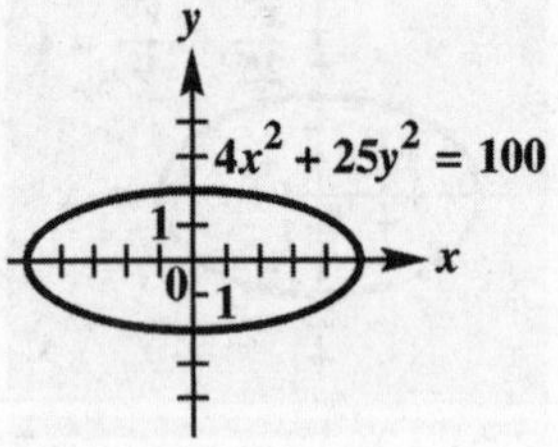

11. $\dfrac{(x-2)^2}{25}+\dfrac{(y-1)^2}{4}=1$

Rewriting the equation, we have $\frac{(x-2)^2}{5^2}+\frac{(y-1)^2}{2^2}=1$. The center is (2, 1). Since $a = 5$ is associated with x^2, the major axis of the ellipse is horizontal. The vertices are on a horizontal line through (2, 1), while the endpoints of the minor axis are on the vertical line through (2, 1). The vertices are 5 units to the left and right of the center at (–3, 1) and (7, 1). The endpoints of the minor axis are 2 units below and 2 units above the center at (2, –1) and (2, 3). The domain is [–3, 7]. The range is [–1, 3]. To find the foci, we need to find c such that $c^2 = a^2 - b^2$.

$$c^2 = a^2 - b^2 \Rightarrow c^2 = 25-4 \Rightarrow c^2 = 21 \Rightarrow c = \sqrt{21}$$

Since the major axis lies on $y=1$, the foci are $\left(2-\sqrt{21}, 1\right)$ and $\left(2+\sqrt{21}, 1\right)$.

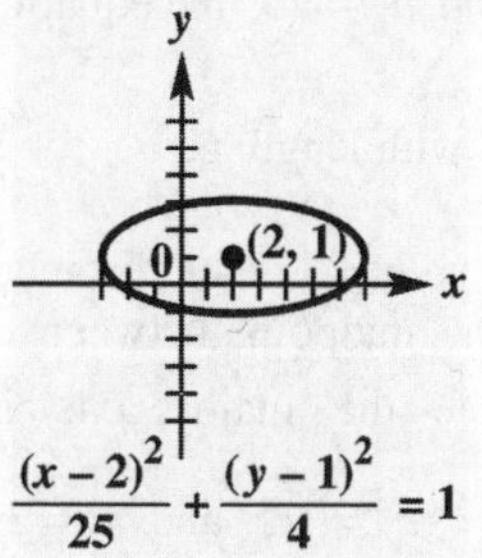

13. $\dfrac{(x+3)^2}{16}+\dfrac{(y-2)^2}{36}=1$

Rewriting the equation, we have $\frac{(x+3)^2}{4^2}+\frac{(y-2)^2}{6^2}=1$. The center is (–3, 2). We have $a = 6$ and $b = 4$. Since $a = 6$ is associated with y^2, the major axis of the ellipse is vertical. The vertices are on the vertical line through (–3, 2), and the endpoints of the minor axis are on the horizontal line through (–3, 2). The vertices are 6 units below and 6 units above the center at (–3, –4) and (–3, 8). The endpoints of the minor axis are 4 units to the left and 4 units to the right of the center at (–7, 2) and (1, 2). The domain is [–7, 1]. The range is [–4, 8]. To find the foci, we need to find c such that $c^2 = a^2 - b^2$.

$$c^2 = a^2 - b^2 \Rightarrow c^2 = 36-16 \Rightarrow c^2 = 20 \Rightarrow c = \sqrt{20} = 2\sqrt{5}$$

Since the major axis lies on $x=-3$, the foci are $\left(-3, 2-2\sqrt{5}\right)$ and $\left(-3, 2+2\sqrt{5}\right)$.

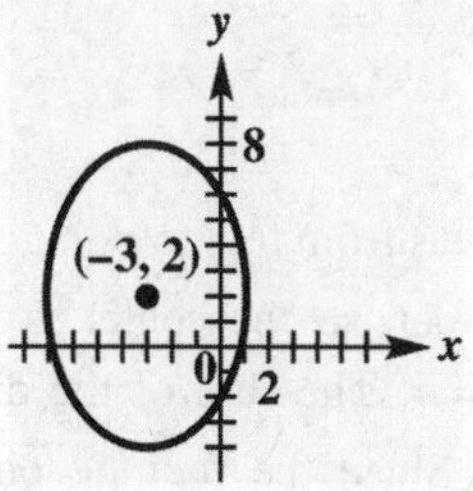

15. x-intercepts ± 5; foci at (–3, 0), (3, 0)

From the given information, $a = 5$ and $c = 3$. To find b^2, use the relation $c^2 = a^2 - b^2$.

$$c^2 = a^2 - b^2 \Rightarrow 9 = 25 - b^2 \Rightarrow b^2 = 16$$

Since the foci are on the x-axis and the ellipse is centered at the origin, the equation has the form $\frac{x^2}{a^2}+\frac{y^2}{b^2}=1$. Since $a^2 = 25$ and $b^2 = 16$, the equation of the ellipse is $\frac{x^2}{25}+\frac{y^2}{16}=1$.

17. Major axis with length 6, foci at (0, 2), (0, –2).
The length of the major axis is $2a$. Thus, we have $2a = 6 \Rightarrow a = 3$. From the foci, we have $c = 2$. Solving for b^2 we have $c^2 = a^2 - b^2 \Rightarrow 4 = 9 - b^2 \Rightarrow b^2 = 5$. Since the foci are on the y-axis and the ellipse is centered at the origin, the equation has the form $\frac{x^2}{b^2} + \frac{y^2}{a^2} = 1$. Since $a = 3 \Rightarrow a^2 = 9$ and and $b^2 = 5$, the equation of the ellipse is $\frac{x^2}{5} + \frac{y^2}{9} = 1$.

19. Center at (5, 2); minor axis vertical, with length 8; $c = 3$.
Since the center is (5, 2) and the minor axis is vertical, the equation has the form $\frac{(x-5)^2}{a^2} + \frac{(y-2)^2}{b^2} = 1$. The length of the minor axis is $2b$, so $b = 4$. Solving for a^2, we have $c^2 = a^2 - b^2 \Rightarrow 9 = a^2 - 16 \Rightarrow a^2 = 25$. Since $b = 4 \Rightarrow b^2 = 16$ and $a^2 = 25$, the equation of the ellipse is $\frac{(x-5)^2}{25} + \frac{(y-2)^2}{16} = 1$.

21. Vertices at (4, 9), (4, 1); minor axis with length 6.

The length of the minor axis is $2b$, so $b = 3$. The distance between the vertices is $9 - 1 = 8$, so $2a = 8$ and thus $a = 4$. The center is the midpoint between the vertices. Thus, the center is located at $\left(\frac{4+4}{2}, \frac{9+1}{2}\right) = \left(\frac{8}{2}, \frac{10}{2}\right) = (4,5)$. Since the major axis is vertical, the equation is of the form $\frac{(x-4)^2}{b^2} + \frac{(y-5)^2}{a^2} = 1$. Since $a = 4 \Rightarrow a^2 = 16$ and $b = 3 \Rightarrow b^2 = 9$, the equation of the ellipse is $\frac{(x-4)^2}{9} + \frac{(y-5)^2}{16} = 1$.

23. Foci at (0, –3), (0, 3); (8, 3) on the ellipse.
The distance between the foci is $3 - (-3) = 6$, so $2c = 6$ and thus $c = 3$. The center is the midpoint between the foci, so the center is (0, 0). Since the foci lie on the y-axis, the major axis is vertical, so the equation is of the form $\frac{x^2}{b^2} + \frac{y^2}{a^2} = 1$.
Now recall from Figure 15 on page 903 of your text, $d(P,F) + d(P,F') = 2a$. If we let $P(8,3)$, $F'(0,-3)$, and $F(0,3)$ represent the point on the ellipse and the foci, respectively, we have the following.

$$d(P,F) + d(P,F') = \sqrt{(8-0)^2 + (3+3)^2} + \sqrt{(8-0)^2 + (3-3)^2} = 10 + 8 = 18 = 2a \Rightarrow a = 9$$

Solving for b^2, we have $c^2 = a^2 - b^2 \Rightarrow 9 = 81 - b^2 \Rightarrow b^2 = 72$. Since $a = 9 \Rightarrow a^2 = 81$ and $b^2 = 72$, the equation of the ellipse is $\frac{x^2}{72} + \frac{y^2}{81} = 1$.

25. Foci at $(0,4)$, $(0,-4)$; sum of distances from foci to point on ellipse is 10.
The center is halfway between the foci, so the center is (0, 0). The distance between the foci is $4 - (-4) = 8$, so $2c = 8$ and thus $c = 4$. The sum of the distances from the foci to any point on the ellipse is 10, so $2a = 10 \Rightarrow a = 5$. Since the foci lie on the y-axis, the equation is of the form $\frac{x^2}{b^2} + \frac{y^2}{a^2} = 1$. Solving for b^2, we have $c^2 = a^2 - b^2 \Rightarrow 4^2 = 5^2 - b^2 \Rightarrow 16 = 25 - b^2 \Rightarrow b^2 = 9$. Since $a = 5 \Rightarrow a^2 = 25$ and $b^2 = 9$, the equation of the ellipse is $\frac{x^2}{9} + \frac{y^2}{25} = 1$.

27. Eccentricity $\frac{3}{4}$, foci at (0, –2), (0, 2).

The foci are on the y-axis, so the equation has the form $\frac{x^2}{b^2}+\frac{y^2}{a^2}=1$. From the foci, we have $c = 2$. Use the eccentricity and c to find a.

$$e=\frac{c}{a}\Rightarrow\frac{3}{4}=\frac{2}{a}\Rightarrow 3a=8\Rightarrow a=\frac{8}{3}$$

Solving for b^2, we have $c^2=a^2-b^2\Rightarrow 2^2=\left(\frac{8}{3}\right)^2-b^2\Rightarrow 4=\frac{64}{9}-b^2\Rightarrow b^2=\frac{64}{9}-\frac{36}{9}=\frac{28}{9}$. Since $a=\frac{8}{3}\Rightarrow a^2=\frac{64}{9}$ and $b^2=\frac{28}{9}$, the equation is $\frac{x^2}{\frac{28}{9}}+\frac{y^2}{\frac{64}{9}}=1$ or $\frac{9x^2}{28}+\frac{9y^2}{64}=1$.

29. $\frac{y}{2}=\sqrt{1-\frac{x^2}{25}}$

Square both sides to get $\frac{y^2}{4}=1-\frac{x^2}{25}\Rightarrow\frac{x^2}{25}+\frac{y^2}{4}=1\Rightarrow\frac{x^2}{5^2}+\frac{y^2}{2^2}=1$, which is the equation of an ellipse centered at the origin with x-intercepts ±5 (vertices) and y-intercepts ±2 (endpoints of minor axis). Since $\sqrt{1-\frac{x^2}{25}}\geq0$, the only possible values of y are those making $\frac{y}{2}\geq0\Rightarrow y\geq0$. The domain is [–5, 5]. The range is [0, 2]. The graph of the original equation is the upper half of the ellipse. By applying the vertical line test, we see that this is the graph of a function.

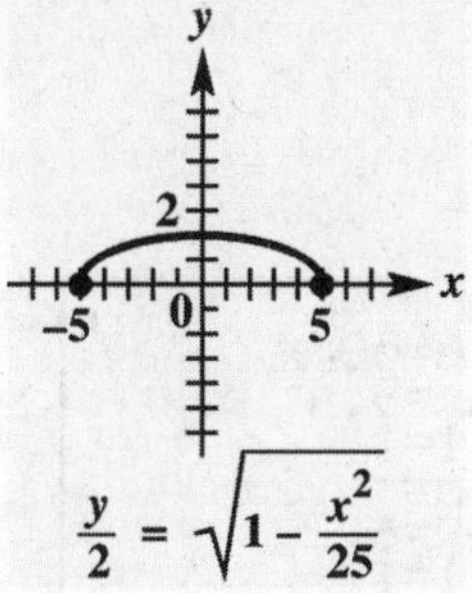

31. $x=-\sqrt{1-\frac{y^2}{64}}$

Square both sides to get $x^2=1-\frac{y^2}{64}\Rightarrow\frac{x^2}{1}+\frac{y^2}{64}=1\Rightarrow\frac{x^2}{1^2}+\frac{y^2}{8^2}=1$, the equation of an ellipse centered at the origin with x-intercepts ±1 (endpoints of minor axis) and y-intercepts ±8 (vertices). Since $-\sqrt{1-\frac{y^2}{64}}\leq0$, we must have $x\leq0$, so the graph of the original equation is the left half of the ellipse. The domain is [–1, 0]. The range is [–8, 8]. The vertical line test shows that this is not the graph of a function.

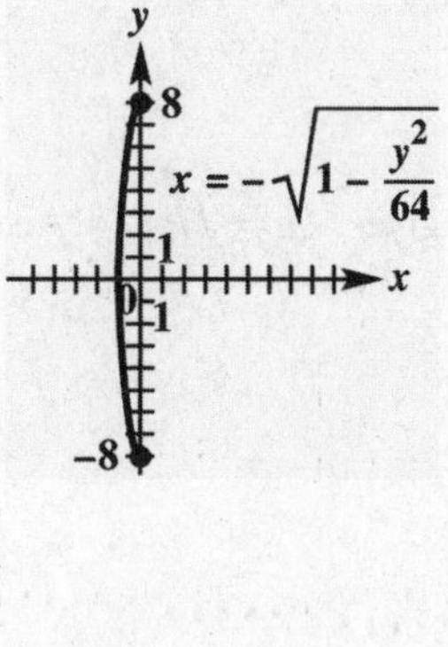

33. Solve for y in the equation of the ellipse.

$$\frac{x^2}{16}+\frac{y^2}{4}=1 \Rightarrow \frac{y^2}{4}=1-\frac{x^2}{16} \Rightarrow y^2=4\left(1-\frac{x^2}{16}\right) \Rightarrow y=\pm\sqrt{4\left(1-\frac{x^2}{16}\right)} \Rightarrow y=\pm 2\sqrt{1-\frac{x^2}{16}}$$

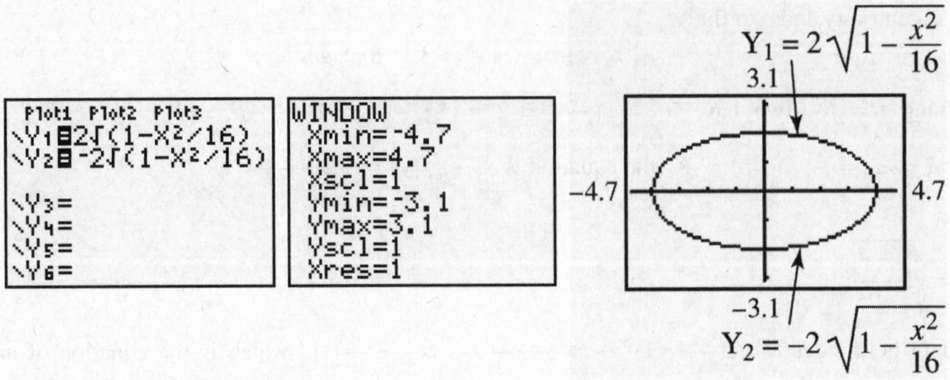

35. Solve for y in the equation of the ellipse.

$$\frac{(x-3)^2}{25}+\frac{y^2}{9}=1 \Rightarrow \frac{y^2}{9}=1-\frac{(x-3)^2}{25} \Rightarrow y^2=9\left(1-\frac{(x-3)^2}{25}\right) \Rightarrow y=\pm\sqrt{9\left(1-\frac{(x-3)^2}{25}\right)} \Rightarrow y=\pm 3\sqrt{1-\frac{(x-3)^2}{25}}$$

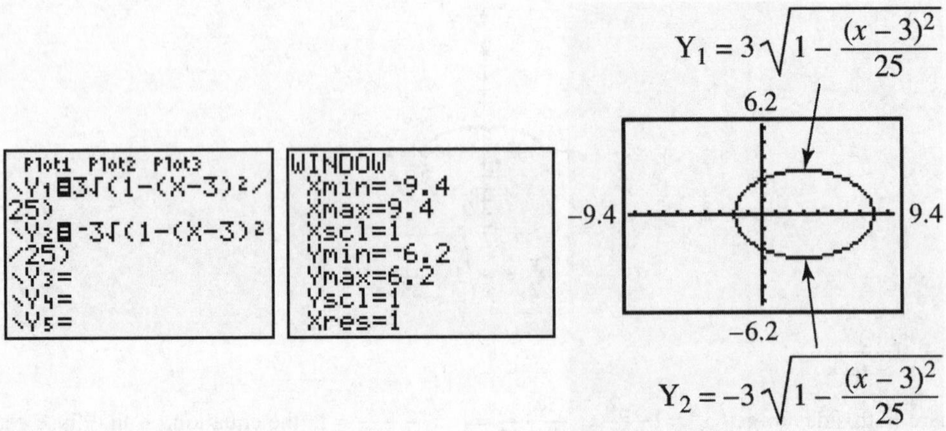

37. $\frac{x^2}{3}+\frac{y^2}{4}=1$

Since $4>3$, $a^2=4$, which gives $a=2$. Also $c=\sqrt{a^2-b^2}=\sqrt{4-3}=\sqrt{1}=1$. Thus, $e=\frac{c}{a}=\frac{1}{2}$.

39. $4x^2+7y^2=28 \Rightarrow \frac{x^2}{7}+\frac{y^2}{4}=1$

Since $7>4$, $a^2=7$, which gives $a=\sqrt{7}$. Also $c=\sqrt{a^2-b^2}=\sqrt{7-4}=\sqrt{3}$. Thus, $e=\frac{c}{a}=\frac{\sqrt{7}}{\sqrt{3}}=\frac{\sqrt{21}}{3}\approx .65$.

41. Answers will vary.

43. Place the half-ellipse that represents the overpass on a coordinate system with the center of the bottom of the overpass at the origin. If the complete ellipse were drawn, the center of the ellipse would be $(0,0)$. Then the half-ellipse will include the points $(0,15),(-10,0)$, and $(10,0)$. The equation is of the form $\frac{x^2}{b^2}+\frac{y^2}{a^2}=1$. Thus, for the complete ellipse, we have $a=15$ and $b=10$. Thus, we have $\frac{x^2}{10^2}+\frac{y^2}{15^2}=1 \Rightarrow \frac{x^2}{100}+\frac{y^2}{225}=1$. To find the equation of the half-ellipse, solve this equation for y and use the positive square root since the overpass is represented by the upper half of the ellipse.

$$\frac{x^2}{100}+\frac{y^2}{225}=1 \Rightarrow \frac{y^2}{225}=1-\frac{x^2}{100} \Rightarrow y^2=225\left(1-\frac{x^2}{100}\right) \Rightarrow y=\sqrt{225\left(1-\frac{x^2}{100}\right)} \Rightarrow y=15\sqrt{1-\frac{x^2}{100}}$$

Find the y-coordinate of the point whose x-coordinate is $\frac{1}{2}(12)=6$.

$$y=15\sqrt{1-\frac{x^2}{100}} \Rightarrow y=15\sqrt{1-\frac{6^2}{100}} \Rightarrow y=15\sqrt{1-\frac{36}{100}} \Rightarrow y=15\sqrt{\frac{64}{100}}=15\sqrt{\frac{16}{25}}=15\left(\frac{4}{5}\right)=12$$

The tallest truck that can pass under the overpass is 12 feet tall.

45. Referring to Example 6 on page 908 of your text, the greatest distance between the comet and the sun is $a+c=3281$ million miles. If $a+c=3281 \Rightarrow c=3281-a$ and $e=\frac{c}{a}$, we have $e=\frac{3281-a}{a}$. Since $e=.9673$, we have $.9673=\frac{3281-a}{a} \Rightarrow .9673a=3281-a \Rightarrow 1.9673a=3281 \Rightarrow a=\frac{3281}{1.9673}\approx 1668$. We then have $c=3281-1668=1613$, which implies $a-c=1668-1613=55$. Thus, the shortest distance between Halley's Comet and the sun is about 55 million miles.

47. **(a)** Use the given values of e and a to find the value of c for each planet. Then use the values of a and c to find the value of b.

Neptune: $e=\frac{c}{a} \Rightarrow c=ea \Rightarrow c=(.009)(30.1) \Rightarrow c=.2709$

$$b^2=a^2-c^2 \Rightarrow b^2=(30.1)^2-(.2709)^2 \Rightarrow b^2\approx 905.9366 \Rightarrow b\approx 30.1$$

Since c = .2709, the graph should be translated .2709 units to the right so that the sun will be located at the origin. It's essentially circular with equation $\frac{(x-.2709)^2}{30.1^2}+\frac{y^2}{30.1^2}=1$.

Pluto: $e=\frac{c}{a} \Rightarrow c=ea \Rightarrow c=(.249)(39.4) \Rightarrow c=9.8106$

$$b^2=a^2-c^2 \Rightarrow b^2=(39.4)^2-(9.8106)^2 \Rightarrow b^2\approx 1456.1121 \Rightarrow b\approx 38.16$$

As with Neptune, we translate the graph by c units to the right so that the sun will be located at the origin. The equation is $\frac{(x-9.8106)^2}{39.4^2}+\frac{y^2}{38.16^2}=1$.

(b) In order to graph these equations on a graphing calculator, we must solve each equation for y. Each equation will be broken down into two functions, so we will need to graph four functions.

Neptune: $\frac{(x-.2709)^2}{30.1^2}+\frac{y^2}{30.1^2}=1 \Rightarrow (x-.2709)^2+y^2=30.1^2 \Rightarrow y=\pm\sqrt{30.1^2-(x-.2709)^2}$

Pluto: $\frac{(x-9.8106)^2}{39.4^2}+\frac{y^2}{38.16^2}=1 \Rightarrow \frac{y^2}{38.16^2}=1-\frac{(x-9.8106)^2}{39.4^2} \Rightarrow y^2=38.16^2\left(1-\frac{(x-9.8106)^2}{39.4^2}\right)$

$$y=\pm\sqrt{38.16^2\left(1-\frac{(x-9.8106)^2}{39.4^2}\right)} \Rightarrow y=\pm 38.16\sqrt{1-\frac{(x-9.8106)^2}{39.4^2}}$$

Graph the following four functions on the same screen.

$$Y_1=\sqrt{30.1^2-(x-.2709)^2};\ Y_2=-\sqrt{30.1^2-(x-.2709)^2}=-Y_1$$

$$Y_3=38.16\sqrt{1-\frac{(x-9.8106)^2}{39.4^2}};\quad Y_4=-38.16\sqrt{1-\frac{(x-9.8106)^2}{39.4^2}}=-Y_3$$

Continued on next page

47. (b) (continued)

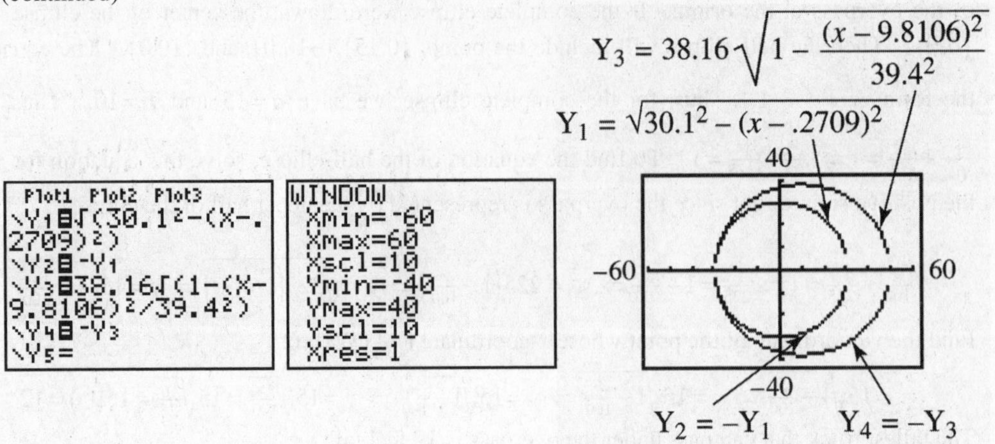

49. The stone and the wave source must be placed at the foci, $(c, 0)$ and $(-c, 0)$. Here $a^2 = 36$ and $b^2 = 9$, so $c^2 = a^2 - b^2 \Rightarrow c^2 = 36 - 9 \Rightarrow c^2 = 27 \Rightarrow c = \sqrt{27} = 3\sqrt{3}$. Thus, the kidney stone and source of the beam must be placed $3\sqrt{3}$ units from the center.

Section 10.3: Hyperbolas

Connections (page 918)
From the definition of a hyperbola, we know the difference of the distances equals the constant $2a$. Substituting the given values, we have $d_1 - d_2 = 2a \Rightarrow 80 - 30 = 2a \Rightarrow 50 = 2a \Rightarrow a = 25$. Since the distance between foci is $2c$, we have $2c = 100 \Rightarrow c = 50$. Using these values, we solve for b^2. We have $b^2 = c^2 - a^2 \Rightarrow b^2 = 50^2 - 25^2 \Rightarrow b^2 = 2500 - 625 \Rightarrow b^2 = 1875$. Substituting these values into the general equation of a hyperbola with a horizontal transverse axis centered at the origin, we get the following.

$$\frac{x^2}{a^2} - \frac{y^2}{b^2} = 1 \Rightarrow \frac{x^2}{625} - \frac{y^2}{1875} = 1$$

Exercises

1. $\dfrac{x^2}{25} + \dfrac{y^2}{9} = 1$

This is an equation of an ellipse with x-intercepts ± 5 and y-intercepts ± 3. The correct graph is C.

2. $\dfrac{x^2}{9} + \dfrac{y^2}{25} = 1$

This is the equation of an ellipse with x-intercepts ± 3 and y-intercepts ± 5. The correct graph is B.

3. $\dfrac{x^2}{9} - \dfrac{y^2}{25} = 1$

This is the graph of a hyperbola with a horizontal transverse axis and x-intercepts ± 3 (no y-intercepts). The correct graph is D.

5. $\frac{x^2}{16}-\frac{y^2}{9}=1$

This equation may be written as $\frac{x^2}{4^2}-\frac{y^2}{3^2}=1$, which has the form $\frac{x^2}{a^2}-\frac{y^2}{b^2}=1$. The hyperbola is centered at (0, 0) with branches opening to the left and right. The graph has vertices at (–4, 0) and (4, 0) (also x-intercepts ± 4). There are no y-intercepts. The domain is $(-\infty,-4]\cup[4,\infty)$. The range is $(-\infty,\infty)$. The foci are on the x-axis. Since $c^2=a^2+b^2 \Rightarrow c^2=16+9 \Rightarrow c^2=25 \Rightarrow c=5$, the foci are (–5, 0) and (5, 0). Since $a=4$ and $b=3$, the asymptotes are $y=\pm\frac{b}{a}x=\pm\frac{3}{4}x$.

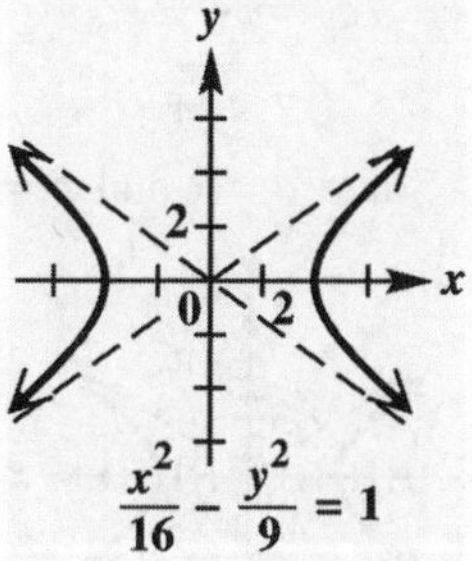

7. $\frac{y^2}{25}-\frac{x^2}{49}=1$

This equation may be written as $\frac{y^2}{5^2}-\frac{x^2}{7^2}=1$, which has the form $\frac{y^2}{a^2}-\frac{x^2}{b^2}=1$. The hyperbola is centered at (0, 0) with branches opening upward and downward. The graph has vertices at (0,–5) and (0,5) (also y-intercepts ± 5). There are no x-intercepts. The domain is $(-\infty, \infty)$. The range is $(-\infty,-5] \cup [5,\infty)$. The foci are on the y-axis. Since $c^2=a^2+b^2$, we have the following.

$$c^2=a^2+b^2 \Rightarrow c^2=25+49 \Rightarrow c^2=74 \Rightarrow c=\sqrt{74}$$

The foci are $\left(0,-\sqrt{74}\right)$ and $\left(0,\sqrt{74}\right)$. Since $a=5$ and $b=7$, the asymptotes are $y=\pm\frac{a}{b}x=\pm\frac{5}{7}x$.

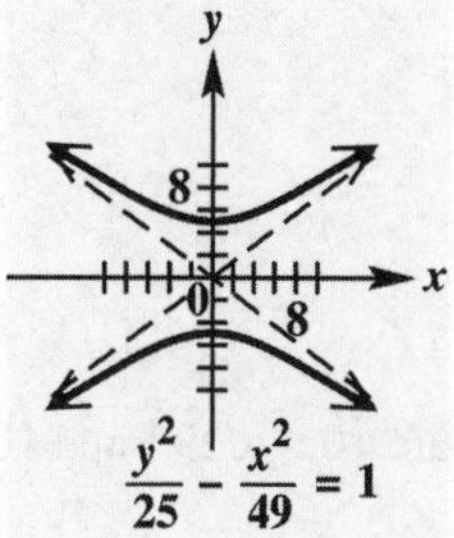

9. $x^2-y^2=9$

This equation may be written as $\frac{x^2}{9}-\frac{y^2}{9}=1 \Rightarrow \frac{x^2}{3^2}-\frac{y^2}{3^2}=1$, which has the form $\frac{x^2}{a^2}-\frac{y^2}{b^2}=1$. The hyperbola is centered at (0, 0) with branches opening to the left and right. The graph has vertices at (–3, 0) and (3, 0) (also x-intercepts ± 3). There are no y-intercepts. The domain is $(-\infty, -3] \cup [3, \infty)$. The range is $(-\infty, \infty)$. The foci are on the x-axis. Since $c^2=a^2+b^2$, we have the following.

$$c^2=a^2+b^2 \Rightarrow c^2=9+9 \Rightarrow c^2=18 \Rightarrow c=\sqrt{18}=3\sqrt{2}$$

The foci are $\left(-3\sqrt{2},0\right)$ and $\left(3\sqrt{2},0\right)$. Since $a=3$ and $b=3$, the asymptotes are as follows.

$$y=\pm\frac{b}{a}x=\pm\frac{3}{3}x=\pm x$$

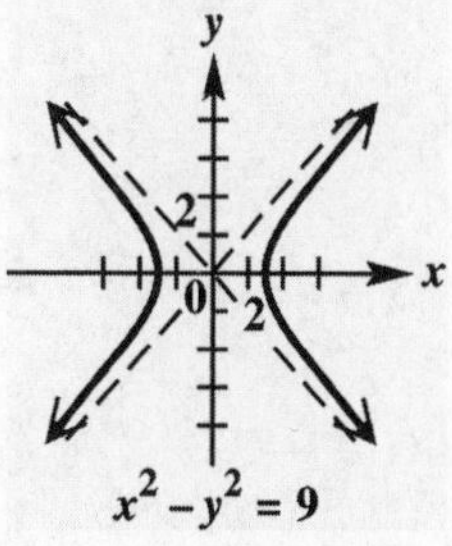

11. $9x^2 - 25y^2 = 225$

This equation may be written as $\frac{x^2}{25} - \frac{y^2}{9} = 1 \Rightarrow \frac{x^2}{5^2} - \frac{y^2}{3^2} = 1$, which has the form $\frac{x^2}{a^2} - \frac{y^2}{b^2} = 1$. The hyperbola is centered at (0, 0) with branches opening to the left and right. The graph has vertices at (–5, 0) and (5, 0) (also x-intercepts ± 5). There are no y-intercepts. The domain is $(-\infty, -5] \cup [5, \infty)$. The range is $(-\infty, \infty)$. The foci are on the x-axis. Since $c^2 = a^2 + b^2$, we have the following.

$$c^2 = a^2 + b^2$$
$$c^2 = 25 + 9$$
$$c^2 = 34$$
$$c = \sqrt{34}$$

The foci are $\left(-\sqrt{34}, 0\right)$ and $\left(\sqrt{34}, 0\right)$. Since $a = 5$ and $b = 3$, the asymptotes are $y = \pm\frac{b}{a}x = \pm\frac{3}{5}x$.

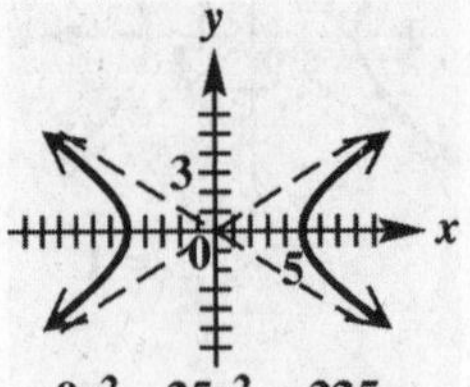

$9x^2 - 25y^2 = 225$

13. $4y^2 - 25x^2 = 100$

This equation may be written as $\frac{y^2}{25} - \frac{x^2}{4} = 1 \Rightarrow \frac{y^2}{5^2} - \frac{x^2}{2^2} = 1$, which has the form $\frac{y^2}{a^2} - \frac{x^2}{b^2} = 1$. The hyperbola is centered at (0, 0) with branches opening upward and downward. The graph has vertices at (0,–5) and (0,5) (also y-intercepts ± 5). There are no x-intercepts. The domain is $(-\infty, \infty)$. The range is $(-\infty, -5] \cup [5, \infty)$. The foci are on the y-axis. Since $c^2 = a^2 + b^2$, we have the following.

$$c^2 = a^2 + b^2$$
$$c^2 = 25 + 4$$
$$c^2 = 29$$
$$c = \sqrt{29}$$

The foci are $\left(0, -\sqrt{29}\right)$ and $\left(0, \sqrt{29}\right)$. Since $a = 5$ and $b = 2$, the asymptotes are $y = \pm\frac{a}{b}x = \pm\frac{5}{2}x$.

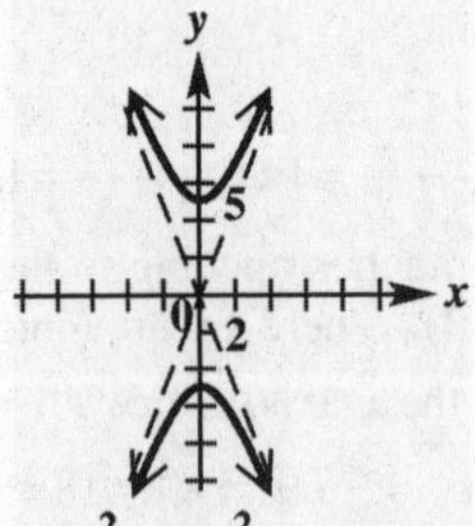

$4y^2 - 25x^2 = 100$

15. $9x^2 - 4y^2 = 1$

This equation may be written as $\frac{x^2}{\frac{1}{9}} - \frac{y^2}{\frac{1}{4}} = 1 \Rightarrow \frac{x^2}{\left(\frac{1}{3}\right)^2} - \frac{y^2}{\left(\frac{1}{2}\right)^2} = 1$, which has the form $\frac{x^2}{a^2} - \frac{y^2}{b^2} = 1$. The hyperbola is centered at (0, 0) with branches opening to the left and right. The graph has vertices at $\left(-\frac{1}{3}, 0\right)$ and $\left(\frac{1}{3}, 0\right)$ (also x-intercepts $\pm\frac{1}{3}$). There are no y-intercepts. The domain is $\left(-\infty, -\frac{1}{3}\right] \cup \left[\frac{1}{3}, \infty\right)$. The range is $(-\infty, \infty)$. The foci are on the x-axis. Since $c^2 = a^2 + b^2$, we have the following.

$$c^2 = a^2 + b^2$$
$$c^2 = \frac{1}{9} + \frac{1}{4}$$
$$c^2 = \frac{4+9}{36}$$
$$c^2 = \frac{13}{36}$$
$$c = \sqrt{\frac{13}{36}} = \frac{\sqrt{13}}{6}$$

The foci are $\left(-\frac{\sqrt{13}}{6}, 0\right)$ and $\left(\frac{\sqrt{13}}{6}, 0\right)$. Since $a = \frac{1}{3}$ and $b = \frac{1}{2}$, the asymptotes are $y = \pm\frac{b}{a}x = \pm\frac{\frac{1}{2}}{\frac{1}{3}}x = \pm\frac{3}{2}x$.

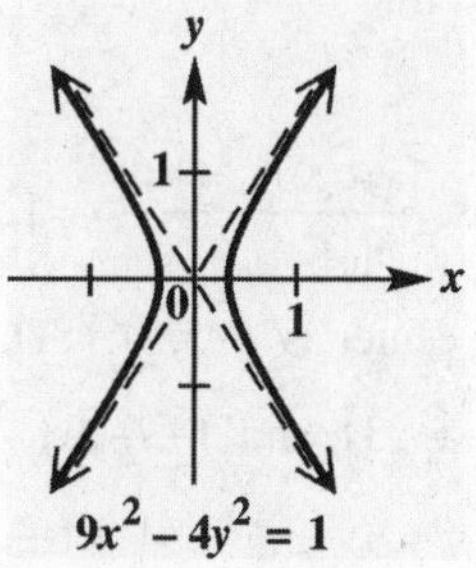

17. $\frac{(y-7)^2}{36} - \frac{(x-4)^2}{64} = 1$

Since this equation can be written as $\frac{(y-7)^2}{6^2} - \frac{(x-4)^2}{8^2} = 1$, it has the form $\frac{(y-k)^2}{a^2} - \frac{(x-h)^2}{b^2} = 1$ where $h = 4$, $k = 7$, $a = 6$, and $b = 8$. The center is (4, 7). The vertices are 6 units above and below the center (4, 7). These points are (4, 1) and (4, 13). The domain is $(-\infty, \infty)$. The range is $(-\infty, 1] \cup [13, \infty)$. Since $c^2 = a^2 + b^2 \Rightarrow c^2 = 36 + 64 \Rightarrow c^2 = 100 \Rightarrow c = 10$, the foci are 10 units below and above the center (4, 7). Thus, the foci are (4, –3) and (4, 17). Since $h = 4$, $k = 7$, $a = 6$, $b = 8$, and $y = k \pm \frac{a}{b}(x - h)$, the asymptotes are $y = 7 \pm \frac{6}{8}(x-4) \Rightarrow y = 7 \pm \frac{3}{4}(x-4)$

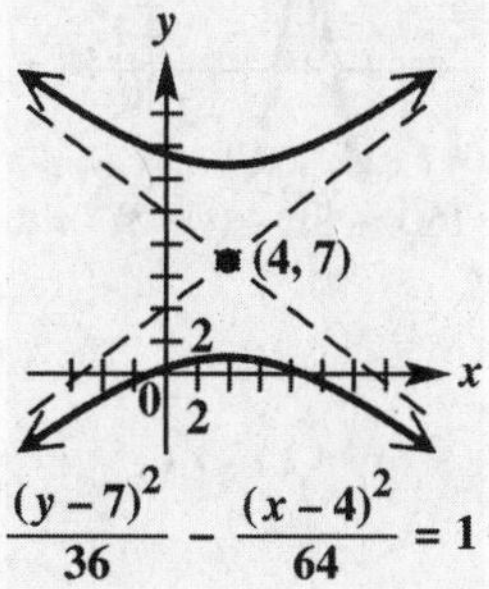

19. $\frac{(x+3)^2}{16}-\frac{(y-2)^2}{9}=1$

Since this equation can be written as $\frac{[x-(-3)]^2}{4^2}-\frac{(y-2)^2}{3^2}=1$, it has the form $\frac{(x-h)^2}{a^2}-\frac{(y-k)^2}{b^2}=1$ where $h=-3$, $k=2$, $a=4$, and $b=3$. The center is $(-3,2)$. The vertices are 4 units left and right of the center $(-3,2)$. These points are $(-7,2)$ and $(1,2)$. The domain is $(-\infty,-7]\cup[1,\infty)$. The range is $(-\infty,\infty)$. Since $c^2=a^2+b^2 \Rightarrow c^2=16+9 \Rightarrow c^2=25 \Rightarrow c=5$, the foci are 5 units left and right of the center $(-3,2)$. Thus, the foci are $(-8,2)$ and $(2,2)$. Since $h=-3$, $k=2$, $a=4$, $b=3$, and $y=k\pm\frac{b}{a}(x-h)$, the asymptotes are $y=2\pm\frac{3}{4}[x-(-3)] \Rightarrow y=2\pm\frac{3}{4}(x+3)$.

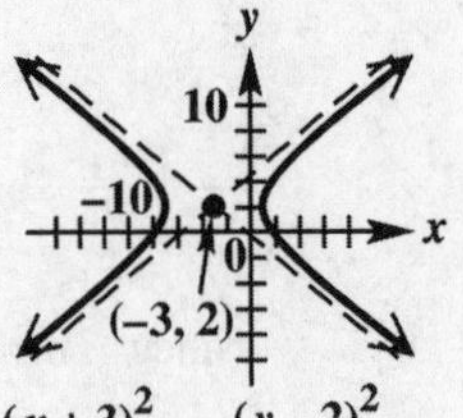

21. $16(x+5)^2-(y-3)^2=1$

Since this equation can be written as $\frac{[x-(-5)]^2}{\left(\frac{1}{4}\right)^2}-\frac{(y-3)^2}{1^2}=1$, it has the form $\frac{(x-h)^2}{a^2}-\frac{(y-k)^2}{b^2}=1$ where $h=-5$, $k=3$, $a=\frac{1}{4}$, and $b=1$. The center is $(-5,3)$. The vertices are $\frac{1}{4}$ unit left and right of the center $(-5,3)$. These points are $\left(-\frac{21}{4},3\right)$ and $\left(-\frac{19}{4},3\right)$. The domain is $\left(-\infty,-\frac{21}{4}\right]\cup\left[-\frac{19}{4},\infty\right)$. The range is $(-\infty,\infty)$. Since $c^2=a^2+b^2 \Rightarrow c^2=\frac{1}{16}+1 \Rightarrow c^2=\frac{1+16}{16} \Rightarrow c^2=\frac{17}{16} \Rightarrow c=\sqrt{\frac{17}{16}}=\frac{\sqrt{17}}{4}$, the foci are $\frac{\sqrt{17}}{4}$ units left and right of the center $(-5,3)$. Thus, the foci are $\left(-5-\frac{\sqrt{17}}{4},3\right)$ and $\left(-5+\frac{\sqrt{17}}{4},3\right)$. Since $h=-5$, $k=3$, $a=\frac{1}{4}$, $b=1$, and $y=k\pm\frac{b}{a}(x-h)$, the asymptotes are as follows.

$$y=3\pm\frac{1}{\frac{1}{4}}[x+(-5)] \Rightarrow y=3\pm4(x+5)$$

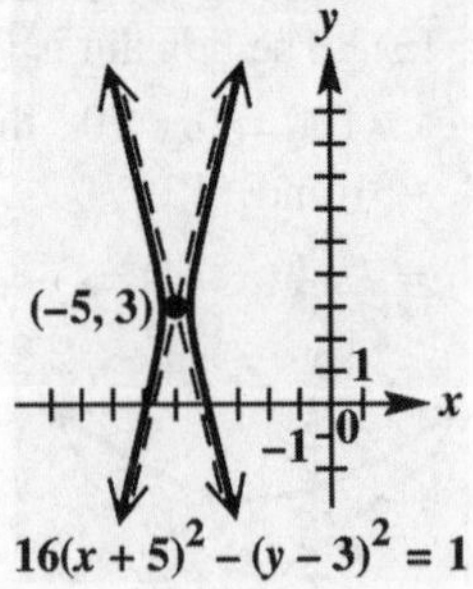

23. $\frac{y}{3}=\sqrt{1+\frac{x^2}{16}}$

Square both to get $\frac{y^2}{9}=1+\frac{x^2}{16}$ or $\frac{y^2}{9}-\frac{x^2}{16}=1$ or $\frac{y^2}{3^2}-\frac{x^2}{4^2}=1$ This is the equation of a hyperbola with center $(0,0)$ and vertices $(0,-3)$ and $(0,3)$. Since $a=3$ and $b=4$ and $y=\pm\frac{a}{b}x$, we have asymptotes $y=\pm\frac{3}{4}x$. The original equation is the top half of the hyperbola. The domain is $(-\infty, \infty)$. The range is $[3, \infty)$. The vertical line test shows this is a graph of a function.

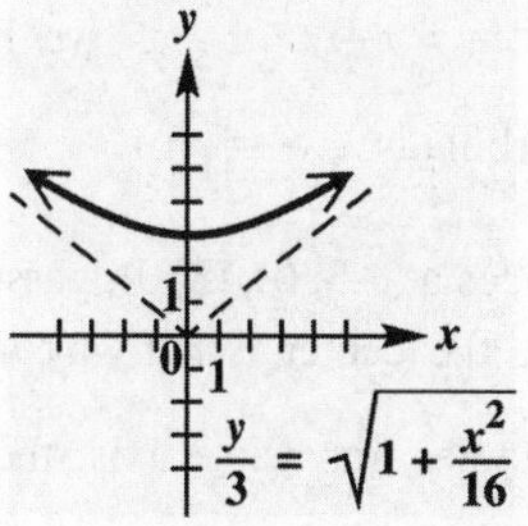

25. $5x=-\sqrt{1+4y^2}$

Square both to get $25x^2=1+4y^2$ or $25x^2-4y^2=1$ or $\frac{x^2}{\left(\frac{1}{5}\right)^2}-\frac{y^2}{\left(\frac{1}{2}\right)^2}=1$. This is the equation of a hyperbola with center $(0,0)$ and vertices $\left(-\frac{1}{5},0\right)$ and $\left(\frac{1}{5},0\right)$. Since $a=\frac{1}{5}$ and $b=\frac{1}{2}$ and $y=\pm\frac{b}{a}x$, we have asymptotes $y=\pm\frac{\frac{1}{2}}{\frac{1}{5}}x$ or $y=\pm\frac{5}{2}x$. The original equation is the left half of the hyperbola. The domain is $\left(-\infty,-\frac{1}{5}\right]$. The range is $(-\infty, \infty)$. The vertical line test shows that this is not the graph of a function.

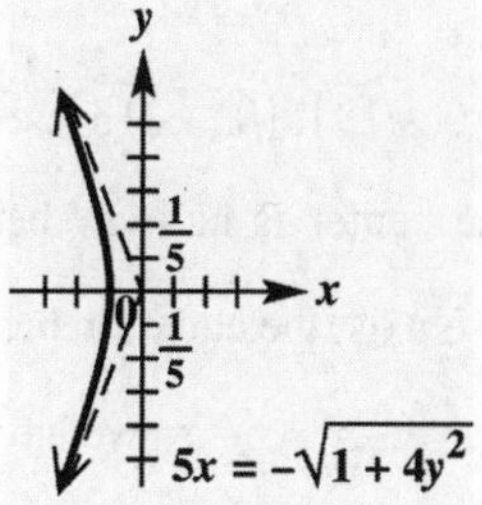

27. $\frac{x^2}{4}-\frac{y^2}{4}=1$

Since $a^2=4$, we have $a=2$. Also, $c=\sqrt{a^2+b^2}=\sqrt{4+4}=\sqrt{8}=2\sqrt{2}$. Thus, $e=\frac{c}{a}=\frac{2\sqrt{2}}{2}=\sqrt{2}\approx 1.4$.

29. $8y^2-4x^2=8 \Rightarrow \frac{y^2}{1}-\frac{x^2}{2}=1$

Since $a^2=1$, we have $a=1$. Also, $c=\sqrt{a^2+b^2}=\sqrt{1+2}=\sqrt{3}$. Thus, $e=\frac{c}{a}=\frac{\sqrt{3}}{1}=\sqrt{3}\approx 1.7$.

31. *x*-intercepts ±4; foci at (–5, 0), (5, 0)

Since the center is halfway between the foci, the center is $(0,0)$. Since the foci are on a horizontal transverse axis, the equation has the form $\frac{x^2}{a^2}-\frac{y^2}{b^2}=1$. The *x*-intercepts are also vertices, so *a* = 4 and thus $a^2=16$. With the given foci, we have *c* = 5. So given $c^2=a^2+b^2$, we have the following.

$$c^2=a^2+b^2 \Rightarrow 5^2=4^2+b^2 \Rightarrow 25=16+b^2 \Rightarrow b^2=9$$

Thus, the equation of the hyperbola is $\frac{x^2}{16}-\frac{y^2}{9}=1$.

33. Vertices at (0, 6), (0, –6); asymptotes $y = \pm\frac{1}{2}x$

Since the center is halfway between the vertices, the center is $(0,0)$. Since the vertices are on a vertical transverse axis, the equation has the form $\frac{y^2}{a^2} - \frac{x^2}{b^2} = 1$ and $a = 6$, which implies $a^2 = 36$. Also, since $y = \pm\frac{1}{2}x = \pm\frac{a}{b}x$, we have $\frac{a}{b} = \frac{1}{2} \Rightarrow \frac{6}{b} = \frac{1}{2} \Rightarrow b = 12 \Rightarrow b^2 = 144$. Thus, the equation of the hyperbola is $\frac{y^2}{36} - \frac{x^2}{144} = 1$

35. Vertices at (–3, 0), (3, 0); passing through (6, 1)

Since the center is halfway between the vertices, the center is $(0,0)$. Since the vertices are on a horizontal transverse axis, the equation has the form $\frac{x^2}{a^2} - \frac{y^2}{b^2} = 1$ and $a = 3$, which implies $a^2 = 9$. Thus, we have $\frac{x^2}{9} - \frac{y^2}{b^2} = 1$. Since the hyperbola goes through the point (6, 1), substitute $x = 6$ and $y = 1$ into the equation and solve for b^2.

$$\frac{x^2}{9} - \frac{y^2}{b^2} = 1 \Rightarrow \frac{6^2}{9} - \frac{1^2}{b^2} = 1 \Rightarrow \frac{36}{9} - \frac{1}{b^2} = 1 \Rightarrow 4 - \frac{1}{b^2} = 1 \Rightarrow -\frac{1}{b^2} = -3 \Rightarrow b^2 = \frac{1}{3}$$

Thus, the equation is $\frac{x^2}{9} - \frac{y^2}{\frac{1}{3}} = 1$ or $\frac{x^2}{9} - 3y^2 = 1$.

37. Foci at $\left(0, \sqrt{13}\right), \left(0, -\sqrt{13}\right)$; asymptotes $y = \pm 5x$

Since the center is halfway between the foci, the center is $(0,0)$. Since the foci are on a vertical transverse axis, the equation has the form $\frac{y^2}{a^2} - \frac{x^2}{b^2} = 1$ and $c = \sqrt{13}$, which implies $c^2 = 13$. Also, since $y = \pm 5x = \pm\frac{5}{1}x = \pm\frac{a}{b}x$, we have $\frac{a}{b} = \frac{5}{1} \Rightarrow a = 5b$ (1). Since $c^2 = a^2 + b^2$, we have $13 = a^2 + b^2$ (2). Substituting equation (1) into equation (2) and solving for b^2, we have the following.

$$13 = a^2 + b^2 \Rightarrow 13 = (5b)^2 + b^2 \Rightarrow 13 = 25b^2 + b^2 \Rightarrow 13 = 26b^2 \Rightarrow b^2 = \frac{1}{2}$$

Since $13 = a^2 + b^2$ and $b^2 = \frac{1}{2}$, we have $13 = a^2 + \frac{1}{2} \Rightarrow 13 - \frac{1}{2} = a^2 \Rightarrow a^2 = \frac{26}{2} - \frac{1}{2} = \frac{25}{2}$.

Thus, the equation of the hyperbola is $\frac{y^2}{\frac{25}{2}} - \frac{x^2}{\frac{1}{2}} = 1$ or $\frac{2y^2}{25} - 2x^2 = 1$.

39. Vertices at (4, 5), (4,1); asymptotes $y = 3 \pm 7(x-4)$

Since the center is halfway between the vertices, the center is located at $\left(\frac{4+4}{2}, \frac{5+1}{2}\right) = \left(\frac{8}{2}, \frac{6}{2}\right) = (4,3)$. (This could have also been determined from the equation of the asymptotes.) Since the vertices are on a vertical transverse axis, the equation has the form $\frac{(y-k)^2}{a^2} - \frac{(x-h)^2}{b^2} = 1$. Since the distance between the vertices is 4, we have $2a = 4 \Rightarrow a = 2$. The slopes of the asymptotes $\pm 7 = \pm\frac{a}{b}$. This yields $\frac{7}{1} = \frac{a}{b} \Rightarrow 7b = a \Rightarrow b = \frac{a}{7}$. Since $a = 2 \Rightarrow b = \frac{2}{7}$. With $a = 2 \Rightarrow a^2 = 4$, $b = \frac{2}{7} \Rightarrow b^2 = \frac{4}{49}$, $h = 4$, and $k = 3$ we have $\frac{(y-3)^2}{4} - \frac{(x-4)^2}{\frac{4}{49}} = 1$ or $\frac{(y-3)^2}{4} - \frac{49(x-4)^2}{4} = 1$.

41. Center at (1, –2); focus at (4, –2); vertex at (3,–2)
Since the center, focus, and vertices are on a horizontal transverse axis, the equation has the form $\frac{(x-h)^2}{a^2}-\frac{(y-k)^2}{b^2}=1$. The distance from the center to the vertex being 2 implies $a = 2$. The focus, (4, –2), is 3 units from the center, so $c=3$. Given that $c^2=a^2+b^2$, $a=2$, and $c=3$, we have $c^2=a^2+b^2 \Rightarrow 3^2=2^2+b^2 \Rightarrow 9=4+b^2 \Rightarrow b^2=5$. With $a=2 \Rightarrow a^2=4$, $b^2=5$, $h=1$, and $k=-2$, we have $\frac{(x-1)^2}{4}-\frac{(y+2)^2}{5}=1$.

43. Eccentricity 3; center at (0, 0); vertex at (0, 7)
Since the center and vertex lie on a vertical transverse axis (the *y*-axis), the equation is of the form $\frac{y^2}{a^2}-\frac{x^2}{b^2}=1$. The distance between the center and a vertex is 7, so $a = 7$. Use the eccentricity to find *c*.

$$e=\frac{c}{a} \Rightarrow 3=\frac{c}{7} \Rightarrow c=21$$

Now find the value of b^2 given $c^2=a^2+b^2$, $a=7$, and $c=21$.

$$c^2=a^2+b^2 \Rightarrow 21^2=7^2+b^2 \Rightarrow 441=49+b^2 \Rightarrow b^2=392$$

Since $a=7 \Rightarrow a^2=49$ and $b^2=392$, the equation of the hyperbola is $\frac{y^2}{49}-\frac{x^2}{392}=1$.

45. Vertices at (–2, 10), (–2, 2); eccentricity $\frac{5}{4}$
Since the vertices lie on a vertical transverse axis, the equation is of the form $\frac{(y-k)^2}{a^2}-\frac{(x-h)^2}{b^2}=1$.
Since the center is halfway between the vertices, the center is located at $\left(\frac{-2+(-2)}{2},\frac{10+2}{2}\right)=\left(\frac{-4}{2},\frac{12}{2}\right)=(-2,6)$.
The distance from the center to each vertex is 4, so $a = 4$. Use the eccentricity to find *c*.

$$e=\frac{c}{a} \Rightarrow \frac{5}{4}=\frac{c}{4} \Rightarrow 20=4c \Rightarrow c=5$$

Now find the value of b^2 given $c^2=a^2+b^2$, $a=4$, and $c=5$.

$$c^2=a^2+b^2 \Rightarrow 5^2=4^2+b^2 \Rightarrow 25=16+b^2 \Rightarrow b^2=9$$

Since $a=4 \Rightarrow a^2=16$, $b^2=9$, $h=-2$, and $k=6$, we have $\frac{(y-6)^2}{16}-\frac{(x+2)^2}{9}=1$.

47. We solve $\frac{x^2}{4}-\frac{y^2}{16}=1$ for *y*.

$$\frac{x^2}{4}-\frac{y^2}{16}=1 \Rightarrow \frac{x^2}{4}-1=\frac{y^2}{16} \Rightarrow y^2=16\left(\frac{x^2}{4}-1\right) \Rightarrow y^2=4x^2-16 \Rightarrow y=\sqrt{4x^2-16}$$

$$y=\pm\sqrt{4\left(x^2-4\right)} \Rightarrow y=\pm 2\sqrt{x^2-4}$$

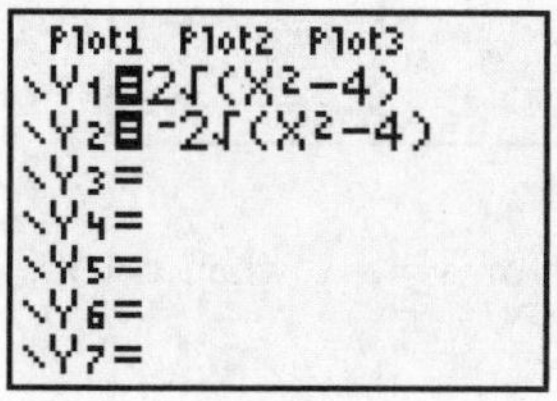

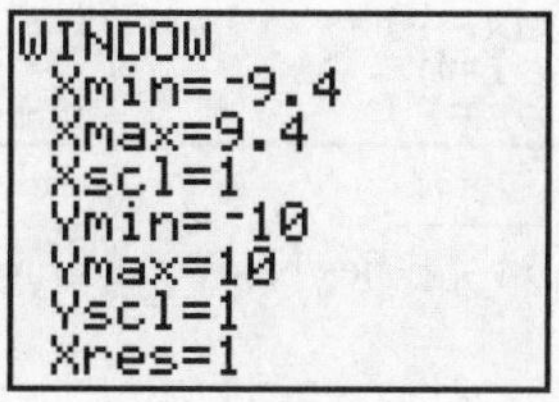

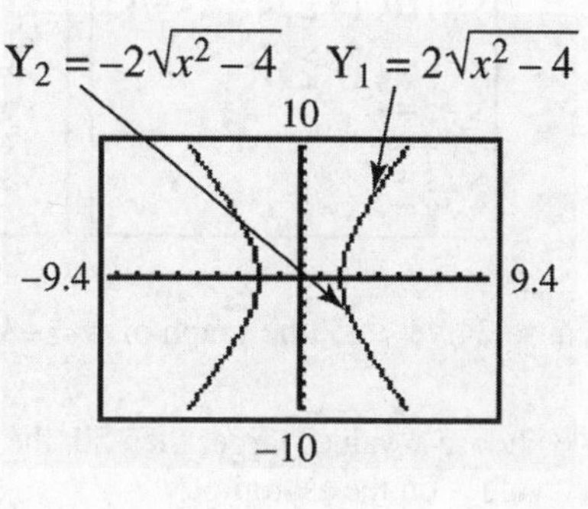

49. We solve $4y^2 - 36x^2 = 144$ for y.

$$4y^2 - 36x^2 = 144 \Rightarrow 4y^2 = 36x^2 + 144 \Rightarrow y^2 = 9x^2 + 36 \Rightarrow y = \pm\sqrt{9x^2 + 36}$$

$$y = \pm\sqrt{9\left(x^2 + 4\right)} \Rightarrow y = \pm 3\sqrt{x^2 + 4}$$

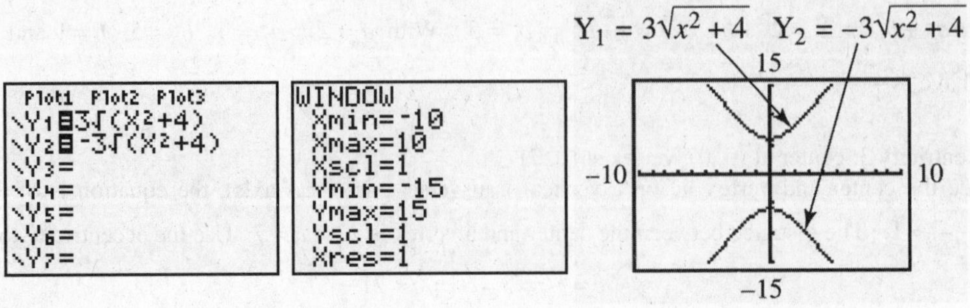

51. Solving $\frac{x^2}{4} - y^2 = 1$ for y, we have $\frac{x^2}{4} - y^2 = 1 \Rightarrow y = \pm\sqrt{\frac{x^2}{4} - 1}$. The positive square root is

$$y = \sqrt{\frac{x^2}{4} - 1} \Rightarrow y = \sqrt{\frac{x^2}{4} - \frac{4}{4}} \Rightarrow y = \sqrt{\frac{x^2 - 4}{4}} \Rightarrow y = \frac{1}{2}\sqrt{x^2 - 4}.$$

52. Writing the equation in the standard form, we have $\frac{x^2}{4} - y^2 = 1 \Rightarrow \frac{x^2}{4} - \frac{y^2}{1} = 1 \Rightarrow \frac{x^2}{2^2} - \frac{y^2}{1^2} = 1$. Since $a = 2$, $b = 1$, and the slopes of the asymptotes are $\pm\frac{b}{a}$, we have the equation of the asymptote with positive slope is $y = \frac{1}{2}x$.

53. $y = \frac{1}{2}\sqrt{x^2 - 4}$

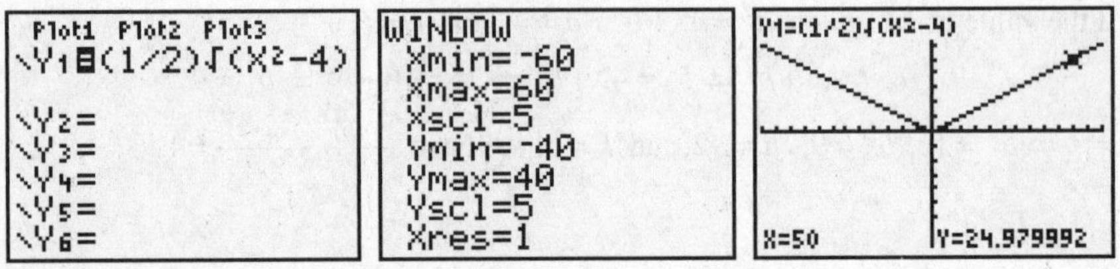

At $x = 50$, $y \approx 24.98$.

54. On the asymptote $y = \frac{1}{2}x$, when $x = 50$, $y = \frac{1}{2} \cdot 50 = 25$.

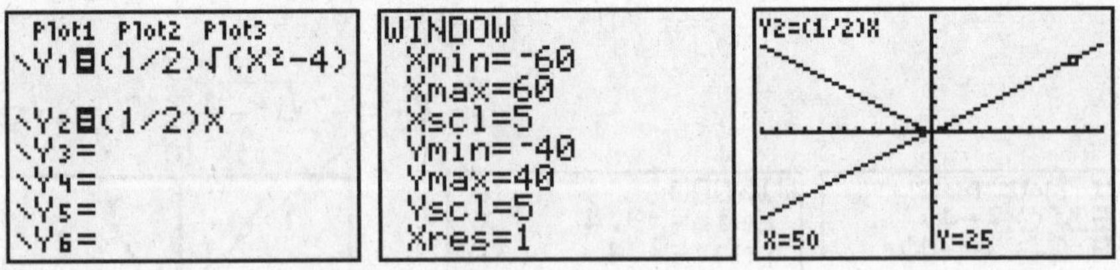

55. Because $24.98 < 25$, the graph of $y = \frac{1}{2}\sqrt{x^2 - 4}$ lies below the graph of $y = \frac{1}{2}x$ when $x = 50$.

56. If we choose x-values larger than 50, the y-values on the hyperbola will be even closer to (or approach) the y-values on the asymptote.

57. (a) We must determine a and b in the equation $\frac{x^2}{a^2}-\frac{y^2}{b^2}=1$. The asymptotes are $y = x$ and $y = -x$, which have slopes of 1 and –1, respectively, so $a = b$. Look at the small right triangle that is shown in quadrant III. The line $y = x$ intersects the x-axis to form 45º angles. Since the right angle vertex of the triangle lies on the line $y = x$, we know that this triangle is a 45º–45º–90º triangle (an isosceles right triangle). Thus, both legs of the triangle have length d, and by the Pythagorean theorem, $c^2 = d^2 + d^2 \Rightarrow c^2 = 2d^2 \Rightarrow c = d\sqrt{2}$ (1). Thus, the coordinates of N are $\left(-d\sqrt{2},0\right)$.

Since $a = b$, we have $c^2 = a^2 + a^2 \Rightarrow c^2 = 2a^2 \Rightarrow c = a\sqrt{2}$ (2). From equations (1) and (2), we have $d\sqrt{2} = a\sqrt{2} \Rightarrow d = a$. Thus, $a = b = d = 5\times10^{-14}$. The equation of the trajectory of A is given by $\frac{x^2}{a^2}-\frac{y^2}{b^2}=1$.

$$\frac{x^2}{a^2}-\frac{y^2}{b^2}=1 \Rightarrow \frac{x^2}{\left(5\times10^{-14}\right)^2}-\frac{y^2}{\left(5\times10^{-14}\right)^2}=1 \Rightarrow x^2-y^2=\left(5\times10^{-14}\right)^2 \Rightarrow x^2-y^2=25\times10^{-28}$$

$$x^2-y^2=2.5\times10^{-27} \Rightarrow x^2=y^2+\left(2.5\times10^{-27}\right) \Rightarrow x=\sqrt{y^2+\left(2.5\times10^{-27}\right)}$$

(We choose the positive square root since the trajectory occurs only where $x > 0$. This equation represents the right half of the hyperbola, as shown in the figure in the textbook.)

(b) The minimum distance between their centers is $c + a = d\sqrt{2} + d$.

$$c+a=d\sqrt{2}+d \Rightarrow c+a=\left(5\times10^{-14}\right)\sqrt{2}+\left(5\times10^{-14}\right) \Rightarrow c+a=\left(\sqrt{2}+1\right)\left(5\times10^{-14}\right)$$

$$c+a\approx12.07\times10^{-14} \Rightarrow c+a\approx1.2\times10^{-13}\text{m}$$

59. Since the center is the origin and the foci lie on a horizontal transverse axis, the equation has the form $\frac{x^2}{a^2}-\frac{y^2}{b^2}=1$. We know from page 913 of your text that $\left|d(P,F')-d(P,F)\right|=2a$ where F and F' are the locations of the foci, in this case $(-c,0)$ and $(c,0)$. Since $d = rt$, the difference between $d(P,F')$ and $d(P,F)$ is $330t$. Thus, $2a = 330t \Rightarrow a = \frac{330t}{2}$. Since $c^2 = a^2 + b^2$, we have the following.

$$c^2=a^2+b^2 \Rightarrow c^2=\left(\frac{330t}{2}\right)^2+b^2 \Rightarrow b^2=c^2-\frac{330^2t^2}{4} \Rightarrow b^2=\frac{4c^2-330^2t^2}{4}$$

Thus, the equation of the hyperbola is $\frac{x^2}{\left(\frac{330t}{2}\right)^2}-\frac{y^2}{\frac{4c^2-330^2t^2}{4}}=1$ or $\frac{x^2}{330^2t^2}-\frac{y^2}{4c^2-330^2t^2}=\frac{1}{4}$.

Section 10.4: Summary of the Conic Sections

1. $x^2+y^2=144 \Rightarrow (x-0)^2+(y-0)^2=12^2$

The graph of this equation is a circle with center $(0,0)$ and radius 12. Also, note in our original equation, the x^2 - and y^2 - terms have the same positive coefficient.

3. $y=2x^2+3x-4 \Rightarrow y=2\left(x^2+\frac{3}{2}x\right)-4 \Rightarrow y=2\left(x^2+\frac{3}{2}x+\frac{9}{16}-\frac{9}{16}\right)-4 \Rightarrow y=2\left(x+\frac{3}{4}\right)^2+2\left(-\frac{9}{16}\right)-4$

$$\Rightarrow y=2\left(x+\frac{3}{4}\right)^2-\frac{9}{8}-4 \Rightarrow y=2\left(x+\frac{3}{4}\right)^2-\frac{41}{8} \Rightarrow y-\left(-\frac{41}{8}\right)=2\left[x-\left(-\frac{3}{4}\right)\right]^2$$

The graph of this equation is a parabola opening upwards with a vertex of $\left(-\frac{3}{4},-\frac{41}{8}\right)$. Also, note our original equation has an x^2 - term, but no y^2 - term.

5. $x-1=-3(y-4)^2$

The graph of this equation is a parabola opening to the left with a vertex of $(1,4)$. Also, note when expanded, our original equation has a y^2 - term, but no x^2 - term.

7. $\frac{x^2}{49}+\frac{y^2}{100}=1 \Rightarrow \frac{x^2}{7^2}+\frac{y^2}{10^2}=1$

The graph of this equation is an ellipse centered at the origin and x-intercepts of 7 and –7, and y-intercepts of 10 and –10. Also, note in our original equation, the x^2 - and y^2 - terms both have different positive coefficients.

9. $\frac{x^2}{4}-\frac{y^2}{16}=1 \Rightarrow \frac{x^2}{2^2}-\frac{y^2}{4^2}=1$

The graph of this equation is a hyperbola centered at the origin with x-intercepts of 2 and –2, and asymptotes of $y=\pm\frac{4}{2}x=\pm 2x$. Also, note in our original equation, the x^2 - and y^2 - terms have coefficient that are opposite in sign.

11. $\frac{x^2}{25}-\frac{y^2}{25}=1 \Rightarrow \frac{x^2}{5^2}-\frac{y^2}{5^2}=1$

The graph of this equation is a hyperbola centered at the origin with x-intercepts of 5 and –5, and asymptotes of $y=\pm\frac{5}{5}x=\pm x$. Also, note in our original equation, the x^2 - and y^2 - terms have coefficients that are opposite in sign.

13. $\frac{x^2}{4}=1-\frac{y^2}{9} \Rightarrow \frac{x^2}{4}+\frac{y^2}{9}=1 \Rightarrow \frac{(x-0)^2}{2^2}+\frac{(y-0)^2}{3^2}=1$

The equation is of the form $\frac{(x-h)^2}{b^2}+\frac{(y-k)^2}{a^2}=1$ with $a=3$, $b=2$, $h=0$, and $k=0$, so the graph of the given equation is an ellipse.

15. $\frac{x^2}{4}+\frac{y^2}{4}=1 \Rightarrow x^2+y^2=4 \Rightarrow x^2+y^2=2^2$

The equation is of the form $(x-h)^2+(y-k)^2=r^2$ with $r=2$, $h=0$, and $k=0$, so the graph of the given equation is a circle.

17. $x^2=25+y^2 \Rightarrow x^2-y^2=25 \Rightarrow \frac{x^2}{25}-\frac{y^2}{25}=1 \Rightarrow \frac{(x-0)^2}{5^2}-\frac{(y-0)^2}{5^2}=1$

The equation is of the form $\frac{(x-h)^2}{a^2}-\frac{(y-k)^2}{b^2}=1$ with $a=5$, $b=5$, $h=0$, and $k=0$, so the graph of the given equation is a hyperbola.

19. $9x^2+36y^2=36 \Rightarrow \frac{x^2}{4}+\frac{y^2}{1}=1 \Rightarrow \frac{(x-0)^2}{2^2}+\frac{(y-0)^2}{1^2}=1$

The equation is of the form $\frac{(x-h)^2}{a^2}+\frac{(y-k)^2}{b^2}=1$ with $a=2$, $b=1$, $h=0$, and $k=0$, so the graph of the given equation is an ellipse.

21. $\frac{(x+3)^2}{16}+\frac{(y-2)^2}{16}=1 \Rightarrow (x+3)^2+(y-2)^2=16 \Rightarrow [x-(-3)]^2+(y-2)^2=4^2$

The equation is of the form $(x-h)^2+(y-k)^2=r^2$ with $r=4$, $h=-3$, and $k=2$, so the graph of the given equation is a circle.

23. $y^2-4y=x+4 \Rightarrow y^2-4y+4-4=x+4 \Rightarrow (y-2)^2-4=x+4 \Rightarrow x+8=(y-2)^2 \Rightarrow x-(-8)=(y-2)^2$

The equation is of the form $x-h=a(y-k)^2$ with $a=1$, $h=-8$, and $k=2$, so the graph of the given equation is a parabola.

25. $(x+7)^2+(y-5)^2+4=0 \Rightarrow (x+7)^2+(y-5)^2=-4$

A sum of squares can never be negative. This equation has no graph.

27. $3x^2+6x+3y^2-12y=12 \Rightarrow x^2+2x+y^2-4y=4 \Rightarrow (x^2+2x+1-1)+(y^2-4y+4-4)=4$

$$\Rightarrow (x+1)^2-1+(y-2)^2-4=4 \Rightarrow (x-1)^2+(y-2)^2=4+1+4$$

$$\Rightarrow (x+1)^2+(y-2)^2=9 \Rightarrow [x-(-1)]^2+(y-2)^2=3^2$$

The equation is of the form $(x-h)^2+(y-k)^2=r^2$ with $r=3$, $h=-1$, and $k=2$, so the graph of the given equation is a circle.

29. $x^2-6x+y=0 \Rightarrow y=-x^2+6x \Rightarrow y=-(x^2-6x+9-9) \Rightarrow y=-(x-3)^2+9 \Rightarrow y-9=-(x-3)^2$

The equation is of the form $y-k=a(x-h)^2$ with $a=-1$, $h=3$, and $k=9$, so the graph of the given equation is a parabola.

31. $-4x^2+8x+y^2+6y=-6 \Rightarrow 4x^2-8x-y^2-6y=6 \Rightarrow 4(x^2-2x+1-1)-(y^2+6y+9-9)=6$

$$\Rightarrow 4(x^2-2x+1-1)-(y^2+6y+9-9)=6 \Rightarrow 4(x-1)^2-4-(y+3)^2+9=6$$

$$\Rightarrow 4(x-1)^2-(y+3)^2=6+4-9 \Rightarrow 4(x-1)^2-(y+3)^2=1$$

$$\Rightarrow \frac{(x-1)^2}{\frac{1}{4}}-\frac{(y+3)^2}{1}=1 \Rightarrow \frac{(x-1)^2}{\left(\frac{1}{2}\right)^2}-\frac{[y-(-3)]^2}{1^2}=1$$

The equation is of the form $\frac{(x-h)^2}{a^2}-\frac{(y-k)^2}{b^2}=1$ with $a=\frac{1}{2}$, $b=1$, $h=1$, and $k=-3$, so the graph of the given equation is a hyperbola.

33. $4x^2-8x+9y^2+54y=-84 \Rightarrow 4\left(x^2-2x+1-1\right)+9\left(y^2+6y+9-9\right)=-84$

$$\Rightarrow 4(x-1)^2-4+9(y+3)^2-81=-84$$

$$\Rightarrow 4(x-1)^2+9(y+3)^2=-84+4+81$$

$$\Rightarrow 4(x-1)^2+9(y+3)^2=1 \Rightarrow \frac{(x-1)^2}{\frac{1}{4}}+\frac{(y+3)^2}{\frac{1}{9}}=1$$

$$\Rightarrow \frac{(x-1)^2}{\left(\frac{1}{2}\right)^2}+\frac{\left[y-(-3)\right]^2}{\left(\frac{1}{3}\right)^2}=1$$

The equation is of the form $\frac{(x-h)^2}{a^2}+\frac{(y-k)^2}{b^2}=1$ with $a=\frac{1}{2}$, $b=\frac{1}{3}$, $h=1$, and $k=-3$, so the graph of the given equation is an ellipse.

35. $4x^2-24x+5y^2+10y+41=0 \Rightarrow 4\left(x^2-6x+9-9\right)+5\left(y^2+2y+1-1\right)=-41$

$$\Rightarrow 4(x-3)^2-36+5(y+1)^2-5=-41$$

$$\Rightarrow 4(x-3)^2+5(y+1)^2=-41+36+5 \Rightarrow 4(x-3)^2+5(y+1)^2=0$$

$$\Rightarrow \frac{4(x-3)^2}{20}+\frac{5(y+1)^2}{20}=0 \Rightarrow \frac{(x-3)^2}{5}+\frac{\left[y-(-1)\right]^2}{4}=0$$

The graph is the point $(3,-1)$.

37. The definition of an ellipse states "an ellipse is the set of all points in a plane the sum of whose distances from two fixed points is constant." Therefore, the set of all points in a plane for which the sum of the distances from the points (5, 0) and (–5, 0) is 14 is an ellipse with foci (5, 0) and (–5, 0).

39. Refer to the Geometric Definition of a Conic Section on page 925 of your text. It gives the relation

[distance of P from F] $= e \cdot$ [distance of P from L].

In this exercise, $e=1\frac{1}{2}=\frac{3}{2}$. Since $e > 1$, this is a hyperbola.

41. From the graph, the coordinates of P (a point on the graph) are (–3, 8), the coordinates of F (a focus) are (3, 0), the equation of L (the directrix) is $x = 27$. By the distance formula, the distance from P to F is $\sqrt{(x_2-x_1)^2+(y_2-y_1)^2}=\sqrt{\left[3-(-3)\right]^2+(0-8)^2}=\sqrt{6^2+(-8)^2}=\sqrt{36+64}=\sqrt{100}=10.$ The distance from a point to a line is defined as the perpendicular distance, so the distance from P to L is $|27-(-3)|=30$. Thus, $e=\frac{\text{Distance of } P \text{ from } F}{\text{Distance of } P \text{ from } L}=\frac{10}{30}=\frac{1}{3}$.

43. From the graph, we see that $F=\left(\sqrt{2},0\right)$ and L is the vertical line $x=-\sqrt{2}$. Choose $(0,0)$, the vertex of the parabola, as P. Distance of P from $F=\sqrt{2}$, and Distance of P from $L=\sqrt{2}$. Thus, we have $e=\frac{\text{Distance of } P \text{ from } F}{\text{Distance of } P \text{ from } L}=\frac{\sqrt{2}}{\sqrt{2}}=1.$

45. From the graph, we see that P = (9, –7.5), F = (9, 0) and L is the vertical line x = 4. Distance of P from $F=7.5$, and Distance of P from $L=5$. Thus, $e=\frac{\text{Distance of } P \text{ from } F}{\text{Distance of } P \text{ from } L}=\frac{7.5}{5}=1.5.$

47. If $\frac{k}{\sqrt{D}} = \frac{2.82\times10^7}{\sqrt{42.5\times10^6}} = \frac{2.82\times10^7}{\sqrt{42.5}\times10^3} \approx .432568\times10^4 \approx 4326$ and $V = 2090$, then we have $V < \frac{k}{\sqrt{D}}$.
Thus, the shape of the satellite's trajectory was elliptic.

49. Answers will vary.

51. To enter the relation $\frac{x^2}{16}+\frac{y^2}{12}=1$ into the graphing calculator, we must solve for *y*.

$$\frac{x^2}{16}+\frac{y^2}{12}=1 \Rightarrow \frac{y^2}{12}=1-\frac{x^2}{16} \Rightarrow y^2=12\left(1-\frac{x^2}{16}\right) \Rightarrow y=\pm\sqrt{12\left(1-\frac{x^2}{16}\right)}$$

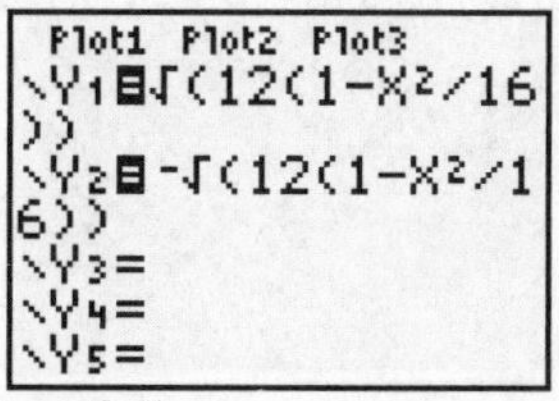

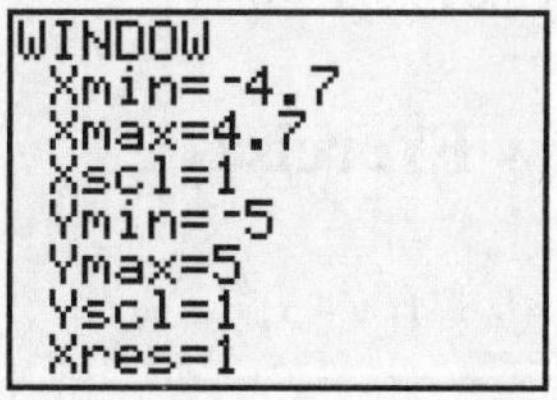

A sampling of points is as follows.

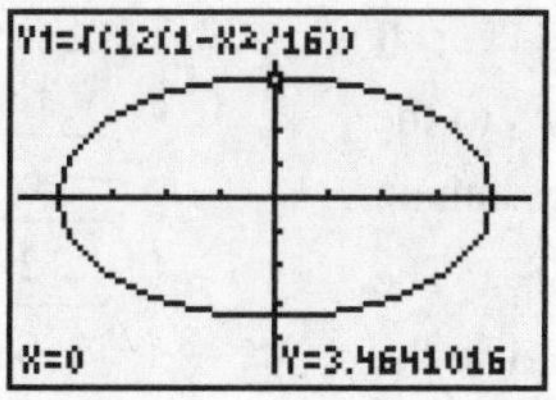

The distance of *P* from $(2,0) \approx \sqrt{(2-0)^2+(0-3.4641016)^2} = \sqrt{4+(-3.4641016)^2} \approx 3.999999987$

The distance of *P* from the line $x=8$ is $|0-8|=8$. We have $3.999999987 \approx \frac{1}{2}(8)=4$.

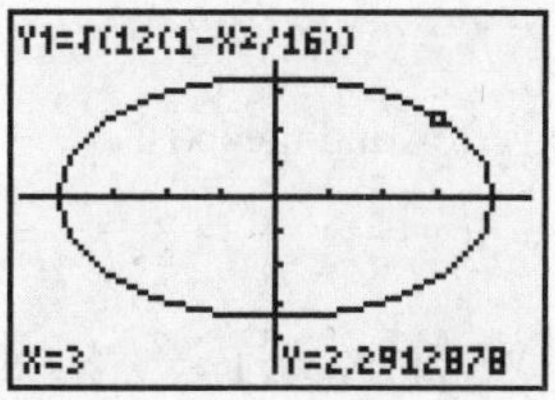

The distance of *P* from $(2,0) \approx \sqrt{(2-3)^2+(0-2.2912878)^2} = \sqrt{1+(-2.2912878)^2} \approx 2.499999956$

The distance of *P* from the line $x=8$ is $|3-8|=5$. We have $2.499999956 \approx \frac{1}{2}(5)=2.5$.

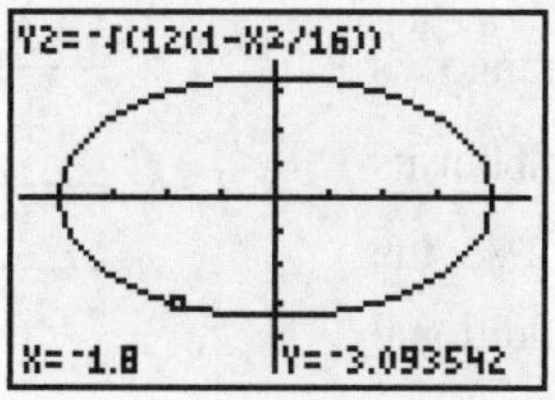

The distance of *P* from $(2,0) \approx \sqrt{\left[2-(-1.8)\right]^2+\left[0-(-3.093542)\right]^2}$

$$= \sqrt{14.44+(3.093542)^2} \approx 4.900000215$$

Continued on next page

51. (continued)

The distance of *P* from the line $x = 8$ is $|-1.8-8| = 9.8$. We have $4.900000215 \approx \frac{1}{2}(9.8) = 4.9$.

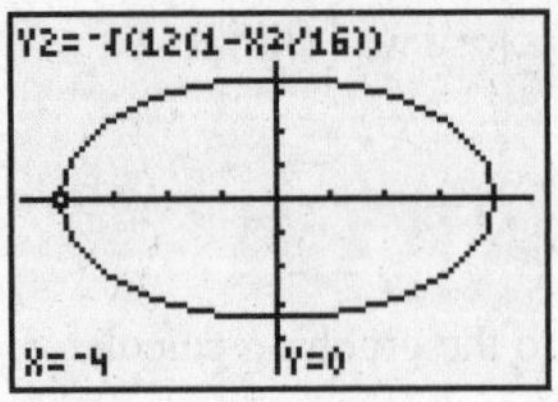

The distance of *P* from $(2,0) \approx \sqrt{[2-(-4)]^2 + (0-0)^2} = \sqrt{36} = 6$

The distance of *P* from the line $x = 8$ is $|-4-8| = 12$. We have $6 = \frac{1}{2}(12)$.

Chapter 10: Review Exercises

1. $x = 4(y-5)^2 + 2 \Rightarrow x - 2 = 4(y-5)^2$

The vertex is $(2,5)$. The graph opens to the right and has the same shape as $x = 4y^2$. It is a translation 5 units up and 2 units to the right of the graph of $x = 4y^2$. The domain is $[2,\infty)$. The range is $(-\infty,\infty)$. The graph is symmetric about its axis, the horizontal line $y = 5$. Use the vertex and axis and plot a few additional points.

x	y
18	7
6	6
2	5
6	4
18	3

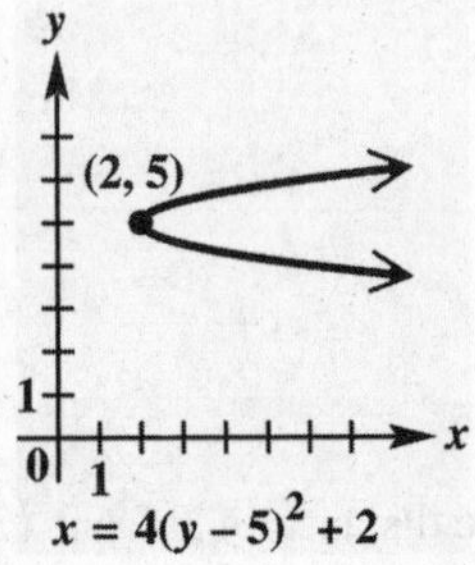

3. $x = 5y^2 - 5y + 3$

Complete the square on *y* to find the vertex and the axis.

$$x = 5y^2 - 5y + 3 \Rightarrow x = 5\left(y^2 - y \quad\right) + 3 \Rightarrow x = 5\left(y^2 - y + \tfrac{1}{4} - \tfrac{1}{4}\right) + 3$$

$$x = 5\left(y - \tfrac{1}{2}\right)^2 + 5\left(-\tfrac{1}{4}\right) + 3 \Rightarrow x = 5\left(y - \tfrac{1}{2}\right)^2 + \left(-\tfrac{5}{4}\right) + \tfrac{12}{4} \Rightarrow x = 5\left(y - \tfrac{1}{2}\right)^2 + \tfrac{7}{4} \Rightarrow x - \tfrac{7}{4} = 5\left(y - \tfrac{1}{2}\right)^2$$

The vertex is $\left(\frac{7}{4}, \frac{1}{2}\right)$. The graph opens to the right and has the same shape as $x = 5y^2$, translated $\frac{7}{4}$ unit to the right and $\frac{1}{2}$ unit up. The domain is $\left[\frac{7}{4}, \infty\right)$. The range is $(-\infty,\infty)$. The graph is symmetric about its axis, the horizontal line $y = \frac{1}{2}$. Use the vertex and axis and plot a few additional points.

x	y
$\frac{27}{4}$	$\frac{3}{2}$
3	1
$\frac{7}{4}$	$\frac{1}{2}$
3	0
$\frac{27}{4}$	$-\frac{1}{2}$

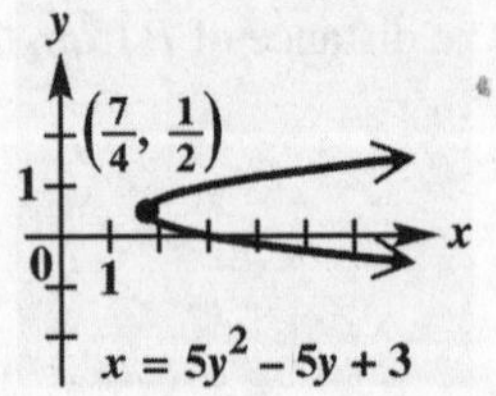

5. The equation $y^2 = -\frac{2}{3}x$ has the form $y^2 = 4px$, so $4p = -\frac{2}{3}$, from which $p = -\frac{1}{6}$. Since the y-term is squared, the parabola is horizontal, with focus $(p,0) = \left(-\frac{1}{6},0\right)$ and directrix, $x = -p$, is $x = \frac{1}{6}$. The vertex is $(0,0)$, and the axis of the parabola is the x-axis. The domain is $(-\infty,0]$. The range is $(-\infty,\infty)$. Use this information and plot a few additional points.

x	y
-6	2
$-\frac{3}{2}$	1
0	0
$-\frac{3}{2}$	-1
-6	-2

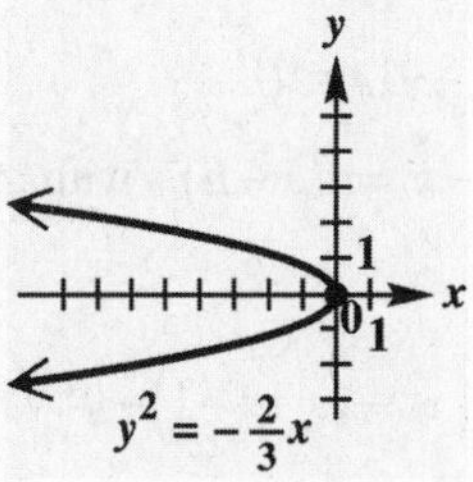

7. The equation $3x^2 = y \Rightarrow x^2 = \frac{1}{3}y$ has the form $x^2 = 4py$, so $4p = \frac{1}{3}$, from which $p = \frac{1}{12}$. Since the x-term is squared, the parabola is vertical, with focus $(0,p) = \left(0,\frac{1}{12}\right)$ and directrix, $y = -p$, is $y = -\frac{1}{12}$. The vertex is $(0,0)$, and the axis of the parabola is the y-axis. The domain is $(-\infty,\infty)$. The range is $[0,\infty)$. Use this information and plot a few additional points.

x	y
2	12
1	3
0	0
-1	3
-2	12

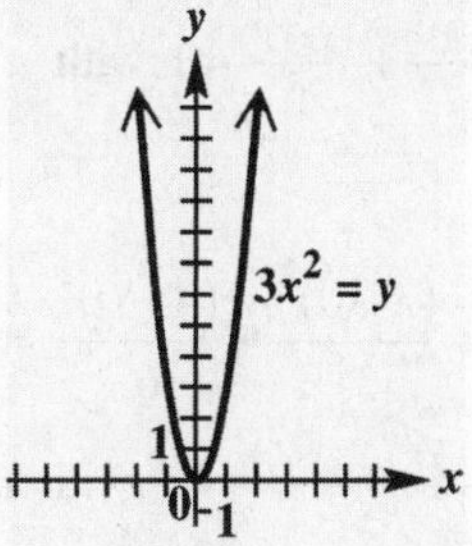

9. A parabola with focus (4, 0) and vertex at the origin is a horizontal parabola. The equation has the form $y^2 = 4px$. Since $p = 4$ is positive, it opens to the right. Substituting 4 for p, we find that an equation for this parabola is $y^2 = 4(4)x \Rightarrow y^2 = 16x$.

11. A parabola passing through $(-3,4)$, opening up, and vertex at the origin has an equation of the form $x^2 = 4py$. Use this equation with the coordinates of the point $(-3,4)$ to find the value of p.

$$x^2 = 4py \Rightarrow (-3)^2 = 4p \cdot 4 \Rightarrow 9 = 16p \Rightarrow \frac{9}{16} = p$$

Thus, an equation of the parabola is $x^2 = 4\left(\frac{9}{16}\right)y \Rightarrow x^2 = \frac{9}{4}y$.

13. $y^2 + 9x^2 = 9 \Rightarrow \frac{x^2}{1} + \frac{y^2}{9} = 1 \Rightarrow \frac{(x-0)^2}{1^2} + \frac{(y-0)^2}{3^2} = 1$

The equation is of the form $\frac{(x-h)^2}{b^2} + \frac{(y-k)^2}{a^2} = 1$ with $a = 3$, $b = 1$, $h = 0$, and $k = 0$, so the graph of the given equation is an ellipse.

15. $3y^2 - 5x^2 = 30 \Rightarrow \frac{y^2}{10} - \frac{x^2}{6} = 1 \Rightarrow \frac{(y-0)^2}{(\sqrt{10})^2} - \frac{(x-0)^2}{(\sqrt{6})^2} = 1$

The equation is of the form $\frac{(y-k)^2}{a^2} - \frac{(x-h)^2}{b^2} = 1$ with $a = \sqrt{10}$, $b = \sqrt{6}$, $h = 0$, and $k = 0$, so the graph of the given equation is a hyperbola.

17. $4x^2 - y = 0 \Rightarrow y = 4x^2 \Rightarrow y - 0 = 4(x-0)^2$

The equation is of the form $y - k = a(x-h)^2$ with $a = 4$, $h = 0$, and $k = 0$, so the graph of the given equation is a parabola.

19. $$\begin{aligned} 4x^2 - 8x + 9y^2 + 36y = -4 &\Rightarrow 4(x^2 - 2x + 1 - 1) + 9(y^2 + 4y + 4 - 4) = -4 \\ &\Rightarrow 4(x-1)^2 - 4 + 9(y+2)^2 - 36 = -4 \\ &\Rightarrow 4(x-1)^2 + 9(y+2)^2 = -4 + 4 + 36 \\ &\Rightarrow 4(x-1)^2 + 9(y+2)^2 = 36 \Rightarrow \frac{(x-1)^2}{9} + \frac{(y+2)^2}{4} = 1 \\ &\Rightarrow \frac{(x-1)^2}{3^2} + \frac{[y-(-2)]^2}{2^2} = 1 \end{aligned}$$

The equation is of the form $\frac{(x-h)^2}{a^2} + \frac{(y-k)^2}{b^2} = 1$ with $a = 3$, $b = 2$, $h = 1$, and $k = -2$, so the graph of the given equation is an ellipse.

21. $4x^2 + y^2 = 36 \Rightarrow \frac{x^2}{9} + \frac{y^2}{36} = 1 \Rightarrow \frac{(x-0)^2}{3^2} + \frac{(y-0)^2}{6^2} = 1$

The equation is of the form $\frac{(x-h)^2}{b^2} + \frac{(y-k)^2}{a^2} = 1$ with $a = 6$, $b = 3$, $h = 0$, and $k = 0$, so the graph of the given equation is an ellipse. It is centered at the origin with vertices at (0, –6) and (0, 6) and endpoints of the minor axis at (–3, 0) and (3, 0). The correct graph is F.

23. $(x-2)^2 + (y+3)^2 = 36 \Rightarrow (x-2)^2 + [y-(-3)]^2 = 6^2$

The equation is of the form $(x-h)^2 + (y-k)^2 = r^2$ with $r = 6$, $h = 2$, and $k = -3$, so the graph of the given equation is a circle. This circle is centered at (2, –3) and has radius 6. The correct graph is A.

25. $(y-1)^2 - (x-2)^2 = 36 \Rightarrow \frac{(y-1)^2}{36} - \frac{(x-2)^2}{36} = 1 \Rightarrow \frac{(y-1)^2}{6^2} - \frac{(x-2)^2}{6^2} = 1$

The equation is of the form $\frac{(y-k)^2}{a^2} - \frac{(x-h)^2}{b^2} = 1$ with $a = 6$, $b = 6$, $h = 2$, and $k = 1$, so the graph of the given equation is a hyperbola. This hyperbola is centered at (2, 1), opening upward and downward, with vertices at (2, –5) and (2, 7). The correct graph is B.

27. $\frac{x^2}{4}+\frac{y^2}{9}=1 \Rightarrow \frac{(x-0)^2}{2^2}+\frac{(y-0)^2}{3^2}=1$

The graph is an ellipse centered at the origin with domain [–2, 2], range [–3, 3], and vertices at (0, –3) and (0, 3). The endpoints of the minor axis are (–2, 0) and (2, 0).

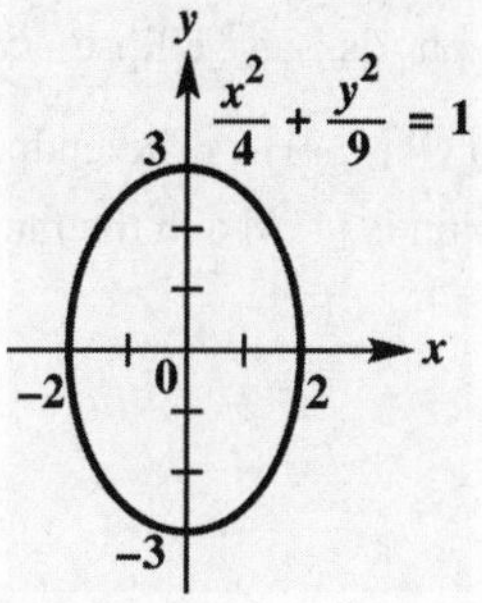

29. $\frac{x^2}{64}-\frac{y^2}{36}=1 \Rightarrow \frac{(x-0)^2}{8^2}-\frac{(y-0)^2}{6^2}=1$

The graph is a hyperbola centered at the origin with domain $(-\infty,-8]\cup[8,\infty)$, range $(-\infty, \infty)$, and vertices (–8, 0) and (8, 0). The asymptotes are the lines $y=\pm\frac{6}{8}x \Rightarrow y=\pm\frac{3}{4}x$.

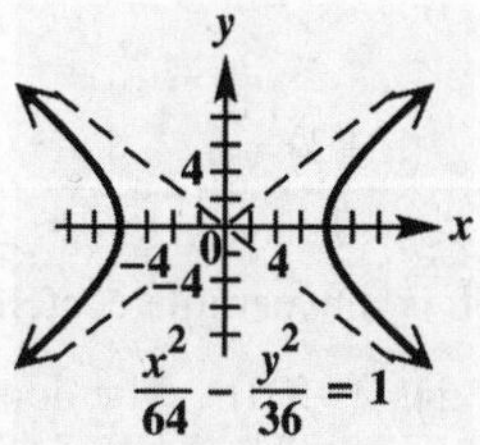

31. $\frac{(x+1)^2}{16}+\frac{(y-1)^2}{16}=1 \Rightarrow (x+1)^2+(y-1)^2=16 \Rightarrow [x-(-1)]^2+(y-1)^2=4^2$

The graph is a circle centered at $(-1,1)$ and radius 4. Its domain is $[-1-4,-1+4]=[-5,3]$. The range is $[1-4,1+4]=[-3,5]$.

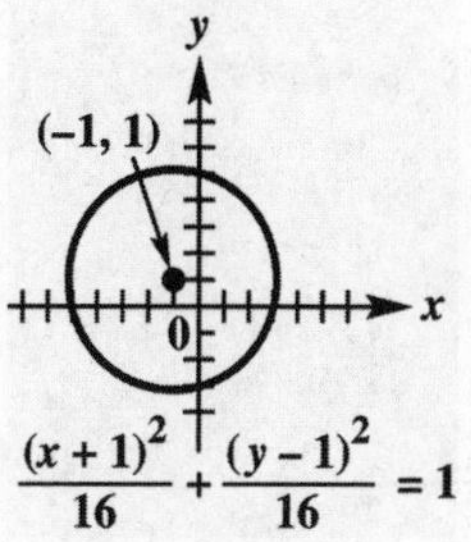

33. $4x^2+9y^2=36 \Rightarrow \frac{x^2}{9}+\frac{y^2}{4}=1 \Rightarrow \frac{(x-0)^2}{3^2}+\frac{(y-0)^2}{2^2}=1$

The graph is an ellipse centered at the origin with domain [–3, 3], range [–2, 2], vertices at (–3, 0) and (3, 0). The endpoints of the minor axis at (0, –2) and (0, 2).

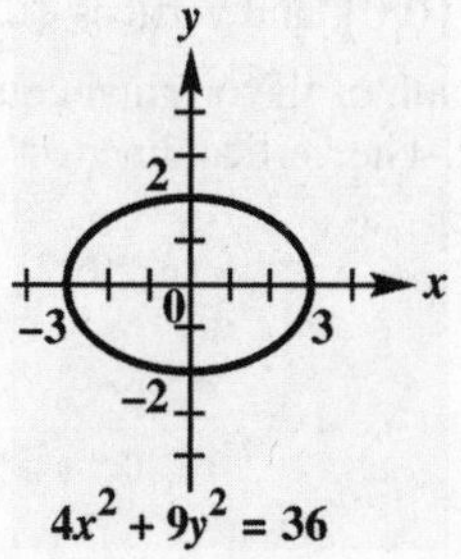

35. $\dfrac{(x-3)^2}{4}+(y+1)^2=1 \Rightarrow \dfrac{(x-3)^2}{2^2}+\dfrac{[y-(-1)]^2}{1^2}=1$

The graph is an ellipse centered at $(3,-1)$. The vertices are $(3-2,-1)=(1,-1)$ and $(3+2,-1)=(5,-1)$. The endpoints of the minor axis are $(3,-1-1)=(3,-2)$ and $(3,-1+1)=(3,0)$. The domain is [1, 5] and the range is [–2, 0].

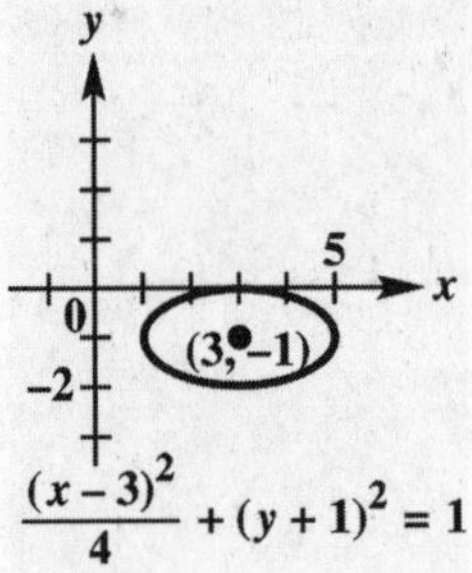

37. $\dfrac{(y+2)^2}{4}-\dfrac{(x+3)^2}{9}=1 \Rightarrow \dfrac{[y-(-2)]^2}{2^2}-\dfrac{[x-(-3)]^2}{3^2}=1$

The graph is a hyperbola centered at $(-3,-2)$. The vertices are located at $(-3,-2-2)=(-3,-4)$ and $(-3,-2+2)=(-3,0)$. The domain is $(-\infty, \infty)$ and the range is $(-\infty, -4] \cup [0, \infty)$. The asymptotes are the lines $y-(-2)=\pm\frac{2}{3}[x-(-3)] \Rightarrow y+2=\pm\frac{2}{3}(x+3) \Rightarrow y=-2\pm\frac{2}{3}(x+3)$.

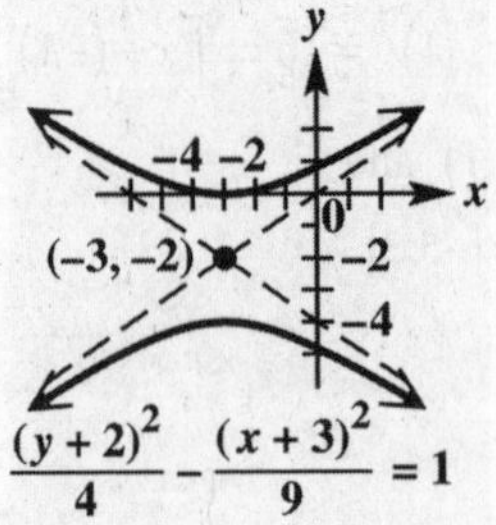

39. $\dfrac{x}{3}=-\sqrt{1-\dfrac{y^2}{16}}$

Square both sides to get $\frac{x^2}{9}=1-\frac{y^2}{16}$ or $\frac{x^2}{9}+\frac{y^2}{16}=1$ or $\frac{x^2}{3^2}+\frac{y^2}{4^2}=1$. This is the equation of an ellipse with center $(0,0)$ and vertices $(0,-4)$ and $(0,4)$. It has endpoints of the minor axis of $(-3,0)$ and $(3,0)$. The graph of the original equation is the left half of this ellipse. The domain is [–3, 0] and the range is [–4, 4]. The vertical line test shows that this relation is not a function.

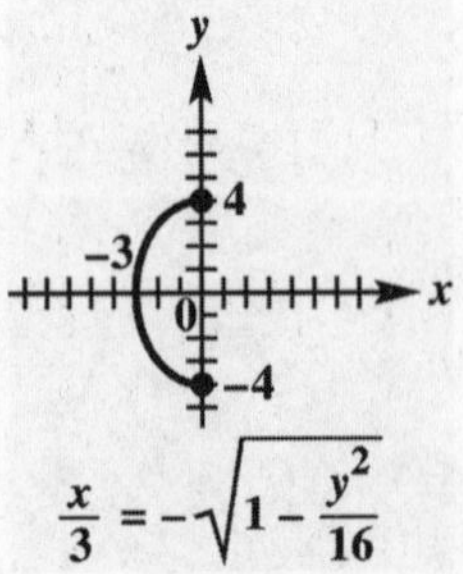

41. $y = -\sqrt{1+x^2}$

Square both sides of the equation to get $y^2 = 1 + x^2$ or $\frac{y^2}{1} - \frac{x^2}{1} = 1$ or $\frac{y^2}{1^2} - \frac{x^2}{1^2} = 1$. This is the equation of a hyperbola with center $(0,0)$ and vertices $(0,-1)$ and $(0,1)$. Since $a = 1$, $b = 1$, and $y = \pm\frac{a}{b}x$, we have asymptotes $y = \pm\frac{1}{1}x \Rightarrow y = \pm x$. The original equation is the bottom half of the hyperbola. The domain is $(-\infty, \infty)$. The range is $(-\infty, -1]$. The vertical line test shows this is a graph of a function.

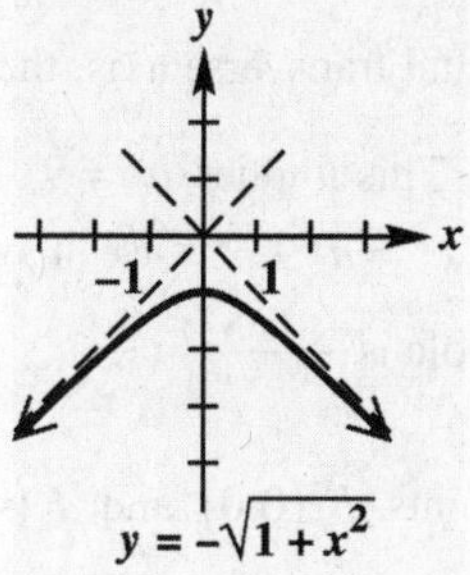

43. Ellipse; vertex at (0, 4), focus at (0, 2), center at the origin
Since the vertex is (0, 4) and the focus is (0, 2), we know that the major axis is vertical and thus, the equation is of the form $\frac{x^2}{b^2} + \frac{y^2}{a^2} = 1$. Since the ellipse is centered at the origin, we have $a = 4$ which implies $a^2 = 16$. Since the ellipse is centered at the origin and a focus is at (0, 2), we have $c = 2$ which implies $c^2 = 4$. Since $c^2 = a^2 - b^2$, we have $c^2 = a^2 - b^2 \Rightarrow 4 = 16 - b^2 \Rightarrow b^2 = 12$. Thus, the equation of the ellipse is $\frac{x^2}{12} + \frac{y^2}{16} = 1$.

45. Hyperbola; focus at $(0,-5)$, transverse axis of length 8, center at the origin
Since the focus is $(0,-5)$, we know that the transverse axis is vertical and thus, the equation is of the form $\frac{y^2}{a^2} - \frac{x^2}{b^2} = 1$. Since the length of the transverse axis is 8, we have $2a = 8 \Rightarrow a = 4$. This implies that $a^2 = 16$. Since the hyperbola is centered at the origin and a focus is at $(0,-5)$, we have $c = 5$ which implies $c^2 = 25$. Since $c^2 = a^2 + b^2$, we have $25 = 16 + b^2 \Rightarrow b^2 = 9$. Thus, the equation of the hyperbola is $\frac{y^2}{16} - \frac{x^2}{9} = 1$.

47. Parabola with focus at (3, 2) and directrix $x = -3$
Since the directrix is $x = -3$, a vertical line, the parabola is of the form $(y-k)^2 = 4p(x-h)$. Since the vertex is halfway between the focus and the directrix, we know that the vertex is $(0,2) = (h,k)$. Because of the orientation of the directrix versus the focus, we know that the parabola opens to the right, so the p value must be positive. By examining the distance between the vertex and the focus or the directrix and the vertex, we know that $p = 3$. Thus, the equation of the parabola is $(y-2)^2 = 4 \cdot 3(x-0)$ or $(y-2)^2 = 12x$.

49. Ellipse with foci at (–2, 0) and (2, 0) and major axis of length 10
Since the foci are at (–2, 0) and (2, 0), we know that major axis is horizontal and the ellipse is centered at the origin. Thus, the equation is of the form $\frac{x^2}{a^2} + \frac{y^2}{b^2} = 1$. Since the foci are at (–2, 0) and (2, 0), we know that $c = 2$, which implies $c^2 = 4$. Since the major axis is of length 10 we have $2a = 10$. This implies that $a = 5$ and $a^2 = 25$. Since $c^2 = a^2 - b^2$, we have $c^2 = a^2 - b^2 \Rightarrow 4 = 25 - b^2 \Rightarrow b^2 = 21$. Thus, the equation of the ellipse is $\frac{x^2}{25} + \frac{y^2}{21} = 1$.

51. Hyperbola with x-intercepts ± 3; foci at $(-5, 0)$, $(5, 0)$
Since the center is halfway between the foci, the center is at the origin. Since the foci are on a horizontal transverse axis, the equation has the form $\frac{x^2}{a^2}-\frac{y^2}{b^2}=1$. The x-intercepts are also vertices, so $a=3$. This implies $a^2=9$. Since the foci at $(-5, 0)$ and $(5, 0)$, we have $c=5$. This implies $c^2=25$. Since $c^2=a^2+b^2$, we have $c^2=a^2+b^2 \Rightarrow 25=9+b^2 \Rightarrow b^2=16$. Thus, the equation of the hyperbola is $\frac{x^2}{9}-\frac{y^2}{16}=1$.

53. The points $F'(0,0)$ and $F(4,0)$ are the foci, so the center of the ellipse is $(2,0)=(h,k)$. Since the foci are on a horizontal axis, the equation is of the form $\frac{(x-h)^2}{a^2}+\frac{(y-k)^2}{b^2}=1$. Since the distance from the center to each of the foci is 2, we have $c=2 \Rightarrow c^2=4$. For any point P on the ellipse, $d(P,F)+d(P,F')=2a=8$, so $a = 4$. Thus, we have $a^2=16$. Since $c^2=a^2-b^2$, we have $c^2=a^2-b^2 \Rightarrow 4=16-b^2 \Rightarrow b^2=12$. Thus, the equation of the ellipse is $\frac{(x-2)^2}{16}+\frac{y^2}{12}=1$.

55. Refer to the chart on page 917 of your text.
Graph A is an ellipse, so $0<e<1$. Graph B is a parabola, so $e = 1$. Graph C is a circle, so $e = 0$. Graph D is a hyperbola, so $e > 1$. Thus, in increasing order of eccentricity, the graphs are C, A, B, D.

57. Since the eccentricity is .964 and $e=\frac{c}{a}$, we have $.964=\frac{c}{a} \Rightarrow c=.964a$. Since the closest distance to the sun is 89 million mi, we have $a-c=89$. Substituting $c=.964a$ into this equation, we have the following.

$$a-c=89 \Rightarrow a-.964a=89 \Rightarrow .036a=89 \Rightarrow a=\frac{89}{.036}=\frac{22{,}250}{9}$$

Since $c=.964a$, we have $c=.964\left(\frac{22{,}250}{9}\right)=\frac{21{,}449}{9}$. Since $c^2=a^2-b^2$, we have the following.

$$c^2=a^2-b^2 \Rightarrow \left(\frac{21{,}449}{9}\right)^2=\left(\frac{22{,}250}{9}\right)^2-b^2 \Rightarrow \frac{460{,}059{,}601}{81}-\frac{495{,}062{,}500}{81}=-b^2 \Rightarrow b^2=\frac{35{,}002{,}899}{81}$$

Since $a^2=\left(\frac{22{,}250}{9}\right)^2=\frac{495{,}062{,}500}{81}\approx 6{,}111{,}883$ and $b^2=\frac{35{,}002{,}899}{81}\approx 432{,}135$, the equation is $\frac{x^2}{6{,}111{,}883}+\frac{y^2}{432{,}135}=1$.

Chapter 10: Test

1. $y=-x^2+6x$
Completing the square on x, we have the following.

$$y=-x^2+6x \Rightarrow y=-\left(x^2-6x+9-9\right) \Rightarrow y=-(x-3)^2+9 \Rightarrow y-9=-(x-3)^2$$

The equation has the form $x-h=a(y-k)^2$. The vertex, (h,k), is $(3,9)$. Since the x-term is squared, the axis is the vertical line $x=h$, or $x=3$. The domain is $(-\infty,\infty)$. The range is $(-\infty,9]$. Using this information and plot a few additional points.

x	y
5	5
4	8
3	9
2	8
1	5

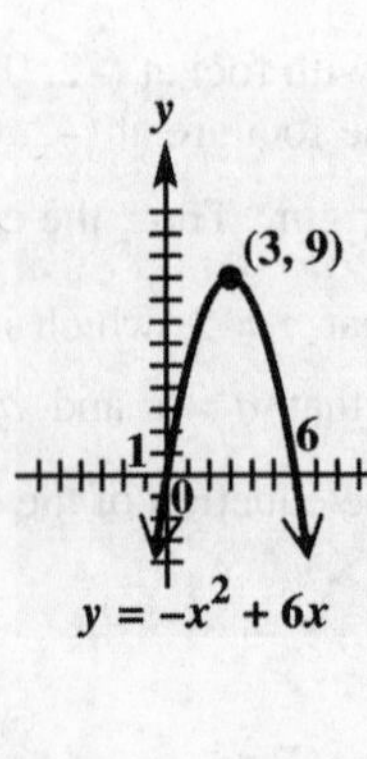

$y=-x^2+6x$

2. $x = 4y^2 + 8y$

Completing the square on y, we have the following.

$$x=4y^2+8y \Rightarrow x=4\left(y^2+2y+1-1\right) \Rightarrow x=4(y+1)^2-4 \Rightarrow x-(-4)=4\left[y-(-1)\right]^2$$

The equation has the form $y-k=a(x-h)^2$. The vertex, (h,k), is $(-4,-1)$. Since the y-term is squared, the axis is the horizontal line $y=k$, or $y=-1$. The domain is $[-4,\infty)$. The range is $(-\infty,\infty)$. Using this information and plot a few additional points.

x	y
12	1
0	0
−4	−1
0	−2
12	−3

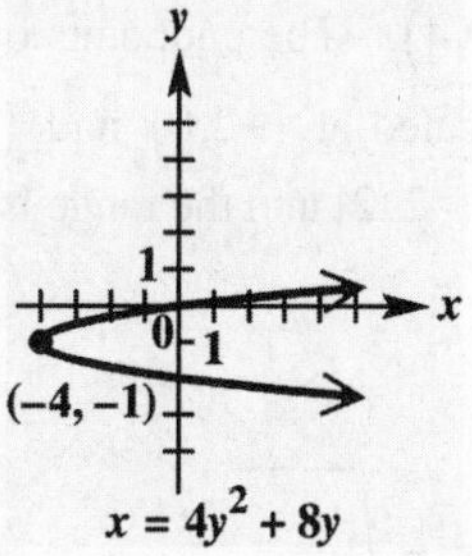

3. Since $x=8y^2 \Rightarrow y^2=\frac{1}{8}x$, the parabola is of the form $y^2=4px$. Thus, we have $4p=\frac{1}{8} \Rightarrow p=\frac{1}{32}$. Since the y-term is squared, the parabola is horizontal, with focus $(p,0)=\left(\frac{1}{32},0\right)$ and directrix, $x=-p$, is $x=-\frac{1}{32}$.

4. Parabola; vertex at $(2,3)$, passing through $(-18,1)$, opening to the left

Since the parabola opens to the left, it is of the form $(y-k)^2=4p(x-h)$. Since the vertex is located at $(2,3)$, we have $(y-3)^2=4p(x-2)$. We can now substitute $x = -18$ and $y = 1$, and solve for p.

$$(1-3)^2=4p(-18-2) \Rightarrow (-2)^2=4p(-20) \Rightarrow 4=-80p \Rightarrow p=-\tfrac{1}{20}$$

Thus, the equation is $(y-3)^2=4\left(-\frac{1}{20}\right)(x-2) \Rightarrow (y-3)^2=-\frac{1}{5}(x-2)$ or alternatively written as $x-2=-5(y-3)^2$.

We could have also stated that since the parabola opens to the left, it is of the form $x-h=a(y-k)^2$. With $(h,k)=(2,3)$, we have $x-2=a(y-3)^2$. Substituting $x = -18$ and $y = 1$, we have the following.

$$-18-2=a(1-3)^2 \Rightarrow -20=a(-2)^2 \Rightarrow -20=4a \Rightarrow a=5$$

Thus, $x-2=-5(y-3)^2$.

5. Answers will vary.

6. $\dfrac{(x-8)^2}{100}+\dfrac{(y-5)^2}{49}=1 \Rightarrow \dfrac{(x-8)^2}{10^2}+\dfrac{(y-5)^2}{7^2}=1$

The graph is an ellipse centered at $(8,5)$. We also have the vertices located at $(8-10,5)=(-2,5)$ and $(8+10,5)=(18,5)$. The endpoints of the minor axis are located at $(8,5-7)=(8,-2)$ and $(8,5+7)=(8,12)$. The domain is [−2, 18] and the range is [−2, 12].

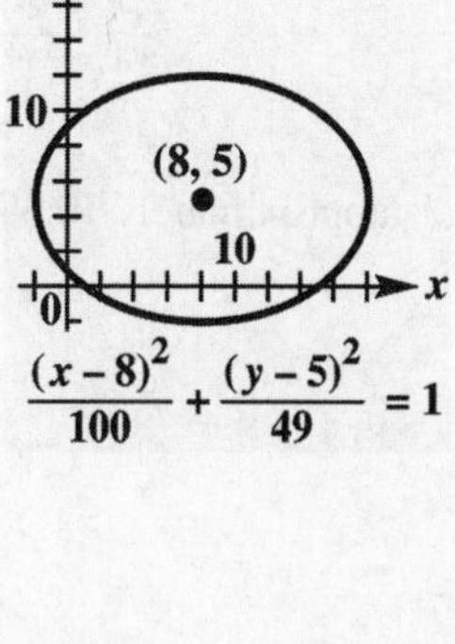

7. $16x^2+4y^2=64 \Rightarrow \frac{x^2}{4}+\frac{y^2}{16}=1 \Rightarrow \frac{x^2}{2^2}+\frac{y^2}{4^2}=1$

The graph is an ellipse centered at the origin The vertices are located at $(0,-4)$ and $(0,4)$. The endpoints of the minor axis are located at $(-2,0)$ and $(2,0)$. The domain is [–2, 2] and the range is [–4, 4].

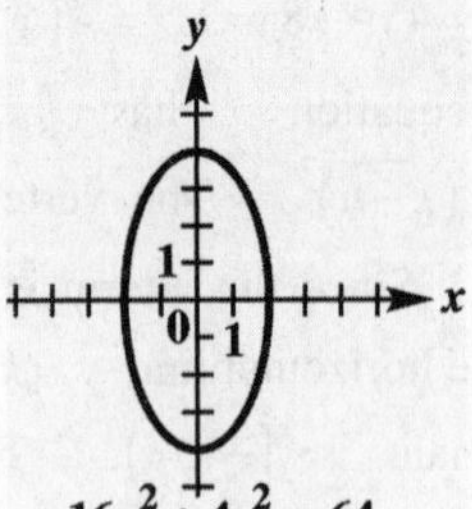

8. $y=-\sqrt{1-\frac{x^2}{36}}$

Square both sides to get $y=-\sqrt{1-\frac{x^2}{36}} \Rightarrow y^2=1-\frac{x^2}{36} \Rightarrow \frac{x^2}{36}+y^2=1 \Rightarrow \frac{x^2}{6^2}+\frac{y^2}{1^2}=1$. This is the equation of an ellipse with vertices (–6, 0) and (6, 0). The endpoints of the minor axis are at (0, –1) and (0, 1). The graph of the original equation is the bottom half of the ellipse. The vertical line test shows that this relation is a function.

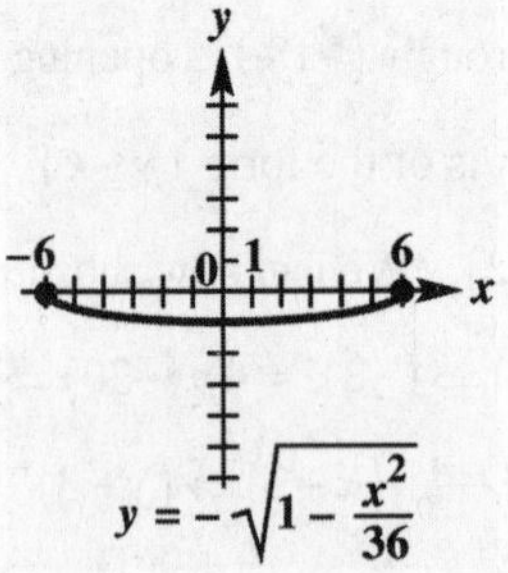

9. Ellipse; centered at the origin, horizontal major axis with length 6, minor axis with length 4
Since the ellipse is centered at the origin and major axis is horizontal, the ellipse has the form $\frac{x^2}{a^2}+\frac{y^2}{b^2}=1$. Since the major axis has length 6, we have $2a=6 \Rightarrow a=3 \Rightarrow a^2=9$. Since the minor axis has length 4, we have $2b=4 \Rightarrow b=2 \Rightarrow b^2=4$. Thus, the equation of the ellipse is $\frac{x^2}{9}+\frac{y^2}{4}=1$.

10. Place the half-ellipse that represents the overpass on a coordinate system with the center of the bottom of the overpass at the origin. If the complete ellipse were drawn, the center of the ellipse would be $(0,0)$. Then the half-ellipse will include the points $(0,12),(-20,0)$, and $(20,0)$. The equation is of the form $\frac{x^2}{a^2}+\frac{y^2}{b^2}=1$. Thus, for the complete ellipse, we have $a=20$ and $b=12$. Thus, we have $\frac{x^2}{20^2}+\frac{y^2}{12^2}=1 \Rightarrow \frac{x^2}{400}+\frac{y^2}{144}=1$.
At a distance of 10 ft from the center of the bottom, $x = 10$. Find the positive y-coordinate of the point on the ellipse with x-coordinate 10.

$$\frac{x^2}{400}+\frac{y^2}{144}=1 \Rightarrow \frac{10^2}{400}+\frac{y^2}{144}=1 \Rightarrow \frac{100}{400}+\frac{y^2}{144}=1 \Rightarrow \frac{1}{4}+\frac{y^2}{144}=1$$

$$\frac{y^2}{144}=\frac{3}{4} \Rightarrow y^2=108 \Rightarrow y=\sqrt{108}\approx 10.39$$

The arch is approximately 10.39 ft high 10 ft from the center of the bottom.

11. $\frac{x^2}{4}-\frac{y^2}{4}=1 \Rightarrow \frac{x^2}{2^2}-\frac{y^2}{2^2}=1$

The graph of the hyperbola is centered at the origin. Since the x^2 - term comes first, the branches open to the right and left, with vertices (–2, 0) and (2, 0). The domain is $(-\infty,-2]\cup[2,\infty)$. The range is $(-\infty, \infty)$. The asymptotes are the lines $y=\pm\frac{2}{2}x=\pm x$.

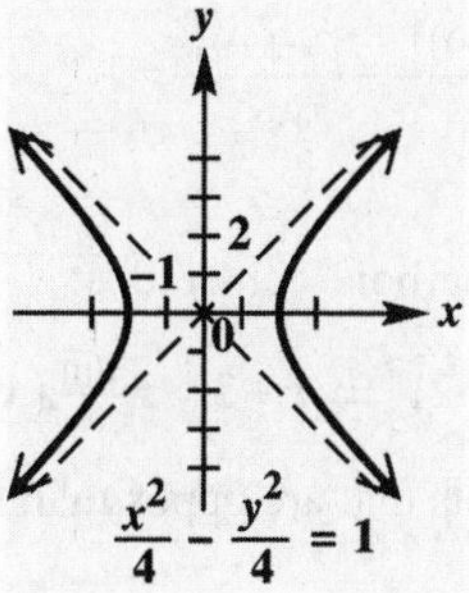

12. $9x^2-4y^2=36 \Rightarrow \frac{x^2}{4}-\frac{y^2}{9}=1 \Rightarrow \frac{x^2}{2^2}-\frac{y^2}{3^2}=1$

The graph of the hyperbola is centered at the origin. Since the x^2 - term comes first, the branches open to the right and left, with vertices (–2, 0) and (2, 0). The domain is $(-\infty,-2]\cup[2,\infty)$. The range is $(-\infty, \infty)$. The asymptotes are the lines $y=\pm\frac{3}{2}x$.

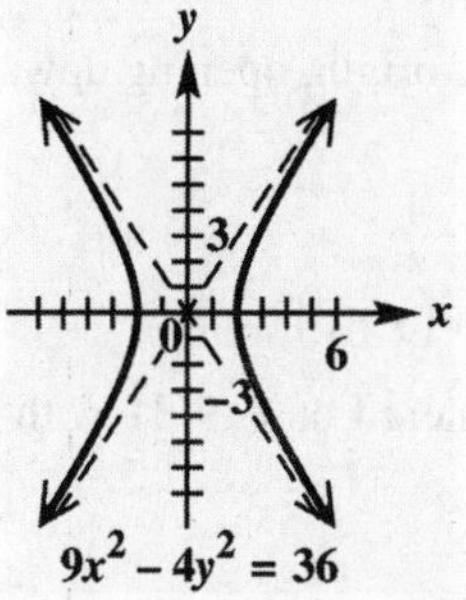

13. Hyperbola; y-intercepts ± 5, foci at (0, –6) and (0, 6)

Since the center is halfway between the foci, the center is $(0,0)$. Since the foci are on a vertical transverse axis, the equation has the form $\frac{y^2}{a^2}-\frac{x^2}{b^2}=1$. The y-intercepts are also vertices, so $a = 5$, and thus $a^2=25$. With the given foci, we have $c = 6$. So given $c^2=a^2+b^2$, we have the following.

$$c^2=a^2+b^2 \Rightarrow 6^2=5^2+b^2 \Rightarrow 36=25+b^2 \Rightarrow b^2=11$$

Thus, the equation of the hyperbola is $\frac{y^2}{25}-\frac{x^2}{11}=1$.

14. $x^2+8x+y^2-4y+2=0 \Rightarrow \left(x^2+8x+16-16\right)+\left(y^2-4y+4-4\right)=-2$

$$\Rightarrow (x+4)^2-16+(y-2)^2-4=-2 \Rightarrow (x+4)^2+(y-2)^2=-2+16+4$$

$$\Rightarrow (x+4)^2+(y-2)^2=18 \Rightarrow [x-(-4)]^2+(y-2)^2=\left(\sqrt{18}\right)^2$$

The graph of this equation is a circle with center $(-4,2)$ and radius $\sqrt{18}$. Also note in our original equation, the x^2 - and y^2 - terms have the same positive coefficient.

15. $5x^2+10x-2y^2-12y-23=0 \Rightarrow 5\left(x^2+2x+1-1\right)-2\left(y^2+6y+9-9\right)=23$

$$\Rightarrow 5(x+1)^2-5-2(y+3)^2+18=23$$
$$\Rightarrow 5(x+1)^2-2(y+3)^2=23+5-18$$
$$\Rightarrow 5(x+1)^2-2(y+3)^2=10 \Rightarrow \frac{(x+1)^2}{2}-\frac{(y+3)^2}{5}=1$$
$$\Rightarrow \frac{\left[x-(-1)\right]^2}{\left(\sqrt{2}\right)^2}-\frac{\left[y-(-3)\right]^2}{\left(\sqrt{5}\right)^2}=1$$

The graph of this equation is a hyperbola centered at $(-1,-3)$ and vertices $\left(-1\pm\sqrt{2},-3\right)$. The asymptotes are $y-(-3)=\pm\frac{\sqrt{5}}{\sqrt{2}}\left[x-(-2)\right] \Rightarrow y+3=\pm\frac{\sqrt{10}}{2}(x+2)$. Also note in our original equation, the x^2 - and y^2 - terms have coefficients that are opposite in sign.

16. $3x^2+10y^2-30=0 \Rightarrow 3x^2+10y^2=30 \Rightarrow \frac{x^2}{10}+\frac{y^2}{3}=1 \Rightarrow \frac{(x-0)^2}{\left(\sqrt{10}\right)^2}+\frac{(y-0)^2}{\left(\sqrt{3}\right)^2}=1$

The graph of this equation is an ellipse centered at the origin and x-intercepts (vertices) of $\pm\sqrt{10}$, and y-intercepts (endpoints of minor axis) of $\pm\sqrt{3}$. Also note in our original equation, the x^2 - and y^2 - terms both have different positive coefficients.

17. $x^2-4y=0 \Rightarrow 4y=x^2 \Rightarrow y=\frac{1}{4}x^2$

This is a parabola with its vertex at the origin, opening upward. Also, note our original equation has an x^2 - term, but no y^2 - term.

18. $(x+9)^2+(y-3)^2=0 \Rightarrow \left[x-(-9)\right]^2+(y-3)^2=0$

This is the equation of a "circle" centered at $(-9,3)$ with radius 0. The graph of this equation is a point.

19. $x^2+4x+y^2-6y+30=0 \Rightarrow \left(x^2+4x+4-4\right)+\left(y^2-6y+9-9\right)=-30$

$$\Rightarrow \left(x^2+4x+4\right)-4+\left(y^2-6y+9\right)-9=-30$$
$$\Rightarrow (x+2)^2+(y-3)^2=-30+4+9 \Rightarrow \left[x-(-2)\right]^2+(y-3)^2=-17$$

This equation has the form of the equation of a circle. However, since r^2 cannot be negative, there is no graph of this equation.

20. Solve the equation $\frac{x^2}{25}-\frac{y^2}{49}=1$ for y.

$$\frac{x^2}{25}-\frac{y^2}{49}=1 \Rightarrow -\frac{y^2}{49}=1-\frac{x^2}{25} \Rightarrow \frac{y^2}{49}=\frac{x^2}{25}-1 \Rightarrow y^2=49\left(\frac{x^2}{25}-1\right)$$
$$y=\pm\sqrt{49\left(\frac{x^2}{25}-1\right)} \Rightarrow y=\pm 7\sqrt{\frac{x^2}{25}-1}$$

Thus, the functions $Y_1=7\sqrt{\frac{x^2}{25}-1}$ and $Y_2=-7\sqrt{\frac{x^2}{25}-1}$ were used to obtain the graph.

Chapter 11

FURTHER TOPICS IN ALGEBRA

Section 11.1: Sequences and Series

Connections (page 938)

1. After the first two terms, each of which is 1, the terms of the sequence are found by adding the two preceding terms. Thus, the third term is $1+1=2$, the fourth is $1+2=3$, and so on.

2. (Assume the original male honeybee is in generation 1.)

   $a_1=1$

   $a_2=1$

   $a_n=a_{n-1}+a_{n-2}$, if $n\ge 3$

Exercises

1. $a_n = 4n + 10$
   Replace n with 1, 2, 3, 4, and 5.
   $n = 1$: $a_1 = 4(1) + 10 = 14$
   $n = 2$: $a_2 = 4(2) + 10 = 18$
   $n = 3$: $a_3 = 4(3) + 10 = 22$
   $n = 4$: $a_4 = 4(4) + 10 = 26$
   $n = 5$: $a_5 = 4(5) + 10 = 30$
   The first five terms are 14, 18, 22, 26, and 30.

3. $a_n=2^{n-1}$
   Replace n with 1, 2, 3, 4, and 5.
   $n = 1$: $a_1=2^{1-1}=2^0=1$
   $n = 2$: $a_2=2^{2-1}=2^1=2$
   $n = 3$: $a_3=2^{3-1}=2^2=4$
   $n = 4$: $a_4=2^{4-1}=2^3=8$
   $n = 5$: $a_5=2^{5-1}=2^4=16$
   The first five terms are 1, 2, 4, 8, and 16.

5. $a_n=\left(\frac{1}{3}\right)^n(n-1)$
   Replace n with 1, 2, 3, 4, and 5.
   $n = 1$: $a_1=\left(\frac{1}{3}\right)^1(1-1)=\left(\frac{1}{3}\right)(0)=0$
   $n = 2$: $a_2=\left(\frac{1}{3}\right)^2(2-1)=\left(\frac{1}{9}\right)(1)=\frac{1}{9}$
   $n = 3$: $a_3=\left(\frac{1}{3}\right)^3(3-1)=\left(\frac{1}{27}\right)(2)=\frac{2}{27}$
   $n = 4$: $a_4=\left(\frac{1}{3}\right)^4(4-1)=\left(\frac{1}{81}\right)(3)=\frac{1}{27}$
   $n = 5$: $a_5=\left(\frac{1}{3}\right)^5(5-1)=\left(\frac{1}{243}\right)(4)=\frac{4}{243}$
   The first five terms are 0, $\frac{1}{9}, \frac{2}{27}, \frac{1}{27}$, and $\frac{4}{243}$.

7. $a_n=(-1)^n(2n)$
   Replace n with 1, 2, 3, 4, and 5.
   $n = 1$: $a_1=(-1)^1[2(1)]=-1(2)=-2$
   $n = 2$: $a_2=(-1)^2[2(2)]=1(4)=4$
   $n = 3$: $a_3=(-1)^3[2(3)]=-1(6)=-6$
   $n = 4$: $a_4=(-1)^4[2(4)]=1(8)=8$
   $n = 5$: $a_5=(-1)^5[2(5)]=-1(10)=-10$
   The first five terms are -2, 4, -6, 8, and -10.

9. $a_n=\dfrac{4n-1}{n^2+2}$
   Replace n with 1, 2, 3, 4, and 5.
   $n = 1$: $a_1=\dfrac{4(1)-1}{(1)^2+2}=\dfrac{4-1}{1+2}=\dfrac{3}{3}=1$
   $n = 2$: $a_2=\dfrac{4(2)-1}{(2)^2+2}=\dfrac{8-1}{4+2}=\dfrac{7}{6}$
   $n = 3$: $a_3=\dfrac{4(3)-1}{(3)^2+2}=\dfrac{12-1}{9+2}=\dfrac{11}{11}=1$
   $n = 4$: $a_4=\dfrac{4(4)-1}{(4)^2+2}=\dfrac{16-1}{16+2}=\dfrac{15}{18}=\dfrac{5}{6}$
   $n = 5$: $a_5=\dfrac{4(5)-1}{(5)^2+2}=\dfrac{20-1}{25+2}=\dfrac{19}{27}$
   The first five terms are 1, $\frac{7}{6}$, 1, $\frac{5}{6}$, and $\frac{19}{27}$.

11. Answers will vary.

13. The sequence of the days of the week has as its domain {1, 2, 3, 4, 5, 6, 7}. Therefore, it is a finite sequence.

15. The sequence 1, 2, 3, 4 has as its domain {1, 2, 3, 4}. Therefore, it is a finite sequence.

17. The sequence 1, 2, 3, 4, ...has as its domain {1, 2, 3, 4, ...}. Therefore, the sequence is infinite.

19. The sequence $a_1 = 3$ and for $2 \le n \le 10$, $a_n = 3 \cdot a_{n-1}$ has as its domain {1, 2, 3, ..., 10}. Therefore, the sequence is finite.

21. $a_1 = -2,\ a_n = a_{n-1} + 3,$ for $n > 1$

This is an example of a recursive definition. We know $a_1 = -2$. Since $a_n = a_{n-1} + 3$,

$n = 2: a_2 = a_1 + 3 = -2 + 3 = 1$

$n = 3: a_3 = a_2 + 3 = 1 + 3 = 4$

$n = 4: a_4 = a_3 + 3 = 4 + 3 = 7.$

The first four terms are –2, 1, 4, and 7.

23. $a_1 = 1,\ a_2 = 1,\ a_n = a_{n-1} + a_{n-2},$ for $n \ge 3$

$n = 3: a_3 = a_2 + a_1 = 1 + 1 = 2$

$n = 4: a_4 = a_3 + a_2 = 2 + 1 = 3$

The first four terms are 1, 1, 2, and 3.

25. $a_1 = 2,\ a_n = n \cdot a_{n-1},$ for $n > 1$

$a_2 = 2 \cdot a_1 = 2 \cdot 2 = 4$

$a_3 = 3 \cdot a_2 = 3 \cdot 4 = 12$

$a_4 = 4 \cdot a_3 = 4 \cdot 12 = 48$

The first four terms are 2, 4, 12, and 48.

27. $$\sum_{i=1}^{5}(2i+1) = [2(1)+1]+[2(2)+1]+[2(3)+1]+[2(4)+1]+[2(5)+1]$$
$$= (2+1)+(4+1)+(6+1)+(8+1)+(10+1) = 3+5+7+9+11 = 35$$

29. $$\sum_{j=1}^{4}\frac{1}{j} = \frac{1}{1}+\frac{1}{2}+\frac{1}{3}+\frac{1}{4} = \frac{12}{12}+\frac{6}{12}+\frac{4}{12}+\frac{3}{12} = \frac{25}{12}$$

31. $$\sum_{i=1}^{4} i^i = 1^1 + 2^2 + 3^3 + 4^4 = 1 + 4 + 27 + 256 = 288$$

33. $$\sum_{k=1}^{6}(-1)^k \cdot k = (-1)^1 \cdot 1 + (-1)^2 \cdot 2 + (-1)^3 \cdot 3 + (-1)^4 \cdot 4 + (-1)^5 \cdot 5 + (-1)^6 \cdot 6$$
$$= -1 \cdot 1 + 1 \cdot 2 + (-1) \cdot 3 + 1 \cdot 4 + (-1) \cdot 5 + 1 \cdot 6 = -1 + 2 - 3 + 4 - 5 + 6 = 3$$

35. $$\sum_{i=2}^{5}(6-3i) = [6-3(2)]+[6-3(3)]+[6-3(4)]+[6-3(5)]$$
$$= (6-6)+(6-9)+(6-12)+(6-15) = 0+(-3)+(-6)+(-9) = -18$$

37. $$\sum_{i=-2}^{3} 2(3)^i = 2(3)^{-2} + 2(3)^{-1} + 2(3)^0 + 2(3)^1 + 2(3)^2 + 2(3)^3$$
$$= 2\left(\tfrac{1}{9}\right) + 2\left(\tfrac{1}{3}\right) + 2(1) + 2(3) + 2(9) + 2(27) = \tfrac{2}{9} + \tfrac{2}{3} + 2 + 6 + 18 + 54 = \tfrac{2}{9} + \tfrac{6}{9} + 80 = 80\tfrac{8}{9} = \tfrac{728}{9}$$

39. $\sum_{i=-1}^{5}\left(i^2-2i\right)=\left[(-1)^2-2(-1)\right]+\left[0^2-2(0)\right]+\left[1^2-2(1)\right]+\left[2^2-2(2)\right]+\left[3^2-2(3)\right]$

$$+\left[4^2-2(4)\right]+\left[5^2-2(5)\right]$$

$$=\left[1-(-2)\right]+(0-0)+(1-2)+(4-4)+(9-6)+(16-8)+(25-10)$$

$$=3+0+(-1)+0+3+8+15=28$$

41. $\sum_{i=1}^{5}\left(3^i-4\right)=\left(3^1-4\right)+\left(3^2-4\right)+\left(3^3-4\right)+\left(3^4-4\right)+\left(3^5-4\right)$

$$=(3-4)+(9-4)+(27-4)+(81-4)+(243-4)=(-1)+5+23+77+239=343$$

43. $\sum_{i=1}^{10}(4i^2-5)=1490$

To find the seq(feature, go to the LIST menu (2nd STAT) go to OPS and choose option 5.

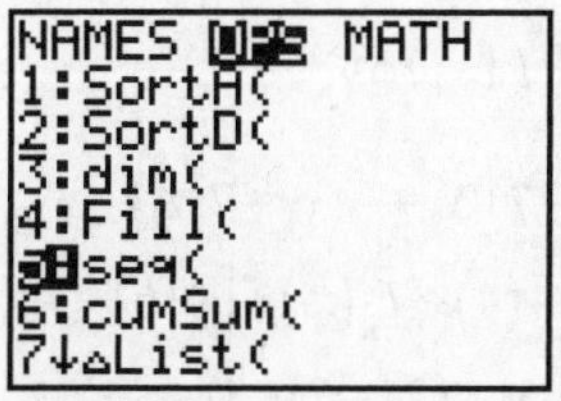

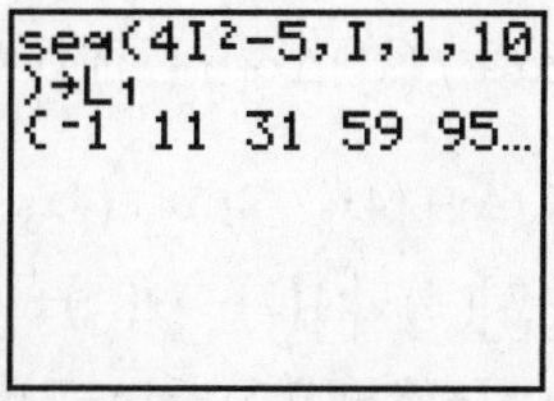

To find the sum(feature, go to the LIST menu (2nd STAT) go to MATH and choose option 5.

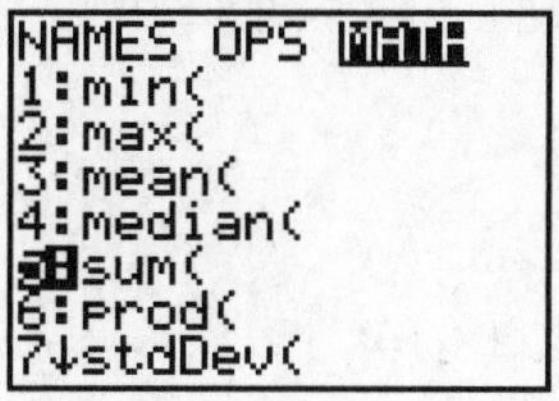

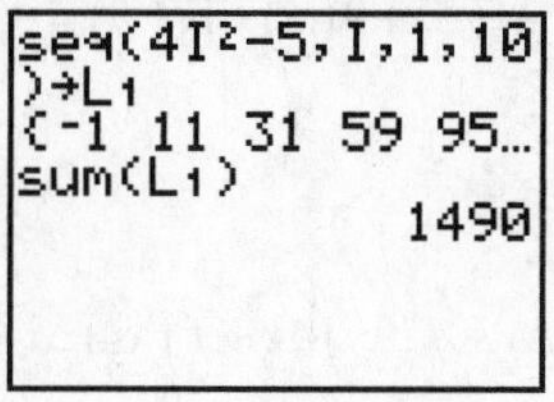

45. $\sum_{j=3}^{9}(3j-j^2)=-154$

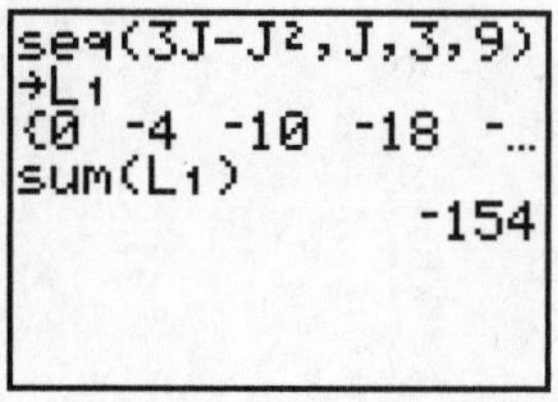

In Exercises 47 – 53, $x_1=-2,\ x_2=-1,\ x_3=0,\ x_4=1,$ and $x_5=2$.

47. $\sum_{i=1}^{5}x_i=x_1+x_2+x_3+x_4+x_5=-2+(-1)+0+1+2=0$

49. $\sum_{i=1}^{5}(2x_i+3)=(2x_1+3)+(2x_2+3)+(2x_3+3)+(2x_4+3)+(2x_5+3)$

$$=\left[2(-2)+3\right]+\left[2(-1)+3\right]+\left[2(0)+3\right]+\left[2(1)+3\right]+\left[2(2)+3\right]$$

$$=(-4+3)+(-2+3)+(0+3)+(2+3)+(4+3)=-1+1+3+5+7=15$$

51. $\sum_{i=1}^{3}(3x_i - x_i^2) = (3x_1 - x_1^2) + (3x_2 - x_2^2) + (3x_3 - x_3^2)$

$= [3(-2) - (-2)^2] + [3(-1) - (-1)^2] + [3(0) - 0^2]$

$= (-6-4) + (-3-1) + (0-0) = -10 + (-4) + 0 = -14$

53. $\sum_{i=2}^{5}\frac{x_i+1}{x_i+2} = \frac{x_2+1}{x_2+2} + \frac{x_3+1}{x_3+2} + \frac{x_4+1}{x_4+2} + \frac{x_5+1}{x_5+2} = \frac{-1+1}{-1+2} + \frac{0+1}{0+2} + \frac{1+1}{1+2} + \frac{2+1}{2+2}$

$= \frac{0}{1} + \frac{1}{2} + \frac{2}{3} + \frac{3}{4} = 0 + \frac{6}{12} + \frac{8}{12} + \frac{9}{12} = \frac{23}{12}$

In Exercises 55 – 59, $x_1 = 0,\ x_2 = 2,\ x_3 = 4,\ x_4 = 6,$ and $\Delta x = .5.$

55. $f(x) = 4x - 7 \Rightarrow f(x_i) = 4x_i - 7$

$\sum_{i=1}^{4} f(x_i)\Delta x = f(x_1)\Delta x + f(x_2)\Delta x + f(x_3)\Delta x + f(x_4)\Delta x$

$= (4x_1 - 7)\Delta x + (4x_2 - 7)\Delta x + (4x_3 - 7)\Delta x + (4x_4 - 7)\Delta x$

$= [4(0) - 7](.5) + [4(2) - 7](.5) + [4(4) - 7](.5) + [4(6) - 7](.5)$

$= (0-7)(.5) + (8-7)(.5) + (16-7)(.5) + (24-7)(.5)$

$= -7(.5) + 1(.5) + 9(.5) + 17(.5) = -3.5 + .5 + 4.5 + 8.5 = 10$

57. $f(x) = 2x^2 \Rightarrow f(x_i) = 2x_i^2$

$\sum_{i=1}^{4} f(x_i)\Delta x = f(x_1)\Delta x + f(x_2)\Delta x + f(x_3)\Delta x + f(x_4)\Delta x$

$= 2(x_1^2)\Delta x + 2(x_2^2)\Delta x + 2(x_3^2)\Delta x + 2(x_4^2)\Delta x$

$= 2(0^2)(.5) + 2(2^2)(.5) + 2(4^2)(.5) + 2(6^2)(.5)$

$= 2(0)(.5) + 2(4)(.5) + 2(16)(.5) + 2(36)(.5) = 0 + 4 + 16 + 36 = 56$

59. $f(x) = \frac{-2}{x+1} \Rightarrow f(x_i) = \frac{-2}{x_i+1}$

$\sum_{i=1}^{4} f(x_i)\Delta x = f(x_1)\Delta x + f(x_2)\Delta x + f(x_3)\Delta x + f(x_4)\Delta x$

$= \left(\frac{-2}{x_1+1}\right)(.5) + \left(\frac{-2}{x_2+1}\right)(.5) + \left(\frac{-2}{x_3+1}\right)(.5) + \left(\frac{-2}{x_4+1}\right)(.5)$

$= \left(\frac{-2}{0+1}\right)(.5) + \left(\frac{-2}{2+1}\right)(.5) + \left(\frac{-2}{4+1}\right)(.5) + \left(\frac{-2}{6+1}\right)(.5)$

$= \left(\frac{-2}{1}\right)(.5) + \left(-\frac{2}{3}\right)(.5) + \left(-\frac{2}{5}\right)(.5) + \left(-\frac{2}{7}\right)(.5)$

$= -1 + \left(-\frac{1}{3}\right) + \left(-\frac{1}{5}\right) + \left(-\frac{1}{7}\right) = \frac{-105}{105} + \left(\frac{-35}{105}\right) + \left(\frac{-21}{105}\right) + \left(\frac{-15}{105}\right) = -\frac{-176}{105}$

61. $\sum_{i=1}^{100} 6 = 100(6) = 600$

63. $\sum_{i=1}^{15} i^2 = \frac{15(15+1)[2(15)+1]}{6} = \frac{15(16)(30+1)}{6} = \frac{15(16)(31)}{6} = \frac{7440}{6} = 1240$

65. $\sum_{i=1}^{5} (5i+3) = \sum_{i=1}^{5} 5i + \sum_{i=1}^{5} 3 = 5\sum_{i=1}^{5} i + 5(3)$

$$= 5\cdot\frac{5(5+1)}{2} + 15 = 5\cdot\frac{5(6)}{2} + 15 = 5\cdot\frac{30}{2} + 15 = 5(15) + 15 = 75 + 15 = 90$$

67. $\sum_{i=1}^{5} \left(4i^2 - 2i + 6\right) = \sum_{i=1}^{5} 4i^2 - \sum_{i=1}^{5} 2i + \sum_{i=1}^{5} 6 = 4\sum_{i=1}^{5} i^2 - 2\sum_{i=1}^{5} i + 5(6)$

$$= 4\cdot\frac{5(5+1)(10+1)}{6} - 2\cdot\frac{5(5+1)}{2} + 30 = 4\cdot\frac{5(6)(11)}{6} - 2\cdot\frac{5(6)}{2} + 30$$

$$= 4\cdot[5(11)] - 2\cdot[5(3)] + 30 = 220 - 30 + 30 = 220$$

69. $\sum_{i=1}^{4} \left(3i^3 + 2i - 4\right) = \sum_{i=1}^{4} 3i^3 + \sum_{i=1}^{4} 2i - \sum_{i=1}^{4} 4 = 3\sum_{i=1}^{4} i^3 + 2\sum_{i=1}^{4} i - 4(4) = 3\cdot\frac{4^2(4+1)^2}{4} + 2\cdot\frac{4(4+1)}{2} - 16$

$$= 3\cdot\frac{16(5)^2}{4} + 2\cdot\frac{4(5)}{2} - 16 = 3\cdot[4(25)] + 2\cdot[2(5)] - 16 = 300 + 20 - 16 = 304$$

In Exercises 71 – 74, there are other acceptable forms of the answers.

71. $\frac{1}{3(1)} + \frac{1}{3(2)} + \frac{1}{3(3)} + \ldots + \frac{1}{3(9)} = \sum_{i=1}^{9} \frac{1}{3i}$

73. $1 - \frac{1}{2} + \frac{1}{4} - \frac{1}{8} + \ldots - \frac{1}{128} = \frac{1}{2^0} - \frac{1}{2^1} + \frac{1}{2^2} - \frac{1}{2^3} + \ldots - \frac{1}{2^7} = \left(\frac{1}{2}\right)^0 - \left(\frac{1}{2}\right)^1 + \left(\frac{1}{2}\right)^2 - \left(\frac{1}{2}\right)^3 + \ldots - \left(\frac{1}{2}\right)^7$

$$= \left(\frac{1}{2}\right)^{1-1} - \left(\frac{1}{2}\right)^{2-1} + \left(\frac{1}{2}\right)^{3-1} - \left(\frac{1}{2}\right)^{4-1} + \ldots - \left(\frac{1}{2}\right)^{8-1}$$

$$= \left(-\frac{1}{2}\right)^{1-1} + \left(-\frac{1}{2}\right)^{2-1} + \left(-\frac{1}{2}\right)^{3-1} + \left(-\frac{1}{2}\right)^{4-1} + \ldots + \left(-\frac{1}{2}\right)^{8-1} = \sum_{k=1}^{8} \left(-\frac{1}{2}\right)^{k-1}$$

For Exercises 75 – 79, enter the set $\{1, 2, 3, \ldots, 10\}$ into L_1. Turn the STAT PLOTS on and clear any functions you have in the $Y=$ screen.

75. $a_n = \dfrac{n+4}{2n}$

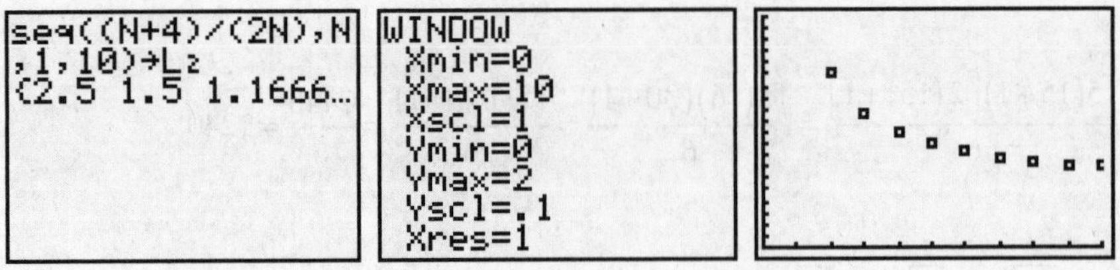

It appears that the sequence converges to $\frac{1}{2}$. The line $y = \frac{1}{2}$ is graphed in the same screen as the plot.

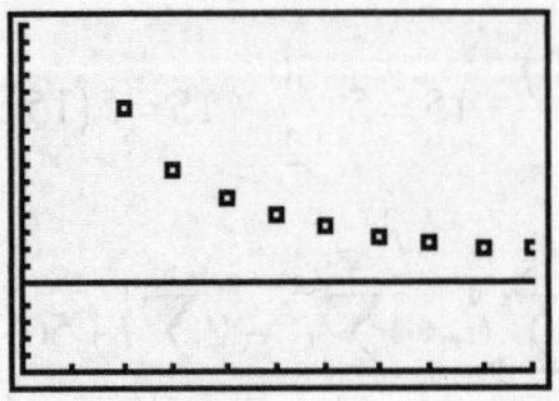

77. $a_n = 2e^n$

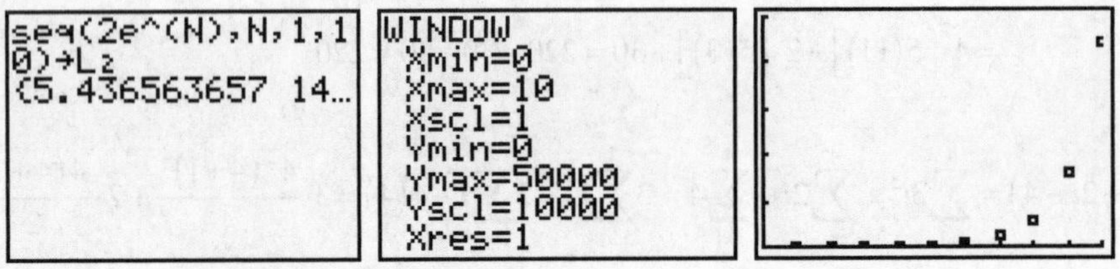

It appears that the sequence diverges.

79. $a_n = \left(1+\dfrac{1}{n}\right)^n$

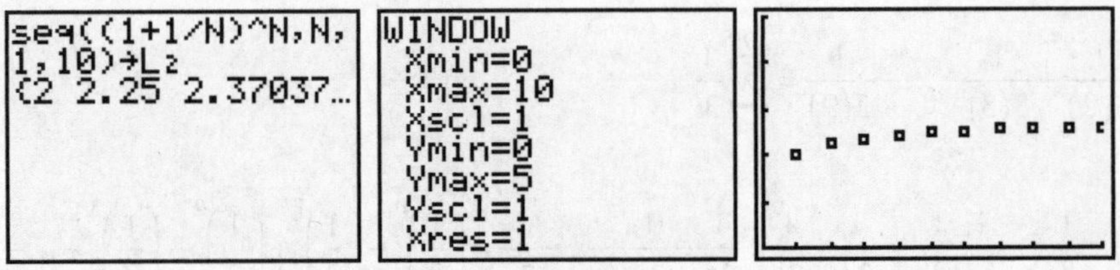

It appears that the sequence converges to $e \approx 2.71828$ The line $y = e$ is graphed in the same screen as the plot.

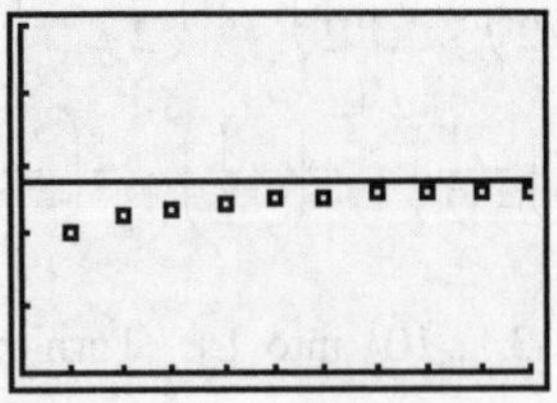

81. (a) $a_1 = 8;\ a_n = 2.9a_{n-1} - .2a_{n-1}^{\ 2}$, for $n > 1$

$a_1 = 8$

$a_2 = 2.9a_1 - .2a_1^{\ 2} = 2.9(8) - .2(8)^2 = 23.2 - 12.8 = 10.4$

$a_3 = 2.9a_2 - .2a_2^{\ 2} = 2.9(10.4) - .2(10.4)^2 = 30.16 - 21.632 = 8.528$

(b) One way to enter the required data into a list is to first enter the set $\{1, 2, 3, \ldots, 20\}$ into L_1. Turn the STAT PLOTS on and clear any functions you have in the Y = screen.

Next, to enter the data from the recursive sequence, we can enter the values in individually as follows.

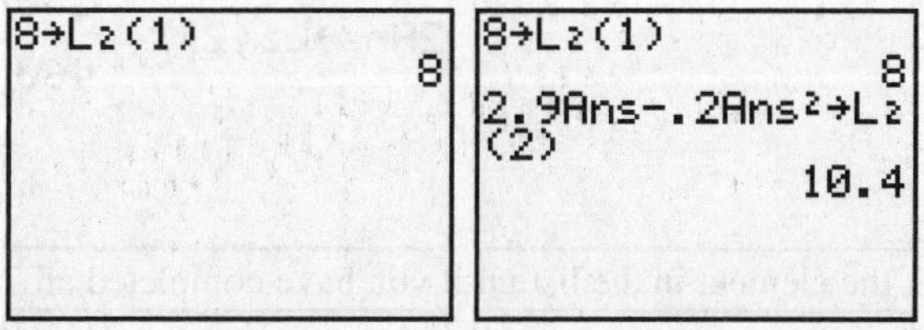

Hit enter, then edit the element in the list until you have completed all 20 elements.

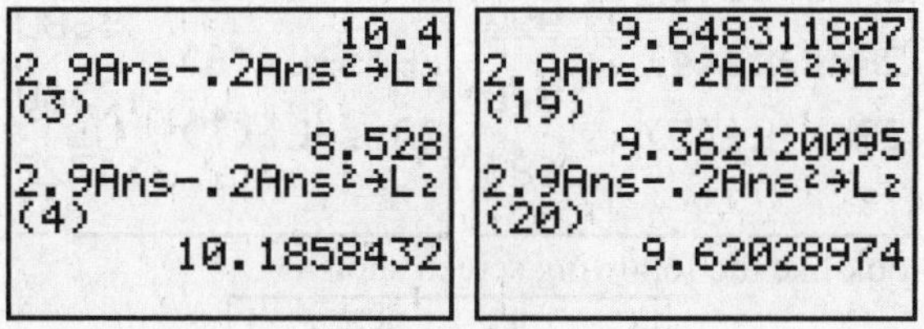

Your lists should look like the following screen shots.

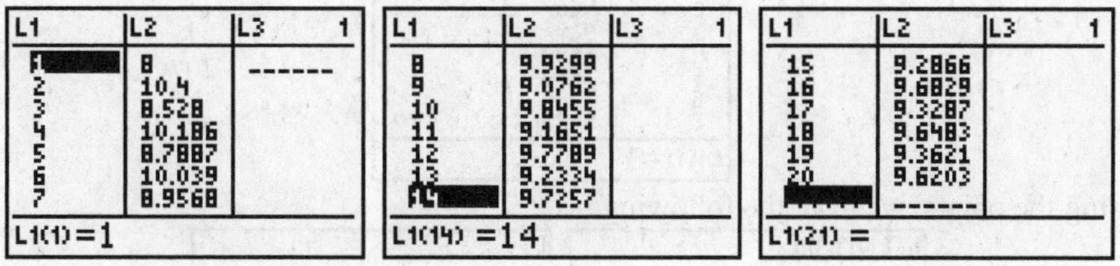

Plotting the points we have the following.

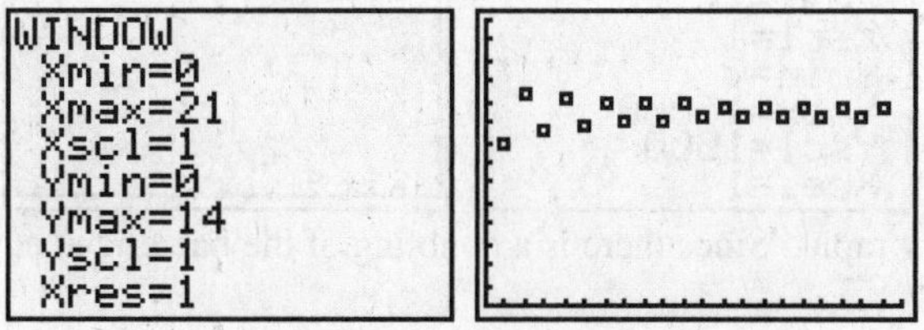

The population density oscillates above and below 9.5 thousand per acre (approximately). The line $y = 9.5$ is graphed in the same screen as the plot.

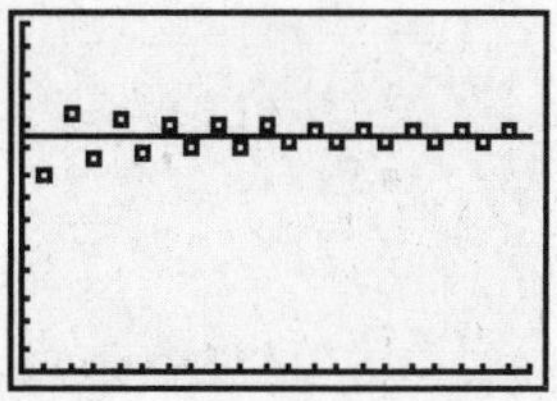

83. **(a)** Since the number of bacteria doubles every 40 minutes, it follows that $N_{j+1} = 2N_j$ for $j \geq 1$.

(b) Two hours is 120 minutes. If $120 = 40(j-1)$, then $3 = j-1 \Rightarrow j = 4$.

Since $N_1 = 230$, $N_2 = 460$, $N_3 = 920$, and $N_4 = 1840$, there will be 1840 bacteria after two hours.

(c) We must graph the sequence $N_{j+1} = 2N_j$ for $j = 1, 2, 3, \ldots, 7$ if $N_1 = 230$. You should clear lists that you may have used in previous exercises and enter the set $\{1, 2, 3, \ldots, 7\}$ into L_1.

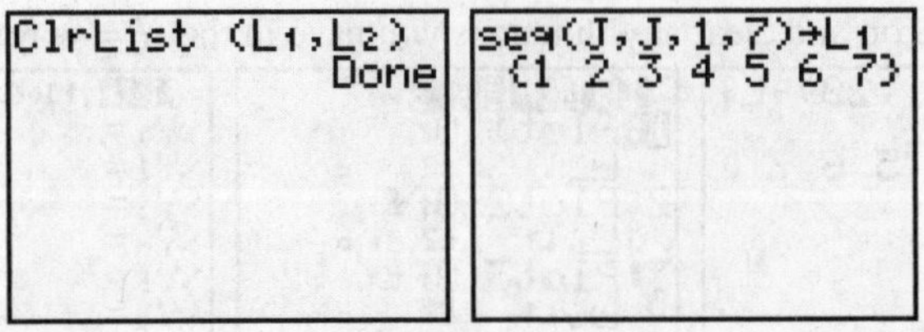

Next, to enter the data from the recursive sequence, we can enter the values in individually as follows.

Hit enter, then edit the element in the list until you have completed all 7 elements.

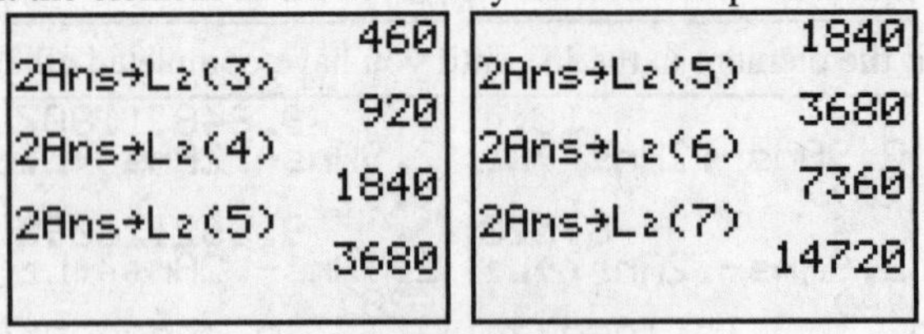

Your lists should look like the following screen shots.

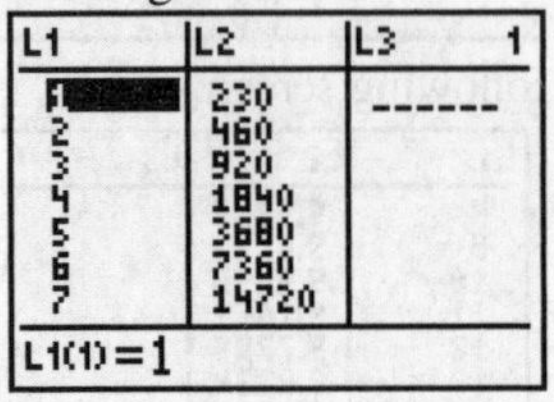

Plotting the points, we have the following.

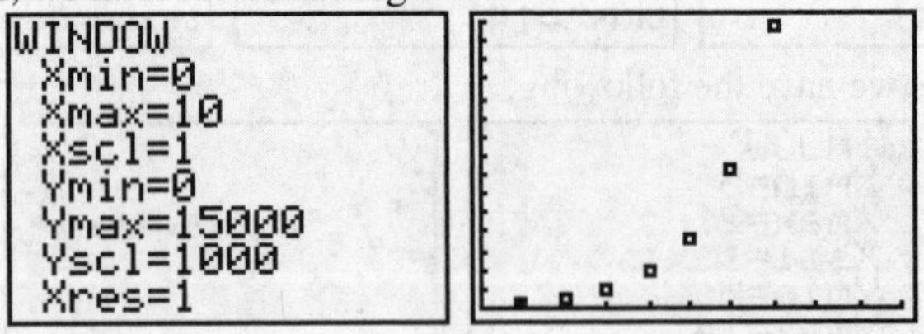

(d) The growth is very rapid. Since there is a doubling of the bacteria at equal intervals, their growth is exponential.

85. (a) Enter the data into the list and determine the linear function is $y = 93.69x + 979.6$.

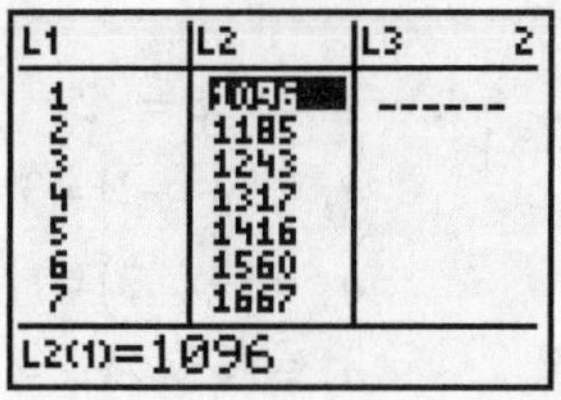

(b) Use the calculator to determine that the quadratic function is $y = 3.167x^2 + 65.19x + 1027$.

(c) Use the calculator to determine that the cubic function is $y = -1.303x^3 + 20.76x^2 - 1.916x + 1092$.

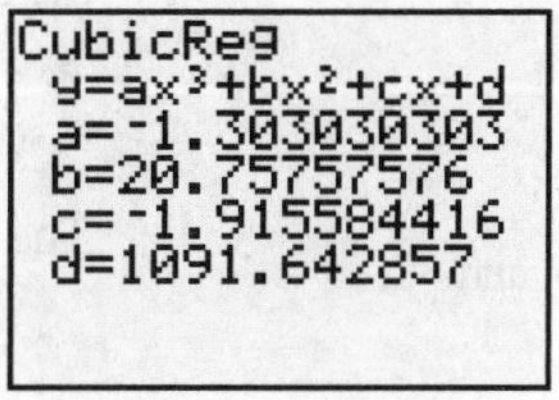

(d) In the year 2003, $x = 9$.

Linear; $y = 93.69(9) + 979.6 \approx \$1823$ (billion)

Quadratic; $y = 3.167(9)^2 + 65.19(9) + 1027 \approx \$1870$ (billion)

Cubic; $y = -1.303(9)^3 + 20.76(9)^2 - 1.916(9) + 1092 \approx \$1806$ (billion)

87. $e^a \approx 1 + a + \frac{a^2}{2!} + \frac{a^3}{3!} + \ldots\ldots + \frac{a^n}{n!}$ where $n! = 1 \cdot 2 \cdot 3 \cdot \cdots \cdot n$

(a) Calculate $e^1 \approx 1 + 1 + \frac{1^2}{2!} + \frac{1^3}{3!} + \frac{1^4}{4!} + \frac{1^5}{5!} + \frac{1^6}{6!} + \frac{1^7}{7!} + \frac{1^8}{8!}$.

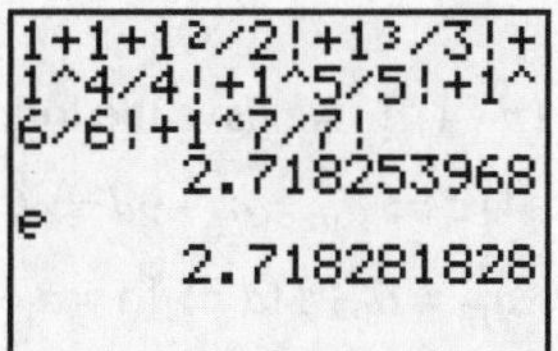

The approximation is accurate to four decimal places.

(b) Calculate $e^{-1} \approx 1 + (-1) + \frac{(-1)^2}{2!} + \frac{(-1)^3}{3!} + \frac{(-1)^4}{4!} + \frac{(-1)^5}{5!} + \frac{(-1)^6}{6!} + \frac{(-1)^7}{7!} + \frac{(-1)^8}{8!}$.

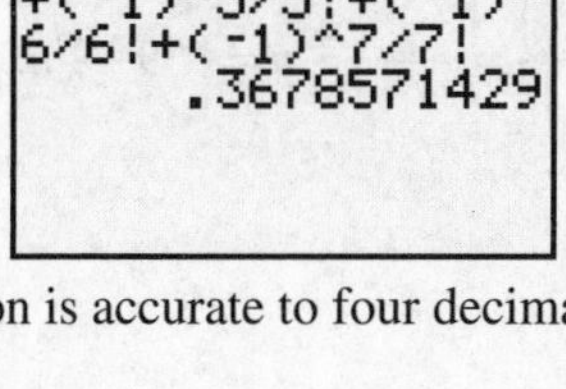

The approximation is accurate to four decimal places.

Section 11.2: Arithmetic Sequences and Series

1. 2, 5, 8, 11, …
$d = a_2 - a_1 = 5 - 2 = 3$

3. 3, –2, –7, –12, …
$d = a_2 - a_1 = -2 - 3 = -5$

5. $x + 3y$, $2x + 5y$, $3x + 7y$, …
$d = a_2 - a_1 = (2x+5y)-(x+3y)$
$= 2x+5y-x-3y = x+2y$

7. $a_1 = 8$ and $d = 6$
Starting with $a_1 = 8$, add $d = 6$ to each term to get the next term.
$a_2 = 8+6 = 14$
$a_3 = 14+6 = 20$
$a_4 = 20+6 = 26$
$a_5 = 26+6 = 32$
The first five terms are 8, 14, 20, 26, and 32.

9. $a_1 = 5$, $d = -2$
$a_2 = 5+(-2) = 3$
$a_3 = 3+(-2) = 1$
$a_4 = 1+(-2) = -1$
$a_5 = -1+(-2) = -3$
The first five terms are 5, 3, 1, –1, and –3.

11. $a_3 = 10$, $d = -2$
$a_4 = 10+d = 10+(-2) = 8$
$a_5 = 8+d = 8+(-2) = 6$
Subtract the common difference –2 to find the earlier terms.
$a_2 = a_3 - d = 10-(-2) = 12$
$a_1 = a_2 - d = 12-(-2) = 14$
The first five terms are 14, 12, 10, 8, and 6.

13. 5, 7, 9, …
$d = a_2 - a_1 = 7 - 5 = 2$
Since $a_n = a_1 + (n-1)d$, we have $a_8 = 5+(8-1)2 = 5+7\cdot 2 = 5+14 = 19$. Also, we have
$a_n = 5+(n-1)2 = 5+2n-2 = 3+2n$.

15. $a_1 = 5$, $a_4 = 15$
Since $a_n = a_1 + (n-1)d$, we have $a_4 = 5+(4-1)d = 15 \Rightarrow 5+3d = 15 \Rightarrow 3d = 10 \Rightarrow d = \frac{10}{3}$.
We now have $a_8 = 5+(8-1)\left(\frac{10}{3}\right) = 5+7\left(\frac{10}{3}\right) = \frac{15}{3}+\frac{70}{3} = \frac{85}{3}$.
Also, we have $a_n = 5+(n-1)\left(\frac{10}{3}\right) = 5+\frac{10}{3}n-\frac{10}{3} = \frac{15}{3}+\frac{10}{3}n-\frac{10}{3} = \frac{5}{3}+\frac{10}{3}n$.

17. $a_{10} = 6$, $a_{12} = 15$
First find a_1 and d. Since $a_n = a_1 + (n-1)d$, we have the following.
$$a_{10} = a_1 + (10-1)d \Rightarrow a_{10} = a_1 + 9d \Rightarrow 6 = a_1 + 9d \quad (1)$$
Also, we have $a_{12} = a_1 + (12-1)d \Rightarrow a_{12} = a_1 + 11d \Rightarrow 15 = a_1 + 11d$ (2).
If we solve the system formed by equations (1) and (2) by the substitution method, we can first solve equation (1) for a_1 to obtain $a_1 = 6-9d$. Substitute $6 - 9d$ for a_1 in equation (2) and solve for d.
$$15 = a_1 + 11d \Rightarrow 15 = (6-9d)+11d \Rightarrow 15 = 6+2d \Rightarrow 9 = 2d \Rightarrow d = \frac{9}{2}$$
Now substitute $d = \frac{9}{2}$ into $a_1 = 6-9d$ to find $a_1 = 6-9\left(\frac{9}{2}\right) = 6-\frac{81}{2} = \frac{12}{2}-\frac{81}{2} = -\frac{69}{2}$.
Now find a_8 and a_n. We have $a_8 = -\frac{69}{2}+(8-1)\left(\frac{9}{2}\right) = -\frac{69}{2}+7\left(\frac{9}{2}\right) = -\frac{69}{2}+\frac{63}{2} = \frac{-6}{2} = -3$.
Also, we have $a_n = -\frac{69}{2}+(n-1)\left(\frac{9}{2}\right) = -\frac{69}{2}+\frac{9}{2}n-\frac{9}{2} = -\frac{78}{2}+\frac{9}{2}n = -39+\frac{9}{2}n$.

19. $a_1 = x,\ a_2 = x+3$

$d = a_2 - a_1 = (x+3) - x = 3$

Since $a_n = a_1 + (n-1)d$, we have $a_8 = x + (8-1)3 = x + 7\cdot 3 = x + 21$. Also, we have $a_n = x + (n-1)3 = x + 3n - 3$.

21. $a_5 = 27,\ a_{15} = 87$

Since $a_{15} = a_5 + 10d$, it follows that $10d = a_{15} - a_5$. This implies $10d = 87 - 27 \Rightarrow 10d = 60 \Rightarrow d = 6$. Since $a_5 = a_1 + 4d$, we have $27 = a_1 + 4(6) \Rightarrow 27 = a_1 + 24 \Rightarrow a_1 = 3$.

23. $S_{16} = -160,\ a_{16} = -25$

Since $S_n = \frac{n}{2}(a_1 + a_n)$, we have $S_{16} = \frac{16}{2}(a_1 + a_{16}) \Rightarrow -160 = 8[a_1 + (-25)] \Rightarrow -20 = a_1 - 25 \Rightarrow a_1 = 5$.

25. The sequence is comprised of the points $\{(1,-2),(2,-1),(3,0),(4,1),(5,2),(6,3)\}$. If the points were connected, they would form a line with slope $m = \frac{y_2 - y_1}{x_2 - x_1} = \frac{-1-(-2)}{2-1} = \frac{1}{1} = 1$. Using the point-slope form of a line, we have the following.

$$y - y_1 = m(x - x_1) \Rightarrow y - (-2) = 1(x-1) \Rightarrow y + 2 = x - 1 \Rightarrow y = x - 3$$

The nth term of the sequence is determined by $a_n = n - 3$.

The domain is $\{1,2,3,4,5,6\}$ and the range is $\{-2,-1,0,1,2,3\}$.

27. The sequence is comprised of the points $\{(1,\frac{5}{2}),(2,2),(3,\frac{3}{2}),(4,1),(5,\frac{1}{2}),(6,0)\}$. If the points were connected, they would form a line with slope $m = \frac{y_2 - y_1}{x_2 - x_1} = \frac{2-\frac{5}{2}}{2-1} = \frac{-\frac{1}{2}}{1} = -\frac{1}{2}$. Using the point-slope form of a line, we have the following.

$$y - y_1 = m(x - x_1) \Rightarrow y - \tfrac{5}{2} = -\tfrac{1}{2}(x-1) \Rightarrow y - \tfrac{5}{2} = -\tfrac{1}{2}x + \tfrac{1}{2} \Rightarrow y = -\tfrac{1}{2}x + 3$$

The nth term of the sequence is determined by $a_n = -\frac{1}{2}n + 3$ or $a_n = 3 - \frac{1}{2}n$.

The domain is $\{1,2,3,4,5,6\}$ and the range is $\{0,\frac{1}{2},1,\frac{3}{2},2,\frac{5}{2}\}$ or $\{0,.5,1,1.5,2,2.5\}$.

29. The sequence is comprised of the points $\{(1,10),(2,-10),(3,-30),(4,-50),(5,-70)\}$. If the points were connected, they would form a line with slope $m = \frac{y_2 - y_1}{x_2 - x_1} = \frac{-10-10}{2-1} = \frac{-20}{1} = -20$. Using the point-slope form of a line, we have the following.

$$y - y_1 = m(x - x_1) \Rightarrow y - 10 = -20(x-1) \Rightarrow y - 10 = -20x + 20 \Rightarrow y = -20x + 30$$

The nth term of the sequence is determined by $a_n = -20n + 30$ or $a_n = 30 - 20n$.

The domain is $\{1,2,3,4,5\}$ and the range is $\{-70,-50,-30,-10,10\}$.

31. 8, 11, 14, ...

Since $a_1 = 8$, $d = a_2 - a_1 = 11 - 8 = 3$, and $S_n = \frac{n}{2}[2a_1 + (n-1)d]$, we have the following.

$$S_{10} = \tfrac{10}{2}[2(8) + (10-1)(3)] = 5[16 + 9(3)] = 5(16+27) = 5(43) = 215$$

33. 5, 9, 13,...

Since $a_1 = 5$, $d = a_2 - a_1 = 9 - 5 = 4$, and $S_n = \frac{n}{2}[2a_1 + (n-1)d]$, we have the following.

$$S_{10} = \tfrac{10}{2}[2(5) + (10-1)(4)] = 5[10 + 9(4)] = 5(10+36) = 5(46) = 230$$

35. $a_2 = 9,\ a_4 = 13$

To find S_{10}, we need a_1 and d. Since $a_4 = a_2 + 2d$, we have $13 = 9 + 2d \Rightarrow 4 = 2d \Rightarrow d = 2$. Also, since $d = a_2 - a_1$, we have $2 = 9 - a_1 \Rightarrow a_1 = 7$. Thus, since $S_n = \frac{n}{2}\left[2a_1 + (n-1)d\right]$, we have $S_{10} = \frac{10}{2}\left[2(7) + (10-1)(2)\right] = 5\left[14 + 9(2)\right] = 5(14 + 18) = 5(32) = 160.$

37. $a_1 = 10,\ a_{10} = 5.5$

To find S_{10}, we need a_1 and d. Since $a_{10} = a_1 + 9d$, we have $5.5 = 10 + 9d \Rightarrow 9d = -4.5 \Rightarrow d = -.5$. Thus, since $S_n = \frac{n}{2}\left[2a_1 + (n-1)d\right]$, we have the following.

$$S_{10} = \frac{10}{2}\left[2(10) + (10-1)(-.5)\right] = 5\left[20 + 9(-.5)\right] = 5\left[20 + (-4.5)\right] = 5(15.5) = 77.5$$

39. The first 80 positive integers form the arithmetic sequence 1, 2, 3, 4, …80. Thus, in the formula $S_n = \frac{n}{2}(a_1 + a_n)$, we have $n = 80, a_1 = 1$, and $a_{80} = 80$. Thus, the sum of the first 80 positive integers is $S_{80} = \frac{80}{2}(1 + 80) = 40(81) = 3240.$

41. The positive odd integers form an arithmetic sequence 1, 3, 5, 7,… with $a_1 = 1$ and $d = 2$. Find the sum of the first 50 terms of this sequence. Since $S_n = \frac{n}{2}\left[2a_1 + (n-1)d\right]$, we have the following.

$$S_{50} = \frac{50}{2}\left[2(1) + (50-1)(2)\right] = 25\left[2 + 49(2)\right] = 25(2 + 98) = 25(100) = 2500$$

43. The positive even integers form an arithmetic sequence 2, 4, 6, 8,… with $a_1 = 2$ and $d = 2$. Find the sum of the first 60 terms of this sequence. Since $S_n = \frac{n}{2}\left[2a_1 + (n-1)d\right]$ we have the following.

$$S_{60} = \frac{60}{2}\left[2(2) + (60-1)(2)\right] = 30\left[4 + 59(2)\right] = 30(4 + 118) = 30(122) = 3660$$

45. $S_{20} = 1090,\ a_{20} = 102$

Since the formula for the sum is $S_n = \frac{n}{2}(a_1 + a_n)$, we have $S_{20} = \frac{20}{2}(a_1 + a_{20})$. This yields $1090 = 10(a_1 + 102) \Rightarrow 109 = a_1 + 102 \Rightarrow a_1 = 7$. To solve for d, we use the fact that $a_n = a_1 + (n-1)d$.

$$a_n = a_1 + (n-1)d \Rightarrow a_{20} = a_1 + (20-1)d \Rightarrow 102 = 7 + 19d \Rightarrow 95 = 19d \Rightarrow d = 5$$

Thus, $a_1 = 7$ and $d = 5$.

47. $S_{12} = -108,\ a_{12} = -19$

Since the formula for the sum is $S_n = \frac{n}{2}(a_1 + a_n)$, we have $S_{12} = \frac{12}{2}(a_1 + a_{12})$. This yields $-108 = 6\left[a_1 + (-19)\right] \Rightarrow -18 = a_1 + (-19) \Rightarrow a_1 = 1$. To solve for d, we use the fact that $a_n = a_1 + (n-1)d$.

$$a_n = a_1 + (n-1)d \Rightarrow a_{12} = a_1 + (12-1)d \Rightarrow -19 = 1 + 11d \Rightarrow -20 = 11d \Rightarrow d = -\frac{20}{11}$$

Thus, $a_1 = 1$ and $d = -\frac{20}{11}$.

49. $\sum_{i=1}^{3}(i+4)$

This is a sum of three terms having a common difference of 1. Thus, in the formula $S_n = \frac{n}{2}(a_1 + a_n)$, we have $a_1 = 1+4 = 5$, $n = 3$, and $a_n = a_3 = 3+4 = 7$. The sum can, therefore, be determined to be

$\sum_{i=1}^{3}(i+4) = S_3 = \frac{3}{2}(a_1 + a_3) = \frac{3}{2}(5+7) = \frac{3}{2}(12) = 18.$

51. $\sum_{j=1}^{10}(2j+3)$

This is the sum of the arithmetic sequence with $a_1 = 2(1)+3 = 5$, $d = 2$, and $n = 10$. Using the formula $S_n = \frac{n}{2}\left[2a_1 + (n-1)d\right]$, we have $\sum_{j=1}^{10}(2j+3) = S_{10} = \frac{10}{2}\left[2(5)+9(2)\right] = 5(10+18) = 5(28) = 140.$

53. $\sum_{i=4}^{12}(-5-8i)$

This is the sum of an arithmetic sequence with $d = -8$ and $a_1 = -5-8(4) = -37$. If i started at 1, there would be 12 terms. Since three terms are missing, $n = 9$. Using the formula $S_n = \frac{n}{2}\left[2a_1 + (n-1)d\right]$, we have the following.

$$\sum_{i=4}^{12}(-5-8i) = S_9 = \frac{9}{2}\left[2(-37)+8(-8)\right] = \frac{9}{2}\left[-74+(-64)\right] = \frac{9}{2}(-138) = -621$$

55. $\sum_{i=1}^{1000} i$

This is the sum of 1000 terms having a common difference of 1. Thus, in the formula $S_n = \frac{n}{2}(a_1 + a_n)$, we have $a_1 = 1$, $n = 1000$, and $a_n = a_{1000} = 1000$. The sum can, therefore, be determined as follows.

$$\sum_{i=1}^{1000} i = S_{1000} = \frac{1000}{2}(1+1000) = 500(1001) = 500{,}500$$

57. $f(x) = mx + b$

$f(1) = m(1) + b = m + b$

$f(2) = m(2) + b = 2m + b$

$f(3) = m(3) + b = 3m + b$

58. The sequence $f(1), f(2), f(3)$ is an arithmetic sequence since the difference between any two adjacent terms is m.

59. Since $d = (3m+b)-(2m+b) = 3m+b-2m-b = m$, the common difference is m.

60. From Exercise 57, we know that $a_1 = m + b$. Also from Exercise 57, we know that $d = m$. Therefore, we have $a_n = a_1 + (n-1)d \Rightarrow a_n = (m+b)+(n-1)m \Rightarrow a_n = m+b+nm-m \Rightarrow a_n = mn + b.$

For Exercises 61 – 63, you will need the sum(and seq(features of your graphing calculator. On the TI-83, the sum(feature is located under the LIST then MATH menu. The seq(feature is under the LIST then OPS menu.

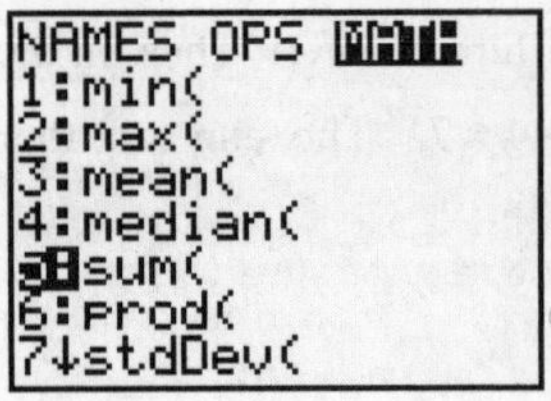

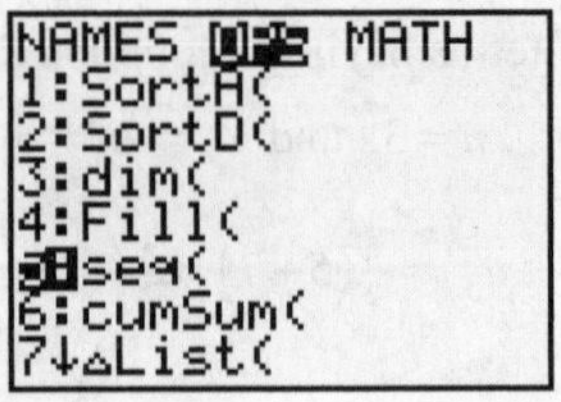

61. $a_n = 4.2n + 9.73$

Using the sequence feature of a graphing calculator, we obtain $S_{10} = 328.3$.

63. $a_n = \sqrt{8}n + \sqrt{3}$

Using the sequence feature of a graphing calculator, we obtain $S_{10} \approx 172.884$.

65. Find the sum of all the integers from 51 to 71.

We need to find $\sum_{i=51}^{71} i = \sum_{i=1}^{71} i - \sum_{i=1}^{50} i = S_{71} - S_{50}$. Since we know $a_1 = 1$, $d = 1$, $a_{50} = 50$, and $a_{71} = 71$, we have $S_{71} = \frac{71}{2}(1+71) = 71(36) = 2556$ and $S_{50} = \frac{50}{2}(1+50) = 25(51) = 1275$. Thus, the sum is $S_{71} - S_{50} = 2556 - 1275 = 1281$.

67. In every 12-hour cycle, the clock will chime 1 + 2 + 3 + …+ 12 times. Since $a_1 = 1$, $n = 12$, $a_{12} = 12$, and $S_n = \frac{n}{2}(a_1 + a_n)$, we have $S_{12} = \frac{12}{2}(1+12) = 6(13) = 78$. Since there are two 12-hour cycles in 1 day, every day, the clock will chime $2(78) = 156$ times. Since there are 30 days in this month, the clock will chime $156(30) = 4680$ times.

69. In this exercise, we have $a_1 = 49{,}000$, $d = 580$, and $n = 5$. Using $a_n = a_1 + (n-1)d$, we need to find a_{10}. Since $a_{11} = 49{,}000 + (11-1)580 = 49{,}000 + 10(580) = 49{,}000 + 5800 = 54{,}800$, we would expect that five years from now, the population will be 54,800.

71. The longest rung measures 28 in., and the shortest measures 18 in. Since the rungs are uniformly tapered, the sum of the lengths of these 31 supports can be thought of as the sum of an arithmetic sequence with $a_1 = 28$, $a_n = a_{31} = 18$, and $n = 31$. Since $S_n = \frac{n}{2}(a_1 + a_n)$, we have the following.

$$S_{31} = \frac{31}{2}(a_1 + a_{31}) = \frac{31}{2}(28+18) = \frac{31}{2}(46) = 713$$

Thus, a total of 713 in. of material would be needed.

73. If $a_1, a_2, a_3, \ldots$ is an arithmetic sequence, then $a_n = a_1 + (n-1)p_a$ (where p_a is the common difference for this sequence). Also, if $b_1, b_2, b_3, \ldots$ is an arithmetic sequence, then $b_n = b_1 + (n-1)p_b$ (where p_b is the common difference for this sequence). Since $d_n = a_n + c \cdot b_n$, we have the following.

$$d_n = a_n + c \cdot b_n$$
$$d_n = \left[a_1 + (n-1)p_a\right] + c \cdot \left[b_1 + (n-1)p_b\right]$$
$$d_n = a_1 + (n-1)p_a + c \cdot b_1 + c \cdot (n-1)p_b$$
$$d_n = (a_1 + c \cdot b_1) + (n-1)(p_a + c \cdot p_b)$$

Thus, d_n is an arithmetic sequence whose first term is $a_1 + c \cdot b_1$ and common difference is $p_a + c \cdot p_b$.

75. Since the sequence $\log 2, \log 4, \log 8, \log 16, \ldots$ is the same $\log 2^1, \log 2^2, \log 2^3, \log 2^4, \ldots$, it has a general term of $a_n = \log 2^n$. Notice that we have $a_2 - a_1 = \log 4 - \log 2 = \log \frac{4}{2} = \log 2$ and $a_3 - a_2 = \log 8 - \log 4 = \log \frac{8}{4} = \log 2$. In general, we have the following.

$$a_n - a_{n-1} = \log 2^n - \log 2^{n-1} = \log \frac{2^n}{2^{n-1}} = \log 2^{n-(n-1)} = \log 2^{n-n+1} = \log 2^1 = \log 2$$

Thus, $\log 2, \log 4, \log 8, \log 16, \ldots$ is an arithmetic sequence whose first term is $\log 2$ and common difference is $\log 2$.

Section 11.3: Geometric Sequences and Series

For Exercises 1 – 3, we are examining the geometric sequence 1, 2, 4, 8,… . As stated on page 957 of your text, the *n*th term of a geometric sequence is given by $a_n = a_1 r^{n-1}$, where a_1 is the first term and r is the common ratio. For this situation, $a_n = 1 \cdot 2^{n-1} = 2^{n-1}$.

1. day 10

(a) $a_{10} = 2^{10-1} = 2^9 = 512$ cents or \$5.12

(b) Since $S_n = \dfrac{a_1(1-r^n)}{1-r}$ for $r \neq 1$, we have $S_{10} = \dfrac{1(1-2^{10})}{1-2} = \dfrac{1-1024}{-1} = \dfrac{-1023}{-1} = 1023$ cents or \$10.23.

3. day 15

(a) $a_{15} = 2^{15-1} = 2^{14} = 16{,}384$ cents or \$163.84

(b) Since $S_n = \frac{a_1(1-r^n)}{1-r}$ for $r \neq 1$, we have $S_{15} = \frac{1(1-2^{15})}{1-2} = \frac{1-32{,}768}{-1} = \frac{-32{,}767}{-1} = 32{,}767$ cents or \$327.67.

5. $a_1 = 5,\ r = -2$

$a_5 = a_1 r^{5-1} = 5(-2)^4 = 5(16) = 80$

$a_n = a_1 r^{n-1} = 5(-2)^{n-1}$

7. $a_2 = -4,\ r = 3$

We need to determine a_1. Since $a_2 = a_1 r^{2-1} \Rightarrow -4 = a_1(3)^1 \Rightarrow -4 = a_1(3) \Rightarrow a_1 = -\frac{4}{3}$, we have the following.

$$a_5 = a_1 r^{5-1} = -\tfrac{4}{3}(3)^4 = -\tfrac{4}{3}(81) = -108 \text{ and } a_n = a_1 r^{n-1} = -\tfrac{4}{3}(3)^{n-1}$$

9. $a_4 = 243$, $r = -3$

We need to determine a_1. Since $a_4 = a_1 r^{4-1} \Rightarrow 243 = a_1(-3)^3 \Rightarrow 243 = a_1(-27) \Rightarrow a_1 = -9$, we have the following.

$$a_5 = a_1 r^{5-1} = -9(-3)^4 = -9(81) = -729 \text{ and } a_n = a_1 r^{n-1} = -9(-3)^{n-1}$$

Note that $(-9)(-3)^{n-1} = -(-3)^2(-3)^{n-1} = (-3)^{2+n-1} = -(-3)^{n+1}$, so $a_n = -(-3)^{n+1}$ is an equivalent formula for the *n*th term of this sequence.

11. $-4, -12, -36, -108, \ldots$

First find *r*. Since $r = \frac{a_2}{a_1}$, we have $r = \frac{-12}{-4} = 3$. Also, given that $a_1 = -4$, we have the following.

$$a_5 = a_1 r^{5-1} = -4(3)^4 = -4(81) = -324 \text{ and } a_n = a_1 r^{n-1} = -4(3)^{n-1}$$

13. $\frac{4}{5}, 2, 5, \frac{25}{2}, \ldots$

First find *r*. Since $r = \frac{a_2}{a_1}$, we have $r = \frac{2}{\frac{4}{5}} = 2\left(\frac{5}{4}\right) = \frac{5}{2}$. Also, given that $a_1 = \frac{4}{5}$, we have the following.

$$a_5 = a_1 r^{5-1} = \frac{4}{5}\left(\frac{5}{2}\right)^4 = \frac{4}{5}\left(\frac{625}{16}\right) = \frac{125}{4} \text{ and } a_n = a_1 r^{n-1} = \frac{4}{5}\left(\frac{5}{2}\right)^{n-1}$$

Note that $\left(\frac{4}{5}\right)\left(\frac{5}{2}\right)^{n-1} = \frac{2^2}{5^1} \cdot \frac{5^{n-1}}{2^{n-1}} = \frac{5^{n-2}}{2^{n-3}}$, so $a_n = \frac{5^{n-2}}{2^{n-3}}$ is an equivalent formula for the *n*th term of this sequence.

15. $10, -5, \frac{5}{2}, -\frac{5}{4}, \ldots$

First find *r*. Since $r = \frac{a_2}{a_1}$, we have $r = \frac{-5}{10} = -\frac{1}{2}$. Also, given that $a_1 = 10$, we have the following.

$$a_5 = a_1 r^{5-1} = 10\left(-\frac{1}{2}\right)^4 = 10\left(\frac{1}{16}\right) = \frac{5}{8} \text{ and } a_n = a_1 r^{n-1} = 10\left(-\frac{1}{2}\right)^{n-1}$$

17. $a_2 = -6$, $a_7 = -192$

Using $a_n = a_1 r^{n-1}$, we have $a_2 = a_1 r = -6$. This yields $a_1 = \frac{-6}{r}$. Also, $a_7 = a_1 r^6 = -192$.

Substituting $a_1 = \frac{-6}{r}$ into $a_1 r^6 = -192$ equation and solving for *r*, we have the following.

$$a_1 r^6 = -192 \Rightarrow \left(\frac{-6}{r}\right) r^6 = -192 \Rightarrow -6r^5 = -192 \Rightarrow r^5 = 32 \Rightarrow r^5 = 2^5 \Rightarrow r = 2$$

Since $a_1 = \frac{-6}{r}$, we have $a_1 = \frac{-6}{2} = -3$.

19. $a_3 = 50$, $a_7 = .005$

Using $a_n = a_1 r^{n-1}$, we have $a_3 = a_1 r^2 = 50$. This yields $a_1 = \frac{50}{r^2}$. Also, $a_7 = a_1 r^6 = .005$.

Substituting $a_1 = \frac{50}{r^2}$ into $a_1 r^6 = .005$ equation and solving for *r*, we have the following.

$$a_1 r^6 = .005 \Rightarrow \left(\frac{50}{r^2}\right) r^6 = .005 \Rightarrow 50r^4 = .005 \Rightarrow r^4 = .0001 \Rightarrow r^4 = .0001 \Rightarrow r = \pm .1$$

If $r = -.1$, then $a_1 = \frac{50}{(-.1)^2} = \frac{50}{.01} = 5000$. If $r = .1$, then $a_1 = \frac{50}{(.1)^2} = \frac{50}{.01} = 5000$.

21. $2, 8, 32, 128, \ldots$

First find *r*. Since $r = \frac{a_2}{a_1}$, we have $r = \frac{8}{2} = 4$. Also, given that $a_1 = 2$, $n = 5$, and $S_n = \frac{a_1(1-r^n)}{1-r}$, we have $S_n = \frac{a_1(1-r^n)}{1-r} = \frac{2(1-4^5)}{1-4} = \frac{2(1-1024)}{-3} = \frac{2(-1023)}{-3} = \frac{-2046}{-3} = 682$.

23. $18, -9, \frac{9}{2}, -\frac{9}{4}, \ldots$

First find r. Since $r = \frac{a_2}{a_1}$, we have $r = \frac{-9}{18} = -\frac{1}{2}$. Also, given that $a_1 = 18$, $n = 5$, and $S_n = \frac{a_1(1-r^n)}{1-r}$, we have $S_n = \frac{a_1(1-r^n)}{1-r} = \frac{18\left[1-\left(-\frac{1}{2}\right)^5\right]}{1-\left(-\frac{1}{2}\right)} = \frac{18\left[1-\left(-\frac{1}{32}\right)\right]}{\frac{3}{2}} = \frac{18\left(\frac{32}{32}+\frac{1}{32}\right)}{\frac{3}{2}} = 18\left(\frac{33}{32}\right)\left(\frac{2}{3}\right) = 18\left(\frac{11}{16}\right) = \frac{99}{8}$.

25. $a_1 = 8.423$, $r = 2.859$

Since $S_n = \frac{a_1(1-r^n)}{1-r}$, we have $S_5 = \frac{8.423\left[1-(2.859)^5\right]}{1-2.859} \approx 860.95$.

27. $\sum_{i=1}^{5} 3^i$

For this geometric series, $a_1 = 3^1 = 3$, $r = 3$, and $n = 5$. Since $S_n = \frac{a_1(1-r^n)}{1-r}$, we have the following.

$$\sum_{i=1}^{5} 3^i = S_5 = \frac{3(1-3^5)}{1-3} = \frac{3(1-243)}{-2} = \frac{3(-242)}{-2} = 3(121) = 363$$

29. $\sum_{j=1}^{6} 48\left(\frac{1}{2}\right)^j$

For this geometric series, $a_1 = 48\left(\frac{1}{2}\right)^1 = 48\left(\frac{1}{2}\right) = 24$, $r = \frac{1}{2}$, and $n = 6$. Since $S_n = \frac{a_1(1-r^n)}{1-r}$, we have the following.

$$\sum_{j=1}^{6} 48\left(\frac{1}{2}\right)^j = S_6 = \frac{24\left[1-\left(\frac{1}{2}\right)^6\right]}{1-\frac{1}{2}} = \frac{24\left(1-\frac{1}{64}\right)}{\frac{1}{2}} = \frac{24\left(\frac{64}{64}-\frac{1}{64}\right)}{\frac{1}{2}} = 24\left(\frac{63}{64}\right)(2) = 24\left(\frac{63}{32}\right) = \frac{189}{4}$$

31. $\sum_{k=4}^{10} 2^k$

This series is the sum of the fourth through tenth terms of a geometric sequence with $a_1 = 2^1 = 2$ and $r = 2$. To find this sum, find the difference between the sum of the first ten terms and the sum of the first three terms.

$$\sum_{k=4}^{10} 2^k = \sum_{k=1}^{10} 2^k - \sum_{k=1}^{3} 2^k = \frac{2(1-2^{10})}{1-2} - \frac{2(1-2^3)}{1-2} = \frac{2(1-1024)}{-1} - \frac{2(1-8)}{-1} = \frac{2(-1023)}{-1} - \frac{2(-7)}{-1} = 2046 - 14 = 2032$$

Note: We could also consider $\sum_{k=4}^{10} 2^k$ as a geometric series with $a_1 = 2^4 = 16$ and $r = 2$. If the sequence started with $k = 1$, there would be 10 terms. Since it starts with 4, three of the terms are missing, so there are seven terms and $n = 7$. Thus we have the following.

$$\sum_{k=4}^{10} 2^k = S_7 = \frac{16(1-2^7)}{1-2} = \frac{16(1-128)}{-1} = \frac{16(-127)}{-1} = 2032$$

33. The sum of an infinite geometric series exists if $|r| < 1$.

35. 12, 24, 48, 96, …

Since $r = \frac{a_2}{a_1}$, we have $r = \frac{24}{12} = 2$. The sum of the terms of this infinite geometric sequence would not converge since $r = 2$ is not between –1 and 1.

37. –48, –24, –12, –6, …

Since $r = \frac{a_2}{a_1}$, we have $r = \frac{-24}{-48} = \frac{1}{2}$. Since $-1 < r < 1$, the sum converges.

39. $2 + 1 + \frac{1}{2} + \frac{1}{4} + \ldots$ is a geometric series with $r = \frac{a_2}{a_1} = \frac{1}{2}$ and $a_1 = 2$. Since $S_n = \frac{a_1\left(1 - r^n\right)}{1 - r}$, we have

$S_n = \frac{2\left[1 - \left(\frac{1}{2}\right)^n\right]}{1 - \frac{1}{2}} = \frac{2\left[1 - \left(\frac{1}{2}\right)^n\right]}{\frac{1}{2}}$. Similar to Example 7, we have $\lim_{n\to\infty} \left(\frac{1}{2}\right)^n = 0$. Thus, we obtain

$$\lim_{n\to\infty} S_n = \lim_{n\to\infty} \frac{2\left[1 - \left(\frac{1}{2}\right)^n\right]}{\frac{1}{2}} = \frac{2(1-0)}{\frac{1}{2}} = \frac{2}{\frac{1}{2}} = 4.$$

41. $18 + 6 + 2 + \frac{2}{3} + \ldots$

For this geometric series, $a_1 = 18$ and $r = \frac{6}{18} = \frac{1}{3}$. Because $-1 < r < 1$, this series converges. We have

$$S_\infty = \frac{a_1}{1 - r} = \frac{18}{1 - \frac{1}{3}} = \frac{18}{\frac{2}{3}} = 18 \cdot \frac{3}{2} = 27.$$

43. $\frac{1}{4} - \frac{1}{6} + \frac{1}{9} - \frac{2}{27} + \ldots$

For this geometric series, $a_1 = \frac{1}{4}$ and $r = \frac{-\frac{1}{6}}{\frac{1}{4}} = -\frac{1}{6} \cdot \frac{4}{1} = -\frac{2}{3}$. Because $-1 < r < 1$, this series converges. We have $S_\infty = \frac{a_1}{1 - r} = \frac{\frac{1}{4}}{1 - \left(-\frac{2}{3}\right)} = \frac{\frac{1}{4}}{\frac{5}{3}} = \frac{1}{4} \cdot \frac{3}{5} = \frac{3}{20}$.

45. $\sum_{i=1}^{\infty} 3\left(\frac{1}{4}\right)^{i-1}$

For this geometric series, $a_1 = 3\left(\frac{1}{4}\right)^{1-1} = 3\left(\frac{1}{4}\right)^0 = 3 \cdot 1 = 3$ and $r = \frac{1}{4}$. Because $-1 < r < 1$, this series converges. We have $S_\infty = \frac{a_1}{1 - r} = \frac{3}{1 - \frac{1}{4}} = \frac{3}{\frac{3}{4}} = 3 \cdot \frac{4}{3} = 4$.

47. $\sum_{k=1}^{\infty} (.3)^k$

For this geometric series, $a_1 = (.3)^1 = .3$ and $r = .3$. Because $-1 < r < 1$, this series converges. We have $S_\infty = \frac{a_1}{1 - r} = \frac{.3}{1 - .3} = \frac{.3}{.7} = \frac{3}{7}$.

49. $g(x) = ab^x$

$g(1) = ab^1 = ab$

$g(2) = ab^2$

$g(3) = ab^3$

50. The sequence $g(1)$, $g(2)$, $g(3)$ is a geometric sequence because each term after the first is a constant multiple of the preceding term. The common ratio is b.

51. From Exercise 49, $a_1 = ab$. From Exercise 50, $r = b$. Therefore, $a_n = a_1 r^{n-1} = ab(b)^{n-1} = ab^n$.

52. Answers will vary.

For Exercises 53 – 55, you will need the sum(and seq(features of your graphing calculator. On the TI-83, the sum(feature is located under the LIST then MATH menu. The seq(feature is under the LIST then OPS menu.

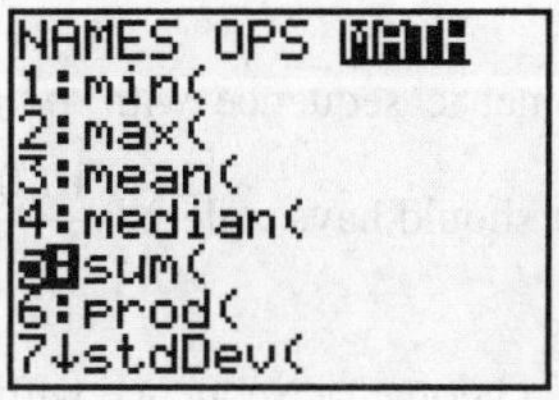

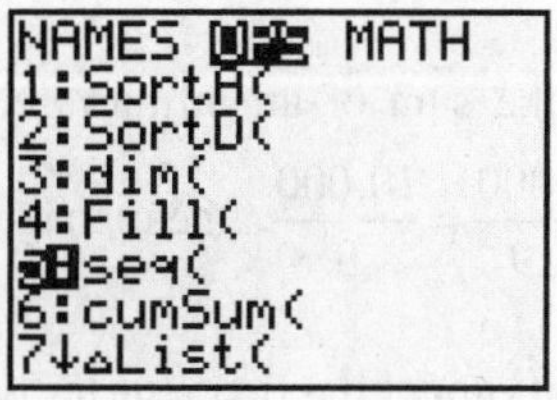

53. $\sum_{i=1}^{10} (1.4)^i$

Using the sequence feature of a graphing calculator, we obtain $S_{10} \approx 97.739$.

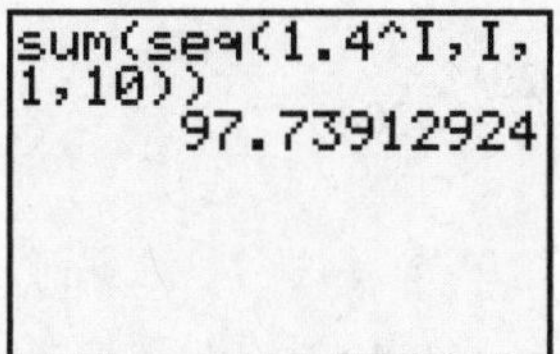

55. $\sum_{j=3}^{8} 2(.4)^j$

Using the sequence feature of a graphing calculator, the sum is approximately .212.

57. (a) $a_n = 1276(.916)^n$

$a_1 = 1276(.916)^1 = 1168.816 \approx 1169$ and $r = .916$

(b) $a_n = 1276(.916)^n$

$a_{10} = 1276(.916)^{10} \approx 531$

$a_{20} = 1276(.916)^{20} \approx 221$

This means that a person who is 10 years from retirement should have savings of 531% of his or her annual salary; a person 20 years from retirement should have savings of 221% of his or her annual salary.

59. (a) Since the first term is a_1 and the common ratio is r, we have $a_n = a_1 \cdot 2^{n-1}$.

(b) If $a_1 = 100$, we have $a_n = 100 \cdot 2^{n-1}$. Since 100 = 10^2 and 1,000,000 = 10^6, we need to solve the equation $10^2 \cdot 2^{n-1} = 10^6$. Divide both sides by 10^2 to obtain $2^{n-1} = 10^4$. Take the common logarithm (base 10) of both sides and solve for n.

$$\log 2^{n-1} = \log 10^4 \Rightarrow (n-1)\log 2 = 4 \Rightarrow n-1 = \frac{4}{\log 2} \Rightarrow n = \frac{4}{\log 2} + 1 \approx 14.28$$

Since the number of bacteria is increasing, the first value of n where $a_n > 1{,}000{,}000$ is 15.

(c) Since a_n represents the number of bacteria after 40(n – 1) minutes, a_{15} represents the number after $40(15-1) = 40 \cdot 14 = 560$ minutes or 9 hours, 20 minutes.

61. Since there are 200 insects in the first generation, $a_1 = 200$. The r value will be 1.25. Thus, $a_n = a_1 r^{n-1} \Rightarrow a_5 = 200(1.25)^{5-1} = 200(1.25)^4 = 488.28125$. There are approximately 488 fruit flies in the fifth generation.

63. Use the formula for the sum of an infinite geometric sequence with $a_1 = 1000$ and r = .1. Since $S_\infty = \frac{a_1}{1-r} = \frac{1000}{1-.1} = \frac{1000}{.9} = \frac{10{,}000}{9}$, the manager should have ordered $\frac{10{,}000}{9}$ units of sugar.

65. Use the formula for the sum of the first n terms of a geometric sequence with $a_1 = 2$, r = 2, and n = 5.

$$S_n = \frac{a_1(1-r^n)}{1-r} \Rightarrow S_5 = \frac{2(1-2^5)}{1-2} = \frac{2(1-32)}{-1} = \frac{2(-31)}{-1} = 62$$

Going back five generations, the total number of ancestors is 62. Next, use the same formula with $a_1 = 2$, r = 2, and n =10.

$$S_{10} = \frac{2(1-2^{10})}{1-2} = \frac{2(1-1024)}{-1} = \frac{2(-1023)}{-1} = 2046$$

Going back ten generations, the total number of ancestors is 2046.

67. When the midpoints of the sides of an equilateral triangle are connected, the length of a side of the new triangle is one-half the length of a side of the original triangle. Use the formula for the nth term of a geometric sequence with $a_1 = 2$, $r = \frac{1}{2}$, and n = 8.

$$a_n = a_1 r^{n-1} \Rightarrow a_8 = (2)\left(\tfrac{1}{2}\right)^{8-1} = (2)\left(\tfrac{1}{2}\right)^7 = (2)\left(\tfrac{1}{128}\right) = \tfrac{1}{64}$$

The eighth triangle has sides of length $\frac{1}{64}$ m.

69. Option 1 is modeled by the arithmetic sequence $a_n = 5000 + 10{,}000(n-1)$ with the following sum.

$$S_n = \tfrac{n}{2}\left[2a_1 + (n-1)d\right] \Rightarrow S_{30} = \tfrac{30}{2}\left[2a_1 + (30-1)d\right] \Rightarrow S_{30} = 15[2a_1 + 29d]$$
$$\Rightarrow S_{30} = 15\left[2(5000) + 29\cdot 10{,}000\right] \Rightarrow S_{30} = 15[10{,}000 + 290{,}000]$$
$$\Rightarrow S_{30} = 15(300{,}000) = 4{,}500{,}000$$

Thus, the first option will pay you \$4,500,000 for the month's work. Option 2 is modeled by the sequence $a_n = .01(2)^{n-1}$ with the following sum.

$$S_n = \frac{a_1\left(1-r^n\right)}{1-r} \Rightarrow S_{30} = \frac{a_1\left(1-r^{30}\right)}{1-r} \Rightarrow S_{30} = \frac{.01\left(1-2^{30}\right)}{1-2} \Rightarrow S_{30} = \frac{.01(1-1{,}073{,}741{,}824)}{-1}$$
$$\Rightarrow S_{30} = -.01(-1{,}073{,}741{,}823) \Rightarrow S_{30} = 10{,}737{,}418.23$$

The second will pay you \$10,737,418.23. You should choose Option 2; it pays better.

71. The future value of an annuity uses the formula $S_n = \dfrac{a_1(1-r^n)}{1-r}$, where r = 1 + interest rate.

The payments are \$1000 for 9 yr at 3% compounded annually, so $a_1 = 1000$, r = 1.03, and n = 9.

$$S_9 = \frac{1000\left[1-(1.03)^9\right]}{1-1.03} \approx 10{,}159.11$$

The future value is \$10,159.11.

73. The future value of an annuity uses the formula $S_n = \dfrac{a_1(1-r^n)}{1-r}$, where r = 1 + interest rate.

The payments are \$2430 for 10 yr at 1% compounded annually, so $a_1 = 2430$, r = 1.01, and n = 10.

$$S_{10} = \frac{2430\left[1-(1.01)^{10}\right]}{1-1.01} \approx 25{,}423.18$$

The future value is \$25,423.18.

75. $S = R\left[\dfrac{(1+i)^n - 1}{i}\right]$ where $R = 2430$, $i = .01$, and $n = 11$.

$$S = 2430\left[\frac{(1.01)^{11} - 1}{.01}\right] \approx 28{,}107.41$$

The balance after 11 years is \$28,107.41.

77. For deposits made annually for twenty-five years, we need to find $S = R\left[\dfrac{(1+i)^n - 1}{i}\right]$ where

$R = 2000$, $i = .03$, and $n = 25$. Thus, we have $S = 2000\left[\dfrac{(1.03)^{25} - 1}{.03}\right] \approx 72{,}918.53$.

The total amount in Michael's IRA will be \$72,918.53.

79. In the formula $S_n = \dfrac{a_1\left(1-r^n\right)}{1-r}$, we are considering the sum $a_1 + a_1r + a_1r^2 + ... + a_1r^{n-1}$. With an annuity with deposits at the end of each year, this summation is actually the reversed since the last deposit will not receive interest. Reversing the summation we have the following.

$$a_1r^{n-1} + a_1r^{n-2} + ... + a_1r^2 + a_1r + a_1$$

Now the first term of this series represents the first amount deposited having gone through $n-1$ compound periods (since it is deposited at the end of the first year). The value of r is $1+i$, where i is the interest rate in decimal form. The value of a_1 is the equal amounts of money that are deposited annually. If we call this value R, then the formula $S_n = \dfrac{a_1\left(1-r^n\right)}{1-r}$ becomes $S = \dfrac{R\left(1-(1+i)^n\right)}{1-(1+i)}$. This simplifies as follows.

$$S = \frac{R\left(1-(1+i)^n\right)}{1-(1+i)} \Rightarrow S = \frac{R\left(1-(1+i)^n\right)}{1-1-i} \Rightarrow S = R\frac{1-(1+i)^n}{-i} \Rightarrow S = R\frac{(1+i)^n - 1}{i}$$

81. If $a_1, a_2, a_3, ...$ is a geometric sequence, then $a_n = a_1r_a^{\,n-1}$ (where r_a is the common ratio for this sequence). Also, if $b_1, b_2, b_3, ...$ is a geometric sequence, then $b_n = b_1r_b^{\,n-1}$ (where r_b is the common ratio for this sequence). Since $d_n = c \cdot a_n \cdot b_n$, we have the following.

$$d_n = c \cdot a_n \cdot b_n$$
$$d_n = c \cdot a_1r_a^{\,n-1} \cdot b_1r_b^{\,n-1}$$
$$d_n = c \cdot a_1 \cdot b_1\left(r_a^{\,n-1} \cdot r_b^{\,n-1}\right)$$
$$d_n = c \cdot a_1 \cdot b_1\left(r_a \cdot r_b\right)^{n-1}$$

Thus, d_n is a geometric sequence whose first term is $c \cdot a_1 \cdot b_1$ and common ratio is $r_a \cdot r_b$.

Summary Exercises on Sequences and Series

1. 2, 4, 8, 16, 32,... is a geometric sequence with $r = 2$.

Notice $2(2) = 4$, $4(2) = 8$, $8(2) = 16$, and $16(2) = 32$.

3. $3, \frac{1}{2}, -2, -\frac{9}{2}, -7, ...$ is an arithmetic sequence with $d = -\frac{5}{2}$.

Notice $3 + \left(-\frac{5}{2}\right) = \frac{1}{2}$, $\frac{1}{2} + \left(-\frac{5}{2}\right) = -2$, $-2 + \left(-\frac{5}{2}\right) = -\frac{9}{2}$, and $-\frac{9}{2} + \left(-\frac{5}{2}\right) = -7$.

5. $\frac{3}{4}, 1, \frac{4}{3}, \frac{16}{9}, \frac{64}{27}, ...$ is a geometric sequence with $r = \frac{4}{3}$.

Notice $\frac{3}{4}\left(\frac{4}{3}\right) = 1$, $1\left(\frac{4}{3}\right) = \frac{4}{3}$, $\frac{4}{3}\left(\frac{4}{3}\right) = \frac{16}{9}$, and $\frac{16}{9}\left(\frac{4}{3}\right) = \frac{64}{27}$.

7. $\frac{1}{2}, \frac{1}{3}, \frac{1}{4}, \frac{1}{5}, \frac{1}{6}, ...$ is neither an arithmetic sequence nor a geometric sequence.

Notice $\frac{1}{2} + \left(-\frac{1}{6}\right) = \frac{1}{3}$ but $\frac{1}{3} + \left(-\frac{1}{6}\right) \neq \frac{1}{4}$, so the sequence is not arithmetic.

Also, $\frac{1}{2}\left(\frac{2}{3}\right) = \frac{1}{3}$ but $\frac{1}{3}\left(\frac{2}{3}\right) \neq \frac{1}{4}$, so the sequence is not geometric.

9. The sequence 3, 6, 12, 24, 48,... is geometric with $a_1 = 3$ and $r = 2$. Thus, we have the following.

$$a_n = a_1 r^{n-1} \Rightarrow a_n = 3(2)^{n-1}$$

Since $\sum_{i=1}^{n} a_1 r^{i-1} = S_n = \frac{a_1(1-r^n)}{1-r}$, we have the following.

$$\sum_{i=1}^{10} 3(2)^{i-1} = S_{10} = \frac{3(1-2^{10})}{1-2} = \frac{3(1-1024)}{-1} = -3(-1023) = 3069$$

11. The sequence $4, \frac{5}{2}, 1, -\frac{1}{2}, -2, \ldots$ is arithmetic with $a_1 = 4$ and $d = -\frac{3}{2}$. Thus, we have the following.

$$a_n = a_1 + (n-1)d \Rightarrow a_n = 4 + (n-1)\left(-\tfrac{3}{2}\right) \Rightarrow a_n = 4 - \tfrac{3}{2}n + \tfrac{3}{2} \Rightarrow a_n = \tfrac{11}{2} - \tfrac{3}{2}n$$

Since $\sum_{i=1}^{n} [a_1 + (i-1)d] = S_n = \frac{n}{2}[2a_1 + (n-1)d]$, we have the following.

$$\sum_{i=1}^{10} \tfrac{11}{2} - \tfrac{3}{2}i = S_{10} = \frac{10}{2}\left[2(4) + (10-1)\left(-\tfrac{3}{2}\right)\right] = 5\left[8 + 9\left(-\tfrac{3}{2}\right)\right] = 5\left[8 + \left(-\tfrac{27}{2}\right)\right] = 5\left(-\tfrac{11}{2}\right) = -\tfrac{55}{2}$$

13. The sequence 3, −6, 12, −24, 48,... is geometric with $a_1 = 3$ and $r = -2$. Thus, we have the following.

$$a_n = a_1 r^{n-1} \Rightarrow a_n = 3(-2)^{n-1}$$

Since $\sum_{i=1}^{n} a_1 r^{i-1} = S_n = \frac{a_1(1-r^n)}{1-r}$, we have the following.

$$\sum_{i=1}^{10} 3(2)^{i-1} = S_{10} = \frac{3\left[1-(-2)^{10}\right]}{1-(-2)} = \frac{3(1-1024)}{3} = -1023$$

15. $\sum_{i=1}^{\infty} \frac{1}{3}(-2)^{i-1}$ is an infinite geometric series with $a_1 = \frac{1}{3}$ and $r = -2$. Since $|r| = 2 > 1$, this series diverges.

17. $\sum_{i=1}^{25} (4-6i)$ is an arithmetic series with $a_1 = -2$ and $d = -6$. Since the sum of the first n terms of an arithmetic series is $S_n = \frac{n}{2}[2a_1 + (n-1)d]$, we have the following.

$$\sum_{i=1}^{25} (4-6i) = S_{25} = \frac{25}{2}[2(-2) + (25-1)(-6)] = \frac{25}{2}[-4 + 24(-6)]$$
$$= \frac{25}{2}[-4 + (-144)] = \frac{25}{2}(-148) = -1850$$

19. $\sum_{i=1}^{\infty} 4\left(-\frac{1}{2}\right)^i$ is an infinite geometric series with $a_1 = -2$ and $r = -\frac{1}{2}$. Since $|r| = \frac{1}{2} < 1$, then the sum of this series is $S = \frac{a_1}{1-r} = \frac{-2}{1-\left(-\frac{1}{2}\right)} = \frac{-2}{\frac{3}{2}} = -\frac{4}{3}$.

21. $\sum_{j=1}^{12} (2j-1)$ is an arithmetic series with $a_1 = 1$ and $d = 2$. To use the formula $S_n = \frac{n}{2}(a_1 + a_n)$, we need find a_{12} (the last term). Since $a_{12} = 2(12) - 1 = 24 - 1 = 23$, we have the following.

$$\sum_{j=1}^{12} (2j-1) = S_{12} = \frac{12}{2}(1+23) = 6(24) = 144$$

Section 11.4: The Binomial Theorem

1. $\frac{6!}{3!3!} = \frac{6\cdot5\cdot4\cdot3\cdot2\cdot1}{3\cdot2\cdot1\cdot3\cdot2\cdot1} = \frac{6\cdot5\cdot4}{3\cdot2\cdot1} = 20$

3. $\frac{7!}{3!4!} = \frac{7\cdot6\cdot5\cdot4\cdot3\cdot2\cdot1}{3\cdot2\cdot1\cdot4\cdot3\cdot2\cdot1} = \frac{7\cdot6\cdot5}{3\cdot2\cdot1} = 35$

5. $\binom{8}{3} = \frac{8!}{3!5!} = \frac{8\cdot7\cdot6\cdot5\cdot4\cdot3\cdot2\cdot1}{3\cdot2\cdot1\cdot5\cdot4\cdot3\cdot2\cdot1} = \frac{8\cdot7\cdot6}{3\cdot2\cdot1} = 56$

7. $\binom{10}{8} = \frac{10!}{8!2!} = \frac{10\cdot9\cdot8!}{8!\cdot2\cdot1} = \frac{10\cdot9}{2\cdot1} = 45$

9. $\binom{13}{13} = \frac{13!}{13!0!} = \frac{13!}{13!\cdot1} = 1$

11. $\binom{n}{n-1} = \frac{n!}{(n-1)!\left[n-(n-1)\right]!} = \frac{n!}{(n-1)!(n-n+1)!} = \frac{n!}{(n-1)!1!} = \frac{n(n-1)!}{(n-1)!} = n$

13. ${}_8C_3 = \frac{8!}{3!(8-3)!} = \frac{8!}{3!5!} = \frac{8\cdot7\cdot6}{3\cdot2\cdot1} = 56$

15. ${}_{100}C_2 = \frac{100!}{2!(100-2)!} = \frac{100!}{2!98!} = \frac{100\cdot99}{2\cdot1} = 4950$

17. ${}_4C_0 = \frac{4!}{0!(4-0)!} = \frac{4!}{1\cdot4!} = 1$

19. The first term in the expansion of $(2x+3y)^4$ is $(2x)^4 = 16x^4$ and the last is $(3y)^4 = 81y^4$.

21. $(x+y)^6 = x^6 + \binom{6}{1}x^5y + \binom{6}{2}x^4y^2 + \binom{6}{3}x^3y^3 + \binom{6}{4}x^2y^4 + \binom{6}{5}xy^5 + y^6$

$= x^6 + \frac{6!}{1!5!}x^5y + \frac{6!}{2!4!}x^4y^2 + \frac{6!}{3!3!}x^3y^3 + \frac{6!}{4!2!}x^2y^4 + \frac{6!}{5!1!}xy^5 + y^6$

$= x^6 + 6x^5y + \frac{6\cdot5}{2\cdot1}x^4y^2 + \frac{6\cdot5\cdot4}{3\cdot2\cdot1}x^3y^3 + \frac{6\cdot5}{2\cdot1}x^2y^4 + 6xy^5 + y^6$

$= x^6 + 6x^5y + 15x^4y^2 + 20x^3y^3 + 15x^2y^4 + 6xy^5 + y^6$

23. $(p-q)^5 = [p+(-q)]^5$
$$= p^5 + \binom{5}{1}p^4(-q) + \binom{5}{2}p^3(-q)^2 + \binom{5}{3}p^2(-q)^3 + \binom{5}{4}p(-q)^4 + (-q)^5$$
$$= p^5 + \frac{5!}{1!4!}p^4(-q) + \frac{5!}{2!3!}p^3q^2 + \frac{5!}{3!2!}p^2(-q)^3 + \frac{5!}{4!1!}pq^4 + (-q)^5$$
$$= p^5 + 5p^4(-q) + \frac{5\cdot 4}{2\cdot 1}p^3q^2 + \frac{5\cdot 4}{2\cdot 1}p^2(-q)^3 + 5pq^4 + (-q)^5$$
$$= p^5 - 5p^4q + 10p^3q^2 - 10p^2q^3 + 5pq^4 - q^5$$

25. $(r^2+s)^5 = (r^2)^5 + \binom{5}{1}(r^2)^4 s + \binom{5}{2}(r^2)^3 s^2 + \binom{5}{3}(r^2)^2 s^3 + \binom{5}{4}(r^2)s^4 + s^5$
$$= r^{10} + \frac{5!}{1!4!}r^8s + \frac{5!}{2!3!}r^6s^2 + \frac{5!}{3!2!}r^4s^3 + \frac{5!}{4!1!}r^2s^4 + s^5$$
$$= r^{10} + 5r^8s + \frac{5\cdot 4}{2\cdot 1}r^6s^2 + \frac{5\cdot 4}{2\cdot 1}r^4s^3 + 5r^2s^4 + s^5$$
$$= r^{10} + 5r^8s + 10r^6s^2 + 10r^4s^3 + 5r^2s^4 + s^5$$

27. $(p+2q)^4 = p^4 + \binom{4}{1}p^3(2q) + \binom{4}{2}p^2(2q)^2 + \binom{4}{3}p(2q)^3 + (2q)^4$
$$= p^4 + \frac{4!}{1!3!}p^3(2q) + \frac{4!}{2!2!}p^2(4q^2) + \frac{4!}{3!1!}p(8q^3) + 16q^4$$
$$= p^4 + 4p^3(2q) + \frac{4\cdot 3}{2\cdot 1}p^2(4q^2) + 4p(8q^3) + 16q^4$$
$$= p^4 + 8p^3q + 24p^2q^2 + 32pq^3 + 16q^4$$

29. $(7p+2q)^4 = (7p)^4 + \binom{4}{1}(7p)^3(2q) + \binom{4}{2}(7p)^2(2q)^2 + \binom{4}{3}(7p)(2q)^3 + (2q)^4$
$$= 2401p^4 + \frac{4!}{1!3!}(343p^3)(2q) + \frac{4!}{2!2!}(49p^2)(4q^2) + \frac{4!}{3!1!}(7p)(8q^3) + 16q^4$$
$$= 2401p^4 + 4(686p^3q) + \frac{4\cdot 3}{2\cdot 1}(196p^2q^2) + 4(56pq^3) + 16q^4$$
$$= 2401p^4 + 2744p^3q + 6(196p^2q^2) + 224pq^3 + 16q^4$$
$$= 2401p^4 + 2744p^3q + 1176p^2q^2 + 224pq^3 + 16q^4$$

31. $(3x-2y)^6 = (3x)^6 + \binom{6}{1}(3x)^5(-2y) + \binom{6}{2}(3x)^4(-2y)^2 + \binom{6}{3}(3x)^3(-2y)^3$

$+\binom{6}{4}(3x)^2(-2y)^4 + \binom{6}{5}(3x)(-2y)^5 + (-2y)^6$

$= 729x^6 + \frac{6!}{1!5!}(243x^5)(-2y) + \frac{6!}{2!4!}(81x^4)(4y^2) + \frac{6!}{3!3!}(27x^3)(-8y^3)$

$+\frac{6!}{4!2!}(9x^2)(16y^4) + \frac{6!}{5!1!}(3x)(-32y^5) + 64y^6$

$= 729x^6 - 6(486x^5y) + \frac{6\cdot 5}{2\cdot 1}(324x^4y^2) - \frac{6\cdot 5\cdot 4}{3\cdot 2\cdot 1}(216x^3y^3)$

$+\frac{6\cdot 5}{2\cdot 1}(144x^2y^4) - 6(96xy^5) + 64y^6$

$= 729x^6 - 2916x^5y + 15(324x^4y^2) - 20(216x^3y^3) + 15(144x^2y^4) - 576xy^5 + 64y^6$

$= 729x^6 - 2916x^5y + 4860x^4y^2 - 4320x^3y^3 + 2160x^2y^4 - 576xy^5 + 64y^6$

33. $\left(\frac{m}{2}-1\right)^6 = \left(\frac{m}{2}\right)^6 + \binom{6}{1}\left(\frac{m}{2}\right)^5(-1) + \binom{6}{2}\left(\frac{m}{2}\right)^4(-1)^2 + \binom{6}{3}\left(\frac{m}{2}\right)^3(-1)^3$

$+\binom{6}{4}\left(\frac{m}{2}\right)^2(-1)^4 + \binom{6}{5}\left(\frac{m}{2}\right)(-1)^5 + (-1)^6$

$= \frac{m^6}{64} - \frac{6!}{1!5!}\left(\frac{m^5}{32}\right) + \frac{6!}{2!4!}\left(\frac{m^4}{16}\right) - \frac{6!}{3!3!}\left(\frac{m^3}{8}\right) + \frac{6!}{4!2!}\left(\frac{m^2}{4}\right) - \frac{6!}{5!1!}\left(\frac{m}{2}\right) + 1$

$= \frac{m^6}{64} - 6\left(\frac{m^5}{32}\right) + \frac{6\cdot 5}{2\cdot 1}\left(\frac{m^4}{16}\right) - \frac{6\cdot 5\cdot 4}{3\cdot 2\cdot 1}\left(\frac{m^3}{8}\right) + \frac{6\cdot 5}{2\cdot 1}\left(\frac{m^2}{4}\right) - 6\left(\frac{m}{2}\right) + 1$

$= \frac{m^6}{64} - \frac{3m^5}{16} + 15\left(\frac{m^4}{16}\right) - 20\left(\frac{m^3}{8}\right) + 15\left(\frac{m^2}{4}\right) - 3m + 1$

$= \frac{m^6}{64} - \frac{3m^5}{16} + \frac{15m^4}{16} - \frac{5m^3}{2} + \frac{15m^2}{4} - 3m + 1$

35. $\left(\sqrt{2}r + \frac{1}{m}\right)^4 = \left(\sqrt{2}r\right)^4 + \binom{4}{1}\left(\sqrt{2}r\right)^3\left(\frac{1}{m}\right) + \binom{4}{2}\left(\sqrt{2}r\right)^2\left(\frac{1}{m}\right)^2 + \binom{4}{3}\left(\sqrt{2}r\right)\left(\frac{1}{m}\right)^3 + \left(\frac{1}{m}\right)^4$

$= \left(\sqrt{2}r\right)^4 + \frac{4!}{1!3!}\left(\sqrt{2}r\right)^3\left(\frac{1}{m}\right) + \frac{4!}{2!2!}\left(\sqrt{2}r\right)^2\frac{1}{m^2} + \frac{4!}{3!1!}\left(\sqrt{2}r\right)\frac{1}{m^3} + \frac{1}{m^4}$

$= 4r^4 + 4\left(2\sqrt{2}\right)r^3\left(\frac{1}{m}\right) + \frac{4\cdot 3}{2\cdot 1}\left(2r^2\right)\frac{1}{m^2} + 4\left(\sqrt{2}r\right)\frac{1}{m^3} + \frac{1}{m^4}$

$= 4r^4 + \frac{8\sqrt{2}r^3}{m} + (6)\frac{2r^2}{m^2} + \frac{4\sqrt{2}r}{m^3} + \frac{1}{m^4}$

$= 4r^4 + \frac{8\sqrt{2}r^3}{m} + \frac{12r^2}{m^2} + \frac{4\sqrt{2}r}{m^3} + \frac{1}{m^4}$

37. $(4h-j)^8$

Using the formula $\binom{n}{k-1}x^{n-(k-1)}y^{k-1}$ with $n = 8$, $k-1 = 5$, and $n-(k-1) = 3$, the sixth term of the expansion is $\binom{8}{5}(4h)^3(-j)^5 = \frac{8!}{5!3!}(64h^3)(-j^5) = \frac{8\cdot7\cdot6}{3\cdot2\cdot1}(64h^3)(-j^5) = 56(-64h^3j^5) = -3584h^3j^5$.

39. $(a^2+b)^{22}$

Use the formula $\binom{n}{k-1}x^{n-(k-1)}y^{k-1}$ with $n = 22$, $k = 15$, $k-1 = 14$, and $n-(k-1) = 8$. The fifteenth term of the expansion is as follows.

$$\binom{22}{14}(a^2)^8(b)^{14} = \frac{22!}{14!8!}(a^{16})(b^{14}) = \frac{22\cdot21\cdot20\cdot19\cdot18\cdot17\cdot16\cdot15}{8\cdot7\cdot6\cdot5\cdot4\cdot3\cdot2\cdot1}(a^{16}b^{14}) = 319,770a^{16}b^{14}.$$

41. $(x-y^3)^{20}$

Use the formula $\binom{n}{k-1}x^{n-(k-1)}y^{k-1}$ with $n = 20$, $k = 15$, $k-1 = 14$, and $n-(k-1) = 6$. The fifteenth term of the expansion is as follows.

$$\binom{20}{14}(x)^6(-y^3)^{14} = \frac{20!}{14!6!}(x^6)(y^{42}) = \frac{20\cdot19\cdot18\cdot17\cdot16\cdot15}{6\cdot5\cdot4\cdot3\cdot2\cdot1}(x^6y^{42}) = 38,760x^6y^{42}.$$

43. $(3x^7+2y^3)^8$

This expansion has nine terms, so the middle term is the fifth term. Using the formula $\binom{n}{k-1}x^{n-(k-1)}y^{k-1}$ with $n = 8$, $k = 5$, $k-1 = 4$, and $n-(k-1) = 4$, the fifth term is as follows.

$$\binom{8}{4}(3x^7)^4(2y^3)^4 = \frac{8!}{4!4!}(3^4x^{28})(2^4y^{12}) = \frac{8\cdot7\cdot6\cdot5}{4\cdot3\cdot2\cdot1}(81x^{28})(16y^{12})$$
$$(70)(1296x^{28}y^{12}) = 90,720x^{28}y^{12}$$

45. If the coefficients of the fifth and eighth terms in the expansion of $(x+y)^n$ are the same, then the symmetry of the expansion can be used to determine n. There are four terms before the fifth term, so there must be four terms after the eighth term. This means that the last term of the expansion is the twelfth term. This in turn means that $n = 11$, since $(x+y)^{11}$ is the expansion that has twelve terms.

47. Using a calculator, we obtain the exact value $10! = 3,628,800$. Using Stirling's formula, we obtain the following.

$$10! \approx \sqrt{2\pi(10)}\cdot10^{10}\cdot e^{-10} \approx 3,598,695.619$$

48. Since $\frac{3,628,800-3,598,695.619}{3,628,800} \approx .00830$, the percent error is approximately .830%.

49. Using a calculator, we obtain the exact value 12! = 479,001,600. Using Stirling's formula, we obtain the following.

$$12! \approx \sqrt{2\pi(12)} \cdot 12^{12} \cdot e^{-12} \approx 475{,}687{,}486.5$$

Since $\frac{479{,}001{,}600 - 475{,}687{,}486.5}{479{,}001{,}600} \approx .00692$, the percent error is approximately .692%.

50. Using a calculator, we obtain the exact value 13! = 6,227,020,800. Using Stirling's formula, we obtain the following.

$$13! \approx \sqrt{2\pi(13)} \cdot 13^{13} \cdot e^{-13} \approx 6{,}187{,}239{,}475$$

Since $\frac{6{,}227{,}020{,}800 - 6{,}187{,}239{,}475}{6{,}227{,}020{,}800} \approx .00639$, the percent error is approximately .639%.

As n gets larger, the percent decreases

For Exercises 51 – 53, we will be using the first four terms of the following formula.

$$(1+x)^n = 1 + nx + \frac{n(n-1)}{2!}x^2 + \frac{n(n-1)(n-2)}{3!}x^3 + \ldots$$

51. $(1.02)^{-3} = (1+.02)^{-3}$

$$\begin{aligned}
&= 1 + (-3)(.02) + \frac{(-3)(-3-1)}{2!}(.02)^2 + \frac{(-3)(-3-1)(-3-2)}{3!}(.02)^3 \\
&= 1 - .06 + \frac{(-3)(-4)}{2 \cdot 1}(.0004) + \frac{(-3)(-4)(-5)}{3 \cdot 2 \cdot 1}(.000008) \\
&= 1 - .06 + 6(.0004) - 10(.000008) \\
&= 1 - .06 + .0024 - .00008 \\
&= .94232 \approx .942
\end{aligned}$$

53. $(1.01)^{1.5} = (1+.01)^{1.5}$

$$\begin{aligned}
&= 1 + (1.5)(.01) + \frac{(1.5)(1.5-1)}{2!}(.01)^2 + \frac{(1.5)(1.5-1)(1.5-2)}{3!}(.01)^3 \\
&= 1 + .015 + \frac{(1.5)(.5)}{2 \cdot 1}(.0001) + \frac{(1.5)(.5)(-.5)}{3 \cdot 2 \cdot 1}(.000001) \\
&= 1 + .015 + .375(.0001) - .0625(.000001) \\
&= 1 + .015 + .0000375 - .0000000625 \\
&= 1.0150374375 \approx 1.015
\end{aligned}$$

Section 11.5: Mathematical Induction

1. Let S_n be the statement $1+3+5+...+(2n-1)=n^2$.

$S_1: 1=1^2 \Rightarrow 1=1,$ which is true.

$S_2: 1+3=2^2 \Rightarrow 4=4,$ which is true.

$S_3: 1+3+5=3^2 \Rightarrow 9=9,$ which is true.

$S_4: 1+3+5+7=4^2 \Rightarrow 16=16,$ which is true.

$S_5: 1+3+5+7+9=5^2 \Rightarrow 25=25,$ which is true.

Now prove that S_n is true for every positive integer *n*.

Step 1: Show that the statement is true when *n* = 1.

S_1 is the statement $1=1^2 \Rightarrow 1=1,$ which is true.

Step 2: Show that S_k implies S_{k+1}, where S_k is the statement $1+3+5+...+(2k-1)=k^2$, and S_{k+1} is the statement $1+3+5+...+(2k-1)+\left[2(k+1)-1\right]=(k+1)^2$.

Start with S_k: $1+3+5+...+(2k-1)=k^2$ and add the $(k+1)$ st term, $\left[2(k+1)-1\right]$, to both sides of this equation.

$$1+3+5+...+(2k-1)=k^2$$
$$1+3+5+...+(2k-1)+\left[2(k+1)-1\right]=k^2+\left[2(k+1)-1\right]$$
$$1+3+5+...+(2k-1)+\left[2(k+1)-1\right]=k^2+(2k+2-1)$$
$$1+3+5+...+(2k-1)+\left[2(k+1)-1\right]=k^2+2k+1$$
$$1+3+5+...+(2k-1)+\left[2(k+1)-1\right]=(k+1)^2$$

It has been shown that S_k implies S_{k+1}. Therefore, the statement S_n is true for every positive integer value of *n*.

3. S_n is the statement $3+6+9+...+3n=\dfrac{3n(n+1)}{2}$.

(a) *Verify the statement for* $n=1$.

$$3(1)=\frac{3(1)(1+1)}{2} \Rightarrow 3=\frac{6}{2} \Rightarrow 3=3,$$ which is true. Thus, S_n is true for $n=1$.

(b) *Write the statement for* $n=k$.

$$3+6+9+...+3k=\frac{3k(k+1)}{2}$$

(c) *Write the statement for* $n=k+1$.

$$3+6+9+...+3k+3(k+1)=\frac{3(k+1)\left[(k+1)+1\right]}{2}$$

Continued on next page

3. (continued)

(d) *Assume the statement is true for $n=k$. Use algebra to change the statement in part (b) to the statement in part (c).*

Add the $(k+1)$ st term, $3(k+1)$, to both sides of this equation.

$$3+6+9+\ldots+3k=\frac{3k(k+1)}{2}$$
$$3+6+9+\ldots+3k+3(k+1)=\frac{3k(k+1)}{2}+3(k+1)$$
$$3+6+9+\ldots+3k+3(k+1)=\frac{3k(k+1)+6(k+1)}{2}$$
$$3+6+9+\ldots+3k+3(k+1)=\frac{3k^2+3k+6k+6}{2}$$
$$3+6+9+\ldots+3k+3(k+1)=\frac{3k^2+9k+6}{2}$$
$$3+6+9+\ldots+3k+3(k+1)=\frac{3(k^2+3k+2)}{2}$$
$$3+6+9+\ldots+3k+3(k+1)=\frac{3(k+1)(k+2)}{2}$$
$$3+6+9+\ldots+3k+3(k+1)=\frac{3(k+1)[(k+1)+1]}{2}$$

(e) *Write a conclusion based on Steps (a) – (d).*

Since S_n is true for $n=1$ and $n=k+1$ when it is true for $n=k$, S_n is true for every positive integer *n*.

5. S_n is the statement $2+4+8+\ldots+2^n=2^{n+1}-2$.

(a) *Verify the statement for $n=1$.*

$2^1=2^{1+1}-2\Rightarrow 2=2^2-2\Rightarrow 2=4-2\Rightarrow 2=2$, which is true. Thus, S_n is true for $n=1$.

(b) *Write the statement for $n=k$.*

$$2+4+8+\ldots+2^k=2^{k+1}-2$$

(c) *Write the statement for $n=k+1$.*

$$2+4+8+\ldots+2^k+2^{k+1}=2^{(k+1)+1}-2$$

(d) *Assume the statement is true for $n=k$. Use algebra to change the statement in part (b) to the statement in part (c).*

Add the $(k+1)$ st term, 2^{k+1}, to both sides of this equation.

$$2+4+8+\ldots+2^k=2^{k+1}-2$$
$$2+4+8+\ldots+2^k+2^{k+1}=2^{k+1}-2+2^{k+1}$$
$$2+4+8+\ldots+2^k+2^{k+1}=2\cdot 2^{k+1}-2$$
$$2+4+8+\ldots+2^k+2^{k+1}=2^1\cdot 2^{k+1}-2$$
$$2+4+8+\ldots+2^k+2^{k+1}=2^{(k+1)+1}-2$$

(e) *Write a conclusion based on Steps (a) – (d).*

Since S_n is true for $n=1$ and $n=k+1$ when it is true for $n=k$, S_n is true for every positive integer *n*.

7. S_n is the statement $1^2+2^2+3^2+\ldots+n^2=\frac{n(n+1)(2n+1)}{6}$.

(a) *Verify the statement for* $n=1$.

$1^2=\frac{1(1+1)(2\cdot 1+1)}{6}\Rightarrow 1=\frac{1(2)(2+1)}{6}\Rightarrow 1=\frac{2(3)}{6}\Rightarrow 1=1$, which is true. Thus, S_n is true for $n=1$.

(b) *Write the statement for* $n=k$.

$$1^2+2^2+3^2+\ldots+k^2=\frac{k(k+1)(2k+1)}{6}$$

(c) *Write the statement for* $n=k+1$.

$$1^2+2^2+3^2+\ldots+k^2+(k+1)^2=\frac{(k+1)[(k+1)+1][2(k+1)+1]}{6}$$

(d) *Assume the statement is true for* $n=k$. *Use algebra to change the statement in part (b) to the statement in part (c).*

Add the $(k+1)$ st term, $(k+1)^2$, to both sides of this equation.

$$1^2+2^2+3^2+\ldots+k^2=\frac{k(k+1)(2k+1)}{6}$$

$$1^2+2^2+3^2+\ldots+k^2+(k+1)^2=\frac{k(k+1)(2k+1)}{6}+(k+1)^2$$

$$1^2+2^2+3^2+\ldots+k^2+(k+1)^2=\frac{k(k+1)(2k+1)+6(k+1)^2}{6}$$

$$1^2+2^2+3^2+\ldots+k^2+(k+1)^2=\frac{(k+1)[k(2k+1)+6(k+1)]}{6}$$

$$1^2+2^2+3^2+\ldots+k^2+(k+1)^2=\frac{(k+1)(2k^2+k+6k+6)}{6}$$

$$1^2+2^2+3^2+\ldots+k^2+(k+1)^2=\frac{(k+1)(2k^2+7k+6)}{6}$$

$$1^2+2^2+3^2+\ldots+k^2+(k+1)^2=\frac{(k+1)(k+2)(2k+3)}{6}$$

$$1^2+2^2+3^2+\ldots+k^2+(k+1)^2=\frac{(k+1)(k+2)(2k+2+1)}{6}$$

$$1^2+2^2+3^2+\ldots+k^2+(k+1)^2=\frac{(k+1)[(k+1)+1][2(k+1)+1]}{6}$$

(e) *Write a conclusion based on Steps (a) – (d).*

Since S_n is true for $n=1$ and $n=k+1$ when it is true for $n=k$, S_n is true for every positive integer *n*.

9. S_n is the statement $5\cdot 6+5\cdot 6^2+5\cdot 6^3+\ldots+5\cdot 6^n=6\left(6^n-1\right)$.

(a) *Verify the statement for* $n=1$.

$5\cdot 6^1=6\left(6^1-1\right)\Rightarrow 5\cdot 6=6(6-1)\Rightarrow 30=6(5)\Rightarrow 30=30$, which is true. Thus, S_n is true for $n=1$.

(b) *Write the statement for* $n=k$.

$$5\cdot 6+5\cdot 6^2+5\cdot 6^3+\ldots+5\cdot 6^k=6\left(6^k-1\right)$$

(c) *Write the statement for* $n=k+1$.

$$5\cdot 6+5\cdot 6^2+5\cdot 6^3+\ldots+5\cdot 6^k+5\cdot 6^{k+1}=6\left(6^{k+1}-1\right)$$

(d) *Assume the statement is true for* $n=k$. *Use algebra to change the statement in part (b) to the statement in part (c).*

Add the $(k+1)$ st term, $5\cdot 6^{k+1}$, to both sides of this equation.

$$5\cdot 6+5\cdot 6^2+5\cdot 6^3+\ldots+5\cdot 6^k=6\left(6^k-1\right)$$
$$5\cdot 6+5\cdot 6^2+5\cdot 6^3+\ldots+5\cdot 6^k+5\cdot 6^{k+1}=6\left(6^k-1\right)+5\cdot 6^{k+1}$$
$$5\cdot 6+5\cdot 6^2+5\cdot 6^3+\ldots+5\cdot 6^k+5\cdot 6^{k+1}=6\left[\left(6^k-1\right)+5\cdot 6^k\right]$$
$$5\cdot 6+5\cdot 6^2+5\cdot 6^3+\ldots+5\cdot 6^k+5\cdot 6^{k+1}=6\left[6\cdot 6^k-1\right]$$
$$5\cdot 6+5\cdot 6^2+5\cdot 6^3+\ldots+5\cdot 6^k+5\cdot 6^{k+1}=6\left(6^{k+1}-1\right)$$

(e) *Write a conclusion based on Steps (a) – (d).*

Since S_n is true for $n=1$ and $n=k+1$ when it is true for $n=k$, S_n is true for every positive integer *n*.

11. S_n is the statement $\frac{1}{1\cdot 2}+\frac{1}{2\cdot 3}+\frac{1}{3\cdot 4}+\ldots+\frac{1}{n(n+1)}=\frac{n}{n+1}$.

(a) *Verify the statement for* $n=1$.

$\frac{1}{(1)(1+1)}=\frac{1}{1+1}\Rightarrow\frac{1}{(1)(2)}=\frac{1}{2}\Rightarrow\frac{1}{2}=\frac{1}{2}$, which is true. Thus, S_n is true for $n=1$.

(b) *Write the statement for* $n=k$.

$$\frac{1}{1\cdot 2}+\frac{1}{2\cdot 3}+\frac{1}{3\cdot 4}+\ldots+\frac{1}{k(k+1)}=\frac{k}{k+1}$$

(c) *Write the statement for* $n=k+1$.

$$\frac{1}{1\cdot 2}+\frac{1}{2\cdot 3}+\frac{1}{3\cdot 4}+\ldots+\frac{1}{k(k+1)}+\frac{1}{(k+1)\left[(k+1)+1\right]}=\frac{k+1}{(k+1)+1}$$

Continued on next page

11. (continued)

(d) *Assume the statement is true for $n=k$. Use algebra to change the statement in part (b) to the statement in part (c).*

Add the $(k+1)$ st term, $\frac{1}{(k+1)\left[(k+1)+1\right]}$, to both sides of this equation.

$$\frac{1}{1\cdot2}+\frac{1}{2\cdot3}+\frac{1}{3\cdot4}+\ldots+\frac{1}{k(k+1)}=\frac{k}{k+1}$$

$$\frac{1}{1\cdot2}+\frac{1}{2\cdot3}+\frac{1}{3\cdot4}+\ldots+\frac{1}{k(k+1)}+\frac{1}{(k+1)\left[(k+1)+1\right]}=\frac{k}{k+1}+\frac{1}{(k+1)\left[(k+1)+1\right]}$$

$$\frac{1}{1\cdot2}+\frac{1}{2\cdot3}+\frac{1}{3\cdot4}+\ldots+\frac{1}{k(k+1)}+\frac{1}{(k+1)\left[(k+1)+1\right]}=\frac{k}{k+1}+\frac{1}{(k+1)(k+2)}$$

$$\frac{1}{1\cdot2}+\frac{1}{2\cdot3}+\frac{1}{3\cdot4}+\ldots+\frac{1}{k(k+1)}+\frac{1}{(k+1)\left[(k+1)+1\right]}=\frac{k(k+2)+1}{(k+1)(k+2)}$$

$$\frac{1}{1\cdot2}+\frac{1}{2\cdot3}+\frac{1}{3\cdot4}+\ldots+\frac{1}{k(k+1)}+\frac{1}{(k+1)\left[(k+1)+1\right]}=\frac{k^2+2k+1}{(k+1)(k+2)}$$

$$\frac{1}{1\cdot2}+\frac{1}{2\cdot3}+\frac{1}{3\cdot4}+\ldots+\frac{1}{k(k+1)}+\frac{1}{(k+1)\left[(k+1)+1\right]}=\frac{(k+1)^2}{(k+1)(k+2)}$$

$$\frac{1}{1\cdot2}+\frac{1}{2\cdot3}+\frac{1}{3\cdot4}+\ldots+\frac{1}{k(k+1)}+\frac{1}{(k+1)\left[(k+1)+1\right]}=\frac{k+1}{k+2}$$

$$\frac{1}{1\cdot2}+\frac{1}{2\cdot3}+\frac{1}{3\cdot4}+\ldots+\frac{1}{k(k+1)}+\frac{1}{(k+1)\left[(k+1)+1\right]}=\frac{k+1}{(k+1)+1}$$

(e) *Write a conclusion based on Steps (a) – (d).*

Since S_n is true for $n=1$ and $n=k+1$ when it is true for $n=k$, S_n is true for every positive integer *n*.

13. S_n is the statement $\frac{1}{2}+\frac{1}{2^2}+\frac{1}{2^3}+\ldots+\frac{1}{2^n}=1-\frac{1}{2^n}$.

(a) *Verify the statement for $n=1$.*

$\frac{1}{2^1}=1-\frac{1}{2^1}\Rightarrow\frac{1}{2}=1-\frac{1}{2}\Rightarrow\frac{1}{2}=\frac{1}{2}$, which is true. Thus, S_n is true for $n=1$.

(b) *Write the statement for $n=k$.*

$$\frac{1}{2}+\frac{1}{2^2}+\frac{1}{2^3}+\ldots+\frac{1}{2^k}=1-\frac{1}{2^k}$$

(c) *Write the statement for $n=k+1$.*

$$\frac{1}{2}+\frac{1}{2^2}+\frac{1}{2^3}+\ldots+\frac{1}{2^k}+\frac{1}{2^{k+1}}=1-\frac{1}{2^{k+1}}$$

Continued on next page

13. (continued)

(d) *Assume the statement is true for $n=k$. Use algebra to change the statement in part (b) to the statement in part (c).*

Add the $(k+1)$ st term, $\frac{1}{2^{k+1}}$, to both sides of this equation.

$$\frac{1}{2}+\frac{1}{2^2}+\frac{1}{2^3}+\ldots+\frac{1}{2^k}=1-\frac{1}{2^k}$$

$$\frac{1}{2}+\frac{1}{2^2}+\frac{1}{2^3}+\ldots+\frac{1}{2^k}+\frac{1}{2^{k+1}}=1-\frac{1}{2^k}+\frac{1}{2^{k+1}}$$

$$\frac{1}{2}+\frac{1}{2^2}+\frac{1}{2^3}+\ldots+\frac{1}{2^k}+\frac{1}{2^{k+1}}=1-\frac{1\cdot 2}{2^k . 2}+\frac{1}{2^{k+1}}$$

$$\frac{1}{2}+\frac{1}{2^2}+\frac{1}{2^3}+\ldots+\frac{1}{2^k}+\frac{1}{2^{k+1}}=1-\frac{2}{2^{k+1}}+\frac{1}{2^{k+1}}$$

$$\frac{1}{2}+\frac{1}{2^2}+\frac{1}{2^3}+\ldots+\frac{1}{2^k}+\frac{1}{2^{k+1}}=1-\frac{1}{2^{k+1}}$$

(e) *Write a conclusion based on Steps (a) – (d).*

Since S_n is true for $n=1$ and $n=k+1$ when it is true for $n=k$, S_n is true for every positive integer *n*.

15. $2^n > 2n$

If $n = 1$, we have $2^1 > 2\cdot 1$ or $2 > 2$, which is false.

If $n = 2$, we have $2^2 > 2\cdot 2$ or $4 > 4$, which is false.

If $n = 3$, we have $2^3 > 2\cdot 3$ or $8 > 6$, which is true.

For $n \geq 3$, the statement is true. The statement is false for $n = 1$ or 2.

17. $2^n > n^2$

If $n = 1$, we have $2^1 > 1^2$ or $2 > 1$, which is true.

If $n = 2$, we have $2^2 > 2^2$ or $4 > 4$, which is false.

If $n = 3$, we have $2^3 > 3^2$ or $8 > 9$, which is false.

If $n = 4$, we have $2^4 > 4^2$ or $16 > 16$, which is false.

If $n = 5$, we have $2^5 > 5^2$ or $32 > 25$, which is true.

For $n \geq 5$, the statement is true. The statement is false for $n = 2$, 3, or 4.

19. Let S_n be the statement $(a^m)^n = a^{mn}$. (Assume that a and m are constant.)

Step 1: Show that the statement is true when $n = 1$.

S_1 is the statement $\left(a^m\right)^1 = a^{m\cdot 1} \Rightarrow a^m = a^m$, which is true.

Step 2: Show that S_k implies S_{k+1}, where S_k is the statement $\left(a^m\right)^k = a^{mk}$, and S_{k+1} is the statement $\left(a^m\right)^{k+1} = a^{m(k+1)}$.

$$\left(a^m\right)^k = a^{mk}$$
$$\left(a^m\right)^k \cdot \left(a^m\right)^1 = a^{mk} \cdot \left(a^m\right)^1$$
$$\left(a^m\right)^{k+1} = a^{mk} \cdot a^m$$
$$\left(a^m\right)^{k+1} = a^{mk+m}$$
$$\left(a^m\right)^{k+1} = a^{m(k+1)}$$

It has been shown that S_k implies S_{k+1}. Therefore, the statement S_n is true for every positive integer value of n.

21. Let S_n be the statement $2^n > 2n$, if $n \geq 3$.

Step 1: Show that the statement is true when $n = 3$.

S_3 is the statement $2^3 > 2 \cdot 3 \Rightarrow 8 > 6$, which is true.

Step 2: Show that S_k implies S_{k+1}, where S_k is the statement $2^k > 2k$, and S_{k+1} is the statement $2^{k+1} > 2(k+1)$.

$$2^k > 2k$$
$$2^k \cdot 2 > 2k \cdot 2$$
$$2^k \cdot 2^1 > 4k$$
$$2^{k+1} > 2k + 2k$$

Since $k \geq 3$ we have $2k > 2$.

$$2^{k+1} > 2k + 2k > 2k + 2$$
$$2^{k+1} > 2k + 2$$
$$2^{k+1} > 2(k+1)$$

It has been shown that S_k implies S_{k+1}. Therefore, the statement S_n is true for every positive integer value of n greater than or equal to 3.

23. Let S_n be the statement: If $a > 1$, then $a^n > 1$.

Step 1: Show that the statement is true when $n = 1$.

S_1 is the statement, If $a > 1$, then $a^1 > 1$, which is obviously true since $a = a^1$.

Step 2: Show that S_k implies S_{k+1}, where S_k is the statement: If $a > 1$, then $a^k > 1$. S_{k+1} is the statement: If $a > 1$, then $a^{k+1} > 1$.

If $a > 1$, then $a^k > 1$.

$$a^k > 1 \Rightarrow a^k \cdot a > 1 \cdot a$$

$$a^k \cdot a^1 > a \Rightarrow a^{k+1} > a$$

Since $a > 1$ we have the following.

$$a^{k+1} > a > 1$$

$$a^{k+1} > 1$$

Note: Since $a > 1 > 0$, we did not need to be concerned about changing the direction of the inequality.

It has been shown that S_k implies S_{k+1}. Therefore, the statement S_n is true for every positive integer value of n.

25. Let S_n be the statement: If $0 < a < 1$, then $a^n < a^{n-1}$.

Step 1: Show that the statement is true when $n = 1$.

S_1 is the statement: If $0 < a < 1$, then $a^1 < a^{1-1}$. Since $a^1 < a^{1-1} \Rightarrow a < a^0 \Rightarrow a < 1$, which is true.

Step 2: Show that S_k implies S_{k+1}, where S_k is the statement: If $0 < a < 1$, then $a^k < a^{k-1}$. S_{k+1} is the statement: If $0 < a < 1$, then $a^{k+1} < a^{(k+1)-1}$.

If $0 < a < 1$, then $a^k < a^{k-1}$.

$$a^k < a^{k-1}$$

$$a^k \cdot a^1 < a^{k-1} a^1$$

$$a^{k+1} < a^{(k-1)+1}$$

$$a^{k+1} < a^{(k+1)-1}$$

Note: Since $0 < a < 1$, we did not need to be concerned about changing the direction of the inequality.

It has been shown that S_k implies S_{k+1}. Therefore, the statement S_n is true for every positive integer value of n.

27. Let S_n be the statement: If $n \ge 4$, then $n! > 2^n$, where $n! = n(n-1)(n-2)\cdots(3)(2)(1)$.

Step 1: Show that the statement is true when $n = 4$.

S_4 is the statement $4! > 2^4 \Rightarrow 4(3)(2)(1) > (2)(2)(2)(2) \Rightarrow 24 > 16$, which is true.

Step 2: Show that S_k implies S_{k+1}, where S_k is the statement $k! > 2^k$, and S_{k+1} is the statement $(k+1)! > 2^{k+1}$.

$$k! > 2^k$$
$$k!(k+1) > 2^k(k+1)$$
$$(k+1)! > 2^k(k+1)$$

Since $k+1 > 2$, we have the following.

$$(k+1)! > 2^k(k+1) > 2 \cdot 2^k$$
$$(k+1)! > 2 \cdot 2^k \Rightarrow (k+1)! > 2^1 \cdot 2^k$$
$$(k+1)! > 2^{1+k} \Rightarrow (k+1)! > 2^{k+1}$$

Note: Since $k+1 > 0$, we did not need to be concerned about changing the direction of the inequality.

It has been shown that S_k implies S_{k+1}. Therefore, the statement S_n is true for every positive integer value of n greater than or equal to 4.

29. Let S_n be the number of handshakes of the n people is $\frac{n^2-n}{2}$.

Since 2 is the smallest number of people who can shake hands, we need to prove this statement for every positive integer $n \ge 2$.

Step 1: Show that the statement is true for $n = 2$. S_2 is the statement that for two people, the number of handshakes is $\frac{2^2-2}{2} = \frac{4-2}{2} = \frac{2}{2} = 1$, which is true.

Step 2: Show that S_k implies S_{k+1}, where S_k is the statement: k people shake hands in $\frac{k^2-k}{2}$ ways and S_{k+1} is the statement: $k+1$ people shake hands in $\frac{(k+1)^2-(k+1)}{2}$ ways.

Start with S_k and assume it is a true statement: For k people, there are $\frac{k^2-k}{2}$ handshakes.

If one more person joins the k people, this $(k + 1)$st person will shake hands with the previous k people one time each. Thus, there will be k additional handshakes. Thus, the number of handshakes for $k + 1$ people is as follows.

$$\frac{k^2-k}{2} + k = \frac{k^2-k}{2} + \frac{2k}{2} = \frac{k^2+k}{2} = \frac{(k^2+2k+1)-(k+1)}{2} = \frac{(k+1)^2-(k+1)}{2}$$

This shows that if S_k is true, S_{k+1} is true.

Since both steps for a proof by the generalized principle of mathematical induction have been completed, the given statement is true for every positive integer $n \ge 2$.

31. The number of sides of the nth figure is $3\cdot 4^{k-1}$ (from Exercise 30). To find the perimeter of each figure, multiply the number of sides by the length of each side. In each figure, the lengths of the sides are $\frac{1}{3}$ the lengths of the sides in the preceding figure. To find the perimeter of the nth figure, P_n, we try to find a pattern.

$$P_1 = 3(1) = 3$$
$$P_2 = 3\cdot 4\left(\tfrac{1}{3}\right) = 4$$
$$P_3 = 3\cdot 4^2\left(\tfrac{1}{9}\right) = \tfrac{16}{3}, \text{ and so on.}$$

This gives a geometric sequence with $a_1 = 3$ and $r = \frac{4}{3}$. Thus, $P_n = a_1 r^{n-1} \Rightarrow P_n = 3\left(\frac{4}{3}\right)^{n-1}$. The result may also be written as $P_n = \frac{3^1\cdot 4^{n-1}}{3^{n-1}} \Rightarrow P_n = \frac{4^{n-1}}{3^{-1}\cdot 3^{n-1}} \Rightarrow P_n = \frac{4^{n-1}}{3^{n-2}}$.

33. With 1 ring, 1 move is required. With 2 rings, 3 moves are required. Note that $2^2 - 1 = 3 = 2 + 1$. With 3 rings, 7 moves are required. Note that $2^3 - 1 = 7 = 2^2 + 2 + 1$. With n rings, the number of moves required are $2^{n-1} + 2^{n-2} + \ldots + 2^1 + 1$. This is a geometric series with $a_1 = 1$ and $r = 2$. The sum would be $\dfrac{a_1\left(1-r^n\right)}{1-r} = \dfrac{1\left(1-2^n\right)}{1-2} = \dfrac{1-2^n}{-1} = 2^n - 1$. Thus, S_n is the statement: For n rings, the number of required moves is $2^n - 1$. To prove this statement using mathematical induction, we perform the following steps.

Step 1: Show that the statement is true when $n = 1$.

S_1 is the statement: For 1 ring, the number of required moves is $2^1 - 1 = 2 - 1 = 1$, which is true.

Step 2: Show that S_k implies S_{k+1}, where S_k is the statement: For k rings, the number of required moves is $2^k - 1$. S_{k+1} is the statement: For $k+1$ rings, the number of required moves is $2^{k+1} - 1$.

Assume k + 1 rings are on the first peg. Since S_k is true, the top k rings can be moved to the second peg in $2^k - 1$ moves. Now move the bottom ring to the third peg. Since S_k is true, move the k rings on the second peg on top of the largest ring on the third peg in $2^k - 1$ moves. The total number of moves is $\left(2^k - 1\right) + 1 + \left(2^k - 1\right) = 2\cdot 2^k - 1 = 2^1\cdot 2^k - 1 = 2^{k+1} - 1$. Since S_n is true for $n = 1$ and $n = k + 1$ when is true for $n = k$, S_n is true for every positive integer n.

Section 11.6: Counting Theory

1. $P(12,8) = \dfrac{12!}{(12-8)!} = \dfrac{12!}{4!} = \dfrac{12\cdot 11\cdot 10\cdot 9\cdot 8\cdot 7\cdot 6\cdot 5\cdot 4\cdot 3\cdot 2\cdot 1}{4\cdot 3\cdot 2\cdot 1}$
$= 12\cdot 11\cdot 10\cdot 9\cdot 8\cdot 7\cdot 6\cdot 5 = 19{,}958{,}400$

3. $P(9, 2) = \dfrac{9!}{(9-2)!} = \dfrac{9!}{7!} = \dfrac{9\cdot 8\cdot 7!}{7!} = 9\cdot 8 = 72$

5. $P(5, 1) = \dfrac{5!}{(5-1)!} = \dfrac{5!}{4!} = \dfrac{5\cdot 4!}{4!} = 5$

7. $C(4,2)=\binom{4}{2}=\frac{4!}{(4-2)!2!}=\frac{4!}{2!2!}=\frac{4\cdot 3\cdot 2!}{2!2!}=\frac{4\cdot 3}{2\cdot 1}=6$

9. $C(6,0)=\binom{6}{0}=\frac{6!}{(6-0)!0!}=\frac{6!}{6!\cdot 1}=1$

11. $\binom{12}{4}=\frac{12!}{(12-4)!4!}=\frac{12!}{8!4!}=\frac{12\cdot 11\cdot 10\cdot 9\cdot 8!}{8!4!}=\frac{12\cdot 11\cdot 10\cdot 9}{4!}=\frac{12\cdot 11\cdot 10\cdot 9}{4\cdot 3\cdot 2\cdot 1}=495$

13. ${}_{20}P_5=1,860,480$

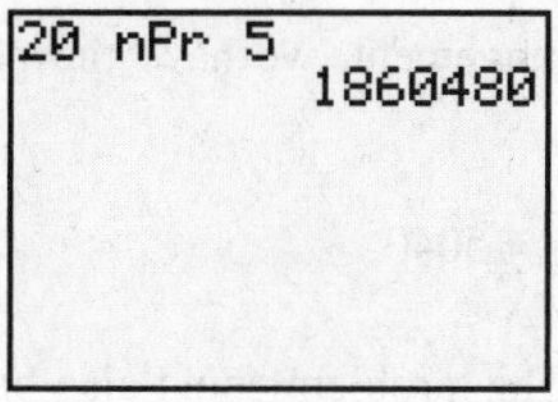

15. ${}_{15}P_8=259,459,200$

17. ${}_{20}C_5=15,504$

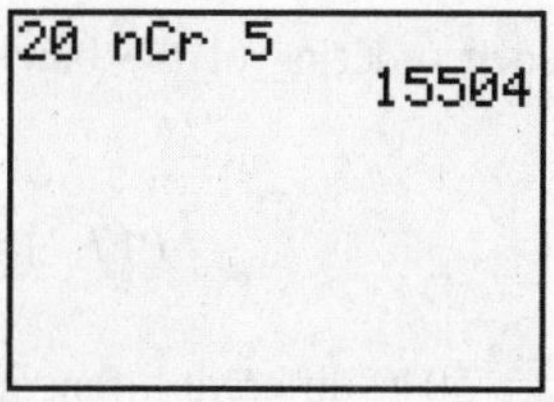

19. $\binom{15}{8}=C(15,8)=6435$

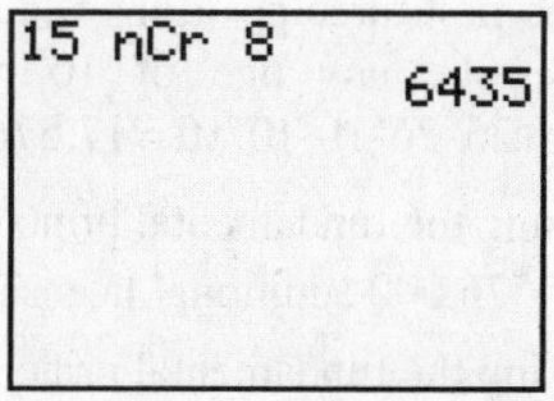

21. **(a)** Since the order of digits in a telephone number does matter, this involves a permutation.

(b) Since the order of digits in a Social Security number does matter, this involves a permutation.

(c) Since the order of the cards in a poker hand does not matter, this involves a combination.

(d) Since the order of members on a committee of politicians does not matter, this involves a combination.

(e) Since the order of numbers of the "combination" on a combination lock does matter, this involves a permutation.

(f) Since the order does not matter, the lottery choice of six numbers involves a combination.

(g) Since the order of digits and/or letters on a license plate does matter, this involves a permutation.

23. Using the fundamental principle of counting we have $5\cdot 4\cdot 2=40$. There are 40 different homes available if a builder offers a choice of 5 basic plans, 4 roof styles, and 2 exterior finishes.

25. **(a)** There are two choices for the first letter, K and W. The second letter can be any of the 26 letters of the alphabet except for the one chosen for the first letter, so there are 25 choices. The third letter can be any of the remaining 24 letters of the alphabet, so there are 24 choices. The fourth letter can be any of the remaining 23 letters of the alphabet, so there are 23 choices.

Therefore, by the fundamental principle of counting, the number of possible 4-letter radio-station call letters is $2\cdot 25\cdot 24\cdot 23=27,600$.

Continued on next page

25. (continued)

(b) There are two choices for the first letter. Because repeats are allowed, there are 26 choices for each of the remaining 3 letters.

Therefore, by the fundamental principle of counting, the number of possible 4-letter radio-station call letters is $2\cdot 26\cdot 26\cdot 26 = 35{,}152$.

(c) There are two choices for the first letter. There are 24 choices for the second letter since it cannot repeat the first letter and cannot be R. There are 23 choices for the third letter since it cannot repeat any of the first two letters and cannot be R. There is only once choice for the last letter since it must be R.

Therefore, by the fundamental principle of counting, the number of possible 4-letter radio-station call letters is $2\cdot 24\cdot 23\cdot 1 = 1104$.

27. Since each ordering of the blocks is considered a different arrangement, we have the permutation, $P(7,7)$.

$$P(7,7) = \frac{7!}{(7-7)!} = \frac{7!}{0!} = \frac{7\cdot 6\cdot 5\cdot 4\cdot 3\cdot 2\cdot 1}{1} = 5040$$

There are 5040 different arrangements of the 7 blocks. Note: This problem could also be solved by using the fundamental principle of counting. There are 7 choices for the first block, 6 for the second, 5 for the third, etc. The number of arrangements would be $7\cdot 6\cdot 5\cdot 4\cdot 3\cdot 2\cdot 1 = 5040$.

29. (a) The first three positions could each be any one of 26 letters, and the second three positions could each be any one of 10 digits. Using the fundamental principle of counting, we have $26\cdot 26\cdot 26\cdot 10\cdot 10\cdot 10 = 17{,}576{,}000$. Thus, 17,576,000 license plates were possible.

(b) Using the fundamental principle of counting, we have $10\cdot 10\cdot 10\cdot 26\cdot 26\cdot 26 = 17{,}576{,}000$. 17,576,000 additional license plates were made possible by the reversal.

(c) Using the fundamental principle of counting, we have $26\cdot 10\cdot 10\cdot 10\cdot 26\cdot 26\cdot 26 = 456{,}976{,}000$. 456,976,000 plates were provided by prefixing the previous pattern with an additional letter.

31. Since order does matter, we have the permutation, $P(8, 8) = \frac{8!}{(8-8)!} = \frac{8!}{0!} = \frac{8\cdot 7\cdot 6\cdot 5\cdot 4\cdot 3\cdot 2\cdot 1}{1} = 40{,}320$.

32. Since the order does matter, we have the following permutation.

$$P(10, 7) = \frac{10!}{(10-7)!} = \frac{10!}{3!} = \frac{10\cdot 9\cdot 8\cdot 7\cdot 6\cdot 5\cdot 4\cdot 3!}{3!} = 10\cdot 9\cdot 8\cdot 7\cdot 6\cdot 5\cdot 4 = 604{,}800$$

33. He has 6 choices for the first course, 5 choices for the second, and 4 choices for the third. Thus, the student has $6\cdot 5\cdot 4 = 120$ possible schedules according to the fundamental principle of counting.

35. The number of ways in which the 3 officers can be chosen from the 15 members is given by the following permutation.

$$P(15,3) = \frac{15!}{(15-3)!} = \frac{15!}{12!} = \frac{15\cdot 14\cdot 13\cdot 12!}{12!} = 15\cdot 14\cdot 13 = 2730$$

37. **(a)** $P(5,5)=\frac{5!}{(5-5)!}=\frac{5!}{0!}=\frac{5\cdot4\cdot3\cdot2\cdot1}{1}=120$

The letters can be arranged in 120 ways.

(b) $P(3,3)=\frac{3!}{(3-3)!}=\frac{3!}{0!}=\frac{3\cdot2\cdot1}{1}=6$

The first three letters can be arranged in 6 ways.

39. We want to choose 4 group members out of 30 and the order is not important. The number of possible groups is $C(30,4)=\binom{30}{4}=\frac{30!}{(30-4)!4!}=\frac{30!}{26!4!}=\frac{30\cdot29\cdot28\cdot27\cdot26!}{26!4!}=\frac{30\cdot29\cdot28\cdot27}{4\cdot3\cdot2\cdot1}=27,405.$

41. **(a)** We want to choose 4 extras from a choice of 6 extras and order is not important. The number of different hamburgers that can be made is $C(6,4)=\binom{6}{4}=\frac{6!}{(6-4)!4!}=\frac{6!}{2!4!}=\frac{6\cdot5\cdot4!}{2!4!}=\frac{6\cdot5}{2\cdot1}=15.$

(b) Since one of the four choices is fixed, we now want to choose 3 extras from a choice of 5 extras and order is not important. The number of different hamburgers that can be made is given by the following.

$$C(5,3)=\binom{5}{3}=\frac{5!}{(5-3)!3!}=\frac{5!}{2!3!}=\frac{5\cdot4\cdot3!}{2!3!}=\frac{5\cdot4}{2\cdot1}=10$$

43. This problem involves choosing 2 members from a set of 5 members. There are $C(5,2)$ such subsets.

$$C(5,2)=\binom{5}{2}=\frac{5!}{(5-2)!2!}=\frac{5!}{3!2!}=\frac{5\cdot4\cdot3!}{3!2!}=\frac{5\cdot4}{2\cdot1}=10$$

There are 10 different 2-card combinations.

45. Since 2 blue marbles are to be chosen and there are 8 blue marbles, this problem involves choosing 2 members from a set of 8 members. There are $C(8,2)$ ways of doing this.

$$C(8,2)=\binom{8}{2}=\frac{8!}{(8-2)!2!}=\frac{8!}{6!2!}=\frac{8\cdot7\cdot6!}{6!2!}=\frac{8\cdot7}{2\cdot1}=28$$

47. There are 5 liberal and 4 conservatives, giving a total of 9 members. Three members are chosen as delegates to a convention.

(a) There are $C(9,3)$ ways of doing this.

$$C(9,3)=\binom{9}{3}=\frac{9!}{(9-3)!3!}=\frac{9!}{6!3!}=\frac{9\cdot8\cdot7\cdot6!}{6!3!}=\frac{9\cdot8\cdot7}{3\cdot2\cdot1}=84$$

84 delegations are possible.

(b) To get all liberals, we must choose 3 members from a set of 5, which can be done $C(5,3)$ ways.

$$C(5,3)=\binom{5}{3}=\frac{5!}{(5-3)!3!}=\frac{5!}{2!3!}=\frac{5\cdot4\cdot3!}{2!3!}=\frac{5\cdot4}{2}=10$$

10 delegations could have all liberals.

Continued on next page

47. (continued)

(c) To get 2 liberals and 1 conservative involves two independent events. First select the liberals. The number of ways to do this is $C(5,2)=\binom{5}{2}=\frac{5!}{3!2!}=\frac{5\cdot4\cdot3!}{3!2!}=\frac{5\cdot4}{2\cdot1}=10.$

Now select the conservative. The number of ways to do this is as follows.

$$C(4,1)=\binom{4}{1}=\frac{4!}{(4-1)!1!}=\frac{4!}{3!1!}=\frac{4\cdot3!}{3!1!}=\frac{4}{1}=4$$

To find the number of delegations, use the fundamental principle of counting. The number of delegations with 2 liberals and 1 conservative is $10\cdot4=40$.

(d) If one particular person must be on the delegation, then there are 2 people left to choose from a set consisting of 8 members. The number of ways to do this is as follows.

$$C(8,2)=\binom{8}{2}=\frac{8!}{(8-2)!2!}=\frac{8!}{6!2!}=\frac{8\cdot7\cdot6!}{6!2!}=\frac{8\cdot7}{2\cdot1}=28$$

28 delegations are possible, which includes the mayor.

49. The problem asks how many ways can Matthew arrange his schedule. Therefore, order is important, and this is a permutation problem. There are $P(8,4)=\frac{8!}{(8-4)!}=\frac{8!}{4!}=\frac{8\cdot7\cdot6\cdot5\cdot4!}{4!}=8\cdot7\cdot6\cdot5=1680$ ways to arrange his schedule.

51. The order of the vegetables in the soup is not important, so this is a combination problem. There are $C(6,4)=\binom{6}{4}=\frac{6!}{(6-4)!4!}=\frac{6!}{2!4!}=\frac{6\cdot5\cdot4!}{2!4!}=\frac{6\cdot5}{2\cdot1}=15$ different soups she can make.

53. Order is important in the seating, so this is a permutation problem. All twelve children will have a specific location; the first eleven will sit down and twelfth will be left standing.

$$P(12,12)=\frac{12!}{(12-12)!}=\frac{12!}{0!}=\frac{12\cdot11\cdot10\cdot9\cdot8\cdot7\cdot6\cdot5\cdot4\cdot3\cdot2\cdot1}{1}=479{,}001{,}600$$

There are 479,001,600 seatings possible.

55. A club has 8 men and 11 women members. There are a total of $8+11=19$ members, and 5 of them are to be chosen. Order is not important, so this is a combination problem.

(a) Choosing all men implies of the 8 men, choose 5.

$$C(8,5)=\binom{8}{5}=\frac{8!}{(8-5)!5!}=\frac{8!}{3!5!}=\frac{8\cdot7\cdot6\cdot5!}{3!5!}=\frac{8\cdot7\cdot6}{3\cdot2\cdot1}=56$$

56 committees having 5 men can be chosen.

(b) Choose all women implies of the 11 women, choose 5.

$$C(11,5)=\binom{11}{5}=\frac{11!}{(11-5)!5!}=\frac{11!}{6!5!}=\frac{11\cdot10\cdot9\cdot8\cdot7\cdot6!}{6!5!}=\frac{11\cdot10\cdot9\cdot8\cdot7}{5\cdot4\cdot3\cdot2\cdot1}=462$$

462 committees having 5 women can be chosen.

Continued on next page

55. (continued)

(c) Choosing 3 men and 2 women involves two independent events, each of which involves combinations.

First, select the men. There are 8 men in the club, so the number of ways to do this is as follows.

$$C(8,3)=\binom{8}{3}=\frac{8!}{(8-3)!3!}=\frac{8!}{5!3!}=\frac{8\cdot7\cdot6\cdot5!}{5!3!}=\frac{8\cdot7\cdot6}{3\cdot2\cdot1}=56$$

Now, select the women. There are 11 women in the club, so the number of ways to do this is as follows.

$$C(11,2)=\binom{11}{2}=\frac{11!}{(11-2)!2!}=\frac{11!}{9!2!}=\frac{11\cdot10\cdot9!}{9!2!}=\frac{11\cdot10}{2\cdot1}=55$$

To find the number of committees, use the fundamental principle of counting. The number of committees with 3 men and 2 women is $56\cdot55=3080$.

(d) Choose no more than 3 women.
This means choose 0 women (and 5 men) or choose 1 woman (and 4 men) or choose 2 women (and 3 men) or choose 3 women (and 2 men). For each of these choices, we use the fundamental principle of counting. Thus, the number of possible committees with no more than 3 women is $C(11,0)\cdot C(8,5)+C(11,1)\cdot C(8,4)+C(11,2)\cdot C(8,3)+C(11,3)\cdot C(8,2)$.

$$C(11,0)\cdot C(8,5)+C(11,1)\cdot C(8,4)+C(11,2)\cdot C(8,3)+C(11,3)\cdot C(8,2)$$

$$=\binom{11}{0}\cdot\binom{8}{5}+\binom{11}{1}\cdot\binom{8}{4}+\binom{11}{2}\cdot\binom{8}{3}+\binom{11}{3}\cdot\binom{8}{2}$$

$$=\frac{11!}{(11-0)!0!}\cdot\frac{8!}{(8-5)!5!}+\frac{11!}{(11-1)!1!}\cdot\frac{8!}{(8-4)!4!}+\frac{11!}{(11-2)!2!}\cdot\frac{8!}{(8-3)!3!}+\frac{11!}{(11-3)!3!}\cdot\frac{8!}{(8-2)!2!}$$

$$=\frac{11!}{11!0!}\cdot\frac{8!}{3!5!}+\frac{11!}{10!1!}\cdot\frac{8!}{4!4!}+\frac{11!}{9!2!}\cdot\frac{8!}{5!3!}+\frac{11!}{8!3!}\cdot\frac{8!}{6!2!}$$

$$=1\cdot\frac{8\cdot7\cdot6\cdot5!}{3!5!}+\frac{11\cdot10!}{10!1!}\cdot\frac{8\cdot7\cdot6\cdot5\cdot4!}{4!4!}+\frac{11\cdot10\cdot9!}{9!2!}\cdot\frac{8\cdot7\cdot6\cdot5!}{5!3!}+\frac{11\cdot10\cdot9\cdot8!}{8!3!}\cdot\frac{8\cdot7\cdot6!}{6!2!}$$

$$=1\cdot\frac{8\cdot7\cdot6}{3\cdot2\cdot1}+11\cdot\frac{8\cdot7\cdot6\cdot5}{4\cdot3\cdot2\cdot1}+\frac{11\cdot10}{2\cdot1}\cdot\frac{8\cdot7\cdot6}{3\cdot2\cdot1}+\frac{11\cdot10\cdot9}{3\cdot2\cdot1}\cdot\frac{8\cdot7}{2\cdot1}$$

$$=1\cdot56+11\cdot70+55\cdot56+165\cdot28=56+770+3080+4620=8526$$

8526 committees having no more than 3 women can be chosen.

57. For the first lock, there are 10 choices for the first, second, and third digits. Thus, the number of combinations on the first lock is $10\cdot10\cdot10=1000$. This is the same for the second lock, that is, it also has 1000 different combinations. Since each of the locks is independent from the other, we use the fundamental principle of counting. We have a total of $1000\cdot1000=1{,}000{,}000$ combinations possible.

59. Each of the 12 switches has two possible settings. Since each switch is independent from the others, there is a total of $2\cdot2\cdot2\cdot2\cdot2\cdot2\cdot2\cdot2\cdot2\cdot2\cdot2\cdot2=2^{12}=4096$ codes possible.

61. Because the keys are arranged in a circle, there is no "first" key. The number of distinguishable arrangements is the number of ways to arrange the other three keys in relation to any one of the keys, which is $P(3,3)=\frac{3!}{(3-3)!}=\frac{3!}{0!}=\frac{3!}{1}=3\cdot2\cdot1=6$.

In Exercises 63 – 69, we will be using the formulas $P(n,r)=\dfrac{n!}{(n-r)!}$ and $\dbinom{n}{r}=\dfrac{n!}{(n-r)!r!}$, where $r\le n$.

63. Show $P(n,n-1)=P(n,n)$.

$$P(n,n-1)=\frac{n!}{\left[n-(n-1)\right]!}=\frac{n!}{(n-n+1)!}=\frac{n!}{1!}=\frac{n!}{1}=\frac{n!}{0!}=\frac{n!}{(n-n)!}=P(n,n)$$

65. Show $P(n,0)=1$.

$$P(n,0)=\frac{n!}{(n-0)!}=\frac{n!}{n!}=1$$

67. Show $\dbinom{n}{0}=1$.

$$\binom{n}{0}=\frac{n!}{(n-0)!0!}=\frac{n!}{n!0!}=\frac{n!}{n!1}=\frac{n!}{n!}=1$$

69. Show $\dbinom{n}{n-r}=\dbinom{n}{r}$.

$$\binom{n}{n-r}=\frac{n!}{\left[n-(n-r)\right]!(n-r)!}=\frac{n!}{(n-n+r)!(n-r)!}=\frac{n!}{r!(n-r)!}=\frac{n!}{(n-r)!r!}=\binom{n}{r}$$

71. (a) log 50! = log 1 + log 2 + log 3 + … + log 50

Using a sum and sequence utility on a calculator, we obtain the following.

$$\log 50!\approx 64.48307487$$
$$50!\approx 10^{64.48307487}$$
$$50!\approx 10^{.48307487}\times 10^{64}$$
$$50!\approx 3.04140932\times 10^{64}$$

```
sum(seq(log(N),N
,1,50,1)
         64.48307487
10^Ans
        3.04140932E64
```

Computing the value directly, we obtain $50!\approx 3.04140932\times 10^{64}$.

```
50!
        3.04140932E64
```

(b) log 60! = log 1 + log 2 + log 3 + … + log 60

Using a sum and sequence utility on a calculator, we obtain the following.

$$\log 60!\approx 81.92017485$$
$$60!\approx 10^{81.92017485}$$
$$60!\approx 10^{.92017485}\times 10^{81}$$
$$60!\approx 8.320987113\times 10^{81}$$

```
sum(seq(log(N),N
,1,60,1)
         81.92017485
10^Ans
       8.320987113E81
```

Computing the value directly, we obtain $60!\approx 8.320987113\times 10^{81}$.

```
60!
       8.320987113E81
```

Continued on next page

71. (continued)

(c) log 65! = log 1 + log 2 + log 3 + … + log 65

Using a sum and sequence utility on a calculator, we obtain the following.

$$\log 65! \approx 90.91633025$$
$$65! \approx 10^{90.91633025}$$
$$65! \approx 10^{.91633025} \times 10^{90}$$
$$65! \approx 8.247650592 \times 10^{90}$$

Computing the value directly, we obtain $65! \approx 8.247650592 \times 10^{90}$.

72. **(a)** $P(47,13) = \dfrac{47!}{(47-13)!} = \dfrac{47!}{34!} = 47 \cdot 46 \cdot 45 \cdot \ldots \cdot 35$

$$\log P(47, 13) = \log 47 + \log 46 + \log 45 + \ldots + \log 35$$
$$\log P(47, 13) \approx 20.94250295$$
$$P(47, 13) \approx 10^{20.94250295}$$
$$P(47, 13) \approx 10^{.94250295} \times 10^{20}$$
$$P(47, 13) \approx 8.759976613 \times 10^{20}$$

Computing the value directly, we obtain $P(47,13) \approx 8.759976613 \times 10^{20}$.

(b) $P(50,4) = \dfrac{50!}{(50-4)!} = \dfrac{50!}{46!} = 50 \cdot 49 \cdot 48 \cdot 47$

$$\log P(50, 4) = \log 50 + \log 49 + \log 48 + \log 47$$
$$\log P(50, 4) \approx 6.74250518$$
$$P(50, 4)) \approx 10^{6.74250518}$$
$$P(50, 4) \approx 5{,}527{,}200$$

(This is in fact the exact value of $P(50,4)$.)

Computing the value directly, we obtain $P(50,4) = 5{,}527{,}200$.

Continued on next page

72. (continued)

(c) $P(29,21)=\dfrac{29!}{(29-21)!}=\dfrac{29!}{8!}=29\cdot 28\cdot 27\cdot\ldots\cdot 9$

$$\log P(29,\,21)=\log 29+\log 28+\log 27+\ldots+\log 9$$
$$\log P(29,\,21)\approx 26.34101830$$
$$P(29,\,21)\approx 10^{26.34101830}$$
$$P(29,\,21)\approx 10^{.34101830}\times 10^{26}$$
$$P(29,\,21)\approx 2.19289732\times 10^{26}$$

Computing the value directly, we obtain $P(29,\,21)\approx 2.19289732\times 10^{26}$.

Section 11.7: Basics of Probability

1. Let H = heads, T = tails.
The only possible outcome is a head. Hence, the sample space is $S=\{H\}$.

3. Since each coin can be a head or a tail and there are 3 coins, the sample space is as follows.
$S=\{(H,\,H,\,H),\,(H,\,H,\,T),(H,\,T,\,H),(T,\,H,\,H),\,(H,\,T,\,T),\,(T,\,H,\,T),(T,\,T,\,H),\,(T,\,T,\,T)\}$

5. The sample space is $S=\{(1,1),\,(1,2),\,(1,3),\,(2,1),\,(2,2),\,(2,3),\,(3,1),\,(3,2),\,(3,3)\}$.

7. **(a)** "The result is heads" is the event $E_1=\{H\}$. This event is certain to occur, $P(E_1)=1$.

(b) "The result is tails" is the event $E_2=\varnothing$. This event is an impossible event, so $P(E_2)=0$.

9. The sample space is $S=\{(1,1),\,(1,2),\,(1,3),\,(2,1),\,(2,2),\,(2,3),\,(3,1),\,(3,2),\,(3,3)\}$, so $n(S)=9$.

(a) The result is a repeated number" is the event $E_1=\{(1,1),\,(2,2),\,(3,3)\}$, so $n(E_1)=3$. The probability is $P(E_1)=\dfrac{n(E_1)}{n(S)}=\dfrac{3}{9}=\dfrac{1}{3}$.

(b) "The second number is 1 or 3" is the event $E_2=\{(1,1),(1,3),(2,1),(2,3),(3,1),(3,3)\}$, so $n(E_2)=6$. The probability is $P(E_2)=\dfrac{n(E_2)}{n(S)}=\dfrac{6}{9}=\dfrac{2}{3}$.

(c) "The first number is even and the second number is odd" is the event $E_3=\{(2,1),\,(2,3)\}$, So, $n(E_3)=2$. The probability is $P(E_3)=\dfrac{n(E_3)}{n(S)}=\dfrac{2}{9}$.

11. For any event E, $0\le P(E)\le 1$. Since $\frac{6}{5}>1$, the student must have made a mistake.

13. **(a)** F
(b) D
(c) A
(d) F
(e) C
(f) B
(g) E

15. There are 15 marbles, so $n(S) = 15$.

(a) E_1 : yellow marbles is drawn

There are three yellow marbles, so $n(E_1) = 3$. The probability is $P(E_1) = \frac{3}{15} = \frac{1}{5}$.

(b) E_2 : black marble is drawn

There are no black marbles so $n(E_2) = 0$. The probability is $P(E_2) = \dfrac{0}{15} = 0$.

(c) E_3 : yellow or white marble is drawn

There are 3 yellow and 4 white marbles so $n(E_3) = 3 + 4 = 7$. The probability is $P(E_3) = \frac{7}{15}$.

(d) E_4 : yellow marble is not drawn

There are 12 non-yellow marbles, so $n(E_4{}') = 12$. The probability is $P(E_4{}') = \frac{12}{15} = \frac{4}{5}$.

The odds in favor of drawing a yellow marble are $\dfrac{P(E_4)}{P(E_4{}')} = \dfrac{\frac{1}{5}}{\frac{4}{5}} = \dfrac{1}{4}$ or 1 to 4.

(e) The probability that a blue marble is drawn is $P(E_2) = \frac{8}{15}$. The probability that a blue marble is not drawn is $P(E_2{}') = 1 - P(E_2) = \frac{7}{15}$. The odds against drawing a blue marble are as follows.

$$\frac{P(E_2{}')}{P(E_2)} = \frac{\frac{7}{15}}{\frac{8}{15}} = \frac{7}{8} \text{ or 7 to 8}$$

17. The sample space for the event of rolling 2 dice is $S = \{(1, 1), (1, 2), (1, 3), \ldots, (6, 6)\}$, so $n(S) = 36$ (See Example 5 on pages 997– 998 of your text.).

(a) The event in which the sum is at least 10 can be represented by $E_1 = \{(4, 6), (5, 5), (5, 6), (6, 4), (6, 5), (6, 6)\}$, so $n(E_1) = 6$. The probability of E_1 is $P(E_1) = \frac{6}{36} = \frac{1}{6}$.

(b) If the event in which the sum is 7 is E_2, then $E_2 = \{(1, 6), (6, 1), (2, 5), (5, 2), (3, 4), (4, 3)\}$, so $n(E_2) = 6$. We have $P(E_2) = \frac{6}{36} = \frac{1}{6}$. The probability of the union of two events, E_2 or E_1, is $P(E_2 \text{ or } E_1) = P(E_2 \cup E_1) = P(E_2) + P(E_1) - P(E_2 \cap E_1)$. Since $P(E_2 \cap E_1) = 0$ and $P(E_1) = \frac{1}{6}$ (from part (a)), we have $P(E_2 \text{ or } E_1) = \frac{1}{6} + \frac{1}{6} - 0 = \frac{2}{6} = \frac{1}{3}$.

(c) The event in which the sum is 2 is $E_3 = \{(1, 1)\}$, so $n(E_3) = 1$, and thus $P(E_3) = \frac{1}{36}$. The event in which both dice show the same number is $E_4 = \{(1, 1), (2, 2), (3, 3), (4, 4), (5, 5), (6, 6)\}$, so $n(E_4) = 6$, and $P(E_4) = \frac{6}{36} = \frac{1}{6}$. The intersection of these two events is $E_3 \cap E_4 = \{1, 1\}$, so $n(E_3 \cap E_4) = 1$, and $P(E_3 \cap E_4) = \frac{1}{36}$. Hence the probability of these two alternate events occurring is as follows.

$$P(E_3 \text{ or } E_4) = P(E_3 \cup E_4) = P(E_3) + P(E_4) - P(E_3 \cap E_4) = \frac{1}{36} + \frac{6}{36} - \frac{1}{36} = \frac{6}{36} = \frac{1}{6}$$

19. The total of all types is $58,930+209,117+43,511+2,744+20,748=335,050$.

(a) $P(\text{of Hispanic origin})=\dfrac{58,930}{335,050}\approx .176$

(b) $P(\text{not white})=1-P(\text{White})=1-\dfrac{209,117}{335,050}=\dfrac{125,933}{335,050}\approx .376$

(c) $P\left(\text{Indian (Native American) or Black}\right)=\dfrac{2,744+43,511}{335,050}=\dfrac{46,255}{335,050}\approx .138$

(d) Let E be "selected resident was Asian."

We have $P(E)=\dfrac{20,748}{335,050}$ and $P(E')=1-P(E)=1-\dfrac{20,748}{335,050}=\dfrac{314,302}{335,050}$. The odds that a randomly selected U.S. resident was an Asian is $\dfrac{P(E)}{P(E')}=\dfrac{\frac{20,748}{335,050}}{\frac{314,302}{335,050}}=\dfrac{10,374}{157,151}$ or 10,374 to 157,151.

21. Each suit has thirteen cards, and the probability of choosing the correct card in that suit is $\frac{1}{13}$. Thus, we have $P(4 \text{ correct choices})=\dfrac{1}{13}\cdot\dfrac{1}{13}\cdot\dfrac{1}{13}\cdot\dfrac{1}{13}=\dfrac{1}{28,561}$. The probability of getting all four picks correct and winning \$5000 is $\dfrac{1}{28,561}\approx .000035$.

23. **(a)** A 40-year old man who lives 30 more years would be a 70-year old man. Let E be "selected man will live to be 70." Then $n(E) = 66,172$. For this situation, the sample space S is the set of all 40-yr-old men, so $n(S) = 94,558$. Thus, the probability that a 40-yr-old man will live 30 more yr is $P(E)=\dfrac{n(E)}{n(S)}=\dfrac{66,172}{94,558}\approx .6998$.

(b) Using the notation and results from part (a), the probability that a 40-yr-old man will not live 430 more yr is $P(E')=1-P(E)=1-.6998=.3002$.

(c) Use the notation and results from parts (a) and (b). In this binomial experiment, we call "a 40-yr-old man survives to age 70" a success. Then $p=P(E)=.6998$ and $1-p=P(E')=.3002$. There are 5 independent trials and we need the probability of 3 successes, so $n = 5$, $r = 3$. The probability that exactly 3 of the 40-yr-old men survive to age 40 is as follows.

$$\binom{n}{r}p^r(1-p)^{n-r}=\binom{5}{3}(.6998)^3(.3002)^{5-3}=\frac{5!}{(5-3)!3!}(.6998)^3(.3002)^2$$
$$=\frac{5!}{2!3!}(.6998)^3(.3002)^2=\frac{5\cdot 4}{2\cdot 1}(.6998)^3(.3002)^2$$
$$=10(.6998)^3(.3002)^2\approx .3088$$

(d) Let F be the event "at least one man survives to age 70." The easiest way to find $P(F)$ is to first find the probability of the complement of the event, F'. F' is the event that "neither man survives to age 70."

Since $P(F')=P(E')\cdot P(E')=(.3002)^2\approx .0901$, we have $P(F)=1-P(F')\approx 1-.0901=.9099$.

25. The amount of growth would be 11,400 – 10,000 = 1400, so the percent growth would be $\frac{1400}{10,000} = .14$. Let E be the event "worth at least \$11,400 by the end of the year." This is equivalent to "at least 14 percent growth" which is equivalent to "14 or 18 percent growth." Thus, we have the following.

$$\begin{aligned} P(E) &= P(\text{14 percent growth or 18 percent growth}) \\ &= P(\text{14 percent growth}) + P(\text{18 percent growth}) = .20 + .10 = .30 \end{aligned}$$

27. In this binomial experiment, we call "smoked less than 10" a success.
Then $n = 10$, $r = 4$, and $p = .45 + .24 = .69$.

$$\begin{aligned} P(\text{4 smoked less than 10}) &= \binom{n}{r} p^r (1-p)^{n-r} = \binom{10}{4} (.69)^4 (1-.69)^{10-4} = \frac{10!}{(10-4)!4!} (.69)^4 (.31)^6 \\ &= \frac{10 \cdot 9 \cdot 8 \cdot 7}{4 \cdot 3 \cdot 2 \cdot 1} (.69)^4 (.31)^6 = 210 (.69)^4 (.31)^6 \approx .042246 \end{aligned}$$

29. $$\begin{aligned} P(\text{smoked between 1 and 19}) &= P(\text{smoked 1 to 9 or smoked 10 to 19}) \\ &= P(\text{smoked 1 to 9}) + P(\text{smoked 10 to 19}) = .24 + .20 = .44 \end{aligned}$$

In this binomial experiment, call "smoked between 1 and 19" a success. Then $p = .44$ and $1 - p = .56$. "Fewer than 2" means 0 or 1, so P(fewer than 2 smoked between 1 and 19) is the following.

$$\begin{aligned} &P(\text{0 smoked between 1 and 19}) + P(\text{1 smoked between 1 and 19}) \\ &= \binom{10}{0} (.44)^0 (56)^{10} + \binom{10}{1} (.44)^1 (56)^9 = 1(1)(56)^{10} + 10(.44)(56)^9 \\ &\approx .003033 + .023831 = .026864 \end{aligned}$$

31. $$\begin{aligned} &P(\text{a student applied to fewer than 4 colleges}) \\ &= P(\text{a student applied 1 college}) + P(\text{a student applied to 2 or 3 colleges}) = .20 + .29 = .49 \end{aligned}$$

33. $$\begin{aligned} &P(\text{a student applied to more than 3 colleges}) \\ &= P(\text{a student applied 4 - 6 college}) + P(\text{a student applied to 7 or more colleges}) = .37 + .14 = .51 \end{aligned}$$

35. In these binomial experiments, we call "the man is color-blind" a success.

(a) For "exactly 5 are color-blind", we have $n = 53$, $r = 5$, and $p = .042$.

$$\begin{aligned} P(\text{exactly 5 are color-blind}) &= \binom{53}{5} (.042)^5 (1-.042)^{53-5} = \frac{53!}{(53-5)!5!} (.042)^5 (.958)^{48} \\ &= \frac{53!}{48!5!} (.042)^5 (.958)^{48} = \frac{53 \cdot 52 \cdot 51 \cdot 50 \cdot 49}{5 \cdot 4 \cdot 3 \cdot 2 \cdot 1} (.042)^5 (.958)^{48} \\ &= 2{,}869{,}685 (.042)^5 (.958)^{48} \approx .047822 \end{aligned}$$

Continued on next page

35. (continued)

(b) "No more than 5 are color-blind" corresponds to "0, 1, 2, 3, 4, or 5 are color-blind." Then $n = 53$, $r = 0, 1, 2, 3, 4,$ or 5, and $p = .042$.

P(no more than 5 are color-blind)= P(0 are color-blind) + P(1 are color-blind) + P(2 are color-blind) + P(3 are color-blind) + P(4 are color-blind) + P(5 are color-blind)

$$=\binom{53}{0}(.042)^0(1-.042)^{55-0}+\binom{53}{1}(.042)^1(1-.042)^{53-1}+\binom{53}{2}(.042)^2(1-.042)^{53-2}$$
$$+\binom{53}{3}(.042)^3(1-.042)^{53-3}+\binom{53}{4}(.042)^4(1-.042)^{53-4}+\binom{53}{5}(.042)^5(1-.042)^{53-5}$$
$$=\frac{53!}{(53-0)!0!}(1)(.958)^{53}+\frac{53!}{(53-1)!1!}(.042)^1(.958)^{52}$$
$$+\frac{53!}{(53-2)!2!}(.042)^2(.958)^{51}+\frac{53!}{(53-3)!3!}(.042)^3(.958)^{50}$$
$$+\frac{53!}{(53-4)!4!}(.042)^4(.958)^{49}+\frac{53!}{(53-5)!5!}(.042)^5(.958)^{48}$$
$$=\frac{53!}{53!0!}(.958)^{53}+\frac{53\cdot 52!}{52!1!}(.042)^1(.958)^{52}+\frac{53\cdot 52\cdot 51!}{51!2!}(.042)^2(.958)^{51}$$
$$+\frac{53\cdot 52\cdot 51\cdot 50!}{50!3!}(.042)^3(.958)^{50}+\frac{53\cdot 52\cdot 51\cdot 50\cdot 49!}{49!4!}(.042)^4(.958)^{49}$$
$$+\frac{53\cdot 52\cdot 51\cdot 50\cdot 49\cdot 48!}{48!5!}(.042)^5(.958)^{48}$$
$$=1(.958)^{53}+53(.042)^1(.958)^{52}+1378(.042)^2(.958)^{51}+23{,}426(.042)^3(.958)^{50}$$
$$+292{,}825(.042)^4(.958)^{49}+2{,}869{,}685(.042)^5(.958)^{48}$$
$$\approx .102890+.239074+.272514+.203105+.111305+.047822=.976710$$

(c) Let E be "at least 1 is color-blind." Consider the complementary event E': "0 are color-blind." Thus, we have the following.

$$P(E)=1-P(E')=1-\binom{53}{0}(.042)^0(1-.042)^{53-0}=1-\frac{53!}{(53-0)!0!}(1)(.958)^{53}$$
$$=1-\frac{53!}{53!0!}(1)(.958)^{53}=1-(1)(.958)^{53}=1-(.958)^{53}1-.102890=.897110$$

37. (a) First compute $q=(1-p)^I=(1-.1)^2=.9^2=.81$. Then, with $S = 4$, $k = 3$, and $q = .81$, we have the following.

$$P=\binom{S}{k}q^k(1-q)^{S-k}=\binom{4}{3}.81^3(1-.81)^{4-3}=\frac{4!}{(4-3)!3!}.81^3(.19)=4(.81^3)(.19)\approx .404$$

There is about a 40.4% chance of exactly 3 people not becoming infected.

Continued on next page

37. (continued)

(b) Compute $q=(1-p)^I=(1-.5)^2=.5^2=.25$ Then, with S = 4, k = 3, and q = .25, we have the following.

$$P=\binom{S}{k}q^k(1-q)^{S-k}=\binom{4}{3}.25^3(1-.25)^{4-3}=\frac{4!}{(4-3)!3!}.25^3(.75)=4(.25^3)(.75)\approx .047$$

There is about 4.7 % chance of this occurring when the disease is highly infectious.

(c) Compute $q=(1-p)^I=(1-.5)^1=.5$. Then, with S = 9, k = 0, and q = .5, we have the following.

$$P=\binom{S}{k}q^k(1-q)^{S-k}=\binom{9}{0}.5^0(1-.5)^{9-0}=\frac{9!}{(9-0)!0!}(1)(.5)^9=1(1)(.5^9)\approx .002$$

There is about a .2% chance of everyone becoming infected. This means that in a large family or group of people, it is highly unlikely that everyone will become sick even though the disease is highly infectious.

Chapter 11: Review Exercises

1. $a_n=\dfrac{n}{n+1}$

$a_1=\dfrac{1}{1+1}=\dfrac{1}{2};\ a_2=\dfrac{2}{2+1}=\dfrac{2}{3};\ a_3=\dfrac{3}{3+1}=\dfrac{3}{4};\ a_4=\dfrac{4}{4+1}=\dfrac{4}{5};\ a_5=\dfrac{5}{5+1}=\dfrac{5}{6}$

The first five terms are $\frac{1}{2}, \frac{2}{3}, \frac{3}{4}, \frac{4}{5}$, and $\frac{5}{6}$. This sequence does not have a common difference or a common ratio, so the sequence is neither arithmetic nor geometric.

3. $a_n=2(n+3)$

$a_1=2(1+3)=2(4)=8;\ a_2=2(2+3)=2(5)=10;\ a_3=2(3+3)=2(6)=12;$

$a_4=2(4+3)=2(7)=14;\ a_5=2(5+3)=2(8)=16$

The first five terms are 8, 10, 12, 14, and 16. There is a common difference, d = 2, so the sequence is arithmetic.

5. $a_1=5$; for $n\ge 2$, $a_n=a_{n-1}-3$

$a_2=a_{2-1}-3=a_1-3=5-3=2;\ a_3=a_{3-1}-3=a_2-3=2-3=-1;$

$a_4=a_{4-1}-3=a_3-3=-1-3=-4;\ a_5=a_{5-1}-3=a_4-3=-4-3=-7$

The first five terms are 5, 2, –1, –4, and –7. There is a common difference, d = –3, so the sequence is arithmetic.

7. Arithmetic, $a_3=\pi$, $a_4=1$

$d=a_4-a_3=1-\pi$

$a_3=a_1+2d\Rightarrow \pi=a_1+2(1-\pi)\Rightarrow \pi=a_1+2-2\pi\Rightarrow 3\pi-2=a_1$

$a_2=a_1+d\Rightarrow a_2=(3\pi-2)+(1-\pi)\Rightarrow a_2=2\pi-1$

$a_5=a_1+4d\Rightarrow a_5=(3\pi-2)+4(1-\pi)\Rightarrow a_5=3\pi-2+4-4\pi\Rightarrow a_5=-\pi+2$

The first five terms are $3\pi-2$, $2\pi-1$, π, 1, $-\pi+2$.

9. Geometric, $a_1 = -5$, $a_2 = -1$

$r = \frac{a_2}{a_1} = \frac{-1}{-5} = \frac{1}{5}$

$a_3 = a_1 r^2 = -5\left(\frac{1}{5}\right)^2 = -5 \cdot \frac{1}{25} = -\frac{1}{5}$; $a_4 = a_1 r^3 = -5\left(\frac{1}{5}\right)^3 = -5 \cdot \frac{1}{125} = -\frac{1}{25}$

$a_5 = a_1 r^4 = -5\left(\frac{1}{5}\right)^4 = -5 \cdot \frac{1}{625} = -\frac{1}{125}$

The first five terms are $-5, -1, -\frac{1}{5}, -\frac{1}{25}$, and $-\frac{1}{125}$.

11. Geometric, $a_1 = -8$ and $a_7 = -\frac{1}{8}$

Since $a_n = a_1 r^{n-1}$, we have $a_7 = a_1 r^{7-1} \Rightarrow -\frac{1}{8} = -8r^6 \Rightarrow r^6 = \frac{1}{64} \Rightarrow r = \pm\frac{1}{2}$.

There are two geometric sequences that satisfy the given conditions.

If $r = \frac{1}{2}$, $a_4 = (-8)\left(\frac{1}{2}\right)^3 = (-8)\left(\frac{1}{8}\right) = -1$.

Also, $a_n = -8\left(\frac{1}{2}\right)^{n-1}$ or $a_n = -2^3\left(\frac{1}{2}\right)^{n-1} = -\frac{2^3}{2^{n-1}} = -\frac{1}{2^{(n-1)-3}} = -\frac{1}{2^{n-4}} = -\left(\frac{1}{2}\right)^{n-4}$.

If $r = -\frac{1}{2}$, $a_4 = (-8)\left(-\frac{1}{2}\right)^3 = (-8)\left(-\frac{1}{8}\right) = 1$.

Also, $a_n = -8\left(-\frac{1}{2}\right)^{n-1}$ or $a_n = -2^3\left(-\frac{1}{2}\right)^{n-1} = (-2)^3\left(-\frac{1}{2}\right)^{n-1} = \frac{(-2)^3}{(-2)^{n-1}} = \frac{1}{(-2)^{(n-1)-3}} = \frac{1}{(-2)^{n-4}} = \left(-\frac{1}{2}\right)^{n-4}$.

13. $a_1 = 6x - 9$, $a_2 = 5x + 1$

$d = a_2 - a_1 = (5x+1) - (6x-9) = 5x + 1 - 6x + 9 = -x + 10$

$a_n = a_1 + (n-1)d$

$a_8 = a_1 + (8-1)d \Rightarrow a_8 = a_1 + 7d \Rightarrow a_8 = (6x-9) + 7(-x+10) = 6x - 9 - 7x + 70 = -x + 61$

15. $a_2 = 6$, $d = 10$

To first find a_1, we have $a_2 = a_1 + d \Rightarrow 6 = a_1 + 10 \Rightarrow a_1 = -4$

Now, to find S_{12}, we use $S_n = \frac{n}{2}\left[2a_1 + (n-1)d\right]$.

$S_{12} = \frac{12}{2}\left[2(-4) + (12-1)(10)\right] = 6\left[-8 + (11)(10)\right] = 6(-8+110) = 6(102) = 612$

17. $a_3 = 4$, $r = \frac{1}{5}$

$a_4 = a_3 r = 4 \cdot \frac{1}{5} = \frac{4}{5} \Rightarrow a_5 = a_4 r = \frac{4}{5} \cdot \frac{1}{5} = \frac{4}{25}$

19. $a_1 = -1$, $r = 3$

$$S_n = \frac{a_1\left(1-r^n\right)}{1-r} \Rightarrow S_4 = \frac{a_1\left(1-r^4\right)}{1-r} = \frac{-1\left(1-3^4\right)}{1-3} = \frac{-1(1-81)}{-2} = \frac{1}{2}(-80) = -40$$

21. $\sum_{i=1}^{7} (-1)^{i-1}$

This is a geometric series with $a_1 = (-1)^{1-1} = (-1)^0 = 1$ and $r = -1$.

$$S_n = \frac{a_1\left(1-r^n\right)}{1-r} \Rightarrow S_7 = \frac{a_1\left(1-r^7\right)}{1-r} \Rightarrow S_7 = \frac{1\left[1-(-1)^7\right]}{1-(-1)} = \frac{1\left[1-(-1)\right]}{2} = \frac{1 \cdot 2}{2} = 1$$

23. $\sum_{i=1}^{4} \frac{i+1}{i} = \frac{2}{1} + \frac{3}{2} + \frac{4}{3} + \frac{5}{4} = \frac{24}{12} + \frac{18}{12} + \frac{16}{12} + \frac{15}{12} = \frac{73}{12}$

25. Since $\sum_{i=1}^{n} i = \frac{n(n+1)}{2}$, $\sum_{j=1}^{2500} j = \frac{2500(2500+1)}{2} = 1250(2501) = 3{,}126{,}250.$

27. $\sum_{i=1}^{\infty} \left(\frac{4}{7}\right)^i$

This is an infinite geometric series with $a_1 = \left(\frac{4}{7}\right)^1 = \frac{4}{7}$ and $r = \frac{4}{7}$. Since $|r| = \left|\frac{4}{7}\right| < 1$, we can use the formula $S_\infty = \frac{a_1}{1-r}$. Thus, we have $\sum_{i=1}^{\infty} \left(\frac{4}{7}\right)^i = S_\infty = \frac{a_1}{1-r} = \frac{\frac{4}{7}}{1-\frac{4}{7}} = \frac{\frac{4}{7}}{\frac{3}{7}} = \frac{4}{7} \cdot \frac{7}{3} = \frac{4}{3}.$

29. $24 + 8 + \frac{8}{3} + \frac{8}{9} + \ldots$

This is an infinite geometric series with $a_1 = 24$ and $r = \frac{8}{24} = \frac{1}{3}$. Since $|r| = \left|\frac{1}{3}\right| < 1$, we can use the formula $S_\infty = \frac{a_1}{1-r}$. Thus, we have $S_\infty = \frac{a_1}{1-r} = \frac{24}{1-\frac{1}{3}} = \frac{24}{\frac{2}{3}} = 24 \cdot \frac{3}{2} = 36.$

31. $\frac{1}{12} + \frac{1}{6} + \frac{1}{3} + \frac{2}{3} + \ldots$

This is an infinite geometric series with $a_1 = \frac{1}{12}$ and $r = \frac{\frac{1}{6}}{\frac{1}{12}} = 2$. Since $|r| > 1$, the series diverges.

In Exercise 33, $x_1 = 0$, $x_2 = 1$, $x_3 = 2$, $x_4 = 3$, $x_5 = 4$ and $x_6 = 5$.

33. $\sum_{i=1}^{4} (x_i^2 - 6) = (x_1^2 - 6) + (x_2^2 - 6) + (x_3^2 - 6) + (x_4^2 - 6) = (0^2 - 6) + (1^2 - 6) + (2^2 - 6) + (3^2 - 6)$

$= (0-6) + (1-6) + (4-6) + (9-6) = -6 + (-5) + (-2) + 3 = -10$

In Exercises 35 – 37, other answers are possible.

35. $4 - 1 - 6 - \cdots - 66 = 4 + (-1) + (-6) + \cdots + (-66)$

This series is the sum of an arithmetic sequence with $a_1 = 4$ and $d = -1 - 4 = -5$. Therefore, the nth term is $a_n = a_1 + (n-1)d = 4 + (n-1)(-5) = 4 - 5n + 5 = -5n + 9$, or, equivalently, $a_i = -5i + 9$. To find the number of terms in the series, we realize that the last term of the series is –66. Since $a_i = -5i + 9$, we solve $-66 = -5i + 9$ for i.

$$-66 = -5i + 9 \Rightarrow -75 = -5i \Rightarrow i = 15$$

This indicates that the series consists of 15 terms and we have $4 - 1 - 6 - \ldots - 66 = \sum_{i=1}^{15} (-5i + 9)$.

37. $4 + 12 + 36 + \ldots + 972$

This series is the sum of a geometric sequence with $a_1 = 4$ and $r = \frac{12}{4} = 3$. Therefore, the nth term is $a_n = a_1 r^{n-1} \Rightarrow a_n = 4(3)^{n-1}$, or, equivalently, $a_i = 4(3)^{i-1}$. To find the number of terms in the series, we realize that the last term of the series is 972. Since $a_i = 4(3)^{i-1}$, we solve $972 = 4(3)^{i-1}$ for i.

$$972 = 4(3)^{i-1} \Rightarrow 243 = 3^{i-1} \Rightarrow 3^5 = 3^{i-1} \Rightarrow 5 = i-1 \Rightarrow i = 6$$

This indicates that the series consists of 6 terms and we have $4+12+36+\ldots+972 = \sum_{i=1}^{6} 4(3)^{i-1}$.

39.
$$\begin{aligned}(x+2y)^4 &= x^4 + \binom{4}{1}x^3(2y)^1 + \binom{4}{2}x^2(2y)^2 + \binom{4}{3}x^1(2y)^3 + (2y)^4 \\ &= x^4 + \frac{4!}{1!(4-1)!}x^3(2y) + \frac{4!}{(4-2)!2!}x^2(4y^2) + \frac{4!}{3!(4-3)!}x(8y^3) + 16y^4 \\ &= x^4 + \frac{4!}{1!3!}x^3(2y) + \frac{4!}{2!2!}x^2(4y^2) + \frac{4!}{3!1!}x(8y^3) + 16y^4 \\ &= x^4 + 4x^3(2y) + \frac{4\cdot 3}{2\cdot 1}x^2(4y^2) + 4x(8y^3) + 16y^4 \\ &= x^4 + 8x^3y + 24x^2y^2 + 32xy^3 + 16y^4\end{aligned}$$

41.
$$\begin{aligned}\left(3\sqrt{x} - \frac{1}{\sqrt{x}}\right)^5 &= \left[3x^{1/2} + \left(-x^{-1/2}\right)\right]^5 \\ &= \left(3x^{1/2}\right)^5 + \binom{5}{1}\left(3x^{1/2}\right)^4\left(-x^{-1/2}\right) + \binom{5}{2}\left(3x^{1/2}\right)^3\left(-x^{-1/2}\right)^2 \\ &\quad + \binom{5}{3}\left(3x^{1/2}\right)^2\left(-x^{-1/2}\right)^3 + \binom{5}{4}\left(3x^{1/2}\right)\left(-x^{-1/2}\right)^4 + \left(-x^{-1/2}\right)^5 \\ &= 243x^{5/2} + \frac{5!}{1!4!}\left(81x^2\right)\left(-x^{-1/2}\right) + \frac{5!}{2!3!}\left(27x^{3/2}\right)^3\left(x^{-1}\right) \\ &\quad - \frac{5!}{3!2!}(9x)x^{-3/2} + \frac{5!}{4!1!}\left(3x^{1/2}\right)\left(x^{-2}\right) + \left(-x^{-5/2}\right) \\ &= 243x^{5/2} - 5\left(81x^{2+(-1/2)}\right) + \frac{5\cdot 4}{2\cdot 1}\left(27x^{3/2+(-1)}\right) - \frac{5\cdot 4}{2\cdot 1}\left(9x^{1+(-3/2)}\right) + 5\left(3x^{1/2+(-2)}\right) - x^{-5/2} \\ &= 243x^{5/2} - 405x^{3/2} + 270x^{1/2} - 90x^{-1/2} + 15x^{-3/2} - x^{-5/2}\end{aligned}$$

43. The sixth term of the expansion of $(4x-y)^8$ is $\binom{8}{5}(4x)^3(-y)^5$. This simplifies as follows.

$$\binom{8}{5}(4x)^3(-y)^5 = \frac{8!}{5!3!}\left(64x^3\right)\left(-y^5\right) = \frac{8\cdot 7\cdot 6}{3\cdot 2\cdot 1}\left(-64x^3y^5\right) = 56\left(-64x^3y^5\right) = -3584x^3y^5$$

45. The first four terms of $(x+2)^{12}$ are as follows.

$$\begin{aligned}
&(x)^{12}+\binom{12}{1}(x)^{11}(2)+\binom{12}{2}(x)^{10}(2)^2+\binom{12}{3}(x)^9(2)^3 \\
&= x^{12}+\frac{12!}{1!11!}(x^{11})(2)+\frac{12!}{2!10!}(x^{10})(4)+\frac{12!}{3!9!}(x^9)(8) \\
&= x^{12}+12(2x^{11})+\frac{12\cdot 11}{2\cdot 1}(4x^{10})+220(8x^9) \\
&= x^{12}+24x^{11}+264x^{10}+1760x^9
\end{aligned}$$

47. Answers will vary.

49. Let S_n be the statement $1+3+5+7+\ldots+(2n-1)=n^2$.

Step 1: Show that the statement is true for $n = 1$.

S_1 is the statement $2(1)-1=1^2 \Rightarrow 2-1=1 \Rightarrow 1=1$, which is true.

Step 2: Show that if S_k is true, S_{k+1} is also true. S_k is the statement $1+3+5+7+\ldots+(2k-1)=k^2$. and S_{k+1} is the statement $1+3+5+7+\ldots+[2(k+1)-1]=(k+1)^2$.

Start with S_k: $1+3+5+7+\ldots+(2k-1)=k^2$ and add the $(k+1)$ st term, $[2(k+1)-1]$, to both sides of this equation.

$$\begin{aligned}
1+3+5+7+\ldots+(2k-1)&=k^2 \\
1+3+5+7+\ldots+(2k-1)+[2(k+1)-1]&=k^2+[2(k+1)-1] \\
1+3+5+7+\ldots+(2k-1)+[2(k+1)-1]&=k^2+(2k+2-1) \\
1+3+5+7+\ldots+(2k-1)+[2(k+1)-1]&=k^2+(2k+1) \\
1+3+5+7+\ldots+(2k-1)+[2(k+1)-1]&=k^2+2k+1 \\
1+3+5+7+\ldots+(2k-1)+[2(k+1)-1]&=(k+1)^2
\end{aligned}$$

It has been shown that S_k implies S_{k+1}. Therefore, by mathematical induction, S_n is true for every positive integer n.

51. Let S_n be the statement $2+2^2+2^3+\ldots+2^n=2(2^n-1)$.

Step 1: Show that the statement is true for $n = 1$.

S_1 is the statement $2^1=2(2^1-1)\Rightarrow 2=2(2-1)\Rightarrow 2=2(1)\Rightarrow 2=2$, which is true.

Step 2: Show that if S_k is true, S_{k+1} is also true. S_k is the following statement.

$$2+2^2+2^3+\ldots+2^k=2(2^k-1)$$

S_{k+1} is the statement $2+2^2+2^3+\ldots+2^{k+1}=2(2^{k+1}-1)$.

Start with S_k: $2+2^2+2^3+\ldots+2^k=2(2^k-1)$ and add the $(k+1)$ st term, 2^{k+1}, to both sides of this equation.

$$2+2^2+2^3+\ldots+2^k=2(2^k-1)$$
$$2+2^2+2^3+\ldots+2^k+2^{k+1}=2(2^k-1)+2^{k+1}$$
$$2+2^2+2^3+\ldots+2^k+2^{k+1}=2^{k+1}-2+2^{k+1}$$
$$2+2^2+2^3+\ldots+2^k+2^{k+1}=2\cdot 2^{k+1}-2\cdot 1$$
$$2+2^2+2^3+\ldots+2^k+2^{k+1}=2(2^{k+1}-1)$$

It has been shown that S_k implies S_{k+1}. Therefore, by mathematical induction, S_n is true for every positive integer n.

53. $P(9,2)=\dfrac{9!}{(9-2)!}=\dfrac{9!}{7!}=\dfrac{9\cdot 8\cdot 7!}{7!}=72$

55. $\dbinom{8}{3}=C(8,3)=\dfrac{8!}{(8-3)!3!}=\dfrac{8!}{5!3!}=\dfrac{8\cdot 7\cdot 6\cdot 5!}{3\cdot 2\cdot 1\cdot 5!}=56$

57. $C(10,5)=\dfrac{10!}{(10-5)!5!}=\dfrac{10!}{5!5!}=\dfrac{10\cdot 9\cdot 8\cdot 7\cdot 6\cdot 5!}{5!5!}=\dfrac{10\cdot 9\cdot 8\cdot 7\cdot 6}{5\cdot 4\cdot 3\cdot 2\cdot 1}=252$

59. Three independent events are involved. There are 5 choices of style, 3 choices of fabric, and 6 choices of color. Therefore, using the fundamental principle of counting, there are $5\cdot 3\cdot 6=90$ different couches.

61. There are 6 people on the student body council.

(a) In selecting a 3-member delegation, $C(6,3)$ choices are possible.

$$C(6,3)=\binom{6}{3}=\frac{6!}{(6-3)!3!}=\frac{6!}{3!3!}=\frac{6\cdot 5\cdot 4\cdot 3!}{3!3!}=\frac{6\cdot 5\cdot 4}{3\cdot 2\cdot 1}=20$$

20 delegations are possible.

(b) If the president must attend, then there are two slots available for the remaining 5 members, which means there are $C(5,2)$ choices.

$$C(5,2)=\binom{5}{2}=\frac{5!}{2!(5-2)!}=\frac{5!}{2!3!}=\frac{5\cdot 4\cdot 3!}{2!3!}=\frac{5\cdot 4}{2\cdot 1}=10$$

10 delegations are possible if the president must attend.

63. There are 4 spots to be filled by 26 letters and 3 spots by 10 digits. If repeats are allowed, then $26\cdot10\cdot10\cdot10\cdot26\cdot26\cdot26=456{,}976{,}000$ different license plates can be formed. If no repeats are allowed, then $26\cdot10\cdot9\cdot8\cdot25\cdot24\cdot23=258{,}336{,}000$ different license plates can be formed.

65. **(a)** Let E be the event "picking a green marble."

$n(E)=4$ and $n(S)=4+5+6=15$ (total number of marbles). Thus, $P(E)=\frac{n(E)}{n(S)}=\frac{4}{15}$

(b) Let E be the event "picking a black marble."

$n(E)=5$ and $n(S)=15$ (from part (a)). Thus, $P(E)=\frac{n(E)}{n(S)}=\frac{5}{15}=\frac{1}{3}$.

The probability that the marble is not black is given by $P(E')=1-P(E)=1-\frac{1}{3}=\frac{2}{3}$.

(c) Let E be the event "picking a blue marble."

$n(E)=0$ since there are no blue marbles and $n(S)=15$ (from part (a)). Thus, we have $P(E)=\frac{n(E)}{n(S)}=\frac{0}{15}=0$.

(d) Let E be the event "picking a marble that is not white." We have $P(E)=\frac{n(E)}{n(S)}=\frac{9}{15}$ and $P(E')=\frac{n(E')}{n(S)}=\frac{6}{15}$. Thus, the odds in favor of E are $\frac{P(E)}{P(E')}=\frac{\frac{9}{15}}{\frac{6}{15}}=\frac{9}{15}\cdot\frac{15}{6}=\frac{3}{2}$ or 3 to 2.

67. The total number of students polled is $\frac{282{,}200}{1000}=282.2$ (in thousands). Thus, $n(S)=282.2$.

(a) Let E be the event "selected student is conservative politically." Thus, we have the following.

$$P(E)=\frac{n(E)}{n(S)}=\frac{56.51}{282.2}\approx .2002$$

(b) Let L be the event "selected student is on the far left" and R be the event "selected student is on the far right." We have $P(L)=\frac{n(L)}{n(S)}=\frac{7.06}{282.2}\approx .0250$ and $P(R)=\frac{n(E)}{n(S)}=\frac{3.673}{282.2}\approx .0130$ There are no students which are both on the far left and far right, so $n(L\cap R)=0$ and $P(L\cap R)=0$. Thus we have the following.

$$P(L \text{ or } R)=P(L\cup R)=P(L)+P(R)-P(L\cap R)=.0250+.0130-0=.0380$$

(c) Let M be the event "selected student is middle of the road." Then $P(M)=\frac{n(M)}{n(S)}=\frac{143.5}{282.2}\approx .5085$.

Thus, $P(M)=1-P(M')=1-.5085=.4915$.

69. In this binomial experiment, we call rolling a five a success. Then $n=12$, $r=2$, and $p=\frac{1}{6}$.

$$P(2\text{ fives})=\binom{n}{r}p^r(1-p)^{n-r}=\binom{12}{2}\left(\frac{1}{6}\right)^2\left(1-\frac{1}{6}\right)^{12-2}=\frac{12!}{(12-2)!2!}\left(\frac{1}{6^2}\right)\left(\frac{5}{6}\right)^{10}=\frac{12!}{10!2!}\left(\frac{1}{6^2}\right)\left(\frac{5^{10}}{6^{10}}\right)$$

$$=\frac{12\cdot11\cdot10!}{10!2!}\left(\frac{5^{10}}{6^{12}}\right)=\frac{12\cdot11}{2\cdot1}\left(\frac{5^{10}}{6^{12}}\right)=66\left(\frac{5^{10}}{6^{12}}\right)\approx .296$$

Chapter 11: Test

1. $a_n = (-1)^n(n^2+2)$

$n=1: a_1 = (-1)^1(1^2+2) = (-1)(1+2) = -3; n=2: a_2 = (-1)^2(2^2+2) = (1)(4+2) = 6$

$n=3: a_3 = (-1)^3(3^2+2) = (-1)(9+2) = -11; n=4: a_4 = (-1)^4(4^2+2) = (1)(16+2) = 18$

$n=5: a_5 = (-1)^5(5^2+2) = (-1)(25+2) = -27$

The first five terms are –3, 6, –11, 18, and –27. This sequence does not have either a common difference or a common ration, so the sequence is neither arithmetic nor geometric.

2. $a_n = -3\cdot\left(\frac{1}{2}\right)^n$

$n=1: a_1 = -3\left(\frac{1}{2}\right)^1 = -3\left(\frac{1}{2}\right) = -\frac{3}{2}; n=2: a_2 = -3\left(\frac{1}{2}\right)^2 = -3\left(\frac{1}{4}\right) = -\frac{3}{4}$

$n=3: a_3 = -3\left(\frac{1}{2}\right)^3 = -3\left(\frac{1}{8}\right) = -\frac{3}{8}; n=4: a_4 = -3\left(\frac{1}{2}\right)^4 = -3\left(\frac{1}{16}\right) = -\frac{3}{16}$

$n=5: a_5 = -3\left(\frac{1}{2}\right)^5 = -3\left(\frac{1}{32}\right) = -\frac{3}{32}$

The first five terms are $-\frac{3}{2}, -\frac{3}{4}, -\frac{3}{8}, -\frac{3}{16}$, and $-\frac{3}{32}$. This sequence has a common ratio, $r = \frac{1}{2}$, so the sequence is geometric.

3. $a_1 = 2, a_2 = 3, a_n = a_{n-1} + 2a_{n-2},$ for $n \geq 3$

$n=3: a_3 = a_2 + 2a_1 = 3 + 2(2) = 3 + 4 = 7; n=4: a_4 = a_3 + 2a_2 = 7 + 2(3) = 7 + 6 = 13$

$n=5: a_5 = a_4 + 2a_3 = 13 + 2(7) = 13 + 14 = 27$

The first five terms are 2, 3, 7, 13, and 27. There is no common difference or common ratio, so the sequence is neither arithmetic nor geometric.

4. $a_1 = 1$ and $a_3 = 25$

$a_n = a_1 + (n-1)d \Rightarrow a_3 = a_1 + 2d \Rightarrow 25 = 1 + 2d \Rightarrow 2d = 24 \Rightarrow d = 12$

$a_5 = a_1 + (5-1)d \Rightarrow a_5 = a_1 + 4d = 1 + 4(12) = 1 + 48 = 49$

5. $a_1 = 81$ and $r = -\frac{2}{3}$

$a_n = a_1 r^{n-1} \Rightarrow a_6 = 81\left(-\frac{2}{3}\right)^5 = 81\left(-\frac{32}{243}\right) = -\frac{32}{3}$

6. Arithmetic, with $a_1 = -43$ and $d = 12$

$S_n = \frac{n}{2}\left[2a_1 + (n-1)d\right] \Rightarrow S_{10} = \frac{10}{2}\left[2a_1 + (10-1)d\right] = 5\left[2(-43) + 9(12)\right] = 5(-86 + 108) = 5(22) = 110$

7. Geometric, with $a_1 = 5$ and $r = -2$

$$S_n = \frac{a_1(1-r^n)}{1-r} \Rightarrow S_{10} = \frac{5\left[1-(-2)^{10}\right]}{1-(-2)} = \frac{5(1-1024)}{3} = \frac{5(-1023)}{3} = 5(-341) = -1705$$

8. $\sum_{i=1}^{30}(5i+2)$

This sum represents the sum of the first 30 terms of the arithmetic sequence having $a_1 = 5\cdot 1+2 = 7$ and $a_n = a_{30} = 5\cdot 30+2 = 150+2 = 152$. Thus, we have the following.

$$\sum_{i=1}^{30}(5i+2) = S_{30} = \tfrac{n}{2}(a_1+a_n) = \tfrac{30}{2}(a_1+a_{30}) = 15(7+152) = 15(159) = 2385$$

We could have also $\sum_{i=1}^{30}(5i+2) = \sum_{i=1}^{30}5i + \sum_{i=1}^{30}2 = 5\sum_{i=1}^{30}i + \sum_{i=1}^{30}2$

Since $\sum_{i=1}^{n}c = cn$ and $\sum_{i=1}^{n}i = \frac{n(n+1)}{2}$, we have the following.

$$5\sum_{i=1}^{30}i + \sum_{i=1}^{30}2 = 5\cdot\frac{30(30+1)}{2} + 2(30) = 5\cdot\frac{30(31)}{2} + 60 = 5(15)(31) + 60 = 2325 + 60 = 2385$$

9. $\sum_{i=1}^{5}(-3\cdot 2^i)$

This sum represents the sum of the first five terms of the geometric sequence having $a_1 = -3\cdot 2^1 = -6$ and $r = 2$. Thus, we have $\sum_{i=1}^{5}-3\cdot 2^1 = S_5 = \frac{a_1(1-r^n)}{1-r} = \frac{-6(1-2^5)}{1-2} = \frac{-6(1-32)}{-1} = 6(-31) = -186.$

10. $\sum_{i=1}^{\infty}(2^i)\cdot 4$

This is the sum of an infinite geometric sequence with $r = 2$. Since $|r| > 1$, the sum does not exist.

11. $\sum_{i=1}^{\infty}54\left(\frac{2}{9}\right)^i$

This is the sum of the infinite geometric sequence with $a_1 = 54\left(\frac{2}{9}\right)^1 = 54\left(\frac{2}{9}\right) = 12$ and $r = \frac{2}{9}$. Since $\left|\frac{2}{9}\right| < 1$, we can use the summation formula $S_\infty = \frac{a_1}{1-r}$.

$$\sum_{i=1}^{\infty}54\left(\tfrac{2}{9}\right)^i = S_\infty = \frac{a_1}{1-r} = \frac{12}{1-\frac{2}{9}} = \frac{12}{\frac{7}{9}} = 12\cdot\frac{9}{7} = \frac{108}{7}$$

12.
$$\begin{aligned}(x+y)^6 &= x^6 + \binom{6}{1}x^5y + \binom{6}{2}x^4y^2 + \binom{6}{3}x^3y^3 + \binom{6}{4}x^2y^4 + \binom{6}{5}xy^5 + y^6\\
&= x^6 + \frac{6!}{1!5!}x^5y + \frac{6!}{2!4!}x^4y^2 + \frac{6!}{3!3!}x^3y^3 + \frac{6!}{4!2!}x^2y^4 + \frac{6!}{5!1!}xy^5 + y^6\\
&= x^6 + 6x^5y + \frac{6\cdot 5}{2\cdot 1}x^4y^2 + \frac{6\cdot 5\cdot 4}{3\cdot 2\cdot 1}x^3y^3 + \frac{6\cdot 5}{2\cdot 1}x^2y^4 + 6xy^5 + y^6\\
&= x^6 + 6x^5y + 15x^4y^2 + 20x^3y^3 + 15x^2y^4 + 6xy^5 + y^6\end{aligned}$$

13. $(2x-3y)^4=(2x)^4+\binom{4}{1}(2x)^3(-3y)+\binom{4}{2}(2x)^2(-3y)^2+\binom{4}{3}(2x)(-3y)^3+(-3y)^4$

$$=16x^4+\frac{4!}{1!3!}(8x^3)(-3y)+\frac{4!}{2!2!}(4x^2)(9y^2)+\frac{4!}{1!3!}(2x)(-27y^3)+81y^4$$

$$=16x^4-4(24x^3y)+\frac{4\cdot 3}{2\cdot 1}(36x^2y^2)-4(54xy^3)+81y^4$$

$$=16x^4-96x^3y+216x^2y^2-216xy^3+81y^4$$

14. To find the third term in the expansion of $(w-2y)^6$, use the formula $\binom{n}{k-1}x^{n-(k-1)}y^{k-1}$ with $n = 6$ and $k = 3$. Then $k - 1 = 2$ and $n - (k - 1) = 4$. Thus, the third term is as follows.

$$\binom{n}{k-1}x^{n-(k-1)}y^{k-1}=\binom{6}{2}w^{6-2}(-2y)^2=\frac{6!}{2!4!}w^4(4y^2)=\frac{6\cdot 5\cdot 4!}{2!4!}(4w^4y^2)=\frac{6\cdot 5}{2\cdot 1}(4w^4y^2)=60w^4y^2$$

15. $8!=8\cdot 7\cdot 6\cdot 5\cdot 4\cdot 3\cdot 2\cdot 1=40,320$

16. $C(10,\ 2)=\frac{10!}{(10-2)!2!}=\frac{10!}{8!2!}=\frac{10\cdot 9\cdot 8!}{8!2!}=\frac{10\cdot 9}{2\cdot 1}=45$

17. $\binom{7}{3}=C(7,3)=\frac{7!}{(7-3)!3!}=\frac{7!}{4!3!}=\frac{7\cdot 6\cdot 5\cdot 4!}{4!3!}=\frac{7\cdot 6\cdot 5}{3\cdot 2\cdot 1}=35$

18. $P(11,\ 3)=\frac{11!}{(11-3)!}=\frac{11!}{8!}=\frac{11\cdot 10\cdot 9\cdot 8!}{8!}=11\cdot 10\cdot 9=990$

19. Let S_n be the statement $1+7+13+\ldots+(6n-5)=n(3n-2)$.

Step 1: Show that the statement is true for $n = 1$.

S_1 is the statement $6(1)+2=3(1^2)+5(1)\Rightarrow 6+2=3(1)+5\Rightarrow 8=3+5\Rightarrow 8=8$, which is true.

Step 2: Show that if S_k is true, S_{k+1} is also true. S_k is the following statement.

$$1+7+13+\ldots+(6k-5)=k(3k-2)$$

S_{k+1} is the statement $1+7+13+\ldots+[6(k+1)-5]=(k+1)[3(k+1)-2]$.

Start with S_k: $1+7+13+\ldots+(6k-5)=k(3k-2)$ and add the $(k+1)$ st term, $[6(k+1)-5]$, to both sides of this equation.

$$1+7+13+\ldots+(6k-5)=k(3k-2)$$

$$1+7+13+\ldots+(6k-5)+[6(k+1)-5]=k(3k-2)=k(3k-2)+[6(k+1)-5]$$

$$1+7+13+\ldots+(6k-5)+[6(k+1)-5]=3k^2-2k+(6k+6-5)$$

$$1+7+13+\ldots+(6k-5)+[6(k+1)-5]=3k^2+4k+1$$

$$1+7+13+\ldots+(6k-5)+[6(k+1)-5]=(k+1)(3k+1)$$

$$1+7+13+\ldots+(6k-5)+[6(k+1)-5]=(k+1)[(3k+3)-2]$$

$$1+7+13+\ldots+(6k-5)+[6(k+1)-5]=(k+1)[3(k+1)-2]$$

It has been shown that S_k implies S_{k+1}. Therefore, by mathematical induction, S_n is true for every positive integer n.

20. Using the fundamental principle of counting, we have $4 \cdot 3 \cdot 2 = 24$.
There are 24 different kinds of shoes if there are 4 styles, 3 different colors, and 2 different shades.

21. We are choosing three people from a group of ten without regard to order, so there are $C(10, 3)$ ways to do this. Since $C(10, 3) = \frac{10!}{(10-3)!3!} = \frac{10!}{7!3!} = \frac{10 \cdot 9 \cdot 8 \cdot 7!}{7!3!} = \frac{10 \cdot 9 \cdot 8}{3 \cdot 2 \cdot 1} = 120$, there are 120 ways 3 officers can be selected to attend a seminar.

If one black and exactly one Asian officer must be included, we have 1 way to select the black officer, 2 ways to select the Asian officer, and 7 ways to select the remaining officer. Altogether, then, we have $1 \cdot 2 \cdot 7 = 14$ ways to do this.

22. The two women can be selected from the four women in $C(4, 2) = \frac{4!}{(4-2)!2!} = \frac{4!}{2!2!} = \frac{4 \cdot 3}{2 \cdot 1} = 6$ ways.

The two men can be selected from the six men in $C(6, 2) = \frac{6!}{(6-2)!2!} = \frac{6!}{4!2!} = \frac{6 \cdot 5}{2 \cdot 1} = 15$ ways.

Altogether, then, we have $6 \cdot 15 = 90$ ways to do this.

23. Answers will vary.

24. **(a)** $P(\text{red three}) = \frac{n(\text{red three cards})}{n(\text{cards in deck})} = \frac{2}{52} = \frac{1}{26}$

(b) Let F be the event "draw a face card." Each suit contains 3 face cards (jack, queen, and king), so the deck contains 12 face cards. Thus, $n(F) = 12$ and $P(F) = \frac{12}{52} = \frac{3}{13}$. The probability of drawing a card that is not a face card is $P(F') = 1 - P(F) = 1 - \frac{3}{13} = \frac{10}{13}$.

(c) Let K be the event "king is drawn" and S be the event "spade is drawn." There are 4 kings, so $n(K) = 4$ and $P(K) = \frac{4}{52} = \frac{1}{13}$. There are 13 spades, so $n(S) = 13$ and $P(S) = \frac{13}{52} = \frac{1}{4}$. There is one card which is both a king and a spade, so $n(K \cap S) = 1$ and $P(K \cap S) = \frac{1}{52}$. Thus we have the following.

$$P(K \text{ or } S) = P(K \cup S) = P(K) + P(S) - P(K \cap S) = \frac{1}{13} + \frac{1}{4} - \frac{1}{52} = \frac{4}{52} + \frac{13}{52} - \frac{1}{52} = \frac{16}{52} = \frac{4}{13}$$

(d) Consider the event F: "draw a face card." As shown in the solution to part (b), $P(F) = \frac{3}{13}$ and $P(F') = \frac{10}{13}$. Thus, the odds in favor of drawing a face card are as follows.

$$\frac{P(F)}{P(F')} = \frac{\frac{3}{13}}{\frac{10}{13}} = \frac{3}{13} \cdot \frac{13}{10} = \frac{3}{10} \text{ or 3 to 10}$$

25. "At most 2" means "0 or 1 or 2."

$$P(\text{at most 2}) = P(0 \text{ or } 1 \text{ or } 2) = P(0) + P(1) + P(2) = .19 + .43 + .30 = .92$$

The probability that at most 2 light bulbs are defective is .92.

26. In this binomial experiment, we call rolling a five a success. Then $n = 6$, $r = 2$, and $p = \frac{1}{6}$.

$$P(2\text{ fives}) = \binom{n}{r} p^r (1-p)^{n-r} = \binom{6}{2}\left(\frac{1}{6}\right)^2\left(1-\frac{1}{6}\right)^{6-2} = \frac{6!}{(6-2)!2!}\left(\frac{1}{6^2}\right)\left(\frac{5}{6}\right)^4 = \frac{6!}{4!2!}\left(\frac{1}{6^2}\right)\left(\frac{5^4}{6^4}\right)$$

$$= \frac{6\cdot 5\cdot 4!}{4!2!}\left(\frac{5^4}{6^6}\right) = \frac{6\cdot 5}{2\cdot 1}\left(\frac{5^4}{6^6}\right) = 15\left(\frac{5^4}{6^6}\right) \approx .201$$

Appendix A
POLAR FORM OF CONIC SECTIONS

Exercises 1 – 12 are graphed in degree mode.

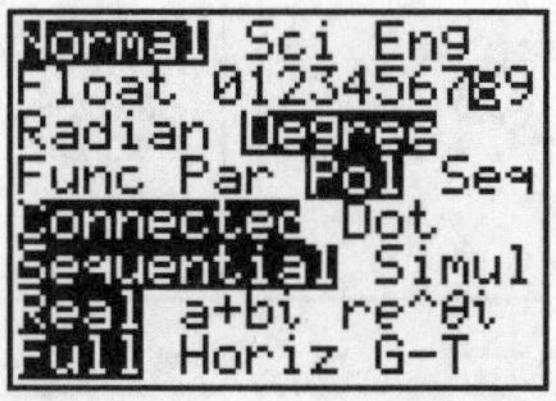

1.

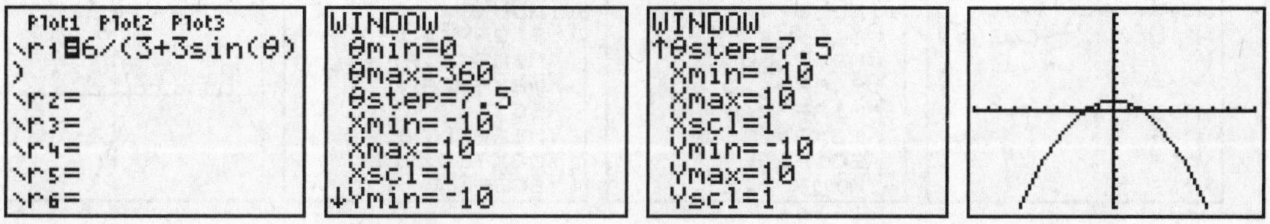

2.

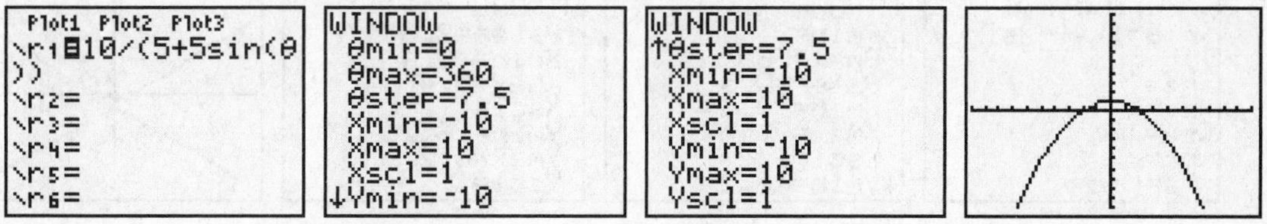

3.

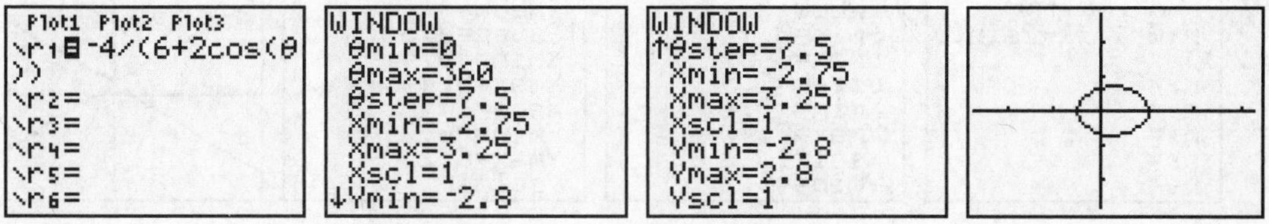

4.

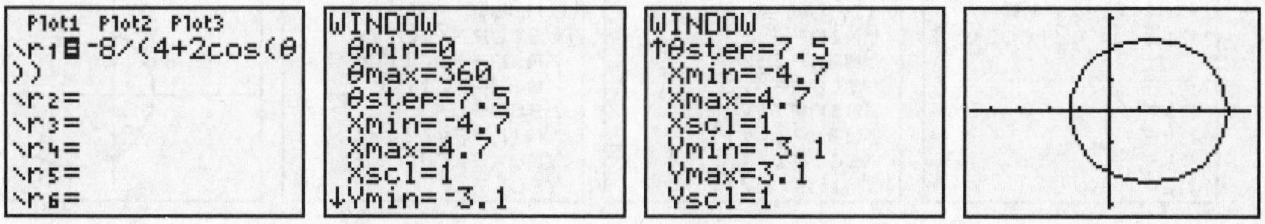

5.

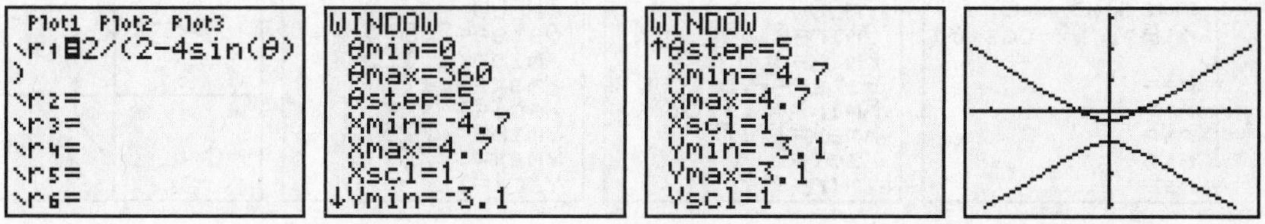

6.

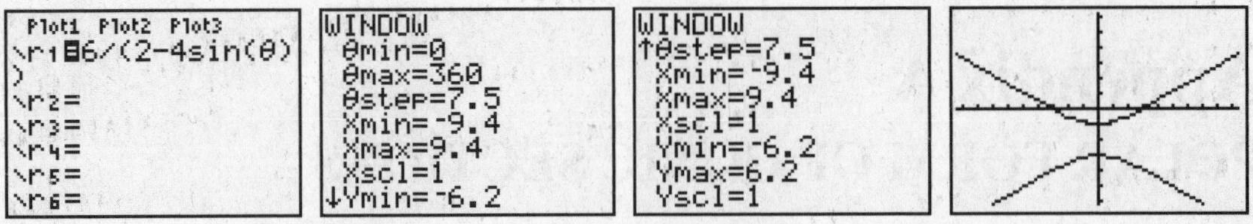

7.

8.

9.

10.

11.

12.

13. Since a parabola with vertical directrix 3 units to the right of the pole has the equation $r = \dfrac{ep}{1+e\cos\theta}$

where $e=1$ and $p=3$, $r = \dfrac{1\cdot 3}{1+1\cos\theta} = \dfrac{3}{1+\cos\theta}$.

14. Since a parabola with vertical directrix 4 units to the left of the pole has the equation $r = \dfrac{ep}{1 - e\cos\theta}$ where $e = 1$ and $p = 4$, $r = \dfrac{1 \cdot 4}{1 - 1\cos\theta} = \dfrac{4}{1 - \cos\theta}$.

15. Since a parabola with a horizontal directrix 5 units below the pole has the equation $r = \dfrac{ep}{1 - e\sin\theta}$ where $e = 1$ and $p = 5$, $r = \dfrac{1 \cdot 5}{1 - 1\sin\theta} = \dfrac{5}{1 - \sin\theta}$.

16. Since a parabola with a horizontal directrix 6 units above the pole has the equation $r = \dfrac{ep}{1 + e\sin\theta}$ where $e = 1$ and $p = 6$, $r = \dfrac{1 \cdot 6}{1 + 1\sin\theta} = \dfrac{6}{1 + \sin\theta}$.

17. A conic section with vertical directrix 5 units to the right of the pole has a polar equation of the form $r = \dfrac{ep}{1 + e\cos\theta}$ where $p = 5$. When $e = \dfrac{4}{5}$, we get the following.

$$r = \frac{\frac{4}{5} \cdot 5}{1 + \frac{4}{5}\cos\theta} \Rightarrow r = \frac{4}{\frac{5 + 4\cos\theta}{5}} \Rightarrow r = \frac{20}{5 + 4\cos\theta}$$

Since $e < 1$, the graph of the equation is an ellipse.

18. A conic section with vertical directrix 6 units to the left of the pole has a polar equation of the form $r = \dfrac{ep}{1 - e\cos\theta}$ where $p = 6$. When $e = \dfrac{2}{3}$, we get the following.

$$r = \frac{\frac{2}{3} \cdot 6}{1 - \frac{2}{3}\cos\theta} \Rightarrow r = \frac{4}{\frac{3 - 2\cos\theta}{3}} \Rightarrow r = \frac{12}{3 - 2\cos\theta}$$

Since $e < 1$, the graph of the equation is an ellipse.

19. A conic section with horizontal directrix 8 units below the pole has a polar equation of the form $r = \dfrac{ep}{1 - e\sin\theta}$ where $p = 8$. When $e = \dfrac{5}{4}$, we get the following.

$$r = \frac{\frac{5}{4} \cdot 8}{1 - \frac{5}{4}\sin\theta} \Rightarrow r = \frac{10}{\frac{4 - 5\sin\theta}{4}} \Rightarrow r = \frac{40}{4 - 5\sin\theta}$$

Since $e > 1$, the graph of the equation is a hyperbola.

20. A conic section with horizontal directrix 4 units above the pole has a polar equation of the form $r = \dfrac{ep}{1 + e\sin\theta}$ where $p = 4$. When $e = \dfrac{3}{2}$, we get the following.

$$r = \frac{\frac{3}{2} \cdot 4}{1 + \frac{3}{2}\sin\theta} \Rightarrow r = \frac{6}{\frac{2 + 3\sin\theta}{2}} \Rightarrow r = \frac{12}{2 + 3\sin\theta}$$

Since $e > 1$, the graph of the equation is a hyperbola.

21. To identify the type of conic, rewrite the equation in standard form to find *e*.

$$r=\frac{6}{3-\cos\theta}\Rightarrow r=\frac{3\cdot 2}{3\left(1-\frac{1}{3}\cos\theta\right)}\Rightarrow r=\frac{2}{1-\frac{1}{3}\cos\theta}$$

Thus, $e=\dfrac{1}{3}$. Since $e<1$, the graph of the equation is an ellipse. To convert to rectangular form, start with the given equation.

$$r=\frac{6}{3-\cos\theta}$$
$$r(3-\cos\theta)=6\Rightarrow 3r-r\cos\theta=6\Rightarrow 3r=r\cos\theta+6$$
$$(3r)^2=(r\cos\theta+6)^2\Rightarrow(3r)^2=(x+6)^2\Rightarrow 9r^2=x^2+12x+36$$
$$9\left(x^2+y^2\right)=x^2+12x+36\Rightarrow 9x^2+9y^2=x^2+12x+36$$
$$8x^2+9y^2-12x-36=0$$

22. To identify the type of conic, rewrite the equation in standard form to find *e*.

$$r=\frac{8}{4-\cos\theta}\Rightarrow r=\frac{4\cdot 2}{4\left(1-\frac{1}{4}\cos\theta\right)}\Rightarrow r=\frac{2}{1-\frac{1}{4}\cos\theta}$$

Thus, $e=\dfrac{1}{4}$. Since $e<1$, the graph of the equation is an ellipse. To convert to rectangular form, start with the given equation.

$$r=\frac{8}{4-\cos\theta}$$
$$r(4-\cos\theta)=8\Rightarrow 4r-r\cos\theta=8\Rightarrow 4r=r\cos\theta+8$$
$$(4r)^2=(r\cos\theta+8)^2\Rightarrow(4r)^2=(x+8)^2\Rightarrow 16r^2=x^2+16x+64$$
$$16\left(x^2+y^2\right)=x^2+16x+64\Rightarrow 16x^2+16y^2=x^2+16x+64$$
$$15x^2+16y^2-16x-64=0$$

23. To identify the type of conic, rewrite the equation in standard form to find *e*. $r=\dfrac{-2}{1+2\cos\theta}$ is in standard form. Thus, $e=2$. Since $e>1$, the graph of the equation is a hyperbola. To convert to rectangular form, start with the given equation.

$$r=\frac{-2}{1+2\cos\theta}$$
$$r(1+2\cos\theta)=-2\Rightarrow r+2r\cos\theta=-2\Rightarrow r=-2r\cos\theta-2$$
$$r^2=(-2r\cos\theta-2)^2\Rightarrow r^2=(-2x-2)^2\Rightarrow x^2+y^2=4x^2+8x+4$$
$$0=3x^2-y^2+8x+4$$

24. To identify the type of conic, rewrite the equation in standard form to find *e*. $r = \dfrac{-3}{1+3\cos\theta}$ is in standard form. Thus, $e = 3$. Since $e > 1$, the graph of the equation is a hyperbola. To convert to rectangular form, start with the given equation.

$$r = \frac{-3}{1+3\cos\theta}$$
$$r(1+3\cos\theta) = -3 \Rightarrow r + 3r\cos\theta = -3 \Rightarrow r = -3r\cos\theta - 3$$
$$r^2 = (-3r\cos\theta - 3)^2 \Rightarrow r^2 = (-3x-3)^2 \Rightarrow x^2 + y^2 = 9x^2 + 18x + 9$$
$$8x^2 - y^2 + 18x + 9 = 0$$

25. To identify the type of conic, rewrite the equation in standard form to find *e*.

$$r = \frac{-6}{4+2\sin\theta} \Rightarrow r = \frac{4\cdot\frac{-6}{4}}{4(1+\frac{1}{2}\sin\theta)} \Rightarrow r = \frac{\frac{-3}{2}}{1+\frac{1}{2}\sin\theta}$$

Thus, $e = \dfrac{1}{2}$. Since $e < 1$, the graph of the equation is an ellipse. To convert to rectangular form, start with the given equation.

$$r = \frac{-6}{4+2\sin\theta}$$
$$r(4+2\sin\theta) = -6 \Rightarrow 4r + 2r\sin\theta = -6 \Rightarrow 4r = -2r\sin\theta - 6$$
$$(4r)^2 = (-2r\sin\theta - 6)^2 \Rightarrow (4r)^2 = (-2y-6)^2 \Rightarrow 16r^2 = 4y^2 + 24y + 36$$
$$16\left(x^2+y^2\right) = 4y^2 + 24y + 36 \Rightarrow 16x^2 + 16y^2 = 4y^2 + 24y + 36 \Rightarrow 16x^2 + 12y^2 - 24y - 36 = 0$$
$$4x^2 + 3y^2 - 6y - 9 = 0$$

26. To identify the type of conic, rewrite the equation in standard form to find *e*.

$$r = \frac{-12}{6+3\sin\theta} \Rightarrow r = \frac{6\cdot -2}{6(1+\frac{1}{2}\sin\theta)} \Rightarrow r = \frac{-2}{1+\frac{1}{2}\sin\theta}$$

Thus, $e = \dfrac{1}{2}$. Since $e < 1$, the graph of the equation is an ellipse. To convert to rectangular form, start with the given equation.

$$r = \frac{-12}{6+3\sin\theta}$$
$$r(6+3\sin\theta) = -12 \Rightarrow 6r + 3r\sin\theta = -12 \Rightarrow 6r = -3r\sin\theta - 12$$
$$(6r)^2 = (-3r\sin\theta - 12)^2 \Rightarrow (6r)^2 = (-3y-12)^2$$
$$36r^2 = 9y^2 + 72y + 144 \Rightarrow 36\left(x^2+y^2\right) = 9y^2 + 72y + 144$$
$$36x^2 + 36y^2 = 9y^2 + 72y + 144 \Rightarrow 36x^2 + 27y^2 - 72y - 144 = 0$$
$$4x^2 + 3y^2 - 8y - 16 = 0$$

27. To identify the type of conic, rewrite the equation in standard form to find *e*.

$$r=\frac{10}{2-2\sin\theta}\Rightarrow r=\frac{2\cdot 5}{2(1-\sin\theta)}\Rightarrow r=\frac{5}{1-\sin\theta}$$

Thus, $e=1$ and the graph of the equation is a parabola. To convert to rectangular form, start with the given equation.

$$r=\frac{10}{2-2\sin\theta}$$
$$r(2-2\sin\theta)=10\Rightarrow 2r-2r\sin\theta=10\Rightarrow 2r=2r\sin\theta+10$$
$$(2r)^2=(2r\sin\theta+10)^2\Rightarrow(2r)^2=(2y+10)^2\Rightarrow 4r^2=4y^2+40y+100$$
$$4(x^2+y^2)=4y^2+40y+100\Rightarrow 4x^2+4y^2=4y^2+40y+100\Rightarrow 4x^2-40y-100=0$$
$$x^2-10y-25=0$$

28. To identify the type of conic, rewrite the equation in standard form to find *e*.

$$r=\frac{12}{4-4\sin\theta}\Rightarrow r=\frac{4\cdot 3}{4(1-\sin\theta)}\Rightarrow r=\frac{3}{1-\sin\theta}$$

Thus, $e=1$ and the graph of the equation is a parabola. To convert to rectangular form, start with the given equation.

$$r=\frac{12}{4-4\sin\theta}$$
$$r(4-4\sin\theta)=12\Rightarrow 4r-4r\sin\theta=12\Rightarrow 4r=4r\sin\theta+12$$
$$(4r)^2=(4r\sin\theta+12)^2\Rightarrow(4r)^2=(4y+12)^2\Rightarrow 16r^2=16y^2+96y+144$$
$$16(x^2+y^2)=16y^2+96y+144\Rightarrow 16x^2+16y^2=16y^2+96y+144\Rightarrow 16x^2-96y-144=0$$
$$x^2-6y-9=0$$

Appendix B
ROTATION OF AXES

1. $4x^2+3y^2+2xy-5x=8$
$A=4,\ B=2,\ C=3$
$B^2-4AC=2^2-4(4)(3)=4-48=-44$
Since $B^2-4AC<0$, the graph will be a circle or ellipse or a point.

2. $x^2+2xy-3y^2+2y=12$
$A=1,\ B=2,\ C=-3$
$B^2-4AC=2^2-4(1)(-3)=4+12=16$
Since $B^2-4AC>0$, the graph will be a hyperbola or two intersecting lines.

3. $2x^2+3xy-4y^2=0$
$A=2,\ B=3,\ C=-4$
$B^2-4AC=3^2-4(2)(-4)=9+32=41$
Since $B^2-4AC>0$, the graph will be a hyperbola or two intersecting lines.

4. $x^2-2xy+y^2+4x-8y=0$
$A=1,\ B=-2,\ C=1$
$B^2-4AC=(-2)^2-4(1)(1)=4-4=0$
Since $B^2-4AC=0$, the graph will be a parabola or one line or two parallel lines.

5. $4x^2+4xy+y^2+15=0$
$A=4,\ B=4,\ C=1$
$B^2-4AC=4^2-4(4)(1)=16-16=0$
Since $B^2-4AC=0$, the graph will be a parabola or one line or two parallel lines.

6. $-x^2+2xy-y^2+16=0$
$A=-1,\ B=2,\ C=-1$
$B^2-4AC=2^2-4(-1)(-1)=4-4=0$
Since $B^2-4AC=0$, the graph will be a parabola or one line or two parallel lines.

7. The *xy*-term is removed from $2x^2+\sqrt{3}xy+y^2+x=5$ by a rotation of the axes through an angle θ satisfying $\cot 2\theta=\frac{A-C}{B}$, where $A=2,\ B=\sqrt{3}$, and $C=1$.

$$\cot 2\theta=\frac{2-1}{\sqrt{3}}\Rightarrow \cot 2\theta=\frac{1}{\sqrt{3}}\Rightarrow \cot 2\theta=\frac{\sqrt{3}}{3}\Rightarrow 2\theta=\cot^{-1}\frac{\sqrt{3}}{3}\Rightarrow 2\theta=60°\Rightarrow \theta=30°$$

8. The *xy*-term is removed from $4\sqrt{3}x^2 + xy + 3\sqrt{3}y^2 = 10$ by a rotation of the axes through an angle θ satisfying $\cot 2\theta = \frac{A-C}{B}$, where $A = 4\sqrt{3}$, $B = 1$, and $C = 3\sqrt{3}$.

$$\cot 2\theta = \frac{4\sqrt{3} - 3\sqrt{3}}{1} \Rightarrow \cot 2\theta = \sqrt{3} \Rightarrow 2\theta = \cot^{-1}\sqrt{3} \Rightarrow 2\theta = 30° \Rightarrow \theta = 15°$$

9. The *xy*-term is removed from $3x^2 + \sqrt{3}xy + 4y^2 + 2x - 3y = 12$ by a rotation of the axes through an angle θ satisfying $\cot 2\theta = \frac{A-C}{B}$, where $A = 3$, $B = \sqrt{3}$, and $C = 4$.

$$\cot 2\theta = \frac{3-4}{\sqrt{3}} \Rightarrow \cot 2\theta = \frac{-1}{\sqrt{3}} \Rightarrow \cot 2\theta = -\frac{\sqrt{3}}{3} \Rightarrow 2\theta = \cot^{-1}\left(-\frac{\sqrt{3}}{3}\right) \Rightarrow 2\theta = 120° \Rightarrow \theta = 60°$$

10. The *xy*-term is removed from $4x^2 + 2xy + 2y^2 + x - 7 = 0$ by a rotation of the axes through $\cot 2\theta = \frac{A-C}{B}$, where $A = 4$, $B = 2$, and $C = 2$.

$$\cot 2\theta = \frac{4-2}{2} \Rightarrow \cot 2\theta = \frac{2}{2} \Rightarrow \cot 2\theta = 1 \Rightarrow 2\theta = \cot^{-1} 1 \Rightarrow 2\theta = 45° \Rightarrow \theta = 22.5°$$

11. The *xy*-term is removed from $x^2 - 4xy + 5y^2 = 18$ by a rotation of the axes through $\cot 2\theta = \frac{A-C}{B}$, where $A = 1$, $B = -4$, and $C = 5$.

$$\cot 2\theta = \frac{1-5}{-4} \Rightarrow \cot 2\theta = \frac{-4}{-4} \Rightarrow \cot 2\theta = 1 \Rightarrow 2\theta = \cot^{-1} 1 \Rightarrow 2\theta = 45° \Rightarrow \theta = 22.5°$$

12. The *xy*-term is removed from $3\sqrt{3}x^2 - 2xy + \sqrt{3}y^2 = 25$ by a rotation of the axes through $\cot 2\theta = \frac{A-C}{B}$, where $A = 3\sqrt{3}$, $B = -2$, and $C = \sqrt{3}$.

$$\cot 2\theta = \frac{3\sqrt{3} - \sqrt{3}}{-2} \Rightarrow \cot 2\theta = \frac{2\sqrt{3}}{-2} \Rightarrow \cot 2\theta = -\sqrt{3} \Rightarrow 2\theta = \cot^{-1}\left(-\sqrt{3}\right) \Rightarrow 2\theta = 150° \Rightarrow \theta = 75°$$

13. Since $\theta = 45°$, then $\sin\theta = \frac{\sqrt{2}}{2}$ and $\cos\theta = \frac{\sqrt{2}}{2}$, and the rotation equations are $x = \frac{\sqrt{2}}{2}x' - \frac{\sqrt{2}}{2}y'$ and $y = \frac{\sqrt{2}}{2}x' + \frac{\sqrt{2}}{2}y'$.

Substituting these values into the given equation yields the following.

$$x^2 - xy + y^2 = 6$$

$$\left(\frac{\sqrt{2}}{2}x' - \frac{\sqrt{2}}{2}y'\right)^2 - \left(\frac{\sqrt{2}}{2}x' - \frac{\sqrt{2}}{2}y'\right)\left(\frac{\sqrt{2}}{2}x' + \frac{\sqrt{2}}{2}y'\right) + \left(\frac{\sqrt{2}}{2}x' + \frac{\sqrt{2}}{2}y'\right)^2 = 6$$

$$\left[\frac{1}{2}x'^2 - 2\left(\frac{1}{2}x'y'\right) + \frac{1}{2}y'^2\right] - \left(\frac{1}{2}x'^2 + \frac{1}{2}x'y' - \frac{1}{2}x'y' - \frac{1}{2}y'^2\right) + \left[\frac{1}{2}x'^2 + 2\left(\frac{1}{2}x'y'\right) + \frac{1}{2}y'^2\right] = 6$$

$$\left(\frac{1}{2}x'^2 - x'y' + \frac{1}{2}y'^2\right) - \left(\frac{1}{2}x'^2 - \frac{1}{2}y'^2\right) + \left(\frac{1}{2}x'^2 + x'y' + \frac{1}{2}y'^2\right) = 6$$

$$\frac{1}{2}x'^2 - x'y' + \frac{1}{2}y'^2 - \frac{1}{2}x'^2 + \frac{1}{2}y'^2 + \frac{1}{2}x'^2 + x'y' + \frac{1}{2}y'^2 = 6$$

$$\frac{1}{2}x'^2 + \frac{3}{2}y'^2 = 6$$

$$\frac{x'^2}{12} + \frac{y'^2}{4} = 1$$

The graph of the equation is an ellipse. This ellipse is centered at the origin and has x' – intercepts $\pm\sqrt{12} = \pm 2\sqrt{3} \approx \pm 3.5$ and y' – intercepts $\pm\sqrt{4} = \pm 2$.

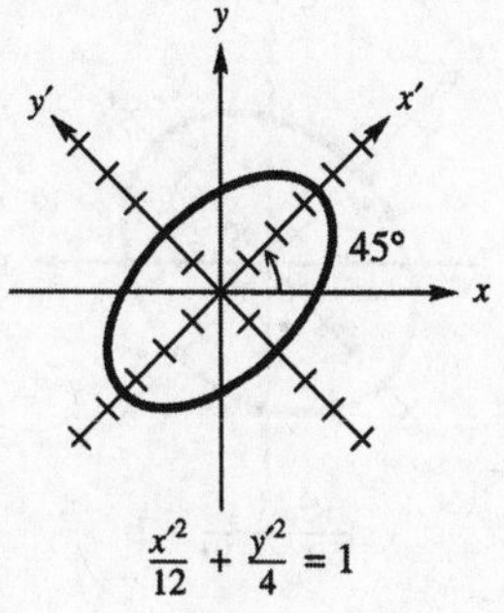

14. Since $\theta = 45°$, then $\sin\theta = \frac{\sqrt{2}}{2}$ and $\cos\theta = \frac{\sqrt{2}}{2}$, and the rotation equations are $x = \frac{\sqrt{2}}{2}x' - \frac{\sqrt{2}}{2}y'$ and $y = \frac{\sqrt{2}}{2}x' + \frac{\sqrt{2}}{2}y'$. Substituting these values into the given equation yields the following.

$$2x^2 - xy + 2y^2 = 25$$

$$2\left(\frac{\sqrt{2}}{2}x' - \frac{\sqrt{2}}{2}y'\right)^2 - \left(\frac{\sqrt{2}}{2}x' - \frac{\sqrt{2}}{2}y'\right)\left(\frac{\sqrt{2}}{2}x' + \frac{\sqrt{2}}{2}y'\right) + 2\left(\frac{\sqrt{2}}{2}x' + \frac{\sqrt{2}}{2}y'\right)^2 = 25$$

$$2\left[\frac{1}{2}x'^2 - 2\left(\frac{1}{2}x'y'\right) + \frac{1}{2}y'^2\right] - \left(\frac{1}{2}x'^2 + \frac{1}{2}x'y' - \frac{1}{2}x'y' - \frac{1}{2}y'^2\right) + 2\left[\frac{1}{2}x'^2 + 2\left(\frac{1}{2}x'y'\right) + \frac{1}{2}y'^2\right] = 25$$

$$2\left(\frac{1}{2}x'^2 - x'y' + \frac{1}{2}y'^2\right) - \left(\frac{1}{2}x'^2 - \frac{1}{2}y'^2\right) + 2\left(\frac{1}{2}x'^2 + x'y' + \frac{1}{2}y'^2\right) = 25$$

$$x'^2 - 2x'y' + y'^2 - \frac{1}{2}x'^2 + \frac{1}{2}y'^2 + x'^2 + 2x'y' + y'^2 = 25$$

$$\frac{3}{2}x'^2 + \frac{5}{2}y'^2 = 25$$

$$\frac{3x'^2}{50} + \frac{y'^2}{10} = 1$$

The graph of the equation is an ellipse. This ellipse is centered at the origin and has x' – intercepts $\pm\sqrt{\frac{50}{3}} = \pm\frac{5\sqrt{2}}{\sqrt{3}} = \pm\frac{5\sqrt{6}}{3} \approx \pm 4.1$ and y' – intercepts $\pm\sqrt{10} \approx \pm 3.2$.

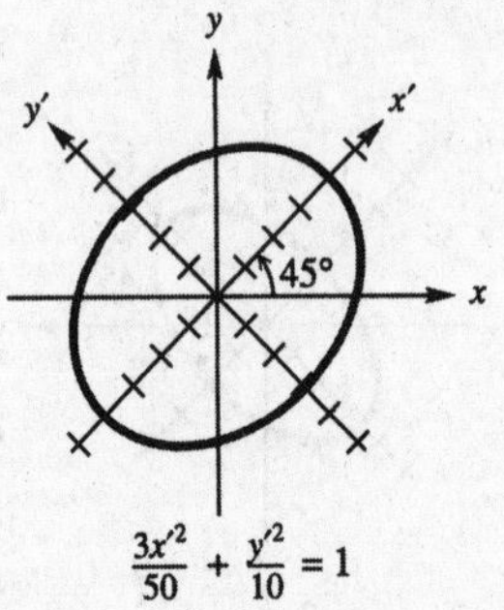

15. If $0<\theta<90°$, then given $\sin\theta=\frac{2}{\sqrt{5}}$, we can find $\cos\theta$.

The side adjacent to θ is the following.

$$\sqrt{\left(\sqrt{5}\right)^2-2^2}=\sqrt{5-4}=\sqrt{1}=1$$

Thus, $\cos\theta=\frac{1}{\sqrt{5}}$.

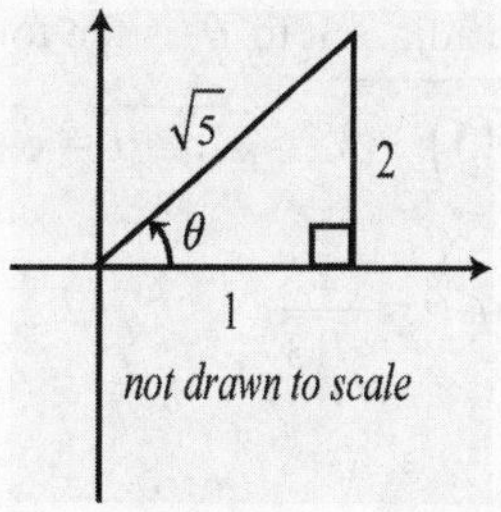

not drawn to scale

The rotation equations are $x=\frac{1}{\sqrt{5}}x'-\frac{2}{\sqrt{5}}y'$ and $y=\frac{2}{\sqrt{5}}x'+\frac{1}{\sqrt{5}}y'$. Substituting these values into the given equation yields the following.

$$8x^2-4xy+5y^2=36$$

$$8\left(\frac{1}{\sqrt{5}}x'-\frac{2}{\sqrt{5}}y'\right)^2-4\left(\frac{1}{\sqrt{5}}x'-\frac{2}{\sqrt{5}}y'\right)\left(\frac{2}{\sqrt{5}}x'+\frac{1}{\sqrt{5}}y'\right)+5\left(\frac{2}{\sqrt{5}}x'+\frac{1}{\sqrt{5}}y'\right)^2=36$$

$$8\left[\frac{1}{5}x'^2-2\left(\frac{2}{5}x'y'\right)+\frac{4}{5}y'^2\right]-4\left(\frac{2}{5}x'^2+\frac{1}{5}x'y'-\frac{4}{5}x'y'-\frac{2}{5}y'^2\right)+5\left[\frac{4}{5}x'^2+2\left(\frac{2}{5}x'y'\right)+\frac{1}{5}y'^2\right]=36$$

$$8\left(\frac{1}{5}x'^2-\frac{4}{5}x'y'+\frac{4}{5}y'^2\right)-4\left(\frac{2}{5}x'^2-\frac{3}{5}x'y-\frac{2}{5}y'^2\right)+5\left(\frac{4}{5}x'^2+\frac{4}{5}x'y'+\frac{1}{5}y'^2\right)=36$$

$$\frac{8}{5}x'^2-\frac{32}{5}x'y'+\frac{32}{5}y'^2-\frac{8}{5}x'^2+\frac{12}{5}x'y'+\frac{8}{5}y'^2+\frac{20}{5}x'^2+\frac{20}{5}x'y'+\frac{5}{5}y'^2=36$$

$$4x'^2+9y'^2=36$$

$$\frac{x'^2}{9}+\frac{y'^2}{4}=1$$

The graph of the equation is an ellipse. With $0<\theta<90°$, we have $\theta=\sin^{-1}\frac{2}{\sqrt{5}}\approx 63.43°$. This ellipse is centered at the origin and has x' – intercepts $\pm\sqrt{9}=\pm3$ and y' – intercepts $\pm\sqrt{4}=\pm2$.

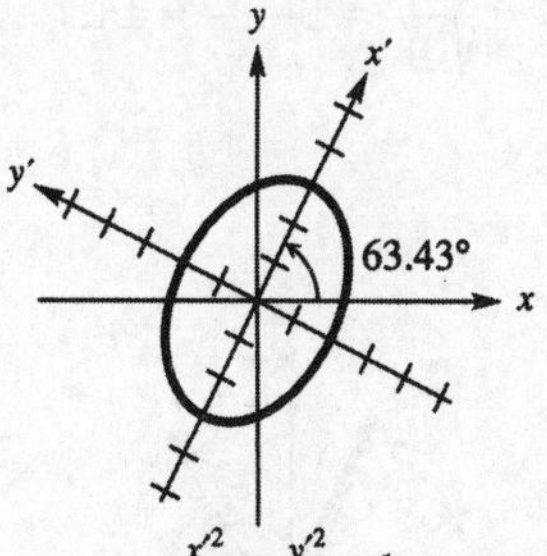

$\frac{x'^2}{9}+\frac{y'^2}{4}=1$

16. If $0<\theta<90°$, then given $\sin\theta=\frac{3}{\sqrt{13}}$, we can find $\cos\theta$.

The side adjacent to θ is the following.

$$\sqrt{\left(\sqrt{13}\right)^2-3^2}=\sqrt{13-9}=\sqrt{4}=2$$

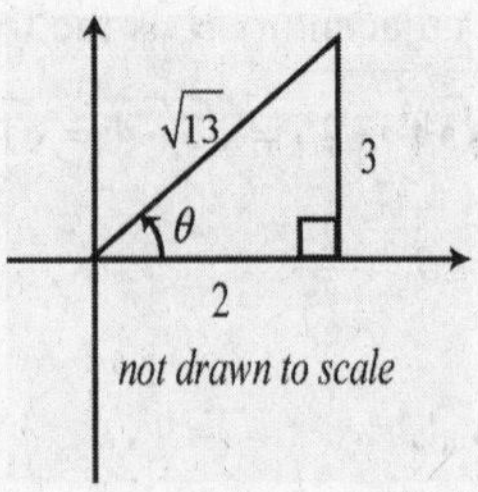

Thus, $\cos\theta=\frac{2}{\sqrt{13}}$.

The rotation equations are $x=\frac{2}{\sqrt{13}}x'-\frac{3}{\sqrt{13}}y'$ and $y=\frac{3}{\sqrt{13}}x'+\frac{2}{\sqrt{13}}y'$. Substituting these values into the given equation yields the following.

$$5y^2+12xy=10$$

$$5\left(\frac{3}{\sqrt{13}}x'+\frac{2}{\sqrt{13}}y'\right)^2+12\left(\frac{2}{\sqrt{13}}x'-\frac{3}{\sqrt{13}}y'\right)\left(\frac{3}{\sqrt{13}}x'+\frac{2}{\sqrt{13}}y'\right)=10$$

$$5\left[\frac{9}{13}x'^2+2\left(\frac{6}{13}x'y'\right)+\frac{4}{13}y'^2\right]+12\left(\frac{6}{13}x'^2-\frac{9}{13}x'y'+\frac{4}{13}x'y'-\frac{6}{13}y'^2\right)=10$$

$$5\left(\frac{9}{13}x'^2+\frac{12}{13}x'y'+\frac{4}{13}y'^2\right)+12\left(\frac{6}{13}x'^2-\frac{5}{13}x'y'-\frac{6}{13}y'^2\right)=10$$

$$\frac{45}{13}x'^2+\frac{60}{13}x'y'+\frac{20}{13}y'^2+\frac{72}{13}x'^2-\frac{60}{13}x'y'-\frac{72}{13}y'^2=10$$

$$\frac{117}{13}x'^2-\frac{52}{13}y'^2=10$$

$$9x'^2-4y'^2=10$$

$$\frac{9x'^2}{10}-\frac{2y'^2}{5}=1$$

The graph of the equation is a hyperbola. This hyperbola is centered at the origin and has vertices on the x'-axis. These vertices are $\pm\sqrt{\frac{10}{9}}=\pm\frac{\sqrt{10}}{3}\approx\pm1.1$. The equations of the asymptotes are

$$y'=\pm\frac{\sqrt{\frac{10}{9}}}{\sqrt{5}}x' \text{ or } y'=\pm\frac{\sqrt{2}}{3}x'.$$

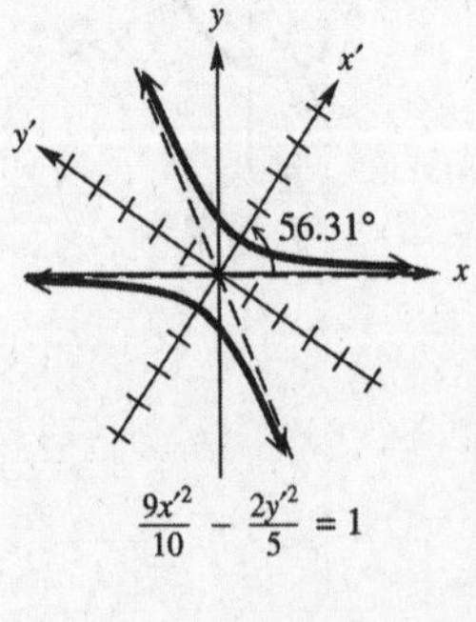

17. $3x^2 - 2xy + 3y^2 = 8$

Since $A = 3$, $B = -2$, and $C = 3$, we have $\cot 2\theta = \dfrac{A-C}{B} = \dfrac{3-3}{-2} = 0$. Also, since $\cot 2\theta = \dfrac{\cos 2\theta}{\sin 2\theta} = 0$, we know $\cos 2\theta = 0$. This yields the following.

$$\sin\theta = \sqrt{\frac{1-\cos 2\theta}{2}} = \sqrt{\frac{1-0}{2}} = \sqrt{\frac{1}{2}} = \frac{\sqrt{2}}{2} \text{ and } \cos\theta = \sqrt{\frac{1+\cos 2\theta}{2}} = \sqrt{\frac{1+0}{2}} = \sqrt{\frac{1}{2}} = \frac{\sqrt{2}}{2}$$

Thus, $\theta = 45°$ and the rotation equations are $x = \frac{\sqrt{2}}{2}x' - \frac{\sqrt{2}}{2}y'$ and $y = \frac{\sqrt{2}}{2}x' + \frac{\sqrt{2}}{2}y'$. Substituting these values into the given equation yields the following.

$$3x^2 - 2xy + 3y^2 = 8$$

$$3\left(\frac{\sqrt{2}}{2}x' - \frac{\sqrt{2}}{2}y'\right)^2 - 2\left(\frac{\sqrt{2}}{2}x' - \frac{\sqrt{2}}{2}y'\right)\left(\frac{\sqrt{2}}{2}x' + \frac{\sqrt{2}}{2}y'\right) + 3\left(\frac{\sqrt{2}}{2}x' + \frac{\sqrt{2}}{2}y'\right)^2 = 8$$

$$3\left[\frac{1}{2}x'^2 - 2\left(\frac{1}{2}x'y'\right) + \frac{1}{2}y'^2\right] - 2\left(\frac{1}{2}x'^2 + \frac{1}{2}x'y' - \frac{1}{2}x'y' - \frac{1}{2}y'^2\right) + 3\left[\frac{1}{2}x'^2 + 2\left(\frac{1}{2}x'y'\right) + \frac{1}{2}y'^2\right] = 8$$

$$3\left(\frac{1}{2}x'^2 - x'y' + \frac{1}{2}y'^2\right) - 2\left(\frac{1}{2}x'^2 - \frac{1}{2}y'^2\right) + 3\left(\frac{1}{2}x'^2 + x'y' + \frac{1}{2}y'^2\right) = 8$$

$$\frac{3}{2}x'^2 - 3x'y' + \frac{3}{2}y'^2 - x'^2 + y'^2 + \frac{3}{2}x'^2 + 3x'y' + \frac{3}{2}y'^2 = 8$$

$$2x'^2 + 4y'^2 = 8$$

$$\frac{x'^2}{4} + \frac{y'^2}{2} = 1$$

The graph of the equation is an ellipse. This ellipse is centered at the origin and has x' – intercepts $\pm\sqrt{4} = \pm 2$ and y' – intercepts $\pm\sqrt{2} = \pm 1.4$.

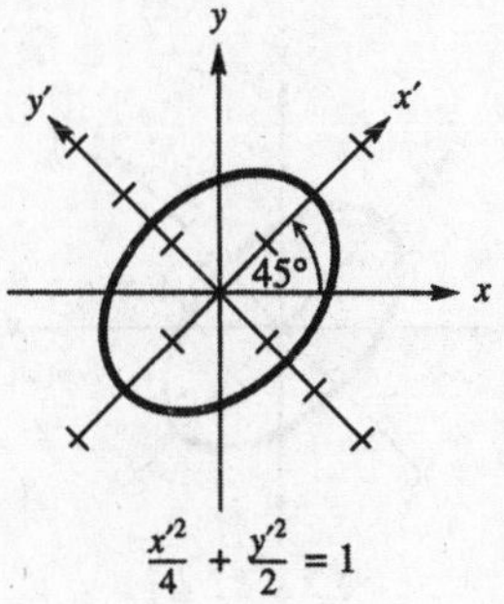

18. $x^2 + xy + y^2 = 3$

Since $A = 1$, $B = 1$, and $C = 1$, we have $\cot 2\theta = \frac{A-C}{B} = \frac{1-1}{1} = 0$. Also, since $\cot 2\theta = \frac{\cos 2\theta}{\sin 2\theta} = 0$, we know $\cos 2\theta = 0$. This yields the following.

$$\sin\theta = \sqrt{\frac{1-\cos 2\theta}{2}} = \sqrt{\frac{1-0}{2}} = \sqrt{\frac{1}{2}} = \frac{\sqrt{2}}{2} \text{ and } \cos\theta = \sqrt{\frac{1+\cos 2\theta}{2}} = \sqrt{\frac{1+0}{2}} = \sqrt{\frac{1}{2}} = \frac{\sqrt{2}}{2}$$

Thus, $\theta = 45°$ and the rotation equations are $x = \frac{\sqrt{2}}{2}x' - \frac{\sqrt{2}}{2}y'$ and $y = \frac{\sqrt{2}}{2}x' + \frac{\sqrt{2}}{2}y'$. Substituting these values into the given equation yields the following.

$$x^2 + xy + y^2 = 3$$

$$\left(\frac{\sqrt{2}}{2}x' - \frac{\sqrt{2}}{2}y'\right)^2 + \left(\frac{\sqrt{2}}{2}x' - \frac{\sqrt{2}}{2}y'\right)\left(\frac{\sqrt{2}}{2}x' + \frac{\sqrt{2}}{2}y'\right) + \left(\frac{\sqrt{2}}{2}x' + \frac{\sqrt{2}}{2}y'\right)^2 = 3$$

$$\left[\frac{1}{2}x'^2 - 2\left(\frac{1}{2}x'y'\right) + \frac{1}{2}y'^2\right] + \left(\frac{1}{2}x'^2 + \frac{1}{2}x'y' - \frac{1}{2}x'y' - \frac{1}{2}y'^2\right) + \left[\frac{1}{2}x'^2 + 2\left(\frac{1}{2}x'y'\right) + \frac{1}{2}y'^2\right] = 3$$

$$\left(\frac{1}{2}x'^2 - x'y' + \frac{1}{2}y'^2\right) + \left(\frac{1}{2}x'^2 - \frac{1}{2}y'^2\right) + \left(\frac{1}{2}x'^2 + x'y' + \frac{1}{2}y'^2\right) = 3$$

$$\frac{1}{2}x'^2 - x'y' + \frac{1}{2}y'^2 + \frac{1}{2}x'^2 - \frac{1}{2}y'^2 + \frac{1}{2}x'^2 + x'y' + \frac{1}{2}y'^2 = 3$$

$$\frac{3}{2}x'^2 + \frac{1}{2}y'^2 = 3$$

$$\frac{x'^2}{2} + \frac{y'^2}{6} = 1$$

The graph of the equation is an ellipse. This ellipse is centered at the origin and has x'-intercepts $\pm\sqrt{2} = \pm 1.4$ and y'-intercepts $\pm\sqrt{6} \approx \pm 2.4$.

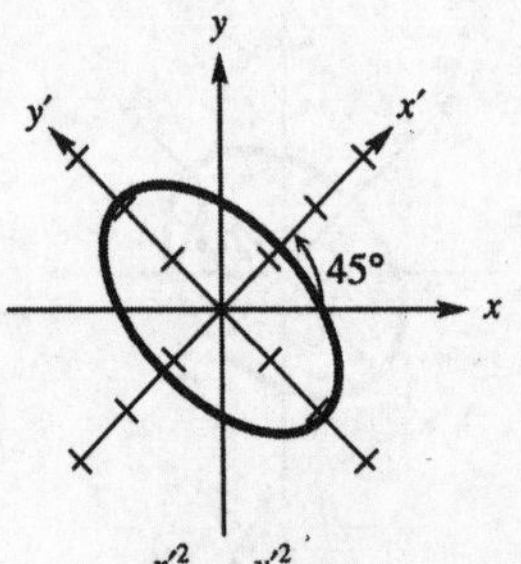

19. $x^2 - 4xy + y^2 = -5$

Since $A = 1$, $B = -4$, and $C = 1$, we have $\cot 2\theta = \frac{A-C}{B} = \frac{1-1}{-4} = 0$. Also, since $\cot 2\theta = \frac{\cos 2\theta}{\sin 2\theta} = 0$, we know $\cos 2\theta = 0$. This yields the following.

$$\sin\theta = \sqrt{\frac{1-\cos 2\theta}{2}} = \sqrt{\frac{1-0}{2}} = \sqrt{\frac{1}{2}} = \frac{\sqrt{2}}{2} \text{ and } \cos\theta = \sqrt{\frac{1+\cos 2\theta}{2}} = \sqrt{\frac{1+0}{2}} = \sqrt{\frac{1}{2}} = \frac{\sqrt{2}}{2}$$

Thus, $\theta = 45°$ and the rotation equations are $x = \frac{\sqrt{2}}{2}x' - \frac{\sqrt{2}}{2}y'$ and $y = \frac{\sqrt{2}}{2}x' + \frac{\sqrt{2}}{2}y'$. Substituting these values into the given equation yields the following.

$$x^2 - 4xy + y^2 = -5$$

$$\left(\frac{\sqrt{2}}{2}x' - \frac{\sqrt{2}}{2}y'\right)^2 - 4\left(\frac{\sqrt{2}}{2}x' - \frac{\sqrt{2}}{2}y'\right)\left(\frac{\sqrt{2}}{2}x' + \frac{\sqrt{2}}{2}y'\right) + \left(\frac{\sqrt{2}}{2}x' + \frac{\sqrt{2}}{2}y'\right)^2 = -5$$

$$\left[\frac{1}{2}x'^2 - 2\left(\frac{1}{2}x'y'\right) + \frac{1}{2}y'^2\right] - 4\left(\frac{1}{2}x'^2 + \frac{1}{2}x'y' - \frac{1}{2}x'y' - \frac{1}{2}y'^2\right) + \left[\frac{1}{2}x'^2 + 2\left(\frac{1}{2}x'y'\right) + \frac{1}{2}y'^2\right] = -5$$

$$\left(\frac{1}{2}x'^2 - x'y' + \frac{1}{2}y'^2\right) - 4\left(\frac{1}{2}x'^2 - \frac{1}{2}y'^2\right) + \left(\frac{1}{2}x'^2 + x'y' + \frac{1}{2}y'^2\right) = -5$$

$$\frac{1}{2}x'^2 - x'y' + \frac{1}{2}y'^2 - 2x'^2 + 2y'^2 + \frac{1}{2}x'^2 + x'y' + \frac{1}{2}y'^2 = -5$$

$$-x'^2 + 3y'^2 = -5$$

$$\frac{x'^2}{5} - \frac{3y'^2}{5} = 1$$

The graph of the equation is a hyperbola. This hyperbola is centered at the origin and has vertices on the x'-axis. These vertices are $\pm\sqrt{5} \approx \pm 2.2$. The equations of the asymptotes are as follows.

$$y' = \pm\frac{\sqrt{\frac{5}{3}}}{\sqrt{5}}x' \text{ or } y' = \pm\frac{\sqrt{3}}{3}x'$$

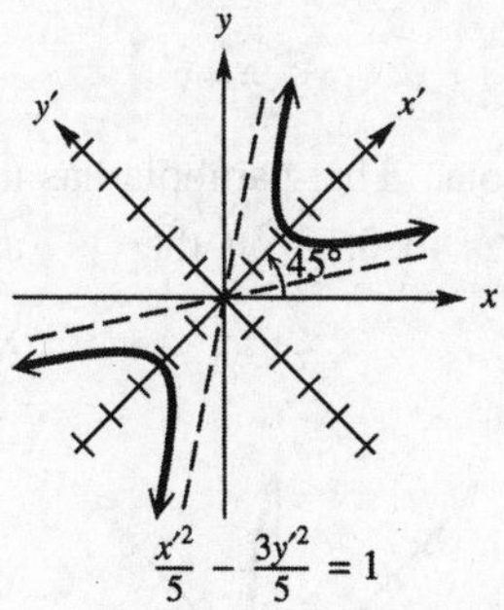

20. $x^2+2xy+y^2+4\sqrt{2}x-4\sqrt{2}y=0$

Since $A=1$, $B=2$, and $C=1$, we have $\cot 2\theta=\frac{A-C}{B}=\frac{1-1}{2}=0$. Also, since $\cot 2\theta=\frac{\cos 2\theta}{\sin 2\theta}=0$, we know $\cos 2\theta=0$. This yields the following.

$$\sin\theta=\sqrt{\frac{1-\cos 2\theta}{2}}=\sqrt{\frac{1-0}{2}}=\sqrt{\frac{1}{2}}=\frac{\sqrt{2}}{2} \text{ and } \cos\theta=\sqrt{\frac{1+\cos 2\theta}{2}}=\sqrt{\frac{1+0}{2}}=\sqrt{\frac{1}{2}}=\frac{\sqrt{2}}{2}$$

Thus, $\theta=45°$ and the rotation equations are $x=\frac{\sqrt{2}}{2}x'-\frac{\sqrt{2}}{2}y'$ and $y=\frac{\sqrt{2}}{2}x'+\frac{\sqrt{2}}{2}y'$. Substituting these values into the given equation yields the following.

$$x^2+2xy+y^2+4\sqrt{2}x-4\sqrt{2}y=0$$

$$\left(\frac{\sqrt{2}}{2}x'-\frac{\sqrt{2}}{2}y'\right)^2+2\left(\frac{\sqrt{2}}{2}x'-\frac{\sqrt{2}}{2}y'\right)\left(\frac{\sqrt{2}}{2}x'+\frac{\sqrt{2}}{2}y'\right)$$

$$+\left(\frac{\sqrt{2}}{2}x'+\frac{\sqrt{2}}{2}y'\right)^2+4\sqrt{2}\left(\frac{\sqrt{2}}{2}x'-\frac{\sqrt{2}}{2}y'\right)-4\sqrt{2}\left(\frac{\sqrt{2}}{2}x'+\frac{\sqrt{2}}{2}y'\right)=0$$

$$\left[\frac{1}{2}x'^2-2\left(\frac{1}{2}x'y'\right)+\frac{1}{2}y'^2\right]+2\left(\frac{1}{2}x'^2+\frac{1}{2}x'y'-\frac{1}{2}x'y'-\frac{1}{2}y'^2\right)+\left[\frac{1}{2}x'^2+2\left(\frac{1}{2}x'y'\right)+\frac{1}{2}y'^2\right]$$

$$+4\sqrt{2}\left(\frac{\sqrt{2}}{2}x'-\frac{\sqrt{2}}{2}y'\right)-4\sqrt{2}\left(\frac{\sqrt{2}}{2}x'+\frac{\sqrt{2}}{2}y'\right)=0$$

$$\left(\frac{1}{2}x'^2-x'y'+\frac{1}{2}y'^2\right)+2\left(\frac{1}{2}x'^2-\frac{1}{2}y'^2\right)+\left(\frac{1}{2}x'^2+x'y'+\frac{1}{2}y'^2\right)$$

$$+4\sqrt{2}\left(\frac{\sqrt{2}}{2}x'-\frac{\sqrt{2}}{2}y'\right)-4\sqrt{2}\left(\frac{\sqrt{2}}{2}x'+\frac{\sqrt{2}}{2}y'\right)=0$$

$$\frac{1}{2}x'^2-x'y'+\frac{1}{2}y'^2+x'^2-y'^2+\frac{1}{2}x'^2+x'y'+\frac{1}{2}y'^2+4x'-4y'-4x'-4y'=0$$

$$2x'^2-8y'=0$$

$$2x'^2=8y'$$

$$x'^2=4y'$$

The graph of the equation is a parabola. This parabola has its vertex on the origin and opens upward, relative to the x'-axis. Its focus is located on the y'-axis. This point is $(x',y')=(0,1)$. The directrix is the line $y'=-1$.

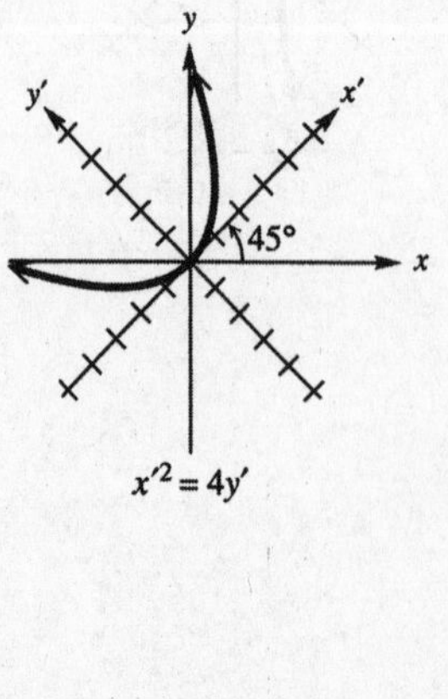

21. $7x^2 + 6\sqrt{3}xy + 13y^2 = 64$

Since $A = 7,\ B = 6\sqrt{3},$ and $C = 13,$ we have $\cot 2\theta = \frac{A-C}{B} = \frac{7-13}{6\sqrt{3}} = -\frac{1}{\sqrt{3}}.$ Thus, we have the following.

$$\cot 2\theta = -\frac{1}{\sqrt{3}} \Rightarrow \cot 2\theta = -\frac{\sqrt{3}}{3} \Rightarrow 2\theta = \cot^{-1}\left(-\frac{\sqrt{3}}{3}\right) \Rightarrow 2\theta = 120° \Rightarrow \theta = 60°$$

Thus, $\sin\theta = \sin 60° = \frac{\sqrt{3}}{2}$ and $\cos\theta = \cos 60° = \frac{1}{2}.$ This yields the following rotation equations.

$$x = \frac{1}{2}x' - \frac{\sqrt{3}}{2}y' \text{ and } y = \frac{\sqrt{3}}{2}x' + \frac{1}{2}y'$$

Substituting these values into the given equation yields the following.

$$7x^2 + 6\sqrt{3}xy + 13y^2 = 64$$

$$7\left(\frac{1}{2}x' - \frac{\sqrt{3}}{2}y'\right)^2 + 6\sqrt{3}\left(\frac{1}{2}x' - \frac{\sqrt{3}}{2}y'\right)\left(\frac{\sqrt{3}}{2}x' + \frac{1}{2}y'\right) + 13\left(\frac{\sqrt{3}}{2}x' + \frac{1}{2}y'\right)^2 = 64$$

$$7\left[\frac{1}{4}x'^2 - 2\left(\frac{\sqrt{3}}{4}x'y'\right) + \frac{3}{4}y'^2\right] + 6\sqrt{3}\left(\frac{\sqrt{3}}{4}x'^2 + \frac{1}{4}x'y' - \frac{3}{4}x'y' + \frac{\sqrt{3}}{4}y'^2\right)$$

$$+13\left[\frac{3}{4}x'^2 + 2\left(\frac{\sqrt{3}}{4}x'y'\right) + \frac{1}{4}y'^2\right] = 64$$

$$7\left[\frac{1}{4}x'^2 - \frac{\sqrt{3}}{2}x'y' + \frac{3}{4}y'^2\right] + 6\sqrt{3}\left(\frac{\sqrt{3}}{4}x'^2 - \frac{1}{2}x'y' + \frac{\sqrt{3}}{4}y'^2\right) + 13\left[\frac{3}{4}x'^2 + \frac{\sqrt{3}}{2}x'y' + \frac{1}{4}y'^2\right] = 64$$

$$\frac{7}{4}x'^2 - \frac{7\sqrt{3}}{2}x'y' + \frac{21}{4}y'^2 + \frac{18}{4}x'^2 - \frac{6\sqrt{3}}{2}x'y' - \frac{18}{4}y'^2 + \frac{39}{4}x'^2 + \frac{13\sqrt{3}}{2}x'y' + \frac{13}{4}y'^2 = 64$$

$$\frac{64}{4}x'^2 + \frac{16}{4}y'^2 = 64$$

$$\frac{x'^2}{4} + \frac{y'^2}{16} = 1$$

The graph of the equation is an ellipse. This ellipse is centered at the origin and has x'– intercepts $\pm\sqrt{4} = \pm 2$ and y'– intercepts $\pm\sqrt{16} = \pm 4.$

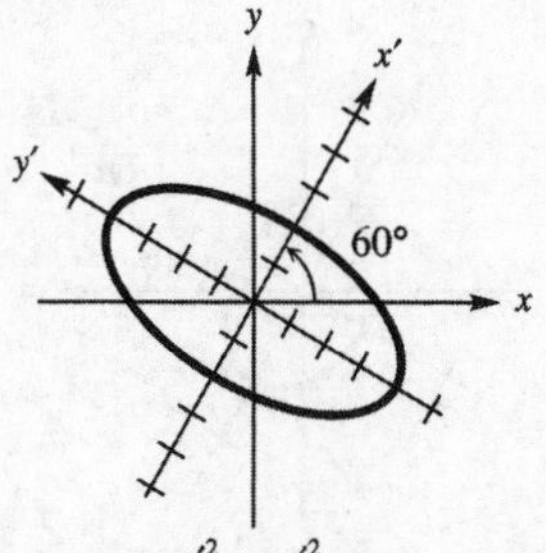

$\frac{x'^2}{4} + \frac{y'^2}{16} = 1$

22. $7x^2+2\sqrt{3}xy+5y^2=24$

Since $A=7,\ B=2\sqrt{3},$ and $C=5$ we have, $\cot 2\theta=\dfrac{A-C}{B}=\dfrac{7-5}{2\sqrt{3}}=\dfrac{1}{\sqrt{3}}$. Thus, we have the following.

$$\cot 2\theta=\frac{1}{\sqrt{3}}\Rightarrow \cot 2\theta=\frac{\sqrt{3}}{3}\Rightarrow 2\theta=\cot^{-1}\left(\frac{\sqrt{3}}{3}\right)\Rightarrow 2\theta=60°\Rightarrow \theta=30°$$

Thus, $\sin\theta=\sin 30°=\dfrac{1}{2}$ and $\cos\theta=\cos 30°=\dfrac{\sqrt{3}}{2}$. This yields the following rotation equations.

$$x=\frac{\sqrt{3}}{2}x'-\frac{1}{2}y' \text{ and } y=\frac{1}{2}x'+\frac{\sqrt{3}}{2}y'$$

Substituting these values into the given equation yields the following.

$$7x^2+2\sqrt{3}xy+5y^2=24$$

$$7\left(\frac{\sqrt{3}}{2}x'-\frac{1}{2}y'\right)^2+2\sqrt{3}\left(\frac{\sqrt{3}}{2}x'-\frac{1}{2}y'\right)\left(\frac{1}{2}x'+\frac{\sqrt{3}}{2}y'\right)+5\left(\frac{1}{2}x'+\frac{\sqrt{3}}{2}y'\right)^2=24$$

$$7\left[\frac{3}{4}x'^2-2\left(\frac{\sqrt{3}}{4}x'y'\right)+\frac{1}{4}y'^2\right]+2\sqrt{3}\left(\frac{\sqrt{3}}{4}x'^2+\frac{3}{4}x'y'-\frac{1}{4}x'y'-\frac{\sqrt{3}}{4}y'^2\right)$$

$$+5\left[\frac{1}{4}x'^2+2\left(\frac{\sqrt{3}}{4}x'y'\right)+\frac{3}{4}y'^2\right]=24$$

$$7\left(\frac{3}{4}x'^2-\frac{\sqrt{3}}{2}x'y'+\frac{1}{4}y'^2\right)+2\sqrt{3}\left(\frac{\sqrt{3}}{4}x'^2+\frac{1}{2}x'y'-\frac{\sqrt{3}}{4}y'^2\right)+5\left(\frac{1}{4}x'^2+\frac{\sqrt{3}}{2}x'y'+\frac{3}{4}y'^2\right)=24$$

$$\frac{21}{4}x'^2-\frac{7\sqrt{3}}{2}x'y'+\frac{7}{4}y'^2+\frac{6}{4}x'^2+\sqrt{3}x'y'-\frac{6}{4}y'^2+\frac{5}{4}x'^2+\frac{5\sqrt{3}}{2}x'y'+\frac{15}{4}y'^2=24$$

$$\frac{32}{4}x'^2+\frac{16}{4}y'^2=24$$

$$\frac{x'^2}{3}+\frac{y'^2}{6}=1$$

The graph of the equation is an ellipse. This ellipse is centered at the origin and has x'– intercepts $\pm\sqrt{3}\approx\pm 1.7$ and y'– intercepts $\pm\sqrt{6}\approx\pm 2.4$.

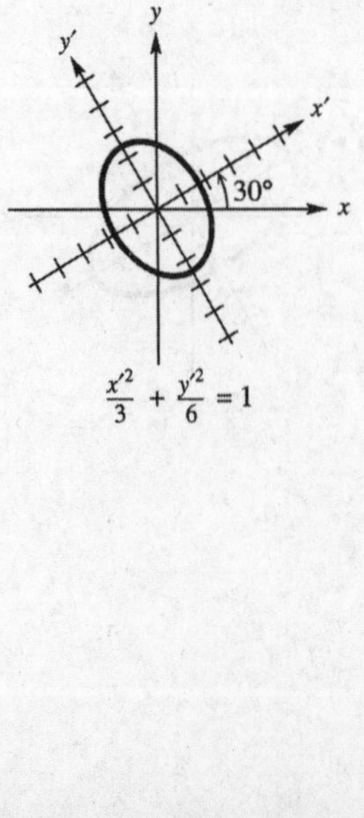

23. $3x^2-2\sqrt{3}xy+y^2-2x-2\sqrt{3}y=0$

Since $A=3,\ B=-2\sqrt{3},$ and $C=1,$ we have $\cot 2\theta=\frac{A-C}{B}=\frac{3-1}{-2\sqrt{3}}=-\frac{1}{\sqrt{3}}$. Thus, we have the following.

$$\cot 2\theta=-\frac{1}{\sqrt{3}}\Rightarrow \cot 2\theta=-\frac{\sqrt{3}}{3}\Rightarrow 2\theta=\cot^{-1}\left(-\frac{\sqrt{3}}{3}\right)\Rightarrow 2\theta=120°\Rightarrow \theta=60°$$

Thus, $\sin\theta=\sin 60°=\frac{\sqrt{3}}{2}$ and $\cos\theta=\cos 60°=\frac{1}{2}$. This yields the following rotation equations.

$$x=\frac{1}{2}x'-\frac{\sqrt{3}}{2}y' \text{ and } y=\frac{\sqrt{3}}{2}x'+\frac{1}{2}y'$$

Substituting these values into the given equation yields the following.

$$3x^2-2\sqrt{3}xy+y^2-2x-2\sqrt{3}y=0$$

$$3\left(\frac{1}{2}x'-\frac{\sqrt{3}}{2}y'\right)^2-2\sqrt{3}\left(\frac{1}{2}x'-\frac{\sqrt{3}}{2}y'\right)\left(\frac{\sqrt{3}}{2}x'+\frac{1}{2}y'\right)+\left(\frac{\sqrt{3}}{2}x'+\frac{1}{2}y'\right)^2$$
$$-2\left(\frac{1}{2}x'-\frac{\sqrt{3}}{2}y'\right)-2\sqrt{3}\left(\frac{\sqrt{3}}{2}x'+\frac{1}{2}y'\right)=0$$

$$3\left[\frac{1}{4}x'^2-2\left(\frac{\sqrt{3}}{4}x'y'\right)+\frac{3}{4}y'^2\right]-2\sqrt{3}\left(\frac{\sqrt{3}}{4}x'^2+\frac{1}{4}x'y'-\frac{3}{4}x'y'-\frac{\sqrt{3}}{4}y'^2\right)$$
$$+\left[\frac{3}{4}x'^2+2\left(\frac{\sqrt{3}}{4}x'y'\right)+\frac{1}{4}y'^2\right]-2\left(\frac{1}{2}x'-\frac{\sqrt{3}}{2}y'\right)-2\sqrt{3}\left(\frac{\sqrt{3}}{2}x'+\frac{1}{2}y'\right)=0$$

$$3\left(\frac{1}{4}x'^2-\frac{\sqrt{3}}{2}x'y'+\frac{3}{4}y'^2\right)-2\sqrt{3}\left(\frac{\sqrt{3}}{4}x'^2-\frac{1}{2}x'y'-\frac{\sqrt{3}}{4}y'^2\right)+\left(\frac{3}{4}x'^2+\frac{\sqrt{3}}{2}x'y'+\frac{1}{4}y'^2\right)$$
$$-2\left(\frac{1}{2}x'-\frac{\sqrt{3}}{2}y'\right)-2\sqrt{3}\left(\frac{\sqrt{3}}{2}x'+\frac{1}{2}y'\right)=0$$

$$\frac{3}{4}x'^2-\frac{3\sqrt{3}}{2}x'y'+\frac{9}{4}y'^2-\frac{6}{4}x'^2+\sqrt{3}x'y'+\frac{6}{4}y'^2+\frac{3}{4}x'^2+\frac{\sqrt{3}}{2}x'y'+\frac{1}{4}y'^2-x'+\sqrt{3}y'-3x'-\sqrt{3}y'=0$$

$$\frac{16}{4}y'^2-4x'=0\Rightarrow 4y'^2=4x'\Rightarrow y'^2=x'$$

The graph of the equation is a parabola. This parabola has its vertex on the origin and opens to the right, relative to the x'−axis. Its focus is located on the x'−axis. This point is $(x',y')=\left(\frac{1}{4},0\right)$.

The directrix is the line $x'=-\frac{1}{4}$.

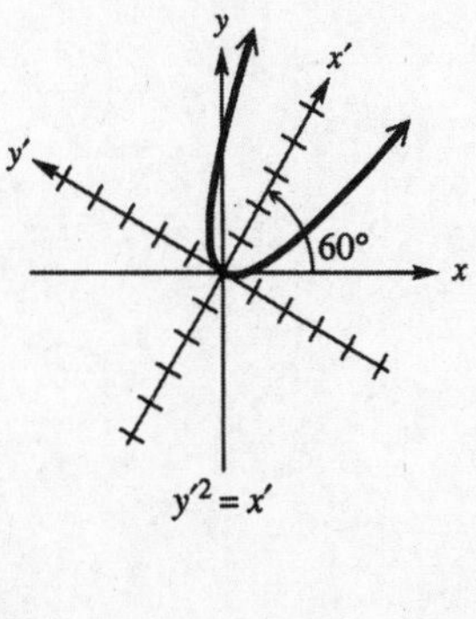

24. $2x^2 + 2\sqrt{3}xy + 4y^2 = 5$

Since $A = 2,\ B = 2\sqrt{3},$ and $C = 4,$ we have $\cot\theta = \dfrac{A-C}{B} = \dfrac{2-4}{2\sqrt{3}} = -\dfrac{1}{\sqrt{3}}.$ Thus, we have the following.

$$\cot 2\theta = -\frac{1}{\sqrt{3}} \Rightarrow \cot 2\theta = -\frac{\sqrt{3}}{3} \Rightarrow 2\theta = \cot^{-1}\left(-\frac{\sqrt{3}}{3}\right) \Rightarrow 2\theta = 120^\circ \Rightarrow \theta = 60^\circ$$

Thus, $\sin\theta = \sin 60^\circ = \dfrac{\sqrt{3}}{2}$ and $\cos\theta = \cos 60^\circ = \dfrac{1}{2}.$ This yields the following rotation equations.

$$x = \frac{1}{2}x' - \frac{\sqrt{3}}{2}y' \text{ and } y = \frac{\sqrt{3}}{2}x' + \frac{1}{2}y'$$

Substituting these values into the given equation yields the following.

$$2\left(\frac{1}{2}x' - \frac{\sqrt{3}}{2}y'\right)^2 + 2\sqrt{3}\left(\frac{1}{2}x' - \frac{\sqrt{3}}{2}y'\right)\left(\frac{\sqrt{3}}{2}x' + \frac{1}{2}y'\right) + 4\left(\frac{\sqrt{3}}{2}x' + \frac{1}{2}y'\right)^2 = 5$$

$$2\left[\tfrac{1}{4}x'^2 - 2\left(\tfrac{\sqrt{3}}{4}x'y'\right) + \tfrac{3}{4}y'^2\right] + 2\sqrt{3}\left(\tfrac{\sqrt{3}}{4}x'^2 + \tfrac{1}{4}x'y' - \tfrac{3}{4}x'y' - \tfrac{\sqrt{3}}{4}y'^2\right) + 4\left[\tfrac{3}{4}x'^2 + 2\left(\tfrac{\sqrt{3}}{4}x'y'\right) + \tfrac{1}{4}y'^2\right] = 5$$

$$2\left(\frac{1}{4}x'^2 - \frac{\sqrt{3}}{2}x'y' + \frac{3}{4}y'^2\right) + 2\sqrt{3}\left(\frac{\sqrt{3}}{4}x'^2 - \frac{1}{2}x'y' - \frac{\sqrt{3}}{4}y'^2\right) + 4\left(\frac{3}{4}x'^2 + \frac{\sqrt{3}}{2}x'y' + \frac{1}{4}y'^2\right) = 5$$

$$\frac{2}{4}x'^2 - \sqrt{3}x'y' + \frac{6}{4}y'^2 + \frac{6}{4}x'^2 - \sqrt{3}x'y' - \frac{6}{4}y'^2 + 3x'^2 + 2\sqrt{3}x'y' + y'^2 = 5$$

$$5x'^2 + y'^2 = 5$$

$$x'^2 + \frac{y'^2}{5} = 1$$

The graph of the equation is an ellipse. This ellipse is centered at the origin and has x' – intercepts $\pm\sqrt{1} = \pm 1$ and y' – intercepts $\pm\sqrt{5} = \pm 2.2.$

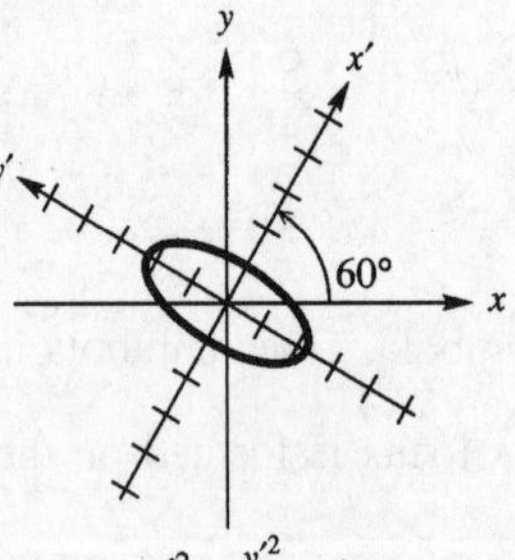

$$x'^2 + \frac{y'^2}{5} = 1$$

25. $x^2 + 3xy + y^2 - 5\sqrt{2}y = 15$

Since $A = 1$, $B = 3$, and $C = 1$, we have $\cot 2\theta = \dfrac{A-C}{B} = \dfrac{1-1}{3} = 0$. Also, since $\cot 2\theta = \dfrac{\cos 2\theta}{\sin 2\theta} = 0$, we know $\cos 2\theta = 0$. This yields the following.

$$\sin\theta = \sqrt{\frac{1-\cos 2\theta}{2}} = \sqrt{\frac{1-0}{2}} = \sqrt{\frac{1}{2}} = \frac{\sqrt{2}}{2} \text{ and } \cos\theta = \sqrt{\frac{1+\cos 2\theta}{2}} = \sqrt{\frac{1+0}{2}} = \sqrt{\frac{1}{2}} = \frac{\sqrt{2}}{2}$$

Thus, $\theta = 45°$ and the rotation equations are $x = \frac{\sqrt{2}}{2}x' - \frac{\sqrt{2}}{2}y'$ and $y = \frac{\sqrt{2}}{2}x' + \frac{\sqrt{2}}{2}y'$. Substituting these values into the given equation yields the following.

$$x^2 + 3xy + y^2 - 5\sqrt{2}y = 15$$

$$\left(\frac{\sqrt{2}}{2}x' - \frac{\sqrt{2}}{2}y'\right)^2 + 3\left(\frac{\sqrt{2}}{2}x' - \frac{\sqrt{2}}{2}y'\right)\left(\frac{\sqrt{2}}{2}x' + \frac{\sqrt{2}}{2}y'\right) + \left(\frac{\sqrt{2}}{2}x' + \frac{\sqrt{2}}{2}y'\right)^2 - 5\sqrt{2}\left(\frac{\sqrt{2}}{2}x' + \frac{\sqrt{2}}{2}y'\right) = 15$$

$$\left[\frac{1}{2}x'^2 - 2\left(\frac{1}{2}x'y'\right) + \frac{1}{2}y'^2\right] + 3\left(\frac{1}{2}x'^2 + \frac{1}{2}x'y' - \frac{1}{2}x'y' - \frac{1}{2}y'^2\right)$$
$$+\left[\frac{1}{2}x'^2 + 2\left(\frac{1}{2}x'y'\right) + \frac{1}{2}y'^2\right] - 5\sqrt{2}\left(\frac{\sqrt{2}}{2}x' + \frac{\sqrt{2}}{2}y'\right) = 15$$

$$\left[\frac{1}{2}x'^2 - x'y' + \frac{1}{2}y'^2\right] + 3\left(\frac{1}{2}x'^2 - \frac{1}{2}y'^2\right) + \left[\frac{1}{2}x'^2 + x'y' + \frac{1}{2}y'^2\right] - 5\sqrt{2}\left(\frac{\sqrt{2}}{2}x' + \frac{\sqrt{2}}{2}y'\right) = 15$$

$$\frac{1}{2}x'^2 - x'y' + \frac{1}{2}y'^2 + \frac{3}{2}x'^2 - \frac{3}{2}y'^2 + \frac{1}{2}x'^2 + x'y' + \frac{1}{2}y'^2 - 5x' - 5y' = 15$$

$$\frac{5}{2}x'^2 - \frac{1}{2}y'^2 - 5x' - 5y' = 15$$

$$5x'^2 - y'^2 - 10x' - 10y' = 30$$

$$5x'^2 - 10x' - y'^2 - 10y' = 30$$

$$5\left(x'^2 - 2x' + 1\right) - \left(y'^2 + 10y' + 25\right) = 30 + 5 - 25$$

$$5\left(x'-1\right)^2 - \left(y'+5\right)^2 = 10$$

$$\frac{\left(x'-1\right)^2}{2} - \frac{\left(y'+5\right)^2}{10} = 1$$

The graph of the equation is a hyperbola with its center at $x' = 1$ and $y' = -5$. By translating the axes of the $x'\,y'$ system down 5 units and right 1 unit, we get an $x''y''$ – coordinate system, in which the hyperbola is centered at its origin. This hyperbola has vertices on the x'' – axis. These vertices are $\pm\sqrt{2} \approx \pm 1.4$. The equations of the asymptotes are $y'' = \pm\frac{\sqrt{2}}{\sqrt{10}}x''$ or $y'' = \pm\frac{\sqrt{5}}{5}x''$.

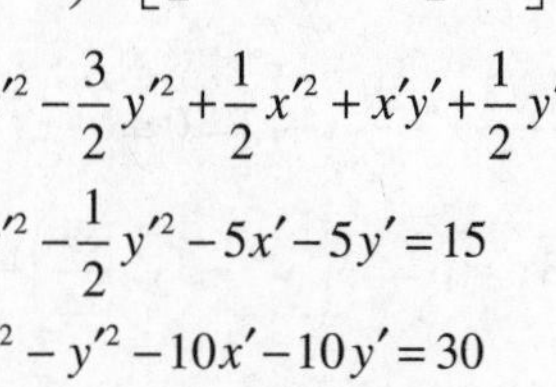

26. $x^2-\sqrt{3}xy+2\sqrt{3}x-3y-3=0$

Since $A=1$, $B=-\sqrt{3}$, and $C=0$, we have $\cot 2\theta=\dfrac{A-C}{B}=\dfrac{1-0}{-\sqrt{3}}=-\dfrac{1}{\sqrt{3}}$. Thus, we have the following.

$$\cot 2\theta=-\frac{1}{\sqrt{3}}\Rightarrow \cot 2\theta=-\frac{\sqrt{3}}{3}\Rightarrow 2\theta=\cot^{-1}\left(-\frac{\sqrt{3}}{3}\right)\Rightarrow 2\theta=120^\circ\Rightarrow\theta=60^\circ$$

Thus, $\sin\theta=\sin 60^\circ=\dfrac{\sqrt{3}}{2}$ and $\cos\theta=\cos 60^\circ=\dfrac{1}{2}$. This yields the following rotation equations.

$$x=\frac{1}{2}x'-\frac{\sqrt{3}}{2}y' \text{ and } y=\frac{\sqrt{3}}{2}x'+\frac{1}{2}y'$$

Substituting these values into the given equation yields the following.

$$x^2-\sqrt{3}xy+2\sqrt{3}x-3y-3=0$$

$$\left(\frac{1}{2}x'-\frac{\sqrt{3}}{2}y'\right)^2-\sqrt{3}\left(\frac{1}{2}x'-\frac{\sqrt{3}}{2}y'\right)\left(\frac{\sqrt{3}}{2}x'+\frac{1}{2}y'\right)+2\sqrt{3}\left(\frac{1}{2}x'-\frac{\sqrt{3}}{2}y'\right)-3\left(\frac{\sqrt{3}}{2}x'+\frac{1}{2}y'\right)-3=0$$

$$\left[\tfrac{1}{4}x'^2-2\left(\tfrac{\sqrt{3}}{4}x'y'\right)+\tfrac{3}{4}y'^2\right]-\sqrt{3}\left(\tfrac{\sqrt{3}}{4}x'^2+\tfrac{1}{4}x'y'-\tfrac{3}{4}x'y'-\tfrac{\sqrt{3}}{4}y'^2\right)+2\sqrt{3}\left(\tfrac{1}{2}x'-\tfrac{\sqrt{3}}{2}y'\right)-3\left(\tfrac{\sqrt{3}}{2}x'+\tfrac{1}{2}y'\right)-3=0$$

$$\left(\frac{1}{4}x'^2-\frac{\sqrt{3}}{2}x'y'+\frac{3}{4}y'^2\right)-\sqrt{3}\left(\frac{\sqrt{3}}{4}x'^2-\frac{1}{2}x'y'-\frac{\sqrt{3}}{4}y'^2\right)+\sqrt{3}x'-3y'-\frac{3\sqrt{3}}{2}x'-\frac{3}{2}y'-3=0$$

$$\frac{1}{4}x'^2-\frac{\sqrt{3}}{2}x'y'+\frac{3}{4}y'^2-\frac{3}{4}x'^2+\frac{\sqrt{3}}{2}x'y'+\frac{3}{4}y'^2+\sqrt{3}x'-3y'-\frac{3\sqrt{3}}{2}x'-\frac{3}{2}y'-3=0$$

$$-\frac{1}{2}x'^2+\frac{3}{2}y'^2-\frac{\sqrt{3}}{2}x'-\frac{9}{2}y'-3=0\Rightarrow -x'^2+3y'^2-\sqrt{3}x'-9y'-6=0$$

$$3y'^2-9y'-x'^2-\sqrt{3}x'=6\Rightarrow 3\left(y'^2-3y'+\frac{9}{4}\right)-\left(x'^2+\sqrt{3}x'+\frac{3}{4}\right)=6+\frac{27}{4}-\frac{3}{4}$$

$$3\left(y'-\frac{3}{2}\right)^2-\left(x'+\frac{\sqrt{3}}{2}\right)^2=12$$

$$\frac{\left(y'-\frac{3}{2}\right)^2}{4}-\frac{\left(x'+\frac{\sqrt{3}}{2}\right)^2}{12}=1$$

The graph of the equation is a hyperbola with its center at $x'=-\dfrac{\sqrt{3}}{2}$ and $y'=\dfrac{3}{2}$. By translating the axes of the $x'\,y'$ system up $\dfrac{3}{2}$ and left $\dfrac{\sqrt{3}}{2}$ units, we get an $x''y''-$coordinate system in which the hyperbola is centered at its origin. This hyperbola has vertices on the $y''-$axis. These vertices are $\pm\sqrt{4}=\pm 2$. The equations of the asymptotes are $y''=\pm\dfrac{\sqrt{4}}{\sqrt{12}}x''$ or $y''=\pm\dfrac{\sqrt{3}}{3}x''$.

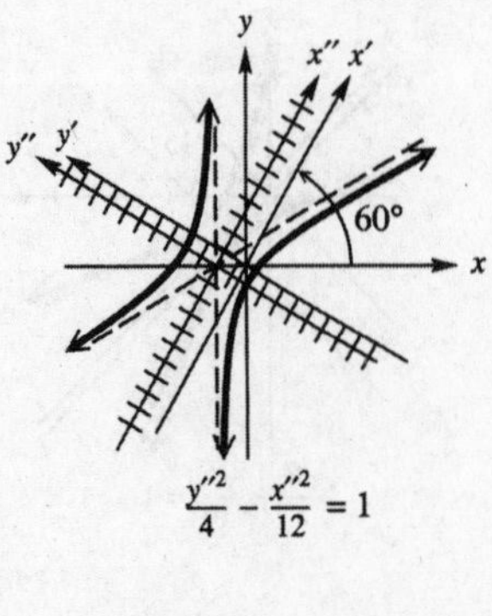

$$\frac{y''^2}{4}-\frac{x''^2}{12}=1$$

27. $4x^2+4xy+y^2-24x+38y-19=0$

Since $A=4,\ B=4,$ and $C=1,$ we have $\cot 2\theta=\dfrac{A-C}{B}=\dfrac{4-1}{4}=\dfrac{3}{4}.$

The hypotenuse of the triangle is the following.

$$\sqrt{3^2+4^2}=\sqrt{9+16}=\sqrt{25}=5$$

Thus, $\cos 2\theta=\dfrac{3}{5}.$

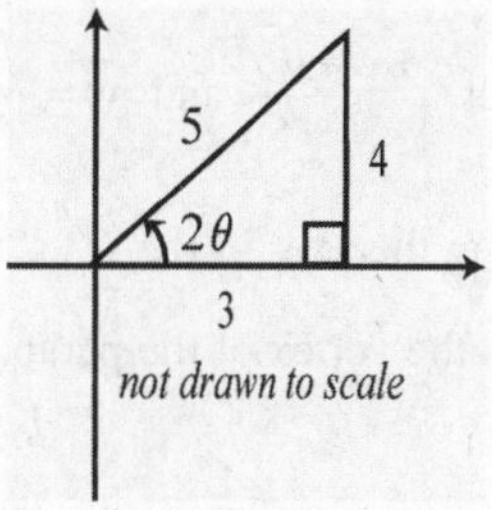

Thus, we have the following.

$$\sin\theta=\sqrt{\frac{1-\cos 2\theta}{2}}=\sqrt{\frac{1-\frac{3}{5}}{2}}=\sqrt{\frac{2}{10}}=\frac{\sqrt{5}}{5}\text{ and }\cos\theta=\sqrt{\frac{1+\cos 2\theta}{2}}=\sqrt{\frac{1+\frac{3}{5}}{2}}=\sqrt{\frac{8}{10}}=\frac{2\sqrt{5}}{5}$$

The rotation equations are $x=\dfrac{2\sqrt{5}}{5}x'-\dfrac{\sqrt{5}}{5}y'$ and $y=\dfrac{\sqrt{5}}{5}x'+\dfrac{2\sqrt{5}}{5}y'$. Substituting these values into the given equation yields the following.

$$4x^2+4xy+y^2-24x+38y-19=0$$

$$4\left(\frac{2\sqrt{5}}{5}x'-\frac{\sqrt{5}}{5}y'\right)^2+4\left(\frac{2\sqrt{5}}{5}x'-\frac{\sqrt{5}}{5}y'\right)\left(\frac{\sqrt{5}}{5}x'+\frac{2\sqrt{5}}{5}y'\right)+\left(\frac{\sqrt{5}}{5}x'+\frac{2\sqrt{5}}{5}y'\right)^2$$
$$-24\left(\frac{2\sqrt{5}}{5}x'-\frac{\sqrt{5}}{5}y'\right)+38\left(\frac{\sqrt{5}}{5}x'+\frac{2\sqrt{5}}{5}y'\right)-19=0$$

$$4\left[\frac{4}{5}x'^2-2\left(\frac{2}{5}x'y'\right)+\frac{1}{5}y'^2\right]+4\left(\frac{2}{5}x'^2+\frac{4}{5}x'y'-\frac{1}{5}x'y'-\frac{2}{5}y'^2\right)+\left[\frac{1}{5}x'^2+2\left(\frac{2}{5}x'y'\right)+\frac{4}{5}y'^2\right]$$
$$-24\left(\frac{2\sqrt{5}}{5}x'-\frac{\sqrt{5}}{5}y'\right)+38\left(\frac{\sqrt{5}}{5}x'+\frac{2\sqrt{5}}{5}y'\right)-19=0$$

$$4\left(\frac{4}{5}x'^2-\frac{4}{5}x'y'+\frac{1}{5}y'^2\right)+4\left(\frac{2}{5}x'^2+\frac{3}{5}x'y'-\frac{2}{5}y'^2\right)+\left(\frac{1}{5}x'^2+\frac{4}{5}x'y'+\frac{4}{5}y'^2\right)$$
$$-24\left(\frac{2\sqrt{5}}{5}x'-\frac{\sqrt{5}}{5}y'\right)+38\left(\frac{\sqrt{5}}{5}x'+\frac{2\sqrt{5}}{5}y'\right)-19=0$$

$$\frac{16}{5}x'^2-\frac{16}{5}x'y'+\frac{4}{5}y'^2+\frac{8}{5}x'^2+\frac{12}{5}x'y'-\frac{8}{5}y'^2+\frac{1}{5}x'^2+\frac{4}{5}x'y'+\frac{4}{5}y'^2$$
$$-\frac{48\sqrt{5}}{5}x'+\frac{24\sqrt{5}}{5}y'+\frac{38\sqrt{5}}{5}x'+\frac{76\sqrt{5}}{5}y'-19=0$$

$$5x'^2-2\sqrt{5}x'+20\sqrt{5}y'-19=0\Rightarrow 5\left(x'^2-\frac{2\sqrt{5}}{5}x'+\frac{1}{5}\right)+20\sqrt{5}y'-19=1$$

$$5\left(x'-\frac{\sqrt{5}}{5}\right)^2=20-20\sqrt{5}y'\Rightarrow\left(x'-\frac{\sqrt{5}}{5}\right)^2=4-4\sqrt{5}y'$$

$$\left(x'-\frac{\sqrt{5}}{5}\right)^2=-4\sqrt{5}\left(y'-\frac{\sqrt{5}}{5}\right)$$

Continued on next page

27. (continued)

The graph of the equation is a parabola. The angle of rotation is $\theta = \sin^{-1}\left(\frac{\sqrt{5}}{5}\right) \approx 26.57°$. Its vertex is located at $x' = -\frac{\sqrt{5}}{5}$ and $y' = \frac{\sqrt{5}}{5}$ and opens in the downward direction, relative to the x'–axis. By translating the axes of the $x'\ y'$ system up $\frac{3}{2}$ and left $\frac{\sqrt{3}}{2}$ units, we get an $x''\ y''$–coordinate system in which the vertex of the parabola is at the origin.

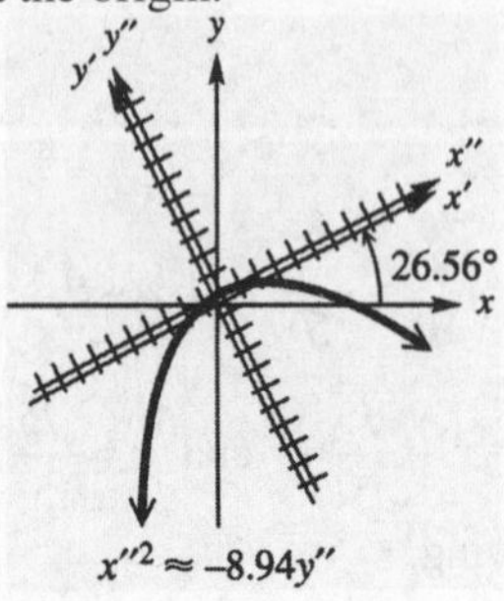

28. $12x^2 + 24xy + 19y^2 - 12x - 40y + 31 = 0$

Since $A = 12\ B = 24$, and $C = 19$, we have $\cot 2\theta = \frac{A-C}{B} = \frac{12-19}{24} = -\frac{7}{24} = \frac{-7}{24}$.

The hypotenuse of the triangle is the following.

$\sqrt{(-7)^2 + 24^2} = \sqrt{49+576} = \sqrt{625} = 25$

Thus, $\cos 2\theta = \frac{-7}{25} = -\frac{7}{25}$.

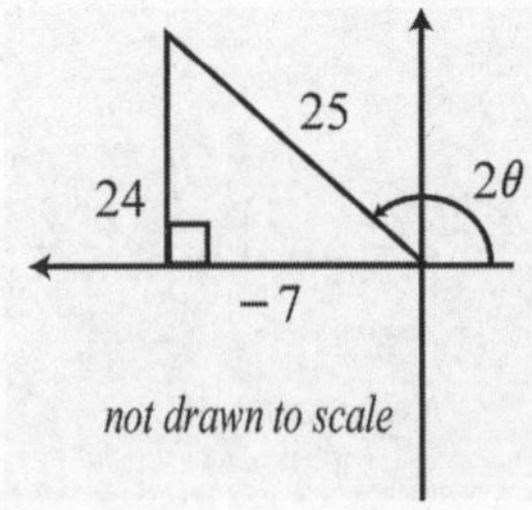

Thus, we have the following.

$$\sin\theta = \sqrt{\frac{1-\cos 2\theta}{2}} = \sqrt{\frac{1-(-\frac{7}{25})}{2}} = \sqrt{\frac{16}{25}} = \frac{4}{5} \text{ and } \cos\theta = \sqrt{\frac{1+\cos 2\theta}{2}} = \sqrt{\frac{1+(-\frac{7}{25})}{2}} = \sqrt{\frac{9}{25}} = \frac{3}{5}$$

The rotation equations are $x = \frac{3}{5}x' - \frac{4}{5}y'$ and $y = \frac{4}{5}x' + \frac{3}{5}y'$. Substituting these values into the given equation yields the following.

Continued on next page

28. (continued)

$$12x^2+24xy+19y^2-12x-40y+31=0$$

$$12\left(\frac{3}{5}x'-\frac{4}{5}y'\right)^2+24\left(\frac{3}{5}x'-\frac{4}{5}y'\right)\left(\frac{4}{5}x'+\frac{3}{5}y'\right)+19\left(\frac{4}{5}x'+\frac{3}{5}y'\right)^2$$
$$-12\left(\frac{3}{5}x'-\frac{4}{5}y'\right)-40\left(\frac{4}{5}x'+\frac{3}{5}y'\right)+31=0$$

$$12\left[\frac{9}{25}x'^2-2\left(\frac{12}{25}x'y'\right)+\frac{16}{25}y'^2\right]+24\left(\frac{12}{25}x'^2+\frac{9}{25}x'y'-\frac{16}{25}x'y'-\frac{12}{25}y'^2\right)$$
$$+19\left[\frac{16}{25}x'^2+2\left(\frac{12}{25}x'y'\right)+\frac{9}{25}y'^2\right]$$
$$-12\left(\frac{3}{5}x'-\frac{4}{5}y'\right)-40\left(\frac{4}{5}x'+\frac{3}{5}y'\right)+31=0$$

$$12\left(\frac{9}{25}x'^2-\frac{24}{25}x'y'+\frac{16}{25}y'^2\right)+24\left(\frac{12}{25}x'^2-\frac{7}{25}x'y'-\frac{12}{25}y'^2\right)$$
$$+19\left(\frac{16}{25}x'^2+\frac{24}{25}x'y'+\frac{9}{25}y'^2\right)-12\left(\frac{3}{5}x'-\frac{4}{5}y'\right)-40\left(\frac{4}{5}x'+\frac{3}{5}y'\right)+31=0$$

$$\frac{108}{25}x'^2-\frac{288}{25}x'y'+\frac{192}{25}y'^2+\frac{288}{25}x'^2-\frac{168}{25}x'y'-\frac{288}{25}y'^2+\frac{304}{25}x'^2$$
$$+\frac{456}{25}x'y'+\frac{171}{25}y'^2-\frac{36}{5}x'+\frac{48}{5}y'-\frac{160}{5}x'-\frac{120}{5}y'+31=0$$

$$28x'^2+3y'^2-\frac{196}{5}x'-\frac{72}{5}y'+31=0$$
$$140x'^2+15y'^2-196x'-72y'+155=0$$
$$140x'^2-196x'+15y'^2-72y'=-155$$
$$140\left(x'^2-1.4x'+.49\right)+15\left(y'^2-4.8y'+5.76\right)=-155+68.6+86.4$$
$$140(x'-.7)^2+15(y'-2.4)^2=0.$$

The angle of rotation is $\theta=\sin^{-1}\left(\frac{4}{5}\right)\approx 53.13°$. The graph of the equation is the point

$(x',y')=(.7,2.4)$.

29. $16x^2+24xy+9y^2-130x+90y=0$

Since $A=16$ $B=24$, and $C=9$, we have $\cot 2\theta=\frac{A-C}{B}=\frac{16-9}{24}=\frac{7}{24}$.

The hypotenuse of the triangle is the following.

$$\sqrt{7^2+24^2}=\sqrt{49+576}=\sqrt{625}=25$$

Thus, $\cos 2\theta=\frac{7}{25}$.

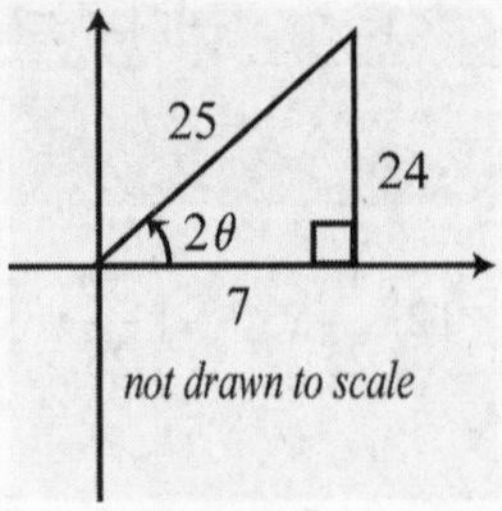

Thus, we have the following.

$$\sin\theta=\sqrt{\frac{1-\cos 2\theta}{2}}=\sqrt{\frac{1-\frac{7}{25}}{2}}=\sqrt{\frac{9}{25}}=\frac{3}{5} \text{ and } \cos\theta=\sqrt{\frac{1+\cos 2\theta}{2}}=\sqrt{\frac{1+\frac{7}{25}}{2}}=\sqrt{\frac{16}{25}}=\frac{4}{5}$$

The rotation equations are $x=\frac{4}{5}x'-\frac{3}{5}y'$ and $y=\frac{3}{5}x'+\frac{4}{5}y'$. Substituting these values into the given equation yields the following.

$$16x^2+24xy+9y^2-130x+90y=0$$

$$16\left(\frac{4}{5}x'-\frac{3}{5}y'\right)^2+24\left(\frac{4}{5}x'-\frac{3}{5}y'\right)\left(\frac{3}{5}x'+\frac{4}{5}y'\right)+9\left(\frac{3}{5}x'+\frac{4}{5}y'\right)^2-130\left(\frac{4}{5}x'-\frac{3}{5}y'\right)+90\left(\frac{3}{5}x'+\frac{4}{5}y'\right)=0$$

$$16\left[\frac{16}{25}x'^2-2\left(\frac{12}{25}x'y'\right)+\frac{9}{25}y'^2\right]+24\left(\frac{12}{25}x'^2+\frac{16}{25}x'y'-\frac{9}{25}x'y'-\frac{12}{25}y'^2\right)$$

$$+9\left[\frac{9}{25}x'^2+2\left(\frac{12}{25}x'y'\right)+\frac{16}{25}y'^2\right]-130\left(\frac{4}{5}x'-\frac{3}{5}y'\right)+90\left(\frac{3}{5}x'+\frac{4}{5}y'\right)=0$$

$$\frac{256}{25}x'^2-\frac{384}{25}x'y'+\frac{144}{25}y'^2+\frac{288}{25}x'^2+\frac{168}{25}x'y'-\frac{288}{25}y'^2+\frac{81}{25}x'^2$$

$$+\frac{216}{25}x'y'+\frac{144}{25}y'^2-104x'+78y'+54x'+72y'=0$$

$$25x'^2-50x'+150y'=0\Rightarrow 25\left(x'^2-2x'\right)=-150y'$$

$$25\left(x'^2-2x'+1\right)=-150y'+25\Rightarrow 25\left(x'-1\right)^2=-150\left(y'-\frac{1}{6}\right)$$

$$\left(x'-1\right)^2=-6\left(y'-\frac{1}{6}\right)$$

The angle of rotation is $\theta=\sin^{-1}\left(\frac{3}{5}\right)\approx 36.87°$. Its vertex is located at $x'=1$ and $y'=\frac{1}{6}$ and opens in the downward direction, relative to the x'-axis. By translating the axes of the x' y' system up $\frac{1}{6}$ and right 1 unit, we get an x'' y''-coordinate system in which the vertex of the parabola is at the origin.

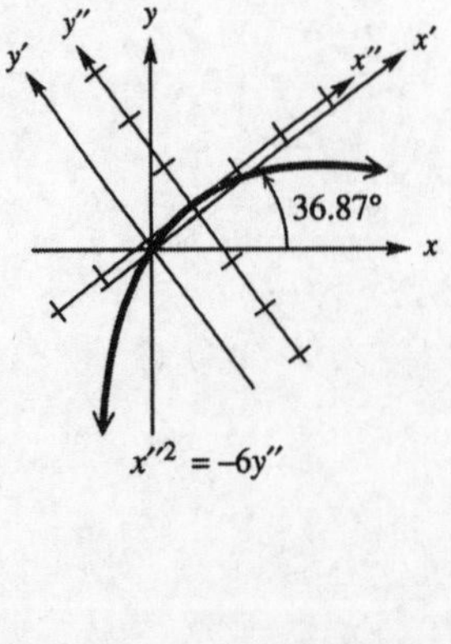

30. $9x^2-6xy+y^2-12\sqrt{10}x-36\sqrt{10}y=0$

Since $A=9$ $B=-6$, and $C=1$, we have $\cot 2\theta=\frac{A-C}{B}=\frac{9-1}{-6}=-\frac{4}{3}=\frac{-4}{3}$

The hypotenuse of the triangle is the following.

$$\sqrt{(-4)^2+3^2}=\sqrt{16+96}=\sqrt{25}=5$$

Thus, $\cos 2\theta=\frac{-4}{5}=-\frac{4}{5}$.

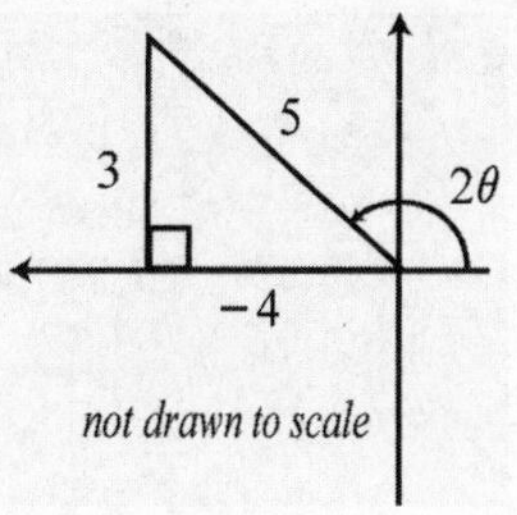

Thus, we have the following.

$$\sin\theta=\sqrt{\frac{1-\cos 2\theta}{2}}=\sqrt{\frac{1-(-\frac{4}{5})}{2}}=\sqrt{\frac{9}{10}}=\frac{3\sqrt{10}}{10} \text{ and } \cos\theta=\sqrt{\frac{1+\cos 2\theta}{2}}=\sqrt{\frac{1+(-\frac{4}{5})}{2}}=\sqrt{\frac{1}{10}}=\frac{\sqrt{10}}{10}$$

The rotation equations are $x=\frac{\sqrt{10}}{10}x'-\frac{3\sqrt{10}}{10}y'$ and $y=\frac{3\sqrt{10}}{10}x'+\frac{\sqrt{10}}{10}y'$. Substituting these values into the given equation yields the following.

$$9x^2-6xy+y^2-12\sqrt{10}x-36\sqrt{10}y=0$$

$$9\left(\frac{\sqrt{10}}{10}x'-\frac{3\sqrt{10}}{10}y'\right)^2-6\left(\frac{\sqrt{10}}{10}x'-\frac{3\sqrt{10}}{10}y'\right)\left(\frac{3\sqrt{10}}{10}x'+\frac{\sqrt{10}}{10}y'\right)+\left(\frac{3\sqrt{10}}{10}x'+\frac{\sqrt{10}}{10}y'\right)^2$$
$$-12\sqrt{10}\left(\frac{\sqrt{10}}{10}x'-\frac{3\sqrt{10}}{10}y'\right)-36\sqrt{10}\left(\frac{3\sqrt{10}}{10}x'+\frac{\sqrt{10}}{10}y'\right)=0$$

$$9\left[\frac{1}{10}x'^2-2\left(\frac{3}{10}x'y'\right)+\frac{9}{10}y'^2\right]-6\left(\frac{3}{10}x'^2+\frac{1}{10}x'y'-\frac{9}{10}x'y'-\frac{3}{10}y'^2\right)+\left[\frac{9}{10}x'^2+2\left(\frac{3}{10}x'y'\right)+\frac{1}{10}y'^2\right]$$
$$-12\sqrt{10}\left(\frac{\sqrt{10}}{10}x'-\frac{3\sqrt{10}}{10}y'\right)-36\sqrt{10}\left(\frac{3\sqrt{10}}{10}x'+\frac{\sqrt{10}}{10}y'\right)=0$$

$$9\left(\frac{1}{10}x'^2-\frac{3}{5}x'y'+\frac{9}{10}y'^2\right)-6\left(\frac{3}{10}x'^2-\frac{4}{5}x'y'-\frac{3}{10}y'^2\right)+\left(\frac{9}{10}x'^2+\frac{3}{5}x'y'+\frac{1}{10}y'^2\right)$$
$$-12\sqrt{10}\left(\frac{\sqrt{10}}{10}x'-\frac{3\sqrt{10}}{10}y'\right)-36\sqrt{10}\left(\frac{3\sqrt{10}}{10}x'+\frac{\sqrt{10}}{10}y'\right)=0$$

$$\frac{9}{10}x'^2-\frac{27}{5}x'y'+\frac{81}{10}y'^2-\frac{18}{10}x'^2+\frac{24}{5}x'y'+\frac{18}{10}y'^2+\frac{9}{10}x'^2+\frac{3}{5}x'y'+\frac{1}{10}y'^2-12x'+36y'-108x'-36y'=0$$

$$10y'^2-120x'=0\Rightarrow 10y'^2=120x'\Rightarrow y'^2=12x'$$

The angle of rotation is $\theta=\sin^{-1}\left(\frac{3\sqrt{10}}{10}\right)\approx 71.57°$. The graph of the equation is a parabola with its vertex at $x'=0$ and $y'=0$. It opens to the right, relative to the x'-axis. No translation of axes is necessary.

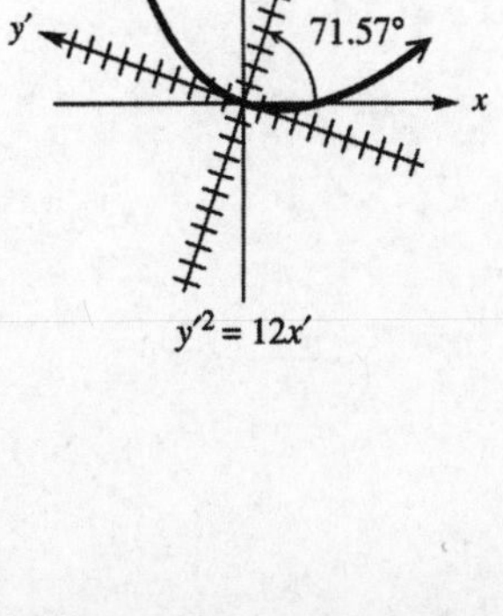

31. If $B = 0$, then $\cot 2\theta$ is undefined. The graph may be translated, but is not rotated.

32. If $A = C$, then $A - C = 0$, $\cot 2\theta = 0$. This implies $2\theta = 90°$, which implies $\theta = 45°$.